76
(1973)

Textbook of
Zoology
Vertebrates

Revised and largely rewritten by the late A. J. MARSHALL, D.Phil., D.Sc.

sometime Professor of Zoology and Comparative Physiology in Monash University

This is the Seventh Edition of *A Textbook of Zoology,* Vol. II

by the late T. JEFFERY PARKER, D.Sc., F.R.S.

sometime Professor of Biology in the University of Otago, Dunedin

and the late WILLIAM A. HASWELL, M.A., D.Sc., F.R.S.

sometime Professor of Biology in the University of Sydney

Macmillan
St. Martin's Press

First Edition 1898
Second Edition 1910
Third Edition 1921
Fourth Edition 1928
Fifth Edition 1930
Sixth Edition 1940
   Reprinted 1943, 1947, 1949, 1951
Seventh Edition 1962
   Reprinted 1963
   Reprinted with corrections 1964
   Reprinted 1966, 1967, 1972

ELBS edition first published 1972

Published by
THE MACMILLAN PRESS LTD
London and Basingstoke
Associated companies in New York
Toronto Dublin Melbourne
Johannesburg and Madras

SBN 333 05391 5 (hard cover)
     333 02829 5 (paper cover)

ELBS edition: SBN 333 14085 0 (paper cover)

Printed in Hong Kong by
Lee Fung-Asco Printers Ltd

*   *   *

In conclusion, it must be pointed out that in order adequately to solve the problems of Zoology they must be approached from all sides. From the time of Cuvier to that of Owen comparative anatomy was the dominant branch of the science, and there was a tendency to depreciate the work of the 'mere' systematist and outdoor naturalist. For the last five and twenty years embryology has been in the ascendant, and the 'mere' anatomist has been somewhat overshadowed. To-day, hopeful signs of a renewed interest in ethology—the study of living animals under natural conditions—are accompanied by a tendency to look upon all laboratory work as necrology rather than biology—the study of corpses rather than of living things. But nothing is more certain than that if the new 'natural history' is to be superior to the old—more scientific, more concerned with the solution of general problems—it can only be by utilising to the full all that has been learnt in the laboratory in the departments of anatomy, physiology and embryology. (*Concluding paragraph, Parker and Haswell, 1st ed., 1898.*)

PREFACE TO THE SEVENTH EDITION

IT is now more than sixty years since the initial publication of 'Parker and Haswell'. Many changes were made in Volume II by Forster-Cooper in his Sixth Edition of 1940, but much of the original nineteenth-century text has nevertheless remained relatively unaltered. Consequently no apology is offered for the almost complete revision that follows.

When the publishers invited me to undertake the Seventh Edition they were kind enough to give me a free hand. For a while I thought of altering the whole scheme of the volume to one of my own devising. However, I decided (like my immediate predecessor) against the disruption of the 'general plan of a text-book that has served well so many generations of students'.

In general I have attempted, within the limits of available space, to retain basic morphology and yet at the same time emphasise functional aspects and, where possible, present animals as living creatures rather than as laboratory specimens. In this I have been helped by my wife, Jane Marshall, whose otherwise unacknowledged pen-drawings are scattered through the text: a collaboration, incidentally, that was responsible once or twice for minor domestic dissension owing to the conflicting claims of art and accuracy.

An innovation in the present volume is the inclusion of the elements of a classification under each illustration of a whole, or almost whole, animal. This may help the student more or less painlessly to familiarise himself with the animal's systematic position. Some trouble too, has been taken to provide a lavish cross-reference system so that comparative information can be found quickly and without tediously repetitive consultation of the Index or Contents.

It was at first hoped to include an appendix on the principles (and pitfalls) of systematics but there was no room for it. In any case, students can nowadays easily consult Mayr, Linsley and Usinger's *Methods and Principles of Systematic Zoology* (1953) or Simpson's *The Principles of Classification and a Classification of Mammals* (1945). (The last-named is additionally noteworthy in its lack of the solemnity that so many scientists believe to be indispensable to good scholarship.) Today, with such books readily available, only egotism or perversity, rather than ignorance, can be responsible for an extension of the taxonomic morass into which so many groups have been thrust: an unhealthy swamp that will need the labour of a century to remove.

The question of references has been one of some difficulty. Clearly it is impossible to cite every source of information, most of which has been taken from original papers. A compromise has been made. In the first place, key references, leading to many others, have been included in the bibliography. Where an authority has been cited personally in the text, the publication date has been deliberately omitted. It is believed that it will provide a mild exercise in ingenuity and bibliographic skill for the honours man to discover the source from which he requires further information.

Another debatable point has been the appropriate amount of palæontology that should be given in a text-book of zoology. Some of my colleagues are of the opinion that there was already included rather too much information about fossil forms. I believe, however, that it is impossible to gain a good general understanding of living animals—either in form or function—without an adequate appreciation of what is known of their ancestry. Therefore the fossil sections have been expanded.

The elimination of *Neoceratodus* as the lung-fish 'type', and the substitution of *Protopterus*, needs brief explanation. The former is so rare, and rigidly protected, that not even an Australian student can confidently hope ever to dissect one. Living *Protopterus*, on the other hand, can be bought in unlimited numbers in fish-markets over wide areas of Africa. Thus they are available (for demonstration purposes at least) to university departments anywhere. It may seem surprising, in this view, that *Salmo* is retained as the teleost 'type'. However, there is employed for the purpose today (in the many countries where this book is used) such a wide diversity of bony fishes that any new choice would have only limited and local value.

Had I not had my first systematic instruction in zoology and physiology from students of Haswell, and made my first supervised dissections in the school that he founded, I would never have essayed the present revision. Yet, once begun, the task became surprisingly agreeable. It has been lightened by the rigorous but kindly criticism of friends who read sections of the manuscript dealing with subjects of their special interests. These are as follows:

E. C. Amoroso	A. J. E. Cave	E. W. Knight-Jones	D. L. Serventy
F. J. Aumonier	G. E. H. Foxon	K. A. Kermack	V. B. Sheffer
E. W. Baxter	F. C. Fraser	Dennis Lacy	J. R. Simons
A. d'A. Bellairs	P. H. Greenwood	D. A. McDonald	R. Strahan
Ruth Bellairs	Frank Goldby	J. D. Macdonald	E. I. White
R. J. H. Brown	I. Griffiths	N. B. Marshall	H. P. Whiting
G. H. O. Burgess	R. W. Hayman	J. A. C. Nichol	
P. M. Butler	William Holmes	H. K. Pusey	
D. B. Carlisle	C. Burdon-Jones	W. D. L. Ride	

If this edition is found to be deserving of any commendation, much of it is properly due to them. Some rewrote special pieces, and a few, in addition, provided illustrations (below which acknowledgement is made). Almost all drew my attention to errors or half-truths, including, I have to confess, a few that I succeeded in introducing myself. On occasions, my benefactors disagreed in a most stimulating way among themselves—principally on minor matters of taxonomy and terminology—and so it is more than ever necessary to add on their behalf the customary disclaimer concerning responsibility. Nobody other than myself has seen more than a comparatively small part of the manuscript.

It is a final pleasure to acknowledge the loan by the British Museum (Natural History) of specimens for illustration, and the constant assistance given me by the Library staffs of University College and, particularly, the Zoological Society of London.

A. J. M.

Victoria
Australia 1960

NOTE ON THE 1964 REPRINT

The 1964 reprint with corrections has been improved by the further criticism of some of the above-named, and additionally by valuable comments from Drs. D. F. Dorward, A. K. Lee, and J. W. Warren.

A. J. M.

Victoria
Australia 1964

CONTENTS

CONTENTS

TABLES

ILLUSTRATIONS

SUB-PHYLUM ADELOCHORDATA

CLASS ENTEROPNEUSTA *Balanoglossus*, Whole animal, Fig. 1 (p. 6); in burrow, Fig. 2 (p. 7); median sagittal section, Fig. 3 (p. 8); branchial region, Fig. 4 (p. 9); development, Fig. 5 (p. 12); Fig. 6 (p. 13); tornaria larva, Fig. 7 (p. 14).

CLASS PTEROBRANCHIA *Cephalodiscus*, Colony, Fig. 8 (p. 15); zooid, Fig. 9 (p. 16); visceral relationships, Fig. 10 (p. 17); *Atubaria*, Fig. 11 (p. 18); *Rhabdopleura*, Colony, Fig. 12 (p. 18); male zooid and cœnœcium, Fig. 13 (p. 19).

SUB-PHYLUM TUNICATA (UROCHORDATA)

CLASS ASCIDIACEA *Ascidia*, whole animal, Fig. 15 (p. 23); branchial sac, Fig. 16 (p. 24); pharyngeal region, Fig. 17 (p. 24); circulation and reproduction, Fig. 18 (p. 25); nerve ganglion and associated parts, Fig. 19 (p. 27); nervous system, Fig. 20 (p. 28). Ascidian development: Figs. 21–25 (pp. 29–33). Composite ascidians: *Botryllus*, Fig. 26 (p. 35); a colonial zooid, Fig. 27 (p. 35).

CLASS THALIACEA *Doliolum*, whole animal, Fig. 28 (p. 37); development, Figs. 29–30 (p. 38); asexual zooid, Fig. 31 (p. 39). *Pyrosoma*, Luminous colony, Fig. 32 (p. 40); colonial individuals, Fig. 33 (p. 40). *Salpa*, Asexual form, Fig. 34 (p. 41); oozoid, Fig. 35 (p. 42); nervous system, Fig. 36 (p. 43); development, Fig. 37 (p. 43).

CLASS LARVACEA *Oikopleura*, Animal in 'house', Fig. 38 (p. 45); *Appendicularia*, visceral relationships, Fig. 39 (p. 45).

SUB-PHYLUM ACRANIA

CLASS CEPHALOCHORDATA *Branchiostoma* (**Amphioxus**), Whole animal in sand, Fig. 40 (p. 48); ventral and lateral veins, Fig. 41 (p. 48); visceral relationships, Fig. 42 (p. 50); general anatomy, Fig. 43 (p. 51); pharyngeal region, Fig. 44 (p. 54); blood vascular system, Fig. 45 (p. 55); nephridium, Fig. 46 (p. 56); solenocytes, Fig. 47 (p. 57); nervous system, Fig. 48 (p. 58); development Figs. 49–56 (pp. 60–66).

SUB-PHYLUM CRANIATA (VERTEBRATA)

Introductory Examples: General and Skeletal. 'Ideal' vertebrate, external view, Fig. 57 (p. 79); epidermis, Fig. 58 (p. 82); placoid scale, Fig. 59 (p. 83); cosmoid scale, Fig. 60 (p. 83); ganoid scale, Fig. 61 (p. 84); myomere patterns, Fig. 62 (p. 86); visceral relationships, Fig. 63 (p. 87); vertebral column in embryo, Fig. 64 (p. 89); segmentation, Fig. 65 (p. 89); cranial elements in embryonic *Salmo*, Fig. 66 (p. 90); cartilaginous skull, Fig. 67 (p. 92); bony skull, Fig. 68 (p. 95); pelvic fins, Fig. 69 (p. 98); pectoral fins, Fig. 70 (p. 99); tetrapod girdles, manus, and pes, Fig. 71 (p. 100); dermal and buccal armour; placoid scale and teeth, Fig. 72 (p. 103).

Respiratory System. Pharyngeal region, including branchiogenic organs, Fig. 73 (p. 106); pulmonary lobule, Fig. 74 (p. 107); lungs and swim-bladder, Fig. 75 (p. 108).

Blood-vascular System. In fishes, Fig. 76 (p. 109); course of circulation, Fig. 77 (p. 110); circulation in embryonic air-breather, Fig. 78 (p. 113); cardiac circulation in amphibian and crocodile, Fig. 79 (p. 114); relationship of blood and lymph capillaries, Fig. 80 (p. 116).

Nervous System and Special Senses. Brain and proximal part of cord during development and maturity, Fig. 81 (p. 118); autonomic system, Fig. 82 (p. 119); sympathetic and spinal nerves and cord, Fig. 83 (p. 120); fibre, motor end-plate and muscle, Fig. 84 (p. 121); cord and constituent structures, Fig. 85 (p. 123); cranial and anterior spinal nerves, Fig. 86 (p. 129); lateral-line system in bony, Fig. 87 (p. 136) and cartilaginous fishes, Fig. 88 (p. 137); nasal and buccal cavity in various vertebrates, Fig. 89 (p. 138); eye (macroscopic structures), Fig. 90 (p. 139); retinal structures, Fig. 91 (p. 140); orbit, Fig. 92 (p. 143); audio-equilibration: evolutionary stages, Fig. 93 (p. 144); semi-circular canals and lagena, Fig. 94 (p. 145).

Endocrine System. Hypothalamico-hypophysial relationships, Fig. 95 (p. 149); hypophysial arrangements, Fig. 96 (p. 150); secretory apparatus of testis, Fig. 97 (p. 152).

Urinogenital System. Development and relationships, Fig. 98 (p. 153); kidney circulation and disposal, Fig. 99 (p. 154); nephron, Fig. 100 (p. 155); and probable stages of evolution, Fig. 101 (p. 157); development, Fig. 102 (p. 161).

SUPER-CLASS AGNATHA

CLASS EUPHANERIDA *Jamoytius*, Fig. 103 (p. 167).

CLASS HETEROSTRACI *Pteraspis*, Fig. 104 (p. 168); *Drepanaspis*, Fig. 105 (p. 170).

CLASS ANASPIDA *Rhyncholepis*, Fig. 106 (p. 171).

CLASS OSTEOSTRACI *Hemicyclaspis*, Fig. 107 (p. 171); *Kiaeraspis*, cranial anatomy, Fig 108 (p. 173); *Lanarkia*, Fig. 109 (p. 174).

CLASSES PETROMYZONTIA and MYXINOIDEA *Petromyzon*, whole animal, Fig. 110 (p. 175); buccal funnel, Fig. 111 (p. 177); integumental and epidermal cells of *Myxine* and fishes, Figs. 112–113 (pp. 178–179); *Petromyzon*, trunk region, Fig. 114 (p. 180); skull, Fig. 115 (p. 181); skull and branchial basket in adult, Fig. 116 (p. 182); skull during metamorphosis, Fig. 117 (p. 182); head region, Fig. 118 (p. 183); **Ammocœte** (*Geotria*), head region, Fig. 119 (p. 186); *Petromyzon*, brain, Fig. 120 (p. 188); olfactory and naso-hypophysial ducts, Fig. 121 (p. 189); development, Fig. 122 (p. 190); *Lampetra*, eye and adjacent structures, Fig. 123 (p. 191); *Petromyzon*, cloacal region, Fig. 125 (p. 193); development, Fig. 126 (p. 195); *Lampetra*: (development, Fig. 127 (p. 196); *Myxine* and *Eptatretus*, anterior regions, Fig. 128 (p. 198); *Myxine* skeletal and visceral structures, Fig. 129 (p. 199); skull of adult, Fig. 130 (p. 200); of embryo, Fig. 131 (p. 201); membranous labyrinth, Fig. 132 (p. 202).

SUPER-CLASS GNATHOSTOMATA

CLASS PLACODERMI *Dinichthys*, whole animal, Fig. 133 (p. 206); *Climatius*, head, Fig. 134 (p. 207); *Diplacanthus*, pectoral girdle, Fig. 135 (p. 208); *Acanthodes*, skull, Fig. 136 (p. 209); head region, Fig. 137 (p. 210); *Coccosteus*, skeleton, Fig. 138 (p. 211); *Macropetalichthys*, skeleton, Fig. 139 (p. 212); head and pectoral shield of *Lunaspis* and *Macropetalichthys*, Fig. 140 (p. 213); *Macropetalichthys*, pectoral girdle, Fig. 141 (p. 213); *Pterichthyodes*, skeleton, Fig. 142 (p. 214); *Bothriolepis*, whole animal, Fig. 143 (p. 215); *Gemuendina*, whole animal, and trunk, Figs. 144–145 (pp. 216–217); *Palæospondylus*, skeleton, Fig. 146 (p. 218).

CLASS ELASMOBRANCHII *Carcharodon*, jaws and teeth, Fig. 147 (p. 220); *Cladoselache*, whole animal, Fig. 148 (p. 223); *Ctenacanthus*, whole animal, Fig. 149 (p. 223); *Pleuracanthus*, skeleton, Fig. 150 (p. 224); *Heterodontus*, whole animal, Fig. 151 (p. 225); dentition, Fig. 152 (p. 226); *Chlamydoselachus*, Fig. 153 (p. 227); *Pristis* and *Aetobatis* illustrating adaptation and radiation, Fig. 154 (p. 228).

Example of Class: Dogfish. Whole animal, Fig. 155 (p. 229); vertebral column, Fig. 156 (p. 231); skull and visceral arches, Fig. 157 (p. 232); visceral arches, Fig. 158 (p. 234); pectoral arch and fin, Fig. 159 (p. 235); pelvic arch and fin, Fig. 160 (p. 236); visceral structures, Fig. 161 (p. 238); Respiration and circulation: branchial sac, Fig. 162 (p. 239); head and branchial circulation, Fig. 163 (p. 240); general circulation, Fig. 164 (p. 242); Nervous system: brain, Fig. 165 (p. 244); brain ventricles, Fig. 166 (p. 246); brain and spinal nerves, Fig. 167 (p. 247); dorsal root cranial nerves, Fig. 168 (p. 248); Endocrine and urinogenital elements: adrenal, Fig. 169 (p. 252); male and female urinogenitalia, Fig. 170 (p. 253); kidney and urinary sinus of female, Fig. 171 (p. 254); egg-case of dogfish, Fig. 172 p. 254).

SUB-CLASS BRADYODONTI Representative whole animals, Fig. 173 (p. 257); *Chimæra*, vertebral column, Fig. 174 (p. 259); skull, Fig. 175 (p. 260). *Callorhynchus*, skull, Fig. 176 (p. 261); brain, Fig. 177 (p. 262); urinogenital system, Fig. 178 (p. 263); embryo within egg, Fig. 179 (p. 264).

General Organisation of Elasmobranchii. Skeletal structures: *Scymnorhinus*, spinal column, Fig. 180 (p. 267); *Urolophus*, endoskeleton, Fig. 181 (p. 268); *Heptranchias*, skull, Fig. 182 (p. 269). *Torpedo*, Electric organs, Fig. 183 (p. 271); *Carcharodon*, Mechanism of eye accommodation, Fig. 184 (p. 273); *Cetorhinus*, Urinogenital system, Fig. 185 (p. 277); development, Figs. 186–190 (pp. 279–281).

CLASS OSTEICHTHYES SUPER-ORDER CHONDOSTREI *Palæoniscus*, whole animal and skeleton, Fig. 191 (p. 286); *Helichthys*, whole animal and skeleton, Fig. 192 (p. 287); *Acipenser*, whole animal, Fig. 193 (p. 288); pre-caudal vertebræ, Fig. 194 (p. 289). *Chondrosteus*, skull and pectoral girdle, Fig. 195 (p. 289); *Polypterus*, whole animal, Fig. 196 (p. 290); **SUPER-ORDER HOLOSTEI.** *Dapedius*, whole animal, Fig. 197 (p. 291); *Lepisosteus*, whole animal, Fig. 198 (p. 292); *Amia*, whole animal, Fig. 199 (p. 293). **SUPER-ORDER TELEOSTEI**, *Leptolepis*, whole animal and skull, Fig. 200 (p. 294).

PHYLUM CHORDATA

INTRODUCTION

THE chordates exhibit an astonishing diversity of form, physiology, and habit. The phylum includes such apparently unrelated animals as, for example, sea-squirts and Man. The creatures which fall into this great group are characterised essentially by the possession, at some stage of their life, of one or more of the three fundamental structures which, along with other features, appear to reveal their common ancestry. These structures are as follows:

1. The *chorda dorsalis* or *notochord*. From this structure the phylum takes its name. It occurs in the embryo of most chordates as a long, flexible cord of specialised, vacuolated cells extending from head to tail along the dorsal mid-line. It lies between the alimentary canal and the dorsal cord of the central nervous system. In lower chordates, such as the Tunicata and Cephalo-chorda, the notochord is developed directly and unmistakably from the endo-derm and, in the Adelochorda, a notochord-like structure remains permanently in continuity with that layer. In the Craniata, however, its origin is not so definite: it may originate from cells that are not obviously of endodermal derivation. Sometimes it is enclosed in a firm sheath and forms a stiff, but elastic, structure which supports the neighbouring single, hollow, fluid-filled, non-ganglionated nerve-cord. In the Craniata, with a few exceptions among lower forms, the notochord is replaced more or less completely in the adult by a segmented cartilaginous or bony axial structure, the vertebral column. In vertebrates, traces of the notochord often remain in the adult as vestiges of gelatinous material in the spaces between the centra of the replacing vertebræ.

2. The *branchial clefts*. Visceral clefts constitute another almost universal feature of the Chordata. They occur as a paired series of perforations leading from the pharynx, an anterior section of the alimentary canal, to the lateral surface of the body. Within these clefts are the gills in many aquatic animals. In the creatures equipped with lungs, branchial clefts or branchial grooves are always found in the embryo. In the adults of vertebrates, the branchial

apparatus is sometimes, as we shall see, converted to endocrine and other functions.   In the more lowly members of the Chordata the branchial apparatus is used also as a feeding mechanism.

3. The dorsal, tubular, fluid-filled *central nervous system*, anteriorly differentiated into a brain in advanced forms, is another structure common to most chordates in the larval or later stages of their development.

The Chordata are cœlomate animals.   In the lower sub-phyla the cœlom develops in essentially the same way as in the Echinodermata, the Chætognatha, and the Brachiopoda, *i.e.* by direct outgrowth from the archenteron.   In the Craniata, this enterocœlic origin of the body cavity is no longer definitely traceable, although in some cases indications of it may be detected.

In the Tunicata the body is not segmented, though faint indications of serial repetition of parts are visible in certain groups.   In the Adelochorda there is a division of the cœlom into three parts, each occupying a definite region of the body.   This has led sometimes to the view that these animals are tri-segmented. In the Cephalochorda and Craniata there are numerous segments (see p. 161).

There has been considerable controversy concerning the period and mode of origin of the Chordata.   Lower chordate forms have been discovered in Cambrian strata (see Table 1, p. 3).   Indisputable vertebrate relics (*e.g.* fish-scales) are known from Ordovician deposits more than 400 million years old.   No general agreement has been reached, but today more and more people tend to accept Garstang's suggestion that the Chordata may have evolved from free-swimming auricularian larvæ partly by means of pædomorphosis.   This is evolutionary change involving the retention, in the sexually mature descendant, of characters that occurred in younger stages of the ancestor.   It is now considered certain that pædogenesis (reproduction in a pre-adult form) has been a powerful influence in the elaboration of at least some animal types. 'Ontogeny' wrote Garstang in 1922 (in reference to this and the so-called Biogenetic 'Law' of Haeckel) 'does not recapitulate Phylogeny : it creates it'.

Clues to the origin of vertebrates have been sought by men ever since the dawn of evolutionary thought.   It was natural to seek them among the invertebrates, both the living and the extinct, and various possibilities have been suggested.   However, the adult forms of most, if not all, diploblastic or triploblastic invertebrates are so specialised as to general form, and especially in regard to the situation and structure (with imposed physiological limitations) of their individual organ systems, that it is difficult or impossible to imagine them as ancestral to the Chordata.

Towards the end of the last century Garstang and Willey looked for possible chordate progenitors in the *youthful* stages of various invertebrate animals. They produced suggestive information that the evolution of ancestral chordate forms from the larvæ of echinoderm-like animals is by no means impossible. Although echinoderms and chordates exhibit striking similarities in early

TABLE I. Ages in millions of years of geological periods and epochs, as estimated approximately, by various workers (modified after Young).[1]

	Zeuner	Bullard	Romer	Holmes	Schuchert and Dunbar	Compromise adopted	Time since begining of period	Sediment thickness (ooo ft.)
Pleistocene .	I	5	—	I	—	I	I	4
Pliocene .	—	15	—	15	—	9	10	13
Miocene .	30	25	—	20	—	15	25·	21
Oligocene .	—	18	—	15	—	10	35	15
Eocene .	—	16	—	20	—	15	50	14
Palaeocene .	(40)	—	—	—	—	10	60	—
Cretaceous .	40	76	50	50	80	60	120	64
Jurassic .	40	23	35	30	35	30	150	20
Triassic .	(40)	30	35	40	25	30	180	25
Permian .	35	15	25	30	40	30	210	13
Carboniferous	50	47	85	60	70	60	270	40
Devonian .	(35)	44	50	40	40	30	300	37
Silurian .	30	18	30	30	40	30	330	15
Ordovician .	50	47	90	50	70	90	420	40
Cambrian .	60	47	70	100	90	90	510	40

development, and agree in other features as well, the adult forms of the various star-fishes and their allies are organised with such peculiarity and complexity that at first sight such a hypothesis might seem utterly invalid. But if we follow Garstang's proposition that a series of changes may have taken place in primitive echinoderm larvæ that were not unlike today's auricularians, we have a succession of pictures that must carry weight with anybody who approaches the problem without prejudice. Garstang pointed out that the ciliated bands and underlying nervous tissue of a larval form might become accentuated and fused to form the forerunner of the dorsal neural tube. Such a view is free from the powerful objections that can legitimately be raised against attempts to consider that a dorsal nervous system might be derived from the nervous tissues of any adult invertebrate and, in addition, it is not at variance with the principle of neurobiotaxis, which insists that a concentration of nervous material evolves in the area of maximum environmental stimulation. Among other changes, it was suggested that the ciliated adoral band feeding-mechanism could become the endostyle which is a characteristic of the protochordates (see p. 24). It will be recalled, too, that in the auricularian a pore brings the body cavity into communication with the external environment, and that this pattern is repeated in various lower chordates. 'If the nervous system and endostyle are formed in the way suggested, all that is required to turn the echinoderm larva into a chordate is the formation of the notochord and the piercing of the gill-slits' (de Beer). It has to be recognised that such hypothetical changes are radical, and

[1] The term *Liassic* (or Lias) is often applied to a richly fossiliferous blue limestone deposit in the Lower Jurassic. In North America the Carboniferous is divisible into upper *Mississippian* and lower *Pennsylvanian* periods.

no convincing explanation of their development has as yet been given. It is, however, logical tentatively to assume that the modified larval form proposed above could become sexually mature and that the neotenous animal which resulted may have been the ancestral stock from which today's chordates evolved.

Neither has any general agreement been reached as to the most appropriate classification within the Phylum Chordata. In the present volume its members will be considered in the following broad grouping :

Sub-phyla Adelochordata (Hemichordata)
Tunicata (Urochordata)
Acrania (Cephalochordata)
Craniata (Vertebrata)

Members of the first three of the above groups are usually referred to as the Protochordata, although, as we shall see, all authorities do not unquestionably admit the Adelochorda as chordate animals. Some hold that they should occupy a phylum to themselves. It has to be remembered that although the notochord is clearly homologous in the Tunicata and Acrania, such homology has certainly not been established with complete assurance in the Adelochorda. However, in the Adelochorda there occurs an endoskeletal element which develops as an outgrowth from the antero-dorsal part of the gut into the proboscis, and this proboscis diverticulum may perhaps be a truly notochordal structure. Again, all protochordates except *Rhabdopleura* (Adelochorda) (p. 19) possess lateral pharyngeal perforations at some stage of development. However, in other Adelochorda such perforations not only occur, but also undergo multiplication by a characteristic method, involving the dorsal downgrowth of dividing 'tongue-bars'. An identical means of multiplication is found in Acrania, and traces of the method may be discerned in young stages of certain Tunicata. The nerve cord is constant in its origin in all chordates in that it arises from the median dorsal ectoderm. In Adelochorda, the Pterobranchia lack a neurocœle, but Enteropneusta possess, in part of the dorsal nerve cord, either a neurocœle or vestigial cavities. Again excepting the Adelochorda, all chordates (and only chordates) possess at least some elements of a true tail which, without viscera, nevertheless contains muscular, nervous, and notochordal elements. (In the Craniata, including Man, it contains vertebræ.)

In addition to the morphological evidence of affinity briefly presented above, it is noteworthy that chordates utilise in their muscles a phosphagen that is a compound of the amino-acid creatine and not, as in the case of most invertebrates studied, a compound of arginine. *Both* forms of phosphagen have been reported in the Adelochorda, Tunicata and certain of the Echinodermata. At the same time, too much should not be made of this, since the creatine compound has recently been demonstrated in many polychætes, whilst other polychætes possess arginine compounds. There is up to the present little other biochemical evidence of possible affinities.

SUB-PHYLUM ADELOCHORDATA (HEMICHORDATA)

THE Adelochorda fall into two groups. The first, the Class Enteropneusta, is composed of worm-like, simply-organised burrowing marine animals such as *Balanoglossus*, *Glossobalanus*, *Ptychodera*, and *Saccoglossus*. The second group, the Class Pterobranchia, includes only three genera, *Cephalodiscus*, *Rhabdopleura*, and *Atubaria*. These, too, live in the sea. They are colonial and sedentary. The two classes have in common the peculiar structure of the stomochord (presumed notochord), the division of the body into three regions (which are sometimes looked upon as representing three segments), and certain other features.

CLASS ENTEROPNEUSTA

Balanoglossus,[1] the so-called acorn-worm, may be used as a convenient type.

External Characters and Cœlom.—Balanoglossus (Fig. 1) is a soft-bodied, cylindrical, superficially worm-like animal. Much of its surface is ciliated. The size varies extremely in the different species, some being only 2 or 3 centimetres long while other species grow to a length of $2\frac{1}{2}$ metres. It is divisible into three regions. In front there is a large muscular, generally ovoid *proboscis* (*prob.*), with a small axial cavity. Immediately behind the proboscis and encircling its base is a prominent fold—the *collar* (*col.*). The third region or *trunk* is long and nearly cylindrical, but somewhat depressed. The degree of flattening varies between species.

Balanoglossus lives in the sea, usually in shallow water, burrowing in sand or mud by means of its proboscis. One species has been found swarming on the surface of the sea. Numerous glands in the integument secrete a viscid matter to which grains of sand adhere in such a way as to form a fragile temporary tube. The proboscis (Fig. 3, *p.*) has thick muscular walls and its cavity the *proboscis-cœlom* (*p. c.*) opens to the exterior usually by a single minute aperture—the *proboscis-pore* (*p. p.*). Occasionally two such apertures are present. In some species the proboscis-pore does not communicate with the proboscis-cœlom, but terminates blindly, and may send off a narrow tubular diverticulum which opens into the neurocœle. The narrow posterior part or 'neck' of the proboscis is strengthened by a layer of cartilage-like or *chondroid* tissue, which supports the blood-vessels. The collar is also muscular. It may

---

[1] The name Balanoglossus is used here as a general designation rather than as a strictly generic name.

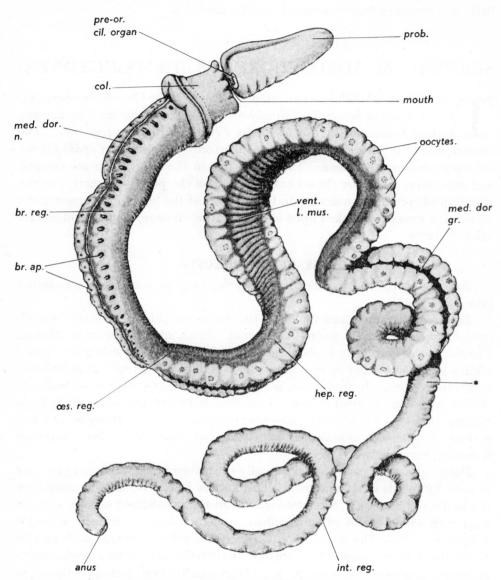

FIG. 1.—Order **Enteropneusta,** Family **Harrimanidæ,** *Protoglossus.* *P. koehleri.* *br. ap.* branchial apertures; *br. reg.* branchial region; *col.* collar; *hep. reg.* hepatic region; *int. reg.* intestinal region; *med. dor. gr.* median dorsal groove between left and right genital ridges; *med. dor. n.* median dorsal nerve; *œs. reg.* œsophageal region; *oocytes* (in genital sacs); *pre-or. cil. organ.* pre-oral ciliary organ; *prob.* proboscis; *vent. l. mus.* ventral longitudinal muscle; * posterior limit of hepatic region. (Drawn by C. Burdon-Jones.)

contain one or two cœlomic cavities. When two are present, the right and left cavities are separated from one another by dorsal and ventral mesenteries. They are completely cut off from the proboscis-cavity. The collar cavity (*c. c.*) and also that of the proboscis (*p. c.*) are crossed by numerous strands of connective tissue which give the region a spongy appearance. The collar-cavity communicates with the exterior by a pair of *collar-pores*, and short ciliated tubes (canals) leading into the first gill-pouches.

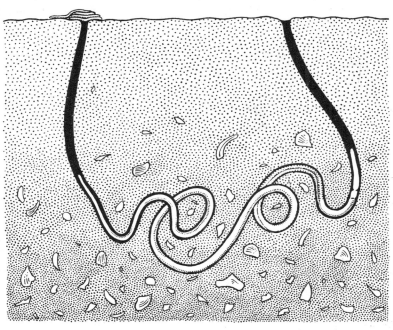

FIG. 2.—**Balanoglossus: The animal in its burrow.** Locomotory power is concentrated in the proboscis, collar and ventral ciliary band. As *Saccoglossus* burrows, fine muddy sand is swallowed. From this organic material is extracted. Inorganic and organic residues resembling worm-castings are voided through the anus. (Redrawn after C. Burdon-Jones.)

On the dorsal surface of the anterior part of the trunk is a double row of small pores—the branchial apertures (Fig. 1, *br. ap.*). Each row is situated in a long furrow. These pores increase in number during growth. In some species the most anterior are overlapped by a posterior prolongation of the collar called the *operculum*. A pair of longitudinal *genital ridges* extends throughout a considerable part of the body behind and, in the region of the branchial apertures. They contain the internally situated gonads. These ridges are so prominent in some of the genera as to form a pair of wing-like lateral folds (Fig. 4, *g.*), but in other genera they are absent. Behind the branchial region in some genera are two rows of prominences formed by the hepatic cæca. The trunk is irregularly ringed. This annulation, which is entirely superficial and does not correspond to an internal segmentation, is most strongly marked posteriorly. The cœlom of the trunk is divided into two lateral closed cavities by a vertical partition (*dorsal* and *ventral mesenteries, d. m* and *v.,* Fig. 4).

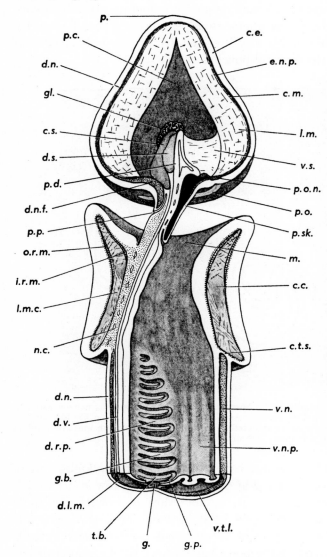

FIG. 3.—**Balanoglossus: Saccoglossus.** Median sagittal section of anterior end showing general details of anatomy. *c. c.* collar-cœlom; *c. e.* ciliated epithelium; *c. m.* circular muscle; *c. s.* cardiac sac; *c. t. s.* collar-trunk septum; *d. l. m.* dorsal longitudinal muscle; *d. n.* dorsal nerve thickening; *d. n. f.* dorsal nerve fan; *d. r. p.* dorsal respiratory pharynx; *d. s.* dorsal sinus or 'heart'; *d. v.* dorsal blood vessel; *e. n. p.* epidermal nerve plexus; *g.* gill-pore; *g.b.* gill-bar; *gl.* glomerulus; *g. p.* gill-pouch; *i. r. m.* inner ring musculature of collar; *l. m.* longitudinal muscle band; *l. m. c.* longitudinal muscles of collar; *m.* mouth; *n. c.* neurocord and neurocœle; *o. r. m.* outer ring musculature of collar; *p.* proboscis; *p. c.* proboscis-cœlom; *p. d.* buccal diverticulum; *p. p.* proboscis pore; *p. o.* preoral ciliary organ; *p. o. n.* nerve thickening associated with ciliary organ; *p. sk.* proboscis skeleton; *t. b.* tongue bar; *v. n.* ventral nerve thickening; *v. n. p.* ventral nutritive pharynx; *v. s.* ventral septum; *v. t. l.* ventro-lateral muscle band of left side of trunk. (Drawn by C. Burdon-Jones.)

Alimentary Canal and Associated Structures.—The mouth (Fig. 3, *m.*) is situated ventrally at the base of the proboscis, within the collar. Into the dorsal half of the anterior portion of the alimentary canal open the internal gill-slits. Each of these is in the form of a long narrow U, the two limbs separated by a narrow process—the *tongue-bar* (*t. b.*)—containing a prolongation of the body-cavity. In most of the Enteropneusta the internal gill-slits lead into *gill-pouches*. These in turn communicate with the exterior by the gill-pores. In the genus *Ptychodera* (Fig. 4), however, there are no gill-pouches ; the U-shaped gill-slits lead directly to the exterior. The bars between the gill slits have skeletal supports each of which is composed of a number of parts. Each consists of a dorsal basal portion and three long narrow rods. One rod is median and two are lateral. The median one, which is bifurcated at the end, lies in the septum or interval between two adjoining gill-sacs. The two lateral rods lie in the neighbouring tongues. In most species a number of trans-

verse rods—the *synapticulæ*—connect together the tongues and the adjoining septa, and are supported by slender processes of the skeleton.

The remainder of the alimentary canal is a nearly straight tube, giving off, in its middle part, paired *hepatic cæca*, which (mainly in the Ptychoderidæ) bulge outwards in the series of external prominences already mentioned. Posteriorly it terminates in an anal aperture situated at the posterior extremity of the body. In the posterior part of its extent in some Ptychoderidæ the intestine presents a ventral median ridge-like outgrowth of its epithelium—the *pygochord*. Throughout its length the intestine lies between the dorsal and

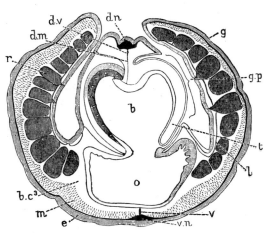

FIG. 4.—**Balanoglossus: *Ptychodera*.** Transverse section of the branchial region in : *b.* branchial part of alimentary canal; *b.* c³, cœlom of trunk; *d. m.* dorsal mesentery; *d. n.* dorsal nerve; *d. v.* dorsal vessel; *e.* epidermis with nerve layer (black) at its base; *g.* genital wing; *g. p.* branchial aperture (gill-pore) encroached upon by tongue (*t*); *l.* lateral septum; *m.* longitudinal muscles; *o.* digestive part of pharynx; *r.* reproductive organ; *t.* tongue; *v.* ventral mesentery and ventral vessel; *v. n.* ventral nerve. (From Harmer, after Spengel.)

ventral divisions of the vertical partition. These act as mesenteries.

Food particles are driven backwards towards the mouth by the action of cilia on the proboscis. Some are swept directly into the mouth with the so-called respiratory current. This is caused mainly by *lateral cilia* on the sides of the gill-bars. These drive water outwards through the branchial apertures and so more fresh water is continually drawn in through the mouth to replace that which is driven out. Other particles of food, silt and sand are entrapped by mucus secreted from the surface of the proboscis. This mucus, with its contents, is drawn into the alimentary canal, partly by the respiratory current and partly by the action of cilia which line the buccal cavity and the gut generally. Immediately anterior to the mouth, on the postero-ventral surface of the proboscis, is a special *ciliary organ* (Fig. 3, *p. o.*), equipped with sensory cells.

A sample of the particles which enter the mouth passes over the surface of this organ. The sand or mud, which is taken into the gut, is eventually passed out at the anus as castings. These can be seen on the surface of the sand in a form resembling that of earth-worm castings (Fig. 2).

A series of pores (*gastro-cutaneous pores*), variously arranged in the different genera, connect the alimentary canal with the surface. They are unciliated, but probably represent vestigial gill-openings, retained, as passive drainage channels, at the posterior limit of the pharynx which has been modified to perform muscular movements, concerned with compacting the ingested sand and food.

Proboscis or Buccal Diverticulum (Stomochord). The dorsal wall of the part of the digestive canal immediately following the mouth gives off a *diverticulum* (Fig. 3, *p. d.*) that runs forward some distance into the basal part of the proboscis after giving off a short ventral branch. The diverticulum contains a narrow lumen, and its wall is composed of a single layer of long and very narrow cells, each of which contains a vacuole. This layer of cells forming the wall of the diverticulum is continuous with the epithelium of the digestive canal itself, the cells being somewhat modified by the presence of the vacuoles. The diverticulum, because of its structure, and its relations, is sometimes regarded as representing the notochord of the typical Chordata. The restricted form of the notochordal structure may be related to the animal's principal mode of locomotion. There is little doubt that a notochord extending right along the body would be disadvantageous in an animal which moves by thrusting out its proboscis and next drawing forward its body since it would hinder changes in length. There is no trace of the flexural movements associated with the presence of the notochord in typical chordates. Cilia also help Balanoglossus in its locomotion.

In close relationship with the diverticulum on its ventral surface is the remarkable *proboscis-skeleton* (*p. sk.*). This consists of a median part of an hour-glass shape, and with a tooth-shaped process, bifurcating behind into two flattened bars which lie on either side of the buccal cavity.

Blood-vascular System.—This has dorsal and ventral longitudinal trunks. The dorsal vessel (*d. v.*) lies above the stomochord, and ends anteriorly in a sinus, the *dorsal sinus* or *heart* (*d. s.*). This is situated in the posterior part of the proboscis, in close contact with the stomochord. From the posterior part of the sinus is given off a vessel which bifurcates to supply the proboscis. In communication with the sinus in front are a number of vessels forming a plexus, the *glomerulus* (*gl.*). This is a complex organ, possibly excretory, situated at the anterior end of the proboscis diverticulum. From the posterior end of the glomerulus on each side there passes backwards an efferent vessel which breaks up into a plexus. The two plexuses communicate with the ventral vessel enabling venous return. A closed *cardiac sac* (*c. s.*) envelops the dorsal side of the sinus. Its ventral wall is equipped with muscle fibres, and it has been observed to contract rhythmically, assisting the circulation of the blood. Its muscles are too feeble, however, to have more than a local effect. Similar fibres, presumably muscular, are associated with the dorsal and ventral vessels throughout the length of the trunk. These vessels lie in the dorsal and ventral mesenteries. The fibres, which run more or less vertically in contact with the mesenteries, are formed by the adjoining mesoderm cells.

Nervous System.—This in some ways resembles that of the Echinodermata. It consists of dorsal and ventral strands (*d. n.*, *v. n.*) which extend throughout the length of the body. These are merely thickenings of a layer of nerve-fibres which extends over the entire body in the deeper part of the epidermis (Fig. 3). Here and there are *giant nerve-cells*. The part of the dorsal strand which lies in the collar (*neurocord*) is detached from the epidermis. It contains a larger number of the giant nerve-cells than the rest. In some species it encloses a canal, the neurocœle, opening in front and behind. In other species the neurocœle is a closed canal or is represented vestigially by a number of separate cavities (*n. c.*). At the posterior extremity of the collar the dorsal and ventral strands are connected by a ring-like thickening, and there is a thickening around the base of the proboscis. There are no organs of special sense unless the preoral ciliary organ (see p. 9) has this function, but certain cells on the epidermis of the proboscis and on the anterior edge of the collar may be sensory in character. It has been shown that the dorsal and ventral nerve-cords are conduction pathways. If one, or particularly both, are severed, and the proboscis is stimulated, the contraction of the trunk is interfered with. Isolated fragments of the body of Balanoglossus, however, will move reflexly away from tactile stimuli or light.

Locomotion.—This is brought about chiefly by the epidermal cilia (*Saccoglossus*). The cilia of the trunk are capable of synchronised reversal. Ciliary movement is reinforced by peristaltic contraction of the longitudinal muscles which are under the control of the main longitudinal nerve-cords. The animal burrows essentially by peristalsis, and these movements are controlled by the dorsal nerve-cord of the proboscis.

Reproductive Organs.—The sexes are separate, and often differ in shape and colour. The ovaries and testes are simple or branched saccular organs arranged in a double row along the branchial region of the trunk and farther back. They open to the exterior, each by a single pore.

Development.—This varies in different species. In some, e.g. *Saccoglossus.* it is comparatively direct, the larvæ feeding on yolk and not differing markedly from the adults in form. Fertilisation is external. Segmentation is complete and fairly regular, resulting in the formation of a blastula, which is at first rounded, then flattened. On one side of the flattened blastula an invagination takes place. The embryo at this stage is covered with short cilia, with

a ring of stronger cilia. The aperture of invagination closes and the ectoderm and endoderm become completely separate. Hatching generally takes
place at about this stage and the larva swims away, elongates, and a transverse groove (*gr.*) appears (Fig. 5): the mouth is formed by an invagination in the position of the groove. The anus is developed in the position
formerly occupied by the blastopore. Before the mouth appears, a diverticulum is separated off anteriorly from the archenteron. Its cavity gives rise

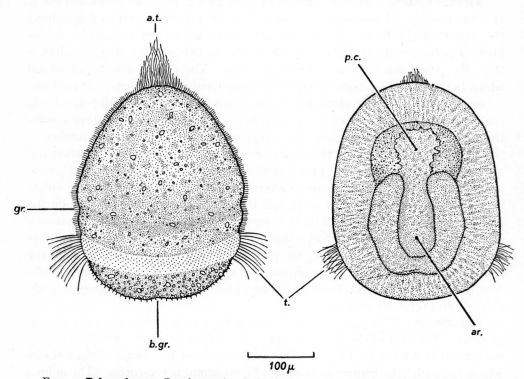

Fig. 5.—**Balanoglossus: Development.** *Left:* Embryo of *Saccoglossus horsti* at hatching stage
(36 hours old). *Right:* The same in optical section (fixed and cleared). *a. t.* apical tuft; *ar.*
archenteron; *b. gr.* blastopore groove; *gr.* first annular groove; *p. c.* proboscis cœlom; *t.* telotroch.
(After Burdon-Jones.)

to the cœlomic cavity of the proboscis. The paired cœlomic cavities of the
collar and of the trunk are formed as outgrowths, either from the posterior wall
of the proboscis cavity, or directly from the wall of the archenteron. By the
appearance of another transverse groove (Fig. 6) the body of the embryo
becomes divided into anterior, middle, and posterior parts. These are the
beginnings of the proboscis, the collar, and the trunk respectively. The
branchial region is marked off by the appearance of a pair of apertures, the
first pair of branchial slits or gill-pores (*g. p.*). Other pairs subsequently
develop behind these.

In the species that undergo a metamorphosis the embryo assumes a larval form termed **Tornaria** (Fig. 7). This stage is somewhat like an echinoderm larva; in fact, it was not until the adelochordate life-history became known that it was conclusively proved that the ciliated tornaria was not a larval echinoderm. It has a looped ciliated band, sometimes lobed, sometimes pro-

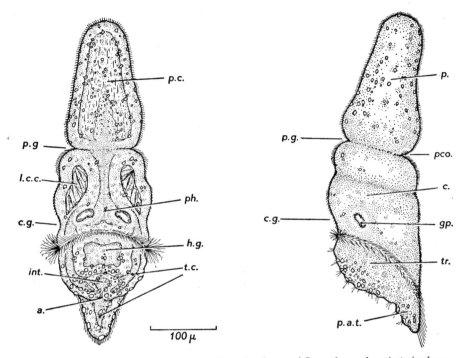

FIG. 6.—**Balanoglossus: Development.** Creeping larva of *Saccoglossus horsti* at six days.

Left: Dorsal view, showing median dorsal reduction of telotroch and continuity of trunk cœlom into tail.

Right: Lateral view, showing forward inclination of grooves, complete tri-metamerism of body and postero-ventral extension of telotroch.

a. anus; *c.* collar; *c. g.* collar groove; *g. p.* gill-pore; *h. g.* hepatic region of gut; *int.* intestine; *p.* proboscis; *p. c.* proboscis cœlom; *p. g.* proboscis groove; *ph.* definitive pharynx and œsophagus; *l. c. c.* left collar cœlom; *p. a. t.* post-anal tail rudiment; *p. c. o.* pre-oral ciliary organ; *tr.* trunk; *t. c.* trunk cœlom. (After Burdon-Jones.)

duced into tentacles, which follows a winding course over most of the preoral surface and has a postoral loop round the mouth. This is termed the *circum-oral ciliated band* (*c. b.*). Its function is to collect the food, which consists of any minute organisms and organic particles that may be suspended in the surrounding water. Further posteriorly, a ring of large cilia encircles the body. This *telotroch* (*t.*) is the main locomotor organ. Some forms have an additional ring of smaller cilia round the posterior (anal) end. At the anterior end, in the middle of the preoral lobe, is an ectodermal thickening, the *apical plate* (*a. pl.*), containing nerve-cells and eye-spots, and, like the apical plate of a trochophore, constituting the nerve-centre of the larva. This disappears in the adult. There is a short alimentary canal with mouth and anus.

At metamorphosis the ciliated bands are lost, the preoral part of the body becoming uniformly ciliated to form the proboscis. A constriction separates this from the collar. The trunk gradually elongates and the gill-slits begin to appear. In some species the neurocord is formed by the separating off of the deeper portion of the ectoderm along the middle line. In others it is

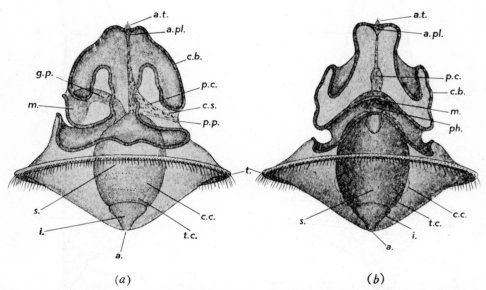

(a)   (b)

FIG. 7.—**Balanoglossus: Development.** Tornaria larva (1–1·5 mm) of *Glossobalanus*. *Left:* Lateral and *Right:* Ventral view: *a.* anal aperture; *a. t.* apical tuft of cilia; *a. pl.* apical plate; *c. b.* circumoral ciliated band; *c. c.* region in which the collar cœlom develops; *c. s.* cardiac sac; *g. p.* position in which gill-pouches develop on the pharynx; *i.* intestine; *m.* mouth; *p. c.* proboscis cœlom; *ph.* pharynx; *p. p.* proboscis pore; *s.* stomach; *t.* telotroch; *t. c.* region in which trunk cœlom develops. (Drawn by C. Burdon-Jones.)

formed by a longitudinal infolding of the whole thickness of the layer, which becomes cut off to form a medullary plate with its edges overlapped by the adjacent ectoderm.

CLASS PTEROBRANCHIA

Three living genera—*Cephalodiscus*, *Rhabdopleura* and *Atubaria*—occur. They are colonial and sedentary, but are nevertheless closely related to the Enteropneusta. They resemble them in having the body divided into three parts or regions—a *proboscis* with a proboscis-cavity, a *collar* with two collar-cavities communicating with the exterior by a pair of collar-pores, and a *trunk* with two distinct lateral cavities. They also have a structure resembling a notochord with the same relations to the nervous system as in Balanoglossus.

They all differ from Balanoglossus firstly in having the alimentary canal bent on itself, so that the anal opening is situated not far from the mouth and secondly, in the presence of arms bearing tentacles arising from the collar. *Cephalodiscus*, moreover, has only a single pair of gill-pores. *Rhabdopleura* lacks such openings, their places being taken, apparently, by a pair of ciliated grooves. *Cephalodiscus* and *Rhabdopleura* live in associations or colonies secreting a common case or investment.

Cephalodiscus has an investment (Fig. 8) in the form of a branching gelatinous structure, which is in some species beset with numerous short filiform processes, and contains a number of tubular cavities (with external openings) occupied by zooids. The latter (Fig. 9) are not in organic continuity, so that, though enclosed in a common investment, they do not form a colony in the sense in which the word is used in describing the hydroid zoophytes. They have a feature in common with such a colony in that they multiply by the formation of buds ; but these become detached before they are mature. With the collar-region (*c.*) is connected a series of usually eight to sixteen 'arms' (*t. p.*). Each of these is beset, except in the case of the male of one species, with numerous very fine pinnately-arranged tentacles. Each arm contains a prolongation of the collar-cavity. The proboscis (Fig. 10, *pr.*) is a shield-shaped lobe overhanging the mouth. Its cavity communicates with the exterior by two proboscis-pores (*p. p.*). The cavities of the collar communicate with the exterior by a pair of ciliated passages opening by the collar-pores. Behind the collar-region on each side is a

Fig. 8.—Order **Pterobranchia,** Family **Cephalodiscidæ.** *Cephalodiscus.* Small portion of a gelatinous colony of *C. dodecalophus* probably measuring about 6″ × 9″. The main stems, bearing branches with filiform processes, vary in breadth from 5 to 15 mm., according to the degree of flattening of the cœnœcium. The main trunks of a colony are attached to stones, sponges or to some other solid substratum. The entire colony tends to lie horizontally rather than erect. (After MacIntosh.)

small area in which the body-wall and that of the pharynx are coalescent. This area is perforated by an opening, the *gill-pore* (*g. p.*). Great numbers of cilia occur on the arms and proboscis. A nerve-strand, dorsal ganglion, or collar-cord, containing nerve-fibres and ganglion-cells, is situated on the dorsal side of the collar deep in the epidermis (*c. n.*). It is prolonged on to the dorsal surface of the proboscis and the dorsal surface of the arms. It is not hollow. On the ventral side of this nerve-strand is a very slender cylindrical cellular cord (*p. d.*) which is continuous behind with the epithelium of the pharynx. This is homologous with the diverticulum of Balanoglossus, and perhaps homologous with the notochord of the Chordata.

Atubaria (Fig. 11), described by Sato as recently as 1936, resembles *Cephalodiscus* in general appearance, but lacks a protective investment. *A. heterolopha* was dredged from a depth of 200–300 metres a few miles from Tokyo Bay when a number of females were found attached to a colony of an athecate hydroid. It is free-living and about 1·5 mm. long. Adults possess four pairs of tentaculate plumes or 'arms' arranged in two rows. These are of different lengths. The antero-internal pair are longest, differing from the others in being club-shaped (Fig. 11). Immature specimens lack arms, bearing merely a single pair of rod-like processes. The collar region is short and thick, and between collar and trunk there are dorsal genital, and ventral mouth apertures. The anal aperture is below the genital opening. The trunk is perforated by a pair of oblique branchial slits (leading to the pharynx) and tapers basally, tail-like extremity. *Atubaria* the *proboscis*, and paired cavities of the collar extend into the

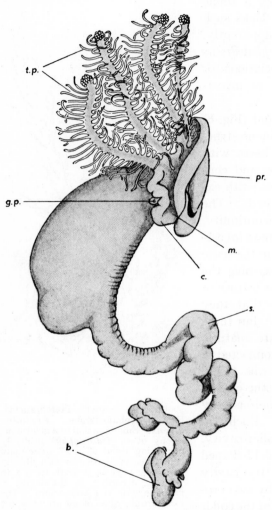

FIG. 9.—*Cephalodiscus:* **Zooid.** The zooid, with budding stalk, has a total length of about 4 mm. Numerous individuals occupy the structure shown in Fig. 8. *b.* buds; *c.* collar; *g. p.* gill-pore; *m.* mouth; *pr.* proboscis; *s.* stalk; *t. p.* tentaculate plumes. (Drawn by C. Burdon-Jones.)

with no attachment disc, into a long exhibits three cœloms: a single cavity in the *proboscis*, and paired cavities inside both collar and trunk. Those of the collar extend into the arms.

The stomochord (the so-called 'notochord') occurs as 'a slender tube, with a small but distinct lumen, surrounded by about a dozen cells' (Komai). It runs obliquely from the dorsal wall of the buccal cavity nearly to the centre of the *proboscis*, where it ends blindly. The spacious buccal cavity bears a ridge on its dorsal wall and internal to this ridge is a short median diverticulum.

The pharynx has folded walls and is lined with ciliated cells. The œsophagus is a funnel-shaped sac which leads to a large sac-like stomach occupying most of the trunk somite. A pylorus separates the stomach from the intestine which ascends to the anus just below the ovary, oviduct, and genital aperture. The mode of reproduction is unknown. The cerebral ganglion lies on the dorsal side of the proboscis giving off anterior and posterior nerve trunks.

Blood-vascular system.— This includes a heart (Fig. 10, *h*.), cardiac sac (*c. s.*), dorsal and ventral vessels, and resembles that of the Enteropneusta.

Reproduction. — Some species of *Cephalodiscus* are hermaphrodite. In most the sexes are separate. The posterior end of the body is drawn out into an appendage on which buds are developed (Fig. 9). A pair of ovaries (Fig. 10, *ov*.) lie in the trunk-cavity, and there is a pair of

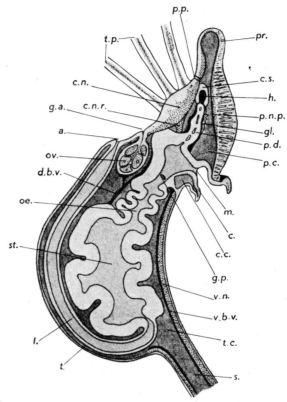

Fig. 10.—*Cephalodiscus:* **Visceral relationships.** The collar septum omitted to show the circumœsophageal nerve ring. *a.* anal aperture; *c.* collar; *c. c.* collar cœlom; *c. n.* collar cord; *c. n. r.* circumœsophageal nerve ring; *c. s.* cardiac sac; *d. b. v.* dorsal blood vessel; *gl.* glomerulus; *g. a.* genital aperture; *g. p.* gill-pore; *h.* heart; *i.* intestine; *m.* mouth; *oe.* œsophagus; *ov.* ovary; *p. c.* proboscis cœlom; *p. d.* proboscis diverticulum; *p. n. p.* proboscis nerve plexus; *p. p.* proboscis pore; *pr.* proboscis; *s.* stalk; *st.* stomach; *t.* trunk; *t. c.* trunk cœlom; *t. p.* tentaculate plumes; *v. b. v.* ventral blood vessel; *v. n.* ventral nerve. (Drawn by C. Burdon-Jones.)

oviducts (*ovd.*) lined by elongated, pigmented epithelium. The development, which is direct (without a free-swimming larval stage), takes place in passages in the investment. In one species, the segmentation is complete, but unequal, and a gastrula is formed by invagination. In another, the segmentation is incomplete, and a gastrula is formed by delamination.

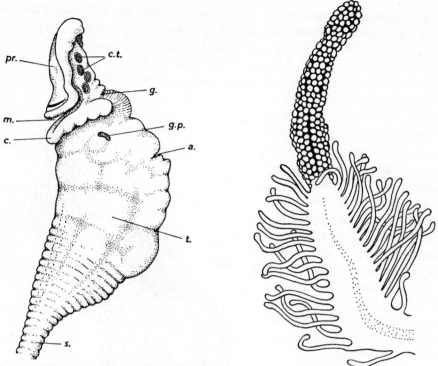

FIG. 11.—Order **Pterobranchia**, Family **Cephalodiscidæ**. *Atubaria*. *A. heterolopha*, a free-living pterobranch, without gelatinous investment (cf. Fig. 8). *Left:* Lateral view of left side. Tentaculate plumes omitted. The total length of the animal with plumes is about 1·25 mm. *Right:* Tentaculate plume, one of a pair from the anterior row. *a.* anus; *c.* collar; *c. t.* cut ends of tentaculate plumes of which there are two rows of four; *g.* genital aperture; *g. p.* gill-pore; *m.* mouth; *pr.* proboscis; *s.* stalk; *t.* trunk. (Drawn by C. Burdon-Jones, modified after Sato.)

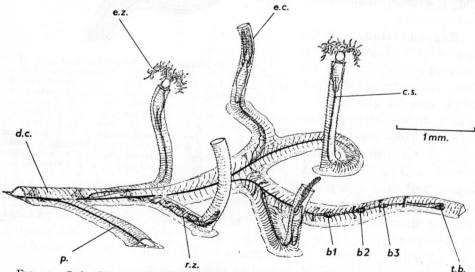

FIG. 12.—Order **Pterobranchia**, Family **Rhabdopleuridæ**. *Rhabdopleura*. A small portion of a colony of *R. normani* showing the inter-relationship of the zooids and a branch carrying a terminal bud and the buds that it has proliferated: *b1, b2, b3,* young buds; *c. s.* contractile stalk; *d. c.* decumbent cœnœcium; *e. c.* erect cœnœcium; *e. z.* extended zooid; *p.* pectocaulus (or black stolon); *r. z.* retracted zooid; *t. b.* terminal bud (or blastozooid). (Drawn by C. Burdon-Jones.)

Rhabdopleura (Fig. 12) occurs in colonies of zooids organically connected together by a creeping stolon and enclosed in, though not in organic continuity with, a system of branching membranous tubes (*d. c.*). The collar region bears a pair of hollow arms (Fig. 13), each with a double row of slender tentacles (*te.*).

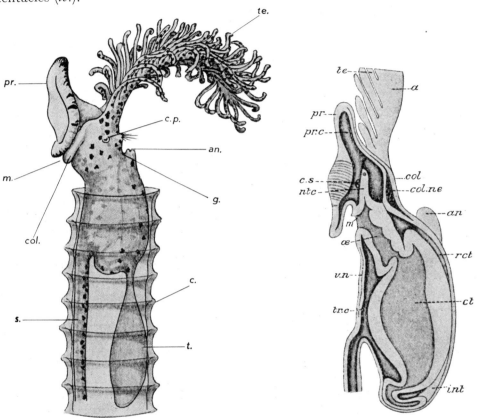

FIG. 13.—***Rhabdopleura.* Mature male zooid and cœnœcium.** The total length of zooid is about 1·5 mm. (Drawn by C. Burdon-Jones.)

Right: Diagrammatic median sagittal section of the above with the gonad and duct omitted. (After Schepotieff.)

a. arm; *an.* anal aperture; *c.* cœnœcium; *col.* collar; *col. ne.* collar nerve; *c. p.* collar pore; *c. s.* cardiac sac; *g.* genital aperture; *int.* intestine; *m.* mouth; *ntc.* proboscis diverticulum; *œ.* œsophagus; *pr.* proboscis; *pr. c.* proboscis cœlom; *rct.* rectum; *s.* stalk or pedicle; *st.* stomach; *t.* testis; *te.* tentacles; *tr. c.* trunk cœlom; *v. n.* ventral nerve.

There are two collar-pores (*c. p.*), each leading into a ciliated canal with an internal funnel, and also a pair of proboscis-pores. The notochord and the nervous system resemble those of *Cephalodiscus*. In *Rhabdopleura* the zooids are of separate sexes, but the colony is hermaphrodite, although it is formed by budding. A free-swimming larval stage occurs.

Cephalodiscus has been found at various widely separated localities in the southern hemisphere. Species occur also off the coast of Japan and Korea.

Some live in shallow water.   None has been found at a greater depth than about 300 fathoms.   *Eocephalodiscus* occurred in the Upper Cretaceous. *Rhabdopleura* has been found in widely separated localities (*e.g.* Shetlands and South Australia).   It seems doubtful if more than one species occurs.

Affinities.—Not all zoologists agree with the inclusion of the Adelochorda among the chordates.   Perhaps, too, the term Hemichorda is inadvisable, since this implies the presence of half a true notochord, a question much in dispute.   Bateson was the first to attempt to homologise the foregut diverticulum of Enteropneusta with the notochord of the Tunicata, Acrania, and the vertebrates, and although this concept was soon criticised by Spengel, it nevertheless gained ground.   There is to-day, however, a growing scepticism. Komai has suggested that the stomochord may be homologous with the anterior pituitary gland (p. 149).   The Adelochorda is probably at least a greatly modified branch from the base of the chordate tree.   The gill-slits, with their tongue-bars, and the dorsal tubular neurocord, are important pointers in this direction.   If the Adelochorda are chordates, it is of special interest that they show many resemblances to the phylum Echinodermata.   The tornaria larva, for instance, is very like an echinoderm larva.

Kozlowski's work on graptolites (by the use of hydrofluoric acid on fossils in a silicious matrix) has now revealed fine skeletal details that suggest that these animals, formerly placed with the Hydrozoa or Ectoprocta, are perhaps most closely allied to the Pterobranchia, and therefore may constitute a chordate class Graptolita.   The tubular skeletons, composed of a succession of concentric rings (each of two half-circles) appeared in the Middle Cambrian, became universal in the Ordovician, and faded slowly and disappeared in the Lower Carboniferous.   Graptolites were colonial, a number of polyps living in each theca budded from a stem or stipe.   Five orders—Dendroidea, Tuboidea, Camaroidea, Stolonoidea and Graptoloidea—have been erected.

SUB-PHYLUM TUNICATA (UROCHORDATA)

THREE main divisions of this ancient group have been recognised : (1) the sessile Ascidiacea, (2) the Thaliacea, and (3) the Appendicularia.   Each has an organisation which, when taken as a whole, is 'significantly unique in itself' (Berrill).   The tunicates are marine.   The Ascidiacea are all sessile, whilst the other two groups are pelagic.   They are especially interesting for several reasons.   They undergo a remarkable series of changes in the course of their life-history.   Some exhibit an *alternation of generations* quite as marked as that existing among so many invertebrates.   In most tunicates there is a *retrogressive metamorphosis* almost, if not quite as striking as that which has been described among the parasitic copepods or the Cirripedia.   The sessile form and ciliary feeding mechanism link the adult tunicates with the pterobranchs, *Rhabdopleura* and *Cephalodiscus*.   Multiplication by budding, so common in the lower groups of invertebrates, but exceptional or absent in the higher, is of very general occurrence in the Tunicata.

The free-swimming tunicate larva is unquestionably chordate in character. In by far the greater number of cases it would be impossible by the study of the adult alone to establish its relation with the Chordata. The affinities of the Tunicata can be determined with certainty only when life-histories are followed out, for the notochord and other significant structures are lost in the later stages of metamorphosis. Although the solitary ascidians were observed by Aristotle (who named them *Thalia*) it was not until the second half of the nineteenth century that Kowalevsky established their chordate relationship.

CLASS ASCIDIACEA

The sessile ascidians have colonised practically every marine habitat from rocky shore to ocean depths, but most species live in shallow coastal waters. They are distributed from the equator to polar seas, and most families are cosmopolitan. This widespread scattering of their kind is consequent upon the fact that although the adults are stationary, the larvæ are well adapted for distribution by ocean currents. The group can be tabulated briefly as follows :

CLASS ASCIDIACEA
  Order Enterogona
    Sub-order Aplousobranchia
      Families Clavelinidæ
             Polycitoridæ
             Polyclinidæ
             Didemnidæ
    Sub-order Phlebobranchiata
      Families Cionidæ
             Diazonidæ
             Perophoridæ
             Corellidæ
             Ascidiidæ
             Hypobythiidæ
             Agnesiidæ
  Order Pleurogona
    Sub-order Stolidobranchiata
      Families Styelidæ
             Pyuridæ
             Molgulidæ

EXAMPLE OF THE CLASS.—THE ASCIDIAN OR SEA-SQUIRT (ASCIDIA)

Sea-squirts occur often in large associations adhering to rocky shores. Some species are found in great numbers attached to wharf-piles. When touched, the ascidian ejects with considerable force two fine jets of sea-water which come from two apertures on its free end. The shape of the ascidian, however, can be profitably studied only in the case of specimens that are completely immersed in the sea-water, for specimens not so immersed always undergo contraction (Fig. 14). In an uncontracted specimen the general shape is that of a short cylinder with a broad base by which it is fixed to the rock. The free end presents a large rounded *oral aperture*, and some little distance from it on one side is a second *atrial aperture* of similar character. Experiments with floating particles reveal that a strong current of water flows steadily

into the oral, and out of the atrial aperture. When the animal is removed from the water both apertures become narrowed (so as to be almost completely closed) by the contraction of sphincters of muscular fibres which surround them. At the same time the walls of the body contract. Streams of water are forced through the apertures and the bulk of the animal is considerably reduced.

Body-wall and Atrial Cavity.—The outer layer of the body-wall is composed of a tough translucent substance forming a thick *test* or *tunic* (Fig. 15, *test*). This consists largely of *tunicin*, which X-ray diffraction analysis has identified with *cellulose*, a characteristic plant product not perhaps otherwise found in animals, except in some 'plant-like' Protozoa. The test of an ascidian is frequently referred to as a cuticle. It is a cuticle in the sense that it lies outside the ectoderm and is derived from that layer in the first instance. There are, however, cells contained in it, which may add to its substance in later stages. They seem to be chiefly derived, not from the ecto-derm, but from the underlying mesoderm, from which they migrate through the ectoderm to the outer surface. These

FIG. 14.—Order **Enterogona**, Family **Ascidiidæ**, *Ascidia*. Entire animal seen from the right side. (After Herdman.)

cells are found scattered through the substance of the test. Running through it are also a number of branching tubes lined with cells, each terminal branch ending in a little bulb-like dilation. The interior of each tube is divided into two channels by a longitudinal septum, which, however, does not completely divide the terminal bulb. Through these tubes (which are of the nature of looped blood-vessels) blood circulates, passing along one channel, through the terminal bulb, and back through the other channel.

When the test is divided (Fig. 15), the soft wall of the body or *mantle* (*mant.*) comes into view. The mantle is suspended within the test and is usually attached firmly to it only round the oral and atrial apertures. The mantle (body-wall) consists of the ectoderm with underlying layers of connective-tissue enclosing muscle fibres. It follows the general shape of the test, and at the two apertures is produced into short and wide tubular prolongations, which are known respectively as the *oral* and *atrial siphons* (Fig. 18, *or. siph.*, *atr. siph.*). These are continuous at their margins with the margins of the apertures of the test, and round the openings are the strong sphincter muscles by which closure is effected. In the rest of the mantle the muscular fibres are arranged in an irregular network, crossing one another in all directions, but for the most part either longitudinally or trans-versely. Within the body-wall is a cavity, the *atrial* or *peribranchial cavity* (*atr. cav.*), communicating with the exterior through the atrial aperture. This cavity is not a cœlom, for it is formed entirely by involution from the outer surface.

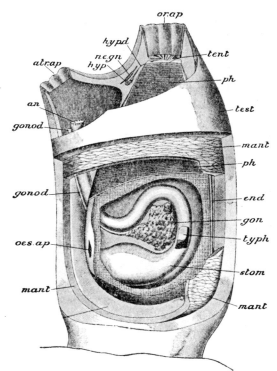

Pharynx.—The oral aperture leads by a short and wide oral passage (*stomodæum*) into a chamber of large dimensions, the *pharynx* or *branchial chamber* (Fig. 15, *ph.*). This is a highly characteristic organ of the Tuni-cata. Its thin and delicate walls are pierced by a number of slit-like apertures, the *stigmata* (Fig. 18, *stigm.*), arranged in trans-verse rows. Through these the cavity of the pharynx communi-cates with the atrial or peribran-chial cavity,[1] which completely surrounds it except along one side. The edges of the stigmata are beset with numerous strong cilia. These drive currents of water from the pharynx into the atrial cavity. The ciliary action

Fig. 15.—*Ascidia*: **Visceral relationships.** The greater part of the test and mantle has been removed from that side so as to bring into view the relation of these layers and of the internal cavities and the course of the alimentary canal, etc. *an.* anus; *atr. ap.* atrial aperture; *end.* endostyle; *gon.* gonad; *gonod.* gonoduct; *hyp.* neural gland; *hyp. d.* duct of neural gland; *mant.* mantle; *ne. gn.* nerve-ganglion; *oes. ap.* aperture of œsophagus; *or. ap.* oral aperture; *ph.* pharynx; *stom.* stomach; *tent.* tentacles; *test,* test; *typh.* typhlosole. (After Herdman.)

draws a current in through the oral aperture, and drives it through the stigmata into the atrial cavity. From there it reaches the exterior through the atrial aperture. The stigmata (Fig. 16) are elongated longitudinally. Groups of from three to ten gill-slits are usually separated by strongly developed internal longitudinal bars which are sometimes thicker and more prominent than the

[1] A distinction is sometimes made between the lateral parts of this space (*peribranchial cavities,* right and left) and the median unpaired (dorsal) part (*atrial cavity*, or *cloaca*), in which the two peribranchial cavities coalesce, and which leads to the exterior through the atrial aperture.

horizontal or transverse bars that separate neighbouring rows.   In all of these
bars run blood-vessels.   Extending across the atrial cavity from the body-wall

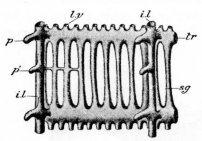

to the wall of the pharynx are a number of
bands of vascular mesodermal tissue, the
connectives or trabeculæ (Fig. 17, *vas. tr.*).

It has already been mentioned that the
atrial cavity does not completely surround
the pharynx.   This is owing to the fact that
the wall of the pharynx is united with the
mantle (Fig. 17).

Along the line of adhesion the inner surface of the pharynx presents a thickening in
the form of a pair of ventral longitudinal
folds separated by a groove.   This specialised grooved thickening is the *endostyle*
(*end.*).

FIG. 16.—*Ascidia:* **Stigmata.** Single
mesh of the branchial sac, seen from
inside.   *i. l.* internal longitudinal bar;
l. v. longitudinal vessel; *p. p'.* papillæ
projecting inwards from the branchial
bar; *sg.* stigma; *tr.* transverse vessel.
(After Herdman.)

The cells covering the endostyle are large and of two kinds—*ciliated cells*
and *gland-cells*.   They are equipped with cilia at their free ends.   These cilia
drive floating particles that come
within their influence outwards
towards the oral aperture.   The
gland cells secrete and discharge
a viscid mucous matter.   Anteriorly the endostyle is continuous with a ciliated ridge
which runs circularly round the
anterior end of the pharynx.   In
front of, and parallel with, this
circular ridge is another ridge of
similar character: these are the
peripharyngeal ridges.   The groove
between them is the *peripharyngeal
groove*.   Dorsally, *i.e.* opposite the
endostyle,   the   posterior   peripharyngeal ridge passes into a
median, much more prominent,
longitudinal ridge, the *dorsal lamina*
(*dors. lam.*), which runs along the
middle of the dorsal surface of the

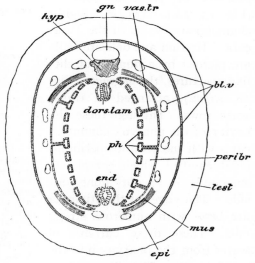

FIG. 17.—*Ascidia:* **Pharyngeal region.** *bl. v.*
blood-vessels; *dors. lam.* dorsal lamina; *epi.*
epidermis; *end.* endostyle; *gn.* ganglion; *hyp.*
neural gland; *mus.* muscular layer of wall of body;
peribr. peribranchial cavity; *ph.* pharynx; *test,*
test; *vas. tr.* vascular trabeculæ.   (After Julin.)

pharynx to the opening of the œsophagus.   In the living animal the lamina
is capable of being bent to one side in such a way as to form a deep groove.
The mucus secreted by the gland-cells of the endostyle is driven from it by the

ciliated cells and conveyed laterally round the inner surface of the pharyngeal wall, mainly by the action of small *frontal cilia*, which are borne on the gill-bars and project into the lumen of the pharynx. As the mucus passes across the stigmata, it entangles microscopic organisms that are contained in the out-going water and carries them round to the dorsal lamina. This bears cilia which drive the mucus and the contained food posteriorly to the opening of the œsophagus through which they are in-gested.

Some little distance in front of the anterior periph-aryngeal ridge, at the inner or posterior end of the oral siphon, is a circlet of delicate *tentacles* (Fig. 18, *tent.*).

Alimentary Canal.—The œsophagus (Figs. 15, 18, *œs.*) leads from the pharynx (near the posterior end of the dorsal lamina) to the stomach (*stom.*), which, together with the in-testine, lies embedded in the mantle on the left-hand side. The stomach is a large fusi-form sac with comparatively thick glandular walls which are said to secrete a strong carbohydrate-splitting enzy-me and weaker proteolytic and lipolytic ferments as well. Along its inner wall is a thickening—the *typhlosole*. There is no liver. A system of delicate tubules, the *pyloric gland*, ramifies over the wall

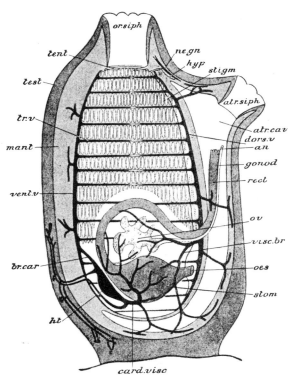

FIG. 18.—*Ascidia:* **Circulation and reproduction.** The test and mantle have been removed. *an.* anus; *atr. cav.* atrial cavity; *atr. siph.* atrial siphon; *br. car.* branchio-cardiac vessel; *card. visc.* cardio-visceral vessel; *dors. v.* dorsal vessel; *gonod.* gonoduct; *ht.* heart; *hyp.* neural gland; *mant.* mantle; *ne. gn.* nerve-ganglion; *œs.* œsophagus; *or. siph.* oral siphon; *ov.* ovary; *rect.* rectum; *stigm.* stigmata; *stom.* stomach; *tent.* tentacles; *test.* test; *tr. v.* transverse vessel; *vent v.* ventral vessel; *visc. br.* viscero-branchial vessel. (From Herdman, after Perrier.)

of the intestine and is connected with a duct opening into the stomach. Little is known of its significance: both digestive and excretory functions have been suggested. The thin-walled intestine is bent around into a double loop and runs forward to terminate in an anal aperture (*an.*) situated in the atrial cavity.

Blood Vascular System.—The system is well developed. The heart (Fig. 18, *ht.*) is a simple muscular sac, situated near the stomach in the pericardium.

The last-named is entirely cut off from the surrounding spaces in which the blood is contained.   Its mode of pulsation is remarkable.   The contractions are of a peristaltic character, and follow one another from one end of the heart to the other for a certain time. Then follows a short pause, and when the contractions begin again they flow in the opposite direction.   Thus the direction of the current of blood through the heart is reversed at regular intervals. There are no true vessels, the blood circulating through a system of channels or sinuses devoid of epithelial lining, and of spaces or lacunæ, forming a hæmocœle.   In the description that follows, therefore, the word vessel is not used in its strict sense.   At each end of the heart is given off a large 'vessel'. That given off ventrally, the *branchio-cardiac vessel* (*br. car.*), runs along the middle of the ventral side of the pharynx below (externally to) the endostyle and gives off a number of branches which extend along the bars between the rows of stigmata.   These branches give rise to smaller branches which pass between the stigmata of each row.   The vessel given off from the dorsal end of the heart—the *cardio-visceral* (*card. visc.*)—breaks up into branches which ramify over the surface of the alimentary canal and other organs.   This system of visceral vessels or lacunæ opens into a large sinus, the *viscero-branchial* (*visc. br.*).   This runs along the middle of the dorsal wall of the pharynx externally to the dorsal lamina, and communicates with the dorsal ends of the series of transverse branchial vessels.   In addition to these principal vessels there are numerous lacunæ extending everywhere throughout the body, and a number of branches, given off both from the branchio-cardiac and cardio-visceral vessels, ramify, as already stated, in the substance of the test.

The direction of the circulation through the main vessels differs according to the direction of the contraction of the heart.   When the heart contracts in a dorso-ventral direction, the blood flows through the branchio-cardiac trunk to the ventral wall of the pharynx and through the transverse vessels.   After undergoing oxygenation in the finer branches between the stigmata, it reaches the viscero-branchial vessel, by which it is carried to the system of visceral lacunæ.   From these it flows back to the heart through the cardio-visceral vessel.   When the contractions take the opposite direction, the course of this main current of the blood is reversed.   Because capillaries are absent, ascidian blood and tissue fluid are intermingled.   Lymphocytes, phagocytic macrophages (including ingested substances), have been recognised, as well as vacuolated compartment cells (reserve food-containers) and other coloured and colourless cells.

Some but not all ascidians possess a green vanadium-containing pigment which is carried in special *vanadocytes* and also flows free in the plasma.   This has been claimed, but not proved, to be a respiratory pigment.   In fact, there is some evidence that the oxidation potential of the pigment is too low for it to function in this way.   The exact method of respiration is still unknown.   In some ascidians niobium, and very little vanadium occurs (Carlisle).

Excretion seems to be carried out by the *nephrocytes* circulating in the blood. These cells contain particles of urates and xanthine which are disposed of by storage, in the form of concretions, in special *excretory vesicles* or *renal organs*.

Nervous System.—This is of an extremely simple character. There is a single *neural ganglion* (Figs. 15, 17, 18 and 19, *ne. gn.*, *gn.* and *n. g.*) which lies between the oral and atrial apertures, embedded in the mantle. This is elongated in the dorso-ventral direction, and gives off at each end nerves which pass to the various parts of the body. In deganglionated individuals reflexes such as the so-called 'cross reflex' (whereby touching one siphon causes the other to close before the one stimulated) and body contraction are radically impaired.

Neural Gland.—This (Figs. 15, 18, *hyp.* ; Fig. 19, *gld.*, and Fig. 20, *n. gl.*) lies on the ventral side of the neural ganglion and is sometimes considered to be homologous with at least part of the hypophysis in vertebrates. This is still a controversial subject, though there appears to be good evidence that the neural gland is of a secretory nature. A duct (Fig. 19, *dct.*, and Fig. 20, *gl. d.*) runs forward from it and opens into the cavity of the pharynx ; the termination of the duct is dilated to form the *ciliated funnel*, and this is folded on itself to form a prominence, the *dorsal tubercle*, which projects into the cavity of the pharynx.

Reproductive System.—The sexes are united. The ovary and the testis are situated close together on the left-hand side of the body in the intestinal loop. Continuous with the gonad is a duct—an oviduct or sperm-duct, as the case may be. This

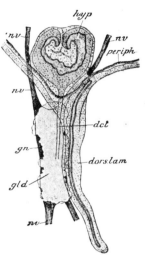

FIG. 19.—*Ascidia:* **Dorsal tubercle, nerve-ganglion, and associated parts.** From below. *dct.* duct of neural gland; *dors. lam.* dorsal lamina; *gld.* neural gland; *gn.* ganglion; *hyp.* dorsal tubercle; *nv.*, *nv.* nerves; *periph.* peripharyngeal ridge. (After Julin.)

opens into the atrial cavity close to the anus. If sex products from another individual are drawn into the mouth, with the incurrent sea water, it is found that some of the eggs or sperm become lodged in the ciliated funnel. It has been suggested that the neural gland thereupon secretes a substance similar to, or even identical with, the gonadotrophic hormone produced by the anterior lobe of the pituitary of vertebrates (Fig. 96, p. 150). There is evidence that the adjacent ganglion is sensitive to this hormone and responds by nervous stimulation of the gonads to release their gametes. In this way adjacent individuals may be stimulated to spawn at the same time, ensuring fertilisation. It is not impossible that the anterior pituitary may have evolved from a ' neural gland ' which was responsible for synchronisation of spawning in a somewhat ascidian-like ancestor.

Development and Metamorphosis.—In the Ascidiacea fertilisation usually takes place after the ova have passed out from the atrial cavity. But in a few simple, and most (if not all) compound forms fertilisation takes place in the atrium, or in the swollen, terminal portion of the oviduct, or in a special outgrowth of the atrium, serving as a brood-sac. After internal fertilisation the zygotes may be discharged immediately (as in most species of *Polycarpa*), retained until the 2- or 32-cell stage (*P. pomaria*), or discharged as blastulæ or gastrulæ ; or expulsion may be delayed until the tailed larval stage is attained. Self-fertilisation is usually rendered impossible by ova and sperms becoming mature at different times. Sometimes, however, both ripen simultaneously.

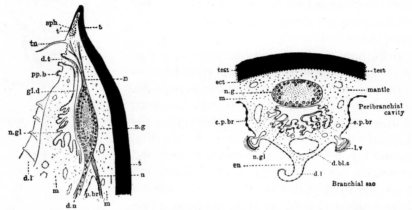

Fig. 20.—*Ascidia:* **Nervous system.** Antero-dorsal aspect showing relationships with the layers of the body; *Left:* in sagittal section; *Right:* in transverse section. *d. bl. s.* dorsal blood-vessel; *d. l.* dorsal lamina; *d. n.* dorsal nerve; *d. t.* dorsal tubercle; *ect.* ectoderm; *en.* endoderm; *e. p. br.* epithelium of peribranchial cavity; *gl. d.* duct of neural gland; *l. v.* points to the ciliated epithelium covering a longitudinal vessel of branchial sac (pharynx); *m.* mantle; *n.* nerve; *n. g.* ganglion; *n. gl.* neural gland; *p. br.* peribranchial cavity; *pp. b.* periphargyngeal band; *sph.* oral sphincter; *t., t'.* test; *tn.* tentacle. (After Herdman.)

At the same time, simultaneous maturation of eggs and spermatozoa does not necessarily imply self-fertilisation. Attempted *in vitro* fertilisations with gametes of a single individual almost always fail.

A somewhat complicated series of membranes invests the ovum. The maturing oocyte is enclosed in a layer of flat cells. These are the primitive *follicle-cells*—derived in most species from undifferentiated cells of the ovary. On the surface of this layer is developed a structureless basal membrane. The follicle-cells increase by division and soon form a sphere of cubical cells. Certain of the cells migrate into the interior of the sphere and form a layer on the surface of the ovum. Others penetrate into the latter so as to lie in the superficial strata of the yolk. The layer of cells on the surface of the ovum are termed the *test-cells* (Fig. 21, *e*) : they afterwards develop on the outer surface a thin structureless layer, the *chorion* (*d*), and internal to them is formed a gelatinous layer (*x*) through which the test-cells in a degenerated condition become scattered. Meantime, external to the follicle-cells, between them and the basal membrane, has appeared a layer of flattened epithelial cells. This, with the basal membrane, is lost before the egg is discharged. In all the simple ascidians, with the exception of the few in which development takes place internally, the protoplasm of the follicle-cells (Fig. 21, c) is greatly vacuolated, so as to appear frothy. The cells become greatly enlarged, projecting like papillæ on the surface and buoying up the developing ovum.

Segmentation is complete and approximately equal, but in the eight-cell stage four of the cells are smaller and four larger. The smaller, situated on the future dorsal side, are the beginning of the endoderm. The four larger form the greater part, if not the whole, of the ectoderm. In the following stages the ectoderm cells multiply more rapidly than the endoderm, so that they soon become the smaller. In the sixteen-celled stage the embryo (Fig. 22, A) has the form of a flattened blastula (*placula*) with ectoderm on one side and endoderm on the other, and with a small segmentation-cavity. The transition to the gastrula stage is, in most ascidians, effected by a process intermediate in character between embolic and epibolic invagination; in some the invagination is of a distinctly epibolic character. In the former case the ectoderm cells continue to increase more rapidly than the endoderm. The whole embryo becomes curved, with the concavity on the endodermal side, and the ectoderm extends over the endo-

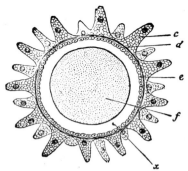

Fig. 21.—*Ciona:* **Development.** Fertilised egg from the oviduct after the basal membrane and layer of flattened cells have been thrown off. c. follicle-cells; d. chorion; e, test-cells; f, ovum; x, gelatinous layer. (From Korschelt and Heider, after Kupffer.)

derm, the two layers coming to lie in close contact and the segmentation-cavity thus becoming obliterated. The concavity deepens until the embryo assumes the form of a saucer-shaped gastrula with an archenteron and a blastopore, which is at first a very wide aperture extending along the whole of the future dorsal side. The blastopore gradually becomes constricted (Fig. 22, B). The closure takes place anteriorly, extending backwards. The opening is eventually reduced to a small pore at the posterior end of the dorsal surface.

The embryo elongates in the direction of the future long axis. The dorsal surface becomes recognisable by being flatter, while the ventral remains convex. The ectoderm cells bordering the blastopore are distinguished from the rest by their more cubical shape. These cells form the earliest rudiment of the nervous system. They become arranged, as the blastopore undergoes contraction, in the form of a *medullary plate* on the dorsal surface. On the surface of this plate appears a *medullary groove*. This is bounded by right and left *medullary folds*, which pass into one another behind the blastopore.

The medullary folds grow upwards and inwards over the medullary groove. They unite together (*D*), the union beginning behind and progressing forwards in such a way as to form a canal, the *neurocœle*, in the hinder portion of which is the opening of the blastopore. In this process of closing-in of the medullary groove, the fold which passes round behind the blastopore takes an important part, growing forwards over the posterior portion of the canal. The blastopore, thus enclosed in the medullary canal, persists for a time as a small opening

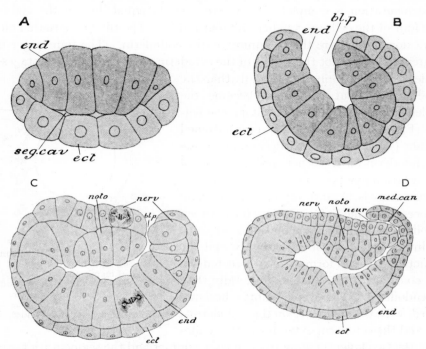

Fig. 22.—*Clavellina:* **Development.** Early stages: *A*, flattened blastula; *B*, early gastrula; *C*, approximately median optical section of more advanced gastrula in which the blastopore has become greatly reduced and in which the first rudiment of the notochord is discernible; *D*, similar view of a later larva in which the medullary canal has begun to be closed in posteriorly. *bl. p.* blastopore; *ect.* ectoderm; *end.* endoderm; *med. can.* medullary canal; *nerv.* cells destined to give rise to the nerve-cord; *neur.* neuropore; *noto.* notochord; *seg. cav.* segmentation cavity. (*A* and *B* from Korschelt and Heider, after Seeliger; *C* and *D* after Van Beneden and Julin.)

—the *neurenteric canal*—by which the neurocœle and enteric cavity are placed in communication. At the anterior end of the medullary canal, owing to its incomplete closure in this region, there remains for a time an opening—the *neuropore* (Fig. 23, *neur.*)—leading to the exterior.

A *notochord* (Figs. 22, *C*, *D*, 23 and 24, *noto.*) is formed from certain of the cells of the wall of the archenteron along the middle line of the dorsal side. These are arranged to form an elongated cord of cells which becomes completely constricted off from the endoderm of the wall of the archenteron, and comes to lie between the latter and the medullary groove. Laterally, certain cells of the endoderm divide to give rise to a pair of longitudinal strands of cells—the rudiments of the mesoderm (Fig. 23, *mes.*). During this process of mesoderm-formation, there are no diverticula developed from the archenteron.

The embryo (Fig. 23, *B*) now becomes pear-shaped, the narrow part being the rudiment of the future tail. As this narrow portion elongates, the part of the enteric cavity which it contains soon disappears, coming to be represented only by a strand of endoderm cells. This strand gives rise in the middle to the backward extension of the notochord, laterally to the mesoderm of the tail, and ventrally to a cord of endoderm cells continuous with the wall of the enteric cavity in front.

The caudal region rapidly increases in length. The anterior or trunk region, at first round, becomes oval. At its anterior end there appear three processes of the ectoderm, the rudiments of the *adhesive papillæ* (Fig. 24, *adh.*), organs by which the larva subsequently becomes fixed. The ectoderm cells at an early stage secrete the rudiments of the cellulose test. In the caudal region, this forms longitudinal dorsal and ventral flaps which take on the function of unpaired fins.

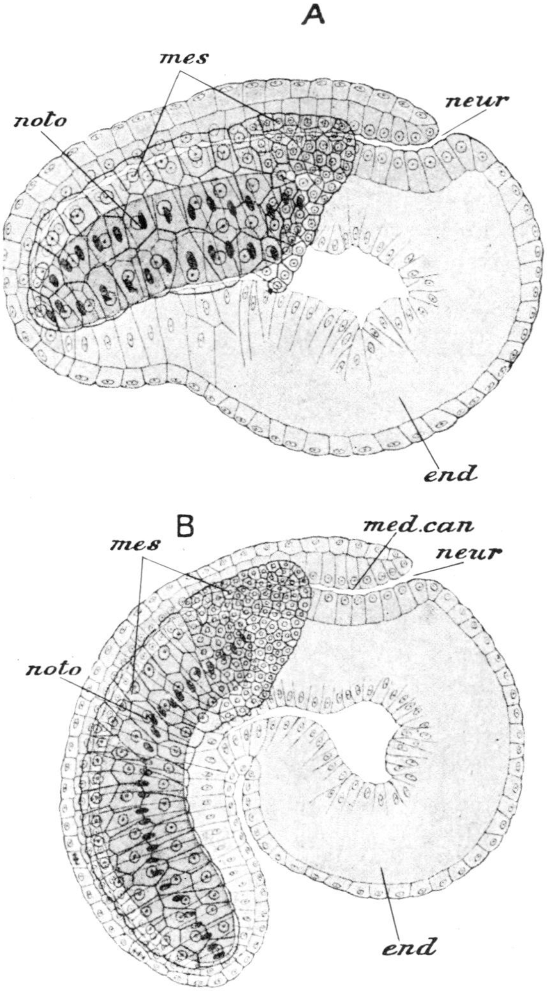

The medullary canal becomes enlarged at its anterior

Fig. 23.—*Clavellina*: **Development.** Later stages: *A*, approximately median optical section of a larva in which the medullary canal (neurocœle) has become enclosed throughout, communicating with the exterior only by the neuropore at the anterior end and with the archenteron by the neurenteric canal; *B*, larva with a distinct rudiment of the tail and well-formed mesoderm-layer and notochord. Letters as in preceding figure; in addition, *mes.* mesoderm. (After Van Beneden and Julin.)

end. A vesicular outgrowth from this enlarged anterior portion forms the *sense-vesicle* (*sens. ves.*). The posterior narrow part forms the caudal portion of the central nervous system (spinal cord). Masses of pigment in relation to the sense-vesicle early form the rudiment of the two larval sense-organs, otocyst (or statocyst), and eye.   The part behind this presents a thickened wall with a narrow lumen.   This is known as the *ganglion of the trunk.*

The embryonic alimentary canal consists of two regions, a wide region situated altogether in front of the notochord, and a narrower portion situated behind in the region of the notochord.   The wider anterior part gives rise to the pharynx.   The posterior part gives rise to the œsophagus, stomach, and intestine.   The mouth-opening is formed shortly before the escape of the embryo from the egg.   An ectodermal invagination is formed at the anterior end, and an endodermal diverticulum from the archenteron grows out to meet it. Then the two coalesce and the oral passage is thus formed.   The stomach and

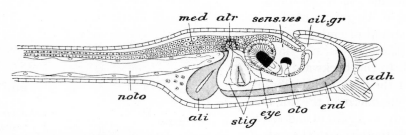

FIG. 24.—*Ascidia:* **Development.**   Free-swimming larva of *Ascidia mammillata,* lateral view. *adh.* adhesive papillæ; *ali.* alimentary canal; *atr.* atrial aperture; *cil. gr.* ciliated diverticulum, becoming ciliated funnel; *end.* endostyle; *eye,* eye; *med.* nerve-cord (ganglion of trunk); *noto.* notochord; *oto.* otocyst; *sens. ves.* sense-vesicle; *stig.* earliest stigmata.   (From Korschelt and Heider, after Kovalevsky.)

intestine of the larva of most species have no lumen and the organism does not feed.

The rudiments of the heart and pericardial cavity first appear as a hollow outgrowth from the archenteron.   This outgrowth subsequently becomes constricted off and involuted to form a double-walled sac.   The inner layer of the sac forms the wall of the heart, while the outer layer gives rise to the wall of the pericardium.

The first beginnings of the atrial cavity appear as a pair of invaginations of the ectoderm which grow inwards and form a pair of pouches, each opening on the exterior by an aperture.   There is a difference of opinion as to some points in the history of these atrial pouches.   It remains uncertain to what extent the ectoderm and endoderm respectively share in the formation of the atrial cavity.   Spaces, into the formation of which the two ectodermal diverticula at least largely enter, eventually grow round the pharynx and give rise to the atrial cavity.   Perforations, which become the stigmata, and which are primarily two in number, place the cavity of the pharynx in communication with the surrounding space.   The two openings of the atrial pouches subsequently coalesce to form the single permanent atrial aperture.

It will be useful now, at the cost of a little repetition, to summarise the various characteristics of the larval ascidian at the stage when it escapes from the egg and becomes free-swimming (Fig. 24). In general shape it bears some resemblance to a minute tadpole, consisting of an oval trunk and a long

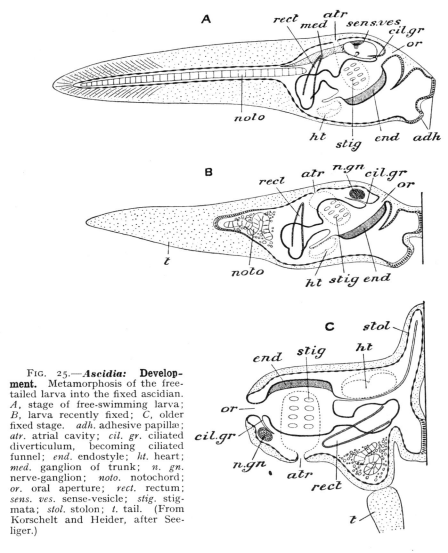

FIG. 25.—*Ascidia:* **Development.** Metamorphosis of the free-tailed larva into the fixed ascidian. *A*, stage of free-swimming larva; *B*, larva recently fixed; *C*, older fixed stage. *adh.* adhesive papillæ; *atr.* atrial cavity; *cil. gr.* ciliated diverticulum, becoming ciliated funnel; *end.* endostyle; *ht.* heart; *med.* ganglion of trunk; *n. gn.* nerve-ganglion; *noto.* notochord; *or.* oral aperture; *rect.* rectum; *sens. ves.* sense-vesicle; *stig.* stigmata; *stol.* stolon; *t.* tail. (From Korschelt and Heider, after Seeliger.)

laterally-compressed tail. The tail is fringed with a caudal fin. This is merely a delicate outgrowth of the thin test covering the whole of the surface. Running through the delicate fringe is a series of striæ, presenting somewhat the appearance of fin-rays. In the axis of the tail there occurs the notochord (Fig. 25, *noto.*), which at this stage consists of a cylindrical cord of gelatinous substance enclosed in a layer of cells. Parallel with this runs, on the dorsal side, the narrow caudal portion of the nerve-cord. At the sides are bands of muscle fibres. In the trunk the nerve-cord is dilated to form the ganglion of the trunk, and, further forwards, expands into the sense-vesicle (*sens. ves.*) with the otocyst or statocyst (Fig. 24, *oto.*) and eye. The enteric canal is distinguishable into pharynx, œsophagus, stomach, and intestine, but is not yet functional since the mouth is covered by the continuous test. The pharynx, however, is already equipped with an endostyle in its ventral floor, and also with varying numbers of stigmata which pierce its walls. The atrial cavity has grown round the pharynx, and opens on the exterior by a single aperture only (*atr.*). The heart and pericardial cavity have been formed. The period in which the larva remains in this free-swimming stage varies between species. In *Botryllus* the free-swimming period is from 90 to 180 seconds. In other species it may last a month. Generally it lasts only a day or two. Then the larva fixes itself by the adhesive papillæ and begins the *retrogressive metamorphosis* by which it attains the adult condition.

The chief changes involved in the retrogressive metamorphosis (Fig. 25) are the increase in the number of pharyngeal stigmata; the diminution, and eventually the complete disappearance, of the tail with the contained notochord and caudal part of the nerve-cord; the disappearance of the eye and the otocyst; the dwindling of the central part of the nervous system which gives rise both to the adult ganglion and to the neural gland; and the gradual development of the reproductive organs. *Thus, from an active free-swimming larva, with complex organs of special sense, and provided with a notochord and well-developed nervous system, there is a retrogression to the fixed inert adult, in which all the parts indicative of affinities with the vertebrates have become aborted, except the gill-slits, endostyle, and other parts of the feeding mechanism.*

In some simple ascidians, and in the composite forms in which development takes place within the body of the parent, the metamorphosis may be considerably abbreviated. But there is always (so far as is known) a tailed larva except in the genera *Molgula* and *Pelonaia*, in which the tailed stage is lacking and only an obscure endodermal rudiment represents the notochord.

GENERAL ORGANISATION OF ASCIDIACEA

General Features.—Among the simple ascidians there is a considerable degree of uniformity of structure, and little need be added here to the account given of the example. Their shape varies a good deal: it is sometimes cylindrical, sometimes globular, sometimes compressed. They are usually sessile and attached by a broad base, often with root-like processes, but in other cases (*e.g. Boltenia*) elevated on a longer or shorter stalk. Most are solitary; but some (the so-called social *ascidians*) multiply by budding, stolons being given off on which new zooids are developed, so that associations or colonies are formed. However, the connection between the zooids is not close, and their tests remain distinct and separate. The test varies considerably in consistency, being sometimes almost gelatinous, transparent or translucent, sometimes tough and leathery. Occasionally it is hardened by encrusting sand-grains or fragments of shells, or by spicules of carbonate of lime. Calcareous spicules may be developed in the substance of the mantle. The apertures always have the same position and re-

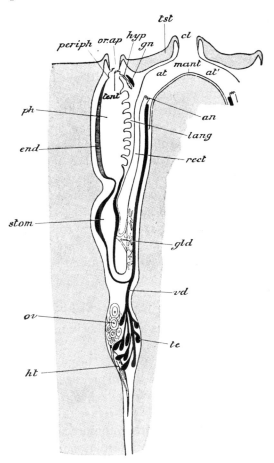

Fig. 27.—**Composite Ascidian.** A colonial zooid. The zooids are in clumps, as seen in a vertical section of the colony. *an.* anus; *at.* atrium; *at'.* atrium of adjoining zooid; *cl.* cloaca common to the two zooids; *end.* endostyle; *gld.* digestive gland; *gn.* nerveganglion; *ht.* heart; *hyp.* neural gland; *lang.* languets; *mant.* mantle; *or. ap.* oral aperture; *ov.* ovary; *periph.* peripharyngeal band; *ph.* pharynx; *rect.* rectum; *stom.* stomach; *te.* testis; *tent.* tentacles; *tst.* test, or common gelatinous mass; *v. d.* vas deferens. (After Herdman.)

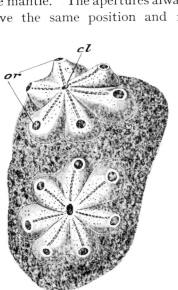

Fig. 26.—Order **Pleurogona,** Family **Styelidæ. Botryllus.** A composite ascidian, *B. violaceus. or.* oral apertures; *cl.* opening of common cloacal chamber. (After Milne-Edwards.)

lations, varying only in their relative prominence. The pharynx varies in its size as compared with the rest of the internal organs, and in the position which it occupies with regard to the various parts of the alimentary canal. It varies, too, in the number and arrangement of the stigmata. The tentacles are sometimes simple, sometimes compound ; and the dorsal lamina may or may not be divided up into a system of lobes or *languets* (Fig. 27, *lang.*).

Composite Ascidians.—In the composite ascidians the zooids are embedded in a common gelatinous mass formed of their united tests. The gelatinous colony thus formed is sometimes flat and encrusting, sometimes branched or lobed, sometimes elevated on a longer or shorter stalk. In certain forms the gelatinous substance is hardened by the inclusion of numerous sand-grains. The arrangement of the zooids differs greatly. Sometimes they occur irregularly dotted over the entire surface without exhibiting any definite arrangement. Sometimes they are arranged in rows or regular groups. In *Botryllus* (Fig. 26) they form star-shaped, radiating sets around a common cloacal chamber into which the atrial apertures of the zooids lead, while the oral apertures are towards their outer ends. In essential structure the zooids (Fig. 26) of such colonies resemble the simple ascidians. At one time it was held that solitary and composite ascidians fell into two distinct Orders. Today it is considered that the ability to bud is primitive in ascidians and that it has been lost independently in several lines. Likewise, the solitary condition is secondary and has been acquired separately in different groups.

CLASS THALIACEA

The thaliaceans are free-swimming tunicates, sometimes simple, sometimes colonial, and never provided with a caudal appendage in the adult condition. The body is transparent. The test is a permanent structure. The muscular fibres of the body-wall are arranged in complete or interrupted ring-like bands, or held diffusely. The mouth and atriopore are situated at opposite ends of the body. The pharynx has either two large, or many small, stigmata leading into an atrial cavity which communicates with the exterior by the atrial aperture. There is usually an alternation of generations of a most remarkable kind. There may, or may not be a tailed larval stage.

Three orders—Doliolida, Pyrosomida, and Salpida—are recognised.

ORDER DOLIOLIDA (CYCLOMYARIA)

The order is restricted to a single family, Doliolidæ, made up of perhaps four genera, *Doliopsis* (= *Anchinia*), *Doliolum* (Figs. 28, 29), *Dolioletta*, and *Dolioloides*. These hermaphrodite animals are in general found in the phytoplankton zone in tropical and sub-tropical seas. The species are commonest down to 200 metres, but 'nurse' forms have been dredged from 3,000 metres. They are rarely found in shallow coastal water, but may occur in vast numbers in suitable areas. They have been studied rarely alive, but nevertheless a good deal has been learnt of their life-histories. The solitary sexual individual or *gonozooid* is barrel-shaped. The test is transparent and delicate, and so it is possible to see clearly the eight characteristic muscle-bands which completely encircle the body (hence the name Cyclomyaria). Unlike the ascidians, the oral and atrial apertures (Fig. 29, *r. ap.*, *atr. ap.*) are at opposite extremities. The relations of the various organs have undergone a corresponding modification. The oral aperture leads into a wide pharynx (Fig. 28, 4) occupying at least the anterior half of the body. The posterior wall of the pharynx alone is usually perforated by stigmata. An endostyle (11) occurs, and a peripharyngeal band; but there is no dorsal lamina. The heart lies immediately posterior to the endostyle in the mid-ventral line. The gut-loop, of variable shape from genus to genus, lies in the ventro-posterior region of the body. The nervous system is composed of a dorsal ganglion which lies in the third or fourth inter-muscular zone (3). Fibres from the ganglion radiate to

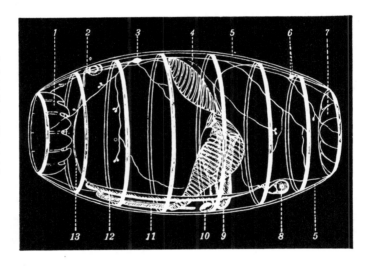

FIG. 28.—Order **Doliolida,** Family **Doliolidæ, Doliolum.** Gonozoid. *1.* oral aperture; *2.* ciliated pit; *3.* ganglion and nerves; *4.* pharynx; *5.* mantle; *6.* sense-cells; *7.* atrial aperture; *8.* ovary; *9.* intestine; *10.* heart; *11.* endostyle; *12.* testis; *13.* peripharyngeal band. (From Young, after Neumann.)

the eight muscle-bands. Branches from each principal fibre terminate in groups of sensory cells (6).

Surrounding each aperture is a series of ten or twelve lobes—the *oral* and *atrial lobes*—in which there are sense organs. The first and last of the muscular hoops serve as sphincters for the two orifices. *Doliolum* moves through the water by jet propulsion. The contraction of the muscle-bands drives water backwards out of the atrial sac and so propels the animal forward.

The reproductive organs—testis (12) and ovary (8)—are in the ventral region. The eggs are discharged into the capacious cloacal aperture and escape into the sea-water where, if fertilised, they develop independently. Development appears to be not unlike that of the simple ascidians in all essential respects. There is total segmentation, followed by the formation of an embolic gastrula. The larva (Fig. 29) has a tail with a notochord (*noto.*) consisting of about forty cells, and a body in which the characteristic muscular bands soon make their appearance. This tailed larva becomes the asexual stage or 'nurse'. By and by the tail aborts, and two processes, one postero-dorsal, the other ventral, known respectively as the *cadophore* (*dors. st.*) and the *ventral stolon* (*vent. st.*), grow out from the body of the larva. On the stolon are formed a number of slight projections or buds. These become constricted off, and in

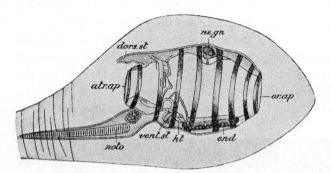

FIG. 29.—**Doliolum: Development.** Late stage in the development of the tailed larva. *atr. ap.* atrial aperture; *dors. st.* cadophore; *end.* endostyle; *ht.* heart; *ne. gn.* nerve-ganglion; *noto.* notochord; *or. ap.* oral aperture; *vent. st.* ventral stolon. (After Uljanin.)

the form of little groups of cells, each consisting of seven strings of cells with an ectodermal investment, creep over the surface of the body (Fig. 30, *e*, and Fig. 31) till they reach the cadophore, to which they attach themselves after multiplying by division. The cadophore soon becomes elongated, and the bud-like bodies attached to it develop into zooids. As the long chain of zooids thus established is further developed, the parent *Doliolum* (Fig. 30) loses its stigmata, its endostyle, and its alimentary canal. At the same time

FIG. 30.—**Doliolum: Development.** Lateral view of asexual stage, showing the early development of the buds. *atr. ap.* atrial aperture; *dors. st.* cadophore; *e.* embryos passing over the surface from the ventral stolon to the cadophore; *ht.* heart; *ne. gn.* nerve-ganglion; *or. ap.* oral aperture; *vent. st.* ventral stolon. (After Uljanin.)

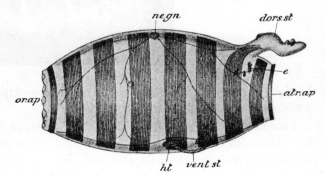

the muscle-bands increase in thickness and the nervous system attains a higher development, until the whole parent comes to play a part like that of the nectocalyx of a siphonophore (Vol. I). Thus, its secondary function is to propel the colony through the water by its contractions.

The zooids of the cadophore consist of two sets, differing from one another in position and in future history—the *lateral zooids* and the *median zooids*. The lateral zooids serve solely to carry on the nourishment and respiration of the colony, and do not undergo any further development. Some of the median buds, on the other hand, become detached and take on the special character of *phorozooids*. When free, each phorozooid carries with it the stalk by means of which it was attached to the stolon. On this stalk there have previously become attached a number of buds which are destined after a time to be developed into the sexual zooids.

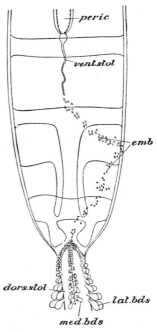

The succession of stages in the life-history of *Doliolum* thus briefly sketched will be seen to succeed one another in the following order : **(1)** sexual form ; **(2)** tailed larva developed sexually from (1) ; **(3)** first asexual form or 'nurse', the direct outcome of (2) ; **(4)** second asexual form (phorozooid) developed on the cadophore of (3) from buds originating on the ventral stolon ; **(5)** the young stages of the sexual form (1) which are of similar origin to (4) and which develop on its stalk.

Berrill should be consulted for a more comprehensive treatment of the Order.

Order Pyrosomida

The strikingly luminescent ('phosphorescent') and distinctive *Pyrosoma* was discovered in the early nineteenth century, but although its anatomy and embryology have been thoroughly investigated, little is yet known of its vital processes. *Pyrosoma* (Fig. 32) is a colonial tunicate, the colony consisting of numerous individuals forming a gelatinous tube that is shaped like a cylinder. Some pyrosomes may grow to about 4 feet long with a tube width of almost a foot. They

FIG. 31.—***Doliolum:* Asexual zooid.** Dorsal view of the posterior aspect showing the course taken by the buds (*emb.*) over the surface from the ventral stolon (*vent. stol.*) to the cadophore (*dors. stol.*) and their growth on the latter. *lat. bds.* lateral buds; *med. bds.* median buds; *peric.* pericardium. (After Barrois.)

are common in warmer seas to a depth of 500 metres ; a few are abyssal. The internal cavity, closed at one end and open at the other, serves as a common cloaca for all the zooids. The oral apertures of the zooids are situated at the outer surface of the cylinder, whilst the atrial apertures (Fig. 33, *atr. ap.*) of the organisms open into the common cloacal cavity. Thus each animal sieves a tiny stream of water from the exterior sea into the lumen of the cylinder. An extensive stream of water is shot out of the open, posterior end of the cylinder and the whole community moves forward by jet propulsion. Velocity is increased by the narrowing of the aperture by means of a diaphragm. The colour and texture of the community vary according to species. Although only one genus—*Pyrosoma*—is generally recognised, it has been suggested that some species should be separated into a second genus *Pyrostremma*.

The *Pyrosoma* zooids of a given colony are seemingly quite independent of each other.   Each individual is characterised by the possession of two body-cavities—the pharynx and the atrium, the latter with two peribranchial extensions.   The gut and gonads lie near the mid-line.   The heart and stolon are situated directly behind the endostyle.   Musculature is weak.   Branchial and atrial sphincters are present, in addition to *circumoral muscles* and paired transverse *atrial muscles*.   The latter connect with the corresponding muscles of neighbouring zooids by means of test fibres.

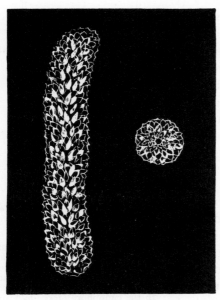

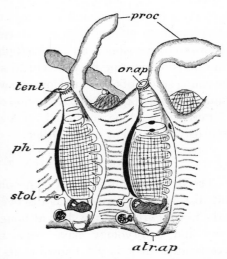

Fig. 32.—Order **Pyrosomida**, Family **Pyrosomidæ, Pyrosoma.**   *Left:* Luminous colony of *P. spinosum*.   *Right:* end view. (Modified after Murray and Hjort.)

Fig. 33.—**Pyrosoma: Colonial individuals.** *atr. ap.* atrial aperture; *or. ap.* oral aperture; *ph.* pharynx; *proc.* processes of test on outer surface of colony; *stol.* stolon on which are developed buds giving rise to new zooids; *tent.* tentacles. (After Herdman.)

The pharynx of *Pyrosoma* is divided.   The prebranchial buccal cavity lies anterior to the peripharyngeal bands.   The branchial sac has the endostyle extending throughout its length.   The peripharyngeal bands are continuous with the ciliated margins of the endostyle and unite dorsally behind the ganglion.   Dorsal languets are recognisable.   The œsophagus is narrow and distinct from the stomach.   A pyloric gland occurs; its relationships are generally similar to those observed in ascidians.   Numerous elongated gill-slits are present.   On each side of the pharynx, immediately over the peripharyngeal bands, lies a flat mass of specialised mesodermal cells enclosed within a blood-sinus.   These are strikingly luminous.   The light is produced by symbiotic bacteria which inhabit the cells and, as the bacteria invade the eggs, light may be produced at all stages of the life-cycle of *Pyrosoma*.   The luminous organs are not innervated. At the same time, they become active only as the result of a stimulus and the whole colony may light up together. In seas where *Pyrosoma* is especially common the light may be sufficiently powerful to enable print to be read. The luminescence is probably a protective device giving warning of unpalatability, and it may have other functions as well.

In *Pyrosoma* development is direct, without a tailed larval stage, and takes place within the body of the parent. The ovum contains a relatively large quantity of food-yolk, and the segmentation is meroblastic. A primary zooid (*cyathozooid*) is formed. This has a stolon which constricts, giving rise to four buds (*blastozooids*), from which the colony develops by further budding. The primary zooid (*cyathozooid*) begins to atrophy. At this stage the young colony, composed of four blastozooids with the remains of the cyathozooid enclosing a mass of yolk (the whole invested in a common cellulose test), passes out from the brood-pouch in which it was developed and reaches the exterior through the cloaca of the parent colony.

ORDER SALPIDA (DESMOMYARIA)

These remarkable animals (Figs. 34, 35) occur in almost every sea. They are most numerous down to 200 metres, but some penetrate to depths as remote

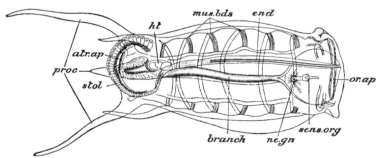

FIG. 34.—*Salpa:* **Oozooid.** Asexual form of *S. democratica* in ventral view. *atr. ap.* atrial aperture; *branch.* dorsal lamina; *end.* endostyle; *ht.* heart; *mus. bds.* muscular bands; *ne. gn.* nerve-ganglion; *or. ap.* oral aperture; *proc.* processes at the posterior end; *sens. org.* sensory organ (ciliated funnel and languet); *stol.* stolon. (After Vogt and Jung.)

as 1,500 metres. They are planktonic tunicates with a transparent, prism-shaped, or cylindrical body reaching from 8 to 190 mm. (exclusive of appendages) according to the species. They are propelled forward by the contraction of muscle-bands which eject water posteriorly. The best-known genus is *Salpa*.

Every species is found in two forms : (1) the *oozooid* or *solitary* form, which develops from an egg, is bilaterally symmetrical, and has a budding stolon but no gonads ; and (2) the *blastozooid* or *aggregate* form, which develops from a bud and has gonads but no stolon. Blastozooids are connected in groups initially, but generally become separate later in life. They are asymmetrical in form.

In the oozooid both branchial and atrial apertures (Figs. 34, 35) are wide and situated at the opposite ends of the body. The test is relatively thin and delicate. A series of seven hoop-like muscles almost, or quite, surrounds the body. The oral muscles, and certain others, strengthen and control the closure of the lower lip. This acts as a valve to shut the mouth when the body-muscles contract to expel water backwards and to propel the animal sharply forward. The atrial muscles act as sphincters. The endostyle and the peripharyngeal bands control the direction of the food-entangling mucus. The entrapped food is drawn into the œsophagus along with mucus strings which stream backwards from all round these bands, forming a conical net. Gill slits are represented only by a pair of large apertures on either side of a single median gill-

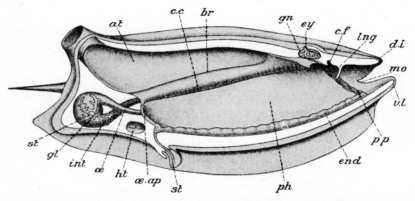

FIG. 35.—Order **Salpida,** Family **Salpidæ.** *Salpa:* **Oozooid.** Lateral view of a section—which is sagittal (longitudinal, vertical, and median) in the oral two-thirds, and oblique in the atrial third. *at.* atrial cavity; *br.* branchia; *c. c.* ciliated crests on the edge of the branchia; *c. f.* ciliated funnel; *d. l.* dorsal lip; *snd.* endostyle; *ey.* eye; *gl.* digestive gland; *gn.* ganglion; *ht.* heart; *int.* intestine; *lng.* languet; *mo.* mouth; *oe.* œsophagus; *œ. ap.* œsophageal aperture; *ph.* pharynx; *pp.* peripharyngeal band; *st.* (right) stolon; *st.* (left) stomach; *v. l.* ventral lip. (After Delage and Hérouard.)

bar, which is really homologous with the dorsal lamina of other forms. The pharyngeal and atrial cavities are incompletely separated by this obliquely running bar. Together they constitute a single large chamber. The remainder of the alimentary canal is divisible into œsophagus, stomach, and gut; the pyloric gland stretches from the stomach over the wall of the intestine. These form a relatively small dark mass called the 'nucleus'. Behind the endostyle, and in the region of the fifth and sixth body-muscle, lies the heart. From between heart and endostyle arises the stolon. In the dorso-anterior region there occurs a horseshoe-shaped eye (*ey.*), which is developed from the dorsal surface, and, associated with this, the dorsal ganglion (Fig. 36). This single ganglion gives off nerves to the various parts of the body. A single large tentacle, the so-called languet (Fig. 35, *lng.*), extends dorsally into the buccal cavity in front of the peripharyngeal bands.

The solitary form described above reproduces asexually. The stolon (which appeared while the oozooid was still an embryo) divides into segments, each of which becomes a sexual blastozooid. Chains of new individuals

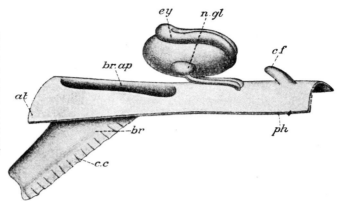

FIG. 36.—*Salpa:* **Nervous system.** Diagrammatic lateral view of the ganglion and neighbouring parts. *at.* wall of atrial cavity; *br.* branchia; *br. ap.* aperture of branchia; *c. c.* ciliated crests of branchia; *c. f.* ciliated funnel; *ey.* eye; *n. gl.* gland (paired) that may represent neural gland; *ph.* wall of pharynx. (After Delage and Hérouard.)

are thus formed. These become detached from the asexual parent, and so the *aggregate* phase arises.

In each individual blastozooid only one ovum forms in the ovary and one testis develops. The testis matures later than the ovum and the latter is fertilised by a sperm from the testis of an individual of an older chain. Development is direct and takes place within the body of the parent. The developing embryo projects into the branchial cavity. The nourishment of the embryo (Fig. 37) is effected by the formation of a *diffusion placenta* through which a close union is brought about between the vascular system of the parent and that of the embryo. The placenta of *Salpa* is partly formed from follicle-cells and ectoderm-cells of the embryo, partly from the cells of the wall of the oviduct. Segmentation is complete. During segmentation there is a migration inwards of some of the cells of the follicle and of the wall of the oviduct.

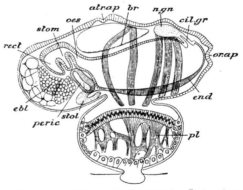

FIG. 37.—*Salpa:* **Development.** Late stage (blastozooid) showing the placental connection with the parent. *atr. ap.* atrial aperture; *br.* branchia; *cil. gr.* ciliated groove; *ebl.* elæoblast (mass of tissue probably representing a vestige of the tail); *end.* endostyle; *n. gn.* nerve-ganglion; *œs.* œsophagus; *or. ap.* oral aperture; *peric.* pericardium; *pl.* placenta; *rect.* rectum; *stol.* stolon; *stom.* stomach. (From Korschelt and Heider, after Salensky.)

These enter the segmenting ovum and pass among the blastomeres. It is not certain what part these inwardly migrating cells play in the development of the embryos. Possibly they act merely as carriers of nourishment, and are broken up and eventually completely absorbed.

There is no tailed larval stage. The embryo develops the muscle-bands and all the characteristic parts of the adult while still enclosed within the body of the parent and nourished by means of the placenta. This sexually-developed embryo, however, does not give rise to a form exactly like the parent, but to one which differs from the latter in certain less important features and notably in the absence of reproductive organs. The sexually formed embryo, in other words, gives rise to an asexual solitary oozooid which escapes to the exterior and then becomes free-swimming. After a time there is developed a process or stolon (*stol.*), on the surface of which are formed a number of bud-like projections. These increase in size as the stolon elongates, and each eventually assumes the form of a sexual *Salpa*. The chain of zooids formed on the stolon breaks off in lengths which swim about intact while reproductive organs develop in the individuals.

CLASS LARVACEA (APPENDICULARIA)

These extraordinary animals are transparent, free-swimming, oceanic tunicates with a permanent tail supported by a skeletal notochord. Most of them are extremely small with a trunk rarely more than 1 mm. long, and a tail generally not more than three times the length of the trunk. A few exceptions, however, occur, and, in particular, the deep-water *Bathochordæus* (Oiko-pleuridæ) grows to the relatively enormous length of 3 inches. The test is represented by a relatively large temporary envelope, the 'house', which is formed with great rapidity, as a secretion from the surface of the ectoderm, and frequently thrown off and renewed. The pharynx has only two stigmata, and these lead directly to the exterior. There is no atrial or peribranchial cavity. The principal ganglion gives off a nerve-cord with ganglionic enlargements running dorsally to the end of the tail. No budding occurs; development takes place without metamorphosis. Appendicularians are widespread in their distribution and are said to occur in Cambrian deposits. The class contains the single Order Copelata. This has been divided into three families: Oiko-pleuridæ, Fritillariidæ, and Kowalevskaiidæ.

General Features.—In shape the Larvacea are not unlike tadpoles, with a rounded body and a long tail-like appendage attached to the ventral side. At the extremity of the body most remote from the tail is the aperture of the mouth. This leads into a comparatively wide pharynx (Fig. 39, *ph.*), in the ventral wall of which (except in *Kowalevskia*) is an endostyle similar to that of the simple ascidian, but comparatively short. Round the pharynx there run obliquely two bands covered with strong cilia—the *peripharyngeal bands*, which join a median dorsal ciliated band. On the ventral side of the pharynx there are two ciliated openings—the *stigmata* (*stig.*), which communicate with the exterior by short passages; the *atrial canals*, situated on either side behind the anus. The axis of the tail is occupied by a cylindrical rod—the *notochord* or *urochord* (*noto.*).

In *Oikopleura* (Fig. 38) the 'house' is a comparatively large structure within which the animal is enclosed. Undulatory movements of the tail cause a current of water to flow in through a pair of incurrent apertures and out through a single excurrent aperture. The former are closed by lattice-works of fine threads, preventing the passage of any but the

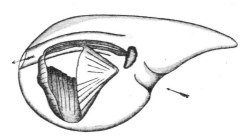

FIG. 38.—Order **Copelata,** Family **Oiko-pleuridæ.** *Oikopleura.* The animal is enclosed in a secreted 'house'. The arrows show the course of the current. (From Herdman, after Fol.)

smallest organisms. In the interior is an elaborate apparatus for filtering out the minute organisms from the water as it passes through. The filtered plankton is sucked into the mouth. Here the processes are not unlike those occurring in the ascidians. Endostyle and peripharyngeal bands are present and a con-

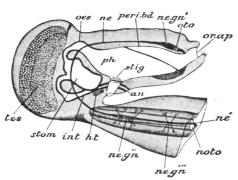

FIG. 39.—Order **Copelata,** Family **Oiko-pleuridæ.** *Appendicularia.* From the right side. *an.* anus; *ht.* heart; *int.* intestine; *ne.* nerve; *ne'.* caudal portion of nerves; *ne. gn'.* principal nerve-ganglion; *ne. gn.'', ne. gn.'''* first two ganglia of nerve of tail; *noto.* notochord; *œs.* œsophagus; *or. ap.* oral aperture; *oto.* otocyst (statocyst); *peri. bd.* peripharyngeal band; *ph.* pharynx; *tes.* testis; *stig.* one of the stigmata; *stom.* stomach. (After Herdman.)

tinuous cord of mucus-entangled prey is drawn into the stomach (Fig. 39). The appendicularians show considerable diversity in the structure of the stomach and digestive apparatus. The intestine (*int.*) ends at the anus (*an.*), which opens on the median ventral line in front of the stigmata.

In most appendicularians the heart consists of a simple, rapidly beating sac, but in others (*Fritillaria*) it is said to be composed of two highly specialised cells which are equipped with fibrillar projections extending and uniting. In *Kowalevskia* the heart is absent altogether.

Two ganglia constitute the essential nervous units of the body. The anterior cerebral ganglion (Fig. 39, *ne. gn'.*) is situated on the dorsal side of the mouth. A large nerve runs forward from this ganglion and divides to form an arch around the mouth; this supplies the sensory cilia of the buccal region. The middle part of the ganglion contains a sensory vesicle with a contained otolith. From the anterior ganglion there runs also a second large nerve which joins the (proximal) caudal ganglion (*ne. gn''*.), situated to the left of the root of the tail. The tail is twisted through 90°, so that its dorsal edge, with its nerve cord, is to the left, as in the tadpole larvæ of many ascidians. The tail muscles, which consist of two rows each of ten cells, are therefore arranged so that each of these rows is above and below the notochord (though morphologically on its right and left sides). The muscle cells are supplied with nerves from a corresponding number of ganglionic enlargements of the nerve cord. This appearance of segmentation is quite different in scale from the segmentation of higher chordates, since it involves individual cells, not somites. The generally minute bodies of Larvacea are composed of remarkably few cells. The notochord, for instance, is formed from about twenty cells in a single row, as compared with about forty such cells in the ascidian tadpole larva.

In one species, *Oikopleura dioica*, individuals are either male, with a single testis, or female, with a single ovary. All other appendicularians, so far as is known, are hermaphrodite. In the posterior part of the trunk there occur a single ovary and a single testis or paired testes. When sexual maturity occurs the ripe ova leave the trunk by rupture of the body-wall, after which the animal gradually dies. The testis has a duct to the exterior. The development of the appendicularian is very like that of the ascidians, except that the former seem to exhibit a precocious differentiation when the various developmental stages are compared.

Affinities.—Several views have been advanced concerning the phylogenetic significance of the tailed appendicularian, and its relationships with the other tunicates and the protochordates in general. Perhaps the most satisfactory hypothesis is that the adult appendicularian, so like the ascidian tadpole, is in fact essentially a neotenic ascidian larva. In this view it is held that the development of sexual maturity, along with other complexities in the larval form, would lead to the elimination of the ancestral adult phase. Subsequent to the above pædomorphosis, other changes may have led to the development of the forms that are living today.

It must be stressed, however, that several authorities believe that appendicularians are merely primitive tunicates and a degenerate offshoot from vertebrate stock. A third view is that they are neotenic doliolids which have retained the tail, lost the cloaca, and converted the test into the appendicularian 'house'.

SUB-PHYLUM ACRANIA (CEPHALOCHORDATA)

THE Acrania consists of a single class—the Cephalochorda—which was once held to include two families : first, the *Branchiostomidæ*, and secondly, the *Amphioxididæ*. The first contains two genera, *Branchiostoma* (which is usually known by the name of one of its sub-genera, *Amphioxus*) and *Asymmetron*. The organisms once believed to belong to the second ' family ' are actually larval individuals of the genus *Asymmetron*.

The Acrania are immensely important in any consideration of the comparative anatomy and systematic relationships of the Chordata. Amphioxus, for example, possesses no separate head, brain, eyes, auditory apparatus, or jaws, yet its nervous and blood vascular systems are clearly of the same general pattern as those which we see more highly elaborated in the fishes, amphibians, reptiles, birds, and mammals. Certain features of the digestive system, too, have much in common with the digestive arrangements of vertebrates. On the other hand, the apparatus of ingestion is strikingly similar to that of the tunicates. At the same time, Amphioxus possesses excretory mechanisms which, in part, resemble not those of the other protochordates, nor that of the Echinodermata, but are, instead, surprisingly akin to those of the flatworms, Mollusca and Annelida (Vol. I). Amphioxus exhibits a well-developed notochord, hollow dorsal nervous system, and gill-slits in the adult as well as in the larval form. Although seemingly primitive and helpless, the Branchiostomidæ are in fact very successful : they occur in suitable habitats all over the world. On the Chinese coast at least one species is sufficiently common to be sold in bulk in the fish-market.

EXAMPLE OF THE SUB-PHYLUM.—THE LANCELET (AMPHIOXUS)

The remarkable little Lancelet,[1] *Branchiostoma lanceolatum* (= *Amphioxus lanceolatus*), which ranges from the Mediterranean to the North Sea, may be taken as a suitable type. The lancelet swims actively, but is primarily a sand-burrowing creature, and is therefore confined to shallow waters. It is a small, almost transparent, superficially fish-like animal, and its length does not exceed 5·8 cm., or less than 2 inches. The body is compressed, elongated, and, as the name suggests, pointed at both ends (Figs. 40 and 41). The anterior two-thirds of the body is roughly triangular in transverse section, having right and left sides inclined towards one another dorsally, and a convex ventral surface. The posterior third is nearly oval in section, the right and left sides meeting above and below in a somewhat sharp edge. Extending along

---

[1] The name Lancelet is the diminutive of the Devon name for the Lance or Sand-eel (*Ammodytes*). The use of the name Amphioxus as a generic term is, strictly speaking, unjustifiable since *Branchiostoma* (given by Costa in 1834) antedates Yarrell's *Amphioxus* by two years.

the whole of the dorsal border is a median longitudinal fold, the *dorsal fin* (*dors. f.*).   This is continued round the posterior end of the body and extends forwards, as the *ventral fin* (*vent. f.*), as far as the region where the oval transverse section passes into the triangular.   The portion of the continuous median fold which extends round the pointed posterior extremity of the body is some-

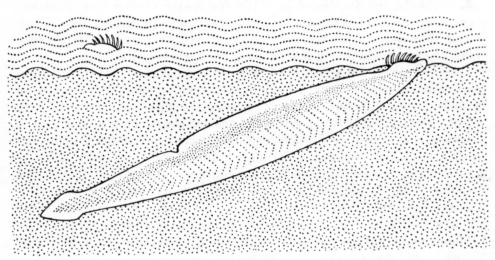

Fig. 40.—Order **Branchiostomida**, Family **Branchiostomidæ**, *Branchiostoma*.   Amphioxus (*B. lanceolatum*) generally lives buried (except for part of the buccal apparatus) in the sandy floor of the shallows.   It is sometimes found in fine shell gravel.   (Redrawn after Hesse, Allee, and Schmidt.)

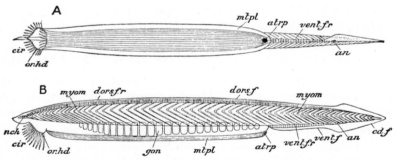

Fig. 41.—**Amphioxus.**   *A*, ventral, *B*, side view of the entire animal.   *an.* anus.   *atrp.* atriopore;   *cd. f.* caudal fin;   *cir.* cirri;   *dors. f.* dorsal fin;   *dors. f. r.* dorsal fin-rays;   *gon.* gonads;   *mtpl.* metapleure;   *myom.* myomeres;   *nch.* notochord;   *or. hd.* oral hood;   *vent. f.* ventral fin;   *vent. f. r.* ventral fin-rays.   (After Kirkaldy.)

what wider than the rest, and may be distinguished as the *caudal fin* (*cd. f.*).   In the anterior two-thirds of the body there is no median ventral fin, but at the junction of each lateral with the ventral surface is a paired longitudinal fold, the *metapleure* (*mtpl.*), which extends forwards to the oral hood mentioned in the next paragraph.   It is important to realise, however, that these fins present none of the structural elaboration that exists in the fins of the true vertebrate fishes.

Below the pointed anterior extremity is a large median aperture surrounded by a frill-like membrane, the *oral hood* (*or. hd.*), the edge of which is beset with numerous tentacles or *cirri* (*cir.*). The oral hood encloses a cup-shaped cavity or *vestibule*, which communicates with the *mouth* (Fig. 43, *mth.*). On the wall of the oral hood is a specially modified tract of the epithelium divided into finger-shaped lobes. The cells of this tract, which is known as the *wheel-organ*, are provided with long cilia. The metachronal waves of the cilia reminded observers of the 'wheel organ' of rotifers, hence the name used. The movements of these cilia collect food particles which fall out of the main stream. Along the roof of the vestibule runs a ciliated groove—the *groove of Hatschek*. Immediately in front of the anterior termination of the ventral fin, and partly enclosed by the metapleures, is a rounded aperture of considerable size, the *atriopore* (*atrp.*). A short distance from the posterior extremity of the body is the *anus* (*an.*), placed asymmetrically on the left side of the central fin. The post-anal portion of the body is distinguished as the *tail*.

Amphioxus ordinarily lives with the greater part of the body buried in sand, only the anterior end with the expanded oral hood protruding. It also swims quickly but erratically, and frequently lies on one side on the sand. It burrows head or tail foremost, with great rapidity. A current of water, used in feeding and respiration, is constantly passing in at the mouth and out at the atriopore.

Body-wall.—The body is covered with an *epidermis* (Fig. 42) formed of a single layer of columnar epithelial cells, some of which are specialised as nerve cells while some are unicellular glands. On the surface of the epidermis is a *cuticle* perforated by pores. The epithelium of the buccal cirri presents at intervals regular groups of sensory cells, some of them bearing stiff sensory hair-like structures, others cilia. Beneath the epidermis is the *dermis*, formed mainly of connective-tissue.

The *muscular layer* (*my., myom.*) is remarkable for exhibiting metameric segmentation. It consists of a large number—about sixty—of muscle-segments or *myomeres*, separated from one another by partitions of dense connective-tissue, the *myocommas*, and having the appearance, in a surface view, of a series of very open V's with their apices directed forwards (Figs. 41 and 43). Each myomere is composed of numerous flat, striated *muscle-plates*, arranged longitudinally, so that each is attached to two successive myocommas. By means of this arrangement the body can be bent from side to side with great rapidity. The myomeres of the right and left sides of the body are not opposite to one another, but have an alternate arrangement. A special set of *transverse muscles* (Fig. 44 *mt.*) extends across the ventral surface of the anterior two-thirds of the body, lying in the floor of the atrial cavity (see below).

Thus in the Lancelet we see for the first time in chordates a clear-cut body segmentation and the consequent ability to swim actively by lateral body flexion effected by the serial contraction of muscle blocks operating

E

synchronously under the control of a relatively elaborate central nervous system (see p. 57). Another striking and characteristic feature of the muscular layer of the body-wall is the immense thickness of its dorsal portion. In the higher worms and many other invertebrate animals the muscles form a layer of approximately equal thickness surrounding the body-cavity, which contains, among other organs, the central nervous system. In vertebrates, on the other hand, the dorsal body-wall is greatly thickened, and in it are contained both the nervous system and the notochord.

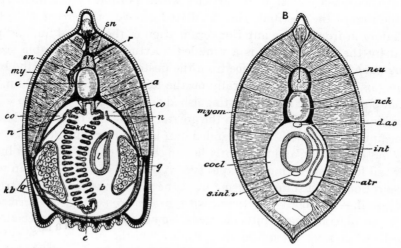

FIG. 42.—**Amphioxus: Visceral relationships.** *A*, Pharyngeal region. *a.* dorsal aortæ; *b.* atrium; *c.* notochord; *co.* cœlom; *e.* endostyle; *g.* gonad; *kb.* branchial lamellæ; *kd.* pharynx; *l.* liver; *my.* myomere; *n.* nephridium; *r.* nerve cord; *sn.* spinal nerves; *B*, Intestinal region. *atr.* atrium; *cœl.* cœlom; *d. ao.* dorsal aorta. *int.* intestine; *myom.* myomere; *nch.* notochord; *neu.* nerve-cord; *s. int. v.* sub-intestinal vein. (*A*, from Hertwig, after Lankester and Boveri; *B*, partly after Rolph.)

Skeleton.—The chief of the skeletal or supporting structures of the Lancelet is the *notochord* (Figs. 42 and 43, *c.*, *nch.*), a cylindrical rod, tapering at both ends, and extending along the whole length of the body in the median plane. It lies immediately above the enteric tract and between the right and left myomeres. It is composed of a peculiar form of cellular tissue known as *notochordal tissue*, formed of large vacuolated cells extending from side to side of the notochord, and having the nuclei confined to its dorsal and ventral regions. Around these cells is a structureless layer, secreted by the cells, enclosed in a *notochordal sheath* of connective-tissue, which is produced dorsally into an investment for the canal enclosing the central nervous system. The notochord, like the parenchyma of plants, owes its resistant character to the vacuoles of its component cells being tensely filled with fluid. This produces a condition of turgescence. The notochord has not the function of most endo-skeletal structures, *i.e.*, to act as a strut against the pull of voluntary muscles.

Rather, it is probable that a principal function of the notochord is to prevent the shortening of the body that would follow the contraction of longitudinal muscles if such an elongated, and somewhat rigid and elastic median rod were absent. In Amphioxus, alone among the chordates, the notochord extends anteriorly in front of the cerebral vesicle. It has been suggested that this prolongation is an adaptation to its habit of burrowing rapidly into the sand.

The oral hood is supported by a ring (Fig. 43, *sk.*) of cartilaginous consistency, made up of separate rod-like pieces arranged end to end, and corresponding in number with the cirri. Each piece sends an off-shoot into the cirrus to which it is related, furnishing it with a skeletal axis.

The pharynx is supported by delicate oblique rods of a firm material, apparently composed of agglutinated elastic fibres, the *gill-rods* (*br. r.*). These will be most conveniently discussed in connection with the pharynx itself. The dorsal fin is supported by a single series and the ventral fin by a double series of *fin-rays* (*dors. f.r.*, *vent. f.r.*), short rods of connective-tissue, continuous with the investment of the neural canal and separated from one another by small cavities (*lymph-spaces*).

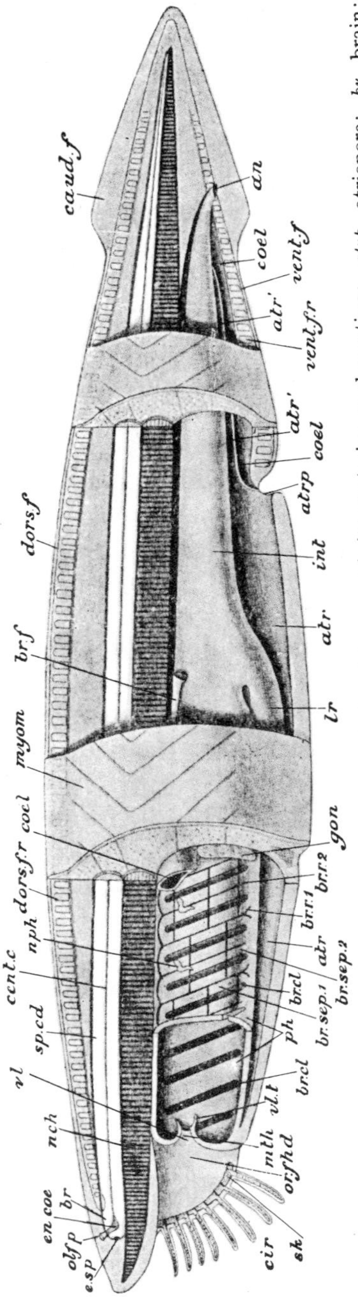

Alimentary Canal and Associated Structures.—The mouth (*mth.*), as already mentioned, lies at the bottom of the vestibule or cavity of the oral hood (*or. f. hd.*). It is a small circular aperture surrounded by a membrane, the *velum* (*vl.*), which acts as a sphincter, and has its free edge produced into a number of *velar tentacles* (*vl. t.*).

Fig. 43.—**Amphioxus: General anatomy.** *an.* anus; *atr.* atrium; *atr'.* its posterior prolongation; *atrp.* atriopore; *br.* brain; *br. cl.* branchial clefts; *br. f.* brown funnel; *br.. sep.* 1, primary, and *br. sep.* 2, secondary branchial lamella; *br. r.* 1, primary, and *br. r.* dorsal fin; *dors. f. r.* dorsal *br. r.* 2, secondary branchial rod; *caud. f.* caudal fin; *cent. c.* neurocele; *cir.* cirri; *cœl.* cœlom; *dors. f.* fin-ray; *en. cœ.* encephalocœle; *e. sp.* eye-spot; *gon.* gonad; *int.* intestine; *br.* liver; *mth.* mouth; *myom.* myomeres; *nch.* noto-chord; *nph.* nephridia; *olf. p.* Kölliker's pit; *or. f. hd.* oral hood; *ph.* pharynx; *sk.* skeleton of oral hood and cirri (dotted); *sp. cd.* nerve-cord; *vent. f.* ventral fin; *vent. f. r.* ventral fin-ray; *vl.* velum; *vl. t.* velar tentacles.

The mouth leads into the largest section of the enteric canal, the *pharynx* (*ph.*), a high, compressed chamber extending through the anterior half of the body. Its walls are perforated by more than a hundred pairs of narrow oblique clefts, the *gill-slits* or *branchial apertures* (*br. cl.*), which place the cavity of the pharynx in communication with the atrium (see below). The posterior end of the pharynx leads to the tubular *intestine* (*int.*), which extends backwards almost in a straight line to the anus.

On the ventral wall of the pharynx is a longitudinal groove, the *endostyle* (Fig. 42, *A, e.*), lined by ciliated epithelium containing groups of gland-cells. This is homologous with the endostyle in the ascidians. A somewhat similar structure, the *epipharyngeal groove*, extends along the dorsal aspect of the pharynx. Its sides are formed by ciliated cells, which, at the anterior end of the groove, curve downwards, as the *peripharyngeal bands*, and join the anterior end of the endostyle.

Just behind the anterior end of the intestine there arises ventrally a blind pouch, the mid-gut diverticulum, the so-called liver (Fig. 43, *lr.*) extending forwards to the right of the pharynx. This is lined with glandular epithelium and secretes digestive enzymes (a lipase and a protease) which are carried into the lumen of the mid-gut by ciliary activity. It is also a place where fat is stored.

The *gill-slits* (*br. cl.*) are long, narrow clefts, which slope antero-dorsally, so obliquely that many always appear in a single transverse section. The clefts are more numerous than the myomeres in the adult, but correspond in number with them in the larva. Hence they are fundamentally metameric, but undergo an increase in number as growth proceeds.

The *branchial lamellæ* (Fig. 43, *br. sep.*, Fig. 42, *A, kb.*), or portions of the pharyngeal wall separating the clefts from one another, are covered by an epithelium which is for the most part endodermal in origin, and is composed of greatly elongated and ciliated cells. On the outer face of each lamella, however, the cells are shorter and not ciliated. These are actually portions of the epithelial lining of the atrium, and of ectodermal origin. Each lamella is supported towards its outer edge by one of the *branchial rods* (Fig. 43, *br. r.*). These are narrow bars united with one another dorsally by loops, but ending below in free extremities which are alternately simple and forked.

The forked bars are the *primary rods* (*br. r.* 1). Those with simple ends are the *secondary* (*br. r.* 2) *branchial rods*. The lamellæ in which they are contained are similarly to be distinguished as *primary lamellæ* (*br. sep.* 1) and *secondary* or *tongue-lamellæ* (*br. sep.* 2). In the young condition, the two clefts between any two primary lamellæ are represented by a single aperture. As development proceeds, a downgrowth takes place from the dorsal edge of the aperture, forming, as in Balanoglossus, a *tongue* which extends downwards, dividing the original cleft into two, and itself becoming a secondary lamella. A further complication is produced by the formation of transverse *branchial junctions* or *synapticulæ*, supported by rods connecting the primary septa with one another at tolerably regular intervals.

Atrium.—The branchial clefts lead into a wide *atrium* which is a chamber occupying most of the space between the body-wall and the pharynx (Figs. 42, B, and 43, *atr.*). It is crescentic in section, surrounding the ventral and lateral regions of the pharynx, but not its dorsal portion. It ends blindly in front. It opens externally, behind the level of the pharynx, by the atriopore (*atrp.*). It is continued backwards by a blind, pouch-like extension (*atr.*) lying to the right of the intestine (Fig. 42, B, *atr.*). The whole cavity is lined by an atrial epithelium of ectodermal origin.

Ingestion, Digestion, and Absorption.—In broad outline these take place as follows : The cirri are turned inwards and form a grating when feeding, excluding sand. At the same time a stream of water, with its contained organic food substances, is sucked into the mouth. This current, as in protochordates generally, is principally due to the activity of the *lateral cilia* which line the gill-slits. These beat outwards into the atrial cavity. The cilia of the wheel-organ beat at right angles to its winding course, in the general direction of the mouth. They cause fine particles, which fall out of the main stream entering the mouth, to collect in shallow grooves between the lobes of the organ. Thence these particles are gradually drawn into the mouth, wrapped in mucus. Within the pharynx sheets of mucus (produced by gland cells in the ventral endostyle) are driven posterodorsally across the gill-slits by the *frontal cilia*. These lie on the surfaces of the gill-bars facing the pharyngeal lumen. The dorsal movement of the mucus is assisted anteriorly by the cilia of the peripharyngeal bands. As the excurrent water passes through the gill-slits, particles of food which remain suspended in it are entrapped by the mucus. The resultant mixture of slime and nourishment is directed into the epipharyngeal groove. The cilia there beat posteriorly, conveying the food-cord into the intestine.

Digestion begins in the mid-gut, where the food is mixed, by ciliary activity, with carbohydrate-, fat-, and protein-splitting enzymes. These are secreted by the epithelium of the diverticulum and mid-gut. Food does not normally enter the diverticulum. Absorption takes place in the hind-gut, and to a lesser degree in the hinder part of the mid-gut. It is also possible that some absorption occurs in the diverticulum. There is evidence that intracellular digestion also occurs at least in the hind-gut (Barrington). Most of the digestion occurs apparently after the food and mucus cord has passed the ilio-colon ring. This is a powerfully ciliated region (at the hind end of the mid-gut) which imparts a rotary movement to the food-cord as it passes into the hind-gut, and where the secretions of the mid-gut are admixed. The mechanical agitation seems to be transmitted to the part of the cord still in the mid-gut, and so possibly facilitates the action of enzymes in that area as well.

Cœlom.—The relationship of the cœlom with the peripheral structures is easily grasped if we think of the whole body essentially as two tubes, firstly, an outer ectodermal layer, and secondly, an inner endodermal alimentary canal. The space between the two is the cœlom, and it is lined by cœlomic epithelium of mesodermal origin. During development this simplicity can be seen much more clearly. Owing to the immense size of the atrium, the cœlomic body-cavity is much reduced. It is represented, in the pharyngeal region, by paired cavities (Fig. 42, *A, co.,* Fig. 43, *cœl.,* Fig. 44, *sc.*) lying one on either side of the dorsal region of the pharynx above the atrium, and connected by narrow canals in the primary branchial lamellæ (Fig 44, right side) with a median longitudinal space below the endostyle (*ec.*). In the intestinal region it entirely surrounds the intestine, but is much reduced on the right side, being displaced by the backward extension of the atrium (Fig. 42, *B, atr.,* Fig. 43, *atr'.*). On the left side a forward extension of it surrounds the liver (Fig. 42, *A, l.*). Separate cavities lie in the metapleures.

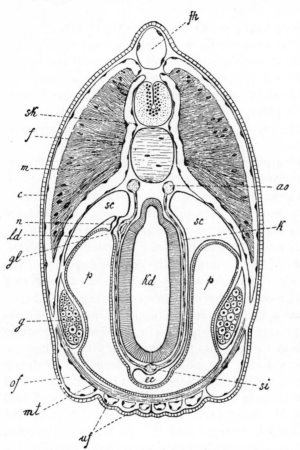

FIG. 44.—**Amphioxus: Pharyngeal region.** Transverse section, passing on the right through a primary, on the left through a secondary branchial lamella. *ao.* dorsal aorta; *c.* dermis; *ec.* endostylar portion of cœlom; *f.* fascia or investing layer of myomere; *fh.* compartment containing fin-ray; *g.* gonad; *gl.* glomerulus (modified part of branchial artery in relation to nephridium); *k.* branchial artery; *kd.* pharynx; *ld.* combined atrial and cœlomic wall (ligamentum denticulatum); *m.* myomere; *mt.* transverse muscle; *n.* nephridium; *of.* metapleural lymph-space; *p.* atrium; *sc.* cœlom; *si.* ventral aorta; *sk.* sheath of notochord and nerve-cord; *uf.* spaces in ventral wall. (From Korschelt and Heider, after Boveri and Hatschek.)

Blood-vascular System.— Although Amphioxus does not possess a heart, its circulatory system is in general outline strikingly similar to those that we see in increasing complexity in the vertebrate series. Although the principal arteries have muscular walls, and the dorsal aorta has an endothelial lining, most blood-vessels are very similar but, owing to certain homologies with the more complex vessels of the Craniata, some of them are called *arteries* and some *veins*.

Lying in the ventral wall of the pharynx, below the endostyle, is a median longitudinal vessel, the *ventral aorta* (Fig. 44, *si.*, Fig. 45, *v. ao.*). This is contractile, and drives the blood forwards. From it are given off, on each side, lateral branches, the *afferent branchial arteries* (Fig. 44, *k.* ; Fig. 45, *af. br. a.*), with small contractile dilations at their bases. These force blood through the vessels of the branchial lamellæ which communicate by cross-branches with similar vessels (*af. br. a'.*) in the secondary or *tongue-lamellæ*. The blood is exposed to what is probably a respiratory current while traversing these vessels. The blood, however, carries no respiratory pigment and no proof of oxygenation in the present situation has yet been obtained. The blood leaves the branchial lamellæ dorsally by *efferent branchial arteries* (*ef. br. a.*). These open on each side into paired longitudinal vessels, the *right* and *left dorsal aortæ* (*d. ao.*), lying

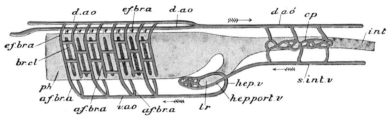

FIG. 45.—**Amphioxus: Blood vascular system.** *af. br. a.* primary afferent branchial vessels; *af. br. a'.* secondary afferent branchial vessels; *br. cl.* branchial cleft; *cp.* intestinal capillaries; *d. ao.* paired dorsal aortæ; *d. ao'.* median dorsal aorta; *e. f br. a.* efferent branchial arteries; *hep. port. v.* hepatic portal vein; *hep. v.* hepatic vein; *int.* intestine; *lr.* liver; *ph.* pharynx; *s. int. v.* sub-intestinal vein; *v. ao.* ventral aorta.

one on either side of the epipharyngeal groove. Anteriorly both dorsal aortæ are continued forwards to the region of the snout. The right aorta is much dilated. Posteriorly they unite with one another, behind the level of the pharynx, into an *unpaired dorsal aorta* (*d. ao'.*). This extends backwards in the middle line, immediately below the notochord and above the intestine.

The unpaired dorsal aorta sends off branches to the intestine. In the intestinal walls, these break up to form a plexus of microscopic capillary-like vessels. From these the blood is collected and poured into a median longitudinal vessel, the *sub-intestinal vein* (Figs. 42, *B*, and 45, *s. int. v.*), lying beneath the intestine. In this trunk the blood flows forwards, and, at the origin of the 'liver', passes into a *hepatic portal vein* (*hep. port. v.*), which extends along the ventral side of the 'liver' and breaks up into minute vessels in that organ. From the 'liver' the blood makes its way into a *hepatic vein* (*hep. v.*), which extends along the dorsal aspect of the digestive gland, and, turning downwards and forwards, joins the posterior end of the ventral aorta.

It will be seen that the vascular system of Amphioxus consists essentially of (*a*) a dorsal vessel represented by the paired and unpaired dorsal aortæ, (*b*) a ventral vessel represented by the sub-intestinal vein and the ventral aorta, and (*c*) commissural vessels represented by the afferent and efferent branchial arteries and the intestinal capillaries. So far the resemblance to the vascular system of annelids is fairly close, but two important differences are to be noted. The blood in the ventral vessel travels forwards, whereas that in the dorsal vessel travels backwards—the precise opposite of what occurs in worms. The ventral vessel is broken up, as it were, into two parts, by the interposition in its course of the minute vessels of the 'liver'. Thus, all the blood from the intestine has to pass through that organ before reaching the ventral aorta. This passage of the intestinal blood supply through the vessels of the 'liver' constitutes what is called the *hepatic portal system*, and is eminently characteristic of vertebrates (pp. 112, 245).

The *blood* is colourless, and appears to contain no leucocytes. It is not confined to the true blood-vessels just described, but occurs also in certain cavities or *lymph-spaces*. The most important of these are the cavities in the dorsal and ventral fins containing the fin-rays (Fig. 44, *fh.*), and paired canals in the metapleures (*of.*). It has been suggested that a

FIG. 46.—**Amphioxus: Nephridium.** Of the left side with part of the wall of the pharynx. (From Willey, after Boveri.)

considerable proportion of the meagre amount of oxygen required by Amphioxus may be taken into the blood-stream through these superficial areas.

Excretory Organs.—The excretory system of Amphioxus is of outstanding interest in that, unlike the blood-vascular and nervous systems, it shows no similarity whatever with that of the Craniata. Neither has it any affinity with that of the Echinodermata.

The principal organs of excretion are about ninety pairs of peculiarly modified *nephridia* (Fig. 43, *nph.*) situated above the pharynx and in relation with the main cœlomic cavities. Each nephridium (Fig. 46) is a bent tube consisting of an anterior vertical and a posterior horizontal limb. The vertical limb ends in a large group of *solenocytes* (flame-cells) (Fig. 47). There are several smaller groups on the horizontal limb. The organ thus closely corresponds to the type of nephridium with closed inner end bearing solenocytes such as occur in certain of the Polychæta and other invertebrate groups. On the ventral surface of the horizontal limb, opposite a secondary branchial lamella, is a single aperture bearing long cilia and opening into the atrium. This corresponds with the *nephridiopore* or external aperture of the typical nephridium. Through this aperture to the atrium are driven the waste nitrogenous products that have been taken up by the solenocytes. Goodrich has calculated that, in a specimen containing some 500 solenocytes about 50µ long in each of its perhaps 200 nephroids, the total excretory length would be no less than 5 metres. (The entire animal is less than 5 centimetres long.)

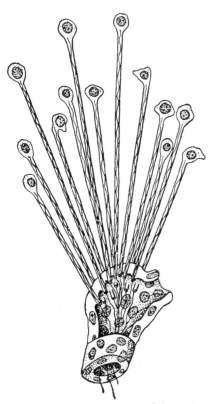

An excretory function has also been assigned to a single pair of organs called the *brown funnels* (Fig. 43, *br. f.*), also situated on the dorsal aspect of the pharynx at its posterior end. Their wide backwardly-directed ends open into the atrium; their narrow anterior ends have been said to communicate with the cœlom.

Nervous System.—The central nervous system of Amphioxus consists of a *dorsal nerve cord* (Fig. 42, *A*, *r*; *B*, *neu.* Fig. 43, *sp. cd.*) lying in the neural canal immediately above the notochord. It is roughly triangular in transverse section. Anteriorly it ends abruptly, some distance behind the anterior end of the notochord.

FIG. 47.—**Amphioxus: Solenocytes.** Showing nuclei, long flagella and the openings into the main excretory canal which leads to the atrium. (From Young, after Goodrich.)

Posteriorly it tapers to a point over the hinder end of the latter. It is traversed by an axial cavity, the *neurocœle* (Fig. 43, *cent. c.*), connected with the mid-dorsal region by a longitudinal cleft—the *dorsal fissure*. At the fore-end of the nerve-tube the neurocœle becomes dilated, forming a considerable cavity, the *encephalocœle* or *cerebral ventricle* (Fig. 43, *en. cœ.*, Fig. 48, *c.v.*). A little behind this the dorsal fissure widens out above to form a trough-like *dorsal dilatation* (*dil.*) covered only by the delicate connective-tissue sheath which invests the whole nerve-tube. The anterior end of the nerve-cord, containing these two cavities, may be considered as a primitive *brain* although it is not distinguishable externally from the remaining portion or *spinal cord*.

The anterior and dorsal region of the brain is produced into a small, hollow-pointed pouch which comes into relation with the olfactory organ and is called the *median olfactory lobe*. Embedded in the posterior and ventral walls of the cerebral ventricle is a structure composed of small cells, the *infundibular organ*. These cells are ciliated, and the organ is probably one of special sense, but this has not been proved. In the young animal the cerebral ventricle opens up by a *neuropore* (Fig. 48, B, *np*.) which subsequently closes.

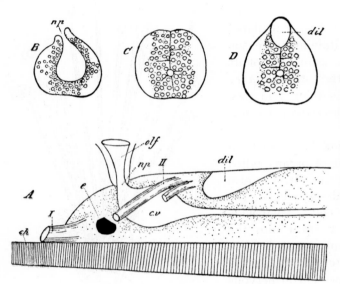

FIG. 48. — **Amphioxus: Nervous system.** *A*, brain and cerebral nerves of a young specimen; *B*, transverse section through neuropore; *C*, behind cerebral ventricle; *D*, through dorsal dilatation. *ch*. notochord; *c. v.* cerebral ventricle; *dil.* dorsal dilatation; *e.* pigment-spot; *np.* neuropore; *olf.* Kölliker's pit; *I, II*, cerebral nerves. (From Willey, after Hatschek.)

The nerve-cord is mainly composed of longitudinal nerve-fibres with abundant nerve-cells mostly grouped around the neurocœle. At intervals *giant nerve-cells* occur. These multipolar cells of immense proportional size are connected with nerve-fibres of unusual thickness, termed *giant fibres*. The peripheral nervous system is simple, but is on the same fundamental pattern that occurs in the Craniata. From the dorsal nerve-cord are given off a dorsal and a ventral nerve-root on each side to every segment. The roots are not united. Each ventral root carries motor-fibres to a myotome. These motor-fibres terminate on muscle-fibres at motor end-plates like those of vertebrates.

The dorsal roots, on the other hand, pass between the myotomes. They carry sensory fibres from the respective segment, and motor-fibres to the non-myotomal muscles of the ventral sections of the body. Some dorsal roots carry fibres which supply the gut-wall where, similar to the vertebrates, a *nerve-plexus* occurs. Two pairs of dorsal roots—the *cerebral nerves* (Fig. 48, I and II)

—arise from the brain in front of the first myomere. The first comes from the anterior extremity and the second from its dorsal region. These bring impulses from the tentacles and sense-organs of the oral hood. There are no corresponding ventral roots in the cephalic region. The walls of the atrium, both ventral and parietal, contain a system of neurones which, lying in or just below the epithelium, have connexions with the central nervous system and may be of sensory as well as motor significance. The presumed sensory fibres which in various regions appear to contribute to the dorsal spinal roots are never aggregated into ganglia as in vertebrates.

Organs of Special Sense.—At the level of the anterior end of the brain is a narrow ciliated depression called *Kölliker's pit* (Figs. 43, 48). This opens externally on the left side of the snout and was once thought to be an organ of smell. It is not innervated. In the larva its cavity is in direct communication with the neurocœle through the *neuropore* (*np.*).

An unpaired *pigment-spot* (*e.*) in the front wall of the brain is usually referred to as a median *cerebral eye*. However, there is no lens or other accessory apparatus, and experimental evidence seems to show that this so-called eye is not sensitive to light. In fact, it has been suggested that, in this animal which lies with its anterior end protruding from the sand, the function of the pigmented area is actually to *prevent* light from penetrating vertically to the undoubted photoreceptors which occur further down the nerve-cord.

There is no trace of auditory organs. The *groove of Hatschek*, on the roof of the buccal cavity, has had sensory functions ascribed to it, but no proof has been forthcoming. Lastly, the sensory cells on the buccal cirri probably give these organs important tactile and perhaps other functions.

Reproductive System.—The sexes are separate, but apart from the reproductive organs there is no difference between male and female. The *gonads* (Figs. 42*A*, Fig. 43, *gon.*, and 44, *g.*) occur as about twenty-six pairs of pouches arranged metamerically along the body-wall. They project into the atrium and largely fill its cavity. The inner or mesial face of each pouch is covered by atrial epithelium which is pushed inwards by the growth of the gonads. Within this, and completely surrounding the reproductive organ, is a single layer of epithelium which is shown by development to be cœlomic. Hence each gonad is surrounded by a closed cœlomic sac.

When ripe, the inner walls of the gonadal pouches burst. The ova or sperms then make their way into the atrium and are thence (according to both Kowalevsky and Hatschek) emitted through the mouth to the external water. The laid eggs are covered by a thin *vitelline membrane*, to which a second, inner *peri-vitelline membrane* is added, the substance of which is derived from droplets in the protoplasm.

Development.—After maturation (Fig. 49, *A*) and fertilisation in the surrounding sea-water, the membranes separate from the developing egg, leaving a wide space around it. Segmentation is complete, there being very little yolk. It begins by a sagittal cleft dividing the egg into two (*B*), and is followed by a second cleft, also meridional, at right angles to the first (*D*). Next, an

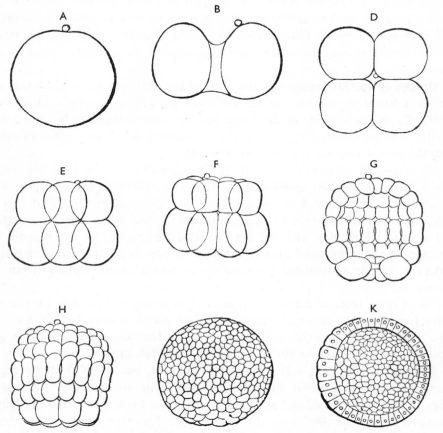

Fig. 49.—**Amphioxus: Development.** Segmentation of the oosperm. *D*, the four-celled stage from above; *G*, vertical section of *H*; *K*, vertical section of the blastula stage *I*. (From Korschelt and Heider, after Hatschek.)

approximately equatorial cleavage takes place, and so the embryo now consists of eight cells (*E*), of which the four belonging to the upper hemisphere, distinguished by the presence of the polar bodies, are smaller than the lower four. Apertures at the poles lead into a central cavity. Further meridional and latitudinal divisions take place, and the embryo becomes a *blastula* (*I, K*). It now encloses a spacious blastocœle. The cells on its lower pole (megameres) are larger than the rest (micromeres). The polar apertures disappear owing to the closer approximation of the cells.

Invagination then takes place (Fig. 50, *A*), due to the rapid multiplication of the micromeres. The lower pole of the blastula is gradually pushed in until the whole lower hemisphere is in complete contact with the upper hemisphere and the blastocœle is obliterated (*B*). The *gastrula* thus formed is at first basin-shaped, having a very wide blastopore, but its cavity (the archenteron) gradually deepens, and the blastopore is reduced to a comparatively narrow aperture (*C*). At the same time the aspects of the body are marked out. The dorsal surface becomes flattened, the ventral convex. The blastopore marks the posterior end and is distinctly dorsal in position. Cilia are developed from the ectoderm cells and their vibration causes the embryo to rotate within its membrane.

The ectoderm cells forming the median portion of the flattened dorsal surface now become differentiated and sink below the rest, giving rise to the

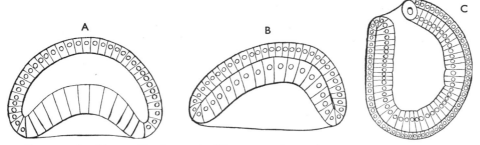

FIG. 50.—**Amphioxus: Development.** Three stages in the formation of the gastrula. (From Korschelt and Heider, after Hatschek.)

medullary plate (Fig. 51, *A*, *mp.*). The ordinary ectoderm cells on each side of this plate rise up as a pair of longitudinal *medullary folds* (*hb.*), extend towards the middle line, and unite (*B*, *hb.*) to cover the medullary plate. The latter bends upwards at the sides and becomes trough-like instead of flat (*C*).· The two sides come in contact with one another above and so the plate is converted into a tube, the nerve-cord (*D*, *n.*). This encloses a central canal, the *neurocœle*, which continues dorsally into a narrow cleft. The medullary folds extend behind the blastopore and unite: the result is that the blastopore now opens into the neurocœle and becomes known as the *neurenteric canal* (Fig. 52, *A*, cn.). Anteriorly the folds remain apart up to a late period, so that the neurocœle opens externally in front by a wide aperture, the *neuropore* (Figs. 53, and 54, *np.*).

While the central nervous system is thus being formed, the wall of the archenteron develops dorso-laterally a pair of longitudinal folds (* in Fig. 51, *A* and *B*). The cavities in these, continuous with the archenteron, are the beginnings of the enterocœlic system. Transverse folds appear and divide the longitudinal folds into segments, with the result that the archenteron comes to have appended to it dorso-laterally a paired series of offshoots, the *enterocœlic* or *cœlomic pouches* (Fig. 51, *mk.*), arranged metamerically. In this way segmentation is established. At this period the embryo ruptures its containing membrane and begins free existence. Before long the cœlomic pouches separate from the archenteron and take on the form of a series of closed *cœlomic sacs* or *somites* (Fig. 51, *C, D*), lying between ectoderm and endoderm. From the walls of these sacs the mesoderm is derived. Their cavities unite and

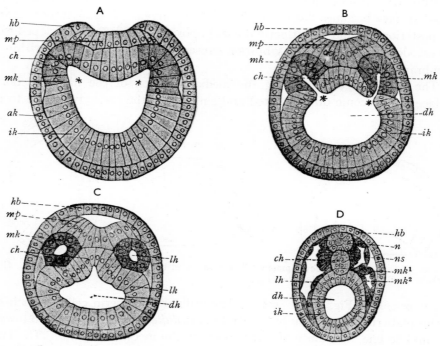

FIG. 51.—**Amphioxus: Development.** Four stages in the development of the notochord, nervous system, and mesoderm. *ak.* ectoderm; *ch.* notochord; *dh.* cavity of archenteron; *hb.* ridge of ectoderm growing over medullary plate; *ik.* endoderm; *lh.* cœlom; *mk.* cœlomic pouch; *mk¹.* parietal layer of mesoderm; *mk².* visceral layer; *mp.* medullary plate; *n.* nerve-cord; *ns.* mesoblastic somite; * = archenteron. (From Korschelt and Heider, after Hatschek.)

become the cœlom. This is therefore an *enterocœle* like that of *Sagitta* and the Echinodermata.

While the cœlomic sacs are in course of formation a median groove appears along the dorsal wall of the archenteron (Fig. 51, *B, C, ch.*). It deepens, its inner walls unite, and it becomes a solid rod, the *notochord* (*D, ch.*), lying immediately beneath the nerve-tube. The ordinary endoderm cells soon unite beneath it and so shut it off from the archenteron. It will be seen that the notochord, like the nerve-cord, never exhibits any trace of segmentation. At its first formation it stops short of the anterior end of the archenteron: its final extension to the end of the snout is a subsequent process.

New cœlomic pouches are formed in regular order from before backwards, the embryo at the same time elongating and becoming laterally compressed and pointed fore and aft. At the anterior end the *mouth* (Fig. 53, *m.*) appears

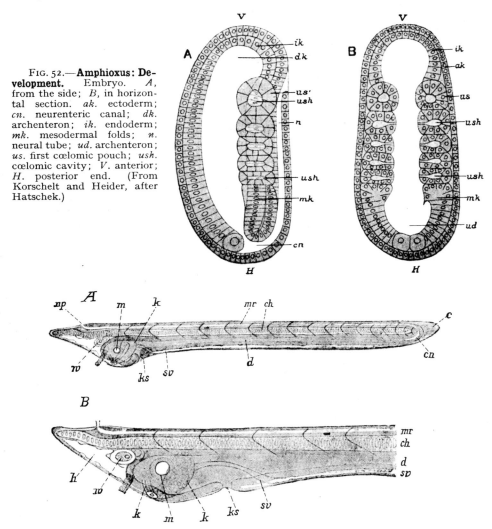

FIG. 52.—**Amphioxus: Development.** Embryo. *A*, from the side; *B*, in horizontal section. *ak.* ectoderm; *cn.* neurenteric canal; *dk.* archenteron; *ik.* endoderm; *mk.* mesodermal folds; *n.* neural tube; *ud.* archenteron; *us.* first cœlomic pouch; *ush.* cœlomic cavity; *V.* anterior; *H.* posterior end. (From Korschelt and Heider, after Hatschek.)

FIG. 53.—**Amphioxus: Development.** *A*, young larva; *B*, anterior end more highly magnified. *c.* provisional tail-fin; *ch.* notochord; *cn.* neurenteric canal; *d.* enteric canal; *h.* cœlom of head; *k.* club-shaped gland; *k'.* its external aperture; *ks.* first gill-slit; *m.* mouth; *mr.* nerve-cord; *n. p.* neuropore; *sv.* sub-intestinal vein; *w.* pre-oral pit. (From Korschelt and Heider, after Hatschek.)

on the left side of the body as a small aperture, which soon increases greatly in size. On the ventral surface another small aperture, the *first gill-slit* (*ks.*), makes its appearance, and soon shifts over to the right side. Here it forms a direct communication between the pharynx and the exterior, like the stigmata

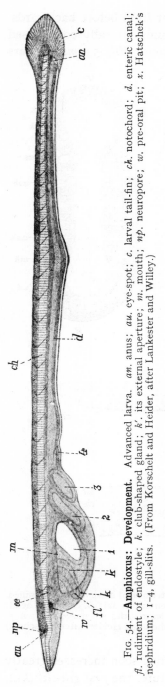

FIG. 54.—**Amphioxus: Development.** Advanced larva. *an.* anus; *au.* eye-spot; *c.* larval tail-fin; *ch.* notochord; *d.* enteric canal; *fl.* rudiment of endostyle; *k.* club-shaped gland; *k'.* its external aperture; *m.* mouth; *np.* neuropore; *w.* pre-oral pit; *x.* Hatschek's nephridium; 1–4, gill-slits. (From Korschelt and Heider, after Lankester and Willey.)

of the Appendicularia (Larvacea). There is at present no trace of the atrium.

The anterior end of the alimentary canal has meanwhile grown out into a pair of pouches, which become shut off as closed sacs. Of these, the right gives rise to the cœlom of the head (*h.*), and the left to a depression called the *preoral pit* (*w.*), which opens on the exterior and from which the groove of Hatschek and the wheel-organ are afterwards formed. The preoral pit also gives rise to *Hatschek's nephridium* (Fig. 54, *x.*), a narrow ciliated tube which opens into the anterior part of the pharynx, and runs forwards to terminate blindly in the roof of the oral hood. It disappears completely in the adult.

On the floor of the archenteron in the neighbourhood of the mouth a depression appears and gives rise to a structure known as the *club-shaped gland* (*k.*), which may be a modified gill-cleft. Posteriorly the neurenteric canal closes and the anus appears.

We left the mesoderm in the form of separate paired somites, arranged metamerically in the dorsal region of the embryo. These increase in size, and extend both upwards and downwards, each presenting a *somatic layer* (Fig. 51, D, $mk.^1$) in contact with the external ectoderm, and a *splanchnic layer* ($mk.^2$) in contact with the nervous system and notochord dorsally, and with the enteric canal ventrally. At about the level of the ventral surface of the notochord a horizontal partition is formed in each cœlomic pouch (Fig. 51, D, C), separating it into a dorsal and ventral portion. The dorsal section is distinguished as the *protovertebra* or *myotome* (*ns.*), and its cavity as the *myocœle* or muscle-cavity. The ventral section is called the *lateral plate mesoderm* or *splanchnotome*, and its cavity forms a segment of the cœlom.

The lateral plates now unite with one another in pairs below the enteric canal, their cavities becoming continuous. At the same time the cavities of successive lateral plates are placed in communication with one another by the absorption of their ad·

jacent (anterior and posterior) walls. In this way the cavities of the entire series of ventral plates, right and left, unite to form the single unsegmented cœlom of the adult, their walls giving rise to the cœlomic epithelium.

At the same time the cells of the splanchnic layer of the protovertebræ become converted into muscular fibres, which nearly fill the myocœle, and give rise to the myomere. The myocommas arise from the adjacent anterior and posterior walls of the protovertebræ. An outpushing of the splanchnic layer, at about the level of the ventral surface of the notochord, grows upwards between the myomere externally and the notochord and nerve-tube internally. From the cells lining this pouch the connective-tissue sheath of the notochord and neural canal arises and perhaps also the fin-rays. From the parietal layer of the protovertebræ is formed the dermis or connective-tissue layer of the skin.

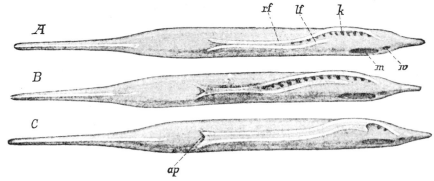

FIG. 55.—**Amphioxus: Development.** Ventral aspect of three larvæ showing the development of the atrium. *ap.* atriopore; *k.* gill-slits; *lf.* left metapleural fold; *m.* mouth; *rf.* right metapleural fold; *w.* pre-oral pit. (From Korschelt and Heider, after Lankester and Willey.)

The larva increases in size, and becomes very long and narrow, with a pointed anterior end and a provisional caudal fin posteriorly (Fig. 53, *c*). As growth proceeds, new segments are added behind those already formed. The notochord grows forwards to the anterior end of the snout, and the eye-spot (*au.*) and olfactory pit appear. The latter is an ectodermal pit which communicates with the neurocœle by the still open neuropore (*np.*). The mouth (*m.*) attains a relatively immense size and remains on the left side.

Additional gill-slits arise behind the one already mentioned. They all make their appearance near the middle ventral line, and gradually shift over to the right side. At first they correspond with the myomeres, so that the segmentation of the pharynx is part of the general metamerism of the body. Altogether, fourteen clefts are produced in a single longitudinal series. Above, *i.e.* dorsal to them, a second longitudinal series makes its appearance, containing eight clefts, so that at this stage there are two parallel rows of gill-slits on the right side of the body, and none on the left. But as growth proceeds, the first or ventral series gradually travels over to the left side, producing a symmetrical arrangement, and at the same time the first slit and the last five of the first or definitely left series close up and disappear. Thus the numbers are equalised on the two sides. At first each gill-slit is simple, but before long a fold grows down from its dorsal edge, and, extending ventrally, divides the single aperture into two. This fold is the secondary or tongue-lamella. The original bars of tissue between the undivided slits become the primary lamellæ.

While the development of the gill-slits is proceeding, the atrium is in course of formation. Paired longitudinal ridges, the *metapleural folds* (Fig. 55, *lf.*, *rf.*,

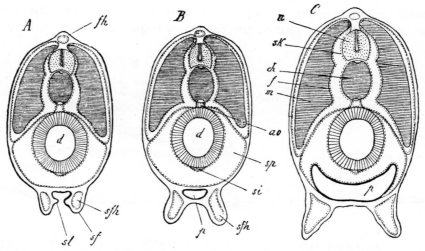

FIG. 56.—**Amphioxus: Development.** Diagrammatic transverse sections of three larvæ to show the development of the atrium. *ao.* aorta; *d.* intestine; *f.* fascia (layer of connective-tissue on inner surface of myomere); *fh.* cavity for dorsal fin-ray; *m.* myomere; *n.* nerve cord; *p.* atrium; *sf.* metapleural fold; *sfh.* metapleural lymph-space; *si.* sub-intestinal vein; *sk.* sheath of notochord and nerve-cord; *sl.* sub-atrial ridge; *sp.* cœlom. (From Korschelt and Heider, after Lankester and Willey.)

Fig. 56, *sf.*), appear on the ventral side of the body, behind the gill-slits, and gradually extend forwards, dorsal to them. Their arrangement is very asymmetrical in correspondence with that of the clefts themselves. On the inner face of each fold, *i.e.* the face which looks towards its fellow of the opposite side, a longitudinal, *subatrial ridge* (Fig. 56, *A*, *sl.*) appears. The two subatrial ridges meet and coalesce. A canal (*B*, *p.*) is formed immediately below the ventral body-wall. This canal is the commencement of the atrium. It is at first quite narrow, but gradually it extends upwards on each side (*C*, *p.*) until it attains its full dimensions. It is at first open, both in front and behind. The posterior opening remains as the atriopore, but the anterior opening becomes gradually shifted forwards as the fusion of the subatrial ridges proceeds (Fig. 56, *B* and *C*). Finally it is completely closed. In this way the gill-slits come to open, not directly on the exterior, but into a cavity formed by the union of paired ridges of the body-wall, and therefore lined by ectoderm.

The mouth gradually passes to the ventral surface, and undergoes a relative diminution in size. A fold of integument develops round it and forms the oral hood, which is probably a stomodæum. The endostyle appears on the right of the pharynx (Fig. 54, *fl.*), and is at first rod-shaped, then V-shaped. Ultimately the limbs of the V unite in the middle ventral line. The gill-slits increase in number and become more and more vertically elongated. The provisional caudal fin disappears. The gonads arise from the outer and ventral regions of the protovertebræ in the form of pouches, which gradually assume the permanent form previously described.

Affinities.—The Lancelet has had a chequered zoological history. Pallas, the eighteenth-century naturalist who first studied it, considered it to be a slug, and placed it among the Gastropoda. When its chordate character became evident it was for a long time placed among the fishes as the type of a distinct order. On further study it became obvious that an animal without skull, true brain, heart, auditory organs, paired eyes, or kidneys, and with a pharynx surrounded by an atrium, must be widely separated from the lowliest fish.

There was still, however, no suspicion of any connection between Amphioxus and the Tunicata until the development of both was worked out and it was shown that in several fundamental points (*e.g.*, the formation of the nervous system and the notochord) there was a close resemblance. The likeness is further emphasised by the presence of an endostyle, an epipharyngeal groove (dorsal lamina), and peripharyngeal bands, which are used in an essentially similar method of endopharyngeal filter-feeding in both forms. Such a feeding mechanism is not found in any other animals except Enteropneusta, the ammocœte larva of cyclostomes (p. 196), and the larvæ of some amphibians. The mechanism occurs so widely in protochordates that it is generally thought to be the primitive mode of feeding in the phylum Chordata. Those chief exponents of the method, the ascidians, were once said to be obviously degenerate, but are now regarded by some zoologists as essentially primitive in habit, and as having evolved the tadpole larva as a dispersal phase in the life-history. Pædomorphosis (which probably gave rise to the Larvacea, as we have seen) could then have produced the stock from which higher chordates arose.[1] The most plausible suggestion yet made to account for the

---

[1] Berrill holds that vertebrates may have evolved from a neotenous ascidian tadpole that matured as a free-swimming organism exploiting the rich pastures of shallow continental seas. (Thaliacians and appendicularians are the direct but modified survivors; the relationship of the Adelochorda (p. 5) remains obscure.) The hypothetical vertebrate ancestor elaborated its sensory and motor equipment and ascended coastal rivers, Amphioxus (p. 47) being a degenerate littoral relic of an intermediate phase of evolution. Within the river systems there arose a relatively simple unarmoured ostracoderm (p. 171), the vertebrate prototype.

Berrill discusses in detail questions of lower chordate relationships, and a brief introductory chapter summarises speculations from the time of St. Hilaire (1818) until the present day (see also p. 213).

changes in position of the gill-slits, and other organs, which occur during the development of Amphioxus is that these are relics of the changes that might have occurred, during metamorphosis, in a hypothetical ascidian ancestor.

Alternatively (and much less probably), Amphioxus may be a specialised and degenerate descendant of the Agnatha (jawless vertebrate hagfishes, lampreys, and their allies, p. 176). According to this view, the acquired specialisations are the multiplication of the gill-slits and myomeres, the asymmetry, and the complicated larval history. The supposed losses by degeneration include the simplification of the brain, the absence of eyes, otic capsules, exoskeleton, and generative ducts. Such losses are perhaps not impossible, but the presence of true nephridia with flame-cells (structures otherwise unknown in the Chordata) lends no support to the above hypothesis.

The evidence as to the real position of the Acrania is still insufficient, but investigations have tended to bring them nearer to the Craniates than has often been suspected. It is probable that Amphioxus and its allies resemble in many fundamental respects the fish-like creatures that existed in Silurian seas, and it is possible that the modern fishes of today evolved from animals of much the same kind.

GENERAL INTRODUCTION TO CRANIATE (VERTEBRATE) FORMS

THE Craniata includes the agnathans, fishes, amphibians, reptiles, birds, and mammals, or, in other words, vertebrate animals with a skull, a highly complex brain, a muscular heart of three or four chambers, and, almost always (see p. 343), red blood-corpuscles.

The Craniata may be defined as Euchorda in which the notochord is not continued to the end of the snout, but stops short beneath the fore-brain, some distance from its anterior end. A skull is always present, and there are usually paired limbs. The pharynx is of moderate dimensions, and is perforated by not more than seven pairs of gill-slits except in some cyclostomes (p. 175). The gill-pouches do not open into an atrium. The liver is massive, and not obviously tubular. The renal tubules unite to form large paired kidneys and open into ducts which discharge into or near the posterior end of the intestine. The brain is complex, and there are at least ten pairs of cranial nerves. Except in cyclostomes the spinal nerves are formed by the union of dorsal and ventral roots. Paired eyes of great complexity, derived in part from the brain, are present. There is a pair of auditory organs. There is typically a single pair of gonads. The reproductive products are usually discharged by ducts derived from the renal system. There is never a typical invaginate gastrula, and the mesoderm arises in the form of paired longitudinal bands which subsequently become segmented. The cœlom is nearly always developed as a schizocœle.

In spite of the obvious and striking diversity of organisation among Craniata —between, for instance, a lamprey, a pigeon, and Man—there is a fundamental unity running through the whole group, both in the general arrangement of the various systems of organs and the structure of the organs themselves. The range of variation in the whole of the classes included in the division is, in fact, considerably less than in many single classes of invertebrates—for instance, Hydrozoa or Crustacea. Hence it is convenient to begin with a preliminary account of the Craniata as a whole. In this way needless repetition will be avoided.

An abbreviated classification of the group is as follows:

SUB-PHYLUM CRANIATA (VERTEBRATA)

Super-class Agnatha
   Classes Euphanerida (Silurian)
           Heterostraci (Pteraspida) (Ordovician-Devonian)
           Anaspida (Silurian–Devonian)
           Osteostraci (Cephalaspida) (Silurian–Devonian)
           Petromyzontia (?—Recent)
           Myxinoidea (?—Recent)

Super-class Gnathostomata
   Classes Placodermi (Silurian–Permian)
           Elasmobranchii (Devonian–Recent)
           Osteichthyes (Devonian–Recent)
           Amphibia (Devonian–Recent)
           Reptilia (Carboniferous–Recent)
           Aves (Jurassic–Recent)
           Mammalia (Triassic–Recent)

CRANIATE TISSUES

The numerous cell-types containing the living, self-perpetuating protoplasm (nucleus and cytoplasm) of the vertebrate body are aggregated in different arrangements to form materials of the following principal kinds:

Epithelial tissue.—*Simple* (single-layered) *epithelia*: columnar (ciliated and non-ciliated), cuboidal, squamous (pavement). *Pseudostratified*: columnar (ciliated and non-ciliated). *Compound* (stratified) *epithelia*: stratified columnar, stratified cuboidal, stratified squamous, stratified transitional.

Connective tissue.[1]—Fibrous and cellular material embedded in an amorphous ground substance. It consists of yellow elastic fibres, white collagenous fibres, reticular fibres; and mainly fibroblasts, histiocytes, fat cells, and mast cells (*mastzellen*). It can be roughly subdivided into: *Loose connective tissue* or areolar tissue (as in sub-cutaneous layers of the integument); *dense connective tissue* (as in the sheaths surrounding muscles and nerves).

Adipose tissue.—Usually considered as a separate tissue, but it is merely connective tissue in which enough cells develop sufficient fat and are aggregated together to form an apparently definite tissue.

Blood.—This consists of *plasma*, a watery fluid containing small amounts of various salts, protein, lipid, and glucose. In this medium lie *erythrocytes* (red blood cells or corpuscles); *leucocytes* (white blood cells) including

[1] In many histology textbooks the term *connective tissue* embraces adipose tissue, blood, cartilage, and bone. In usage one generally employs the term in the manner referred to above.

polymorphs (mainly neutrophils, also eosinophils and basophils), monocytes and lymphocytes; *thrombocytes* (nucleated spindle cells) typically in
sub-mammalian groups, or *blood platelets*, typically in mammals.

Lymph.—The fluid in the lymphatics. Essentially similar to plasma but
with greatly reduced protein content and containing lymphocytes.

Cartilage.—*Hyaline. Fibrous. Elastic.*

Bone.[1]

Muscle.—*Striated* (skeletal, striped, somatic, or voluntary). *Smooth*
(visceral, plain, unstriped, or involuntary). *Cardiac* (heart).

Neural tissue.

The various individual organs and systems are composed, in varying
complexity, of the above classes of material which seem to originate as follows :

Ectodermal Derivatives.—Epithelium of the skin (epidermis) and its appendages, such as the hair, nails, feathers, sebaceous, sweat, and mammary and
other glands. Epithelium of the buccal and anal areas, including the various
salivary glands and epithelial derivatives such as the enamel of the teeth.
Epithelium of the lower part of the urethra. Epithelium of the nasal passages
and associated glands. Epithelium of the glands and canals and that of the
conjunctiva, crystalline lens, retina, and some of the intrinsic muscles of the eye.
Epithelium lining the external auditory meatus, the membranous labyrinth,
the spinal canal, the aqueduct, and the IVth, IIIrd, and lateral ventricles of the
brain, as well as nerve-cells and nerve-fibres. The pituitary and pineal glands.

In addition, the derivatives of the *neural crest* are ectodermal in origin.
They include most of the branchial arch cartilages and parts of the trabeculæ
cranii (at least in Amphibia) ; the ganglia of the spinal, and some of the
cranial, nerves ; parts of the autonomic nervous system ; probably the pia
and arachnoid, and possibly the Schwann cells ; probably the adrenal medulla
and other chromaffin tissues ; parts of some of the teeth ; and the pigment cells.

Mesodermal Derivatives.—Dermis and most of the skeleton (except trabeculæ of the chondrocranium jaws and gill arches). Dentine. All the
connective tissues, including blood. The spleen, lymph tissue, and peritoneum.
The adrenal cortex and the endothelial lining of the heart and blood-vessels.
Epithelium of the uriniferous tubules, ureters, tests (and ducts). Epithelium
of the ovary and Graafian follicles. Epithelium of the oviducts, uterus, and
the upper part of the vagina. Muscular tissues.

Endodermal Derivatives.—Epithelium of the alimentary canal from pharynx
to, and including, the rectum as well as that of all the glands opening into it,
including liver and pancreas. Epithelium of the Eustachian tube and tympanic

---

[1] Stensio and Ørvig have suggested that there is no clear distinction between bone and dentine
in the earliest vertebrates and that the primitive exoskeletal element is not the placoid scale but
the *lepidomorium*. This consists of a bony core, the apical part of which is modified to dentine
and surrounded by enamel. The whole structure arises around a single looped blood vessel.

cavity and that of the larynx, trachea, bronchi, and alveoli. Thyroid and parathyroid glands and the embryonic rudiment of the thymus. Epithelium of the urinary bladder, female urethra as well as that of the upper parts of the male urethra and associated glands.

The *germ-layer theory*, involving many of the above facts, was put forward by von Baer in 1828. It states that : (1) in normal embryos the materials from which the organs develop are arranged in three layers—ectoderm, mesoderm, and endoderm ; and (2) in different animals homologous structures arise from corresponding layers.

But, as de Beer has pointed out, the second part of the theory cannot nowadays be maintained. For example, the anterior thymus may form from ectoderm and endoderm (*Salmo* and the marsupial *Trichosurus*), from endoderm alone (*Oryctolagus* and *Homo*), or from ectoderm alone (*Sus* and the mole, *Talpa*). Numerous comparable examples have caused the germ-layer theory to fall into disrepute among modern embryologists. Some structures, formerly thought to be of mesodermal origin, are now known to be derived from the neural crest. The existence of the germ layers, however, cannot be denied (even though their structure may vary somewhat in different groups) and this makes it difficult to abandon the concept entirely. Perhaps for the time being there is little harm in this, provided that it is remembered clearly that the derivatives of the germ layers are not necessarily homologous in different animals.

THE CRANIATE BODY

The internal tissues of vertebrates are covered and protected by an *integument* (p. 82) which varies remarkably in structure and function from one group to another. The underlying tissues are moulded around, and mechanically supported by, an endoskeletal framework of cartilage, bone, or both. These support the more pliable *soft tissues*, and sometimes form protective compartments such as the cranium, vertebral canal, and thorax. They develop special surfaces, including depressions and projections, for the attachment of muscles, tendons, and ligaments. Many serve also as mobile, articulated levers which allow the free movement of various parts of the body and of the animal as a whole. Although bone, which is peculiar to vertebrates, is found at an early stage in the evolution of the Agnatha (p. 166), it is convenient first to deal with cartilage.

Cartilage is resilient, flexible, but to some degree rigid. It is developed from embryonic mesenchyme and composed of cartilage cells (*chondrocytes*) enclosed within small spaces (lacunæ) and embedded in a matrix composed of connective tissue fibres and amorphous ground substance. The amount and type of its constituent fibres determine whether a cartilage is *hyaline*, *elastic*, or *fibrous*. The last-named is predominantly composed of collagenous fibres and is extremely tough. It is found in joints and in parts of tendons (sinews) that undergo friction against, or are inserted on, bone. Elastic cartilage is permeated with yellow elastic fibres, and occurs in areas of great flexibility (*e.g.* epiglottis and mammalian pinna). Hyaline cartilage consists of amorphous ground-substance laced with numerous collagenous fibres. This type of cartilage is the most widespread form and may persist over the embryonic period, or be replaced by bone (*e.g.* p. 95). Except over articular surfaces, cartilage is covered by a dense connective tissue sheath or *perichondrium*. The amorphous substance of cartilage is compression-resistant; the internal collagenous fibres resist tension. Blood vessels penetrate the substance of the larger cartilages by means of *cartilage canals*, but, in general, chondrocytes are nourished by simple diffusion.

A cartilaginous structure has a consistency not unlike that of very firm jelly. A jelly, if unsupported, would collapse under a weight, yet 'may resist it successfully if wrapped in a piece of sacking whose fibres take up the upward thrust due to the downward pressure of the weight. . . . The jelly-like, firm, matrix [of cartilage] with contained cells resists compression, but the resistance offered is strengthened by the collagen fibres of the perichondrium and the matrix' (Murray). Cartilage can grow at any point within its bulk. It is sufficiently strong, as we shall see, to support in water the bulk of a shark between 40 and 50 feet in length. In cartilaginous animals there is sometimes an impregnation of cartilage with mineral salts (p. 231), but this must not be confused with true bone. There is some evidence that the calcium deposited in this way interferes with the diffusion of nutrient material to, and gases from, the chondrocytes. If mineralisation proceeds too far the chondrocytes tend to die. Bone formation, as we will see below, is brought about by the calcification of an intercellular substance without interfering with the nutrition of the parent tissue.

Bone is a complicated, living tissue made up of cells and collagenous fibres in an amorphous ground-substance impregnated with tricalcium phosphate and other salts. The term 'bone matrix' is usually employed to refer to the whole of the non-cellular constituents. The matrix is made up of numerous concentric rings of thin lamellæ through which run numerous anastomosing *Haversian canals* admitting arterioles, venules, and nerve-fibres. *Interstitial lamina* occupy the spaces between each such *Haversian system*. Within this interstitial material are minute spaces (lacunæ). Radiating canaliculi link the lacunæ with others and ultimately with a Haversian canal, although the canaliculi of one 'system' do not apparently connect with another. An *osteocyte* or bone-cell occupies each lacuna. These are thought to be derived from *osteoblasts*, which, in the growing animal, are probably responsible for the deposition of the inorganic components of bone. The bone is surrounded by another specialised connective tissue, the *periosteum*, the inner part being a vascular *osteogenic layer* containing undifferentiated, potential osteoblasts. The periosteum, too, is pierced by blood vessels, as is also the *medullary* or *marrow cavity*, with its *hæmatopœtic* (blood-forming) *tissue*.

Bone-growth occurs partly by means of sub-periostial deposition of osseus material (membrane bone) and partly by endochondrial ossification. Re-modelling by resorption and by new bone formation subsequently takes place. At the same time, ossification extends towards the still cartilaginous ends of the bone, and, at the extremities themselves, *secondary centres* of ossification may arise. This results in the formation of bony *epiphyses*, which, however, remain separated from the shaft by thin, plate-like *epiphysial cartilage*. In fishes, crocodilians, and chelonians the epiphysial region remains cartilaginous.

All viscera and other tissues are associated in greater or less degree with *connective tissue* (Fig. 80, p. 116). This acts as a secondary support in either simple or specialised form. Connective tissue surrounds vessels as *perivascular sheaths*; nerve tissue as *perineural sheaths*; and many glands as thickened *fibrous capsules*. Around muscles it forms *epimysial sheaths*. It forms also *intermuscular septa*. Individual muscle *fasciculi*, forming the substance of the muscle, are held together by delicate connective tissue sheaths or peri-mysia. *Bursæ* (small, fluid-containing, friction-reducing, and otherwise protective sacs where *tendons* are in contact with each other, or with bones) are formed of connective tissue lined with *mesothelium*. The tendons them-selves (the function of which is to exert a concentrated pull at the *musculo-tendinous junction*, see below) are composed almost exclusively of white collagenous fibres. Such cords are formed of flexible and relatively non-elastic tissue and are of great tensile strength and transmit the muscle-pull to the structure on which the tendon is *inserted*. *Fascia*—both *superficial* and *deep* —is connective tissue differentiated into sheets which in the case of superficial fascia sometimes constitute a fat-containing *panniculus adiposus* (*e.g.* Cetacea, Man). Superficial fascia, immediately below the connective tissue of the *dermis* (p. 116), may carry sufficient adipose tissue to modify surface contours, and is of æsthetic and sexual selection significance in Man. Deep fasciæ lie in inti-mate protective, and sometimes tensile, association with muscles, bones, and other structures, and may merge with the periosteum of bone in surface areas. Connective tissue forms also *perichondrium*, the sheath of hyaline cartilage (p. 72), as well as cord-like *ligaments* which run from bone to bone, particularly in the neighbourhood of movable joints. It forms also *aponeuroses* (if sheet-like) as well as *mesenteries* and *meninges*.

In certain specialised situations ossifications (*sesamoid bones*) appear in tendons (*e.g.* patella in certain mammals, *os falciforme* in moles (p. 731)). Such structures are different from heterotopic bone arising adventitiously in fibrous (*e.g.* scar) tissue. Different too are the *visceral bones* (p. 94): (1) the *os cordis* in ungulates which persists in Man as a dense fibrous mass between the atrioventricular and aortic apertures, (2) *os palpebræ* in the eyelid of Crocodilia, and (3) the *os penis* (*os priapi, baculum*) which arises as a rod- or plate-like bone (of very variable form) in the fibrous septum dividing the corpora cavernosa of 'a few insectivores' (Kingsley) and most, if not all, rodents, bats, carnivores, and Primates (excluding Man). This bone can be massive: in the Walrus it reaches a length of 23 inches and a weight of more than 1 lb. 12 oz.

Within the supporting framework of bone, cartilage, and connective tissue lie the *muscles*, all of which possess in high degree the property of *contractility*. These are of three kinds: (1) *skeletal* or *somatic* (*striated*), (2) *visceral* (*unstriated, plain,* or *smooth*), and (3) *cardiac* (*heart*), which exists in an obviously syncytial arrangement and exhibits certain resemblances to the other two. The two first-named are often spoken respectively of as 'voluntary' and 'involuntary' muscles. In general, such terms are not inappropriate, but it should be remembered that (for example) although the ciliary muscles controlling the curvature of the mammalian eye-lens are unstriped or 'plain', the eye can be nevertheless focused at will.

Skeletal or *striped muscle* consists of numerous individual, elongated, fibres which are supplied by rich vascular plexuses. Each fibre is enclosed by a sheath or *sarcolemma* and consists of a finely granular cytoplasm (*sarcoplasm*) containing many peripherally situated nuclei. Embedded in the sarcoplasm are numerous fine fibrils (*myofibrils*) arranged longitudinally. Each myofibril bears a regular series of transverse light and dark striations. These are responsible for the characteristic striped appearance of each fibre. Fibres may be red, white, or transitional, and both red and white fibres often occur in the same muscle, especially in the Mammalia. The dark colour is due to the relative abundance of *myoglobin*, or muscle hæmoglobin, which is related to blood hæmoglobin, from which it receives the oxygen used in muscle metabolism.

Functionally, striated muscle must be considered in relation to the nervous and skeletal systems. Nerves activate muscles, and these then act upon cartilage, bones, tendons, fascia, ligaments, skin, and other structures. The *origin* and *insertion* of a muscle are respectively its relatively fixed and mobile points of attachment. For example, in the *gastrocnemius* muscle of the leg the proximal end is attached at its origin to the femur and the distal end at its insertion on the foot. A muscle originates at its *head*, the main mass of its fleshy fibres is the *belly*, and it inserts at its *tail* (but nowadays the last term is seldom used). Muscles may insert by either fleshy or fibrous portions.

The arrangement of the constituent fibres of relatively simple muscles is parallel to the direction of pull. *Pennate* muscles, on the other hand, have the fibres arranged obliquely in relation to the attachment. In *unipennate* muscles the fleshy fibres approach the insertion from one direction; in *bipennate* elements there is a dual convergence; and in *multipennate* there is a multiple convergence. Muscles may be named according to shape (e.g. *deltoideus*, *trapezius*), structure (*triceps*, *digastricus*), situation (*pectoralis*, *brachialis*), attachments (*coracohumeralis*, *sternocoracoideus*), action (*flexor tarsi*, *abductor*), and other characteristics.

The essential function of striped or voluntary muscles is to approximate two points, *e.g.* moving manus to mouth by flexing the forearm. *Flexion* bends; it reduces the angle between two parts. *Extension* widens the angle, sometimes rearranging limbs to the straight position. *Protraction* and *retraction* draw bones forward and backward respectively. In relation to some structures such terms can be synonymous with flexion and extension. *Adduction* and *abduction* are the respective movements of a structure toward or away from an axis (*e.g.* the midline of an animal). *Elevators* raise, and *depressors* lower a part (such as the lower jaw). *Pronation* turns the palm downward (by rotation of the radius in relation to the ulna), whilst *supination* arranges the palm in the reverse position.

Muscular activity is carried out by the contraction of individual fibres on an 'all-or-none' principle. A group of fibres innervated by a single nerve-fibre is called a *motor-unit*, and gradation of the contraction depends on varying the number of motor-units in action. No entire muscle acts alone. Along with the prime-mover, *synergists* and *antagonists* operate in ancillary capacities in carrying out what may be apparently the most simple skeletal re-arrangement. The contraction—and even the *tone*—of muscle is maintained by motor nerves, individual fibres of which terminate as *motor end-plates* applied to individual muscle fibres (Fig. 84). In all animals, and in homiothermal forms particularly, muscle activity produces heat, which may be conserved by special devices (pp. 559, 781, 883). In some mammals reflex shivering contractions, resulting in compensatory heat production, occur when the body temperature falls below an optimum degree.

Visceral, smooth, or *plain muscles* lack the characteristic striæ of skeletal fibres. They are controlled by the autonomic nervous system (p. 119). Vertebrate animals (or their eggs) are thrust into the world by such muscles, and thenceforward the circulation of the blood (with its contained food substances and oxygen), the digestion of food, the secretion by glands, the elimination of metabolites, and the maintenance of many other vital functions depend on its routine, involuntary activity. Thus, for example, plain or smooth muscle is found in the walls of the gut, lungs, blood vessels, bladder, genitalia, and various glands. In these it is, among numerous other functions, concerned with peristalsis and retroperistalsis, changes in the vascular tone and the control of blood pressure, with the control of air passages (bronchi), excretory rates, thermoregulation (in birds and mammals), and with the discharge of sexual products and so on. Visceral fibres are uninucleate, spindle-shaped bodies which lack a sarcolemma and lie in intimate association in sheets, the individual fibres perhaps bound together by delicate reticular tissue. Although the activity of visceral muscles is essentially controlled by innervation from the autonomic nervous system, local nerve plexuses occur, and there is abundant experimental evidence of an intrinsic nervous mechanism in certain areas (*e.g.* gut).

Cardiac muscle is confined to the heart, but in some forms it extends into the roots of the great vessels (*e.g.* in the conus arteriosus of the dogfish, p. 240). It is essentially similar to skeletal or striated muscle in structure, except that the sarcolemma is much thinner; the nuclei are central in position; and the fibres branch and possess conspicuous *intercalated discs* interposed among the other fine transverse striations. The branched fibres lack obvious boundaries and were previously regarded as syncitial. Although the heart-beat is myogenic in origin (p. 109), its frequency is under autonomic control (p. 119). Sympathetic nerves innervate the branched fibres; para-sympathetic (vagal) terminations are restricted (in the higher mammals) to the atria and the atrio-ventricular bundle (p. 882). All living tissues are connected with the rhythmically pumping heart by means of a closed system of *supplying* arteries and arterioles, and of *draining* venules and veins. Between arterial and venous elements are *capillary beds* and *tissue spaces* (Fig. 80). Only in the spleen, liver, bone-marrow and some endocrine glands does the blood come into closer contact with the general tissues.

Arteries get progressively narrower, and are required to withstand less blood pressure, the further they go from the heart. As they progressively bifurcate, their total cross-section is increased, and there is a corresponding reduction in circulation rate. The elastin and collagen content of arteries varies greatly with situation and diameter. In cross-section, an artery is lined by an endothelium, which is sheathed by a *lamina elastica*, in turn surrounded by a tough fibrous *tunica media* (of elastin, collagen, and muscular fibres), and by an outermost *tunica externa* (principally of collagen material). By the time arteries narrow to a diameter of about 0·1–2 mm. the tunica media is almost solely muscular, and they are now arterioles, innervated by the autonomic system. Their tone can be altered, thus regulating the blood supply to skin and viscera. Arterioles empty into even narrower, thin-walled *capillaries*, each perhaps composed of a fragile *perivascular* layer of connective tissue and an endothelial lining. In lower craniates these, too, are contractile. In all groups these link up to form a *capillary network*, the richness of which varies according to the nutritive and concomitant requirements of their situation.

Between the capillaries and the other tissues lie *tissue spaces* containing *tissue fluid*. Across these must pass gaseous, nutritional, excretory, and other materials. The capillary walls are highly permeable to all but the largest molecules, *i.e.* proteins. These are retained in the capillary, and exert an osmotic pressure *into* the capillary, whereas movement outward from the capillary is determined by the excess hydrostatic pressure over the osmotic pressure at its arteriolar end. At the venule end, hydrostatic pressure is less than osmotic pressure, and so water and its solutes (*e.g.* metabolites) move back in again. Some fluid passes into *lymph capillaries* (*lymphatics*) as *lymph* which contains some protein, and much the same inorganic components as blood. It contains also *lymphocytes*, but lacks red cells and blood platelets, which cannot penetrate the blood capillary walls. By means of *lymph hearts* or *valves* (according to the type of animal), the fluid is at length forced back into the general circulation, the disposition of the conducting vessels and their entry into the venous system varying from group to group.

Meanwhile, altered capillary blood flows into *venules*, the walls of which are strengthened by a definitive sheath of connective tissue. Venules in turn unite to form *veins*. These are lined with endothelium, but, although veins have basically the same structure as arteries, the remaining layers are often difficult to distinguish. There is a great diminution of both elastic and muscular tissue. In higher craniates, venous return in many veins is facilitated by the presence of valves that prevent back-flow. Blood can be forced forward against gravity, and pooling avoided, by the movement of adjacent skeletal muscles and other means, including, in animals with closed thoracic respiration, the negative intra-thoracic pressures.

Arteries and veins usually run in close proximity to each other, and in certain situations a small artery or an arteriole, by means of a special neuro-muscular mechanism, delivers blood directly into a neighbouring venule, thus short-circuiting the capillary network and forming an *arterio-venous anastomosis*. Such anastomoses appear to be best developed in situations where metabolic activity is intermittent (*e.g.* gut), or where a relatively unimpeded circulation will better subserve thermoregulation (*e.g.* skin, membranous wings, etc.) in homiothermous animals (p. 883).

In the lower craniates in particular (and in higher groups as well) wide *blood sinuses*, sheathed only in endothelium, occur at definite points. These may replace capillaries and allow of a uniquely intimate relationship between blood and tissue, and the performance of special functions in liver, spleen, bone marrow, and adrenal glands. In certain lower craniates (see p. 243) sinusoidal dilations occur in the great veins and are part of a specialised mechanism of venous return.

We have seen that the above fundamental tissues, and (as is obvious) the various living components of structures such as skin, teeth, receptor organs, and the numerous viscera, must all possess a nerve supply. A brief outline of the nervous system is given on pp. 116–135).

External characters.—The body (Fig. 57) is bilaterally symmetrical, elongated in an antero-posterior direction, and usually more or less cylindrical. It is divisible into three regions : (1) the *head*, which contains the brain, the

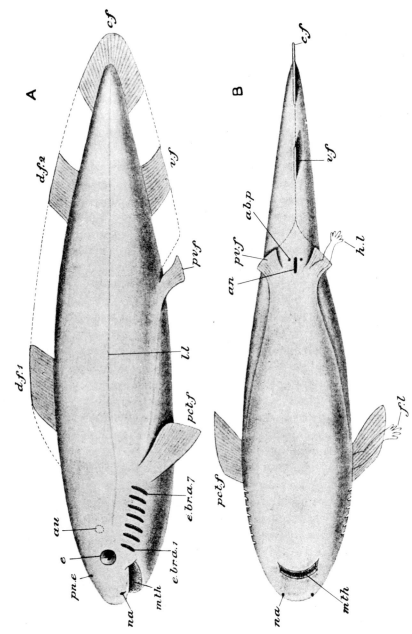

FIG. 57.—**Sub-phylum Craniata: External views of an " ideal " vertebrate.** *ab. p.* abdominal pore; *au.* position of auditory organ; *an.* anus; *c. f.* caudal fin; *d. f. 1,* first, and *d. f. 2,* second dorsal fin; *e.* paired eye; *e. br. a. 1,* first, and *e. br. a. 7,* seventh gill-cleft; *f. l.* fore-limbs; *h. l.* hind-limb; *l. l.* lateral line; *mth.* mouth; *na.* nasal aperture; *pct. f* pectoral fin; *pn. e.* pineal organ; *pv. f.* pelvic fin; *v. f.* ventral fin. The dotted line in *A* indicates a continuous median fin.

chief sensory organs, and the mouth and pharynx ; (2) the *trunk*, to which the cœlom is confined, and which contains the principal digestive, circulatory, excretory, and reproductive organs ; and (3) the *tail*, or region situated posteriorly to the cœlom and anus. *Viscera* do not extend into the tail. At the same time, it should be remembered that functionally the expression may refer in fishes and fish-like animals to pre-anal parts that nevertheless undergo lateral undulations (p. 86). Between the head and trunk there is frequently a narrow *neck*, into which the cœlom does not extend. In aquatic vertebrates the tail is normally of great size, not marked off externally from the trunk. In mammals it is usually greatly reduced in diameter, and has the appearance of a mere unpaired posterior appendage.

The *mouth* (*mth.*) is generally a transverse aperture placed at or near the anterior end of the head. Near it, either dorsal or ventral in position, are the paired *nostrils* or *anterior nares* (*na.*). In various widely unrelated fishes and fish-like vertebrates there have arisen *internal nares* by which the paired olfactory organs communicate with the buccal cavity (see also Fig. 89, p. 138). A peculiar arrangement exists in myxinoids. An unpaired terminal nostril leads into a duct that opens into the pharynx. Through this passes the respiratory current (p. 199). This water enters the nostril, crosses the olfactory epithelium, and traverses the pharynx and finally the gills. This specialisation is of course not homologous with the paired structures that have occasionally arisen among teleosts of burrowing habit (*e.g.* stargazer, *Astroscopus*, and certain echelid and ophichthid eels), nor are any of the above arrangements phylogenetically related to the internal nares of lung-fishes (p. 361). Although the internal nares of the Dipnoi (secondarily lost in the Cœlacanthini, p. 356) are of course homologous with those subserving respiration in the Amphibia (p. 412), and in tetrapods generally, there is no good evidence that they were utilised in breathing by ancestral crossopterygians. Certainly modern lung-fishes appear to respire essentially by gulping in air through the buccal cavity (p. 365). While æstivating too, *Protopterus* breathes through the mouth. It is not improbable that internal nares served initially as adjuncts to the olfactory organs, making for a more rapid and efficient testing of the environment than do the blind respiratory sacs characteristic of fishes in general. Other air-breathing fishes (e.g. *Periophthalmus, Clarias*, p. 338, *Polypterus*, p. 290) do not possess internal nares.

The *eyes* (*e*) are paired and vary greatly in structure and efficiency. On the dorsal surface of the head there is sometimes more or less indication of a vestigial median eye or *pineal organ* (*pn. e.*) (see pp. 189, 345). Posterior to the paired eyes are the *auditory organs* (*au.*), the position of which is indicated in the higher forms by an *auditory aperture*.

On the sides of the head, behind the mouth, are a series of openings, the *gill-slits* or *external branchial apertures* (*e. br. a.* 1–7). They are rarely more than seven in number, and in air-breathing forms disappear more or less completely in the adult. In the higher fishes a fold, the *operculum* (Fig. 205, *op*; p. 304), articulates with the hyoid arch immediately in front of the first gill-slit and extends backwards, covering the branchial apertures. In the larvæ of urodeles there occurs a somewhat similar opercular flap. In frogs the structure covers the external gills and gill-slits, and even the site of the fore-limbs. In the placoderms (p. 205) the operculum is supported by the mandibular arch.

On the ventral surface at the junction of the trunk and tail is the *anus* (*an.*). Distinct *urinary* and *genital apertures*, or a single *urinogenital aperture*, are sometimes found either in front of or behind the anus. More commonly the urinary and genital ducts open into the termination of the alimentary canal, or *cloaca*, so that there is only a single egestive opening, known as the *cloacal aperture*. On either side of this there may be a small *abdominal pore* (*ab. p.*) (of doubtful function) communicating with the cœlom.

In fishes and some amphibians (p. 380) the trunk and tail are produced in the middle dorsal line into a vertical fold or *median fin*, which is continued round the end of the tail and forwards in the middle line to the anus. This continuous fin frequently becomes broken up into distinct *dorsal* (*d. f. 1* and *2*), *ventral* (*v. f.*), and *caudal* (*cd. f.*) *fins*, which may assume very various forms. In the higher classes all trace of median fins disappears (*cf.*, however, analogous structures in *Ichthyosaurus* (p. 491) and the Cetacea (p. 780)).

Fishes also possess *paired fins*. Immediately posterior to the last gill-slit is a more or less horizontal outgrowth, the *pectoral fin* (*pct. f.*), while a similar but smaller structure, the *pelvic fin* (*pv. f.*), arises at the side of the anus.

In all Craniata above the fishes, *i.e.* from the Amphibia upwards, the paired fins are replaced by *fore-* and *hind-limbs* (*f. l., h. l.*), each consisting of three divisions—*upper-arm* (*brachium*), *fore-arm* (*antebrachium*), and *hand* (*manus*) in the one case ; *thigh* and *shank* (*leg*), and *foot* (*pes*) in the other. Both hand and foot normally terminate in five fingers or *digits*. The *pentadactyle limb* thus formed is an obvious adaptation to land-life and is characteristic of *tetrapods*. The paired fins, or limbs (as the case may be), are almost the only lateral appendages possessed by vertebrates, if we except the barbels possessed by certain fishes (p. 338) and 'balancers' of urodele larvæ.

Body-wall and Internal Cavities.—The body is covered externally by a *skin* consisting of two principal layers, an outer and stratified epithelial layer, the *epidermis* (Fig. 58), derived from the ectoderm of the embryo, and an inner or connective-tissue layer, the *dermis* or *corium* of mesodermal origin (p. 71). In terrestrial vertebrates (p. 385) the superficial layers (*stratum corneum*) are dead, flattened, and *keratinised* (horny). The outermost cells are constantly abraded and replaced from below. In fishes (Fig. 58) a keratinised *layer* probably never occurs. New cells for the replenishment of the outer layers are produced by division of cells in the Malpighian layer (*stratum Malpighii*), which lies at the base of the epidermis. In the Agnatha (p. 164) and the true fishes the connective tissue-fibres of the dermis almost all run parallel to the surface, and do not form a felt-like mass of fibres running in all directions, as in mammals.

Although the epidermis of fish is usually many layered, exceptionally it may be only two cells thick, as in many Syngnathidæ. The *basal layer* always consists of undifferentiated epidermal cells, although here and there throughout the epidermis may usually be found *wandering cells* (*wanderzellen*) which are

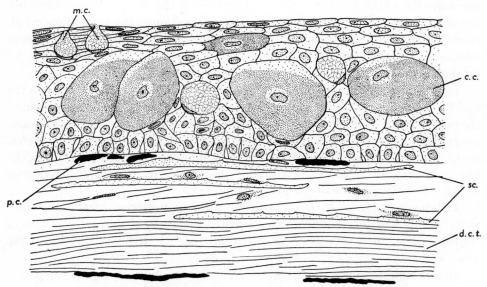

FIG. 58.—**Integument: Epidermis of fish.** Tench (*Tinca*). Vertical section: *c. c.* club cells; *d. c. t.* deep connective tissue; *m. c.* mucous cells; *p. c.* pigment cells; *sc.* scale (see also Fig. 112, p. 178). The club cells do not occur very near the surface but are nevertheless lost when the epidermis is abraded. Although there is some flattening of the surface cells, keratinisation does not usually occur in fishes. (Drawn by G. H. O. Burgess.)

capable of amœboid movement and enter into the epidermis from the under-lying connective tissue. Just above the basal layer there often occur the earliest stages in the development of the various types of secretory cell. Keratin occurs only in certain specialised epidermal structures (*e.g.* lamprey teeth and possibly the 'pearl organs' of cyprinids). Secretory glands are very rare in fishes, but secretory *gland cells* are always found. *Mucous cells* occur in the epidermis of all fishes. These are usually of the goblet-cell type with a basal semi-lunar nucleus and a theca of cytoplasm surrounding the secretion (Fig. 58), but in some fishes (and agnathans) other types of mucous cell are found (as for instance in *Myxine*, Fig. 197). The lubricating secretions from mucous or slime cells are variously held to (1) reduce surface drag, (2) produce a surface difficult for predators to grip, (3) prevent the lodgment of organisms, and (4) assist in the control of osmosis. There is reason to believe that the two last-mentioned functions are important.

The skin of vertebrates is rarely naked and is usually provided with protective structures of various kinds, such as scales, bony plates, feathers, or hair. Scales of the fishes are of different shapes, such as *cycloid*, *ctenoid*, or *rhomboid*, but it is the structure rather than the shape that is of importance and of value in classification. There are three main kinds of scales in fishes : the *placoid*, the *cosmoid*, and the *ganoid*. The placoid scale

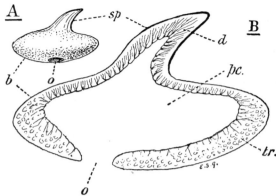

FIG. 59.—Integument: **Placoid scale.** Median dorsal denticle scale of *Raja blanda*. *A*, left side view; *B*, section, enlarged; *b*. basal plate; *d*. dentinal tubules; *o*. opening of pulp cavity; *s. p.* projecting spine; *tr.* trabecular dentine. (After Goodrich.)

(Fig. 59), with an ectodermal cap of enamel and a body of dentine surrounding a pulp-chamber, has essentially the same composition as a tooth. In the

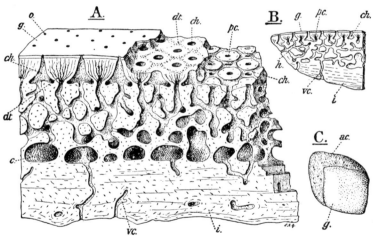

FIG. 60.—Integument: **Cosmoid scale.** *A*, piece of a thick transverse section enlarged; *B*, section through the hind edge, enlarged; *C*, outer view of a complete scale. Carboniferous rhipidistian *Megalichthys*. *ac*. anterior region covered by next scale; *c*. large vascular cavity; *ch*. chamber of cosmine layer; *dt*. canaliculi of cosmine; *g*. thin outermost layer; *h*. irregular vascular canals; *i*. isopedine layer; *o*. opening of chamber of cosmine layer on surface; *pc*. pulp cavity from which canaliculi radiate; *vc*. vertical canal leading to vascular cavity. (After Goodrich.)

elasmobranchs, in which the placoid scale is characteristic, there is a clear transition from the scales on the body to the teeth on the jaws. They lie superficially and, if lost, can be continually replaced.

The cosmoid scale (Fig. 60) lies deeper in the dermis, and consists of three layers. The outer *cosmine layer* is formed of an acellular substance somewhat like dentine. This contains vascular spaces and fine radiating-tubules. On the outer surface it has a thin layer of the hard, glossy *vitrodentine*. The middle *vascular layer* is formed of bone perforated by numerous anastomosing canals for the blood-vessels. The bottom *isopedine layer* consists of several laminæ of bone lying parallel to one another, through which at intervals run canals for blood-vessels passing to the vascular layer. Cosmoid scales are not shed, and during growth expand by the addition of cosmine round the edge of the upper surface

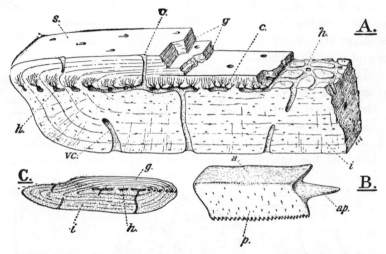

FIG. 61.—**Integument: Ganoid scale.** *A*, diagrammatic and enlarged view of a piece of scale from the carboniferous palæoniscoid *Plectrolepis* (= *Eurynotus*). *B*, outer view of a complete scale; *C*. transverse section of a scale. *a*. anterior covered region; *ap*. articulating process; *c*. fine canaliculi of cosmine layer; *g*. ganoine layer; *h*. system of horizontal canals; *i*. isopedine layer; *o*. opening of vertical canals on the outer surface; *p*. exposed posterior shiny part of the scale; *s*. outer surface; *vc*. vertical canal. (After Goodrich.)

and by addition to the isopedine layers below. It is possible that the vitrodentine covering of the scale can be resorbed and replaced at intervals during the life of the fish, but not all authorities are agreed upon this point. Cosmoid scales are found only in the crossopterygians (p. 353), but in living forms much of the characteristic structure of the scale has been lost.

The *ganoid* scale (Fig. 61) is composed of layers of acellular *ganoine* on the upper surface which pass into layers of isopedine below. Between these two layers are two more. The upper resembles cosmine and the lower one the vascular layers (see above), but these are not universally present and may be much reduced. The growth of the ganoid scale differs from that of the cosmoid in that fresh layers are laid down on the top of the scale as well as on the underside. This type of scale and its derivatives is confined to the Actinopterygii

(p. 283). A superficially similar type of scaling is found in acanthodian fishes (p. 207).

Scales and bony plates occur in the higher vertebrata, but their relation to those of the fishes is still obscure. In reptiles and birds the scales and feathers, and in mammals the hair, are epidermal in origin and are formed of a tough, horny, sulphur-containing protein termed *keratin*. Details of the structure are given in the accounts of the respective classes.

Beneath the skin is the *muscular layer*. The homology of the lateral musculature of all fish-like chordates, from the Acrania (p. 47) to teleost fishes (p. 239), is well established. The action of this musculature causes lateral undulation of the body and is much the same in each group, although considerable differences in the degree of efficiency (as measured by speed and agility in locomotion) are manifest. Such muscles contract serially. In association with an extensive and serial connective-tissue system, they act in relation to the flexible, yet resistant central notochord (see below). There is fossil evidence that optimal locomotion was probably achieved by fish-like chordates in the early Palæozoic (p. 3), and the general pattern of musculature has not changed significantly since. Forms existing to-day exhibit three principal types of lateral muscle architecture: (1) *amphioxine*, embracing the Acrania, (2) *cyclostomine*, including recent agnathous chordates, and (3) *piscine*, comprising the cartilaginous fishes (Elasmobranchii) and the bony fishes (Actinopterygii). (The external appearance of the lateral musculature of representatives of each of these groups, with individual elements offset, is shown in Fig. 62.) In detail, the lateral layer consists of zigzag muscle-segments or *myomeres*, separated from one another by partitions of connective tissue, or *myocommas*, and formed of longitudinally disposed muscle-fibres. The myomeres are not placed at right angles to the long axis of the body, but are directed from the median vertical plane outwards and backwards, and are at the same time convex in front and concave behind, so as to have a cone-in-cone arrangement (Fig. 63, *C*). Each myomere, moreover, is divisible into a dorsal (*d. m.*) and a ventral (*v. m.*) portion. In the higher groups this segmental arrangement, though present in the embryo, is lost in the adult, the myomeres becoming converted into more or less longitudinal bands having an extremely complex arrangement.

All three types of lateral musculature mentioned above possess the common function of bending the animal from side to side, achieving locomotor force as mentioned above. In each instance pull is exerted obliquely to the notochord (Fig. 63) and the long axis of the body. 'The myomeres pull at once laterocraniad and latero-caudad to bend the body from its position of equilibrium, or rest, into concavity. If continued, this movement would lead to a condition of instability, in which the vectors of the forces applied would pass across the axis of bending and the body would be distorted' (Nursall). However, this

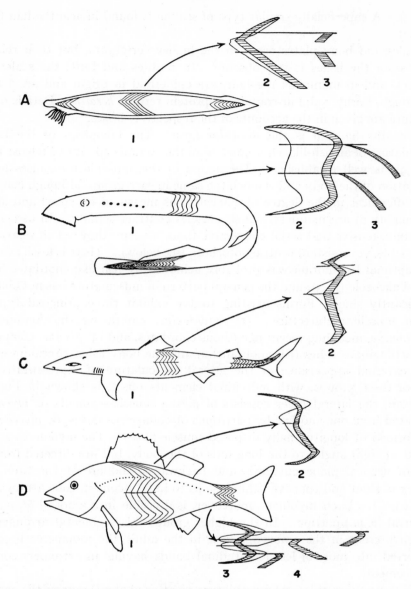

FIG. 62.—**Musculature: Myomere pattern of fishes and fish-like chordates.**

A. **Amphioxine:** (1) lateral view of *Amphioxus*; (2) lateral view of an individual myomere; (3) horizontal sections through myomere.

B. **Cyclostomine:** (1) lateral view of *Petromyzon*; (2) lateral view of an individual myomere; (3) horizontal sections through myomere.

C. **Piscine:** (1) lateral view of *Squalus*; (2) lateral view of an individual myomere from body region.

D. **Piscine:** (1) lateral view of *Perca*; (2) lateral view of an individual myomere from body region; (3) lateral view of a myomere from caudal peduncle; (4) horizontal sections through myomere of caudal peduncle. (All drawings are semi-diagrammatic.) (After Nursall.)

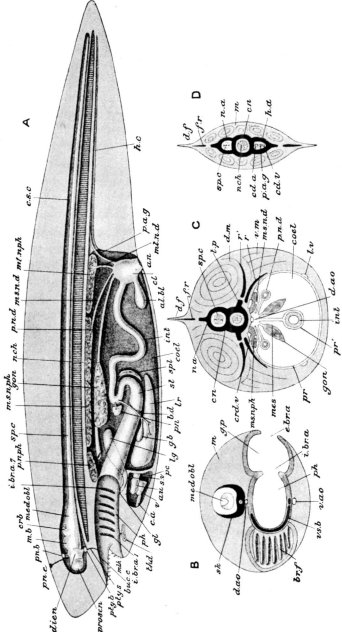

FIG. 63.—**Visceral relationships: "Ideal" craniate.** *A*, sagittal section; *B*, transverse section of the head; *C*, of the trunk; *D*, of the tail. *al. bl.* allantoic bladder; *an.* anus; *au.* auricle; *b. d.* bile-duct; *br. f.* branchial filaments; *buc. c.* buccal cavity; *c. a.* conus arteriosus; *cd. a.* caudal artery; *cd. v.* caudal vein; *cœl.* cœlom; *cn.* centrum; *crb.* cerebellum; *crd. v.* cardinal vein; *c. s. c.* cerebrospinal cavity; *d. ao.* dorsal aorta; *dien.* diencephalon; *d. f.* dorsal fin; *d. m.* dorsal muscles; *e. br. a.* external branchial aperture; *f. r.* fin-ray; *g. b.* gall-bladder; *gl.* glottis; *gon.* gonad; *g. p.* gill-pouch; *h. a.* hæmal arch; *h. c.* hæmal canal; *i. br. a.* internal branchial apertures; *int.* intestine; *lg.* lung; *lr.* liver; *l. v.* lateral vein; *m.* muscles; *m. b.* mid-brain; *med. obl.* medulla oblongata; *mes.* mesentery; *ms. n. d.* mesonephric duct; *mes. nph.* mesonephros; *mth.* mouth; *mt. n. d.* metanephric duct; *mt. nph.* metanephros; *n. a.* neural arch; *nch.* notochord; *p. a. g.* post-anal gut; *pc.* pericardium; *ph.* pharynx; *pn.* pancreas; *pn. b.* pineal body; *p. n. d.* pronephric duct; *pn. e.* pineal sense-organ; *p. nph.* pronephros; *pr.* peritoneum, parietal layer, and *pr'.* visceral layer; *prosen.* prosencephalon; *pty. b.* pituitary body; *pty. s.* pituitary sac; *v.* sub-peritoneal rib; *r'.* intermuscular rib; *sk.* skull; *sp. c.* spinal cord; *spl.* spleen; *st.* stomach; *s. v.* sinus venosus; *thd.* thyroid; *t. p.* transverse process; *v.* ventricle; *v. ao.* ventral aorta; *v. m.* ventral muscles; *vs. b.* visceral bar.

is prevented by the length of the body and its resistance to compression. At the same time, restorative forces are applied on the opposite (now convex) side of the body and these supplant the original bending movement. Thus the animal becomes concave on the other side. Actual locomotion is achieved by the reaction with the water of lateral waves set up by the rapid serial contraction of myomeres antero-posteriorly along the sides of the body. The myomeres are attached to the centra, neural and hæmal spines of the vertebrae and to the inter-muscular myocommas. Longitudinal ligamentous (p. 74) secondary attachments, formed by the apposition of deep *myosepta*, sometimes occur, especially in selachians. In the myosepta of some species there occur *intermuscular bones* (p. 94).

In the trunk the muscular layer encloses the *cœlom* (Fig. 63, *A* and *C, cœl.*). The muscular layer, as in Amphioxus, is not of even diameter throughout, but is greatly thickened dorsally, so that the cœlom is, as it were, thrown towards the ventral side. Its dorsal portion, moreover, is excavated by a canal, the *neural* or *cerebrospinal cavity* (*c. s. c.*), in which the central nervous system is contained, and the anterior portion of which is always dilated, as the *cranial cavity*, for the brain. Thus a transverse section of the trunk has the form of a double tube. In the head, neck, and tail (*B, D*), the cœlom is absent in the adult, and the muscles occupy practically the whole of the interval between the skin and the skeleton. In the tail, however, there is found a *hæmal canal* (*h. c.*) containing connective-tissue, and representing a virtual backward extension of the cœlom. This canal contains the principal caudal artery and vein. The fins, or fore- and hind-limbs, are moved by longitudinal muscles derived from those of the trunk. All the voluntary muscles of Craniata are *striated*.

The cœlom is lined by *peritoneum* (*C, pr.*), a membrane formed of an outer layer of connective-tissue, a middle muscle layer, and an inner layer of cœlomic epithelium bounding the cavity, and thus forming the innermost layer of the body-wall. In fishes the cœlom is divided into two chambers: a large *abdominal cavity* containing the chief viscera, and a small forwardly-placed *pericardial cavity* (*A, pc.*) containing the heart, and lined by a detached portion of peritoneum known as the *pericardium*. In mammals there is a vertical muscular partition, the *diaphragm*, dividing the cœlom into an anterior chamber or *thorax* containing the heart and lungs, and a posterior chamber or *abdomen* containing the remaining viscera. In birds a somewhat similar but less massive, oblique septum occurs behind the liver and anterior to the other viscera.

Skeleton.—The hard parts or supporting structures of Craniata fall into two categories—the *exoskeleton* and the *endoskeleton*. The **exoskeleton** consists of bony or horny deposits in the skin, and may be either epidermal or dermal, or both, but is never cuticular, like the armour of an arthropod or the shell of a mollusc. The epidermal exoskeleton is always formed by the cornification or conversion into horn of epidermal cells, and may take the form of scales, feathers, hairs, claws, nails, horns, and hoofs. The dermal exoskeleton occurs as either bony or horn-like deposits in the dermis, such as the scales and dermal fin-rays of fishes, and the bony armour of a sturgeon, crocodile, or armadillo.

The **endoskeleton** presents an immense range of variation in the different classes and orders. As in Amphioxus, the axis of the entire skeletal system is formed by the *notochord* (Fig. 64, *nch.*), an elastic rod made of peculiar vacuolated cells (Figs. 64, 65, *nch.*) and covered by a laminated *sheath* (*sh. nch.*) with an *external elastic membrane* (*el. m.*) around it. The whole sheath is, in the Craniata, a cuticular product of the superficial notochordal cells (*nch. c.*), being developed as a secretion from their outer or free surfaces. The noto-

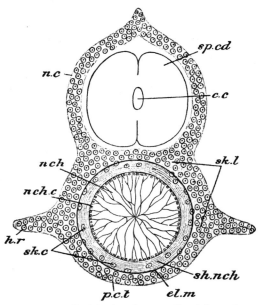

FIG. 64. **Vertebral column: Craniate embryo.** *c. c.* central canal; *el. m.* external elastic membrane; *h. r.* hæmal ridges; *n. c.* neural arch; *nch.* notochord; *nch. c.* notochordal cells; *p. c. t.* perichordal tube; *sh. nch.* sheath of notochord; *sk. c.* skeletogenous cells migrating into notochordal sheath; *sk. l.* skeletogenous layer; *sp. cd.* spinal cord. (Modified from Balfour and Gadow.)

chord lies in the middle line of the dorsal body-wall between the cerebrospinal cavity above, and the cœlom below. It is developed as a median rod of cells

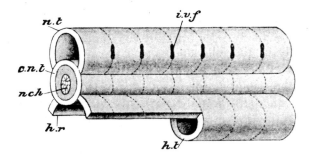

FIG. 65.—**Vertebral column: Segmentation.** *c. n. t.* perichordal tube; *h. r.* hæmal ridge; *h. t.* hæmal arch; *i. v. f.* intervertebral foramen; *n. t.* neural arch; *nch.* notochord. The dotted lines indicate the segmentation into vertebræ.

detached, in the neurula, from the continuous chordo-mesoderm sheet of the gastrula. Posteriorly it extends to the end of the tail, but in front it always stops short of the anterior end of the head, ending near the middle of the brain immediately behind the compound *pituitary body* (Fig. 63, *A*, *pty. b.*). The extension of the nervous system in front of the notochord is one of the most striking differences between the Craniata and the Acrania (p. 47). In the latter the notochord is uniquely prolonged to a considerable distance beyond the anterior end of the nerve-tube during the elongation of the larva (p. 62).

In the majority of living Craniata the notochord is a purely embryonic structure, and all but the anterior end of it is replaced in the adult by the *vertebral column*. The cells of mesoderm (sclerotome) surrounding the notochord become concentrated around the sheath and give rise to the *skeletogenous layer* (Fig. 64, *sk. l.*), some of the cells of which (*sk. c.*) may migrate through the elastic membrane into the sheath itself. In this way the notochord becomes surrounded by a cellular investment which soon takes on the structure of cartilage, and may be called the *perichordal tube* (Fig. 64, *p. c. t.*, and Fig. 65, *c. n. t.*). The skeletogenous layer also grows upwards, and gives rise to an inverted tunnel of cartilage (p. 72), the *neural arch* (*n. c., n. t.*), enclosing the cerebro-spinal cavity and connected below with the perichordal tube ; and to paired *hæmal ridges* (*h. r.*) of cartilage standing out from the sides of the perichordal tube into the muscles. In the region of the tail these unite below to enclose the *hæmal canal* (*h. c.*) already mentioned. Actually, however, the vertebral column thus constituted is from the first more or less broken up into segments, and in the higher forms is replaced by a chain of bones, the *vertebræ*. These begin a short distance behind the anterior end of the notochord and extend to the extremity of the tail.

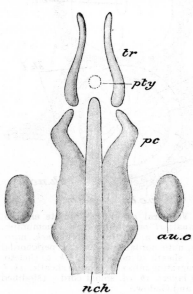

FIG. 66.—**Cranial elements: Embryo Salmon.** From above. *au. c.* auditory capsule; *nch.* notochord; *pc.* parachordal; *pty.* position of pituitary body; *tr.* trabecula. (From a model by Ziegler.)

A vertebra consists essentially of the following parts : (1) a *centrum* or *body* (Fig. 63, C, *cn.*) lying below the spinal canal in the position formerly occupied by the notochord and perichordal tube, and arising either in the skeletogenous layer proper, or in the notochordal sheath after its invasion by skeletogenous cells ; (2) a *neural arch* (*n. a.*) which springs from the dorsal surface of the centrum and encircles the neural canal, representing a segment of the neural tube ; and (3) a pair of *transverse processes* (*t. p.*) which extend outward from the centrum among the muscles and represent segments of the hæmal ridges. To these are often attached *ribs* which extend downwards in the body-wall, sometimes between the dorsal and ventral muscles (*r'.*), sometimes immediately external to the peritoneum (*r.*). In the anterior part of the ventral body-wall a cartilaginous or bony *sternum* or breast-bone may be developed. Thus the anterior or thoracic region of the cœlom is enclosed in an articulated bony framework formed of the vertebral column above, the ribs at the sides, and the sternum below. The ribs in these circumstances become segmented each into two parts, a dorsal *vertebral rib*, articulating with a vertebra, and a ventral *sternal rib* with the sternum. The former is usually ossified ; the latter remains as cartilage. In the tail there is frequently a *hæmal arch* (Fig. 63, *D, h. a.*) springing from the ventral aspect of the centrum and enclosing the hæmal canal. Thus the line of centra in the fully-formed vertebral column occupies the precise position of the notochord. The neural arches encircle the spinal portion of the cerebrospinal cavity ; the transverse processes, ribs, and sternum encircle the cœlom ; and the hæmal arches similarly surround the hæmal canal or vestigial cœlom of the tail. As we ascend the craniate series we find every gradation from the persistent notochord of the lampreys and hags, through the imperfectly differentiated vertebræ of sharks and rays, to the complete bony vertebral column of the higher forms.

The vertebræ are equal in number to the myomeres, but are arranged alternately with them, the fibrous partition between two myomeres abutting against the middle of a vertebra, so that each muscle-segment acts upon two adjacent vertebræ. Thus, the myomeres are metameric or segmental structures, and the vertebræ are intersegmental.

In connection with the anterior end of the notochord, where no vertebræ are formed, there are developed certain elements of the *skull* or cephalic skeleton. This structure is eminently characteristic of the whole craniate division, and gives the group its name. The skull makes its first appearance in the embryo in the form of paired cartilaginous plates, the *parachordals* (Fig. 66, *pc.*), lying one on each side of the anterior end of the notochord (*nch.*), and thus continuing forward the line of vertebral centra. In front of the parachordals are developed a pair of curved cartilaginous rods, the *trabeculæ* (*tr.*). These underlie the anterior part of the brain as the parachordals underlie its posterior part. Their hinder ends diverge so as to embrace the pituitary body (*pty.*). Cartilaginous investments are also formed around three prominent paired organs of special sense : 1. a pair of *olfactory capsules* round the organs of smell ; 2. *optic capsules* round the organs of sight ; and 3. *auditory capsules* (*au. c.*) round the organs of hearing and equilibrium. The optic capsule, which may be either cartilaginous or fibrous, remains free from the remaining elements of the skull in accordance with the mobility of the eye. It constitutes, in fact, the *sclerotic* or outer coat of that organ. The olfactory capsules are usually formed in relation to the trabeculæ, and are continuous with those structures from an early stage. The auditory capsules in some cases arise as outgrowths of the parachordals, in others as independent cartilages, each of which, however, soon unites with the parachordal of its own side. As development proceeds, the trabeculæ and parachordals become fused into a single *basal plate* (Fig. 67, *B, b. cr.*) underlying the brain. The skull-floor thus formed gives off vertical upgrowths on each side or, in some groups, the side wall cartilage may be of independent origin. The vertical components close in above to a greater or less extent, and so give rise to a more or less complete *cranium* or *brain-case* enclosing the brain and the organs of olfaction and hearing, and furnishing open cavities or *orbits* for the eyes.

In the continuous solid cranial box thus formed, certain definite regions can be distinguished. These are firstly a posterior or *occipital region*, formed from the parachordals, united or articulated with the anterior end of the vertebral column, and presenting a large aperture, the *foramen magnum*

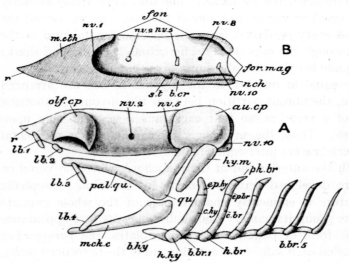

FIG. 67.—**Cartilaginous skull.** *A.* Left side; *B.* in sagittal section. *au. cp.* auditory capsule; *b. br. 1–5*, basi-branchials; *b. cr.* basis cranii; *b. hy.* basi-hyal; *c. br.* cerato-branchial; *c. hy.* cerato-hyal; *ep. br.* epi-branchial; *ep. hy.* epi-hyal; *fon.* fontanelle; *for. mag.* foramen magnum; *h. br.* hypo-branchial; *h. hy.* hypo-hyal; *hy. m.* hyom-andibular; *lb. 1–4*, labial cartilages; *mck. c.* Meckel's cartilage; *m. eth* mesethmoid; *nv. 1—10*, foramina for cranial nerves; *olf. cp.* olfactory capsule; *pal. qu.* palato-quadrate; *ph. br.* pharyngobranchial; *qu.* quadrate; *r.* rostrum; *s. t.* pituitary fossa or sella turcica.

(Fig. 67, *B, for. mag.*). Through this the spinal cord is continuous with the brain. There is secondly an *auditory region* formed by the two prominent auditory capsules (*A, au. cp.*). Thirdly, there is a *trabecular region*, including all the rest. The last-named is again divisible into an *interorbital region*, between the orbits or eye-sockets; an *olfactory region*, constituted by the olfactory capsules (*olf. cp.*) and by a median vertical plate, the *mesethmoid* (*B, m. eth.*), which separates them from one another; and a *pre-nasal region* or *rostrum* (*r.*) extending forwards from the mesethmoid and forming a more or less well-marked anterior prolongation of the cranium. The cavity for the brain (*B*) extends from the foramen magnum behind to the olfactory region in front. Its floor is formed from the basal plate of the embryo and is called the *basis cranii* (*b. cr.*). Its roof is always incomplete, for it contains one or more apertures or *fontanelles* (*fon.*). These are closed only by membranes. Their retention is due to the imperfect union above the side-walls.

In the walls of the brain-case are apertures or *foramina* through which pass the cranial nerves. The most important such apertures are as follows : The *olfactory foramina* (*nv.* 1) are situated at the anterior end of the cerebral cavity, one on each side of the mesethmoid. Through these run the first cranial or olfactory nerves. The *optic foramina* (*nv.* 2) occur in the interorbital region and are traversed by the second cranial or optic nerves. The *trigeminal foramina* (*nv.* 5) lie anterior to the auditory capsule and allow egress to the fifth or trigeminal nerves. The *auditory foramina* (*nv.* 8), in the inner wall of the auditory capsule, carry the short eighth (auditory) nerves. The *vagus foramina* (*nv.* 10), carrying the large wandering tenth or vagus nerve, lie immediately posterior to the auditory capsule.

In addition to the elements of the brain-case—parachordals, trabeculæ, and auditory capsules—there enter into the composition of the skull another set of elements called *visceral bars*. These are cartilaginous rods formed just outside the endodermal lining of the pharynx between the gill-slits. They thus encircle the pharynx like a series of paired half-hoops (Fig. 63, *B, vs. b.*). The corresponding right and left bars become united with one another below by an unpaired cartilage (Fig. 67, *A, b. br.*), forming a *visceral arch*. The unpaired ventral parts may unite successive arches with one another in the middle ventral line, thus giving rise to a more or less basket-like *visceral skeleton*. The visceral skeleton has a segmental arrangement, being arranged in an antero-posterior series, whereas in the cranium there is no clear indication of segmentation. There is, however, no exact correspondence between the segments of the visceral skeleton and the metameres. The visceral arches vary in number from four to nine. The foremost is distinguished as the *mandibular arch*, and lies just behind the mouth. The second is called the *hyoid arch*. The rest are known as *branchial arches* because they support the gills in aquatic forms.

In all Craniata except the Agnatha the mandibular arch becomes modified into *jaws* for the support of the mouth. Each mandibular bar divides into a dorsal and a ventral portion called respectively the *palato-quadrate cartilage* (Fig. 67, *A, pal. qu.*) and *Meckel's cartilage* (*mck. c.*). The palato-quadrates grow forwards along the upper or anterior margin of the mouth, and may unite with one another in the middle line, forming an *upper jaw*. Meckel's cartilages similarly extend along the lower or posterior margin of the mouth and unite in the middle line, forming the *lower jaw*. The *quadrate* (*qu.*), or posterior end of the palato-quadrate furnishes an articulation for the lower jaw, and often acquires a connection with the cranium, thus serving to suspend the jaws from the latter. Thus each jaw arises from the union of paired bars. The final result is two unpaired transverse structures, one lying in the anterior, the other in the posterior margin of the transversely elongated mouth, and moving in a vertical plane.

The hyoid bar usually becomes divided into two parts : a dorsal, the *hyomandibular* (*hy.m.*), and a ventral, the *hyoid cornu*. The latter is again divisible from above downwards into segments called respectively *epi-hyal* (*ep.hy.*), *cerato-hyal* (*c.hy.*), and *hypo-hyal* (*h.hy.*). The median ventral element of the arch, or *basi-hyal* (*b.hy.*), supports the tongue.[1]

Hyoid and mandibular are 'visceral' bones, developing in association with the alimentary tract. Other 'visceral' bones are the *os cordis* in the heart of some ungulates, and the diaphragmatic ossification in camels. The *baculum* (*os penis, os priapi*), an ossification in the fibrous septum between the corpora cavernosa (p. 890) and the *intermuscular* bones of many fishes (p. 301), also come into this category (pp. 74, 88).

In early bony fishes—*e.g.* the Acanthodii (p. 207)—the jaws are attached by ligaments to the neurocranium. The hyoid arch, instead of being modified to support the upper and lower jaws, is as complete as are the posterior arches. The gill-slit lying in front of the hyoid arch, instead of being reduced to a spiracle which may even be closed and disappear, is fully functional as a complete gill. This type of jaw suspension is *autodiastylic*. When the hyomandibular becomes attached to the hinge of the upper and lower jaws, and supports them so that the attachment to the skull is lost, the suspension is termed *hyostylic*. This is the form of attachment of the majority of fishes. In some early forms, and in a few living fishes, there is an attachment to the skull as well as to the hyomandibular. This condition is termed *amphistylic*. It appears that in fishes the autodiastylic attachment is the most primitive. The amphistylic condition was derived from it. The hyostylic condition is the most recent. It is probable that the last-named condition has been arrived at independently in the later Chondrichthyes and bony fishes.

Finally, the upper jaw, instead of merely lying against the skull and attached only by ligaments, as in the autodiastylic phase, may become fused with it. This condition is termed *autosystylic*. Two groups of fishes (Dipnoi and Holocephali) have the jaws attached to the skull and no hyoid suspension, but the condition in each case is different. The Holocephali have a complete hyoid arch which is free from the cranium, a condition which, according to different interpretations, may be an approach to the autodiastylic condition or a secondary modification such as is shown by the skates (p. 226). To this kind of suspension the term *holostylic* has been given. In the Dipnoi and all tetrapods the hyoid arch becomes broken up and the hyomandibular attached to the skull, where it soon enters into the service of the ear region. This condition is usually termed *autostylic*. As this term, however, really covers more than one condition it is now divided into *autosystylic* and *holostylic*.

The branchial arches become divided transversely into dorsoventral seg-

---

[1] Jarvik's reconstruction of the head of *Eusthenopteron* suggests that many structures in the neurocranium are derived from the dorsal components of the three pro-otic visceral arches.

ments called respectively *pharyngo-branchial* (*ph.br.*), *epi-branchial* (*ep.br.*), *cerato-branchial* (*c.br.*), and *hypo-branchial* (*h.br.*). The visceral skeleton thus acquires the character of an articulated framework which allows of the dilatation of the pharynx during swallowing and the inspiration of water and of its more or less complete closure at other times (Fig. 68).

In connection with, and always superficial to, the rostrum, olfactory capsules, and jaws, are frequently found *labial cartilages* (*lb.* 1–4). These sometimes attain considerable dimensions.

In certain fishes (such as elasmobranchs) the cartilages of the skull and vertebral column become more or less encrusted by a superficial granular

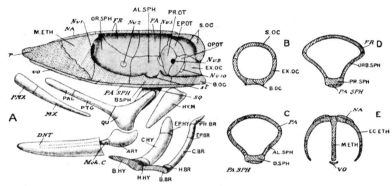

FIG. 68.—**Bony skull.** *A.* Sagittal section; *B.* transverse section of occipital region; *C,* of parietal region; *D,* of frontal region; *E,* of ethmoidal region. Cartilaginous parts are dotted; replacing bones are marked in thick type, investing bones in italics. *Mck. C.* Meckel's cartilage; *Nv. 1—10,* foramina for cranial nerves; *r.* rostrum; *s. t.* sella turcica or pituitary fossa. Replacing bones—AL.SPH. pterosphenoid; ART. articular; B.BR. basi-branchial; B.HY. basi-hyal; B.OC. basi-occipital; B.SPH. basi-sphenoid; C.BR. cerato-branchial; C.HY. ceratohyal; EC.ETH. lateral ethmoid; EP.BR. epi-branchial; EP.HY. epi-hyal; EP.OT. epi-otic; EX.OC. ex-occipital; H.BR. hypo-branchial; H.HY. hypo-hyal; HY.M. hyomandibular; M.ETH. mesethmoid; OP.OT. opisthotic; OR.SPH. orbito-sphenoid; PAL. palatine; PH.BR. pharyngo-branchial; PR.OT. pro-otic; PR.SPH. pre-sphenoid; PTG. pterygoid; QU. quadrate; S.OC. supra-occipital. Investing bones—*DNT.* dentary; *FR.* frontal; *MX.* maxilla; *NA.* nasal; *PA.* parietal; *PA.SPH.* para-sphenoid; *PMX.* premaxilla; *SQ.* squamosal; *VO., v.o.* vomer.

deposit of lime-salts, giving rise to *calcified cartilage* (p. 73). In all the other forms true ossification takes place, the cartilaginous skull becomes complicated, and to a greater or less extent replaced, by distinct *bones*. Of these there are two kinds, *replacing* or '*cartilage*'-bones and *investing* or '*membrane*'-bones. Replacing bones may begin by the deposition of patches of bony matter within the cartilage (*endochondral ossification*).

As development proceeds, the bone first formed (*primary bone*) is mostly replaced by *secondary bone*. Interstitial lamellæ (or lamina, see p. 73) are the persisting primary bone. The perichondrium is transformed to periosteum, giving rise to a subjacent *collar* of bone. This is *perichondral* or *periosteal ossification*.

The bones in question are usually said to be *preformed in cartilage, i.e.*

they replace originally cartilaginous parts. In the case of investing (membrane) bones, centres of ossification also appear, in constant positions, in the fibrous tissue outside the cartilage. They may remain quite independent of the original cartilaginous skull and its replacing bones, so as to be readily removable by boiling or maceration ; or they may eventually become, as it were, grafted on to the cartilage, in which case all distinction between investing and replacing bones is lost in the adult. The investing bones are to be looked upon as portions of the exoskeleton which have retreated from the surface and acquired intimate relations with the endoskeleton.

The replacing bones have a very definite relation to the regions of the cartilaginous cranium. In the occipital region four bones are formed, surrounding the foramen magnum. These are a median ventral *basioccipital* (Fig. 68, *A* and *B*, *B.OC.*), paired lateral *exoccipitals* (*EX.OC.*), and a median dorsal *supraoccipital* (*S.OC.*). In each auditory capsule three ossifications commonly appear. These are a *pro-otic* (*A*, *PR.OT.*) in front, an *opisthotic* (*OP.OT.*) behind, and an *epiotic* over the arch of the posterior semicircular canal of the ear (see below). In front of the basioccipital a bone called the *basisphenoid* (*A* and *C*, *B.SPH.*) is formed in the floor of the skull. The basisphenoid appears in the position of the posterior ends of the trabeculæ, and bears on its upper or cranial surface a depression, the *sella turcica* (*s. t.*), for the reception of the pituitary body. Connected on either side with the basisphenoid are paired bones, the latero- or ptero-sphenoids, which help to furnish the side-walls of the interorbital region. In the Mammalia, their place is taken by the alisphenoids. The basisphenoid is continued forwards by another median bone, the *presphenoid* (*A* and *D*, *PR.SPH.*) with which paired ossifications, the *orbitosphenoids* (*OR.SPH.*), are connected and complete the side-walls of the inter-orbital region. The basioccipital, basisphenoid, and presphenoid together form the basis cranii of the bony skull. A vertical plate of bone, the *mesethmoid* (*M.ETH.*), appears in the posterior portion of the cartilage of the same name. The outer walls of the olfactory capsules may be ossified by paired *ectoethmoids* (*EC.ETH.*).

So far the cranial cavity has its hinder region alone roofed over by bone, *viz.* by the supraoccipital : for the rest of it the replacing bones furnish floor and side-walls only. This deficiency is made good by two pairs of investing bones. These are the *parietals* (*PA.*), formed immediately in front of the supraoccipital and usually articulating below with the pterosphenoids, and the *frontals* (*FR.*), placed in front of the parietals, and often connected below with the orbitosphenoids. A pair of *nasals* (*NA.*) are developed above the olfactory capsules and immediately in advance of the frontals. Below the base of the skull two important investing bones make their appearance, the *vomer* (*vo.*)— which may be double—in front, and the *parasphenoid* (*PA.SPH.*) behind.

The result of the peculiar arrangement of replacing and investing bones just described is that the brain-case, in becoming ossified, acquires a kind of secondary segmentation, being clearly divisible in the higher groups, and especially in the Mammalia, into three quasi-segments. These are: (1) the *occipital segment* (*B*), formed by the basioccipital below, the exoccipitals at the sides, and the supraoccipital above [1]; (2) the *parietal segment* (*C*), formed by the basisphenoid below, the alisphenoids laterally, and the parietals above; and (3) the *frontal segment* (*D*), constituted by the presphenoid below, the orbitosphenoids on either side, and the frontals above. It must be observed that this segmentation of the cranium is quite independent of the primary segmentation of the head, which is determined by the presence of myomeres and by the relations of the cerebral nerves.

The cranial bones have constant relations to the cerebral nerves. The olfactory nerves (*A, Nv. 1*) pass out one on either side of the mesethmoid, the optic nerves (*Nv. 2*) through or immediately behind the orbitosphenoids, the fifth nerves (*Nv. 5*) through or immediately behind the pterosphenoids, and the tenth nerves (*Nv. 10*) through or immediately in front of the exoccipitals.

It will be seen that a clear distinction can be drawn between the *primary cranium, chondrocranium*, or *neurocranium* (formed by the fusion of the parachordals, auditory capsules, and trabeculæ, and consisting of an undivided mass of cartilage more or less replaced by bones), and the *secondary cranium* or *osteocranium*, which is modified by the super-addition of investing bones.

A similar distinction may be drawn between the *primary* and *secondary jaws*. The *primary upper jaw*, or palato-quadrate, becomes ossified by three chief replacing bones on each side, the *autopalatine* (*A, PAL.*) in front, then the *autopterygoid* (*PTG.*), and the *quadrate* (*QU.*) behind. The last-named furnishes the articulation for the lower jaw or *mandible*. In the higher classes the front of the primary upper jaw is not a distinct cartilaginous structure, and the palatine and pterygoid are developed as investing bones. The *secondary upper jaw* is constituted by two pairs of investing bones, the *premaxilla* (*PMX.*) and the *maxilla* (*MX.*), which in bony skulls furnish the actual anterior boundary of the mouth, the primary jaw becoming altogether shut out of the gape. The proximal end of the *primary lower jaw* ossifies to form a replacing bone, the *articular* (*ART.*), by which the mandible is hinged. The rest of it remains as a slender, unossified *Meckel's cartilage* (*Mck. C.*), which may disappear entirely in the adult or its symphysial ends may sometimes ossify as *mentomeckelian* bones. The *secondary lower jaw* is formed by a variable number of investing bones, the most important of which is the *dentary* (*DNT.*). In the Mammalia the dentary forms the entire mandible, and articulates, not with the quadrate, but with a large investing bone formed external to the latter, and known as the *squamosal* (*SQ.*).

---

[1] With the occipital segment in many fishes are amalgamated one or several of the most anterior vertebræ.

In the hyoid arch a replacing bone, the *hyomandibular* (*HY.M.*), appears in the cartilage of the same name, and ossifications are also formed in the various segments of the hyoid cornua (*EP.HY.*, *C.HY.*, *H.HY.*, *B.HY.*) and of the branchial arches (*PH.BR.*, *EP.BR.*, *C.BR.*, *H.BR.*, *B.BR.*). In the air-breathing forms both hyoid and branchial arches undergo more or less complete atrophy, the whole gill-bearing apparatus becoming reduced mainly to a small *hyoid bone* (which supports the tongue) and the stapes of the middle ear.

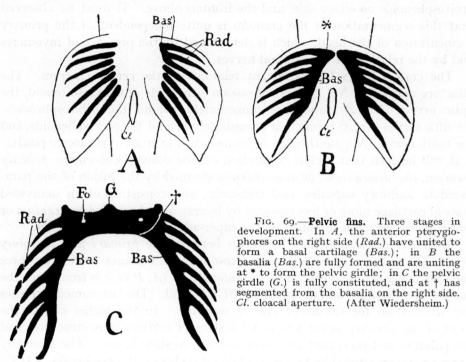

Fig. 69.—**Pelvic fins.** Three stages in development. In *A*, the anterior pterygiophores on the right side (*Rad.*) have united to form a basal cartilage (*Bas.*); in *B* the basalia (*Bas.*) are fully formed and are uniting at * to form the pelvic girdle; in *C* the pelvic girdle (*G.*) is fully constituted, and at † has segmented from the basalia on the right side. *Cl.* cloacal aperture. (After Wiedersheim.)

The skeleton of the median fins is formed of a single row of cartilaginous rays or *pterygiophores* (Fig. 69), lying in the median plane, and primitively more numerous than the vertebræ. They may ossify, and be supplemented by *dermal fin-rays*, of varying composition, developed in the dermis towards the free margin of the fin. The latter are clearly exoskeletal structures.

Both pectoral and pelvic fins are supported by pterygiophores or *radialia* (Fig. 69, *Rad.*). The basal or proximal ends of these are articulated with stout cartilages, the *basalia* (*Bas.*), which are often replaced by bones, that serve to strengthen the fin at its point of union with the trunk.

The structure of the paired fins varies in different groups of fishes (Fig. 70). It is supposed that they arose from an originally continuous fold along each side of the body from which the fins became constricted. This view is to some extent supported by embryological evidence and by the condition of the paired fins of *Cladoselache* (p. 222), which, being without a posterior notch, have the appearance of being the remains of a previously continuous fin.   The rows of spines on each side of the acanthodians (Fig. 134) and of the agnathous Anaspida (Fig. 106) are likewise suggestive of a continuous fold.   When such a fin as that of *Cladoselache* (pleurorhachic type) became free from the body-wall, it would consist of an axis of basalia and a fringe of radialia on the preaxial side.   When more radials appeared on the postaxial side, as in *Pleuracanthus*,

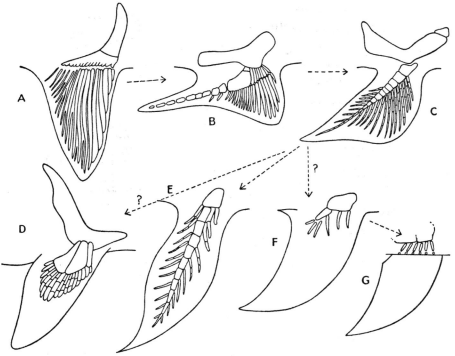

FIG. 70.—**Pectoral fins.**   A, *Cladoselache*; B, *Cladodus*; C, *Pleuracanthus*; D, a 'shark'; E, *Neoceratodus*; F, a primitive Actinopterygian; G, a teleost.   The dotted lines suggest possible lines of *functional* evolution.

the fin reached the condition known as the archipterygium (mesorhachic type). This type of fin is also found in the crossopterygians and dipnoans (p. 353).   In the majority of Chondrichthyes (p. 219) the fin has three basalia, termed the *pro-*, *meso-*, and *meta-pterygium*, respectively, and a number of radialia arranged around them.   The fin of the Polypterini (p. 290) has a somewhat similar appearance, though probably of a different origin.   The Actinopterygii (p. 282) show a further modification, the basalia being lost and the radials reduced to small ossicles which lie within the body-wall, and not in the fin web. Besides the basals and radials, the fins are all strengthened in the free part by fin-rays, which are of several kinds : horny, fibrous, or modified scales.

In all classes above the fishes the paired fins are, as we have seen, replaced by five-toed or *pentadactyle limbs* (see p. 382). These are supported by bones, probably to be looked upon as greatly modified pterygiophores, and obviously serially homologous in the fore- and hind-limbs. In the proximal division of

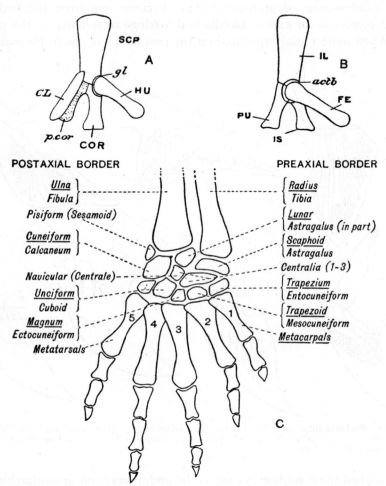

FIG. 71.—**Tetrapod girdles, manus, and pes.** *A*, pectoral, *B*, pelvic girdles, and *C*, generalised skeleton of hand and foot. *actb.* acetabulum; *gl.* glenoid cavity; *p. cor.* pro-coracoid; SCP. scapula; CL. clavicle; COR. coracoid; HU humerus; of shoulder blade. FE. femur; IL. ilium; IS. ischium; PU. pubis. Bones of the fore-limb are underlined. Note that the astragalus is not (as shown in the figure for comparative purposes) composed of two separate elements (see p. 859).

each limb there is a single rod-like bone. In the forelimbs this is the *humerus* (Fig. 71, *HU*.). In the hind-limb it is the *femur* (*FE*.) or thigh-bone. In the middle division there are two elongated bones, an anterior, the *radius*, and a posterior, the *ulna*, in the fore-limb ; an anterior, the *tibia*, and a posterior, the *fibula*, in the hind-limb. Next follow the bones of the hand and foot, which are again divisible into three sets. In the fore-limb these consist of *carpals* or wrist-bones, *metacarpals* or hand-bones, and *phalanges* or finger-bones. In the hind-limb they consist of *tarsals* or ankle-bones, *metatarsals* or foot-bones, and *phalanges* or toe-bones. The carpals and tarsals consist typically of three rows of small nodules of bone or cartilage, the proximal row containing three, the middle two, and the distal five elements.

The three proximal carpals are called respectively *radiale, intermedium,* and *ulnare,* those of the middle row the first and second *centralia,* those of the third row the five *distalia,* the separate elements being distinguished by numbers, counting from the anterior or radial edge of the limb. In the tarsus the bones of the first row are known respectively as *tibiale, intermedium,* and *fibulare,* those of the second row as *centralia,* and those of the third as *distalia.*

The metacarpals and metatarsals are five rod-like bones, one articulating with each distale : they are followed by the phalanges, of which each digit may have from one to five. The first digit of the fore-limb is distinguished as the *pollex* or thumb, that of the hind-limb as the *hallux* or great toe. The fifth digit of each limb is the *minimus.*

In connection with the paired appendages are formed supporting *limb-girdles.* These occur in the portions of the trunk adjacent to the appendages and serve for the articulation of the latter. In the embryonic condition they are continuous with the basalia and are probably ingrowths of the primitive fin-skeleton (Fig. 69). The *shoulder-girdle* or *pectoral arch* has primarily the form of paired bars, which may unite in the middle ventral line so as to form an inverted arch. Each bar—*i.e.* each half of the arch—furnishes a concave or convex *glenoid surface* (Fig. 71, *gl.*) for the articulation of the pectoral fin or fore-limb, and is thereby divided into two portions—a dorsal or *scapular region,* above the glenoid surface, and a ventral or *coracoid region* below it. The coracoid region is again divisible, in all classes above the fishes, into two portions : an anterior, the *pre-coracoid* (*p. cor.*), and a posterior, the *coracoid* proper. Each of these regions commonly ossifies—a replacing bone, the *scapula* (*SCP.*), appearing in the scapular region, another, the *coracoid* (*COR.*), in the coracoid region, while in relation with the pre-coracoid is formed a bone, the *clavicle* (*CL.*), largely or entirely developed independently of pre-existing cartilage.

The constitution of the *hip-girdle,* or *pelvic arch,* is very similar. It consists originally of paired bars, which may unite in the middle ventral line, and are divided by the *acetabulum* (Fig. 71, *actb.*), the articular surface for the pelvic fin or hind-limb, into a dorsal or *iliac region,* and a ventral or *pubo-ischial region,* the last named being again divisible, in all classes above the fishes, into an anterior portion, or *pubis,* and a posterior portion, or *ischium.* Each region is replaced in the higher forms by a bone. The pelvic girdle thus consists of a dorsal *ilium* (*IL.*) serially homologous with the scapula, an antero-ventral *pubis* (*PU.*) which is homologous with the pre-coracoid and clavicle, and a postero-ventral *ischium* (*IS.*) which is homologous with the coracoid. The long bones of the limbs are divisible each into a *shaft*, and proximal and distal *extremities*. When ossification takes place the shaft is converted into a tubular bone, the cartilaginous axis of which is absorbed and replaced by vascular hæmatopœtic (blood-forming) *marrow*. The extremities become simply calcified in the lower forms, but in the higher a distinct centre of ossification may appear in each, forming the *epiphysis*, which finally becomes ankylosed to the shaft.

Alimentary Canal and Associated Structures.—The *alimentary canal* begins at the mouth and is divisible into buccal cavity (Fig. 63, *A, buc. c.*), pharynx (*ph.*), œsophagus, stomach (*st.*), and intestine (*int.*), the latter often communicating with the exterior by the posterior aperture of a *cloaca*, a chamber which also receives the urinary and genital ducts. The *buccal cavity* is developed from the stomodæum of the embryo. The proctodæum gives rise to a very small area in the neighbourhood of the anus, or, when a cloaca, is present, to the external portion of the latter. All the rest of the canal is formed from the mesenteron, and is therefore lined by an epithelium of endodermal origin. In fishes and in the embryos of higher forms the *pharynx* communicates with the exterior by the gill-slits (*i. br. a, 1–7*). It communicates with the stomach by the œsophagus. The *stomach* (*st.*) is usually bent upon itself in the form of a **U**. The *intestine* (*int.*) is generally more or less convoluted, hence the stomach and intestine are together considerably longer than the enclosing abdominal cavity. In the embryo the intestine is sometimes continued backwards into the hæmal canal by an extension called the *post-anal gut* (*p. a. g.*), which may perhaps indicate that the anus has shifted forwards in the course of evolution.

The epithelium of the buccal cavity is usually many-layered, like that of the skin, of which it is developmentally an in-turned portion. The pharynx and œsophagus have also a laminated epithelium, but the rest of the canal is lined by a single layer of cells underlaid by a layer of connective-tissue, the deeper part of which is called the *sub-mucosa*. Epithelium and connective tissue together constitute the *mucous membrane*. The mucous membrane of the stomach and intestine usually contains close-set tubular glands. The digestive and other functions of these glands will be dealt with in individual animal types. Outside the mucous membrane are layers of *smooth* (*plain* or *unstriped*) *muscle*, usually an internal circular and an external longitudinal layer. Externally the intra-cœlomic portion of the canal is invested by peritoneum formed of a layer of connective-tissue next the gut and a single-layered cœlomic epithelium facing the body-cavity.

In connection with the alimentary canal certain very characteristic structures are developed. In the mucous membrane of the mouth calcifications appear and form the *teeth* which, homologous with *placoid scales* (p. 83), usually occur in a row along the ridge of each jaw, but may be developed on the roof of the mouth, on the tongue, and even in the pharynx. A tooth is usually formed of three calcified tissues—*dentine, enamel,* and *cement* (see footnote, p. 71). The bulk of the tooth is made up of dentine (Figs. 72, 59), which occurs in three forms. *Hard dentine* consists of a matrix of animal matter strongly impreg-

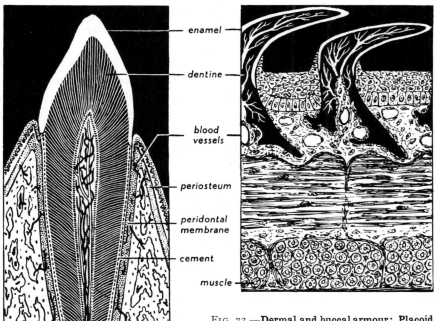

enamel

dentine

blood vessels

periosteum

peridontal membrane

cement

muscle

Fig. 72.—**Dermal and buccal armour: Placoid scales and permanent teeth.** *Left:* Incisor of mammal (*Homo*). The root is buried deep in the jaw-bone. The pulp-cavity is surrounded by a layer of odontoblasts (not arrowed) and contains vascular and nervous tissue that enters through the small *apical foramen. Right:* Placoid scale of selachian. The basal plate (of dentine) is embedded in the *stratum vasculare* of the dermis and receives it as pulp. Septa of the vascular layer connect with the sub-cutaneous tissue overlying the muscles. (Not to scale.) (Redrawn after Hamilton, *et al.,* and Kendall.)

nated with lime-salts and permeated by delicate, more or less parallel, tubules containing organic fibrils. *Vasodentine* is permeated with blood-vessels, and consequently appears red and moist in the fresh condition. *Osteodentine* approaches bone in its structure and mode of development. The free surface of the tooth is usually capped by a layer of enamel, a dense prismatic structure containing not more than 3 to 5 per cent. of animal matter. It is, therefore, the hardest tissue in the body. The cement coats that portion of the tooth which is embedded in the tissues of the jaw, and sometimes forms a thin layer over the enamel; it has practically the structure of bone. At the inner end of the tooth there is frequently an aperture leading into a cavity filled in the fresh condition by the *tooth-pulp*, which is abundantly supplied with nerves and blood-vessels. For tooth development, see p. 862).

In some fishes the scales or elements of the dermal exoskeleton imperceptibly pass into the teeth over the ridges of the jaws, and are identical with them in structure so that there can be no doubt as to the homology of the two. Teeth are, in fact, portions of the exoskeleton which have migrated from the skin into the buccal cavity, and even into the pharynx, and have there increased in size and assumed special functions.

In terrestrial Craniata *buccal glands* open by ducts into the mouth. The most prominent of these are the racemose *salivary glands*, which secrete a fluid that in some animals contains an enzyme capable of converting starch into sugar. There are also two larger, and highly characteristic, digestive glands (*liver* and *pancreas*) in the abdominal cavity, both developed as outpushings of the intestine, but differing greatly from one another in their fully developed state. The liver (Fig. 63) is a dark-red organ of relatively immense size and manifold functions. Among these are the secretion of *bile* (which emulsifies fats), and the formation of *glycogen* (animal starch), which, after being stored in liver-cells, is discharged to the blood in the form of sugar. The liver is formed of a mass of polyhedral cells with numerous minute intercellular spaces which receive the bile secreted from the cells and from which it passes into the hepatic ducts. The pancreas (Fig. 63, *A, pn.*) is a racemose gland that secretes *pancreatic juice*, the various enzymes of which act upon proteins, sugars, and fats. The ducts of both glands usually open into the anterior end of the intestine. That of the liver (*b. d.*) generally (but not always) gives off a blind offshoot ending in a capacious dilatation, the *gall-bladder* (*g. b.*). In this bile is stored. We thus have one or more *hepatic ducts* conveying the bile from the liver and meeting with a *cystic duct* from the gall-bladder, while from the junction a *common bile-duct* leads into the intestine. When a common duct carries both bile and pancreatic juice it is a *hepato-pancreatic duct*.

Another important and characteristic organ in the abdomen of Craniata is the *spleen* (*spl.*), a blood-storage organ of variable size and shape, attached to the stomach by a fold of peritoneum. It has no duct, being connected with the general circulation. It is formed of a pulpy substance containing numerous erythrocytes, many of them in process of disintegration. Dispersed through the pulp are masses of leucocytes (formed by splenic components of the *reticulo-endothelial system*) which pass into the general circulation.

The *parathyroid* and *thymus* glands are each formed in connection with the alimentary canal. The *thyroid* (*thd.*) is developed as an out-pushing of the floor of the pharynx which becomes shut off, and forms an endocrine organ of considerable size. Its final position varies considerably in the different classes.

It is probably homologous with the endostyle of the Tunicata and of Amphioxus, which is an open groove on the ventral side of the pharynx (p. 24). This view is supported by the condition of the parts in the larval Lamprey (p. 196).

The *thymus* is developed from the epithelium of the gill-pouches, usually the 3rd and 4th. In the adult it may take the form of a number of separate gland-like bodies lying above the gills, or may be situated in the neck, or even in the thorax. The thymus is essentially a lymphoid body and probably not an endocrine gland. The endocrine parathyroids also form by budding from the 3rd and 4th gill-pouches (Fig. 73).

The whole intra-abdominal portion of the alimentary canal, as well as the liver, pancreas, spleen, and, indeed, all the abdominal viscera, are supported by folds of peritoneum, called by the general name of *mesentery* (Fig. 63, C, *mes.*) and having the usual relation to the parietal and visceral layers of the peritoneum. Besides providing support, and allowing an essential degree of mobility in contractile (*e.g.* gut) and other structures, mesenteries provide bridges along which blood vascular and nerve connections can reach the viscera.

Organs of Respiration.—Two principal kinds are found in Craniata : water-breathing organs or *gills*, and air-breathing organs or *lungs*. Both may occur in the same species. Gills arise as a series of paired pouches of the pharynx which extend outwards, or towards the surface of the body, and finally open on the exterior by the gill-slits already noticed. Each *gill-pouch* thus communicates with the pharynx by an *internal* and with the outside water by an *external branchial aperture*. It is separated from its predecessor and from its successor in the series by stout fibrous partitions, the *interbranchial septa*. The membrane forming the anterior and posterior walls of the pouches is raised into a number of horizontal ridges, the *branchial filaments*, which are abundantly supplied with blood coursing through thin-walled capillaries. A current of water entering at the mouth passes into the pharynx, thence by the internal gill-slits into the gill-pouches, and finally makes its way out by the external gill-slits, bathing the branchial filaments as it goes. The exchange of carbon dioxide for oxygen takes place in the blood-vessels of the branchial filaments, which are, therefore, the actual organs of external respiration (Fig. 73).

As already mentioned, the walls of the pharynx are supported by the visceral arches, which surround it like a series of incomplete hoops, each half-arch or visceral bar being embedded in the inner or pharyngeal side of an inter-branchial septum. Thus the visceral arches alternate with the gill-pouches, each being related to the posterior set of filaments of one pouch and the anterior set of the next. In the higher bony fishes (*e.g.* a trout) the interbranchial septa become reduced to narrow bars enclosing the visceral arches, so that a double set of free branchial filaments springs from each visceral bar and constitutes a single *gill*. Thus an entire gill or *holobranch* (Fig. 73) is the morphological equivalent of two half-gills—*hemibranchs* or sets of branchial filaments

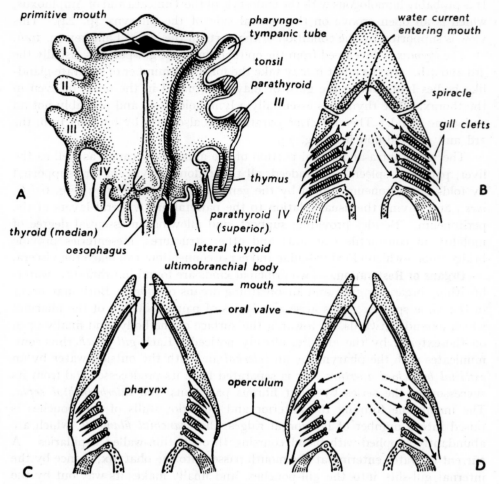

FIG. 73.—**Pharyngeal region: Branchiogenic organs.** *A. Embryonic.* Ventral diagrammatic view of original sites and relationships of branchiogenic endocrine (p. 147) and other structures. Part of the wall is removed to show the interior of the pharyngeal pouches. *B. Adult, selachian.* Diagram, showing relationship of mouth (lacking valve, cf. *C, D* below) and spiracle (1st gill pouch, see p. 94) and the direction of the respiratory current through the gill-clefts (with elongated inter-branchial septa, see Fig. 153, p. 227). *C and D. Adult, teleost.* The 1st pouch becomes a functional gill. Note role of oral valve and opercula in respiration. The œsophageal valve is not shown. (Modified from Boyd, *et al.*, and Storer.)

belonging to the adjacent sides of two consecutive gill-pouches. On the other hand, a gill-pouch is equivalent to the posterior hemibranch of one gill and the anterior hemibranch of its immediate successor.

In some Amphibia (p. 381) water-breathing organs of a different kind are found. These are the *external gills*. They are developed as branched out-growths of the body-wall in immediate relation with the gill-bars. 'Except for their point of origin there is little difference between external and internal gills. The tissues entering into their formation are probably the same' (Noble).

Lungs are found almost universally in Craniata from the Dipnoi (lung-fishes) (p. 361) upwards. They are developed as a hollow outpushing from the ventral wall of the embryonic fore-gut or anterior part of the alimentary

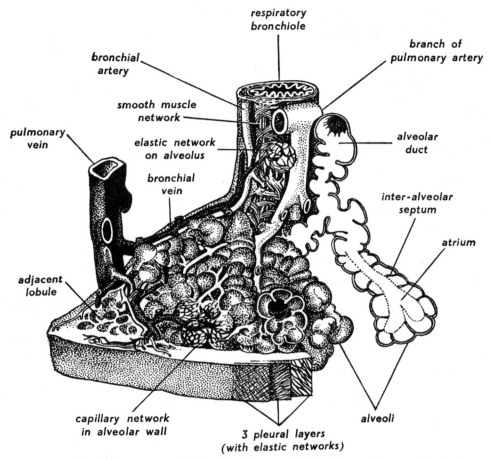

FIG. 74.—**Respiratory system: Portion of a pulmonary lobule in Man.** Nerves omitted. (From Maximov and Bloom, after Braus.)

canal. This passes backwards and upwards, usually dividing into right and left divisions, finally coming to lie in the dorsal region of the cœlom. The inner surface of the single or double lung thus formed is raised into a more or less complex network of ridges and so increases the vascularised surface exposed to the action of the air. In the higher forms, the ridges, increasing in number and complexity, and uniting with one another across the lumen of the lung, convert it into a sponge-like structure. Within, an immense system of *terminal bronchioles* carry inspired air into the minute pouch-like *alveoli*, the walls of which are invested with capillaries. Here gaseous exchanges occur (Fig. 74). The respiratory epithelium is, of course, endodermal. Since (except in birds) the lungs are blind sacs, special mechanisms are necessary for renewing the air contained in them. These are described in the different animal types (*e.g.* p. 371, cf. p. 587). Auxiliary respiratory organs occur in various groups (*e.g.* pp. 338, 339).

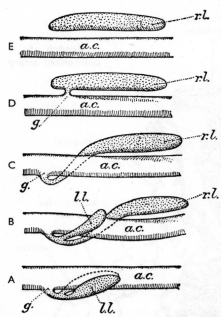

FIG. 75.—**Lung and swim-bladder in Osteichthyes.** From left side. *A*, primitive symmetrical arrangement; *B*, *Polypterus*; *C*, *Neoceratodus*; *D*, Physostomatous Teleost; *E*, Physoclistic Teleost; *a.c.* alimentary canal; *g.* glottis; *l.l.* left lung; *r.l.* right lung. (From Goodrich, after Kerr.)

In many bony fishes, but not in elasmobranchs, there occurs, in approximately the position occupied in air-breathers by the lungs, a structure called the *swim-*, *air-*, or *gas-bladder* (Fig. 75). This organ is often considered to be homologous with the lung, but the structures may, in fact, have evolved independently. The swim-bladder arises in teleosts (p. 293) as an outgrowth from the dorsal or lateral walls of the foregut.

In the lung fishes (p. 361) and the Polypteridæ (p. 290) the lungs, on the other hand, arise as down-growths from the pharyngeal floor (p. 371). Both structures are innervated by the autonomic nervous system (p. 119), but their nervous connections are different. The lungs are supplied by right and left pulmonary arteries which arise from the last pair of epibranchial arteries. In the adult, the swim-bladder receives its arterial blood from the dorsal aorta.

The swim-bladder may be either open or closed. In teleosts it is essentially a *hydrostatic organ* (p. 339), but may be adapted, with the development of alveoli, to respiratory function in inhabitants of swamp-waters of low oxygen content. The swim-bladder can also exist as a pressure register or as an accessory hearing organ, or as an apparatus of sound-production or resonation (p. 340). In some species, especially those which live in the ocean depths, the swim-bladder may be reduced, or even lost, or sometimes converted to fat-storage function.

Blood-vascular System.—This attains a far higher degree of complexity than in any of the groups previously studied. Its essential features can be understood from a general description of the circulatory organs of fishes.

The *heart* (Figs. 63 and 76) is a muscular organ contained in the pericardial cavity and composed of three chambers, the *sinus venosus* (*s. v.*), the *atrium* (*au.*), and the *ventricle* (*v.*). These form a single longitudinal series. The

hindmost, the sinus venosus, opens into the atrium. The atrium opens into the ventricle. They do not, however, lie in a straight line, but in a zigzag fashion, so that the sinus and atrium are dorsal in position, the ventricle ventral. Usually a fourth chamber, the *conus arteriosus* (*c. art.*), is added in front of the ventricle. The various chambers are separated from one another by valvular apertures, varying between groups, which allow blood to flow in one direction only, *viz.*, from behind forwards—*i.e.* from sinus to atrium, atrium to ventricle, and ventricle to conus. The heart is made of *cardiac muscle* which is particularly thick and strong in the ventricle. It is lined internally by endothelium and covered externally by the visceral layer of the pericardium.

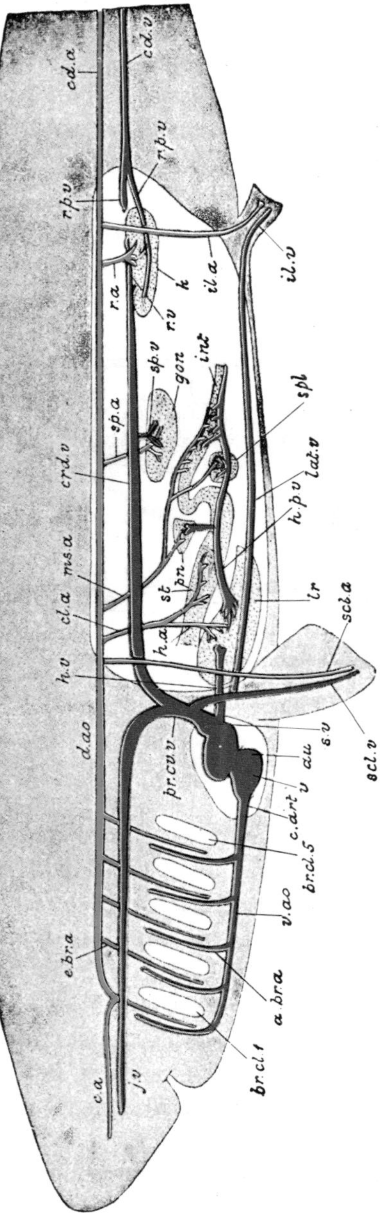

The *myogenic* nature of the heart-beat was first demonstrated in poikilothermous vertebrates. In these the heart-beat originates in the sinus venosus

FIG. 76.—**Blood-vascular system: Fish.** Vessels containing aërated blood red, those containing non-aërated blood blue. *a. br. a.* afferent branchial artery; *au.* atrium; *br. cl. 1–5*, branchial clefts; *c. a.* carotid artery; *c. art.* conus arteriosus; *cd. a.* caudal artery; *cd. v.* caudal vein; *cl. a.* celiac artery; *crd. v.* cardinal vein; *d. ao.* dorsal aorta; *e. br. a.* efferent branchial artery; *gon.* gonad; *h. a.* hepatic artery; *h. p. v.* hepatic portal vein; *h. v.* hepatic vein; *il. a.* iliac artery; *il. v.* iliac vein; *int.* intestine; *j. v.* jugular vein; *k.* kidney; *lat. v.* lateral vein; *lr.* liver; *ms. a.* mesenteric artery; *pn.* pancreas; *pr. cv. v.* precaval vein; *r. a.* renal artery; *r. p. v.* renal portal vein; *v. v.* renal vein; *scl. a.* subclavian artery; *scl. v.* subclavian vein; *sp. a.* spermatic artery; *spl.* spleen; *sp. v.* spermatic vein; *st.* stomach; *s. v.* sinus venosus; *v.* ventricle; *v. ao.* ventral aorta. (After Parker.)

and spreads through the cardiac tissue to other regions. Admixed with the specialised contracting tissue are numerous ganglia and nerve fibres, but the actual wave spreads through the muscle. In chelonians a *coronary nerve* runs in a narrow bridge of cardiac tissue between sinus and ventricle. If this nerve is cut, the transmission wave and cardiac rhythmicity is not interfered with. If the bridge of cardiac muscle is severed, and the coronary nerve left intact, each chamber still contacts, but arhythmically. In Amphibia and reptiles the auricular and ventricular musculature is continuous across the auriculo-ventricular groove, and no specialised bundle of fibres is necessary to transmit the excitation wave. If the cardiac tissue between auricle and ventricle is clamped, the ventricular beat is stopped but later it may begin again spontaneously (myogenically).

Springing from the ventricle (or from the conus when that chamber is present) and passing directly forwards in the middle line below the gills, is a large, thick-walled, elastic blood-vessel, the *ventral aorta* (Figs. 63, *B*, and 76

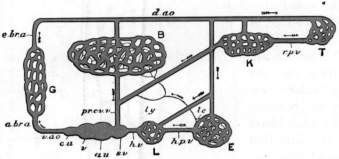

Fig. 77.—**Blood-vascular system.** Course of the circulation in a fish. Vessels containing äerated blood red, those containing non-äerated blood blue, lymphatics black. *B*, capillaries of the body generally; *E*, of the alimentary canal; *G*, of the gills; *K*, of the kidneys; *L*, of the liver; *T*, of the tail. *a. br. a.* afferent branchial arteries; *au.* atrium; *c. a.* conus arteriosus; *d. ao.* dorsal aorta; *e. br. a.* efferent branchial arteries; *h. p. v.* hepatic portal vein; *h. v.* hepatic vein; *lc.* lacteals; *ly.* lymphatics; *pr. cv. v.* precaval veins; *r. p. v.* renal portal veins; *s. v.* sinus venosus; *v.* ventricle; *v. ao.* ventral aorta. The arrows show the direction of the current. (After Parker.)

v. ao.). At its origin, which may be dilated to form a *bulbus arteriosus*, are valves so disposed as to allow of the flow of blood in one direction only, *viz.* from the ventricle into the aorta. It gives off on each side a series of half-hoop-like vessels, the *afferent branchial arteries* (*a. br. a.*), one to each gill. These vessels ramify extensively, and their ultimate branches open into a network of *capillaries* (Fig. 77, *G*). These have walls formed of a single layer of epithelial cells, which permeate the connective-tissue layer of the branchial filaments, and have therefore nothing between them and the surrounding water but the epithelium of the filaments. The blood, driven by the contractions of the heart into the ventral aorta, is pumped into these respiratory capillaries, and there exchanges its superfluous carbon dioxide for oxygen. It then passes from the capillaries into another set of vessels which join with one another, like the tributaries of a river, into larger and larger trunks, finally uniting in each gill, into an *efferent branchial artery* (*e. br. a.*). The efferent arteries of both sides pass upwards and discharge into a median longitudinal vessel, the *dorsal aorta* (*d. ao.*), situated immediately beneath the notochord or vertebral column.   From this trunk, or from the efferent branchial arteries, numerous vessels, the *systemic arteries*, are given off to all parts of the body. The most important of these are the *carotid arteries* (Fig. 76, *c. a.*) to the head, the *subclavian* (*scl. a.*) to the pectoral fins, the *cœliac* (*cl. a.*) and *mesenteric* (*ms. a.*) to the stomach, intestine, liver, spleen, and pancreas, the *renal* (*r. a.*) to the kidneys, the *spermatic* (*sp. a.*) or *ovarian* to the gonads, and the *iliac* (*il. a.*) to the pelvic fins.   After giving off the last-named the aorta is continued as the *caudal artery* (*cd. a.*) to the end of the tail.

With the exception of the capillaries, all the vessels described in the preceding paragraph, including the dorsal and ventral aortæ, are *arteries*.   They are firm, elastic tubes, which do not collapse when empty and usually contain but little blood in the dead animal.   They carry the blood from the heart to the body generally.

The systemic arteries branch and branch again into smaller and smaller trunks (*arterioles*) and finally pour their blood into a capillary network (Fig. 77, *B*, *K*, and *T*) with which all the tissues of the body, except epithelium and cartilage, are permeated.   In these *systemic capillaries* occurs internal or *tissue respiration.*   The blood parts with its oxygen and nutrient constituents to the tissues, and receives from them the various products of destructive metabolism—carbon dioxide, water, and nitrogenous waste.   The systemic, like the respiratory, capillaries are microscopic, and their walls are formed of a single layer of epithelial cells.

We saw that the respiratory capillaries are in connection with two sets of vessels, afferent and efferent.   The same applies to the systemic capillaries, with the important difference that their efferent vessels are not arteries, but thin-walled, non-elastic, collapsible tubes or *venules*.   These receive the deoxygenated blood from the capillaries, and unite into larger and larger trunks, the *veins*, which finally open into one or other of the great veins, presently to be described, by which the blood is returned to the heart.   As a general rule the vein of any part of the body runs parallel to its artery, from which it is at once distinguished by its wider calibre, by its dark colour (due to the contained bluish-purple blood seen through its thin walls), by being gorged with blood after death, by the complete collapse of its walls when empty, and by its possession of valves.   In some cases the veins become dilated into spacious cavities called *sinuses*; but sinuses without proper walls (such as occur in many of the Invertebrata) are never found in the Craniata except in individual organs (liver and spleen).   The veins from the head join to form large, paired *anterior cardinal* (*jugular*) *veins* (Fig. 76, *j. v.*) which pass backwards, one on each side of the head, and are joined by the prominent *posterior cardinal veins* (*crd. v.*) coming from the trunk.   Each jugular unites with the corresponding cardinal to form a large *precaval vein* (*Ductus Cuvieri*) (*pr. cv. v.*) which passes directly downwards and enters the sinus venosus. The blood from the tail returns by a *caudal vein* (*cd. v.*), lying immediately below the caudal artery in the hæmal canal of the caudal vertebræ (Fig. 63, *D*). On reaching the cœlom the caudal vein forks horizontally, and the two branches either become directly continuous with the cardinals or pass one to each kidney under the name of the *renal portal veins* (Fig. 76, *r. p. v.*). In the kidneys they break up into capillaries (Fig. 77, *K*), their blood mingling with that brought by the renal arteries and being finally discharged into the cardinals by the *renal veins* (Fig. 76, *r. v.*). Thus the blood from the tail may either return directly to the heart or may go by way of the capillaries of the kidneys. In the latter case there is said to be a *renal portal system*, the essential characteristic of which is that the kidney has a double blood-supply, one of oxygenated blood from the renal artery, and one of deoxygenated blood from the renal portal vein. In other words, it has two afferent vessels, an artery and a vein, and the latter is further distinguished by the fact that it both begins and ends in capillaries instead of beginning in capillaries and ending in a vein of higher order.

The blood from the gonads is returned to the cardinals by veins called *spermatic* (*sp. v.*) in the male, *ovarian* in the female. That from the paired fins takes, in what appears to be the most typical case, a somewhat curious course. On each side of the body there is a *lateral vein* (*lat. v.*), running in the body-wall and following the course of the embryonic ridge between the pectoral and pelvic fins. It receives, anteriorly, a *subclavian vein* (*scl. v.*) from the pectoral fin, and posteriorly an *iliac vein* (*il. v.*) from the pelvic fin, and in front pours its blood into the precaval.

The veins from the stomach, intestine, spleen, and pancreas join to form a large *hepatic portal vein* (*h. p. v.*), which passes to the liver and there breaks up into capillaries. The portal system among other functions conveys ingested food substances from the intestine to the liver. Thus the liver has a double blood-supply, receiving oxygenated blood by the *hepatic artery* (*h. a.*), a branch of the cœliac, and deoxygenated but food-laden blood by the hepatic portal vein (Fig. 77, *L*). In this way we have a *hepatic portal system* resembling the renal portal system, both in the double blood-supply and in the fact that the afferent vein terminates, as it originates, in capillaries. After circulating through the liver the blood is poured, by *hepatic veins* (*h. v.*), into the sinus venosus. The hepatic portal system, unlike the renal portal system, is of universal occurrence in the Craniata.

In the embryo there is a *sub-intestinal vein*, corresponding with that of Amphioxus, and lying beneath the intestine and the post-anal gut. Its posterior portion becomes the caudal vein of the adult, its anterior portion one of the factors of the hepatic portal vein.

To sum up : The circulatory organs of the branchiate Craniata consist of (*a*) a muscular force-pump, the *heart*, provided with valves and driving the blood into (*b*) a set of thick-walled elastic, afferent vessels, the *arteries* and arterioles, from which it passes into (*c*) a network of microscopic vessels or

capillaries which permeate the tissues, supplying them with oxygen and nutrient material and receiving from them carbon dioxide and other waste products.   From the capillary network the blood is carried off by (*d*) the venules and veins, thin-walled, non-elastic tubes which return it to the heart.   Thus the general scheme of the circulation is simple :   The arteries spring from the heart, or from arteries of a higher order, and end in capillaries.   The veins begin in capillaries and end in vessels of a higher order or in the heart.   Actually, however, two factors complicate the system :   Firstly, the interposition of the gills in the course of the outgoing current, as a result of which we have arteries serving as both afferent and efferent vessels of the respiratory capillaries.   The efferent arteries take their origin in those capillaries after the manner of veins.   Secondly, by the interposition of two very large and important organs, the liver and the kidney, in the course of the returning current, as a result of which we have veins acting as both afferent and efferent vessels of the hepatic and renal capillaries.   The afferent vessels of both organs end in capillaries after the fashion of arteries.

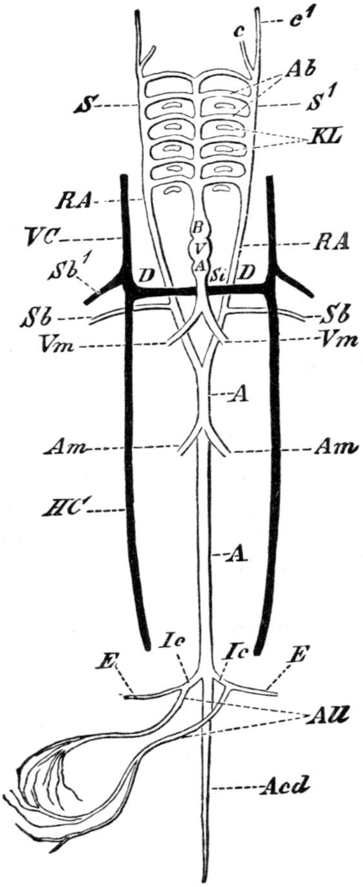

In the embryos of the higher, or air-breathing, Craniata, the circulatory organs agree in essentials with the above description. The most important difference is that, as no gills are present, the branches of the ventral aorta do not break up into capillaries, but pass directly into the dorsal aorta, forming the *aortic arches* (Fig. 78, *Ab*.).   With the

Fig. 78.—**Blood-vascular system: Embryo of an air-breathing craniate.** *A*. dorsal aorta, and auricle; *Ab*. aortic arches; *Acd*. caudal artery; *All*. allantoic arteries; *Am*. vitelline arteries; *B*. ventral aorta; *c*, *c*¹. carotid arteries; *D*. precaval veins; *Ic*, *E*. iliac arteries; *HC*. cardinal veins; *KL*. gill-clefts; *RA*, *S*, *S*¹. roots of dorsal aorta; *Sb*. subclavian arteries; *Sb*¹. subclavian veins; *V*. ventricle; *VC*. jugular vein; *Vm*. vitelline veins.   (After Wiedersheim.)

appearance of the lungs, however, a very profound change occurs in the blood-system.   The last aortic arch of each side now gives off a *pulmonary artery* (Fig. 79, *Ap*.) to the corresponding lung, and the blood, after circulating through the lung capillaries, is returned by a *pulmonary vein* (*lr*.) directly into the left side of the heart and not into an ordinary system vein of higher order. In the atrium a vertical partition is developed, separating a *left auricle* (A^1), which receives the oxygenated blood from the lungs, from a *right auricle* (A), into which is poured the deoxygenated blood of the sinus venosus. In crocodiles, birds, and mammals (B) a further important cardiac specialisation is found : the ventricle also becomes divided into right and left chambers. So we get a four-chambered heart with right and left auricles and right and left ventricles. At the same time the conus arteriosus and sinus venosus cease to exist as distinct chambers. The left auricle receives oxygenated blood from the lungs and passes it into the left ventricle, whence it is propelled through the system. The right auricle receives deoxygenated blood from the system, and passes it into the right ventricle to be pumped into the lungs for aëration. Thus the four-chambered heart of the higher vertebrates is quite different from that of a fish. In the latter the four chambers—sinus venosus, atrium, ventricle, and conus arteriosus—form a single longitudinal series, whereas in a mammal, for instance, the four chambers constitute practically a double heart, there being no direct communication between the auricle and ventricle of the right side, or *respiratory heart*, and those of the left side, or *systemic heart*. The modifications undergone by the arteries and veins in the higher Vertebrata will be considered under the various classes.

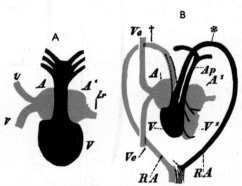

Fig. 79.—**Blood-vascular system: Cardiac circulation. A, an amphibian; B, a crocodile.** *A.* right auricle; *A¹.* left auricle; *Ap.* pulmonary artery; *lr.* pulmonary vein; *RA.* aortic arches; *V.* ventricle; *V¹.* left ventricle; *v, v.* and *Ve, Ve.* pre- and post-cavals. (After Wiedersheim.)

It has been generally believed that the complete division of the heart of birds and mammals into arterial and venous components has evolved independently, but recent studies bring this point into debate. It is not impossible that the inter-ventricular septum may have arisen when the tetrapod ancestors were still fishes and been secondarily lost in recent Amphibia. In the Dipnoi (p. 361), a specialised group far from the main line of vertebrate descent, the heart is almost completely divided. Although it is impossible to derive the modern tetrapod condition from that of the Dipnoi, it may be reasonable to suppose that the interventricular partition is homologous in both lung-fishes and tetrapods. If this is true, the original divided condition must have been present in early amphibians, replaced by a secondary septum in the saurischian reptiles (which gave rise to the birds), and seemingly retained in the therapsids (and so became the interventricular septum in the Mammalia) (Foxon).

In addition to the circulations through the respiratory and systemic hearts (called sometimes the lesser and greater circulations) there is a circulation within the heart itself. This is the *coronary circulation* by which the cardiac tissues are nourished and supplied with oxygen and their excretory products removed. With the exception of the amphibians, the coronary circulation consists of blood vessels which ramify throughout the walls of the heart chambers. The venous blood draining from the heart tissues is collected and returned to the right atrium by the *coronary sinus*.

The coronary circulation in the amphibians is much reduced and supplies only the conus arteriosus; the thin-walled ventricle is nourished by blood passing through into the general circulation.

The *blood* of Craniata is almost always red (*cf.*, however, p. 343). The red respiratory pigment (*hæmoglobin*) is not dissolved in the plasma, as in most red-blooded invertebrates, but is confined to *erythrocytes* (red blood-corpuscles) (p. 70), which float in the plasma. These are usually flat oval discs, the centre bulged out by a large nucleus (*nu.*), but in mammals they are bi-concave non-nucleated, and usually circular. The number and size of red cells vary among animals in regard to altitude and oxygen pressure. *Leucocytes* (white cells) of various kinds also occur (p. 71). The colour of the blood varies with the amount of oxygen taken up by the hæmoglobin. When thoroughly aerated it is of a bright scarlet colour, but assumes a bluish-purple hue after deoxygenation. Oxygenated blood is usually found in arteries, and is often spoken of as *arterial* blood. Deoxygenated, darker blood is usually found in veins and is called *venous*. But it must not be forgotten that an artery, *e.g.* the ventral aorta or the pulmonary artery, may contain venous blood, and a vein, *e.g.* the pulmonary vein, arterial blood. The distinction between the two classes of vessels does not depend upon their contents, but upon their relation to the heart and the capillaries and upon the structure of their walls (pp. 78, 107).

In addition to the blood-vessels the circulatory system of Craniata contains *lymph-vessels* or **lymphatics** (Fig. 77, *ly.*). In most tissues (Fig. 80) there is a lymphatic network of *lymph-capillaries*, interwoven with, but independent of, the blood-capillaries. From this network lymphatic vessels pass off, and finally discharge their contents into one or other of the veins. Many of the lower Craniata possess spacious *lymph-sinuses* surrounding the blood-vessels; and there are communications between the lymphatics and the cœlom by means of minute apertures or *stomata*. The lymphatics contain *lymph*, which is essentially blood *minus* its red cells and most of the plasma proteins. Lymph drains from the tissues: it passes into the lymph capillaries, and thence into the lymphatics. These are efferent vessels, conveying the fluid from the capillaries to the venous system.

The *lymphatic nodes* or *glands* which occur in the course of the vessels contain phagocytic cells, and also add *lymphocytes* to the lymph whence they enter the blood stream. The lymphatics contain valves which prevent back-flow of lymph towards the veins when the vessels are compressed by the surrounding tissues, such as muscle. In some groups there are muscular dilations in some of the lymphatics. These *lymph-hearts* contract rhythmically and actually propel the lymph forwards towards the venous system. The

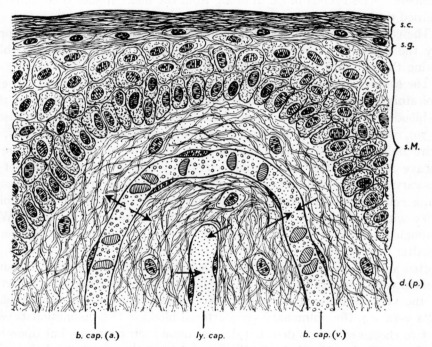

FIG. 80.—**Circulatory system: Relationship of blood and lymph capillaries below epidermis of mammal.** Blood and its contents flow in at the arterial end of the capillary (*b. cap.* (*a.*)), and leave at the venous end (*b. cap.* (*v.*)). Arrows indicate fluid exchanges between a blood capillary, the surrounding tissues, and an adjacent lymph capillary (*ly. cap.*). Other structures are: *d.* (*p.*). dermis (papillary layer; below, and not shown, is the reticular layer); *s. c.* stratum corneum; *s. g.* stratum granulosum; *s. M.* stratum Malpighii. (Modified after Ham.)

lymphatics of the intestine have an important function in the absorption of emulsified fats, and are known as *lacteals*.

Nervous System.—The nervous system attains in the higher vertebrates a structural complexity and functional importance which are probably without parallel in the animal kingdom. It is a system specialised to co-ordinate the activities of the animal in relation to changes in the internal and external environment, such activities including not only the contraction of muscles which may result in overt movement, but also processes in the cardio-vascular, respiratory, digestive, and other systems which are classified as *visceral*. In its most general sense its function may be said to be that of maintaining a condition of equilibrium not only between the internal organs, tissues, and fluids of the body, but also between the body as a whole and its external environment.

To perform these functions the nervous system is equipped with *afferent* or sensory connections which carry information in the form of nervous impulses from organs which are sensitive to external events (*exteroceptive* organs such as the eyes and ears) or to internal events such as changes of tension in muscles, ligaments, and in the walls of viscera, or of the chemical composition of the body-fluids. Nerves capable of responding to these internal events are classified as *interoceptive*, and include *proprioceptors* signalling internal body movements and *visceroceptors* registering mechanical changes in viscera and blood-vessels. Receptor organs, whether extero- or intero-ceptive, vary in relation to special needs. For example, the eyes of nocturnal animals are often larger than those of related diurnal species, since there is a need for greater light-gathering power. Again, those of hunting animals usually look forward (as in the cat), whereas those of hunted animals (*e.g.* the mouse) look laterally, and thus provide a wider field of vision.

As a complement to the afferent connections, *efferent* or motor connections are also present by which *effector* organs such as muscles and glands can be stimulated to perform their characteristic function. In addition, some mechanism is necessary in all more complex animals, by which the information derived from varied receptor organs can be integrated, and by which the activity of the effector organs can be co-ordinated, so as to result in behaviour which is appropriate to the situation which the receptors have revealed.

One other general characteristic of the nervous system must be mentioned. All living tissue is altered to some extent, either temporarily or permanently, by activities which occur within it. In nervous tissue such alterations are particularly important, especially in the higher vertebrates, where they constitute the physical basis of the process of adaptation so far as behaviour is concerned, or, more simply, the physical basis of learning. The nervous system may be altered by stimuli which pass through it, so that on a subsequent occasion it does not react in exactly the same way to similar, or even identical stimuli. At present one can only speculate concerning the physical nature of the change which has occurred, but that a change is there, is shown by the altered reaction obtained. This power of change, the plasticity of nervous tissue, is particularly characteristic of certain parts of the nervous system in the higher vertebrates.

Anatomically the nervous system can be divided into central and peripheral parts (Figs. 81, 82). The *peripheral nervous system* consists mainly of afferent and efferent nerve-fibres, gathered together in nerves which conduct to and from the *central nervous system* in which the integrating and co-ordinating mechanisms are situated. The latter is formed, of course, by the brain and spinal cord. Nerve-fibres are processes (*axons*) of nerve-cells which in the case of the afferent

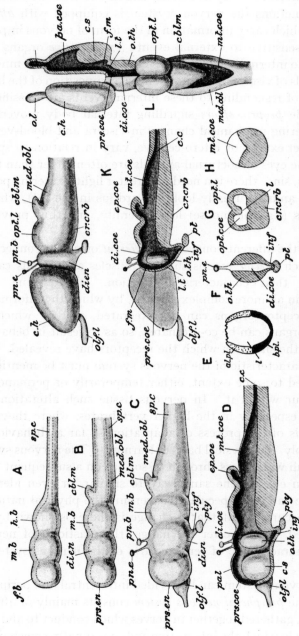

FIG. 81.—**Nervous system: Brain and proximal part of spinal cord during development and maturity.** *A*, first stage, side view, the cavity indicated by a dotted line; *B*, second stage; *C*, side view of fully-formed brain with undivided prosencephalon; *D*, the same in sagittal section; *E*, transverse section of prosencephalon; *F*, of diencephalon; *G*, of mesencephalon; *H*, of medulla oblongata; *I*, side view of brain with cerebral hemispheres; *K*, sagittal section of the same; *L*, dorsal view, the cavities exposed on the right side; *al. pl.* alar, or dorsolateral wall; *b. pl.* basal or ventro-lateral wall; *cblm.* cerebellum; *c. c.* central canal; *cr.crb.* crura cerebri; *c. h.* cerebral hemispheres; *c. s.* corpora striata; *di. coe.* third ventricle; *dien.* diencephalon; *ep. coe.* cerebellar ventricle; *f. b.* fore-brain; *f. m.* foramen of Monro; *h. b.* hind-brain; *inf.* infundibulum; *l.* iter; *l. t.* lamina terminalis; *m. b.* mid-brain; *m. coe.* mesocoele; *med. obl.* medulla oblongata; *mt. coe.* fourth ventricle; *olf. l.* olfactory lobe; *opt. coe.* optic ventricle; *opt. l.* optic lobes; *o. th.* optic thalami; *pa. coe.* lateral or first ventricle; *pal.* pallium; *pn. b.* pineal body (epiphysis); *pn. e.* pineal eye (parietal organ); *prs. coe.* prosocoele; *prs. en.* telencephalon; *pt. pty.* pituitary body; *rh. coe.* rhinocoeles; *sp. c.* spinal cord.

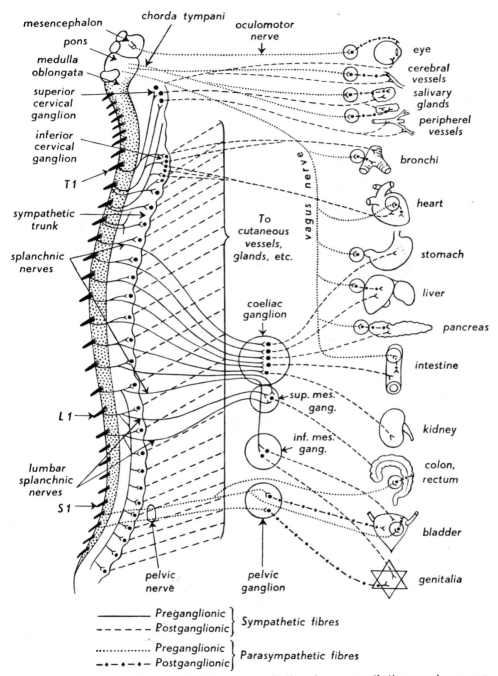

FIG. 82.—**Nervous system: Distribution of sympathetic and parasympathetic nerves in mamma (Man).** (Modified after Kunz.)

fibres are situated in small swellings or *ganglia* on the nerves close to the point where they join the central nervous system (Fig. 83). The cells whose processes form the efferent or motor nerves are situated within the central nervous system, but there is an important exception to this statement. Viscera such as the heart, blood-vessels, intestine, etc., and glands, receive their motor

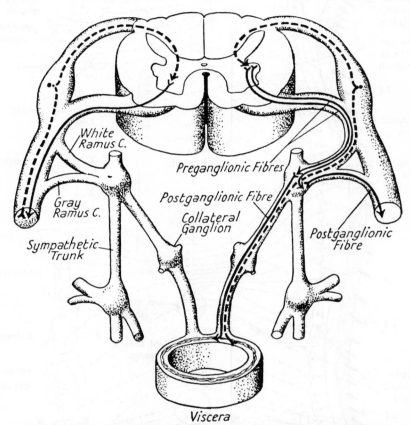

Fig. 83.—**Nervous system: Relationship of the sympathetic system to the spinal nerves and cord.** The main visceral fibres are shown on the right side and, for contrast, the somatic fibres on the left. *Afferent* fibres are indicated by interrupted lines and *efferent* fibres by continuous lines. (From Le Gros Clark, after Cunningham.)

or efferent innervation from a part of the peripheral nervous system which is called *autonomic,* and which consists of two divisions, the sympathetic and para-sympathetic (see below). The fibres which connect with the muscle of a viscus, or the secretory epithelium of a gland, are the processes of cells situated in ganglia outside the central nervous system. On each side of the vertebral column there is a series of such ganglia, two for each segment of the body (Fig. 83). These are known as the ganglia of the sympathetic subdivision of the autonomic nervous system, and they are linked longitudinally to form the two sympathetic chains of ganglia. Although these ganglia may possess some degree of autonomy, they are controlled by the central nervous system through *preganglionic* fibres, which in mammals arise from cells in the thoracic part of the spinal cord.

It will be seen therefore that the sympathetic innervation of a viscus is effected through two nerve-fibres, the one preganglionic, originating in the central nervous system, the other postganglionic, originating in a ganglion and ending in the viscus. It follows that the impulse carried by the pre-ganglionic fibre must be passed on to the postganglionic fibre through a *synaptic junction* in the ganglion. Since preganglionic fibres branch and

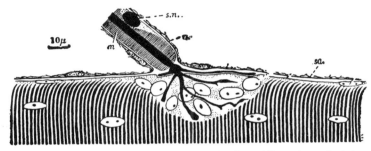

FIG. 84.—**Nervous System: A medullated fibre terminating at its motor end-plate on a striated muscle.** *m.* myelin sheath; *n.* neurilemma; *s. n.* nucleus of Schwann cell; *sa.* sarcolemma. (From Le Gros Clark, after Gutmann and Young.)

ramify widely, many postganglionic fibres may receive impulses from one preganglionic, so that a widespread response may be obtained from a single impulse. This form of innervation is in sharp contrast to that of skeletal muscle, where only one nerve-fibre arising within the central nervous system is involved and where the response is limited to the particular part of a muscle connected to that fibre (Fig. 84).

In addition to the sympathetic chain of ganglia, small and often micro-scopic collections of nerve-cells are found irregularly scattered anterior to the dorsal aorta and in the walls of such viscera as the heart and intestine. These are known as *parasympathetic* ganglia. The fibres which arise from them also innervate viscera, but their action is usually antagonistic to that of the sym-pathetic system; for example, when stimulation of the sympathetic fibre leads to contraction, stimulation of the parasympathetic causes relaxation. The parasympathetic ganglia are also connected to the central nervous system by preganglionic fibres which travel in cranial or sacral nerves from the brain and spinal cord respectively.

The nerves supplying viscera, both afferent and efferent, with their ganglia, are often referred to as the *visceral nervous system*, and are distinguished from the afferent and efferent nerves which supply skin and skeletal muscle which are called *somatic*. The distinction between somatic and visceral is not always clear-cut and there are several nerves whose classification in these terms is uncertain or controversial. This applies particularly to the afferent nerves. On the efferent side, the presence of a peripheral synaptic junction in a sympathetic or parasympathetic ganglion is a criterion for distinguishing the visceral from the somatic type of innervation, although it is not applicable in quite every case. As will be seen, the terms visceral and somatic are also applied within the central nervous system to regions which have predominant connections with these subdivisions of the peripheral system; but again, attempts to place all parts of the central nervous system in one category or the other have not been entirely satisfactory.

The nervous system of all Chordata first appears as a groove in a strip of thickened ectoderm on the dorsal aspect of the embryo. The groove deepens, its lips fuse, and it separates from the surface as a dorsal longitudinal *neural tube*, the cavity of which is called a *neurocœle*. So far the agreement of the Craniata with the lower Chordata is complete, but a fundamental advance is seen in the fact that at a very early stage the anterior end of the neural tube undergoes a marked dilatation and forms the rudiment of the brain, the rest becoming the spinal cord (Fig. 81). Very soon constrictions appear in the dilated part and divide it into three bulb-like swellings or *vesicles*, the *fore-brain*, *mid-brain*, and *hind-brain*, the latter continuous with the *spinal cord*. Functionally there appears to be a primary relationship of the fore-brain with olfaction, the mid-brain with vision, and the hind-brain with the auditory and vestibular apparatus, and also, in aquatic vertebrates, with the sensory inflow from the lateral line organs (p. 135). It is probable that the development of special sense organs at the cranial end of the animal is causally related to the formation of the three vesicles of the brain in this situation.

Structurally the spinal cord is the least differentiated part of the central nervous system. It remains as a longitudinal tube, but the walls thicken greatly and the neurocœle is reduced to a narrow *central canal* lined by columnar ciliated epithelium or *ependyma*. In the thickened walls nerve-cells and a special variety of supporting cells known as *neuroglia* develop. The latter, mainly of ectodermal origin, perform many of the functions of mesodermal connective tissues in other parts of the body.

The nerve-cells or neurones consist of a cell body containing the nucleus and bearing numerous fine branching processes or *dendrites*. There is in addition a single process, the *axon*, which usually gives off only a few branches and often travels for a considerable distance from the cell body. The axons that are covered by a lipoid sheath of *myelin* are said to be *myelinated* or *medullated* (Fig. 84). Somatic and preganglionic visceral axons are generally medullated, whereas post-ganglionic visceral axons are not.

Nervous impulses are received on the dendrites or on the surface of the cell body. Normally conduction in neurones *occurs only in one direction, i.e.* from the dendrites to the cell body, and then away from the cell body along the axon. Neurones are thus said to exhibit *polarity*. The axon loses its sheath and becomes naked just before its termination, so that the impulse which it carries can be passed through a synapse to the dendrite or cell body of another neurone, or through a specialised *end-plate* to a muscle-fibre (Fig. 84). It is clear that

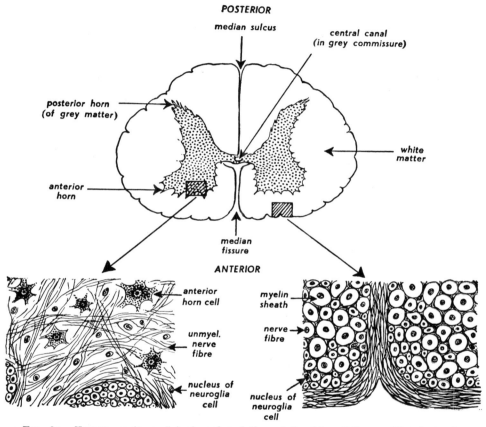

FIG. 85.—**Nervous system: Spinal cord and the relationships of its constituent structures.** *Above:* Transverse section under low power showing distribution of grey and white matter. *Below:* High-power diagrams revealing their contents. (After Ham.)

many axons (such as those which pass from the spinal cord to muscles in the feet) must be of very great length in some animals.

When the spinal cord is cut transversely it can be seen with the naked eye to consist of *grey matter* which is situated around the central canal and has a λ or H shape in section, the whole of the superficial part of the cord consisting of *white matter* (Fig. 85). The grey matter contains cell bodies, dendrites, and the terminations of the axons which are making connections with them, and, of course, the beginnings of the axons arising from the cell bodies. The latter enter the white matter, which is formed of axons running for varying distances cranially or caudally as the *tracts* of the spinal cord. Its whiteness is due to the myelination of these axons. It is clear that the grey matter is the tissue in which interconnections between neurones occur and enable the functions of integration and co-ordination to be carried out. The white matter consists of conducting pathways between different segments of the spinal cord and between the spinal cord and the brain.

The spinal nerves are the only means by which the spinal cord is connected to the receptor and effector organs of the periphery. There is one on each side in each segment of the body, often referred to as a 'mixed spinal nerve', since it contains both afferent and efferent fibres. Each nerve divides as it enters the canal in the vertebral column into two roots, dorsal and ventral. The dorsal root carries all the afferent fibres and has on it the ganglion previously referred to : its fibres enter the dorsal horn of grey matter in the cord. The ventral root consists of efferent fibres which are the axons of cells in the ventral horn of grey matter. In the most primitive living vertebrates (lampreys) (p. 176) the roots do not join. The afferent and efferent fibres run independently to their destinations, and mixed spinal nerves are not formed.

It is customary to classify nerve-fibres as *somatic* and *visceral* according to the structures they supply. The efferent or motor-fibres supplying the striated muscle developed from somites are classified as *somatic motor*, and the sympathetic and parasympathetic pre- and post-ganglionic fibres through which the smooth muscle and glands of viscera are supplied as *visceral motor*. The afferent fibres are similarly classified : 'somatic sensory' fibres are those supplying the skin and sense organs on the surface of the body and all structures developed from somites ; 'visceral sensory' fibres supply viscera, *i.e.* structures developed from lateral plate mesoderm and from endoderm. It must be admitted, however, that in the case of the afferent fibres this classification is not entirely satisfactory. There are many afferent nerves where some justification could be found for placing them in either category.

In all the higher vertebrates visceral motor-fibres leave the spinal cord in the ventral roots of the spinal nerves with the somatic motor-fibres. In cyclostomes and in some fish they are found also, and perhaps entirely in some cases, in the dorsal roots, which do not therefore consist only of afferent fibres in these animals. The functional categories 'somatic sensory', 'visceral motor', etc., in which nerve-fibres can be classified are usually referred to as the *components* of the nerve. *A mixed spinal nerve will normally contain representatives of all the four components so far mentioned.*

Cranially the spinal cord is continuous with the most caudal of the three cerebral vesicles, the hind-brain. The part directly continuous with the spinal cord is the *medulla oblongata* or *myelencephalon*. Here the side walls of the neural tube thicken and fold outwards to form the floor of an enlarged part of the central canal called the 4th ventricle of the brain. Towards the cranial end the hind-brain narrows as it joins the mid-brain at the *isthmus*, and becomes flexed so as to show a ventral convexity. This cranial end of the hind-brain is sometimes distinguished as the *metencephalon*, and it is in this region that the cerebellum develops in all vertebrates (Fig. 81).

The same grey and white matter is found in the hind-brain as was seen in the spinal cord. In the former, however, the grey matter is broken up into more or less discrete masses forming the nuclei of cranial nerves, etc., while the white matter consists chiefly of ascending and descending tracts connecting different parts of the brain with the spinal cord. It is joined by a series of nerves which supply the mouth, pharynx, and branchial arches. Since the last-named are respiratory in function, and the heart and arterial arches are closely related to them both anatomically and functionally, the principal centres controlling cardio-vascular and respiratory functions are found in the hind-brain. This applies to air-breathing as well as aquatic vertebrates, since lungs are also derivatives of the pharynx (p. 107) and the heart always develops first below the floor of the pharynx, though subsequently it may be displaced caudally into a thorax.

In addition to the branchial arch nerves, the hind-brain receives the sensory inflow from the inner ear (vestibular, from the semicircular canals, and auditory) and in aquatic vertebrates from the lateral line system. These sensory systems will be described more fully later. Here it is necessary to say only that, apart from audition, they are mainly concerned with the orientation of the body in space, *i.e.* with *equilibration*. Important centres are therefore found in the hind-brain for the control of position and posture, and it is from these that the *cerebellum*, largely concerned in similar functions, develops.

The form of the cerebellum varies greatly in different vertebrates. In its simplest form (*e.g.* in living Agnatha and Amphibia) it consists of a thin band of nervous tissue which bridges over the 4th ventricle at the cranial end of the hind-brain (metencephalon), and most of its grey matter is spread superficially to form a *cortex*. In fishes, birds, and mammals it is a much larger and more conspicuous structure. The roof of the caudal part of the 4th ventricle remains as a thin and non-nervous layer from which a secretory apparatus called a *choroid plexus* develops. This secretes a watery fluid (very like physiological saline) into the cavity of the ventricle (*cerebrospinal fluid*).

The mid-brain (mesencephalon), immediately cranial to the hind-brain, is less extensively modified from the form of the original neural tube. It becomes bent (the *mid-brain flexure*) so as to present a dorsal convexity which is known as its roof or *tectum*. Here bilateral swellings (into which fibres of the optic nerves grow) are found in all vertebrates. These are the *optic lobes*. Two additional swellings are present in mammals which receive fibres from the auditory centres of the hind-brain. The only motor nerve nuclei in the mid-brain are those which control the movements of the eyeball, the size of the pupil, and the mechanism of accommodation. These are situated more ventrally in the *tegmentum*, and, ventral to them, are found bundles of fibres (particularly well developed in mammals) which connect the fore-brain with lower levels of the nervous system; these are the *crura cerebri*. The *neurocœle* of the mid-brain generally remains small as the *aqueduct* connecting the 4th ventricle of the hind-brain with the ventricles of the fore-brain; in some forms it extends into the optic lobes as *optic ventricles*.

The hind-brain and mid-brain together constitute the *brain-stem*, which, in spite of variations due to differences in the form of the cerebellum and a number of associated structures, preserves a very stable pattern throughout the vertebrate class. It can be thought of as a continuation cranially of the spinal cord, modified by such factors as the inflow of optic and auditory impulses, and the development of special motor mechanisms not present in the spinal cord. The nerves attached to the brain-stem, with the exception of the optic nerve, are in many respects comparable with segmental spinal nerves.

The *fore-brain*, at the cranial end of the neural tube, is more varied in form and also fundamentally different in structure from the spinal cord. It receives impulses directly only from the olfactory nerves and the small nervus terminalis, neither of which is comparable with a spinal nerve. It lies entirely cranial to the notochord and has been called the *archencephalon*, in contrast to the *deuterencephalon*, which lies dorsal to the notochord and includes both brain-stem and spinal cord. At a very early period of development the archencephalon becomes bent ventrally over the end of the notochord. This is the *primary cerebral flexure* and, though permanent, it soon becomes obscured by other changes in this region and is not noticeable in the adult. These two regions, archencephalon and deuterencephalon, show not only fundamental differences in adult structure and in their relationship to the notochord, but important embryological differences as well.

The most cranial part of the fore-brain becomes differentiated as the *telencephalon* or end-brain vesicle, characterised by its connection on either side with the bilateral olfactory apparatus. The caudal part, between the telencephalon and the mid-brain, is the *diencephalon*. The telencephalon possesses thick walls and a thin roof and floor. Its walls are joined by the olfactory nerves in regions differentiated as the *olfactory bulbs* which, in many vertebrates, are drawn out to become pedunculated (the *olfactory peduncles*). Peduncles and bulbs are hollow, containing a prolongation of the neurocœle of the telencephalon. In nearly all vertebrates the lateral walls of the telencephalon also bulge outwards and forwards to form the bilateral *cerebral hemispheres*. These contain a cavity, the *lateral ventricle*, which remains in connection with the cranial end of the neurocœle through an *interventricular foramen* on either side.

This evagination of the cerebral hemispheres is very incomplete in cyclostomes (p. 175) and most fishes. In some of the latter, especially teleosts (p. 239), the evagination of the hemisphere is accompanied by a marked eversion of the dorsal part of the lateral wall which grows downwards and becomes combined with the ventral part of this wall to form a massive collection of nervous tissue in many ways comparable with the *basal ganglia* in the hemispheres of tetrapods. The whole structure is covered by a thin non-nervous membrane which is the stretched roof of the telencephalon.

In lung-fishes (p. 361) and in tetrapods the evagination of the hemispheres is much more complete, and no eversion takes place. The dorsal part of the hemispheres remains comparatively thin as the *pallium*, the region in which the *cerebral cortex* of reptiles (p. 478), birds (p. 592), and mammals (p. 678) will develop ; the ventral part becomes massive as the *basal ganglia*. It should be pointed out that in primitive vertebrates (cyclostomes, fishes, amphibia) the whole hemisphere is dominated by connections from the olfactory bulbs, and is sometimes referred to as an *olfactory lobe* ; in some reptiles and mammals and in all birds, olfactory dominance becomes much reduced.

A small part of the telencephalon remains unaffected by the evagination of the hemisphere and median in position. It is bounded cranially by the *lamina terminalis*, which marks the morphological cranial end of the brain. Its cavity is continuous caudally with that of the diencephalon, so that a median or *third ventricle* is formed. This third ventricle communicates laterally on each side through the interventricular foramina (of Monro) with the lateral ventricles of the hemispheres, and caudally through the aqueduct of the mid-brain with the fourth ventricle of the hind-brain.

As already stated, the diencephalon is a median part of the neural tube between the telencephalon cranially and the mid-brain caudally. Masses of nerve-cells develop in its walls, which form the *thalami* (right and left). These serve largely as relay stations in the course of ascending tracts conveying sensory impulses from the brain-stem and spinal cord to the hemispheres.

These sensory impulses are mainly exteroceptive from the surface of the body and proprioceptive from muscles, ligaments, etc., so that the thalamus has been classed as a somatic sensory centre. It is also connected, however, with a well-developed mass of nervous tissue in the floor of the diencephalon, the *hypothalamus*, which is concerned with the integration of various visceral and metabolic activities. A funnel-shaped diverticulum, the *infundibulum*, grows ventrally from the hypothalamus and comes into relationship with an upgrowth from the roof of the embryonic mouth cavity or stomodæum. From these two outgrowths the anterior and posterior lobes of an important endocrine gland, the *pituitary* or *hypophysis*, are formed (Fig. 81). This is always situated immediately cranial to the notochord between the trabeculæ of the chondrocranium, and retains throughout life its relationship, which is functional as well as developmental, with the hypothalamus. In both bony and carti-laginous fishes a further outgrowth from the infundibulum forms the *saccus vasculosus*, a structure of uncertain function, but possibly sensitive to pressure transmitted from an aquatic environment.

The roof of the diencephalon remains thin and a choroid plexus, similar in structure and function to that of the 4th ventricle, develops in it. Cranially, where it extends into the telencephalon, it forms a saccular outgrowth, the *paraphysis* ; caudally, just before the mid-brain is reached, the pineal apparatus develops. This is represented in mammals by the *pineal organ*, which appears to be vestigial and possibly functionless. In some vertebrates, *e.g.* cyclo-stomes, and many reptiles, two outgrowths are formed in this region (*pineal* and *parapineal*), one or both of which may be sensitive to light and show many of the structural features of an eye (see pp. 189, 345).

The brain of vertebrates is enclosed in the cranial cavity of the skull (*neurocranium*) and the spinal cord in the canal formed between the neural arches and centra of the vertebræ. The whole cerebrospinal cavity is lined by a tough fibrous membrane, the *dura mater*. The connective tissue between the dura mater and the nervous system differentiates into two much thinner membranes, the outer *arachnoid* and the inner *pia mater*, which is everywhere closely applied to the nervous tissue. Between them is the *subarachnoid space* filled with cerebrospinal fluid secreted by the choroid plexuses ; this forms a protective fluid cushion around the brain and spinal cord. Further, by its continuous secretion and resorption into the blood-stream it helps to remove metabolites from the nervous tissue. The dura mater, arachnoid, and pia mater are referred to as the *meninges* or membranes of the nervous system.

The cranial nerves of vertebrates are numbered I to XII, but this mode of designation dates from a period when little was known in detail of the morpho-logy and functions of the nerves in question. The nervus terminalis, which was discovered later, is not included in the series. There is no doubt that in the light of modern knowledge a more satisfactory classification could be devised. The old system is based only on superficial topographical knowledge of the human and mammalian brain and naturally leads to difficulties when applied to vertebrates as a whole. It is still, however, the system in common use, and is employed as a basis for the description which follows.

It has already been noted that most of the cranial nerves are comparable with spinal nerves, or, more accurately, with the roots of spinal nerves, and show evidence of a similar segmental arrangement. This does not apply to three of them, the *nervus terminalis*, the *olfactory* (Ist), and the *optic* (IInd). These must be described individually (Fig. 86).

The **nervus terminalis** is a minute nerve distributed to the mucous membrane of the nasal sac ; a few nerve-cells are scattered along its course and it joins the fore-brain near the ventral end of the *lamina terminalis*. It may contain a

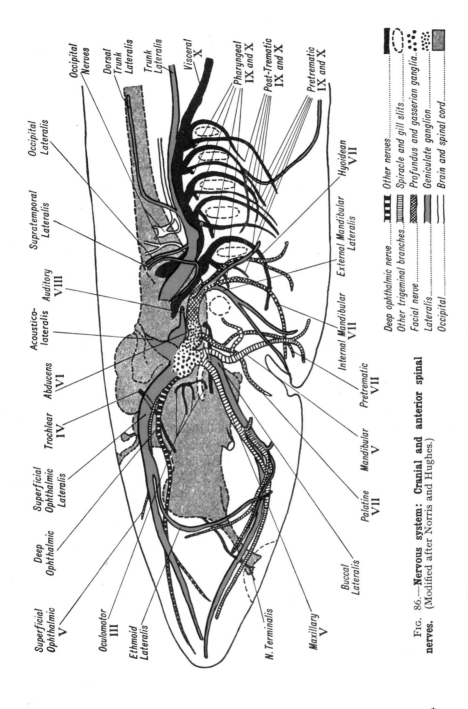

Fig. 86.—**Nervous system: Cranial and anterior spinal nerves.** (Modified after Norris and Hughes.)

few sensory fibres, and possibly autonomic efferent fibres to blood-vessels, but little is known of its functions.

The Ist (**olfactory**) nerve consists of a number of *fila olfactoria* which run from the olfactory receptors of the nasal sac to the olfactory bulbs of the telencephalon.   Though an afferent nerve, it possesses no ganglion.   Its fibres are the processes of the receptor cells.   In these respects it is unique among all the nerves of the vertebrate body.   In many air-breathing vertebrates, notably the Reptilia, a specialised organ, containing receptors of the olfactory type, is found in the naso-buccal region.   This is the *vomeronasal* organ or *organ of Jacobson*.   It is innervated by a special branch of the olfactory nerve (pp. 137, 481).

The IInd (**optic**) nerve runs from the retina of the eye back to the brain. The retina is part of the optic vesicle, which, at an early embryonic stage, developed as an outgrowth from the diencephalic part of the neural tube. Morphologically it is therefore a part of the brain, and the 'nerve' which grows from it is comparable with a tract in the central nervous system rather than with a peripheral nerve.   Although the optic vesicle is a derivative of the forebrain the optic nerve, after decussating in a *chiasma*, grows into the tectum of the mid-brain in all vertebrates below the Mammalia.   In mammals the decussation is incomplete and the majority of fibres enter a part of the thalamus called the *lateral geniculate body*.

The remaining cranial nerves fall into two groups : (1) *somatic motor nerves*, in general comparable with the ventral roots of spinal nerves, and (2) *branchial arch nerves*, comparable with the dorsal roots.

Somatic Motor Nerves.   These are nerves which supply striated muscle developed from somites : the IIIrd (**oculomotor**), IVth (**trochlear**), VIth (**abducens**), and XIIth (**hypoglossal**).   The IIIrd and IVth nerves arise from the mid-brain and the VIth from the cranial end of the hind-brain.   All three supply muscles which move the eyeball ; and the IIIrd also contains fibres which supply smooth muscle within the eyeball (*e.g.* the constrictor muscle of the pupil).   The IIIrd nerve is therefore said to possess a visceral motor in addition to its somatic motor component.   The IVth (trochlear) nerve is exceptional, since it is the only cranial nerve to emerge from the dorsal aspect of the brainstem.   The XIIth (hypoglossal) nerve arises from the ventral surface of the medulla and supplies the hypobranchial musculature, including the muscles of the tongue.   It probably represents the ventral roots of several nerves, since the muscles supplied are developed from several somites.   A hypoglossal nerve cannot be recognised as a cranial nerve in cyclostomes and other primitive vertebrates, where it is probably represented by the ventral roots of the most cranial spinal nerves.

Branchial arch nerves.   This group contains the Vth (**trigeminal**), VIIth (**facial**), IXth (**glossopharyngeal**), Xth (**vagus**), and XIth (**spinal accessory**) nerves. The spinal accessory is not recognised as a separate nerve below the tetrapods, but is represented by a part of the vagus. The VIIIth (**vestibular** and **auditory**) nerve and the **lateral line** nerves will also be described with the branchial arch nerves, since they are closely associated with them. Their position is somewhat equivocal, for they have no functional relationship to the branchial arches or their derivatives.

Apart from the VIIIth, these nerves all have a close relation to the pharyngeal arches and the branchial clefts between them. They all contain afferent fibres, from the skin (somatic afferent) and from the mucous membrane of the mouth and pharynx (visceral afferent), and they all possess ganglia like those of the dorsal roots of spinal nerves. Some of the visceral afferent fibres come from taste receptors and are classed as *special visceral afferent*. In addition, nearly all these nerves contain visceral efferent fibres, some of which supply glands and smooth muscle like visceral efferent fibres elsewhere. Others supply the striated muscle of the pharynx, œsophagus, and visceral arches (including those of the larynx in air-breathing vertebrates). Though striated, these muscles are developed from lateral plate mesoderm and not from somites (p. 161). They are specialised, however, in relation to the movements of the jaws, swallowing, respiration, and phonation, and the nerves supplying them are classed as *special visceral efferent nerves*.

It will be seen that the nerves in this group are all complex and may contain as many as five components : somatic and visceral afferent, special visceral afferent, visceral efferent, and special visceral efferent. The presence of efferent fibres has not been demonstrated in the dorsal roots of spinal nerves in most vertebrates, but they are probably present in the primitive chordate, Amphioxus (p. 47), in cyclostomes (p. 175), and perhaps in fishes (pp. 219, 282). Their presence in this group of cranial nerves is therefore an example of the persistence of a primitive feature in nerves which are in many ways highly specialised.

In general the anatomical pattern of branchial arch nerves is as follows : they possess a main branch which passes posterior to the branchial cleft (*posttrematic*) supplying both skin and muscle and a smaller but similar branch in front of it (*pretrematic*). There is usually a *dorsal cutaneous branch* and another, the *pharyngeal branch*, which passes medially to the mucous membrane of the roof of the pharynx. All these branches are not present in every nerve, just as every component listed is not present in all of them.

The **trigeminal** (Vth) is large and emerges from the cranial part of the hind-brain close to the VII nerve. It soon enters the large *semilunar* or *Gasserian* ganglion, from which its three main branches arise : *ophthalmic, maxillary*, and *mandibular*.

The ophthalmic branch consists of two parts : the *ramus ophthalmicus profundus* and the *ramus ophthalmicus superficialis*. The *R. ophthalmicus profundus* passes deeply through the orbit, supplies sensory fibres to the eyeball, and ends in the skin of the end of the snout.   There are reasons for believing that this deep ophthalmic branch was originally a separate cranial nerve, representing the dorsal root belonging to a premandibular somite, the ventral root to which is the oculomotor nerve.   The superficial ophthalmic branch is the dorsal cutaneous, the maxillary the pretrematic, and the mandibular the post-trematic branch, as in a typical branchial arch nerve.   The gill-slit is represented by the mouth, the gill of course being absent.   The special visceral efferent fibres all run in the mandibular or post-trematic branch and supply the muscles which move the jaws.   It may be called the nerve of mastication. There is no pharyngeal branch.   The ventral root corresponding to this nerve is probably the IVth (trochlear), supplying the superior oblique muscle in the orbit.

The **facial** (VIIth) is the next in this series.   It is a fairly typical branchial arch-nerve, belonging to the hyoid arch.   The sensory ganglion on its root is the *geniculate ganglion*.   Its main or post-trematic branch is the hyomandibular nerve, which supplies the muscles of the hyoid arch.   In mammals these migrate widely to form the superficial muscles of facial expression.

The *chorda tympani* branch of mammals may represent the pretrematic branch, but is more probably the representative of the internal mandibular nerve of fishes, which is post-trematic in position.   It supplies the mucous membrane of the tongue with taste or special visceral sensory fibres and in tetrapods, visceral efferent fibres to salivary glands.   The true pretrematic branch is probably the *prespiracular* nerve of fishes and is reduced or absent in tetrapods.

The *pharyngeal* branch is represented by the *palatine* nerve of fishes, which runs medially above the palato-quadrate bar; it is the *greater superficial petrosal* nerve of mammalian anatomy, and contains visceral afferent and efferent fibres.   The *dorsal cutaneous* branch is small and may be absent.   This is certainly true of tetrapods, but in fishes sensory fibres are more numerous in the VIIth nerve than in higher vertebrates, particularly those serving the taste receptors, which may be distributed widely over the surface of the body.

The IXth or **glossopharyngeal** is the nerve of the third visceral arch.   It is a typical branchial arch nerve with a sensory ganglion, *pre-* and *post-trematic* branches, and a *pharyngeal* branch.   A *dorsal cutaneous* branch is small or absent.

Its afferent fibres come from the mucous membrane of the pharynx and in mammals, where it is the principal nerve of taste, from the posterior part of the tongue.   It also receives afferent fibres from the part of the internal carotid artery in mammals which is developed from the third arterial arch and forms the *carotid sinus* (p. 674).   These, together with other afferents from chemoreceptors in the *carotid body*, are important in cardiovascular reflexes for the adjustment of blood pressure.   Although these fibres from the carotid sinus and carotid body have been investigated chiefly in mammals, similar fibres are probably present in other vertebrates.

The Xth or **vagus** is a large nerve which emerges from the medulla oblongata by several roots which lie in series with the IXth nerve. It probably represents the combined nerves of all the visceral arches caudal to the third. It supplies these arches with the characteristic *pharyngeal, pre-* and *post-trematic* branches. There is also a small *dorsal cutaneous* branch. In the air-breathing tetrapods these branches are represented by *pharyngeal* and *laryngeal* nerves, all of which contain special visceral efferent and visceral afferent fibres. The vagus also supplies the heart and swim-bladder (pp. 108, 361) or lungs (pp. 107–108), structures which develop from the pharynx or in close relation to it. The *pulmonary* branches come from the trunk of the vagus, the *pneumogastric* nerve which continues caudally to supply the oesophagus, stomach, and much of the intestine. It is this wide distribution to viscera which has earned the name 'vagus' or 'wanderer'. The visceral efferent fibres to the heart, lungs, and alimentary canal are classed as 'parasympathetic' and are functionally antagonistic to the sympathetic supply to these viscera in mammals. The vagus also contains numerous visceral afferent fibres which serve important reflexes.

The XIth or **spinal accessory** is probably the nerve of the last (5th or 6th) visceral arch. It is not present in fishes, where it is represented by the most caudal rootlets of the vagus. In mammals, where it was first described, it consists of a *cranial* and a *spinal* part. The cranial part is incompletely separated from the vagus, and supplies motor fibres to the larynx which are distributed in the laryngeal branches of the vagus. The spinal part arises by a series of roots from the cervical part of the spinal cord, independent of the roots of the spinal nerves, and enters the skull and joins the cranial part. Its fibres are distributed to certain muscles of the neck and shoulder girdle which are developed, at least in part, from lateral plate mesoderm related to the caudal end of the pharynx.

The VIIIth or **acoustic** nerve has been left to the last: there is some doubt if it should be included in the branchial arch series. It is a nerve of special sense, which in tetrapods supplies the inner ear. The latter consists of a vestibular part (the semicircular canals, utricle and saccule) concerned with the appreciation of position and movement of the head, and the *lagena* (Fig. 94) or, in mammals, the more complex *cochlea* (Fig. 93), sensitive to auditory vibrations. The nerve therefore consists of *vestibular* and *auditory* subdivisions. The inner ear, however, is probably a highly specialised member of the class of receptors known as *lateral-line* or *neuromast* organs, widely distributed in characteristic patterns on the head and body of aquatic vertebrates (pp. 136, 137, 395). These are sensitive to movement and possibly to vibration of low frequency in the surrounding water, and, since they are superficial in position

TABLE II.   Organisation of the head.

| SOMITE. | MUSCLE. | NERVE | | VISCERAL ARCH. |
		ventral root.	dorsal root.	
1st or premandibular	Superior, inferior, and anterior (internal) rectus, and inferior oblique of eye	IIIrd, Oculomotor	*Ramus ophthalmicus profundus* of V	Trabeculæ of chondrocranium
2nd or mandibular	Superior oblique of eye	IVth, Trochlear	Vth, Trigeminal (excluding the *Ramus ophthalmicus profundus*)	1st, Mandibular
3rd or hyoidean	Posterior (external) rectus of eye	VIth, Abducens	VIIth, Facial	2nd, Hyoid
4th (the somite disappears)	—	—	IXth, Glossopharyngeal	3rd (or the 1st Branchial)
5th and several subsequent somites	Hypobranchial and tongue muscles	XIIth, Hypoglossal	Xth, Vagus XIth, Spinal accessory	4th and subsequent visceral arches

It should be noted that the first three somites, all of which give rise to extrinsic muscles of the eye, are all pre-otic in position. The numbering of the post-otic somites is uncertain, since one and perhaps more than one disappear without giving rise to muscles; the number certainly varies in different vertebrates.

and exteroceptive in function, they are classed as somatic sensory. The nerves supplying these organs enter the central nervous system in close association with the VIIIth nerve as an *anterior* and *posterior lateral line nerve*. The posterior lateral line nerve gives branches to the IXth and Xth cranial nerves and is distributed to the lateral line organs in their territory. The branch to the vagus is particularly large, and soon leaves the trunk of the vagus as what is called its *lateral line branch*. This runs caudally throughout the body supplying the lateral line proper. The anterior lateral line nerve, like the posterior, does not run independently to the organs it supplies, but joins branches of the VIIth and Vth nerves, particularly the hyomandibular branch of the former and the *ramus ophthalmicus superficialis* of the latter.

The lateral line nerves and the VIIIth nerve are sometimes known as the *acoustico-lateral system*, of which only the VIIIth nerve persists in air-breathing vertebrates. The fact that the lateral line nerves join the branchial arch nerves and are distributed with them has led to the idea that a lateral line or special somatic sensory component may have been present in all segmental nerves at an early evolutionary stage. This probably applies only to cranial nerves and gives some justification for the classification of the acoustico-lateral with the branchial arch nerves. It must be pointed out, however, that the sensory ganglia of the acoustico-lateral system develop from ectodermal placodes, which differ in position from those associated with the ganglia of other sensory cranial nerves, and this might be used as a justification for classifying them separately.

That the somatic motor cranial nerves may correspond with the ventral roots of spinal nerves and the branchial arch nerves with the dorsal roots has already been indicated (p. 130). There is also evidence that these cranial nerves are segmentally arranged in relation to somites in the same way as spinal nerves, although, owing to specialisations which result from the presence of special sense organs, jaws, and branchial arches, this is not obvious in the adult body. The position is somewhat clearer in the embryos of the lower Craniata, and the accompanying table is based mainly on evidence from this source.

Sensory Organs.—These vary in form and disposition from group to group. Some are internal—*e.g. kinæsthetic* receptors which apprise the central nervous system of the degree of muscle tension and, in collaboration with sensory components of the inner ear (p. 145), enable the tetrapod to maintain the position it desires. Most sensory organs are distributed on the external surface of the animal and, directly connected with the central nervous system, bring to it information concerning the external environment.

The study of skin receptors has been mostly carried out on Man, and for the past fifty years a theory of punctate sensibility has been generally accepted. This held that four primary modalites—touch, warmth, cold, and pain—operated within the 'law' of specific nervous energies (see Weddell). This concept has been seriously questioned both on physiological and histological grounds. It is now known that various kinds of sensory discrimination are possible in localised regions in the absence of the various cutaneous end-organs postulated by the punctate hypothesis. This is strikingly apparent in the cornea, which is supplied only with free nerve-endings and which, it was formerly believed, was sensitive only to pain. It is now known that touch, warmth, and cold stimuli can be appreciated there as well.

In fishes and some amphibians, characteristic sense-organs known as the *neuromast-organs* or *organs of the lateral-line* occur. Extending along the sides of the trunk and tail is a longitudinal streak, due to the presence either of an open groove or of a tube sunk in the skin, and continued on to the head in the form of branching grooves or canals (Figs. 87, 88). These organs, and certain others in the form of pits or of unbranched canals, are lined with epithelium. Here occur groups of sensory cells—*neuromasts*—which are produced at their free ends into hair-like processes. Neuromasts are innervated by lateral line nerves (see pp. 136, 449), and, at their first appearance in the embryo, are distinct, segmentally arranged patches of sensory epithelium in intimate connection with the ganglia of cranial nerves. Cutaneous sense-organs of the lateral-line system, having at first a metameric arrangement, also occur in the aquatic Amphibia. The neuromast organs enable the animal

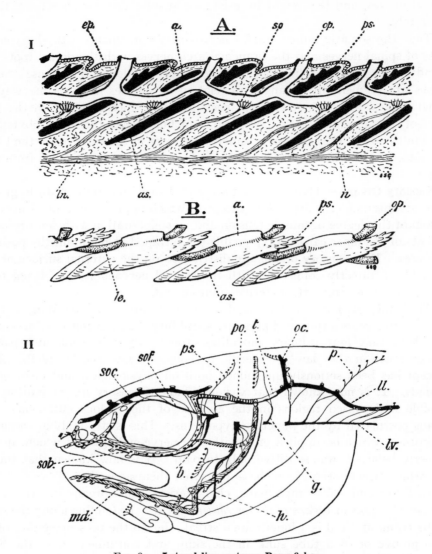

FIG. 87.—**Lateral-line system: Bony fishes.**

I. The relation of the lateral-line canal to the scales on the body of *Perca fluviatilis*. *A*, longitudinal section; *B*, scales and canal seen in side view. *a.* bridge of scale covering the canal; *as.* anterior region of scale; *ep.* epidermis; *lc.* lateral-line canal; *ln.* lateral-line nerve; *n.* nerve to sense organ; *op.* external opening of canal; *ps.* posterior edge of scale; *so.* sense organ in canal.

II. The head of *Amia calva* showing the system of lateral-line canals and their nerve supply (from Allis). *b.* buccal branch of facial nerve; *g.* dorsal branch of glossopharyngeal; *h.* hyomandibular branch of facial; *ll.* lateral-line of trunk; *lv.* lateral-line of vagus; *md.* mandibular canal; *oc.* occipital canal; *p.* pit organs on body; *po.* post-orbital canal; *ps.* pit organs on the head. *sob.* sub-orbital canal; *soc.* supra-orbital canal; *sof.* superior ophthalmic branch of facial. *t.* temporal canal.

to detect vibrations in the water of too low a frequency to form a sound capable of perception by the ear.

Substances suspended in surrounding water or dissolved by saliva are tested by special taste-buds which are composed of groups of narrow, rod-shaped cells. In fishes these are widely distributed in the mouth and branchial cavities, but also on the outer surface of the head, and in some species over almost the whole surface of the body. In higher Craniata they have become chiefly restricted to the moist epithelium of the tongue and soft palate, and are supplied mainly by branches of the glossopharyngeal.

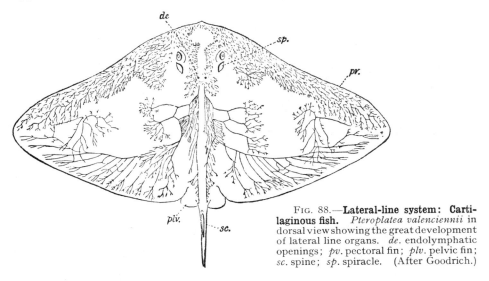

FIG. 88.—**Lateral-line system: Cartilaginous fish.** *Pteroplatea valenciennii* in dorsal view showing the great development of lateral line organs. *de.* endolymphatic openings; *pv.* pectoral fin; *plv.* pelvic fin; *sc.* spine; *sp.* spiracle. (After Goodrich.)

The **olfactory organ** is typically a sac-like invagination of the skin of the snout, anterior to the mouth (Fig. 89). It communicates with the exterior by an *external nostril*. It is paired in all Craniata, except cyclostomes, in which there is a single olfactory sac, supplied, however, by paired olfactory nerves (p. 130). The sac is lined by the olfactory mucous membrane or *Schneiderian membrane*, the epithelium of which contains peculiar, elongated sensory cells. The free ends of these cells are often produced into hair-like processes and the olfactory nerve-fibres consist of processes which run from the base of the cell to the olfactory bulb. In the Dipnoi (p. 361) and all higher groups, the posterior end of each sac communicates with the cavity of the mouth by an aperture called the *posterior nostril*, and an analogous communication occurs in the case of the unpaired organ of the hag-fishes (p. 197).

In many air-breathing vertebrates there is formed an offshoot from the olfactory organ, which, becoming separated, forms a distinct sac lined with olfactory epithelium and which may or may not open into the mouth. This is the *vomeronasal* or *Jacobson's Organ*, by which some animals are able to smell

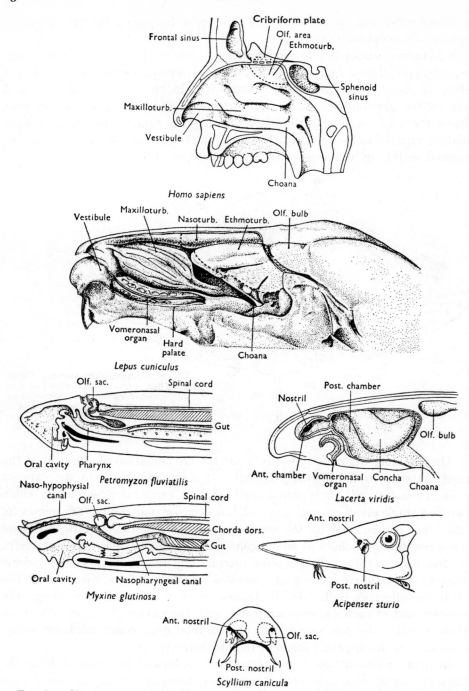

FIG. 89.—**Olfactory apparatus: Nasal cavity and its relationship to the buccal cavity in vertebrate types.** In *Lacerta* (a lizard), *Oryctolagus* (rabbit), and *Homo* (Man) the nasal septum has been removed to display the nasal chambers. The underside of the snout in *Scyllium* (a dogfish) is drawn with the nasal skin fold on the right bent back to show the relationship of the nostrils to the mouth. (From Allison, partly after Matthes.)

substances held in the mouth. The apparatus is supplied by a separate branch of the olfactory nerve. The organ occurs only in tetrapods, being first seen in the Amphibia (p. 381). It reaches a high degree of efficiency in snakes and at least some lizards (p. 543), but is probably of minor significance in chelonians and the Crocodilia. In all birds and in most mammals it occurs during development. In the mammalian embryo it is evident as a distinct groove on the lower medial aspect of each nasal cavity; the duct, however, appears to be cut off from the nasal apparatus in 'higher' groups. In monotremes the organ remains readily identifiable in the adult and is equipped with a turbinal process projecting into its lumen.

The paired **eye** (Fig. 90), of varying but more or less globular shape, lies in the orbit. It consists essentially of the light-sensitive *retina*, connected by the optic tract to the brain, enclosed within a capsule and equipped with apparatus for collecting light and focusing it upon the retina.

The external part of the capsule, the *sclerotic*, consists of dense fibrous tissue which may contain cartilage and in some cases plates of bone. Where it is exposed to the light the

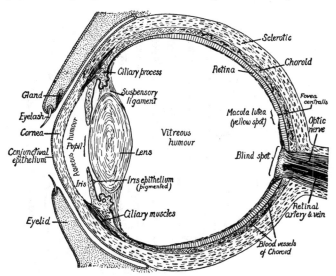

FIG. 90.—**Eye: Macroscopic structures in mammal.** (After Dakin.)

dense fibrous tissue is replaced by a peculiar variety of connective tissue which is transparent; this part of the capsule is called the *cornea*, and is covered on both its outer and inner surfaces with epithelium. The whole external coat has the character of a spherical case, mostly opaque (the sclerotic), but with a circular transparent window (the cornea). The curvature of the cornea is not the same as the sclerotic; almost flat in fishes, it bulges outwards in terrestrial vertebrates.

Lining the sclerotic is the second coat, the *choroid*, consisting of highly vascular connective tissue, pigment cells, and in certain situations smooth muscle fibres. The choroid is in intimate contact with the sclerotic, but at the corneal margin it is continued as the anterior surface of a membrane, the *iris*, which is separated by a space (the *anterior chamber of the eye*) from the cornea. In this region its degree of pigmentation gives the characteristic colour to the eye, and it is perforated by a circular or slit-like aperture, the *pupil*. In most vertebrates the size of the pupil can be varied by two sets of smooth muscle-fibres in the iris : radiating fibres which dilate, and circular fibres which constrict the pupil. Just behind the iris, and close to its peripheral margin, the choroid is thrown into radiating folds which project into the eyeball and contain smooth muscle-fibres, of importance in the mechanism of accommodation. These folds are the *ciliary processes*.

The *retina* (Fig. 91) lines the surface of the choroid and extends forwards over the ciliary processes to form the posterior surface of the iris; it ends at the

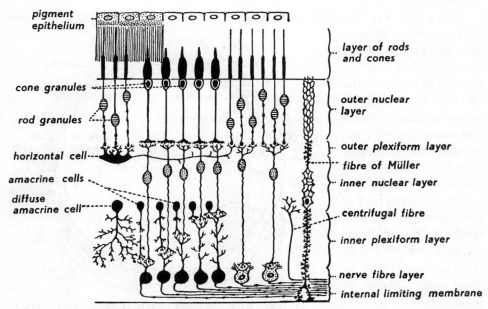

FIG. 91.—**Vision: Retinal structure.** In general, the retina of diurnal animals is rich in cones. That of nocturnal animals possesses a predominance of rods making for high sensitivity to light with a sacrifice of acuity and colour vision. Some animals (*e.g.* certain bats) apparently possess no cones; others (*e.g.* many reptiles, some mammals) no rods. (Redrawn from Gray, after Cajal.)

pupillary margin. Only the posterior part of the retina (the *pars optica*) is light-sensitive; this extends almost to the ciliary processes and ends along an irregular line, the *ora serrata*. The part of the retina which extends over the ciliary processes (*pars ciliaris*) and on to the inner surface of the iris (*pars iridica*) is not light sensitive and is comparatively simple in structure.

Throughout the retina consists essentially of two layers. The outer of these is a single layer of *cuboidal* or low columnar heavily pigmented cells, the *pigment layer*. The inner layer is also a simple cuboidal epithelium in the pars iridica (where it is pigmented) and in the pars ciliaris of the retina. In the pars optica, behind the ora serrata it becomes highly complex, containing the light-sensitive elements and nerve-cells and fibres which form the beginning of the pathway by which optic stimuli are conveyed to the brain. The light-sensitive elements are highly specialised cells which from their shape are classified as *rods* or *cones*. They are placed perpendicular to the surface in intimate contact with the outer pigment layer already referred to; their inner ends connect with small bipolar nerve-cells which in turn connect with larger nerve-cells (the *ganglion cells*) still nearer the inner surface of the retina. From the ganglion cells arise fibres which are at first situated on the inner surface of the retina; they all converge on a small circular area, usually to the nasal side of the posterior pole of the eyeball, called the *optic disc*, and here they pierce the coats of the eyeball to become the optic nerve. It will be noted that in order to reach the light-sensitive elements adjacent to the outer pigmented layer, light-rays must pass through the layers of nerve-fibres, ganglion cells, and bipolar cells. A retina of this type is called 'inverted' and is characteristic of vertebrates. In some invertebrates (*e.g.* cephalopods) eyes superficially similar to the vertebrate eye may be found, but the light-sensitive elements form the innermost layer of the retina, which is therefore of fundamentally different construction.

The biconvex lens lies immediately behind the iris. It is formed from layers of fibres, each derived from a single cell, and is enclosed in a capsule. It is attached round its periphery by a suspensory ligament to the ciliary processes. In mammals this ligament is under tension, which can be relaxed when the ciliary muscle contracts and draws the ciliary processes closer to the lens. This allows the lens to assume a more nearly spherical shape, thus shortening its focal lengths and producing accommodation for near vision. Different mechanisms which serve the same function have been developed in other vertebrate classes.

The space between the cornea and the iris is called the *anterior chamber* of the eye; it communicates through the pupillary opening with a narrow space between the front of the lens and the iris, the *posterior chamber*. Both chambers are filled with a watery fluid, the *aqueous humour*. The greater part of the cavity of the eye, bounded in front by the lens and the ciliary processes and for the rest of its extent by the pars optica of the retina, is filled with a transparent jelly-like substance, the *vitreous body*. The cornea, aqueous humour, lens, and vitreous body together constitute the dioptric apparatus, which focuses an image of external objects on the retina. The iris is a diaphragm by which the amount of light which enters can be regulated.

Among many nocturnal forms (*e.g.* domestic cat), and some animals living in muddy waters, the receptivity of the eye is enhanced by a reflecting plate, the *tapetum lucidum*. Generally this lies in the choroid. It varies considerably, and has arisen independently in different groups. It may be formed of silvery connective tissue, or a layer of guanin granules or other material.

The tapetum often reflects a characteristic colour, *e.g.* the 'fiery' eye of the Crocodilia.

The mode of **development** of the eye is as characteristic as its structure. At an early stage of development a hollow outgrowth—the *optic vesicle*—is given off from each side of the fore-brain. It grows out and touches the ectoderm at the side of the head. This ectoderm becomes thickened and invaginates. Eventually it forms a closed sac and separates from the rest of the ectoderm. The sac is the rudiment of the lens; it has thick walls and a small cavity. Meanwhile the optic vesicle has also invaginated and become converted into a two-layer *optic cup*. Its cavity, originally continuous with the neurocœle, becomes obliterated. The invagination of the vesicle to form the cup does not take place symmetrically. It occurs obliquely from the external (posterior) and ventral aspect of the vesicle, so that the optic cup is incomplete along one side where there is a cleft—the *choroid fissure*. This is afterwards closed by the union of its edges. The outer layer of the optic cup becomes the pigmentary layer of the retina. From its inner layer the rest of that tissue, including the rods and cones, is formed. The stalk of the optic cup occupies, in the embryonic eye, the place of the optic nerve, but the actual fibres of the nerve are formed as backward growths from the nerve-cells of the retina to the brain.

Mesoderm grows in between the developing lens and the external ectoderm. From this the main substance of the cornea and its inner or posterior epithelium are formed. The adjacent ectoderm becomes the external epithelium or conjunctiva. Mesoderm also enters the optic cup through the choroid fissure and becomes the vitreous body. Lastly, the mesoderm immediately surrounding the optic cup is differentiated to form the choroid, the iris, and the sclerotic. Thus the paired eye is derived from both mesoderm and ectoderm. The *substantia propria* of the cornea, the sclerotic, choroid and vitreous body are mesodermal. The superficial epithelium of the cornea, and the lens, are derived from the surface ectoderm directly; the retina and optic nerve are derived from the central nervous system and are therefore indirectly ectodermal in origin.

The eyeball is moved by six muscles (Fig. 92). Four of these arise from the inner wall of the orbit, and pass, diverging as they go, to their insertion round the equator of the eye. One of them is dorsal in position, and is called the *superior rectus* (*sup. rect.*), a second ventral, the *inferior rectus*, a third anterior, the *anterior* or *internal rectus*, and a fourth posterior, the *posterior* or *external rectus* (*post. rect.*). The usual names (internal and external) of the two last-named muscles originate from their position in Man, in which, because the eye looks forwards instead of outwards, its anterior surface becomes internal, its posterior surface external. The two remaining muscles usually arise from the anterior region of the orbit, and are inserted respectively into the dorsal and ventral surface of the eyeball. They are the *superior* and *inferior oblique* muscles. The eye muscles are remarkably similar throughout the vertebrates: few structures have remained more ' conservative ' (Gilbert).

The Apparatus of Audition and Equilibration. The receptor organ concerned with these functions is the *membranous labyrinth*, situated on either

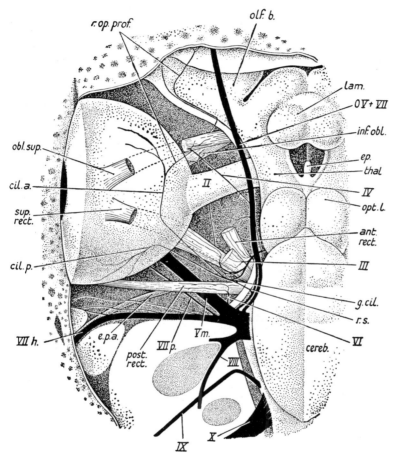

FIG. 92.—**Orbit: Neural and muscular relationships in a cartilaginous fish.** (Dogfish.) *ant. rect.* anterior rectus; *cereb.* cerebellum; *cil. a., cil. p.* anterior and posterior ciliary nerves; *e.p.a.* efferent pseudobranchial artery; *ep.* epiphysis; *g. cil.* ciliary ganglion; *inf. obl.* inferior oblique; *lam.* lamina terminalis of cerebrum; *O.V.* and *VII,* superficial ophthalmic branch of trigeminal and facial; *obl. sup.* superior oblique; *olf. b.* olfactory bulb; *opt. l.* optic lobe; *post. rect.* posterior rectus; *r. op. prof.* ramus ophthalmicus profundus of trigeminal; *r. s.* sensory root of ciliary ganglion; *sup. rect.* superior rectus; *thal.* thalamus; *II* to *X,* cranial nerves. (After Young.)

side of the hind-brain in all vertebrates; it is often called the *inner ear*, especially in tetrapods, in which a *middle* and *external ear* may also be present (Fig. 93). The latter is concerned with the collection of sound vibrations, and the former with their transmission to the inner ear, where they are translated into nervous impulses carried by the VIIIth cranial nerve to the brain. It is, of course, the

membranous labyrinth, or inner ear, which is the essential receptor organ, and
it serves a double function : it is sensitive to vibrations which can be appreciated as sound, and it is sensitive also to movements of the head and to the

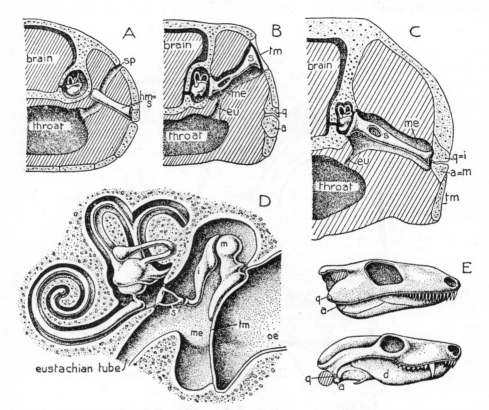

Fig. 93.—**Audio-equilibration: Series of evolutionary stages in vertebrate types.** *A.* Cross-
section of half of a fish skull in the ear region. The ear structures consist only of the deep-lying
sacs and semicircular canals. *B.* An amphibian. The hyomandibular bone (*hm*) of the fish is
pressed into service as a sound transmitter, the stapes (*s*); the first gill slit, the spiracle (*sp*),
becomes the Eustachian tube (*eu*) and the middle-ear cavity (*me*), while the outer end of the
spiracle is closed by the tympanic membrane (*tm*). *C.* A mammal-like reptile. The stapes
passes close to two skull bones (*q*, quadrate; *a*, articular) which form the jaw joint. *D.* Man (the
ear region only, on a larger scale). The two jaw-joint bones have been pressed into service as
accessory ossicles, the malleus (*m*) and the incus (*i*). *E.* A primitive land animal and a mammal-
like reptile to show the relation of the eardrum to the jaw joint. At first in a notch high on the
side of the skull (the otic notch) occupying the place of the fish spiracle, it shifts in mammal-like
reptiles to the jaw region. In mammals the jaw comes to be formed of one bone only (*d*, the
dentary), and the bones of the jaw-joint region are freed to act as accessory hearing organs; *oe*,
tube of outer ear. (After Romer.)

position of the head in relation to the gravitational pull. These functions are
located in different parts of the labyrinth and are served by the auditory and
vestibular divisions of the VIIIth nerve respectively. These divisions are
always present, although the nerve is often referred to simply as the *auditory
nerve.*

Embryologically the inner ear is formed from a localised thickening of ectoderm, the *otic placode*, on either side of the hind-brain. This placode becomes depressed to form a flask-shaped *otic vesicle*, which in most vertebrates loses its connection with the surface ectoderm. The otic placode lies in series with similar placodes from which lateral line organs (p. 135) are developed; the inner ear which develops from it is therefore thought to represent a highly specialised lateral line organ and to belong to the *acoustico-lateral system*.

At first simple, the otic vesicle soon becomes divided by a constriction into a dorsal *utriclus* and a ventral *sacculus* which remain in communication throughout life and are imperfectly differentiated from each other in primitive vertebrates. From the utricle three *semicircular canals* are formed. These lie in planes at right angles to one another: one anterior, one posterior (both vertical), and one external and horizontal. The canals remain in communication with the utricle, but as the anterior and posterior canals have their adjacent limbs united, there are in all only five openings. Each canal is dilated at one end to form an *ampulla*, which is situated anteriorly in the anterior and external canals and posteriorly in the posterior canal (Fig. 94).

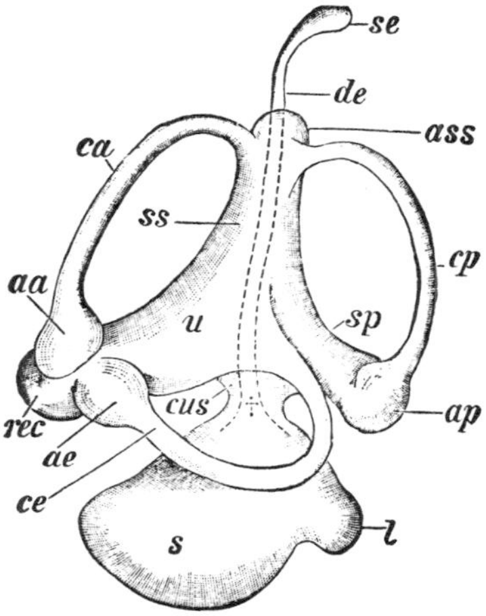

FIG. 94.—**Audio-equilibrium.** *aa.* ampulla of anterior canal, *ae.* of horizontal canal, *ap.* of posterior canal; *ass.* apex of superior utricular sinus; *ca.* anterior, *ce.* horizontal, *cp.* posterior semi-circular canal; *cus.* canal uniting sacculus with utriculus; *de.* endolymphatic duct; *l.* lagena; *rec.* utricular recess; *s.* sacculus; *se.* endolymphatic sac; *sp.* posterior utricular sinus; *ss.* superior utricular sinus; *u.* utriculus. (After Wiedersheim.)

The ventral compartment, or *sacculus*, gives off a blind pouch, the *lagena*, which in mammals becomes elongated and coiled to form the *cochlear duct*. The saccule and lagena (or cochlear duct) are concerned with auditory function; the utricle and semicircular canals with sense of position and movement. The membranous labyrinth is filled with fluid, the *endolymph*, and becomes surrounded by the cartilage or bone of the auditory capsule, a part of the chondrocranium (p. 97).

The cartilage, or bone, adapts itself to the form of the membranous labyrinth, and the complex cavity so formed is called the *bony labyrinth*. It presents a large excavation (the *vestibule*) for the utricle and saccule, and tunnel-like passages for the semicircular canals and lagena. It is from the spirally coiled form of the latter that the term *cochlea* ('snail') is derived. The membranous labyrinth fits loosely in the bony labyrinth, so that it is separated from its capsule in most regions by a narrow *perilymphatic space*. This communicates with the *subarachnoid space* around the brain by means of the *aqueductus cochlearis* and is filled with perilymph which is very like cerebrospinal fluid (p. 125).

The actual sensory receptors are patches of neuro-epithelial cells which are found in particular situations in the wall of the membranous labyrinth. The cells are flask-shaped, with long hair-like processes which project into the endolymph in the cavity of the labyrinth ; the terminal filaments of the VIIIth nerve ramify round their bases. The neuro-epithelial cells are surrounded by supporting cells, and are found in the *cristæ* in the ampullæ of the semicircular canals, in the *maculæ* of the utricle and the saccule, and in the lagena or cochlear duct. In the latter they form the receptive element of the *organ of Corti* in mammals. Each group of epithelial cells has its hair-like processes in contact with, or embedded in, a gelatinous mass, which, particularly in the macula of the utricle, contains crystals of calcium salts and forms an *otolith* or *otolithic membrane*. Otoliths are very conspicuous in fishes where they are of varying size and number. Owing to their weight, changes in position alter the stresses transmitted from the otoliths to the hair-cells, and it is probable that this constitutes the stimulus which is appreciated as 'position sense'. Similar effects can be produced by movements of the head, owing to the inertia of the otoliths, or by vibration in the endolymph, the latter constituting a stimulus which can be appreciated as sound.

The membranous labyrinth is the only auditory apparatus possessed by fishes (except for such accessory apparatus as the *Weberian ossicles* found in many teleosts ; p. 342). The change from water to land, when the first tetrapods arose, necessitated important additions to deal with vibrations conveyed through air instead of the denser medium of water. The most obvious of these is the ear-drum or *tympanum*, a membrane on or near the surface of the body, and separated from the otic capsule and labyrinth by a cavity developed as a diverticulum of the pharynx—probably the spiracular pouch. This cavity is the *middle-ear*.

Vibrations are transmitted across the middle ear from the ear-drum to the labyrinth, or inner ear, by a bony rod, the *columella*, in amphibians, reptiles, and birds. The columella represents the upper element of the hyoid arch (the hyomandibula), which is no longer required for jaw-suspension owing to the acquisition of the condition of autostyly (p. 94). The outer ends of the hyomandibula (columella) becomes embedded in the tympanum and the inner end fits into an opening in the otic capsule, the *fenestra ovalis*. In mammals the columella is found as a small stirrup-shaped bone, the *stapes*, which still fits into the fenestra ovalis ; two other bones, however, the *incus* and the *malleus*, have been added to connect it to the tympanum, so that vibrations are transmitted by a chain of three ossicles instead of by a single bone. Both the incus and the malleus are derived from the jaw skeleton, the incus being the *quadrate* and the malleus the hinder end of Meckel's cartilage, the *articular*. These bones have been freed from their original function of providing a joint for the lower jaw by the development of a new articulation between the dentary and the squamosal bones (p. 97). It is probable that the ossicular chain is a more efficient mechanism than the single columella for the transmission of vibrations to the inner ear, possibly by increasing their force and diminishing their amplitude, but the details of its mode of action are not entirely clear. In mammals the ear-drum has sunk below the surface, with which it remains connected by a tubular *external auditory meatus*. A *pinna* is also developed and serves to reflect sound vibrations into the meatus. The pinna and meatus together constitute the *external ear* (Fig. 93, p. 144).

The evidence, both palæontological and embryological, for the morphological changes which have occurred in the bony structures associated with the ear, is remarkably complete. The evolution of the ear-drum and middle ear is less well understood.

Endocrine Organs.—As recently as the end of the last century the animal body was considered essentially as a group of complicated, little-understood organs, the functions of which, however, were probably explicable in terms of the co-ordinating and integrating nervous system (p. 116). Despite the earlier work of Bordeau, Claude Bernard, Berthold, Brown-Sequard, and many others, it was not until 1902 that the work of Bayliss and Starling promoted a general acceptance of the idea of *chemical reflexes*. Largely due to the work of Pavlov, it was at the turn of the century generally considered that pancreatic secretion, for example, was entirely under neural control. Bayliss and Starling now showed that even after denervation of the mammalian pancreas, the organ still secreted when acid entered the small intestine from the stomach. Injection of hydrochloric acid into the general circulation did not stimulate pancreatic outflow, so Bayliss and Starling ground up intestinal mucosa, injected a weak acid filtrate into the general circulation, and observed a flow of pancreatic juice. They called the activating mucosal substance *secretin* and described it as a *hormone*.

In 1925 Mellanby showed that purified secretin mainly stimulated the outflow of water and bicarbonate from the pancreas, whereas stimulation of the vagus produced a juice rich in enzymes. Later, in 1942, there was discovered a second hormone, *pancreozymin*. This stimulates enzyme secretion, so that duodenal hormones can cause the production of normal pancreatic juice in the absence of vagal activity. Normally the *nervous action* of the vagus (p. 133) initiates secretion, often anticipating the arrival of food in the duodenum: the slower activating *endocrine action* becomes dominant later.

After the discovery of secretin, several organs, whose functions had been only vaguely surmised, were shown to be partly or wholly endocrine in function (see below). Leaving *neurohumors* and other hormone-like substances out of consideration, hormones are in general produced by highly vascular aggregations of specialised epithelial cells which, lacking ducts, pour their secretions as trace substances into the bloodstream, by which they are carried throughout

the body.   Their precise mode of action is unknown.   Hormones act on
particular tissues (*target organs*) and cause specific effects.   The target organ
may be another endocrine gland which itself may be in turn caused to secrete,
and thus reflexly influence other target organs.   Sometimes the increased
activity of the secondarily stimulated endocrine gland will result in a hormonal
'feed-back' that inhibits the action of the initial mover in the series.   Thus, for
example, the anterior pituitary gland produces *gonadotrophic hormones* which
activate the gonads, and these in turn produce sex hormones which, along with
other special effects (*e.g.* the changes occurring at puberty), to some degree
control also the subsequent activity of the anterior pituitary.   Such a reciprocal
relationship occurs also between anterior pituitary and the thyroid gland in
some vertebrates.   Again, the hormones of two entirely different glands sometimes operate in a balanced synergism (*e.g.* *œstrogen* from the ovary and *progesterone* from the corpus luteum together prepare the mammalian uterus for the
implantation of the fertilised egg even while it is still descending the oviduct).

Endocrine glands occur in the protochordates (p. 27) and are already
established in the general vertebrate pattern in the Agnatha (p. 176).   Generally, if not always, individual glands have arisen by the functional and structural
metamorphosis of tissues that previously subserved other ends.   For a pictorial
example of this see Fig. 97, p. 152.   Thus, too, the thyroid (for example) has
developed (in phylogeny) from the endostyle (p. 52) of ancestral chordates.
The thyroid is of special interest in that it can be demonstrated that its homologue in the Lamprey arises in much the same way during ontogeny, *i.e.* in the
developmental histology of the individual (p. 197).   Likewise, each *season* the
male bird develops a fresh complement of secretory interstitial cells from unspecialised connective tissue.   Certain fishes and amphibians likewise seasonally develop *lobule-boundary cells*, of secretory function, from fibroblasts (Fig.
97).

Work on the comparative biochemistry and evolution of hormones is still
in its infancy.   Individual hormones which differ comparatively little in their
chemical structure are capable of the most strikingly diverse effects.   Again,
hormones that are (in the present state of knowledge) indistinguishable may
cause quite different effects in various classes of animals: for example, the
differential influence of adenohypophysial *prolactin* in birds and mammals
(see below).   The evolution of the endocrine system has involved the differentiation of chemical substances and special means of producing them on one
hand, and of specific tissue responses on the other.   However, it must not be
thought that the hormone is simply a 'key' to 'unlock' a response.   Most tissue
reactions (*e.g.* lactation) require a plurality of hormonal influences.   Further,
alien substances will sometimes bring about endocrine effects (*e.g.* the advent
of comb-growth and spermatogenesis after the administration of sulphonamide
to diseased chickens).

There is some evidence that hormones have been evolved from metabolites. Pituitary, parathyroid, and pancreatic hormones are proteins; *thyroxin* (from the thyroid) and *adrenalin* (from the adrenal medulla) are derivatives of the amino-acid tyrosine. The gonads, corpus luteum, and the adrenal cortex (or interrenal tissue) produce *steroid* hormones.

Individual endocrine glands are briefly dealt with later under the various

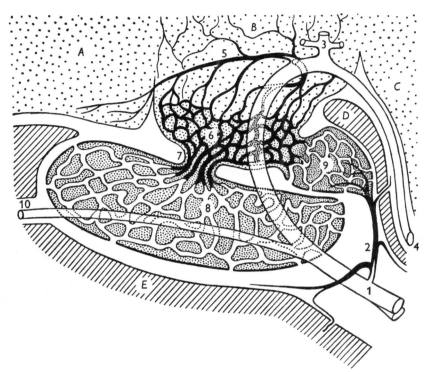

FIG. 95.—**Neuro-endocrine system: Hypothalamico-hypophysial relationships in a bird** (Pigeon, *Columba*). *A.* optic chiasma; *B.* diencephalon; *C.* medulla oblongata; *D.* dorsum sellæ; *E.* osseus floor of sella. *1.* internal carotid artery; *2.* inferior hypophysial artery; *3.* anterior ramus and *4.* posterior ramus of internal carotid; *5.* infundibular artery; *6.* primary capillary plexus on the eminentia; *7.* portal vessels; *8.* secondary plexus in pars distalis; *9.* capillary bed in pars neuralis; *10.* internal ophthalmic artery. (The capillary nets are simplified, and the peri-hypophysial veins omitted.) (From Marshall, modified after Wingstrand.)

classes. Their functions are best known in homæothermic animals with which the following summary is mostly concerned:

Pituitary gland (hypophysis). The pituitary is connected with the hypothalamus by the infundibulum (Figs. 95, 96) and lies in the *sella turcica*, an excavation of the basisphenoid. 'No other single structure in the body is so doubly protected, so centrally placed, so well hidden' (Cushing). The *hypophysial portal system* connects the pars distalis (see Table III, p. 151) with the hypothalamus. The flow is in the direction of the gland to which is carried a neurohumor that influences the anterior lobe of the pituitary. The production by the hypophysis of hormones which influence other organs stimulated the epigram of Long that it is the 'conductor of the glandular orchestra'. It must be remembered, however, that certain target organs within the 'orchestra' have the capacity to modulate the activity of the 'conductor' and, further, that after hypophysectomy at least some of them (thyroid, adrenal cortex) continue to function at reduced level.

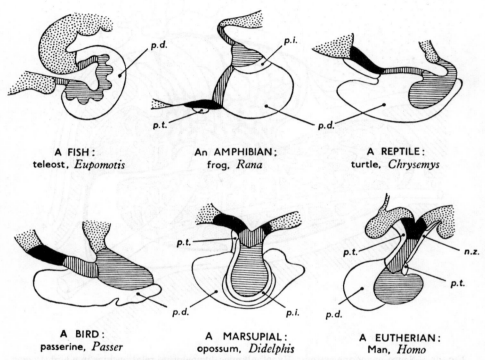

A FISH:
teleost, *Eupomotis*

An AMPHIBIAN;
frog, *Rana*

A REPTILE:
turtle, *Chrysemys*

A BIRD:
passerine, *Passer*

A MARSUPIAL:
opossum, *Didelphis*

A EUTHERIAN:
Man, *Homo*

FIG. 96.—**Hypophysial arrangements: Vertebrate types.** There is considerable variation within each animal class. *p.d.* pars distalis; *p.i.* pars intermedia; *p.t.* pars tuberalis; *n.z.* neural zone. (Modified after Green.)

The pituitary differs in the arrangement of its constituent parts from group to group as shown in Fig. 93. The *pars distalis* secretes *gonadotrophins* of which the *follicle stimulating hormone* (F. S. H.) activates ovarian follicles or, as the *tubule-ripening hormone* (T. R. H.), stimulates spermatogenesis in the testis tubules. *Luteinising hormone* (L. H.) is also gonadotrophic in function, causing the luteal reaction in the ovary that results in the formation of its corpus luteum (or corpora lutea). As the *interstitial cell stimulating hormone* (I. C. S. H.) it activates the interstitial Leydig cells in the male.

The *adrenocorticotrophic* hormone (A. C. T. H.) influences the cortical tissue of the adrenal gland (or its homologue) and the *thyrotrophic hormone* (T. S. H.)

TABLE III. Division of the hypophysis. (After Green, modified from Rioch, Wislocki, and O'Leary.)

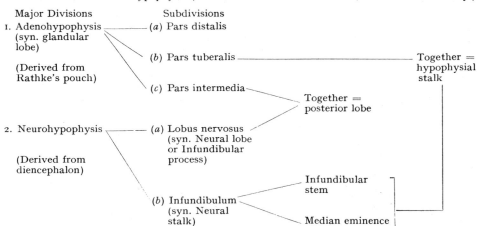

stimulates the thyroid gland. The *lactogenic hormone* influences the mammary gland (after its initial stimulation by œstrogen) and, as *prolactin*, leads to broodiness, certain forms of maternal behaviour, the production of crop-milk in pigeons (p. 583) and brood-patches in many widely diverse species (p. 560).

The *somatotrophic* or *growth hormone* (S. T. H.) influences growth in some classes. Disfunction may lead to giantism or dwarfism. This hormone has not been proved to exist in birds. Hypophysectomy in birds, however, does cause dwarfism, but growth can be restored by prolactin administration.

The 'posterior lobe' (Fig. 96) is in direct neural communication with the brain. From it have been extracted *vasopressin* (A. D. H.) of essentially anti-diuretic, but with some vaso-constrictor function, and *oxytocin*, which aids milk ejection, and uterine contraction at term. The work of E. and B. Scharrer, Bargmann, and others suggests that posterior lobe hormones are secreted in the hypothalamus. They may be stored, and perhaps modified, in the posterior pituitary before final discharge.

The *pars intermedia* is absent in birds and mammals but is prominent in lower vertebrates. *Intermedin* causes melanophore-expansion (p. 450). However, a substance with the properties of intermedin (when administered to frogs and reptiles) has been extracted from the pars distalis of birds.

Thyroid gland. Formed as a pharyngeal diverticulum, this gland is encapsulated by fibrous connective tissue and contains vesicles that are lined with specialised epithelium which holds thyroid colloid. The epithelial cells withdraw iodine from the bloodstream. After combination with the amino-acid tyrosine, and further modifications, there is formed the hormone *thyroxin* which has a stimulating effect on body metabolism in general and specific effects in various classes of animals (see *e.g.* pp. 421, 456).

Parathyroid glands. These minute bodies are developed from the third and fourth gill-pouches and produce *parathormone* which controls the distribution of blood calcium and phosphates.   For *ultimobranchial glands*, see p. 347.

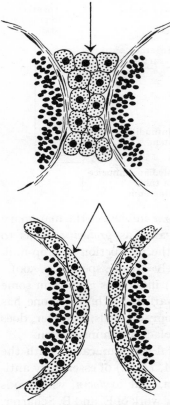

FIG. 97.—**Secretory arrangements: Vertebrate testis.** The interstitial Leydig cells (of connective tissue origin) (above) form the typical vertebrate pattern (Agnatha to Mammalia) except (below) in certain fishes and non-anuran amphibians where there has been a shift in hormone production to specialised connective tissue cells (*boundary cells*) in the walls of the seminiferous tubules. (After Marshall and Lofts.)

Adrenal gland.   These are paired compound glands of two physiologically and anatomically distinct parts—the *medullary* tissue and the *cortex*. The latter interdigitates with the former in Amphibia, Reptilia, Aves, and monotremes and is homologous with the inter-renal glands of sub-amphibian forms.   The *medulla* arises from neural crest ectoderm (as do also the sympathetic nerve trunks) and, under sympathetic control, secretes *adrenalin*, which prepares the animal for fight or flight.   Thus adrenalin, among numerous other effects, increases cardiac rate and vasoconstriction, elevates blood sugar level, and relaxes the bronchii to increase lung ventilation.   In general, parasympathetic stimulation causes antagonistic effects.   Chromaffin tissue is found in various viscera in fishes (see p. 380).

The 'cortical' tissue produces steroid hormones of three principal kinds: (1) *mineralocorticoids* concerned with the retention of sodium and the release of potassium in the kidney, (2) *glucocorticoids* important in the regulation of blood-sugar levels and glycogen deposition, and (3) *gonadoids*, perhaps of relatively little importance under normal conditions.

Gonads. *Interstitial cells* occur in the testes (Fig. 97) and produce the steroid *testosterone* (male sex hormone) which has profound effects on sexual characters and behaviour. The testes produce also œstrogens.   In the ovary *œstrogenic cells* of various kinds produce female sex hormones (œstrogens).   These influence sexual characters and behaviour.   Androgens, too, are formed in the ovary and are, incidentally, responsible for comb-growth in the hens of domestic fowl.

Corpus luteum.   This is a temporary endocrine organ formed by the multiplication of luteal cells in the empty follicle after ovulation.   These produce *progesterone* which is important in the maintenance of pregnancy.

Pancreas.   Apart from its exocrine function (p. 104) this gland is studded internally with endocrine *islets of Langerhans*, which produce the hormone *insulin*, which partly controls blood-sugar level. A high blood-sugar level stimulates the secretion of insulin which lowers blood-sugar by promoting its

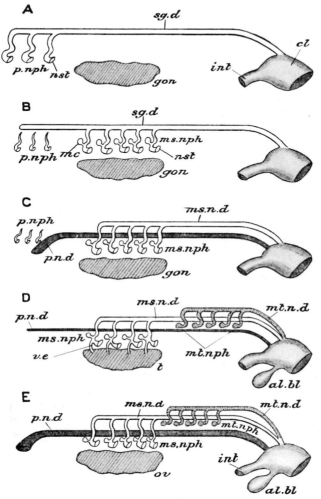

FIG. 98.—**Urinogenital system: Development and relationships.** *A*, development of pronephros and pronephric duct; *B*, atrophy of pronephros, development of mesonephros; *C*, differentiation of pro- and mesonephric ducts; *D*, development of metanephros; male type; *E*, female type. *al. bl.* allantoic bladder; *cl.* cloaca; *gon.* gonad; *int.* intestine; *m. c.* Bowman's capsule; *ms. n. d.* meso-nephric duct; *ms. nph.* mesonephros; *mt. n. d.* metanephric duct; *mt. nph.* metanephros; *nst.* nephrostome; *ov.* ovary; *p. n. d.* and *sg. d.* pronephric duct; *p. nph.* pronephros; *t.* testis; *v. e.* vasa efferentia.

storage (as glycogen in liver and muscles), increasing peripheral utilisation, and preventing its over-production from ingested fats and protein (see also p. 146).

For **placental hormones** see p. 905 and for pineal function in lower vertebrates, pp. 189, 345, 347. The lymphoid *thymus* has been often claimed, without convincing evidence, to possess endocrine functions. The same is true of *brown fat*, which some have believed to be an endocrine 'hibernation gland'. Brown fat occurs as a lobular, and superficially gland-like tissue. It is 'histogenetically and physiologically different from ordinary yellow or white adipose tissue (Fawcett), but has since been found also in widely unrelated, non-hibernating mammals (e.g. *Rattus* and the rhesus monkey, *Macaca*).

Urinogenital Organs.—In all Craniata there is so close a connection between the organs of renal excretion and those of reproduction that the two systems are conveniently considered together as the urinogenital organs.

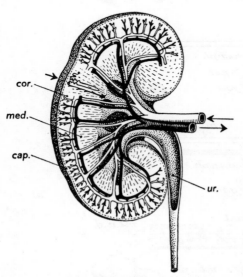

Speaking generally, the excretory organ consists basically of three parts, all paired and situated along the dorsal wall of the cœlom: the *pronephros* ('fore-kidney') (Fig. 98, *A*, *p. nph.*), the *mesonephros* ('mid-kidney') (*ms. nph.*), and the *metanephros* ('hind-kidney') (*mt. nph.*). Each of these is provided with a duct, the *pro-* (*p. n. d.*), *meso-* (*ms. n. d.*), or *meta-nephric* (*mt. n. d.*) *duct*, which opens into the cloaca. The gonads (*gon.*) lie in the cœlom suspended from its dorsal wall by a fold of peritoneum. In some cases their products are discharged into the cœlom and make their exit by genital pores, but more usually the pronephric duct in the female assumes the functions of an oviduct and the mesonephric duct in the male those of a spermiduct. The pronephros is almost always functionless in the adult, and usually

FIG. 99.—**Excretory system: Circulation and disposal in mammalian kidney.** The kidney is the *viscus elegantissimum* of the early anatomists. The arrow near the capsule (*cap*) shows the relationship of the nephron (Fig. 100) with cortex (*cor*) and medulla (*med*). Myriad collecting tubules open into the pelvis from which the urine is conveyed by the ureter (*ur*) to the storage bladder. (Modified after Homer Smith.)

disappears altogether. The mesonephros is generally the functional kidney in the lower (anamniote) (pp. 153, 253) Craniata, in which no metanephros is developed, and the mesonephric duct, in addition to carrying the seminal fluid of the male, acts as a urinary duct.

In the higher forms (amniotes) (p. 457) the early developed mesonephros largely atrophies. In these, the metanephros is the adult functional kidney, and the metanephric duct becomes the true ureter (Fig. 99).

The *kidney* (meso- or meta-nephros) of the adult is a massive highly vascular structure containing vast numbers of convoluted *urinary tubules* (Fig. 100), separated from one another by connective-tissue. The tubules are lined by a single layer of glandular epithelial cells and each ends blindly in Bowman's capsule, a globular dilatation. In many of the lower Craniata, a branch goes off from the tubule, near the Malpighian body, and, passing to the ventral surface of the kidney, ends in a ciliated funnel-like body (Fig. 98 *A*, *nst.*), resembling the nephridiostome of a worm, and, like it, opening into the cœlom. At their opposite ends the tubules join with one another, and finally discharge into the urinary duct.

The renal arteries branch extensively in the kidney, so that each of the countless Malpighian corpuscles is supplied by a minute *afferent* arteriole (Fig. 100, *aff. a.*). This invaginates the wall of *Bowman's capsule* and breaks up in a bunch of looped capillaries, the *glomerulus*, suspended in the interior of the capsule. The blood is carried from the glomerulus by an *efferent vessel* (*eff. v.*), which joins the general capillary system of the kidneys, forming a network over the urinary tubules. Finally the blood is returned from this network to the renal vein. The components of the above apparatus differ greatly (even within a single order) according to the ex-

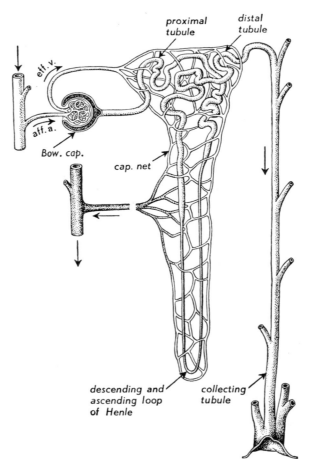

FIG. 100.—**Excretory system: A renal unit (nephron) of a terrestrial mammal.** To the encapsulated glomerulus (within Bowman's capsule) comes blood from the arterial circulation. Fluid, containing solutes of small molecular size (*e.g.* urea, NaCl), is filtered and sent into the convoluted tubule. This is enmeshed in capillaries into which fluid and beneficial substances are reabsorbed for canalisation back into the venous system. Discarded material flows down the collecting tubule into the kidney pelvis (see Fig. 99). (Modified after Homer Smith.)

cretory requirements of the animal and the environment in which it exists. In general, however, blood pressure forces fluids, salts, and waste metabolites of small molecular size to filter from the tuft of capillaries into the Bowman's capsule. The apparatus is impermeable to blood-cells and plasma proteins.

The stranded plasma proteins, however, exert an osmotic pressure which tends to retain fluid and solutes within the capillaries. Depending upon the inter-action of these factors, varying amounts of protein-free filtrate are allowed to flow into the confluent renal tubule. From here quantities of fluid, together with glucose and beneficial salts, can be reabsorbed through the tubule walls into the bloodstream via the adjacent capillary net. The remaining substances are excreted as urine or its equivalent.

All vertebrates, whether aquatic or terrestrial, are constantly exercised to maintain the integrity of their internal environment. The historic migrations between salt and fresh water and on to dry land have been made possible partly by manifold modifications (slime, exoskeletal structures, sweat-glands, gill, and kidney adaptations, etc.) in the structures that are involved in con-servation or elimination of internal fluids and the regulation of the concentra-tion of their contained salts. An animal is in large degree a system of physio-logical membranes. When iso-osmotic sea-animals (with watery tissues rich in the salts of the surrounding sea) explored the rivers they must have developed or already possessed (Fig. 101) a mechanism that prevented the fatal dis-ruption of their salt balance by the osmotic inflow of fresh water (see p. 164). The development of a waterproof exoskeleton by ostracoderms probably improved such protection, as well as conferring obvious advantages against predators (p. 166).

The kidney (meso- or meta-nephros) is the primary organ of excretion, al-though gills, lungs, skin, intestine, and other structures are important in this respect among different groups. The structure of the primary renal unit, the *nephron*, though differing in detail between animals of various habitats, preserves a basic similarity that can be traced from the hypothetical proto-vertebrate arrangement throughout the craniate series (Fig. 101). The kidney is segmental and mesodermal in origin (see below) and there is little reason to doubt that the vertebrate ancestor bore pairs of bilaterally symmetri-cal mesodermal nephric tubules (cf. however, Amphioxus, p. 47), which communicated through cœlomic nephrostomes with the external environment (or with some other structure opening thereto) and which discharged fluid and metabolites and probably sexual products as well. In such a structure (Fig. 101 A) the cœlomic cavity participated in excretion and a 'relatively feeble stream of cœlomic fluid would serve to wash the excretion out of the tubules ... with this meagre equipment the protovertebrate tried to enter the brackish lagoons or freshwater rivers of the Palæozoic continents' (Homer Smith) (see, however, p. 164).

Now, however much the external surface might come to be guarded by slime or exoskeletal modifications, a considerable amount of fresh water would be absorbed during feeding and respiration. The evolution of efficient homeo-stasis, therefore, inevitably depended upon the development of a more elaborate excretory mechanism in which the newly emergent, or at least increasingly efficient, force-pump—the heart—could play an important part.

So, perhaps, arose the glomerulus (Fig. 101 B). The blood was now driven continuously into an arteriole which entered the open nephrostome and which branched into a knot of semi-permeable capillaries. Through the glomeruli large quantities of fluid and salts could be eliminated into the renal tubule, while, at the same time, suspended blood cells and proteins (of larger molecular

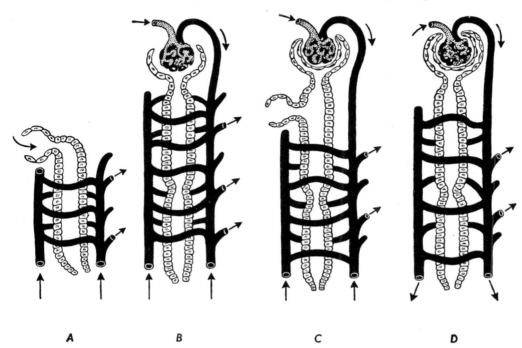

| A | B | C | D |

FIG. 101.—**Excretion and osmoregulation: Probable stages in the evolution of the vertebrate nephron.** *A*, the hypothetical protovertebrate tubule drained the cœlom through the open nephrostome (cœlomostome); *B*, earliest vertebrates developed the glomerulus in loose association with the cœlomostome as a more efficient excretory device under hydrostatic (blood) pressure; *C*, the glomerulus later became sealed in a Bowman's capsule, though with the retention, in some species, of a cœlomostome; which has disappeared in advanced vertebrates (*D*) (see Fig. 100). (After Homer Smith.)

size) were conserved. The glomerular capillaries were in turn canalised back into the venous system. Indications of this arrangement occur in the embryonic piscine pronephros and persist in the pericardial cavity of the adult *Myxine* (p. 197).

Probably an added refinement was the closure and invagination of the nephrostome (characteristic of the adult forms of extant vertebrates), possibly in association with an unmodified nephrostome (Fig. 101 *C*), which was later lost (Fig. 101 *D*) upon the perfection of the apparatus of glomerular filtration and tubule reabsorption (Fig. 100).

Meanwhile paired internal channels arose to carry urine into the cloaca. With the emergence of such enhanced excretory efficiency, various alternative mechanisms for the discharge of gametes arose (Fig. 98). The transitional animals referred to above had no need to conserve water; and in freshwater fishes of to-day tubule reabsorption appears to be very limited. Undoubtedly, the tetrapods inherited the glomerular apparatus through the crossopterygian line (p. 353) and have themselves come to adopt many interesting excretory specialisations in relation to later changes in habitat (*e.g. see* pp. 158, 548, 889). Fishes that took to the sea, on the other hand, were compelled to ingest salt water and developed a remarkable excretory apparatus at the gill-surface (p. 318) and so succeeded in maintaining the stability of their internal environment. In general (excluding the ureotelic elasmobranchs, p. 253), marine fishes have reduced their glomerular equipment and, it follows, urine output. Some species have become aglomerular (p. 347).

The evolution of the glomerulus was concerned in an interesting way with advances in the venous system in general. The renal capillaries early received blood at low pressure from a variety of sources which contributed to the renal portal system that still persists in fishes, frogs, reptiles and, to some extent, in birds. It was advantageous that the blood flowing through the glomeruli should do so at relatively high pressure. The capillaries, after leaving the Malpighian corpuscles, unite with those carrying blood from the renal portal system in a peri-tubule network, and thereafter the two groups cannot be distinguished. They unite as the renal vein and carry 'purified' blood back to the heart for re-distribution. In the Mammalia, however, the renal portal system has disappeared in the adult. The blood enters at high pressure through the renal artery (a branch of the dorsal aorta). The capillary network contains only post-glomerular blood, which is carried by the renal vein to the post-caval vein and the heart.

The *development* of the kidney reveals a resemblance to the cœlomoducts of annelids (Vol. I) which would hardly be suspected from its adult structure. The pronephros (Fig. 98, *A, p. nph.*) originates as a small number of coiled tubes formed from mesoderm in the body-wall at the anterior end of the cœlom. They are arranged metamerically, and each opens into the cœlom by a ciliated funnel (*nst.*). Obviously such tubes are cœlomoducts. Their chief peculiarity is that their outer ends do not open directly to the exterior, but into a longitudinal tube, the *pronephric* or *segmental duct* (*sg. d.*), which passes backwards, and discharges into the cloaca. It seems probable that this arrangement is to be explained by supposing that the cœlomoducts originally opened externally into a longitudinal groove, which, by the apposition of its edges, was converted into a tube. All the tubules of the pronephros open, by their ciliated funnels, into the narrow anterior end of the cœlom. Into this projects a branch of the aorta ending in a single large glomerulus or 'glomus'.

The pronephros soon degenerates. Its tubules lose their connection with the pronephric duct (*B*), but in the meantime fresh tubules appear in the segments posterior to the pronephros, and together constitute the mesonephros or *Wolffian body* (*B, ms. nph.*). From this structure the permanent kidney is formed in most of the lower Craniata. The mesonephric tubules open at one end into the pronephric duct (*sg. d.*), at the other, by ciliated funnels (*nst.*), into the cœlom. A short distance from the funnel each gives off a blind pouch, which dilates at the end and forms a Malpighian capsule (*m. c.*). A branch from the aorta that enters it gives rise to a glomerulus.

In elasmobranchs the pronephric duct now becomes divided by a longitudinal partition into two tubes. One retains its connection with the mesonephros and is known as the mesonephric or *Wolffian duct* (*C, ms. n. d.*). The other has no connection with the tubules, but opens into the cœlom in the region of the vanishing pronephros, and is called the *Müllerian duct* (*p. n. d.*). In most Craniata the Müllerian appears quite independently of the Wolffian duct. The latter is then simply the pronephric duct after its union with the mesonephric tubules.

In the higher vertebrates, from reptiles to mammals, a diverticulum (*D, E, mt. n. d.*) is given off from the posterior end of the Wolffian duct, and this grows forwards and becomes connected with the hindmost tubules. In this way a *metanephros* (*mt. nph.*) is formed. This forms the permanent kidney and a metanephric duct (*mt. n. d.*), which gives rise to the *ureter*. The Wolffian body ceases its renal function, and becomes a purely vestigial organ in the female while its residue in the male provides the *epididymis*.

In many fishes there is a dilatation of the mesonephric duct, the *urinary bladder*, which serves as a receptacle for the urine. In the higher Craniata the ventral wall of the cloaca sends off a pouch, the *allantoic bladder* (*al. bl.*), which serves the same purpose, although morphologically an entirely different structure.

The *gonads* (*gon.*) are developed as ridges growing from the dorsal wall of the cœlom and covered by cœlomic epithelium, from the cells of which, as in so many of the lower animals, the ova and sperms are derived. The testes consist of lobules (fishes) or tubules (tetrapods), lined with spermatogenetic epithelium, and usually discharge their products through delicate *vasa efferentia* (*D, v. e.*) into the Wolffian duct, but in some groups into the coelom (*e.g. Petromyzon*, p. 176). The sperms are always small, and motile. Between the tubules occur *Leydig* or *interstitial cells* which collectively form an endocrine gland which produces the male sex hormone (*testosterone*). The ovary is formed basically of connective-tissue or *stroma*. It is covered by specialised epithelium, certain of the cells of which become enlarged to form ova which become spread through the stroma. In the majority of cases the ova are discharged from the surface of the ovary into the cœlom and thus into the open ends of the Müllerian ducts (*E, p. n. d.*). These thus function simply as oviducts, having no connection in the adult with the urinary system. In some groups the ova and the sperms are shed into the cœlom and escape by the genital pores, and in many bony fishes the ovary is a hollow organ (as in Arthropoda (Vol. I)) discharging its ova into an internal cavity. From there they are carried by a duct that is continuous with the gonad. The ovary has specialised cells that produce female sex hormone (*œstrogen*).

In close topographical relation with the urinogenital organs are found the endocrine *inter-renal glands* (p. 276) or, in tetrapods, *adrenal* (*suprarenal*) *glands* of compound structure and function. The adrenals are developed partly from ridges of the dorsal wall of the cœlom, *i.e.* from mesoderm, partly from the sympathetic ganglia. Adrenal tissue may be segmentally arranged in certain lower groups (p. 380).

Development.—The ova of Craniata are usually telolecithal, but the amount of food-yolk varies within wide limits. When it is small in quantity, cleavage is complete but usually unequal, when abundant, incomplete, and discoidal. In the latter case the embryo proper is formed, as in cephalopods, from a comparatively small portion of the zygote, the rest giving rise to a large yolk-sac and, in the higher forms, to other embryonic membranes.

There is never a typical invaginated gastrula, as in Amphioxus, but in some of the lower Craniata a gastrula stage is formed by a combination of inpushing and overgrowth. Details will be given in the sections on the various groups.

The mode of development of the mesoderm and of the cœlom differs strikingly from the process we saw in Amphioxus. At an early stage the mesoderm is found in the form of paired longitudinal bands (Fig. 102, *A, msd.*) lying one on each side of the middle line. Here they are separated from one another by the notochord (*nch.*), and completely fill the space between the ectoderm and the endoderm. Each mesoderm-band becomes differentiated into a dorsal portion, the *vertebral plate*, bounding the nervous system and notochord, and a ventral portion, the *lateral plate*, surrounding the mesenteron. The vertebral plate undergoes metameric segmentation, becoming divided into a row of squarish masses, *somites* or *mesodermal segments* (*B, pr. v.*). The lateral plate splits into two layers, a somatic (*som.*), adherent to the ectoderm, a splanchnic (*spl.*), to the endoderm. The space between the two is the cœlom (*cœl.*), which is thus a *schizocœle*, or cavity hollowed out of the mesoderm, and is, except in the head-region in the lampreys (p. 176), at no stage in communication with the mesenteron, as are some of the cœlomic pouches of Amphioxus.

In *Lampetra*, approximately the first score of segments are segmentally *separate*, sausage-shaped chambers extending from myotomes down to the bottom of the lateral 'plate' material so that this structure is not, in fact, a plate. Behind the anterior segments the cœlom arises in the lateral plate as a *continuous* cavity (as in the higher Craniata) and there is no such segmentation of the lateral plate region posteriorly. The above points are of high phylogenetic interest.

In most craniates the cœlom extends upwards into each somite. This arrangement is only temporary, and these somitic cavities soon disappear. From the dorsal portions of the somites are formed the *dermatomes* (which give rise to the dermis); and the *myotomes* (from which myomeres develop). From their medial portions arise the *sclerotomes*.

The development of the principal organs has been described in general terms along with a general account of the organs themselves. It will be

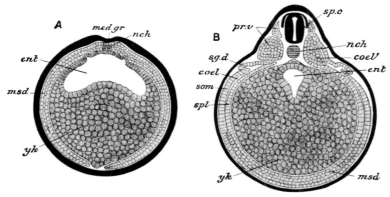

Fig. 102.—**Development: (A) earlier and (B) later embryos of frog.** *cœl.* cœlom; *cœl'.* prolongation of cœlom into a somite; *ent.* mesenteron; *med. gr.* medullary groove; *msd.* mesoderm; *nch.* notochord; *pr. v.* somites; *sg. d.* segmental duct; *som.* somatic layer of mesoderm; *sp. c.* spinal cord; *spl.* splanchnic layer of mesoderm; *yk.* yolk-cells. (After A. M. Marshall.)

convenient to defer further consideration of this subject until we come to deal with the development of the various types of Craniata, and with the embryological characteristics of the classes and sub-classes.

Metamerism.—A tendency, more or less strongly marked, to a serial repetition of parts is to be observed in a number of different systems of organs. Instances of this have already been pointed out in the skeleton, and the muscular, nervous, and excretory systems. This phenomenon seems to lead to the conclusion that the structure of the Craniata can be understood only when they are regarded as metamerically-segmented animals.

Segmentation in the Craniata, however, is never visible on the exterior. Even in the case of organs which present metameric characters, the metamerism often appears indefinite and uncertain. Thus the segmentation of the spinal column, which in the adult is most pronounced of all, does not coincide with the segmentation of the muscular and nervous system. Yet when we take the phenomena of embryonic development into account, it becomes sufficiently clear that in the Craniata we are dealing with animals possessing a metameric segmentation of the same general type as that possessed by Amphioxus and that the apparent anomalies are due to processes of secondary modification.

It is in the trunk region that the metamerism is most strongly pronounced, and that more particularly in the lower groups. In the head there is great specialisation in co-ordination with the presence of the brain, the chief organs of special sense, and the mouth and jaws. Therefore, though there are indications of metamerism of various parts, it is only by the study of development that it is possible to interpret the structure of the head in terms of a metameric segmentation which becomes so much modified in the adult animal. When the development is followed out, it becomes evident that (as in the Arthropoda, Vol. I) the head in Craniata is formed as a result of a process of fusion between a number of metameres, the individuality of which is evident in early stages (more particularly among lower forms) and is most pronounced in the region behind the auditory capsules.

SUB-PHYLUM CRANIATA (VERTEBRATA)

INTRODUCTION

VARIOUS classifications of Vertebrata have been proposed, but agreement has been reached on only one point—*i.e.* that this great group is essentially divisible into two unequal sections: (1) The jawless Agnatha (composed of a small number of primitive but highly specialised fish-like animals), and (2) the Gnathostomata, which embraces all other vertebrates from the true fishes to the Mammalia, including Man. In the past each of these distinctive assemblages has been sometimes accorded the rank of sub-phylum, but, however radically they differ in their buccal and visceral skeletal anatomy in the adult, such an arrangement seems untenable when we consider the criteria on which the three more primitive chordate sub-phyla have been erected and, equally, when we survey the many fundamental similarities existing between these two craniate groups. In recent years there has been a tendency to consider the Agnatha and Gnathostomata as 'branches', 'groups', or 'super-classes' of a single, and final, sub-phylum of the animal kingdom, and that is the arrangement followed here.

We are faced now, as we shall be confronted again, with the perennially vexed question as to what classificatory status various included groups should be accorded. For example, different authorities assign the Euphanerida (p. 167) variously to Family, Order, and Class. At the present stage of our knowledge, the conventional arrangements of many fossil, and even living, groups are essentially provisional and arbitrary. We shall see later, for example, that the 'Orders' erected by ornithologists have no validity whatever when judged by criteria employed by ichthyologists and herpetologists. No arrangement in any group can hope to be universally agreed at the present time. As mentioned above, several opinions are available concerning the most valid form of representation within each branch of the sub-phylum Vertebrata.[1]

---

[1] Goodrich recognised three branches of craniates: the Ostracodermi, including all the fossil agnathans; the Cyclostomata, including the lampreys and hags; and the Gnathostomata. Stensiö and Jarvik classify the Agnatha into the Sub-classes Cephalaspidomorphi, including the cephalaspids, anaspids, and lampreys; and the Pteraspidomorphi, including the pteraspids and hags. Romer includes all except the pteraspids in the Sub-class Cephalaspidomorphi.

SUPER-CLASS AGNATHA

Classes **Euphanerida** (Silurian)
         Heterostraci (**Pteraspida**) (Ordovician–Devonian)
         Anaspida (Silurian–Devonian)
         Osteostraci (**Cephalaspida**) (Silurian–Devonian)
         Petromyzontia (?—Recent)
         Myxinoidea (?—Recent)

It is almost certain that we know only a small proportion of the Agnatha that existed during the Palæozoic.   Further, next to nothing is known of their ancestry.   The earliest known vertebrate relics come from the Ordovician, and the nature of these makes it possible that the first vertebrate animals appeared in the Cambrian (Table I, p. 3).   Opinion is sharply divided as to whether the first true vertebrates were fresh-water or marine in habitat.   It is possible that the relatively strongly swimming vertebrates may have arisen in fresh water, where such powers would enable them to withstand river currents sweeping seawards.   The vertebrate kidney, so different from the excretory apparatus of Amphioxus (p. 47), possibly arose during the slow colonisation of coastal and inland waters (p. 156).   The earliest fresh-water chordates no doubt took in surrounding fluid by osmosis through the permeable regions of the body.   The water had to be discharged.   At the same time it was necessary for vital solutes to be retained, and waste metabolites to be discarded, if the integrity of the internal environment were to be maintained. Pioneer movement into brackish and fresh water would impose the necessity for considerable elaboration of the simple mesodermal funnels of excretion which carried fluid from cœlom to the exterior.   In any case there arose a device which made it possible for the power of the heart-pump to be used to eliminate unwanted fluid, and contained substances, through a filter (Fig. 100). This seems to have been at first a relatively simple knot of capillaries near each tubule mouth.   Upon this basic regulatory mechanism there have been imposed the many modifications made necessary by the re-colonisation of sea-water, and the exploitation of land, including deserts and other environmental niches.   A good case can be made out that all vertebrates, whatever their habitat to-day, are of fresh-water ancestry (see Romer, Homer Smith).

But even stronger evidence, perhaps, can be adduced for an opposite view (see Krogh, Watson, Robertson).   While it is undeniable that most fossils of very early vertebrates so far discovered have come from fresh-water sediments (*e.g.* see p. 174), it is equally true that the *earliest known* remains (plates and scales of Middle Ordovician ostracoderms) were unearthed from sandstone that, judged by an associated, and indubitably marine, invertebrate fauna, was *not* of fresh-water origin.   It has been suggested, but not established, that these fragments are the remnants of fresh-water animals that were washed downstream and incorporated in littoral deposits. As indicated above, there have been suggestions that the powerful lateral body flexure of vertebrates would help the earliest fresh-water craniates to withstand currents tending to sweep them seawards. But it is perhaps equally easy to believe that the development of such enhanced locomotion and stability could occur in the relative turmoil of the ocean, and that such *pre-adapted* (p. 385) ancestral forms could then swim against estuarine currents to colonise the brackish and fresh-water streams and lakes in which so many have left their bones.

It should be remembered too that all three protochordate groups, the Adelochordata (p. 5), Tunicata (p. 20), and Acrania (p. 47), are, and perhaps always have been, restricted to the sea. Again, it is possible that the glomerular kidney (p. 101) existed in marine protovertebrates, thus additionally pre-adapting them for life in fresh water. Finally, the blood of some extant agnathans (myxinoids, p. 197) has an ionic constitution strikingly similar to that of the surrounding sea: ' this may well be a primary feature, derived directly from marine chordate ancestors ' (Robertson).

The first vertebrate group of which numerous specimens are available is the Agnatha. The first common representatives of these were fresh-water, bottom-living animals of the Silurian (p. 3). Groups continued to expand during the Devonian, when they attained their maximum development. Between that time (some 270 to 300 million years ago), and the present day, little is known of them. Extant agnathans, unlike most of the early forms, lack bones, true teeth, and other durable parts, and that is probably why fossils are unknown.

It has been sometimes claimed that the not uncommonly found *conodonts* are the teeth of unknown armoured agnathans. This is unlikely. Conodonts, however, should perhaps for the time being find a place in a volume of the present character, and this is probably the best place to discuss them. They are small (0·2–3 mm. long), cone- or tooth-shaped, widely distributed, fossils which show a great deal of variation but fall possibly into two groups, *laminated* and *fibrous*. Their chemical composition is essentially bone-like and not very different from that of the armour of Devonian fishes (p. 285). Laminated conodonts occur in sedimentary strata from the Ordovician to the Triassic. Fibrous conodonts occur possibly only in Ordovician deposits and may represent a distinct group. A highly suspect binomial classification has been erected, and subscribed to, in many of the several hundred papers dealing with conodonts.

Conodonts seem to be formed by the accretion of material around a basal (but not pulp-) cavity. Radial canals, extending from cavity to surface, occur. The fibrous specimens often have very bone-like material attached to them. A few lamellar specimens have a similar attachment. There is some evidence that conodonts were regenerated when broken, but they show little evidence of wear.

These enigmatic objects have been variously held to be the branchial filters, or skeletal supports, of primitive vertebrates or, sometimes, the teeth of Agnatha or of primitive elasmobranch fishes. They have also been claimed to be the teeth, or copulatory organs, of worms. Some have believed them to be part of the armour of crustaceans or to be allied to the radular teeth of gastropods. Rhodes, the latest reviewer, concludes that : (1) 'if of vertebrate origin they may represent some group . . . other than fishes, now extinct, and, apart from the conodonts, entirely unknown', or (2) they may be masticatory organs of annelid affinity. Apart from their anatomy and chemistry, the one thing that is perfectly clear is that nobody at present has any real idea of their function or identity.

The Agnatha, apart from their antiquity *per se*, are of great interest in possessing *true bone* in the oldest groups. It was for many years confidently held that cartilage was the forerunner of bone. To-day, however, it is now widely agreed, with de Beer, that bone is the more primitive material and that cartilage in the adult is probably a neotenous phenomenon. On palæontological evidence Romer has reached the same conclusion concerning its antiquity. It has not yet been proved, but there are excellent reasons for supposing, that cartilage may be essentially an adaptation of embryonic tissue in the adult form. Although it could be held that Silurian and Devonian dermal bone (as well as skeletal bone in the Cephalaspida) might be derived from cartilage of an even earlier date, there is no doubt that the earliest known vertebrate fragments (from the Ordovician, about 400 million years ago) were ossified. Stensiö believes it possible that bone arose as early as the Lower Ordovician, or perhaps even in the Upper Cambrian. There is no evidence of a progressive increase in ossification in any craniate group.

The early agnathans were generally heavily armoured (Figs. 104, 105). There is no certainty why this was so. Their buccal arrangements reveal that they did not devour each other. The fresh-water forms were isolated from attacks by large predacious marine invertebrates. There is evidence, however, that large water-scorpions (Eurypterida, Vol. I) with formidable claws and mouth-parts existed in the same aquatic environment. These animals were allied to to-day's arachnids, and reached a length of about 9 feet—perhaps the biggest size attained by arthropods. It is an interesting fact that when faster fishes came to replace the early slow-moving armoured agnathan types in the succeeding Devonian period, the eurypterids also faded and disappeared. Homer Smith, on the other hand, believes that the armour of Silurian and Devonian forms was a defence against ' the osmotic invasion of fresh-water rather than the claws and tail-spines of eurypterids '. There is little doubt that dermal ossification would in fact provide such defence; but it would seem that, if protection against osmotic inflow was the primary factor involved, this may well have been obtained by more economical means. Further, many contemporary animals were not protected in this way (*e.g.* see Fig. 103).

CLASS EUPHANERIDA

Perhaps the most primitive vertebrate yet described was the totally unarmoured *Jamoytius kerwoodi*, described by White from the Scottish Silurian (Fig. 103). First thought to be allied to *Lasanius* (p. 171), *Jamoytius* was only about 7 inches long. It was blunt headed, with a rounded, somewhat elongated, body. With the ' possible exception of the supports of the median

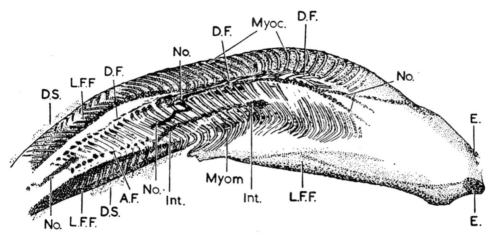

FIG. 103.—Class **Euphanerida**, Family **Jamoytiidæ**. *Jamoytius kerwoodi*. Specimen (lacking tail) shown in three-quarter view, at about ⅜th of natural size. *A. F.* anal fin supports; *D. F.* dorsal fin supports; *D. S.* displaced skin; *E.* eye; *Int.* contents of intestine; *L. F. F.* lateral finfold; *Myoc.* septal spaces; *Myom.* myomere; *No.* notochord. The above is one of the illustrations used in White's description of the new order, family and species.

fins', there is no indication of internal calcification. It had relatively enormous and widely separated eye-regions, a brief anal fin, and a dorsal fin continuous along the posterior two-thirds of the body. The intestine was short and straight. There was a persistent notochord and myotomes that were simple in arrangement. No evidence of gill pouches opening to the exterior has been found.

White believes that the nakedness of *Jamoytius* is a primary character and that earlier members of this apparently unspecialised group may have constituted the stock from which gnathostomes as well as agnathans were derived. There is a further suggestion that the Acrania (*e.g.* Amphioxus) (p. 68) arose as degenerate forms from animals such as the present one. Gregory has suggested that ' the boneless *Jamoytius* may well have been on the way towards Amphioxus, while the bony *Cephalaspis* (p. 172) may have been on or near the line leading to the lampreys'. This view, however, implies that *Jamoytius* was secondarily naked.

The unusual name *Jamoytius* is derived from that of the late J. A. Moy-Thomas, a distinguished worker in the present field who tragically died at the height of his powers.

CLASS HETEROSTRACI (PTERASPIDA)

A great deal is now known of the three armoured agnathan groups of the Palæozoic. These, the Heterostraci, Anaspida, and Osteostraci, and probably

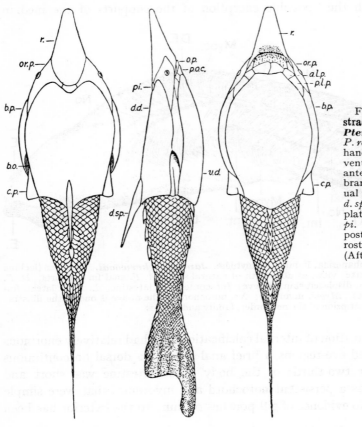

FIG. 104.—Class **Heterostraci**, Family **Pteraspidæ**. *Pteraspis.* Restoration of *P. rostrata* from dorsal (left-hand figure) lateral and ventral views. *a. l. p.* anterior lateral plate; *b. p.* branchial plate; *c. p.* cornual plate; *d. d.* dorsal disc; *d. sp.* dorsal spine; *o. p.* oral plate; *or. p.* orbital plate; *pi.* pineal plate; *p. l. p.* posterior lateral plate; *r.* rostrum; *v. d.* ventral disc. (After E. I. White.)

the naked lampreys and hags as well, are clearly related. None, however, appears to have been directly derived from another. Each stock probably branched successively from the ancestral stem in the order used below.

The Heterostraci, although probably more advanced than the Euphanerida (see above), are known to have existed in the Middle Ordovician, from which plates of *Astraspis* have been described. Such animals (e.g. *Pteraspis*, Fig. 104) were apparently seldom more than a foot long, although some grew to a length of 5 feet. They became more plentiful in the Upper Silurian and Lower Devonian and persisted into the Upper Devonian. They possessed a broad, depressed head protected by a carapace of exoskeletal plates. The eyes were widely separated, and lateral in position. There was a sub-ventral mouth at the extreme anterior end of the body which was equipped with probably mobile plates. White has suggested that this buccal apparatus was protrusible and able to scoop up bottom-mud and the contained organic material that served as food.

There were no fins on the body. The tail behind the carapace was laterally compressed, downwardly turned (*hypocercal*), and protectively covered with over-lapping rhomboid scales of the same composition as the plates of the carapace. The Heterostraci differed widely from the Osteostraci (see below) in several essential points. There are no traces of a median nostril and there are strong indications that the olfactory organ was a paired structure opening into the roof of the mouth. The plates and scales lacked bone-cells. The plates were formed of three layers, of which the outer was composed of a substance allied to dentine. The middle layer was formed of vascular 'bone'; the lower was laminated. The gill-pouches, apparently of the adult cyclostome pattern, united as a single exhalent pore placed rather far back on the sides of the carapace. There was no sign of the complicated and prominently innervated sensory organ formerly thought to be one of electrical discharge (Fig. 108, p. 173).

The four groups which form the Heterostraci (Paleaspidæ, Cyathaspidæ, Pteraspidæ (Fig. 104), and Drepanaspidæ (Fig. 105)) were distinguished from one another by the number of plates in the carapace. The Paleaspidæ had an undivided upper shield; the Cyathaspidæ had it divided into four plates; the Pteraspidæ nine and the Drepanaspidæ twelve major and many smaller plates.

A description of *Pteraspis rostrata*, a species of the best-known genus, will serve for the remainder. The carapace was somewhat elongated and rect-angular in section. The dorsal surface was composed of nine plates, of which three, the *rostral*, *pineal*, and large *dorsal*, were unpaired. The remaining six plates formed three pairs. These are the *orbital* (in which lay the eye-sockets), the *branchial* (with the single gill opening at the posterior border), and just behind these, the *cornual plates*. In the adult all these plates were bound together by a fusion of their inner laminæ. There was a prominent median spine inserted at the base of the dorsal disc. On the ventral surface, a large unpaired plate covered most of the area except for a number of small *oral plates* round the lower border of the mouth. Immediately behind these were three pairs of small plates, the *post-oral* and the anterior and posterior *laterals*. The trunk was covered with thick rectangular scales and there was a series of thorn-like scales along the upper and lower surface. From impressions of the internal surface of the upper carapace it seems clear that there were seven pairs of gill pouches. An X-like impression just behind the pineal opening has been interpreted as evidence of two semicircular canals (see p. 145) on each side. There was a prominent lateral line system (see p. 135).

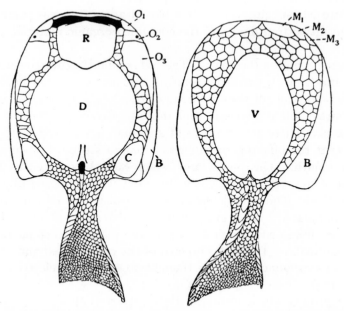

FIG. 105.—Class **Heterostraci**, Family **Drepanaspidæ**. *Drepanaspis*. Dorsal and ventral views. *D. gemündenensis*. *C*, cornual plate; *D*, median dorsal plate; *M₁–M₃*, ventral oral plates; *O₁–O₃*, ocular plates; *R*, rostral plate; *V*, ventral plate; *B*, branchial plate. (From Stensiö, after Kiær.)

CLASS ANASPIDA

Anaspids share some characters with the pteraspids but show a greater resemblance to the cephalaspids (Osteostraci) although, it should be emphasised again, they sprang from a common ancestry and were derived from neither. They were fish-shaped animals, a few inches long, with a downwardly turned tail (*hypocercal*) (Fig. 106). The internal, presumably cartilaginous, skeleton is unknown, but a highly developed dermal skeleton was present. The scales on the head were small and showed a complicated arrangement which differed in pattern in different genera. The scales on the trunk were arranged in lateral and ventral series, which, with a set of tall lateral scales, showed great resemblance to the condition found in cephalaspids, as does also the mode of their articulation. There are no paired appendages, unless a pair of pectoral spines represented them. There was an anal spine, and a series of ridge spines along the dorsal surface. The eyes were lateral, and the pineal and naso-hypophysial openings were placed on the top of the head in relatively the same position as in the cephalaspids. A series of gill openings, varying in number in different genera, were placed in front of the pectoral spine. The mouth had a shape that resembled that of jawed animals, but there is no evidence that jaws

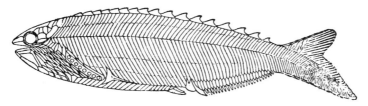

FIG. 106.—Order **Anaspida**, Family **Birkeniidæ**: *Rhyncholepis parvulus.* (After Kiær.

existed. *Lasanius,* from the Upper Silurian, was almost unarmoured except for dorsal and pectoral spines. There were several groups. *Birkenia, Rhyncholepis* (Fig. 106), *Saarolepis* (= *Anaspis*) are typical genera.

CLASS OSTEOSTRACI (CEPHALASPIDA)

The cephalaspids (Fig. 107) had developed prominent ' pectoral fins ' and a heterocercal tail. Much splendidly preserved material has been discovered, allowing a relatively clear picture of their essential features. They were bottom-living animals with a single *naso-hypophysial opening* placed far back

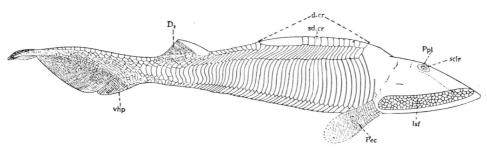

FIG. 107.—Order **Osteostraci**, Family **Cephalaspidæ**. *Hemicyclaspis.* *H. murchisoni.* D_2 dorsal fin; *d. cr.* dorsal crest of trunk; *sd. cr.* dorsal scutes; *Ppl.* pineal plates; *sclr.* sclerotic ring; *lsf.* lateral 'sensory field'; *Pec.* pectoral fin; *vhp.* caudal fin. (After Stensiö.)

on the head. The head region was expanded and flattened. It was protected by a hard, bony carapace or head-shield which was often ornamented with tubercles, and usually produced on each side into a backwardly directed 'horn' which left a bay, or *pectoral sinus*, between itself and the trunk. Beneath the true dermal bone in at least some cephalaspids there occurred a fragile and continuously ossified endocranium, equally curious both in shape and constitution. This was usually cartilaginous in later forms. The body was protected by rows of scales in which true bone-cells were present. A dorsal fin occurred.

Two Orders, Cephalaspidiformes (Fig. 107) and Tremataspidiformes, are generally recognised.

In *Cephalaspis*, the most completely known genus, there was, as mentioned above, a pair of lobed appendages arising from the pectoral sinus on each side. These were *neomorphs*, and therefore not homologous with the pectoral fins of vertebrates. Of the internal anatomy, too, a good deal is known. The brain, with its ten pairs of cranial nerves, was closely comparable with that of the living cyclostomes, but in addition there was a well-developed system arising in the acoustico-lateralis region. From here five pairs of stout vessels ran to depressions on the upper surface of the head-shield. By analogy with such modern forms as torpedoes (p. 271), Stensiö suggested that these nerves and depressions formed a kind of electric organ (Fig. 108).

There are good reasons for believing this theory to be invalid. Westoll has reinterpreted the so-called ' electric fields ' as a sensory organ. He believes them probably to have been ' receptors of vibrationary stimuli ', consisting of invaginated pockets, probably derived from placodes, and richly supplied by neuromast organs innervated by the acoustico-lateralis system. In short, they possibly compensated for the relatively reduced lateral line system (p. 135), which was in them much less extensive than that of the Heterostraci existing in the same habitat. Watson, too, is of the opinion that they may constitute a sensory apparatus that might allow ' pressure waves incident on the head to be conveyed along the fluid-filled canals to the ear '.

Cephalaspis was a bottom dweller. The eyes were placed close together on the top of the cephalic shield, with the pineal aperture between them. It is possible that the pineal was a photoreceptor which helped the animal gauge the depth of water and, by means of pituitary hormones, protectively control its colour in a manner comparable with that of the ammocœte larva of *Petromyzon* (p. 196). The *naso-hypophysial* opening was a little anterior to the pineal aperture. (See p. 345.)

The ventral mouth was followed on each side by ten pairs of gill-pouches, of which the first two (anterior and spiracular gill-cleft) were innervated by the ophthalmicus profundus and trigeminal nerves respectively. Each such nerve, then, was in *Cephalaspis* a typical *branchiomeric* nerve, *i.e.* one associated with a functional gill-slit. We will see that in jawed animals (pp. 205, 210) these nerves supply apparently quite unrelated structures (*i.e.* the snout and jaws). This remarkable change in situation and function has been dictated by the enlargement of the mouth and buccal cavity in relation to the shift to macrophagous habits. The corners of the mouth migrated backwards, obliterating the first, and absorbing the second, pairs of gills (Fig. 137). For many reasons it now appears certain that in this way the mouth came into proximity with the branchial arch (posterior to the second pair of previously functional gills),

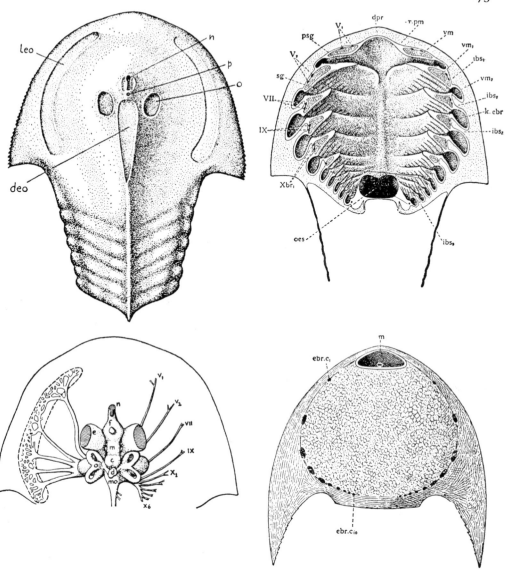

Fig. 108.—**Osteostraci: Cranial anatomy of *Kiœraspis.***

Upper left: top view of head and anterior part of trunk region: *deo.* dorsal sensory (supposed 'electric') organ; *leo.* lateral organ; *n.* opening of single dorsal nostril and hypophysis; *o.* orbit; *p.* pineal opening.

Lower left: diagrammatic dissection of top of head, to show brain, nerves, and sense organs. Nerves to sensory organ shown on the left; other major nerves (numbered) on right, arranged in a series corresponding to the gilt slits. *c.* Cerebellum; *d.* nerve to dorsal sensory field; *e.* orbit; *f.* forebrain; *m.* midbrain; *mo.* medulla oblongata; *n.* opening for nostril and hypophysis; *o.* ear region (two canals). In this and the next figure Roman numerals indicate cranial nerves.

Upper right: restoration of ventral surface of head, with the plates covering the throat removed, showing the ten gill sacs and the small, anteriorly placed mouth. *dpr.* mouth; *ibs.* partitions between gill sacs; *kebr.* ducts from gill pouches to surface; *œs.* œsophagus; *psg.* a prespiracular gill pouch lost in higher vertebrates; *rpm.* rostral region in front of gills; *sg.* gill pouch corresponding to the spiracle of higher fishes; *vm.* muscles of gill pouches.

Lower right: restoration of ventral surface of head, covered by small plates: *ebrc.* opening of the gills; *m.* mouth. (From Romer, after Stensiö.)

and the skeleton of this arch and its musculature came to be modified into a powerful masticating apparatus, *i.e.* the modern jaw.

In *Cephalaspis* the whole of the ventral mouth and gill region was supported by a system of small, tessellated, bony plates, constituting the *oro-branchial area*. The considerably expanded gills had nothing in common with those of fishes. It has been suggested that their structure resembled that found in lampreys of to-day (p. 175) or, alternatively, perhaps that of the ammocœte larva (p. 196). It is generally held that ostracoderms strained organic particles from debris sucked in from the floor of fresh-water lakes and streams : the small ventral mouth, dorsal eyes, and generally flattened form point to this conclusion.

The Osteostraci ranged from the Upper Silurian to the Upper Devonian, and a considerable number of genera and species is known. They showed great variation in the proportions of the cephalic shield and in its ornamentation. Representative genera are *Cephalaspis, Hemicyclaspis, Ateleaspis, Benneviaspis, Kiæraspis* (Fig. 108), *Didymaspis, Thyestes*, and others.

The tremataspids differ from other cephalaspids chiefly in the absence of the pectoral sinus, and, in consequence, of the paired appendages. The cephalic shield was well developed, and extended backwards on to the trunk. The lateral sensory fields were divided into anterior and posterior portions. The members of some genera of the Cephalaspidiformes were transitional in shape; the two groups were clearly allied.

THE ' CŒLOLEPIDA '

FIG. 109.—***Lanarkia spinosa,*** possibly related to the Heterostraci and formerly often placed with 'Order' Cœlolepida. Restored outline in the position in which it occurs as a fossil, the head being flattened and the tail twisted round so as to appear in profile. On each side a much-enlarged dermal denticle is shown. (From the *Cambridge Natural History*, after Traquair.)

Several genera of small fish-like animals which usually appear as flattened impressions with a broad head-region, a somewhat fusiform body, and a heterocercal or hypocercal (*e.g. Cœlolepis*) tail have been described. They occurred from the Upper Ordovician to the Devonian. Their armour appeared to be restricted to minute denticles (Fig. 109) that produced, in some forms at least, a shagreen surface perhaps not unlike that of selachians (p. 267). It has often been considered that the ' Cœlolepida ' forms a single well-defined assembly. Westoll, however, has made it very probable that two or more structurally distinct groups exist. One such is represented by *Thelodus* and *Lanarkia* (Fig. 109) and another by *Cephalopterus*.

The first group were related to the Heterostraci and the second to the

Osteostraci. Other forms (*e.g. Phlebolepis, Cœlolepis*) showed certain resemblances to the Anaspida. It is still uncertain whether the cœlolepids represent, or include (1) forms that belonged to each of the above groups and never became ossified, (2) secondarily unossified types that descended from armoured ancestors, and (3) the 'larval' stages of animals that might have developed dermal ossifications at a later stage of their development.

EXTANT AGNATHA (CYCLOSTOMATA)

Lampreys and hags, the only surviving agnathans, are often grouped together in the Class or Order Cyclostomata, distinguished from all other living craniates by the possession of pouched gills and a single nostril, and the primitive absence of jaws or paired fins. However, such features, which are shared with one or other of the fossil groups, do not provide evidence that hags and lampreys are more closely related to each other than they are to the earliest agnathans. It seems probable that the lampreys are related to a cephalaspid-anaspid stock, but the affinities of the hags are very doubtful. In view of this it is advisable to regard the Cyclostomata as a 'group of convenience' and to treat the lampreys and hags as separate Classes of the Agnatha.

CLASS PETROMYZONTIA

This group comprises the lampreys, Agnatha with a round sucking mouth, a pharynx which ends blindly, and (like the cephalaspids) a naso-hypophysial sac opening by a single nostril on the dorsal surface of the head. There are about half a dozen genera, differing from one another only in minor anatomical features. *Petromyzon* (Fig. 110) occurs on both coasts of the North Atlantic, and *Entosphenus* on both coasts of the North Pacific. *Geotria* occurs along the southern coast of Australia, and in New Zealand, Chile, and Argentina.

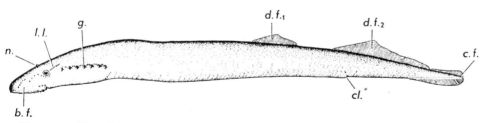

FIG. 110.—Class **Petromyzontia**, Family **Petromyzonidæ**. *Petromyzon*. Adult Lamprey (*P. marinus*). *b. f.* buccal funnel; *c. f.* caudal fin; *cl.* cloaca; *d. f.*₁,₂ 1st and 2nd dorsal fins; *g.* external gill aperture; *l. l.* lateral line organs; *n.* nasal aperture. (Drawn by R. Strahan.)

Mordacia is restricted to the Southern Pacific. The remaining genera, all Holarctic, appear to be degenerate descendants of the Northern genera already mentioned.

EXAMPLE OF THE CLASS:—
THE LAMPREY (PETROMYZON)

Three species of lamprey are common in European river systems. The Sea-lamprey (*P. marinus*) attains a length of a metre, the Lampern, or common fresh-water lamprey (*Lampetra fluviatilis*), reaches a length of about 90 cm., and the Sandpride, or lesser Fresh-water Lamprey (*L. planeri*), does not exceed 45 cm. in length.

Two quite different phases occur in the life-cycle of *Petromyzon*. The larval phase or *ammocœte* feeds on microscopic particles by means of an endostyle not unlike that of Amphioxus. The adult has a suctorial mouth, and a rasping apparatus that enables it to cling to fishes and feed on their tissues. Comparatively little is known about the habits and life-cycle of even the common species. The adult lives in the sea for most of its life. It attaches itself to a fish, rasps away some of the host tissue, and then feeds on its blood. It is often found in this situation when the host is caught. At the onset of its single breeding season it migrates coastwards and ascends a river into fresh water. In Europe this occurs in the autumn, when great numbers of *L. fluviatilis* invade favoured streams. They are not infrequently used as food, though more particularly in past eras, as the sad fate of Henry I of England will recall.

In some instances they ascend rapids in their urge to reach the breeding-ground, and cling to the rocks with their suckers between leaps forward and upward. During this migratory phase the gut atrophies and they cannot feed. They are sustained by fat reserves accumulated sub-cutaneously and in the body-muscles. Towards the end of winter the gonads become mature. Secondary sexual characters develop—a prominent anal fin in the female, and a *penial-tube* and a thickening at the base of the dorsal fin in the male.

In the spring, lampreys aggregate in pairs in shallow spawning-grounds and build their nests. They move stones from the stream-bed with their suckers and construct a sandy floor with a crescentic ridge on the downstream border. Although copulation occurs (the male clinging to the female by means of its buccal funnel), fertilisation is external. Both eggs and spermatozoa (which are ejected through the penial tube and are very short-lived) are extruded into the surrounding water, whence they are carried by the current into the interstices of the stony rim of the nest. After each of the numerous short matings, sand is stirred up from the floor of the nest by vigorous tail movements, and this serves to embed the eggs more firmly among the stones. It is said that the seasonally developed anal fin of the female assists in this operation. When spawning is completed, the adults drop away from the nest and die within several days.

It is of great interest that lampreys that inhabit lakes in North America (where their ancestors were isolated) have successfully adapted themselves to live their whole lives in fresh water, but nevertheless move a few miles up lake-side streams at the onset of the breeding season.

External Characters.—The head and trunk (Figs. 110, 111) are nearly cylindrical, with the tail-region compressed or flattened from side to side. At the anterior end, and directed downwards, is a large, basin-like depression, the *buccal funnel* (*b. f.*), surrounded by a marginal membrane (*m. m.*) outside of which arise the overlapping *oral fimbriæ* (*o. f.*) and the longer, sensory *cirri* (*c.*). The inside of the buccal funnel is beset with radiating rows of yellow *horny teeth* (*i. o., l. t., s. o.*). The teeth rest on cartilaginous pads and are principally mesodermal in origin, and therefore not homologous with true vertebrate teeth, which first appear in fishes.

From the bottom of the buccal funnel there projects a prominence, the so-called 'tongue', bearing even larger horny teeth (*t. t.*), and having immediately above it the narrow *mouth* (*m.*). On the dorsal surface of the head is a single median *nostril* (*n.*), and immediately behind it a transparent area of skin indicates the position of the pineal organ. The paired eyes have no eyelids, but are covered by a transparent area of skin. The gill-slits (*g.*) are seven pairs of small apertures on the sides of the head, the first a little behind the eyes. On the ventral surface, marking the junction between trunk and tail, is the very small *anus* lying in a slight de-

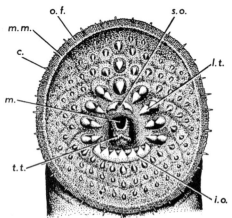

FIG. 111.—*Petromyzon :* **Buccal funnel.** *c.* cirrus; *i. o.* infra-oral tooth plates; *l. t.* lateral bicuspid tooth; *m.* mouth; *m. m.* marginal membrane; *o. f.* oral fimbriæ; *s. o.* supra-oral tooth; *t. t.* tongue tooth. (Redrawn after Bigelow and Schroeder.)

pression. Immediately behind it is a small papilla pierced at its extremity by the *urinogenital aperture* (*cl.*). There is no trace of paired appendages. Two dorsal fins of approximately equal dimensions (separated by a notch) and a caudal fin are present, the second dorsal being continuous with the caudal. All these fins are median and unpaired. As previously mentioned, the sexes during the period of gonad maturation can be distinguished by the number and structure of the fins and, in addition, by the appearance of a penial tube in the male. This is formed by the junction of the cloacal margins. At this period, too, the cloacal margins of the female become distended and sometimes reddened. The *skin* is soft and slimy and, as in *Myxine*, lacking in exoskeletal structures (Fig. 112). Among extant forms scales, like true teeth, do not appear until we ascend further the chordate stem. Keratin (p. 85) does not occur in the epidermis although it possibly forms the caps on the 'teeth' (p. 184). As the outermost layers of the epidermis become worn away by abrasion, new cells are added by division of those at the base of the layer. Thus, these forms differ from Amphioxus and resemble the higher vertebrates in their possession of a several-layered, more durable, epidermis. Underlying the epidermis is a layer of collagen and elastic fibres which forms the *cutis*. This layer contains also pigment-cells or *chromatophores*. The pigment in these star-shaped cells changes

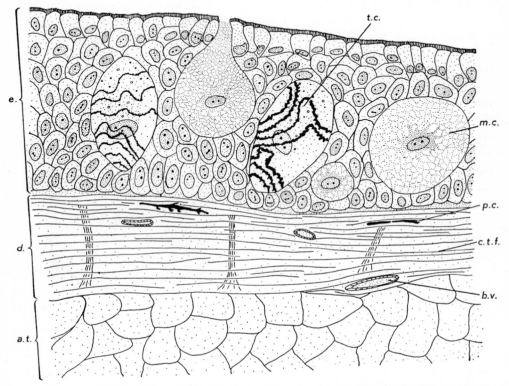

FIG. 112.—***Myxine:*** **Integument.** Vertical section showing structure and cell-types in *M. glutinosa*. *a. t.* adipose tissue; *b. v.* blood vessels; *c. t. f.* connective tissue fibres; *d.* dermis; *e.* epidermis; *m. c.* mucous cell; *p. c.* pigment cell; *t. c.* thread cell. (Thread cells are peculiar to the Myxinidæ. Their mucous cells are atypical in that the nucleus lies in the centre of the cell (cf. Fig. 113, 1). (Drawn by G. H. O. Burgess.)

its position under various conditions of illumination. Thus the 'colour' of the lamprey changes from pallid to dusky and vice versa. This faculty is particularly well shown in the larva (p. 196).

The epidermis is equipped also with numerous unicellular glands which secrete a slime which makes *Petromyzon* difficult, or impossible to hold with the bare hand. In addition, two other types of secretory cell are formed (Fig. 113). One, the *granular cell*, is of yet unknown function. The second, the *club cell* (*Kolbenzelle*), is an elongated cell with hyaline cytoplasm. These are found also in certain teleosts, notably in Anguillidæ (eels). There have been suggestions that club cells are neural (but fibres have not been demonstrated to end in them), or scab-forming (but at least in *Anguilla* and *Tinca* such is not the case).   On the other hand, there is evidence that club cells contribute to the

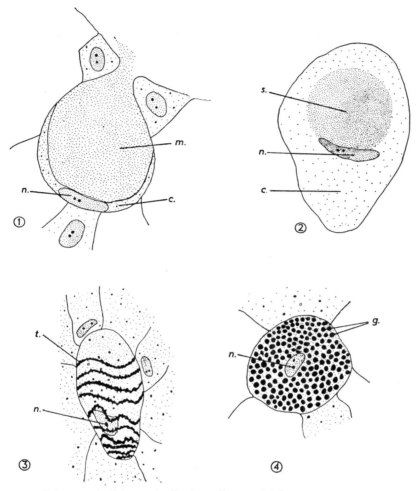

Fig. 113.—**Integument: Epidermal cells of agnathans and fishes.** 1. Mucous cell of *Salmo trutta*; 2. club cell of *Conger conger*; 3. thread cell of *Myxine glutinosa*; 4. granular cell of *Petromyzon marinus*.

c. cytoplasm; g. granules; n. nucleus; m. mucus cell; t. 'thread' in thread cell.   (Drawn by G. H. O. Burgess.)

sliminess of eels in which mucous cells are present only in relatively small numbers.

The segmental sense-organs take the form of a *lateral line* (p. 136).   These organs are restricted to fishes and fish-like vertebrates (including tadpoles of Amphibia).   In lampreys, lateral line organs are not enclosed in a canal, but are exposed to the exterior.

Endoskeleton.—The *axial skeleton* of the trunk is simple. There is a persistent notochord (Fig. 114, *nc.*) with a tough sheath composed of an inner fibrous and an outer elastic layer. This longitudinal central rod probably prevents the body from shortening when the muscle segments contract and drive the animal forward. Attached to the sides of the notochord are small, vertical,

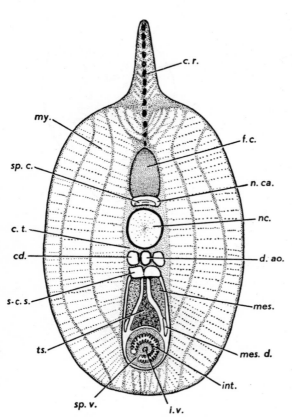

rods of segmentally arranged cartilage, bounding the spinal canal on each side, and which correspond to the rudimentary neural and interneural arches. In the caudal region these fuse into a single plate perforated by foramina for the spinal nerves and send off processes to the base of the fin. For the rest of its length the spinal canal is enclosed only by tough, pigmented connective-tissue. Slender rods of cartilage support the median fins.

The *cranium* also is primitive in structure. Its floor is formed by a *basal plate* (Fig. 115, *b. pl.*), made by the union of the parachordals and trabeculæ, surrounding posteriorly the anterior end of the notochord. Immediately anterior to the notochord is a large aperture, the *basi-cranial fontanelle* (*b. cr. f.*), due to the non-union of the posterior ends of the trabeculæ. Through this passes the naso-hypophysial sac (Fig. 118, *na. hyp.*; Fig. 121, *pty. p.*) extending

FIG. 114.—***Petromyzon:*** **Trunk region.** Transverse section. *cd.* posterior cardinal vein; *c. t.* connective tissue; *c. r.* cartilaginous rods ('fin rays'); *d. ao.* dorsal aorta; *f. c.* fat column; *int.* intestine; *i. v.* intra-intestinal vein; *mes.* mesonephros; *mes. d.* mesonephric duct; *my.* myotome; *n. ca.* spinal canal; *nc.* notochord; *s-c. s.* sub-cardinal venous sinus; *sp. c.* spinal cord; *sp. v.* spiral valve; *ts.* testis. (Drawn by R. Strahan.)

from the olfactory sac to the ventral surface of the notochord. Lateral walls extend upwards from each side of the basal plate, but the roof of the cranium is formed by membrane except at one point. Here a narrow transverse bar (*cr. r.*) extends across between the side-walls and furnishes a rudimentary roof. United with the posterior end of the basal plate and forming the end of the neurocranium are the *otic capsules* (Fig. 115, *au. c*). The side-walls are pierced by apertures for the cranial nerves. So far the skull is typical, though extremely simple; its remaining parts, however, are in many cases very difficult of interpretation.

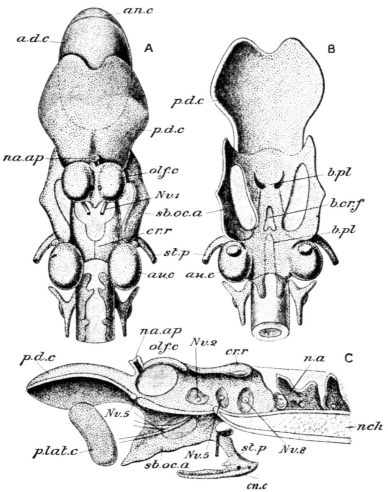

FIG. 115.—*Petromyzon:* **Skull.** Dorsal (*A*), ventral (*B*), and sectional (*C*) views of *P. marinus.* The cartilaginous parts are dotted. *a. d. c.* anterior dorsal cartilage; *an. c.* annular cartilage; *au. c.* auditory capsule; *b. cr. f.* basi-cranial fontanelle; *b. pl.* basal plate; *cn. c.* cornual cartilage; *cr. r.* cranial roof; *n. a.* neural arch; *na. ap.* nasal aperture; *nch.* notochord; *Nv.* 1, olfactory nerve; *Nv.* 2, 5, and 8, foramina for the optic, trigeminal, and auditory nerves; *Nv* 5′, trigeminal nerve; *olf. c.* olfactory capsule; *p. d. c.* posterior dorsal cartilage; *p. lat. c.* posterior lateral cartilage; *sb. oc. a.* sub-ocular arch; *st. p.* styloid process. (After W. K. Parker.)

The *olfactory capsule* (*olf. c.*) is an unpaired concavo-convex plate which supports the posterior wall of the olfactory sac and is pierced by paired apertures for the olfactory nerves. It is unique in being united to the cranium by fibrous tissue only. Extending outwards and downwards from each side of the basal plate is an inverted arch of cartilage, called the *subocular arch* (Figs. 116 and 117, *s. o. a.*) because it supports the eye. From its posterior end a slender *styloid process* (*st. p.*) passes directly downwards and is connected at its lower end

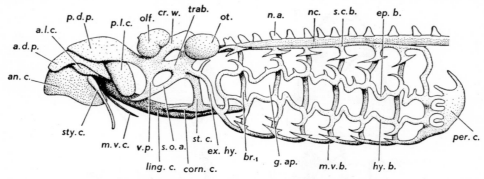

Fig. 116.—***Petromyzon*: Skull and branchial basket in adult.** *P. marinus. a. d. p.* anterior dorsal plate; *a. l. c.* anterior lateral cartilage; *an. c.* annular cartilage; *br.₁* 1st branchial bar; *corn. c.* cornual cartilage; *cr. w.* cranial wall; *ep. b.* epitrematic bar; *ex. hy.* extrahyal bar; *g. ap.* gill aperture; *hy. b.* hypotrematic bar; *ling. c.* lingual cartilage; *m. v. b.* median ventral bar; *m. v. c.* median ventral cartilage; *n. a.* neural arch; *nc.* notochord; *olf.* olfactory capsule; *ot.* otic capsule; *p. d. p.* posterior dorsal plate; *per. c.* pericardial cartilage; *p. l. c.* posterior lateral cartilage; *s. c. b.* subchordal bar; *s. o. a.* subocular arch; *st. c.* styloid cartilage; *sty. c.* stylet cartilage; *trab.* trabecula; *v. p.* vertical pillar of subocular arch. (Modified after Parker.)

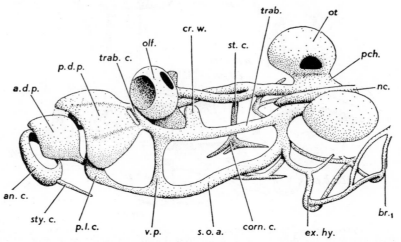

Fig. 117.—***Lampetra*: Skull during metamorphosis.** (Tongue skeleton omitted.) *L. planeri. a. d. p.* anterior dorsal plate; *an. c.* annular cartilage; *br.₁* 1st branchial bar; *corn. c.* cornual cartilage; *cr. w.* cranial wall; *ex. hy.* extrahyal bar; *nc.* notochord; *olf.* olfactory capsule; *ot.* otic capsule; *pch.* parachordal; *p. d. p.* posterior dorsal plate; *p. l. c.* posterior lateral cartilage; *s. o. a.* subocular arch; *st. c.* styloid cartilage; *sty. c.* stylet cartilage; *trab.* trabecula; *trab. c.* trabecular commissure; *v. p.* vertical pillar of subocular arch. (Drawn by R. Strahan, reconstructed after Damas.)

with a small *cornual cartilage* (*corn. c.*). These two cartilages arise in a similar manner to the skeleton of the gills and probably represent the reduced arch of the mandibular somite. The styloid process has been identified with the extra-mandibular cartilage of gnathostomes (p. 203), and the cornual cartilage may possibly represent the mandibular cartilage. In close relation with the angle of the subocular arch is an upwardly directed plate, the *posterior lateral cartilage* (*p. l. c.*).

Connected with the anterior end of the basal plate is the large bilobed *posterior dorsal plate* (*p. d. p.*). Below and projecting in front of it is the *anterior dorsal plate* (*a. d. p.*). Also supporting the upper lip are the paired *anterior lateral cartilages* (*a. l. c.*) which arise in the premandibular somite and possibly represent the internal visceral arch of that segment. The great ring-shaped *annular cartilage* (*an. c.*) supports the edge of the buccal funnel and carries at its sides two backwardly directed rods, the *stylet cartilages* (*sty. c.*).

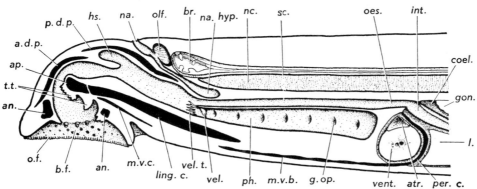

FIG. 118.—*Petromyzon:* **Head region of adult.** (Diagrammatic half-section.) *a. d. p.* anterior dorsal plate; *an.* annular cartilage; *ap.* apical cartilage; *atr.* atrium; *b. f.* buccal funnel; *br.* brain; *cœl.* cœlom; *gon.* gonad; *g. op.* opening to gill; *hs.* hydrosinus; *int.* intestine; *l.* liver; *ling. c.* lingual cartilage; *m. v. b.* median ventral bar of branchial skeleton; *m. v. c.* median ventral cartilage (copula); *na.* nostril; *na. hyp.* naso-hypophysial duct; *nc.* notochord; *œs.* œsophagus; *o. f.* oral fimbriæ; *olf.* olfactory capsule; *p. d. p.* posterior dorsal plate; *per. c.* pericardial cartilage; *ph.* pharynx; *s.c.* spinal cord; *t. t.* tongue teeth; *vel.* velum; *vel. t.* velar tentacles; *vent.* ventricle. (Drawn by R. Strahan.)

The 'tongue' is supported by a long unpaired *lingual cartilage* (Fig. 118, *ling. c.*). This is tipped in front by a small median, and a pair of still smaller lateral, cartilages. Below it occurs a slender T-shaped *median ventral cartilage* (*m. v. c.*). The visceral skeleton differs remarkably from the ordinary craniate type and has many elements which cannot be homologised with it. It is most probably represented in the extra-branchial cartilages of the lower gnathostomes, the inner series, which forms the bulk of the branchial skeleton, being absent from the post-mandibular segments in the lamprey.

The visceral skeleton consists of a *branchial basket* formed, on each side, of nine irregularly curved vertical bars of cartilage (Fig. 116, *br.*₁). The first is placed almost immediately posterior to the styloid cartilage and is homologous with the extra-hyal cartilage of elasmobranchs (p. 219). The second lies immediately in front of the first gill-cleft, and the remaining seven just behind the seven gill-clefts. These bars are united together by four

longitudinal rods.   One, the *subchordal bar* (*s. c. b.*), lies alongside the notochord and is connected in front with the cranium.   Two others, the *epitrematic bar* (*ep. b.*) and *hypotrematic bar* (*hy. b.*), are placed respectively above and
below the gill-clefts.   The fourth, the *median ventral bar* (*m. v. b.*), is situated
close to the middle ventral line and is partly fused with its fellow of the opposite
side.   The posterior vertical bar is connected with a cup-like *pericardial
cartilage* (*per. c.*), which supports the posterior and lateral walls of the pericardium.   The whole branchial basket lies external to the gill-pouches and
branchial arteries, not, like typical visceral arches, in the walls of the pharynx.

The median fins are supported by delicate cartilaginous rods (Fig. 114, *c. r.*,
Fig. 125, *cr.*).   These are more numerous than the myomeres, and lie parallel to
one another in the substance of the fin, extending downwards to the fibrous
neural tube.   The structure of the cartilage is peculiar and varies in different
parts.   It has very little matrix.   Such rods are probably not homologous
with the fin-rays of true fishes (p. 307).

The **muscles** of the trunk and tail are arranged in myomeres which take a
zigzag course.   In the branchial region they are divided into dorsal and
ventral bands, which pass respectively above and below the gill-slits ; but in
the trunk there is no division into dorsal and ventral parts.   A great mass
of radiating muscle is inserted into the buccal funnel, and the 'tongue' has
an extremely complex musculature which derives its nerve-supply from the
trigeminal nerve.

Alimentary Canal and Associated Structures.—The *teeth* are laminated horny
cones.   Beneath them lie mesodermal papillæ (covered with ectoderm) which
bear a superficial resemblance to the germs of true calcified teeth.   When
worn out they are succeeded by others developed at their bases.   Opening
into the mouth below the tongue are paired ducts which lead from the two
buccal glands.   These are embedded in the *basilaris muscles* and appear to
secrete a substance which prevents the coagulation of the blood of the host.
The mouth leads into a *buccal cavity* (Fig. 118, *b. f.*) formed from the stomodæum of the embryo, and communicating behind with two tubes placed one
above the other.   The dorsal of these is the œsophagus (*œs.*) ; the ventral canal
is the *respiratory tube* (*ph.*), or pharynx.   Guarding the entrance to the latter
is a curtain-like fold, the *velum* (*vel.*).   The œsophagus extends above the
pericardium and enters the *intestine* (*int.*) through a valvular aperture.   The
intestine is unconvoluted.   Its anterior end is slightly dilated, and is the only
representative of a stomach.   Its posterior end is widened to form the *rectum*
(Figs. 110, 125), which ends at a cloaca.   As Barrington has shown, true gastric
digestion involving the action of pepsin does not seem to occur until we reach
the true fishes (as far as the vertebrates of to-day are concerned).   The development of the capacious stomach is correlated with the ancient change from
micro- to macro-phagy (p. 206).   Although a stomach is lacking in some of the

higher fishes (p. 336), it is probable that in the Agnatha its absence is a primitive, rather than a secondary, feature.

The whole of the intestine of *Petromyzon* is formed from the mesenteron of the embryo, and the blastopore becomes the anus, there being no proctodæum. The lumen of the intestine is crescentic owing to the presence of a *typhlosole* in which lie the anterior mesenteric artery and hepatic portal vein. Between these vessels and the wall of the typhlosole is a reticular tissue whose cavities communicate with capillaries. Blood cells of all types are formed in this spleen-like tissue and passed from there to the blood. The typhlosole takes a slightly spiral course along the intestine and is hence known as the *spiral valve* (Fig. 114, *sp. v.*). There is no continuous mesentery, but only a number of narrow supporting bands.

The *liver* (Fig. 118, *l.*) is a large bilobed organ. Gall-bladder and bile-duct occur in the larva, but are at least sometimes absent in the adult. There is no pancreas as such. In both larval and adult lampreys, however, there occur in the gut epithelium aggregations of seemingly secretory cells of two different kinds. There is suggestive experimental evidence that one kind (*zymogen cells*) produce a proteolytic enzyme, and that the other sort is involved in carbohydrate metabolism. This second, probably endocrine, group has no communication with the lumen of the intestine. It arises in the larva as ' cords of cells' of one type (Barrington), and forms what have been termed *follicles of Langerhans*. These may be homologous with the islets of Langerhans (p. 153) of higher forms. Both secretory elements—hypothetical endocrine and zymogen—occur in the sub-mucosa at the anterior end of the broader mid-gut. The follicles of Langerhans are aggregated near the entrance of the bile-duct. It must be emphasised, however, that the two elements, though occurring in the same region, are not as intimately associated as are the acinous cells and insulin-producing elements in the compound pancreas of the Gnathostomata (p. 203).

Respiratory Organs.—Adult lampreys differ from all other Vertebrata in that the pharynx ends blindly. By virtue of this difference it is referred to, perhaps unnecessarily, as the ' respiratory tube ' (Fig. 118, *ph.*). In the ammocœte (p. 196) the pharynx communicates posteriorly with a short, narrow œsophagus but, during metamorphosis, this connection is lost and the œsophagus becomes extended forward dorsal to the respiratory tube and opens separately into the buccal cavity.

The respiratory organs are typical gill-pouches. They have the form of biconvex lenses, with numerous gill-lamellæ developed on the inner surfaces, and are separated from one another by wide interbranchial septa. The gills are much less pouch-like in the ammocœte, where they open widely into the pharynx (Fig. 119). In the embryo an additional gill pouch rudiment occurs in front of the first of the adult series.

Circulatory System.—The blood-vascular system shows a radical advancement from the primitive Amphioxus plan in the possession of a distinct heart. The *atrium* (Fig. 118, *atr.*) is situated to the left of the *ventricle* (*v.*) and receives blood from a small *sinus venosus* (*s. v.*). There is no conus arteriosus, but the proximal end of the ventral aorta presents a slight dilatation or *bulbus arteriosus*. Both afferent and efferent branchial arteries supply each the posterior hemibranch of one gill-pouch and the anterior hemibranch of the next. They are thus related to the gills, not to the gill-pouches. In addition to the paired *jugulars* there is a median ventral *inferior jugular vein* returning blood from the lower parts of the head. There is no renal portal system (p. 244), the two

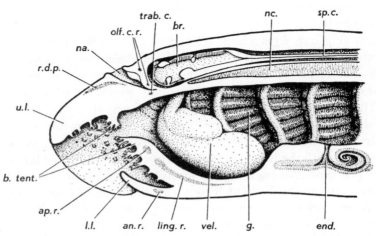

FIG. 119.—**Geotria: Ammocœte head region.** (Diagrammatic half-section of *G. australis*.) *an. r.* rudiment of annular cartilage (mucocartilage); *ap. r.* rudiment of apical cartilage (mucocartilage); *br.* brain; *b. tent.* buccal tentacles; *end.* endostyle; *g.* gill; *ling. r.* rudiment of lingual cartilage (mucocartilage); *l. l.* lower lip; *na.* nasal aperture; *nc.* notochord; *olf. c. r.* rudiment of olfactory capsule (cartilage); *r. d. p.* rostro-dorsal plate (mucocartilage); *sp. c.* spinal cord; *trab. c.* trabecular commissure (cartilage); *u. l.* upper lip; *vel.* velum.   (Drawn by R. Strahan.)

branches of the *caudal vein* being continued directly into the *cardinals*. Blood from the kidneys drains into two *sub-cardinal sinuses* (Fig. 114, *s.-c.s.*) which connect by numerous small passages with the cardinal veins above. The *left precaval* disappears in the adult, so that the jugulars and cardinals of both sides open into the *right precaval*. On the sides of the segmental arteries and veins occurs diffuse *chromaffin tissue* (p. 152). There is evidence that an extract of this tissue has properties strongly resembling that of mammalian *adrenalin*. Such tissue may represent a diffuse adrenal medulla. Islets of cells around the lateral and ventral walls of the cardinal veins have been thought possibly to represent adrenal *cortical tissue* (p. 152).

The *erythrocytes* of the blood contain a respiratory pigment, *hæmoglobin*, which is intermediate in many of its properties between the hæmoglobins of invertebrates and those of gnathostomes.

As previously mentioned, the formation of blood cells, *hæmatopoiesis*, occurs primarily in the spiral valve. In the adult, this function is shared with the *reticular tissue* of the kidney. The erythrocytes, in common with those of true fishes, amphibians, reptiles, and birds, retain their nucleus throughout the life of the corpuscle. The presence of hæmoglobin and a force-pump, the heart, enormously increases the capacity of the circulatory system to transport speedily the oxygen (taken in at the gills) to the tissues throughout the body. An extensive system of *lymphatic sinuses* (p. 116) also occurs.

Nervous System.—This, too, shows a great advance on that of Amphioxus. An elaborate brain is developed along with a system of cranial nerves. It is of great interest, however, that the dorsal and ventral roots of the spinal nerves are unjoined, and therefore retain the Amphioxus plan. Similar to those of Amphioxus, and differing from those of other vertebrates, the nerves of the Lamprey and other cyclostomes are unmyelinated. The spinal cord is wholly composed of transparent grey matter. It contains no blood-vessels, but is dorso-ventrally flattened in a manner that may possibly allow metabolic exchanges to take place without them. As in the fishes and other vertebrates, the nerve cell-bodies are arranged around the narrow central canal, but synaptic contacts occur at the periphery of the cord in what would be the 'white matter' in other vertebrates. This arrangement gives rise to a *neuropil* (nerve felt-work). In this, afferent sensory fibres terminate in close proximity to the dendrites of motor-cells whose axons become associated in the ventral nerve-roots. It is thus probable that the motor-fibres can be stimulated directly as a result of sensory impulses initiated by contact with environmental stimuli. The connection between brain and motor-fibres appears to be by means of the large and prominent *Müller's fibres* which originate from giant cells in the mid- and hind-brain and probably stimulate motor-cell dendrites in the ventral region of the cord.

The brain (Figs. 120, 121) exhibits the typical pattern that is found throughout the vertebrate series. Some of the structures that are well-developed in the higher forms occur in a relatively primitive condition. This of course is essentially a reflection of the life of the animal. The *optic lobes* (Figs. 120, 121, *opt. l.*) are very imperfectly differentiated in the tectum of the mid-brain. In the hind-brain the small size of the *cerebellum* is remarkable. This organ occurs as a mere transverse band roofing over the anterior end of the 4th ventricle, and its lack of complexity is not surprising when we observe the Lamprey's mode of locomotion even when it is not being transported by its host. The rest of the hind-brain is highly developed ; among other functions it controls the powerful sucking structures by means of the trigeminal nerve. The central region of the tectum of the mid-brain is epithelial and is related to a vascular thickening of the overlying pia-mater which forms a choroid plexus, so that when the membranes are removed an aperture is left. No choroid

plexus is found in the mid-brain of higher vertebrates, where such structures
are limited to the fore- and hind-brain.

On the dorsal border of the lateral wall of the diencephalon are two *ganglia
habenulæ*, the right (*r. gn. hb.*) being much larger than the left (*l. gn. hb.*).
These constitute an *epithalamus* and are connected to the *pineal apparatus*.

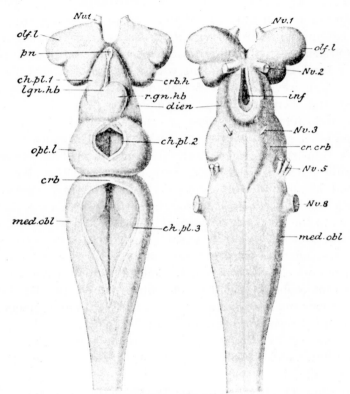

FIG. 120.—**Petromyzon: Brain.** Dorsal (*left*) and ventral (*right*) views of *P. marinus*. *ch. pl.* 1,
anterior choroid plexus forming roof of prosencephalon and diencephalon; *ch. pl.* 2, aperture in
roof of mid-brain exposed by removal of middle choroid plexus; *ch. pl.* 3, metacœle exposed by
removal of posterior choroid plexus; *crb.* cerebellum; *cr. crb.* crura cerebri; *crb. h.* olfactory
lobes ; *dien.* diencephalon; *inf.* infundibulum; *l. gn. hb.* left habenular ganglion; *med. obl.* medulla
oblongata; *Nv.* 1, olfactory, *Nv.* 2, optic, *Nv.* 3, oculo-motor, *Nv.* 5, trigeminal, and *Nv.* 8, auditory
nerves; *olf. l.* olfactory bulbs; *opt. l.* optic lobes; *pn.* pineal eye; *r. gn. hb.* right ganglion
habenulæ. (After Ahlborn.)

This consists of the *pineal eye* which lies against a transparent area of the cranial
roof and the smaller *parapineal body* lying below and somewhat behind it. A
stalk containing nerve-fibres leads from the pineal eye to the right habenular
ganglion, and a similar one from the parapineal body leads to the left habenular
ganglion. Since the habenular ganglia are paired structures, it would seem
that pineal and parapineal eyes were originally paired and have only secondarily come to lie one on top of the other. The pineal eye contains a pigmented

retina with sensory cells, and a flattened imperfect lens. In the parapineal body these structures are extremely reduced and hardly recognisable.

The pineal apparatus is better developed than in any of the higher forms now living, and Young has shown that it is of vital importance in the everyday life of the Lamprey. As light conditions in the environment change, so does the colour of the larval form. The pineal apparatus is photosensitive, and it seems that impulses are conveyed *via* the well-developed *hypothalamus* (in the ventral region of the diencephalon) to the endocrine *pituitary gland*. The pituitary or *hypophysis* is closely applied to the hypothalamus : there is no hypophysial stalk, such as is developed in the higher Vertebrata. The gland is a compound one, consisting of a comparatively large *pars anterior* and

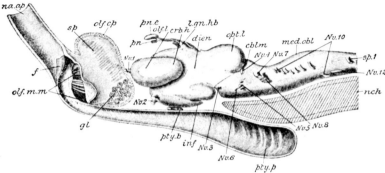

Fig. 121.—*Petromyzon:* **Brain with olfactory and naso-hypophysial ducts.** *Cblm.* cerebellum; *crb. h.* olfactory lobe; *dien.* diencephalon; *f.* fold in nasal duct; *gl.* accessory olfactory organ; *inf.* infundibulum; *l. gn. hb.* left habenular ganglion; *med. obl.* medulla oblongata; *na. ap.* nostril; *nch.* notochord; *Nv.* 1, olfactory nerve; *Nv.* 2, optic n.; *Nv.* 3, oculomotor n.; *Nv.* 4, trochlear n.; *Nv.* 5, trigeminal n.; *Nv.* 6, adbucens n.; *Nv.* 7, facial n.; *Nv.* 8, auditory n.; *Nv.* 10, vagus n.; *Nv.* 12, hypoglossal n.; *olf. cp.* olfactory capsule; *olf. l.* olfactory bulb; *olf. m. m.* olfactory mucosa; *opt. l.* optic lobe; *pn.* parapineal organ; *pn. e.* pineal eye; *pty. b.* pituitary gland; *pty. p.* hypophysial sac; *sp.* median septum of olfactory capsule; *sp.* 1, dorsal root of first spinal nerve. (Combined from figures by Ahlborn and Kænsche.)

a flattened *pars intermedia*. These are separated from the third ventricle by a thin tract of epithelial tissue which may represent the pars nervosa (of the posterior lobe) of higher forms. There is experimental evidence that the expansion of melanophores, causing the Lamprey's skin to darken, is caused by a secretion from the intermedia when this is stimulated by nerve impulses originating from the pineal.

In front of the diencephalon are paired bean-like masses, the cerebral hemispheres, each consisting of a small posterior portion, the *olfactory lobe* (*crb. h.*) and a larger *olfactory bulb* (*olf. l.*).

The cavity of the fore-brain extends laterally into these hemispheres to form rudimentary lateral ventricles. The part of the lateral ventricle which is contained in the olfactory bulb is sometimes referred to as the *rhinocœle*.

Organs of Special Sense.—The external nostril (Fig. 110, *n.*; Fig. 118, *na.*) leads by a short passage into a rounded *olfactory sac* (Fig. 118, *olf.*) placed just in front of the brain and having its posterior wall raised into ridges covered by the olfactory mucous membrane (Fig. 121, *olf. m. m.*). Here are located specialised olfactory receptor-cells, and from these travel axons which become aggregated in the short *olfactory nerve* (Fig. 120, *nv. 1*). This joins the highly organised *olfactory bulb* (*olf. l.*) close by. From the bottom of

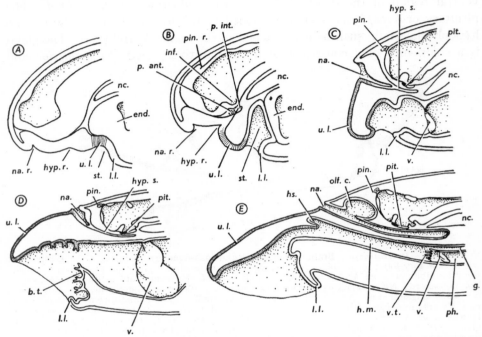

FIG. 122.—*Petromyzon:* **Development.** Five stages in the development of the cavities of the anterior part of the body. A, B, C—successive embryonic stages; D—ammocœte; E—adult. *b. t.* buccal tentacles; *end.* endoderm; *g.* œsophagus; *h. m.* hind-mouth; *hs.* hydrosinus; *hyp. r.* hypophysial rudiment; *hyp. s.* hypophysial sac; *inf.* infundibulum; *l. l.* lower lip; *na.* nasal aperture; *na. r.* nasal rudiment; *nc.* notochord; *olf. c.* olfactory capsule; *p. ant.* pars anterior of pituitary; *ph.* pharynx; *pin.* pineal eye; *pin. r.* pineal rudiment: *p. int.* pars intermedia of pituitary; *pit.* pituitary gland; *st.* stomodæum; *u. l.* upper lip; *v.* velum; *v. t.* velar tentacles. (Drawn by R. Strahan, after various authors.)

the olfactory sac is given off a large naso-hypophysial sac (Fig. 118, *n. hyp.*, Fig. 121, *pty. p.*) which extends downwards and backwards between the brain and the skull-floor, passes through the basicranial fontanelle, and ends blindly below the anterior end of the notochord. This elongated, compressible pouch seems to act in a manner analogous to the rubber bulb of a pipette. The expanded and closed end of the pouch lies directly above the dorsal wall of the pharynx and between the first pair of gill-pouches. Directly above the pouch is the un-yielding anterior end of the notochord (Fig. 121, *nch.*). Respiratory movements squeeze the water in the pouch in a forward direction out through the nostril (*na. ap.*) situated on the dorsal surface of the head.   When the pressure relaxes, a fresh stream of water flows into the pouch, and thus comes in contact with the olfactory receptor-organs.   If the aperture is experimentally blocked, the Lamprey no longer swims away from noxious substances liberated in its vicinity.

The relations between the olfactory sac, naso-hypophysial sac, and the pituitary body are extraordinary.   In the embryo, before the stomodæum (Fig. 122, *A*, *st.*) communicates with the gut, two unpaired ectodermal invaginations appear in front of the mouth.   The foremost of these is the *nasal rudiment* (*na. r.*).   The other (which is situated between the olfactory sac and the

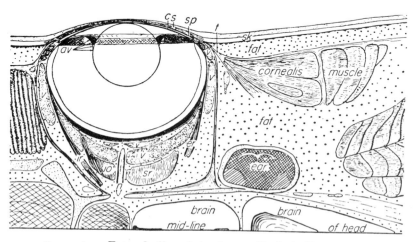

Fig. 123.—*Lampetra:* **Eye and adjacent structures.**   (*L. fluviatilis*, anterior end to the left.) Accommodation is accomplished by alteration of the shape of the eyeball by the extrinsic *cornealis* muscle.   The tendon of this muscle is inserted on the rim of the spectacle, a specialised window-like area of transparent skin.   Muscle contraction draws the spectacle taut and flattens the subjacent cornea.   This in turn is in close contact with the lens which is thus pushed closer to the retina.   The elasticity of sclera and vitreous body, and the equality of the intra-ocular pressure, returns the eyeball to the resting shape.   *av.* anterior surface of vitreous; *c.* cornea; *er.* external rectus; *io.* inferior oblique; *ir.* internal rectus; *s.* spectacle; *sk.* skin; *sp.* space between spectacle and cornea; *sr.* superior rectus; *t.* tendon of cornealis; *v.* venous sinuses (cushioning the eyeball).   (After Walls.)

mouth) is the hypophysial rudiment (*hyp. r.*), which in this case opens just outside the stomodæum instead of within it as in other Craniata.   Its inner or blind end extends to the ventral surface of the fore-brain and terminates just below the infundibulum (*inf.*).   As development proceeds, the olfactory and hypophysial invaginations become sunk in a common pit (*B*), which, by the growth of the immense upper lip (*up. l.*), is gradually shifted to the top of the head (*C, D*).   In the ammocœte (p. 196), this common naso-hypophysial cavity extends only a short distance under the forebrain.   The hypophysial rudiment grows out as a thin plate of tissue.   This buds off (1) the intermedia, which interdigitates with the nervous tissue from the floor of the third ventricle, and (2) the anterior body of the pituitary gland.   Later, all connection with the

naso-hypophysial cavity is lost.   At metamorphosis the last-named grows out
into its adult condition independently of the pituitary gland.   The peculiar
monorhinal condition of the lamprey is due to the hypertrophy of the upper
lip.   This, in turn, is related to the function of the upper lip, which is the burrowing organ of the ammocœte.   We may therefore assume, with Watson, that
the cephalaspids, anaspids, and hags similarly possessed ancestors in which the
upper lip performed this function.

The paired *eyes* of *Petromyzon* are essentially similar to those of other
vertebrates.   Each is moved by six external muscles, as in higher forms, but
the arrangement of these is peculiar.   The accommodation of the eye is brought
about by an extraordinary arrangement (Fig. 123).   A remarkable *cornealis
muscle*, which arises from the special-
isation of two anterior myotomes, *pulls
on the cornea from one side and flattens
it.   This corneal movement thrusts the
lens in towards the retina.*   Thus, the
whole lens moves in a manner roughly
similar to the lens of a camera, being
moved back and forth in relation to the
photographic plate.   It is said that the
cornea of the lamprey does not move
when the position of the rest of the eye
is altered by the extrinsic muscles.

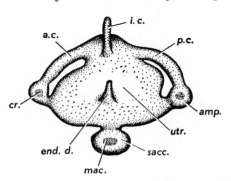

Fig.   124.—*Petromyzon:* **Membranous
labyrinth** (left).   *a. c.* anterior semicircular
canal; *amp.* ampulla; *cr.* crista; *end. d.*
endolymphatic duct; *i. c.* invagination canal;
mac. macula; *p. c.* posterior semicircular
canal; *sacc.* sacculus; *utr.* utriculus.   (Redrawn from Neal and Rand, after Hesse.)

The membranous labyrinth (Fig.
124) is remarkable in having only two
semi-circular canals.   These, the *anterior* (*a. c.*) and *posterior semi-circular
canals* (*p. c.*), curve at right angles to each other and are equipped with a
sacculus (*sacc.*) and *utriculus* (*utr.*).   Little or nothing is known concerning the
actual hearing capacity of *Petromyzon*.   Sensory apparatus within the above
compartments appreciates changes in the animal's orientation, and resultant
nerve-impulses lead to appropriate reflex movements and keep it on an even
keel.

In cyc ostomes the *lateral line* sense-organs (p. 136) are relatively simple and
are exposed to the surrounding water.   They occur in the head region and in
a single line extending along each side of the body.   They are innervated by
cranial nerves ; those on the body and tail are connected to the central nervous
system by a branch of the vagus.

There is experimental evidence that *skin photoreceptor organs* occur in the
tail of the ammocœte larva at least ; the work of Young suggests that the caudal
lateral line organs are involved.   Finally, *organs of taste* occur in the wall of
the pharynx between the gill-sacs.

Urinogenital System.—This shows a great advance on that of Amphioxus. Complicated organs of excretion, the *kidneys* (Figs. 114, 125, *mes.*), have appeared. These enable the animal to eliminate excess fluid and waste nitrogenous and other substances, and at the same time maintain an appropriate osmotic balance whether it is living in a fresh- or a salt-water medium. The kidneys are long, strap-shaped bodies developed from the *mesonephros* of the embryo. The essential renal units within the adult kidney are numerous minute Malphigian corpuscles. Each contains a 'knot' of microscopic blood-

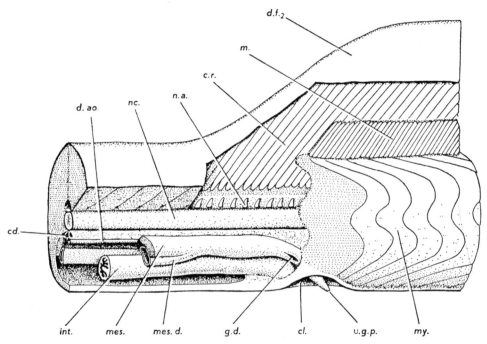

Fig. 125.—***Petromyzon :* Cloacal region.** *P. marinus. cd.* posterior cardinal vein; *cl.* cloaca; *c. r.* cartilaginous rods ('fin rays'); *d. ao.* dorsal aorta; *d. f.₂* second dorsal fin; *g. d.* genital pore; *int.* intestine; *m.* muscles of fin; *mes.* mesonephros; *mes. d.* mesonephric duct; *my.* myotome; *n. a.* neural arch; *nc.* notochord; *u. g. p.* urinogenital papilla. (Redrawn after Goodrich.)

vessels, the *glomerulus*, and opens into a winding tubule (p. 155). The heart-beat pumps blood through the glomeruli. Excess fluids and excretory products are shed down the tubules towards the exterior.

Each kidney is attached along one edge to the dorsal wall of the body-cavity by part of the peritoneum. Along the other (free) edge runs the *mesonephric duct* (Fig. 114, *mes. d.*), which opens posteriorly into a small *urinogenital sinus* placed just behind the rectum. This opens by a *urino-genital papilla* into a pit, the *cloaca*, in which the alimentary canal also ends. The side-walls of the sinus are pierced by a pair of small apertures, the *genital pores* (Fig. 125, *g. d.*), which place its cavity in communication with the cœlom.

The kidneys contain lymphoid tissue where, as has been mentioned, blood cells may be formed. This tissue also performs a phagocytic function by destroying old blood cells and removing suspended material from the circulation.

The sexes are separate in the adult. However, sexual differentiation occurs at a comparatively late stage, and so both oocytes and spermatocytes may be found in a single gonad in the young Lamprey. The gonad (Fig. 118, *gon.*, Fig. 114, *ts.*) is unpaired. The ovary in the female ruptures and extrudes eggs directly into the cœlom, as in higher vertebrates. The testis, however, is unique among vertebrates in the manner in which it discharges its spermatozoa. The sperm-containing follicles of the testis rupture and the spermatozoa, like the ova, are shed into the cœlom. The gametes escape through the pair of genital pores mentioned above. These, alike in each sex, lead as short canals to the urinogenital sinus from which eggs or sperms escape to the exterior where fertilisation takes place. In adult males there occur prominent aggregations of interstitial *Leydig-cells* in the typical vertebrate arrangement (Fig. 97, p. 152).

Development.—The egg is *telolecithal*, having a considerable accumulation of yolk in the vegetal hemisphere. In correspondence with this, cleavage is complete but unequal, a condition comparable with that in the frog (p. 418). Early segmentation divides the animal hemisphere into a number of small, relatively yolk-less *micromeres* (Fig. 126, *A*, *micr.*), and the vegetal hemisphere into a smaller number of yolky *macromeres* (*A*, *y. end.*). A cavity, the *blastocœle* (*blc.*), develops between these two cell layers. The faster-dividing micromeres grow around to enclose the macromeres and also invaginate through a crescentic groove, the *dorsal lip* (*B*, *d. l.*) of the *blastopore* (*B*, *blp.*) just below the equator of the egg. As development proceeds, the blastopore moves towards the vegetal pole of the embryo (*C*) and later passes it (*D*). In contrast to the condition in *Rana* (p. 418), the position of the blastopore bears no relation to the plane of the first cleavage. The process of invagination through the blastopore gives rise to the cavity of the archenteron (*C*, *arch.*). The ventral wall of this cavity is formed from the macromeres, while the dorsal and lateral walls are formed from invaginated *chorda-mesoderm* (*C*, *ch. m.*) which later develops into the notochord (*D*, *nch.*) and somites (*F*, *som.*). Somewhat later, a groove appears in the endodermal floor and the sides of the groove come together to form an endodermal roof (*F*, *end. r.*) to the gut. Apart from this contribution, the macromeres take no part in organ-building. At the time of hatching they still retain considerable food stores. Owing to the mass of this tissue, the lumen of the archenteron is much narrower than in Amphioxus.

By the completion of gastrulation, the blastopore has taken up a position at the postero-ventral end. The development of the central nervous system differs widely from the corresponding process in Amphioxus, and is only approached among the Craniata by the bony fishes. The dorsal surface becomes flattened along a narrow longitudinal area, and along this a groove appears. This terminates immediately in front of the blastopore. The area along which the groove runs soon becomes raised up above the general surface and forms a narrow longitudinal elevation. Sections of this stage show that the ectoderm has developed a thickening along the course of the longitudinal groove, and this comes to grow downwards towards the archenteron as a

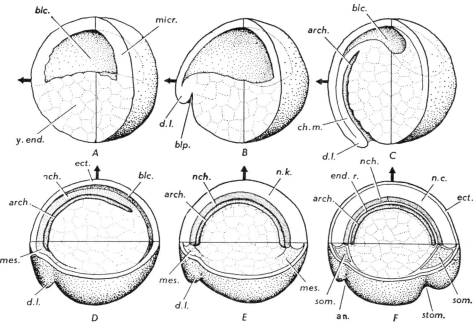

FIG. 126.—*Petromyzon:* **Development.** Successive stages in gastrulation shown in reconstructions from which parts of the embryo have been removed to reveal internal structures. The centre of gravity shifts during gastrulation and this affects the orientation so that the region marked by the arrow eventually comes to lie dorsally. The shift in orientation is a gradual one, but for convenience is shown in two stages. *an.* anus; *arch.* archenteron; *blc.* blastocœle; *blp.* blastopore; *ch. m.* chorda-mesoderm; *d. l.* dorsal lip of blastopore; *ect.* ectoderm; *end. r.* endodermal roof of archenteron; *mes.* mesoderm; *micr.* micromere layer; *n. c.* nerve cord; *nch.* notochord; *n. k.* neural keel; *som.* somite; *stom.* stomodæal invagination; *y. end.* yolky endoderm. (Drawn by R. Strahan, reconstructed from Brachet after Weissenberg and de Sely-Longchamps.)

solid longitudinal *neural keel*. This is the rudiment of the central nervous system. Subsequently the keel becomes separated off from the surface ectoderm, and lies below it as a solid cord. It is only at a considerably later period that a lumen appears in this cord, and gives rise to the ventricles of the brain and the central canal of the spinal cord. In contrast to the condition in Amphioxus, somite formation is limited to the dorsal mesoderm on either side of the mid-line, a feature which is also characteristic of the remainder of the Craniata. The blastopore does not close; it is converted into an anal aperture, so that there is no proctodæum. The dorsal lip of the blastopore, very prominent from the first, is produced into the rudiment of the tail region. The mouth is developed later than the anal aperture by stomodæal invagination. The membrane previously separating the fore-gut from the mid-gut becomes the *velum* (Fig. 122, *v.*) of the larva.

The young is hatched as an *ammocœte larva* (Fig. 127) some 10 mm. long. This differs from the adult in several important respects. The median fin is continuous. There is a semi-circular, hood-shaped *upper lip* (*u. l.*) instead of the suctorial buccal funnel of the adult. Teeth are absent. A set of branched *buccal tentacles* (Fig. 119, *b. tent.*) guards the entrance to the alimentary canal. Behind the tentacles lies the velum (*vel.*), a pair of cup-shaped structures attached to the anterior wall of the pharynx. These act as paddles and maintain a stream of water through the pharynx. In this they are assisted by pumping movements of the pharynx. Although the ammocœte burrows in mud, it feeds by taking in fairly clean water from the oral end of its burrow. The endostyle (*end.*), homologous with that of Amphioxus, passes a stream of mucus forward along a groove in the floor of the pharynx to a pair of *peripharyngeal grooves* behind the velum. Movements of the velum dislodge strands of mucus which form a sort of net across the entrance to the pharynx. Further down the pharynx, the strands come together to form a cord which passes to the œsophagus. Propulsion is now achieved by the action of *œsophageal cilia*. Food is in this manner filtered from the water current and passed to the digestive region of the alimentary canal without being diluted with a great amount of water. In Amphioxus the feeding current is maintained by cilia; in the ammocœte by muscles.

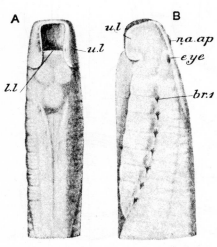

FIG. 127.—*Lampetra:* **Development.** Head of larval *L. fluviatilis.* *A*, from beneath; *B*, from the side. *br.* 1, first branchial aperture; *eye*, eye; *l. l.* lower lip; *na. ap.* nostril; *u. l.* upper lip. (After W. K. Parker.)

This evolution of a *muscular*, in place of a ciliary, ingestive apparatus was an immense step forward in evolution. It enabled a far swifter and greater intake and, consequently, the development and sustenance of far bigger animals.

During its early life the larva spends most of its time buried in a U-shaped burrow in the mud, emerging only at night to change its feeding ground. It swims with its head downwards and then burrows again with great rapidity. Two major instinctive responses combine to maintain the ammocœte in its proper environment : *photokinesis* and *thigmotaxis*. The photokinetic response is shown when ammocœtes are illuminated. Their reaction is to swim in a random fashion until reaching a shaded area, when locomotion becomes much more limited. The thigmotactic response is shown when ammocœtes are given the alternative of a smooth bottom or tubes into which to swim. Spontaneous movements are much fewer when touch receptors are stimulated over a large part of the body-surface than when only a limited number are, so that animals tend to stay in a tube after reaching it, even if the illumination is fairly high. Together these responses lead the animals to seek crevices or burrow in dark places. A batch of *photoreceptors* occur in the skin of the tail, as Young has shown. These presumably act as an extra warning device to prevent the animal from leaving its tail exposed above the burrow.

We have seen that larval lampreys exhibit a muscular feeding device, yet retain an endostyle, a characteristic part of the feeding mechanism of ancestral forms. At the time of metamorphosis, the endostyle becomes modified and develops into an entirely different structure that occurs throughout the rest of the vertebrate series—the endocrine *thyroid* gland. The endostyle loses its mucus-secreting capacity and develops a series of iodine-containing vesicles that are clearly of the same nature as the thyroid follicles of higher animals.

At the same time the buccal region becomes elongated to accommodate the tongue ; and its margin becomes circular. The tentacles recede and are replaced by teeth on the buccal funnel and tongue. The velum becomes reduced, and skeletal rods develop from it to form a filter guarding the respiratory pharynx : food material is thus diverted to the œsophagus, which has already been cut off from the pharynx proper. The gills are modified and open into the pharynx. The naso-hypophysial sac becomes enlarged posteriorly. The larval cranium, which consists of little more than the parachordals, trabeculæ, and olfactory and otic capsules, becomes filled out into the adult condition. The skeleton of the upper lip and tongue, which is absent in the larva, also develops during metamorphosis. The eyes complete their development and move to the surface. The continuous dorsal fin is excavated to form the two dorsal, and single caudal fins ; and the colour of the skin changes from muddy brown to metallic on the dorsal surface. In some species, brilliant-coloured stripes also appear at this stage. The Lamprey now leaves its river habitat for the open sea and begins the carnivorous phase of its life-history.

CLASS MYXINOIDEA

The exclusively marine hags or slime-eels are exemplified by the widespread genera *Myxine*, *Paramyxine*, and *Eptatretus* (= *Bdellostoma*). These inhabit muddy bottoms, where they rest in temporary burrows. They feed on a wide range of dead animals and may perhaps prey upon living polychaetes and

priapuloids. They eat dead or dying fish, but the old view that they are
parasitic upon fishes is incorrect. Their method of feeding is unique among
vertebrates in that they bite with protrusible horny teeth (Fig. 130, *d. pl.*)
which move against each other from side to side. Other unique features
include the direct communication between the nostril and the pharynx, the
existence of auxiliary hearts in the caudal and visceral circulation, and the
fusion of the two semicircular canals form a ring-shaped structure.

COMPARISON OF THE MYXINOIDEA WITH THE LAMPREY

Myxinoids show a much greater range of variation than lampreys. Here
we shall only indicate the points in which they differ from lampreys and from
each other. The body of myxinoids is
cylindrical and from 40 to 80 cm. long.

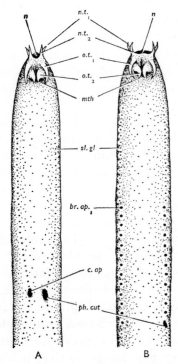

They are remarkable for the immense
amount of slime they can produce when
disturbed. The slime comes from *thread
cells*, peculiar to myxinoids, which occur
singly in the epidermis (Fig. 113) or
massed in the segmental *slime-glands*
(Fig. 128). During cell development a
continuous thread of fibrous protein is
laid down within the membrane. When
the hag is stimulated by agitation or local
pressure, large numbers of these cells
burst, releasing their threads, which are
from 1 to 3μ in diameter and several cm.
in length. The threads absorb water
almost instantaneously and form around
the body a tenacious slimy gel as much as
10 cm. thick. One medium-sized *Myxine*
can gelatinise as much as 500 cc. of sea
water in less than a minute.

FIG. 128.—Class **Myxinoidea: Myxine
glutinosa** (*A*) and *Eptatretus* (= *Bdellostoma*) *stoutii* (*B*) from below. *br. ap.*₁,
first branchial aperture; *c. ap.* common
branchial aperture; *mth.* mouth; *n.* nostril;
*n. t.*₁, ₂ nasal tentacles; *o. t.*₁, ₂ oral tentacles;
ph. cut. aperture of pharyngo-cutaneous
duct; *sl. gl.* slime glands. (Drawn by R.
Strahan.)

The buccal cavity is even longer than
in lampreys, but the mouth is not expanded into a funnel. The mouth and
the nostril are each surrounded by
tentacles (Fig. 128) supported by cartilages (Fig. 130, *tent.* 1–4). There is a
single median palatine tooth (Fig. 129,

pal. t.) above the oral aperture, and two rows of smaller teeth arising from the
dental plate (Fig. 130) on the 'tongue'. The papillæ beneath the cone-like horny

teeth bear a closer superficial resemblance to rudiments (or vestiges) of true calcified teeth than is the case in lampreys ; but it appears that no odontoblasts and no calcified substance of any kind are formed in connection with them. The terminal nostril opens into a tubular nasal duct (Fig. 129, *na. d.*) leading to the olfactory organ and is continuous with the naso-hypophysial duct (*na. hyp.*) which opens into the buccal cavity just anterior to the velum (*vel.*). This is homologous with the velum of the ammocœte and, although having a much more complex structure, performs the same function of maintaining the respiratory current. The continuous flow of water over the olfactory mucosa permitted by this arrangement is probably valuable to a blind scavenger.

The only fin is a narrow caudal fin surrounding the end of the tail. The respiratory organs present striking differences in the major genera. In *Eptatretus* there are in different species six to fourteen very small *external branchial apertures* (*br. ap. 1*) on each side. Each of these communicates by a short *efferent duct* with one of the gill-pouches which is again connected with the pharynx by another tube. Behind and close to the last gill-slit, on the left side, is an aperture leading into a tube, the *pharyngo-cutaneous duct* (*œs. cut.*), which opens directly into the pharynx. In *Myxine* the efferent ducts (Fig. 129, *ef. d.*) all unite together before opening on the exterior, so that there is only a single *external branchial aperture* (*br. ap.*) on each side. The *pharyngo-cutaneous duct* (*œs. cut.*) opens into the left external branchial aperture (*br. ap.*) and

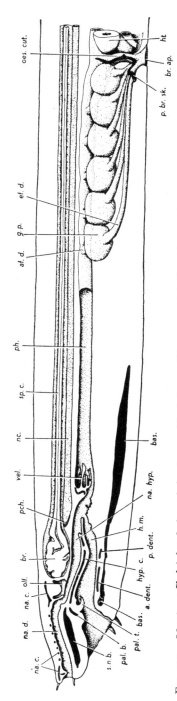

Fig. 129.—*Myxine*: **Skeletal and visceral structures.** *M. glutinosa.* Diagrammatic half-section: *a. dent.* anterior dental cartilage; *af. d.* afferent duct to gill pouch; *bas.* basal cartilage; *br.* brain; *br. ap.* common branchial aperture; *ef. d.* efferent duct from gill pouch; *g. p.* gill pouch; *h. m.* hindmouth; *ht.* heart; *hyp. c.* hypophysial cartilage; *na. c.* nasal cartilages; *na. d.* nasal duct; *na. hyp.* naso-hypophysial duct; *nc.* notochord; *œs. cut.* pharyngo-cutaneous duct; *olf.* olfactory organ; *pal. b.* palatine bar; *pal. t.* palatine tooth; *p. br. sk.* post-branchial skeleton; *pch.* parachordal; *p. dent.* posterior dental cartilage; *ph.* pharynx; *s. n. b.* subnasal bar; *sp. c.* spinal cord; *vel.* velum. (Drawn by R. Strahan, partly after Cole.)

serves for the expulsion of inhaled particles too large to enter the afferent ducts.

The spinal cord (*sp. c.*) is covered only by fibrous tissue.   There is no trace of neural arches in the trunk, but in the posterior part of the caudal region both neural canal and notochord are enclosed in a continuous cartilaginous plate.   Similarly, the roof of the skull is entirely membranous (Fig. 130). The skull has a fundamental similarity to that of lampreys, but this is obvious

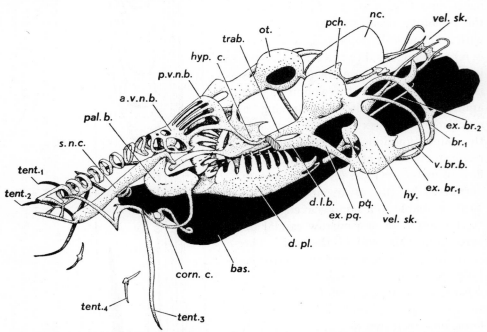

FIG. 130.—***Myxine*: Skull of adult.**   *M. glutinosa.*   Portion of the palatine bar is removed on left side.   *a.v.n.b.* anterior vertical nasal bar; *bas.* basal cartilage; *br.*$_1$ 1st (internal) branchial arch; *corn. c.* cornual cartilage; *d. l. b.* dorsal longitudinal bar; *d. pl.* dental plate; *ex. br.*$_{1, 2}$ 1st and 2nd extrabranchial arches; *ex. pq.* extrapalatoquadrate; *hy.* hyoid arch; *hyp. c.* hypophysial cartilage; *nc.* notochord; *ot.* otic capsule; *pal. b.* palatine bar; *pch.* parachordal; *pq.* palatoquadrate; *p. v. n. b.* posterior vertical nasal bar; *s. n. c.* subnasal cartilage; *tent.*$_{1, 2, 3, 4}$ tentacular cartilages; *trab.* trabecula; *v. br. b.* ventral branchial bar; *vel. sk.* velar skeleton.   (Drawn by R. Strahan, reconstructed from Cole.)

only in the embryo (Fig. 131).   Later developments, associated with the growth of the naso-hypophysial sac, the oral tentacles, and the backward migration of the gills, bring about a considerable distortion.   The *nasal duct* (Fig. 129, *na. d.*) is supported by rings of cartilage (*na. c.*), and the oral tentacles by flexible rods of the same tissue.   The *cornual cartilage* (Fig. 131, *corn. c.*) and the *subnasal cartilage* (*s. n. c.*) represent the skeleton of the upper lip of lampreys and the *basal plates* (Figs. 129 and 131, *bas.*) are, in part, the homologue of the lamprey tongue skeleton.   The *sub-ocular arch* (Fig. 130, *ex. pq.*, *pq.*, *hy.*) represents anteriorly the visceral skeleton of the mandibular arch and posteriorly, the hyoid arch. Of the remaining branchial arches, only the first two are represented, these being the *first extra-branchial cartilage (ex. br. 1.)*, and the *first branchial cartilage (br. 1)*, and the *second extra-branchial cartilage (ex. br. 2)*. In the region of the common branchial apertures a pair of asymmetrical cartilages (Fig. 129, *p. br. sk.*) may represent a posterior remnant of the branchial skeleton.

The myotomes of one side alternate with those of the other.

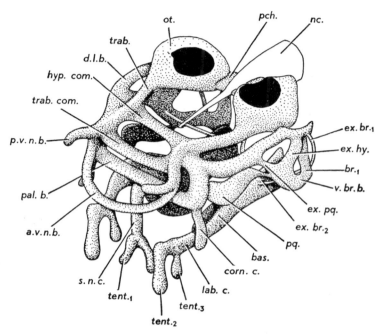

FIG. 131.—**Myxine: Skull of embryo.** *M. glutinosa. a. v. n. b.* anterior vertical nasal bar; *bas.* basal skeleton; *br.₁* 1st (internal) branchial arch; *corn. c.* cornual cartilage; *d. l. b.* dorsal longitudinal bar; *ex. br.₁, ₂* 1st and 2nd extrabranchial arches; *ex. hy.* extrahyal arch; *ex. pq.* extrapalatoquadrate; *hyp. com.* hypophysial commissure; *lab. c.* labial cartilage; *nc.* notochord; *ot.* otic capsule; *pal. b.* palatine bar; *pch.* parachordal; *pq.* palatoquadrate; *p. v. n. b.* posterior vertical nasal bar; *s. n. c.* subnasal cartilage; *tent.₁, ₂, ₃* tentacular cartilages; *trab.* trabecula; *trab. com.* trabecular commissure; *v. br. b.* ventral branchial bar. (Drawn by R. Strahan, reconstructed from Holmgren.)

The intestine is wide. The liver consists of separate anterior and posterior portions, the ducts of which open separately into the gall-bladder. A pancreas-like gland occurs in both *Myxine* and *Eptatretus* in a position comparable with that of the 'insular organ' of lampreys (p. 185). There is no definite spleen, but blood-forming lymphoid tissue is found scattered through the submucosa of the gut. Blood cells may also be formed in the pronephros.

The brain differs considerably from that of *Petromyzon*, especially in the larger olfactory lobes, the reduced ventricles, and the smaller mid-brain. The dorsal and ventral roots of the spinal nerves unite instead of remaining separate.

It is important to realise, however, that the junction is different from that typical of the Gnathostomata.

The eyes are vestigial and sunk beneath the skin, which, as in the ammocœte (p. 196), is light-sensitive. When stimulated these provoke a photokinetic response. The membranous labyrinth (Fig. 132) has only a single semicircular canal, which, having an ampulla at each end, probably represents both anterior and posterior canals (p. 145). Hags lack a pineal organ and a lateral line system. In comparison with lampreys, their sensory system is extremely limited.

The pronephros is retained in adult myxinoids as a pair of small bodies lying dorsal to the pericardial cavity, into which the nephrostomes open. In *Eptatretus*, the tubules open into an incomplete pronephric duct which, however, has no opening to the exterior. *Myxine* lacks a pronephric duct and the tubules end blindly. The functional kidney is the mesonephros, and is specially interesting from the fact that in myxinoids it retains in the adult its primitive segmental arrangement. The 'ureter' sends off in each segment a coiled tubule with a single Bowman's capsule, into which a branch from the aorta enters and forms a glomerulus.

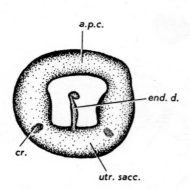

FIG. 132.—*Myxine:* **Membranous labyrinth** (left). *a. p. c.* fused anterior and posterior canals; *cr.* crista; *end. d.* endolymphatic duct; *utr. sacc.* urticulo-sacculus. (Redrawn from Neal and Rand, after Hesse.)

Despite many statements to the contrary, the sexes are probably separate in *Myxine* but, as in Lampreys, differentiation of the immature gonad does not occur until late in life. The female may thus retain an undeveloped testis and the male a rudimentary ovary. The large, cylindrical eggs are enclosed in a horny shell bearing terminal hooked processes.

The early development of *Myxine* is unknown, but there is no reason to assume that it differs markedly from *Eptatretus*, in which segmentation is markedly meroblastic, being confined to one pole of the elongate egg. The blastoderm thus formed extends gradually over the surface of the yolk, which it completely encloses only at a late stage, when the gill-clefts are all formed. *Eptatretus* differs from *Petromyzon* and resembles the majority of the Craniata in the mode of development of the central nervous system. This is formed not from a solid ectodermal keel, but from an open medullary groove. The lips of the groove bend inwards and unite to form a medullary canal. There is no metamorphosis in the life-history.

SUPER-CLASS GNATHOSTOMATA

INTRODUCTION

THE Gnathostomata includes all vertebrates with upper and lower jaws. It comprises a wide range of animals, from fish to the various tetrapod classes, which have in turn been derived from a fish or fish-like ancestor. An entirely satisfactory classification of fishes is not easy to construct, because of the incompleteness of several parts of the fossil record, and the consequent lack of connecting links. Complete agreement as to their arrangement, therefore, has not been reached, and the student will meet with a considerable choice of classifications. It is at least certain that within the old group of Pisces (fishes in the widest sense of the expression) there are fundamental divisions which are of great antiquity. Animals of these divisions appear to have little to do with one another beyond the possession of a possible, but unknown common ancestor at a very remote period.

The old classification of the Gnathostomata into five classes—Pisces, Amphibia, Reptilia, Aves, and Mammalia—has therefore to be modified by the division of the fishes. Here these will be divided into three classes, as follows:

CLASS PLACODERMI (APHETOHYOIDEA)

Sub-classes Acanthodii (Silurian–Permian)
 Arthrodira (Silurian–Devonian)
 Petalichthyida (Devonian)
 Antiarchi (Pterichthyomorphi) (Devonian)
 Rhenanida (Devonian)
 Palæospondylia (Devonian)

CLASS ELASMOBRANCHII (CHONDRICHTHYES, SELACHII)

Sub-class Selachii
 Orders Cladoselachii (Devonian–Permian)
 Pleuracanthodii (Devonian–Triassic)
 Protoselachii (Devonian–Recent)
 Euselachii (Jurassic–Recent)

Sub-class Bradyodonti
   Orders Eubradyodonti (Devonian–Recent)
      Holocephali (Jurassic–Recent)

CLASS OSTEICHTHYES

Sub-class Actinopterygii
   Super-orders Chondrostei (Jurassic–Recent)
      Holostei (Triassic–Recent)
      Teleostei (Jurassic–Recent)

Sub-class Crossopterygii
   Order Rhipidistia
      Sub-orders Osteolepidoti (Devonian–Permian)
         Cœlacanthini (Devonian–Recent)
   Order Dipnoi (Devonian–Recent)

Compared with the tetrapods (p. 381) the three classes mentioned above have certain characters in common. They have organs of respiration and locomotion related to a permanently aquatic life. The chief, and generally the only, respiratory organs are the gills. These are in the form of a series of vascular processes attached to the septa of the branchial arches and persistent throughout life.

The organs of locomotion are the paired pectoral and pelvic fins and the unpaired dorsal, anal, and caudal fins (p. 79). These fins are all supported by fin-rays of dermal origin, in addition to the endoskeletal supports. The fin-rays are of diagnostic significance. A dermal exoskeleton is typically present, but is occasionally secondarily lost. In the endoskeleton the notochord is usually partly replaced by vertebræ, either of bone or cartilage. There is a well-developed skull and a system of visceral arches, of which the first pair form the upper and lower jaws, the latter movably articulated with the skull. Both normally bear teeth (p. 103). The first pair of visceral arches mentioned above are actually the second pair, because primitively there was a premandibular arch that is represented in the Agnatha (p. 164; and see *Petromyzon*, p. 176). There is no middle ear (p. 114) and no allantoic bladder, the latter structure arising for the first time in the Amphibia (p. 381). These two negative characters are therefore also diagnostic.

There are other characters found in one or other of the three classes which, though highly characteristic when they occur, cannot be called diagnostic. It is the unequal distribution of these characters that makes the division of fishes into four classes desirable. A swim-bladder (p. 339), for instance, is normally present (though it may be secondarily lost) in all fishes except elasmobranchs, which never at any time possessed one. In the placoderms and other extinct groups the presence of the swim-bladder can only be surmised. The nasal capsules open by inhalent and exhalent apertures (p. 138). These may be only partly separate, as in the elasmobranchs (p. 230), or completely separate, as in the Actinopterygii, where they are both dorsal in position (p. 298). In the Crossopterygii (p. 353) one pair is external, the other internal in the mouth, although in some very ancient forms the internal nares have been lost. The condition of the circulatory system, the structure of the brain, the urinogenital organs, fins, and scales all yield characters which help to diagnose the various groups.

The kidney is a mesonephros with an occasional persistence of a few pronephric tubules (p. 153). As in all gnathostomes, there are three semicircular canals (p. 145).

CLASS PLACODERMI (APHETOHYOIDEA)

It seems certain that these animals were the earliest jawed vertebrates. They appeared in the Silurian, flourished in the Devonian and Carboniferous, and became extinct in the Permian (p. 3). As mentioned previously, it was once believed that the cartilaginous fishes represented the most primitive type. It now appears evident, however, that the present group of bony animals were the forerunners of some of the modern fishes, and perhaps even of the elasmobranchs. This appearance of bone (accompanied by the development of mobile jaws allied to the advantages conferred by an elaborate nervous system, a heart, and highly developed blood-vascular system) early provided a basis for the later development of animals of extraordinary complexity and adaptive efficiency.

The Placodermi are so called because of their heavy, defensive armour of bony plates (Figs. 133, 135). Members of this polymorphic class show a wide degree of adaptive radiation, and in some instances an appearance so unfishlike that their zoological position has been one of uncertainty. Some have been thought to be Agnatha (p. 164), some as being allied to the Dipnoi (p. 361), and some to the elasmobranchs (p. 219).

All placoderms possess jaws. Hyoid gill-slits persisted, and consequently spiracles had not arisen, and, further, the hyoid arch remained unmodified and *did not support the jaws*—the aphetohyoidean condition was retained (Watson). There thus persisted a type of jaw suspension (p. 94) more primitive than that in any other class of jawed fishes and one, moreover, which probably existed in ancestral gnathostomes. We shall see later that in modern fishes the hyomandibular bone (of the hyoid arch) helps support and brace the jaw against the cranium. It seems probable that the jaws have been derived from paired anterior gill-bars (see p. 93). This evolution of relatively massive jaws appears to have been influential in reducing the first pair of gill-slits and enabling the development of quite separate spiracles which became small apertures of specialised function in the former first gill-slit region.

For many years it was believed that at some early stage of craniate evolution primitive jaws had probably appeared long before the emergence of the hyoid arch as observed today.   It is now known that this anticipated condition did actually occur in the Placodermi.   The hyoid arch was in no sense a jaw support, and the cleft was probably a typical gill-cleft (p. 94).   The placoderm jaw is *autostylic, i.e.* it is articulated by its own processes to the cranium. We see in the buccal arrangements of these Palæozoic placoderms an enormous advance on the Agnatha, but, at the same time, a mechanical and masticatory

FIG. 133.—Sub-class and Order **Arthrodira,** Sub-order **Coccosteidæ.** *Dinichthys.* This carnivorous placoderm, seen here hunting the contemporary shark *Cladoselache* (p. 222), probably reached a length of 26 feet.   The head and thorax were armoured but the posterior parts were unprotected.   (After Heintz.)

efficiency very inferior in comparison with later types of articulation that we shall subsequently examine.

Most placoderms possess paired fins, but these are essentially adaptive organs, variable in the extreme, and no generalised 'ancestral pattern' is shown. At the same time there are a number of other characters which suggest an ultimate common ancestor for all placoderm orders.   The hypothetical condition required for such ancestry is probably most nearly approached by the Acanthodii, which flourished between 200 and 300 million years ago.   It has been suggested, too, that the acanthodians (or their close allies) may have been ancestral to the elasmobranchs, and perhaps other gnathostomes as well. A possible objection to this, however, may be in the acanthodian operculum, which extends over the spiracular region.   At the same time, this operculum was variable, and little is known of its arrangement in the earliest forms. Although in Devonian times the Acanthodii were many and varied, the supposed acanthodians from Silurian deposits are known chiefly from seemingly characteristic scales and dermal fin-bones. It is, perhaps, possible that one of these may have given rise to some, if not all modern gnathostomes.

SUB-CLASS ACANTHODII

These—the so-called 'needle-finned sharks'—are the oldest and least specialised known gnathostomes. Acanthodians were not fish. (See, particularly, Watson on their myotome and lateral line structure.) Appearing

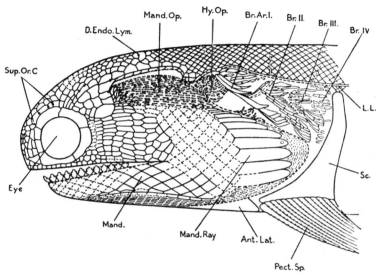

FIG. 134.—Sub-class and Order **Acanthodii.** Family **Brachyacanthidæ.** *Climatius:* Head of *C. reticulatus. Ant. Lat.* antero-lateral dermal bone of the shoulder-girdle; *Br. Ar.* I–IV. dermal elements of the branchial arches and their opercula; *D. Endo. Lym.* foramen ductus endolymphaticus; *Eye,* orbit; *Hy. Op.* hyoid operculum; *L. L.* lateral line; *Mand.* mandible; *Mand. Op.* dorsal part of mandibular operculum; *Mand. Ray,* lower part of mandibular operculum; *Pect. Sp.* pectoral spine; *Sc.* scapula; *Sup. Or. C.* supra-orbital canal. (After Watson.)

first in the Upper Silurian, they reached their maximum development during the Lower Devonian at a time when other classes of fishes were only just beginning to evolve, and persisted until its extinction in the Lower Permian (p. 3).

Westoll separates the Acanthodii from the other Placodermi (see below) to form two separate classes of a ' Grade Aphetohyoidea ', concluding that, although the two groups show many resemblances, neither seems to have been derived from the other. They may have diverged from a not very remote common ancestry.

Acanthodians are fresh-water, superficially shark-like organisms. Usually they have elongated fusiform bodies, which, in the final stages of evolution, became almost eel-like. It is probable that later forms were sea-dwellers. They were generally only a few inches long. The snout was blunt, the mouth terminal, and the eyes large and forwardly placed (Fig. 134). The tail was heterocercal, and the relatively immobile fins were supported each by a strong jacket of dermal bone. There were primitively two dorsal fins (reduced to one in the later forms) and one anal fin. Between the pairs of pectoral and pelvic fins was an intermediate series of pairs of fins increasing in size posteriorly. Primitively this series was more numerous, consisting of as many as five pairs. This suggests a derivation from an originally continuous fin-fold. Later the series became reduced to one small pair, and finally to none.

A pectoral girdle was present (Fig. 135), consisting of a scapular and coracoid part, to which the spine of the fin was affixed. The pectoral fin showed traces of basal elements, as did also the dorsal fin. The peripheral part of the fin was supported by ceratotrichia.

Externally the body was covered with scales of highly characteristic appearance. These had nothing in common with the isolated placoid scales which push through the skin of elasmobranchs (p. 103). They formed a continuous

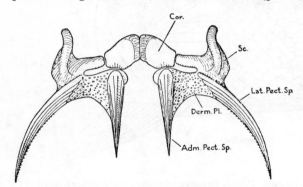

FIG. 135.—*Diplacanthus:* **Pectoral girdle.** *Adm. Pect. Sp.* admedian pectoral spine; *Cor.* coracoid; *Sc.* scapula; *Derm. Pl.* dermal plate; *Lat. Pect. Sp.* lateral pectoral spine. (After Watson.)

dermal armour of true scales which, rhomboid in shape, were formed essentially of a bone-like material. These scales were ornamented with striæ, and were small enough to appear almost granular. The dermal armour extended on to the head (Fig. 134), where the scales were larger, and arranged in a definite pattern. In section they can be seen to have been made up of layers of bone substance in a manner comparable to a ganoid scale (p. 84). Teeth were usually absent, but, when present, seemed to be derived from the modified scales. Further, they appeared to be replaceable as in the elasmobranchs. This, however, was more probably a primitive feature than evidence of any close connection between the two classes.

In the primitive Lower Devonian acanthodian *Climatius* (Fig. 134) there occurred a series of long gill-slits, each of which was overhung by an opercular fold. The largest gill-slit, which was functional as such, was the homologue of the spiracle (Fig. 168, p. 248), its operculum being borne by the jaws. Preservation of some specimens of the much later, Lower Permian *Acanthodes* is sufficiently good to allow a description of the neurocranium, visceral arches, and adjacent structures. Although more specialised than the earlier species, this toothless form nevertheless showed the essential features of the sub-class and class.

The neurocranium (Figs. 136, 137) jaws and branchial arches (Fig. 137) were largely cartilaginous, but ossified in parts by a layer of external peri-chondrial bone, a primitive type of ossification such as occurs also in certain agnathans. The ossifications of the neurocranium resembled in general those of other primitive vertebrates. They consisted of paired lateral and dorsal plates which may fuse. There were anterior, middle, and posterior ventral plates. In front there were five small ossicles, one unpaired, supporting the rostrum. A pair of lateral occipital ossicles, one lying on each side of the

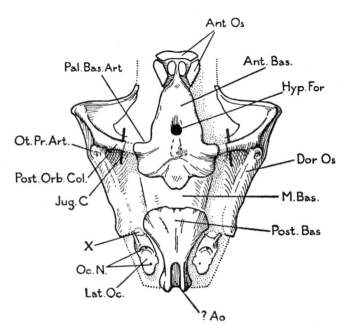

FIG. 136.—*Acanthodes*: **Skull.** Ventral aspect. *Ant. Bas.* anterior basal; *Ant. Os.* anterior ossicles; *? Ao.* groove for dorsal aorta; *Dor. Os.* dorsal bone; *Hyp. For.* hypophysial foramen; *Jug. C.* jugular canal; *Lat. Oc.* lateral occipital; *M. Bas.* middle basal; *Oc. N.* foramina for occipital nerves; *Ot. Pr. Art.* articulation for the otic process; *Pal. Bas. Art.* articulation for the palatobasal process; *Post. Bas.* posterior basal; *Post. Orb. Col.* post-orbital column; *X.* notch for vagus nerve. (After Watson.)

posterior ventral plate, but at a higher level, completes the list. The jaws consisted of a stout palato-quadrate bar for the upper, and the mandible for the lower, portion. The interesting and important point about these elements is that each ossified from two centres. Two centres ossify the upper and two the lower elements. Thus the jaws were formed from four pieces, exactly as are the hyoid and subsequent gill-arches, and so provide further evidence that the jaws were themselves modified gill-arches. Later in life a special ossifica-tion occurred in the otic process. The hyoid arch is complete, and took no part in the jaw suspension. It was supplied throughout its length with gill-rakers. This is sufficient proof that there was a complete hyoid gill-slit. In earlier forms a small operculum was present on each gill-arch, and a larger one on the jaws. In the later forms the mandibular operculum gradually extended back at first to cover the lower part of the gills, and finally to take over the whole function of covering them. This produces an operculum comparable in extent and external appearance with that of the later bony fishes.

The acanthodians may be classified into six families. Of these, four (Brachyacanthidæ, Diplacanthidæ, Ischnacanthidæ, and Gyracanthidæ) possess

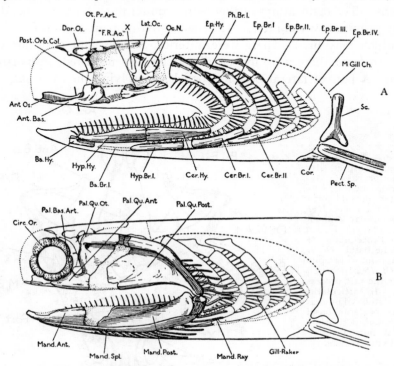

Fig. 137.—*Acanthodes*: **Head region.** Reconstructions: *A*. With the mandible and palatoquadrate removed. *B*. Complete except for the removal of the scales. *Ant. Bas.* anterior basal; *Ant. Os.* anterior ossification in the basis cranii; *Ba. Br. I.* basibranchial; *Cer. Br. I.–II.* ceratobranchials; *Cer. Hy.* ceratohyal; *Circ. Or.* circum-orbital bones; *Cor.* coracoid; *Dor. Os.* dorsal bone of neurocranium; *Ep. Br.* epibranchials 1–4; *F. R. Ao.* foramen for aorta; *Hyp. Br. & Hy.* hypobranchial and hypohyal; *Lat. Oc.* lateral ossification in neurocranium; *M. Gill. Ch.* margin of gill chamber; *Mand. Ant.* anterior ossification of Meckel's cartilage; *Mand. Post.* posterior ossification of Meckel's cartilage; *Mand. Ray.* ray of the mandibular operculum; *Mand. Spl.* mandibular splint; *Oc. N.* foramina for occipital nerve; *Ot. Pr. Art.* articular facet for otic process; *Pal. Bas. Art.* palato-basal articulation; *Pal. Qu. Ant.* anterior bone of palato-quadrate cartilage; *Pal. Qu. Post.* posterior bone of palato-quadrate cartilage; *Pect. Sp.* spine of pectoral fin; *Sc.* scapula; *X*, vagus foramen. (After Watson.)

two dorsal spines. The two remaining families (Mesacanthidæ and Acanthodidæ) have only one. The Brachyacanthidæ (e.g. *Climatius*, Fig. 134), which occurred from the Upper Silurian to the Lower Devonian, is probably the most primitive group (Moy-Thomas).

SUB-CLASS ARTHRODIRA

This group flourished in the Devonian. The Arthrodira were swift predators (Fig. 133, p. 206) which seem, at first sight, to have been very different from acanthodians. In the past some have claimed them to be allied to the lung-fishes (p. 361) or, subsequently, to the elasmobranchs (p. 219). Watson, however, has shown them to be closer to the Acanthodii than was believed. The head was always protected by bony plates which are united to form a strong cranial roof. This was articulated by means of sockets to a pair of condyles on an equally strong bony cuirass covering the anterior parts of the body (Fig. 138). These plates are usually ornamented by tubercles. The remaining free part of the body (where known) tapered to a whip-like tail, and was either naked or, in some, covered with scales. A dorsal fin was commonly present, and a pair of fins on the ventral side must be regarded as representing the pelvics. Free pectoral fins did not occur, but were represented by an immovable bone-sheathed structure on each side, which gradually became reduced almost to extinction. The presence of an operculum which covered the branchial arches can be inferred. The vertebral column, where known, had well-developed neural and hæmal arches but no centra or ribs. Jaws and teeth, the latter rather soon worn down, have been seen in some forms, and may be presumed to have normally been present throughout the group. Arthrodires have been divided into three sub-orders, the Euarthrodira, Ptyctodontida, and Phyllolepida.

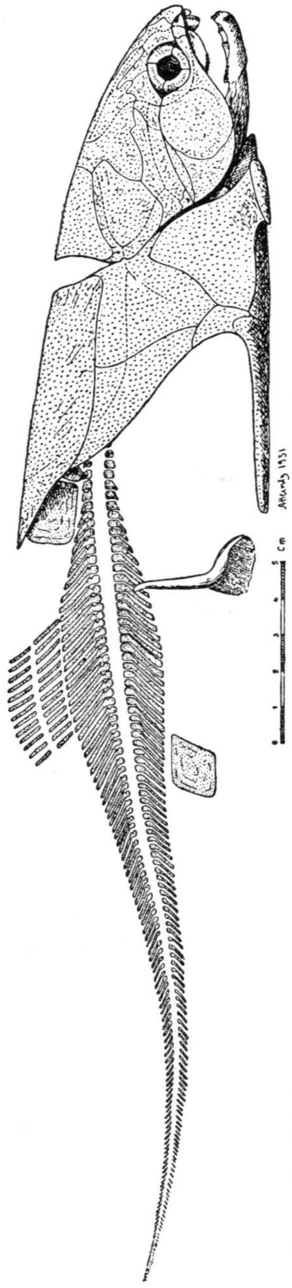

The Euarthrodira contains the most primitive family, the Arctolepida (e.g. *Arctolepis*), which extended from the Lower to the Upper Devonian. The Coccosteidæ (e.g. *Coccosteus*, Fig. 138), *Dinichthys* (Fig. 133, p. 206) ranged from the Middle to Upper Devonian. In this family belonged also the remarkable *Titanichthys*, which may have reached a length of some 30 feet. Its jaws, about 2 feet long, were produced into a beak equipped with shearing blades. The Mylostomidæ (e.g. *Mylostoma*) possessed a plate-like, crushing dentition and are known only from the Upper Devonian. The

FIG. 138.—Sub-class and Order **Arthrodira**, Sub-order **Euarthrodira**, Family **Coccosteidæ**. **Coccosteus**. This placoderm (*C. decipiens*) was about 2 feet long. The cephalic shield of arthrodires was movably articulated with the thoracic carapace fin as was the pectoral fin (not shown). The fin represented above is the pelvic; the diamond-shaped element is the 'anal plate'. (After Heintz.)

Homostiidæ (e.g. *Homostius*), characterised by a dorsoventral compression, existed from the Middle to Upper Devonian.

Fig. 139.—Sub-class and Order **Petalichthyida**, Family **Macropetalichthyidæ.** *Macropetalichthys.* This relatively small, dorso-ventrally flattened placoderm (*M. prumiensis*) possessed pectoral fin-spines probably immovably fixed to the pectoral shield as in arctolepids. (After Broili.)

The sub-order Ptyctodontida was perhaps restricted to the Middle and Upper Devonian and is characterised by a reduction of both cephalic and pectoral armour (e.g. *Rhamphodopsis*). The Phyllolepida are known only from the Upper Devonian. *Phyllolepis* was once considered to be allied to the heterostracan *Drepanaspis* (p. 170), which it superficially resembles.

SUB-CLASS PETALICHTHYIDA

These were Devonian forms (Fig. 139). They somewhat resembled the Arthrodira, but the ball-and-socket joint between the head and body did not exist. Again, the pattern of the head plating was somewhat different, and the pectoral and pelvic fins were constructed on a very different plan. On the other hand, the facts that the neurocranium (Fig. 140) so much resembled that of an arctolepid, and that the hyoid arch took no part in the suspension of the jaws, are evidence that the order is rightly placed with the placoderms. Certain characters have caused some authorities to look upon these fishes as allied to the elasmobranchs. The paired fins in particular have been cited as evidence. The structure of the shoulder-girdle, the tribasal pectoral fin (Fig. 141), and the *Cladoselache*-like pelvic fin are undoubtedly points of resemblance. The shoulder-girdle, however, was equally like the primary girdle of such acanthodians as *Climatius* or *Diplacanthus*. Further, the tribasal pectoral fin is paralleled, except for the absence of a spine, by that of *Acanthodes*. Moreover, a tribasal fin at this period is too advanced in structure to lead to the more simple but later fin of the earliest known elasmobranchs, such as *Cladoselache*. The pelvic fin certainly resembles that of *Cladoselache*, but is of a type that is found equally in the early sturgeons and palæoniscids, and is too generalised and primitive to be of much value as evidence of any particular affinity. Other elasmobranch characters, such as the ventral position of the mouth and the flattening of the neurocranium, may be accounted for as the result of adaptation to a bottom-living life. The different arrangement of the head-plates from the general arthrodire pattern is not so great as appears at first sight. The chief difference is along the mid-dorsal line. This might be put down as the result of a secondary fusion. Both this group and the Rhenanida include primitive members that possessed fin-structures pro-

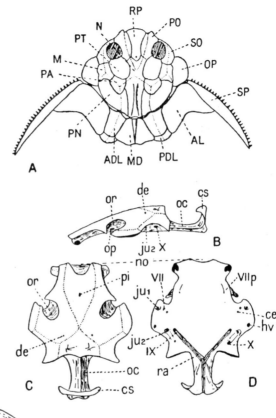

FIG. 140.—**Petalichthyida: Skull and pectoral shield.** A. *Lunaspis heroldi*, in dorsal view. *ADL*. antero-dorsal lateral plate; *AL*. antero-lateral plate; *M*. marginal plate; *MD*. median dorsal plate; *N*. nuchal plate; *OP*. opercular? plate; *PA*. paranuchal plate; *PDL*. postero-dorsal lateral plate; *PN*. postnuchal plate; *PO*. pre-orbital plate; *PT*. postorbital plate; *RP*. rostro-pineal plate; *SO*. sub-orbital plate; *SP*. spinale.

B. *Macropetalichthys rapheidolabis* in lateral, C. in dorsal and D. in ventral view. *ce*. external carotid foramen; *cs*. cranio-spinal process; *de*. ductus endolymphaticus; *hv*. head vein fora-men; *ju* 1-2. anterior and posterior openings of the jugular canal; *no*. position of nasal openings; *oc*. occipital part of skull; *op*. optic foramen; *or*. orbit; *pi*. pineal foramen; *ra*. radix aortæ; *VII*. facial nerve foramen; *VIIp*. foramen for palatine branch of facial nerve; *IX*. foramen for glosso-pharyngeal nerve, *X*. foramen for vagus nerve. (From Moy-Thomas after Gross, Stensiö.)

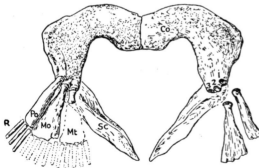

FIG. 141.—*Macropetalichthys:* **Pectoral girdle.** *Co.* coracoid; *Sc.* scapula; *Po.*, *Mo.*, *Mt.* pro-, meso-, and meta-pterygia; *R.* radials. (After Broili.)

tected by a jacket of dermal bone and may be perhaps more properly combined in a single group.

In this sub-class are placed the genera *Macropetalichthys* (Fig. 139) a Middle Devonian form and *Lunaspis* (Fig. 140) of the Lower Devonian. The affinities of certain other supposed members are in doubt.

SUB-CLASS ANTIARCHI (PTERICHTHYOMORPHI)

This is a compact sub-class which was confined to the Devonian period. It contained small fresh-water animals that were common, but apparently left no descendants. Fossils sufficiently well preserved to reveal certain internal details have been found. A spiral valve (p. 237), such as occurs in elasmobranchs, lung-fishes, and cœlacanths, has probably been detected. Further,

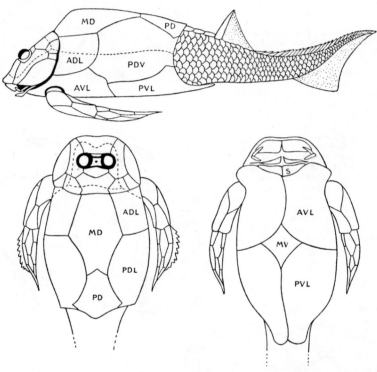

FIG. 142.—Sub-class and Order **Antiarchi,** Family **Asterolepidæ.** *Pterichthyodes.* This group contained small placoderms less than a foot long. Like other aphetohyoideans they had a well-developed lateral line system. Upper figure is *P. milleri* in side view. Left-hand figure in dorsal, right-hand figure in ventral view. *ADL.* antero-dorsolateral; *AVL.* antero-ventrolateral; *MD.* median dorsal; *MV.* median ventral; *PD.* posterior dorsal; *PDL.* posterior dorsolateral; *PVL.* posterior ventrolateral; *S.* semilunar plate. (After Traquair.)

a pair of large backwardly directed sacs communicated with the pharynx and appear to have been lungs (see p. 108).

Like the Arthrodira, the Antiarchi were provided with a strong armour over the head and shoulders, but with a somewhat different arrangement of the plates. There was also a different method of articulation of the head to the body. The sockets in this case were on the cuirass and on the articulating processes on the head. The pectoral appendages were of a much more elaborate structure.

Pterichthyodes (=*Pterichthys*) (Fig. 142) may be taken as the type of the single family (Asterolepidæ). The genera of this group differ only in relatively unimportant details. The eyes were placed close together on the top of the head, a modification which was no doubt responsible for a rearrangement of the neighbouring plates. The cuirass was formed by a large median dorsal and a posterior dorsal plate, both unpaired. Along the sides were the anterior and posterior dorso-laterals. The floor was made up anteriorly by a pair of anterior ventrolateral plates, which enclosed between them a pair of small semilunar plates. Posteriorly it was made up by a pair of posterior ventral plates. Between these pairs lay an unpaired median ventral. The anterior ventrolateral plates had at their sides an excavation which held the condylar head of the 'arms' or pectoral appendages. These were highly developed, and were the leading characteristic of the order. They were formed of a number of plates, closely

Fig. 143.—Sub-class and Order **Antiarchi**, Family **Asterolepidæ**. *Bothriolepis*. This small placoderm was heavily armoured in front and unprotected behind. It possessed weakly developed jaws and ate minute animals or plants (cf. *Dinichthys*, Fig. 133, p. 206). Its pectoral appendages were freely movable and probably sculled the animal along. (From Romer, after Patten.)

united except for a flexible joint dividing them into a proximal and distal section. The fossilised arms are hollow, but were in life provided internally with muscles, nerves, and arteries. The jaw apparatus consisted of a pair of large superognathals, each bearing a notch at the side. Into this was fitted a small elongated element, and this in turn articulated with a third. The system therefore corresponded to some degree with that of *Coccosteus*. The lower jaws were more weakly developed.

The trunk was protected by well-developed scales and terminated in a heterocercal tail with a ventral web. A single dorsal fin was present supported by an anterior spine. A series of fulcral scales ran along the upper border of the body from the fin to the tail. In this genus there were no pelvic fins.

Another well-known genus is *Bothriolepis* (Fig. 143), which had a naked body, an extra plate on the head, and a pair of fleshy protuberances at the ventrolateral border of the cuirass which are supposed to represent a pair of pelvic fins. *Remigolepis* lacked the median joint to the pectoral fins. *Microbrachius* and *Asterolepis*, *Ceraspis*, and *Ceratolepis* are other recorded genera.

SUB-CLASS RHENANIDA

In shape these peculiar, probably placoderm, Devonian animals resembled the modern rays. Their skin, too, was denticulate. However, the denticles were attached to a body-armour. The skull was ossified, and the gills were protected by an operculum. Spiracles have not been found, nor is there any suggestion of hyoid support for the lower jaw. It seems obvious that these animals were bottom gliders, and that the various similarities between them and the later-evolved skates are examples of convergent adaptation. In the Rhenanida the bones were not greatly developed, and became progressively less so in later forms.

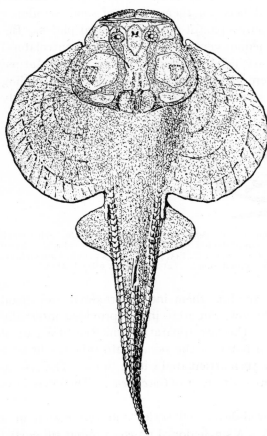

FIG. 144.—Sub-class and Order **Rhenanida,** Family **Gemuendinidæ. *Gemuendina.*** Although superficially skate-like, this ' stegoselachian ' (*G. sturtzi*) belonged to an operculate group that preceded, and was probably not related to, the elasmobranchs. Note the position of the eyes, the pectoral and pelvic fins, and the dorsal spine. (After Broili.)

Gemuendina (Fig. 144) is the best-known form. It had very much the shape of a skate. The head had on the top a central plate of bone, and ranged on each side were three pairs of plates which did not articulate, but were surrounded by areas of skin bearing tubercles. The large pectoral fins were supported by a secondary elongation of the radials, and behind them are the smaller, flattened pelvic fins. The body then tapered to a pointed tail. A dorsal fin was present and supported by an anterior spine much as in *Acanthodes* or *Pterichthyodes*. Behind this fin was a row of dorsal spines, and there was a row of similar spines on each side which started from a point just behind the pelvic fins and ran to join the dorsal row at the end of the tail. The pectoral girdle (Fig. 145) was comparable with that of a ptyctodont (p. 211), but lacked the lateral spine.

The presence of gills supported on branchial arches and covered by an operculum can be demonstrated in some instances, and from them the presence of gills of a similar type can be reasonably inferred in the others. The jaws, when known, showed no signs of any hyoid suspension. From this arrangement, the placoderm condition with its complete hyoid gill-slit naturally follows. The general impression given by these forms is that they were placoderms which were losing their armour, and had developed special fins that enabled them to

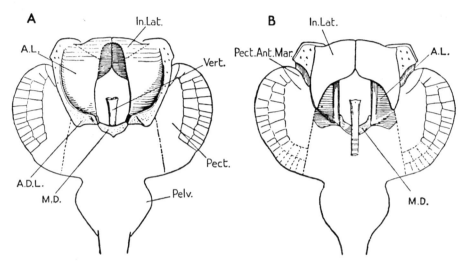

FIG. 145.—*Gemuendina:* **Anterior part of the body with head removed.** Restoration of *G. sturtzi. A. D. L.* antero-dorsolateral; *A. L.* antero-lateral; *In. Lat.* inter-lateral; *M. D.* median dorsal plate; *Pect.* pectoral fin; *Pect. Ant. Mar.* anterior margin of pectoral fin; *Pelv.* pelvic fin; *Vert.* vertebral column. (After Watson.)

exploit the lake- and sea-floor. Only three genera have so far been described: *Gemuendina* (Fig. 144) (Lower Devonian), *Asterosteus* (Middle Devonian), and *Jagorina* (Upper Devonian).

SUB-CLASS PALÆOSPONDYLIA

Palæospondylus (Fig. 146), the sole representative of this group, occurs only in two restricted areas of the Mid-Devonian in Scotland. From the time of its discovery it has been the subject of much speculation, and has in turn been considered either as the larva of a dipnoan fish, of *Coccosteus*, or of an amphibian; as a fish of chondrichthyan affinity, and even as a teleost. For many years the general consensus of opinion was that its nearest affinity was with the Agnatha, and certain of its features led some to see in it a relationship, possibly ancestral, with the Myxinidæ. Moy-Thomas however showed with new as well as old material that *Palæospondylus* was not a member of the

Agnatha, but instead a true gnathostome.   Despite its lack of dermal armour it should probably be placed in a separate sub-class of the placoderms.

Palæospondylus gunni reached a maximum length of about two inches, and occurs in great numbers in certain layers of the flagstones of a small quarry at Achanarras in Scotland.   Unfortunately the preservation of only a very few specimens is sufficiently good to yield details of the structure.   It had a

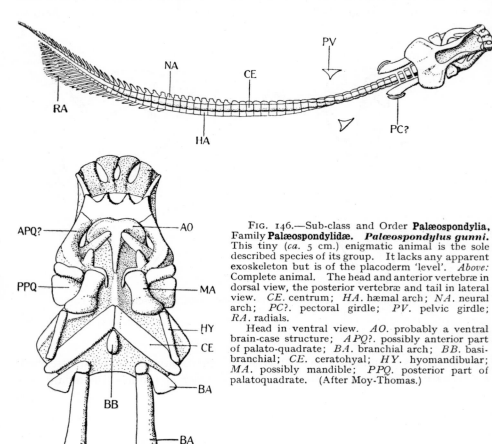

Fig. 146.—Sub-class and Order **Palæospondylia**, Family **Palæospondylidæ**. *Palæospondylus gunni*. This tiny (*ca.* 5 cm.) enigmatic animal is the sole described species of its group.   It lacks any apparent exoskeleton but is of the placoderm 'level'.   *Above:* Complete animal.   The head and anterior vertebræ in dorsal view, the posterior vertebræ and tail in lateral view.   *CE*. centrum; *HA*. hæmal arch; *NA*. neural arch; *PC?*. pectoral girdle; *PV*. pelvic girdle; *RA*. radials.

Head in ventral view.   *AO*. probably a ventral brain-case structure; *APQ?*. possibly anterior part of palato-quadrate; *BA*. branchial arch; *BB*. basibranchial; *CE*. ceratohyal; *HY*. hyomandibular; *MA*. possibly mandible; *PPQ*. posterior part of palatoquadrate.   (After Moy-Thomas.)

depressed skull, a well-calcified vertebral column, and a heterocercal tail.   The lower radials were two-jointed, and the second row of radials was bifurcated (Fig. 146).   Paired fins were present, and traces of pectoral and pelvic girdles have been observed.   In the vertebral column the neural arches were low in front, but gradually lengthened into neural spines towards the caudal region. Ventrally there were short hæmal ribs which posteriorly became hæmal spines. The vertebral centra were stout and ring-shaped.   The neurocranium (Fig.

146), with its ring of tentacles in front, was complicated, and the interpretation of some of its structures presents difficulties. At first sight it gives the impression of a larval condition, but against this view is the fact that much of it was calcified. Further, the vertebral column was fully calcified even in the smallest specimens. The neurocranium is dorso-ventrally compressed, complete and fully calcified on its ventral surface and sides but it lacked a roof, being uncalcified in this region. The auditory capsules were large, and formed the end of the neurocranium. This character is probably not found in any other placoderms, but occurs in the Agnatha (p. 164). The upper jaws (Fig. 146, APQ?, PPQ) were formed by a pair of elements, an anterior and posterior palatoquadrate, on each side. The lower jaws were represented by a single pair which ended bluntly (*MA*). If, as seems possible, there was an anterior uncalcified piece on each side, the jaw apparatus would be comparable to that found in the Acanthodii (Fig. 137). The hyoid arch (*HY*, *CE*) was complete (and took no part in the support of the jaws), but, unlike that of other placoderms, was very different from the succeeding branchial arches. A pair of ventral elements lay posterior to the auditory capsules and represented a branchial arch, and a small element that lay outside the second of these may represent part of the pectoral girdle.

It would seem probable that *Palæospondylus* was an animal of the aphetohyoidean grade. At the same time there is no evidence of its relationship to any known placoderm.

CLASS ELASMOBRANCHII (CHONDRICHTHYES)

INTRODUCTION

This class comprises the living sharks, rays, and chimæras, together with a number of extinct orders. Elasmobranch fishes are generally almost exclusively marine in habit, although a few have successfully colonised brackish and even completely fresh water. Most of them are predacious. They include the largest fishes that ever lived. The biggest known was probably a giant Tertiary species of *Carcharodon*, which may have been about 80 feet in length (Fig. 147). Teeth of this monster measure about 6 inches long, and in shape are very like those of to-day's representatives. Other smaller teeth, but at the same time still larger than those of any living form, have been dredged from the Pacific floor and appear to be of very recent origin. The largest living shark is the oceanic, tropical oviparous whale shark (*Rhinodon*), which reaches nearly 70 feet. It lives on plankton, as does also the Basking Shark (*Cetorhinus*), which grows to a length of 40 feet. Both of these species are harmless to Man, as are, in fact, most elasmobranchs.

The man-eating Great White Shark or White Pointer (*Carcharodon carcharias*) attains a length of 36 feet. It has flat, triangular, serrated teeth, wide at the base and about 3 inches long.   Fundamentalists who have been troubled by the fact of the narrow œsophagus of the large baleen whales, and who are emotionally and spiritually incapable of accepting certain biblical narratives as picturesque allegory, have sometimes held that it was the Great White Shark and not a mammal, that swallowed Jonah.   In any case, sperm whales, sufficiently wide of gape and throat, sometimes enter the Mediterranean Sea.

In the South-west Pacific Ocean, particularly, several man-eating species occur, and this has led to the establishment of elaborate protective measures, including aerial patrols, on eastern Australian beaches.   Unquestionable man-eating sharks are the Black (Common) Whaler (*Galeolamna*) (reaching a length of 12 feet and weighing about 900 lbs.), and the Tiger Shark (*Galeocerdo*) (16 feet and more than 1,400 lbs.).   In addition, the Grey Nurse (*Carcharias*) (9 ft. 6 ins.), and probably the Blue Pointer or Mako (*Isuropsis*) (13 feet) also kill Man.   During this present century more than 120 people were attacked in Australian waters, of whom more than fifty died of hæmorrhage and shock after receiving fearful injuries.   One aboriginal trochus-diver lived after injuries which required 238 stitches (North Queensland, 1939).   During the same period at least ten boats were attacked by sharks, and innumerable dogs, and even horses, have been mauled.   Although at least one shark fatality occurs every summer, this mortality is quite inconsiderable when it is considered that surfing is the principal Austra-

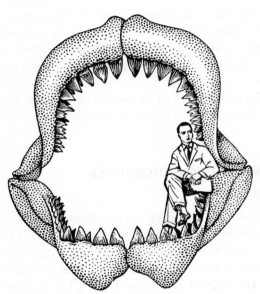

FIG. 147.—*Carcharodon megalodon:* **Teeth and jaws.**   The triangular fang of this Pleistocene shark are up to 6 inches long.   The jaws, restored on the pattern of a modern man-eater, may have had a 6- or 7-foot gape.   (Redrawn from an exhibit in the Am. Mus. Nat. Hist.)

lian sport, and more than 100,000 people expose themselves to some danger each week-end in the surfing season.   It is a remarkable fact that shark attacks are rare in Western Australia and North America.   During the early phases of the war with Japan the United States air force authorities impressed on pilots destined for Pacific service that they had nothing to fear from sharks.   Soon both nations were busily testing repellents (p. 273).

The elasmobranchs are a well-defined group which fall into two clear-cut divisions, the Selachii and the Bradyodonti (see below).   There have been several attempts to ally elasmobranchs with the somewhat shark-like poly-morphic Placodermi (p. 205), but no convincing evidence of anything but very remote relationship has been adduced. It is possible that the elasmobranch ancestor was of placoderm affinity, but the known aphetohyoidean groups were much more closely allied to each other, and of a much lower degree of organisa-tion, than even the most primitive known elasmobranchs. The primary elasmobranch division occurred very early in the history of the class. Sharks with a typically bradyodont dentition (p. 256), and also selachian clado-donts both appear in Upper Devonian deposits. Suggestions that various fragments found in Mid-Devonian and even earlier strata were those of elasmo-branchs have been rejected by most recent authorities.

The elasmobranch skeleton is entirely cartilaginous, but in it there may be occasionally heavy subsidiary mineralisation, although never true bone. This persistent lack of bone led early workers to believe that the sharks and their allies antedated the bony fishes, but this view is now generally abandoned. We know now that bone (p. 74) is an exceedingly primitive material, and in any case the earliest known truly cartilaginous fishes do not seem to have appeared before mid-Devonian. And, in fact, even bony fishes (Actino-pterygii) (p. 285), as distinct from placoderms (p. 205), have been found in Lower Devonian deposits. It is true that cartilaginous structures do not preserve as well as bony ones, but if elasmobranchs are as ancient as was once widely believed it would be expected that teeth of hypothetical, very ancient, species would be preserved and some at least probably found. All in all, it is likely that the elasmobranchs arose from a bony ancestor, and perhaps by neoteny (p. 3). We will see later that the extant Axolotl (p. 456) has arisen because of its capacity to become sexually mature and to reproduce in an essentially larval condition. Cartilage is embryonic tissue. It is by no means improbable that the elasmobranch ancestors became sexually mature while their skeletons remained relatively immature. It is possible that the un-armoured, later placoderms (p. 217) may have reached the soft-bodied con-dition by means of an essentially similar, if not so hypothetically simple, manner as has been discussed above (p. 3). Neoteny, incidentally, has been demonstrated to occur in teleosts (e.g. *Clariallabes*, p. 338).

There is little agreement concerning the most appropriate classification of the cartilaginous fishes. We will use the following :

CLASS ELASMOBRANCHII (CHONDRICHTHYES)
  Sub-class Selachii
    Orders Cladoselachii (Devonian–Permian)
        Pleuracanthodii (Ichthyotomi) (Devonian–Triassic)
        Protoselachii (Devonian–Cretaceous)
        Euselachii (Jurassic–Recent)

Sub-order Pleurotremata (Jurassic–Recent) [1]
Super-families Heterodontoidea (Jurassic–Recent)
Notidanoidea (Jurassic–Recent)
Galeoidea (Jurassic–Recent)
Squaloidea (Jurassic–Recent)
Sub-order Hypotremata (Jurassic–Recent)
Sub-class Bradyodonti (Devonian–Recent)
Orders Eubradyodonti (Devonian–Permian)
Holocephali (Jurassic–Recent)

An operculum is absent (even in *Chlamydoselachus*, frilled sharks), but is present in Holocephali (p. 256). The gill-slits open directly to the exterior and the gills are laminar (p. 106). A cloaca is present. Its aperture serves as a common outlet for the rectum and the renal and reproductive ducts. A uniquely high concentration of blood urea occurs (p. 253). A rhythmically contractile conus arteriosus with several transverse rows of valves is always well developed. The venous system is expanded in places into larger sinuses, which do not occur in other gnathostomes. Other characters are pelvic *claspers* in the male (absent only in one extinct group, the Cladoselachii) and large egg-cases. Fertilisation is always internal. Many species are viviparous (p. 278). The large spiral valve in the short intestine, and the abdominal pores, are characteristic, but occur in some other fishes. The placoid scales are diagnostic.

SUB-CLASS SELACHII
Order Cladoselachii (Pleuropterygii)

These were extinct, shark-like Chondrichthyes with a fusiform body, a heterocercal tail with a large lower lobe, and a horizontal keel-like fin on each side of the caudal peduncle (Fig. 148). There were two dorsal fins, sometimes with a spine in front of the first. There were very prominent pectoral fins and pelvic fins were also present. Each kind had a primitive, very wide, basal attachment to the body and was without the anterior and posterior constriction from the body-wall that is usual in the paired fins of almost all fishes. The skeleton of the fins consisted of parallel cartilages of simple structure. The large sub-terminal mouth (without pronounced rostrum), long sharp teeth, relatively enormous forwardly directed eyes, and generally streamlined form suggesting a hunter of great power and voracity. The body was covered with small denticles. The typically selachian teeth each consisted of a slender, pointed main cusp with smaller lateral cusps fixed on a broad base. The jaw

---

[1] There is much to be said for abandoning the classical Pleurotremata/Hypotremata dichotomy and including the rays as a Super-family Batoidea (Upper Jurassic–Recent) of the Order Euselachii (true sharks). There exist squaloidean forms (*e.g.* monk-fishes, *Squatina*, banjo-fishes, *Rhinobatis*) that seem morphologically intermediate between 'sharks' and 'rays'. The other super-families of the Pleurotremata were distinct in the Lower and Middle Jurassic, whereas the rays first appeared at the top of the Jurassic.

suspension was amphistylic. A well-developed postorbital process engaged the upper jaws and a further, more anterior articulation with the floor of the cranium probably existed. Such a suspension was probably a primitive feature, as was also the absence, unique among elasmobranchs, of claspers (p. 255) in the male. The large notochord was unconstricted. There were paired nostrils, and large scale-like denticles surrounded the eyes. A hyoid arch and five pairs of branchial arches lay behind the jaws. *Cladoselache fyleri* (Fig. 148) from the Upper Devonian (p. 3) is the best-known form, and

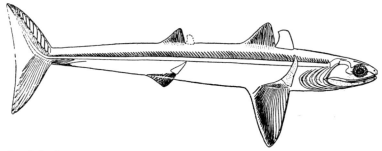

FIG. 148.—Sub-class **Selachii,** Order **Cladoselachii,** Family **Cladoselachidæ.** *Cladoselache.* General structure. *C. fyleri* grew to a length of about 3 feet. In some species, perhaps only in males, there was a small, laterally-compressed spine in front of the anterior dorsal fin. (After Harris.)

Cladodus and *Symmorium* were related forms ranging from the Upper Devonian to the Upper Carboniferous.

It is possible that the Cladoselachii were a group closely allied to the ancestral stock from which the other Chondrichthyes have radiated. Excluding the somewhat specialised Pleuracanthodii mentioned below (p. 224), there seem, broadly speaking, to have been two main radiations. One of these, the Bradyodonti (p. 256), eventually gave rise to the Holocephali (p. 256). The

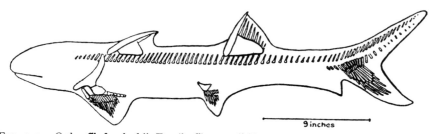

FIG. 149.—Order **Cladoselachii,** Family **Ctenacanthidæ.** *Ctenacanthus.* Some ctenacanths (e.g. *Goodrichia*) were more than twice as long as *C. costellatus,* shown above. (After Moy-Thomas.)

other produced the Ctenacanthidæ and Hybodontidæ (p. 224), which are on the line of the modern sharks and rays. A third group known only from the Devonian is the Coronodontidæ (e.g. *Diademonus, Coronodus*). These possessed peculiar teeth with conical cusps. *Diademonus* was completely covered with minute, ridged scales which strikingly resembled its curious teeth (see Harris). It had pelvic claspers.

The Ctenacanthidæ (Fig. 149) are found from the late Devonian to the Lower Permian. They were ancient dorsal-spined sharks with teeth like those of *Cladoselache*. The jaw suspension was amphistylic. Claspers were absent. The radial elements of the fins were segmented as in modern forms, and so showed a great advance.

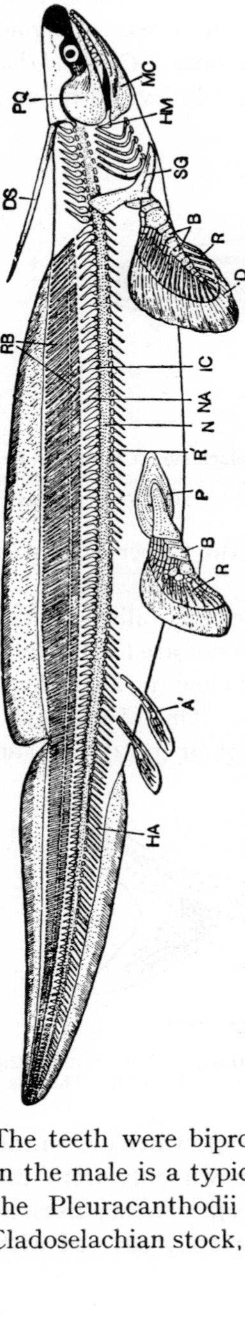

ORDER PLEURACANTHODII
(ICHTHYOTOMI)

The Pleuracanthodii were slender, freshwater, shark-like fishes that appear to have arisen as an early offshoot from the central elasmobranch stem. They extended from the Upper Devonian until the early Triassic. In them the pectoral fin had acquired the form of an 'archipterygium'—an elongated axis extending out from the body and bearing pre- and post, axial rays. The postaxial rays were fewer in number than the pre-axial. This may be a primitive feature. A well-known species, *Pleuracanthus decheni* (Fig. 150), occurred in the Carboniferous and Permian. It was clearly in many respects a specialised form. The long body, the slender diphycercal tail (unusual in early elasmobranchs), the continuous fin-fold along the back, and the anal fin (with its unusual fore and aft duplication and direct suspension from the hæmal arches), and the long, movable spine on the head, all point to a considerable degree of specialisation. Scales have not been observed in any pleuracanth, and are thought to have been absent. The cartilage of the skull, the amphistylic jaws, and the branchial arches were sometimes well calcified.

FIG. 150.—Order **Pleuracanthodii**, Family **Pleuracanthidæ. Pleuracanthus.** Unlike most elasmobranch groups, this late Palæozoic (and barely Triassic) side-line inhabited fresh water. *P. decheni* grew to about 3 feet long. *A'*. ventral fin; *B*. basal fin-cartilages; *D*. dermal margin of fin; *D.S.* dermal fin-spine; *H.A.* hæmal arches; *HM.* hyomandibular; *IC.* inter-neural plates; *MC.* Meckel's cartilage; *N.* notochord; *NA.* neural process and spine; *P.* supposed pelvic cartilage; *PQ.* palatoquadrate; *R.* radial fin-cartilages; *R'*. ribs; *SG.* shoulder girdle.   (After Dean.)

The teeth were bipronged and had a central cusp. The presence of claspers in the male is a typically chondrichthian feature. Like other Chondrichthyes, the Pleuracanthodii are presumed to have branched off from the early Cladoselachian stock, but to have given rise to no successors.

ORDER PROTOSELACHII

The most primitive protoselachian group was probably the Hybodontidæ (e.g. *Hybodus*), the members of which were almost certainly of ctenacanthian ancestry. The order became relatively common in the late Palæozoic and Mesozoic. It was probably composed of numerous sub-groups, but only the Hybodontidæ are well known. A second family (Tristychiidæ) has been

Fig. 151.—Order **Euselachii,** Sub-order **Pleurotremata,** Super-family **Heterodontoidea.** *Heterodontus* (Crested Port Jackson Shark *H. galeatus.*) This harmless eastern Australian species grows to a length of about 4 feet. It may be trawled at a depth of 50 fathoms, but is common in harbours, where its skin and teeth are often stained reddish, perhaps through feeding on large Purple Sea-urchins in the shallows. It is oviparous. The egg-cases are usually found among weed at a depth of about 50 feet. They are about 4 inches long with a flange of seven or eight spirals and terminal anchoring tendrils that may reach a length of seven feet. (Modified after McCulloch.)

erected on material from the lower Carboniferous. The protoselachians differed from the Cladoselachii in two principal ways. Firstly, the pectoral fins were no longer fin-folds but became ' notched at their posterior margins as in modern elasmobranchs ' (Moy-Thomas) and secondly, pelvic claspers had arisen in the males—a feature to be retained by all ' modern ' sharks and their derivatives. The hybodonts retained the amphistylic jaw suspension, but had already evolved narrow-based, flexible fins similar to those of extant forms. In addition to sharp anterior fangs, they developed flattened, crushing posterior teeth, with which they could break the thick shells of molluscs.   It was from the Protoselachii that the Euselachii (p. 226), embracing all modern selachians (but not bradyodonts), arose in the Mesozoic.   Although the hybodonts disappeared in the late Mesozoic, there still exist to-day a few hybodont-like sharks which exhibit many of the ancient characters.   These belong to the genus *Hetero-dontus* (*e.g.* the harmless Port Jackson Shark, Figs. 151, 152), which occurs also in Jurassic strata (p. 3).

Fig. 152.—*Heterodontus:* Dentition. The hybodont condition is retained.   The anterior fangs are pointed.   The posterior elements are rounded and constitute a mechanism adapted to crushing echinoderms and molluscs (cf. Fig. 147, p. 220). (After Deary.)

Order Euselachii

This group is composed of the sharks and rays.   Although these do not occur in vast numbers, as do many species of bony fishes (*e.g.* herring, cod), they are nevertheless abundant in equatorial and temperate seas.

The living and extinct orders which occur from the Jurassic period onward are distinguished, in addition to the general characters of the class, by having numerous teeth developed in continual succession, and by the pectoral fins having three basal pieces (the *pro-*, *meso-*, and *meta-pterygium*), from which a number of pre-axial radials spread out.[1]

The order is divided into two sub-orders, the Pleurotremata (sharks) and the Hypotremata (rays), chiefly on the position of the gill-slits. These are lateral in the first group and ventral in the second.   The division is perhaps essentially one of convenience (see page 222), but other notable differences exist.   In the Pleurotremata the anterior margin of the pectoral fin is free from the body.   The pectoral radials are simple and of few segments, and, as a rule, only the anterior ones reach the free edge of the fin.   The two halves of the pectoral arch are well separated above.   In the Hypotremata, on the other hand, the pectoral fin is joined to the side of the body or to the head.   The pectoral radials are numerous, multi-segmented and bifurcated at the ends.   All of them reach the free edge of the fin. The halves of the pectoral girdle either fuse with one another or else both fuse to the vertebral column.   There is a further difference : the skull of the Pleurotremata is without cartilages attached to the olfactory capsules, and the pterygo-quadrate has a process articulating with, or attached by ligament to, the cranium.

In the skull of the Hypotremata there are paired preorbital cartilages

---

[1] In the hybodonts and in early stages of some Euselachii there are traces of reduced postaxial radials.

attached to the olfactory capsules, which are often very well developed. The pterygo-quadrate has no articulating process to the skull. Finally, in the Pleurotremata the hyomandibular and ceratohyal both bear cartilaginous rays, and both take part in supporting the first gill. The ceratohyal is a single cartilage, and is attached to the lower end of the hyomandibular. In the Hypotremata the hyomandibular lacks rays, and so takes no part in the support of the gill, and the ceratohyal is segmented and attached to the hyomandibular either high up or not at all.

The Pleurotremata can be divided into four super-families: the Heterodontoidea, Notidanoidea, Galeoidea, and Squaloidea.

The Heterodontoidea are accorded ordinal rank by some authorities and relegated to family rank within the Squaloidea by others. One genus, *Heterodontus*, (Fig. 151) survives as an obvious though somewhat modified derivative of *Hybodus* stock (p. 224). The genus occurred in the Jurassic (p. 3).

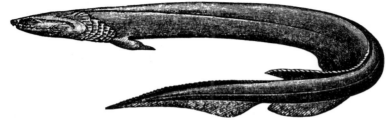

FIG. 153.—Order **Euselachii**, Sub-order **Pleurotremata**, Super-family **Notidanoidea**. *Chlamydoselachus*. *C. anguineus* (Frilled-gilled Shark). This swift and slender shark is found principally, but only relatively rarely, in Japanese waters. Teeth occur in Tertiary deposits. An ally, *Hexanchus*, occurred in the Jurassic. The frills are elongations of inter-branchial septa (p. 106). (After Günther.)

When the Port Jackson Shark (*H. phillippi*) was discovered in the days of Australian colonial settlement in the late eighteenth century it immediately aroused great attention. It still retains the curiously diversified dentition and a sub-terminal mouth. Although the palato-quadrate postorbital articulation has been abandoned, it remains essentially amphistylic. The animal lives chiefly on molluscs, crustacea, and echinoderms. Several species occur in Pacific waters.

The Notidanoidea, too, are archaic survivors. The group includes *Chlamydoselachus* (= *Notidanus*) (the frill-gilled sharks) (Fig. 153); also *Heptranchias* and *Hexanchus*. These animals are characterised by a single dorsal fin (unique to the group), a simple vertebral column, a sub-terminal mouth, and the presence of more than five gill-slits. In the Galeoidea there are two dorsal fins without spines, an anal fin, and five gill-slits. This group includes (1) the Odontaspidæ (Grey Nurse and Goblin Shark), (2) the Isuridæ with numerous genera such as *Lamna* (the mackerel sharks, *e.g.* Porbeagle, *L. nasus*), *Carcharodon*, *Cetorhinus* (Basking Shark), and *Alopias* (Thresher); (3) the Orectolobidæ (carpet and tiger sharks), *Orectolobus* and *Stegostoma*; the Scyliorhinidæ, *Scyliorhinus* (dogfishes); and lastly (4) the Carcharinidæ, with *Carcharinus* (blue sharks), *Galeus* (topes), *Mustelus* (nurse hounds), and *Sphyrna* (hammerheads).

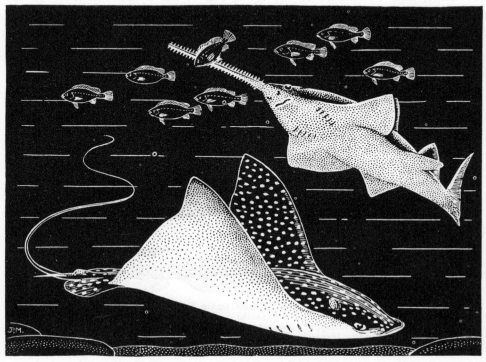

FIG. 154.—Order **Euselachii**, Sub-order **Hypotremata: Radiation and adaptation in selachians.**
Saw-fishes (*Pristis*, Family Pristidæ) are survivors of a group that was common in the Cretaceous.
They are not to be confused with the squaloid saw-sharks (Pristiophoridæ), with which they share
convergent, but not diagnostic characters. Saw-fishes grow to a length of over 24 feet. They
hack and disable their prey before swallowing. Eagle-rays (*Aetobatis*, Family Myliobatidæ)
weigh as much as 400 lbs. *Aetobatis* eats molluscs, sometimes uncovering them by agitating the
sandy sea-floor with its wing-like pectoral fins. Both the above groups are strikingly adapted to
bottom-living. (From photographs and specimens.)

The Squaloidea have two dorsal fins, with or without an anterior spine. The anal fin is usually absent. In this order are placed the Squatinidæ, *Squatina* (angel- or monk-fish), the Squalidæ, *Squalus* (spiny dogfishes), the Pristiophoridæ (saw sharks), and others.

The Hypotremata are sometimes divided into two groups : the Narcobatoidea or electric rays, and the Batoidea, which include all other skates and rays such as the Rhinobatidæ (guitar fishes), the Pristidæ (sawfishes), Myliobatidæ (eagle rays), Raiidæ (true skates and rays) (Fig. 154), etc.

The Sub-class Bradyodonti will be dealt with on p. 256.

EXAMPLE OF THE SUB-CLASS.—A DOGFISH (SCYLIO-RHINUS (= SCYLLIUM), SQUALUS, BRACHÆLURUS, ETC.)

General External Features.—The flesh of these fishes is sold in British fish-shops under the names of 'Rock Salmon' or 'Flake'. The general shape of the body (Fig. 155) is roughly fusiform. At the anterior end it is broader and depressed. Posteriorly it tapers gradually and is compressed from side to side. The head terminates anteriorly in a short, blunt snout. The tail is narrow and bent upwards towards the extremity. The colour is grey with brown markings, or dark brown above, lighter underneath. The entire surface is covered closely with minute hard denticles—*placoid scales* or *dermal teeth*, (p. 103)—which are rather larger on the upper surface than on the lower. These are pointed, and directed somewhat backwards, so that the surface appears rougher when

FIG. 155.—Order **Euselachii**, Sub-order **Pleurotremata**, Super-family **Squaloidea**, Family **Hemiscyllidæ. *Brachælurus waddi*** (Bloch and Schneider, 1801). The Sydney ('Blind' or 'Dusky') Dogfish lives around rocky shores and feeds on small fishes, squid, sea-anemones, crustaceans, and seaweed. It reaches a length of about 3 feet and is ovo-viviparous (Whitley). Above is a drawing of a fœtus about 6 inches long from which the yolk sac has been erased and a suggestion of the lateral line system put in. The dark bands become less prominent with maturity (as occurs in many animals). ' Blind ' is a fisherman's misnomer arising from the fact that the comparatively small eyes are closed upon removal of the fish from water.

the hand is passed over it forwards than when it is passed in the opposite direction. When examined closely each scale is found to be a minute spine situated on a broader base. The spine consists of dentine covered with a layer of enamel. The base is composed of bone-like substance and there is a vascular pulp cavity. The whole scale has thus the same essential structure as a tooth, but, at the same time, the enamel is of different origin from that of mammals, in that it arises in the mesodermal dentine and not as a specifically ectodermal secretion.

Along each side of the head and body runs a faint depressed longitudinal line or slight narrow groove—the *lateral line*, marking the position of the *lateral line canal*. This contains integumentary sense-organs (pp. 136–137).

As in fishes in general, two sets of fins occur—the *unpaired* or *median* fins, and the *paired* or *lateral*. These are all flap-like outgrowths which run vertically and longitudinally in the case of the median fins and nearly horizontally in the case of the lateral. They are flexible, but stiffish (particularly towards the base) owing to the presence of a supporting framework of cartilage. Of the median fins two—the *dorsal*—are situated as the name indicates and are of triangular shape.   The anterior, which is the larger, is situated at about the middle of the length of the body, the other a little further back.   The *caudal fin* fringes the tail.   It consists of a narrower dorsal portion and a broader ventral, continuous with one another round the extremity of the tail, the latter divided by a notch into a larger anterior, and a smaller posterior lobe.   The tail is *heterocercal*, *i.e.* the posterior extremity of the spinal column is bent upwards and lies in the dorsal portion of the caudal fin so that the lobes of the fin have come to be unequal.   The so-called *anal* fin is situated on the ventral surface.   In *Scyliorhinus* it is to be found opposite the interval between the anterior and posterior dorsals.   In *Hemiscyllium* it is situated behind the posterior dorsals, which it resembles in size and shape.

Of the *lateral fins* there are two pairs, the pectoral and the pelvic.   The *pectorals* are situated at the sides of the body, just behind the head.   The *pelvics*, which are the smaller, are placed on the ventral surface, close together, about the middle of the body.   In the males the bases of the pelvic fins are united together in the middle line, and each has connected with it a *clasper* or *copulatory organ*.   The latter is a stiff rod, on the inner and dorsal aspect of which is a groove leading forwards into a pouch-like depression in the base of the fin.

The *mouth*—a transverse, somewhat crescentic opening—is situated on the ventral surface of the head, near its anterior end.   In front and behind it is bounded by the upper and lower jaws, each bearing several rows of teeth with sharp points directed backwards, and adapted for holding and wounding. The teeth are replaced as they become severely worn or broken.   The teeth of elasmobranchs were formerly confidently homologised with those of other vertebrates, but this is now called into question.   In some elasmobranchs accessory teeth are borne on the branchial cartilages.   The nostrils are situated one in front of each angle of the mouth, with which each is connected by a wide groove—the *naso-buccal groove*.   In *Squalus* the outer edge of the groove is prolonged into a narrow subcylindrical appendage—the *barbel*.   A small rounded aperture, the *spiracle*—placed just behind the eye—leads into the large pharynx. In the spiracle is located a leaf-shaped gill-like organ, the *pseudobranch* (p. 205). This may be an organ of special sense.   It is not essentially respiratory in function, since before the blood reaches the pseudobranch it is already oxygenated.   There are five branchial slits on each side of the head behind the spiracle (Fig. 155).   They lead internally into the pharynx.   A large median *cloacal aperture* opens on the ventral surface at the root of the tail between the pelvic fins.   The cloaca is a chamber forming the common outlet for the intestine and the renal and reproductive organs.   A pair of small depressions, the enigmatic *abdominal pores*, are situated behind the cloacal opening and lead into narrow passages opening into the abdominal cavity.

The **skeleton** is composed entirely of cartilage (p. 73), with, in certain places, depositions of calcareous salts. As in vertebrates in general we distinguish two sets of elements in the skeleton—the axial set and the appendicular. The former comprises the skull and spinal column; the latter the limbs and their arches.

The *spinal column* is clearly divisible into two regions—those of the trunk and tail. In the trunk-region each vertebra (Fig. 156, *A* and *B*) consists of a centrum (*c*), neural arch (*n. a.*), and transverse processes (*tr. pr.*). In the caudal region there are no transverse processes, but *inferior* or *hæmal arches* (*C., D., h. a.*) take their place. The centra of all the vertebræ are deeply biconcave or *amphicœlous*, having deep conical concavities on their anterior

FIG. 156. — *Scyliorhinus:* **Vertebral column.** *A* and *B*, from the trunk; *C* and *D*, from the middle of the tail; *A* and *C*, two vertebræ in longitudinal section; *B* and *D*, single vertebræ viewed from one end. *b*, calcified portion of centrum; *c*. centrum; *for*. foramen for dorsal, and *for'*. for ventral root of spinal nerve; *h. a.* hæmal arch (basi-ventral); *h. c.* hæmal canal; *h. sp.* hæmal spine; *i.n.p.* intercalary piece (interdorsal, or interneural plate); *n. a.* neural arch; *n. c.* neural canal; *n. p.* neural plate (basi-dorsal); *n. sp.* neural spine; *ntc.* intervertebral substance (remains of notochord); *r.* proximal portion of rib; *tr. pr.* transverse process (basal stump). (After T. J. Parker.)

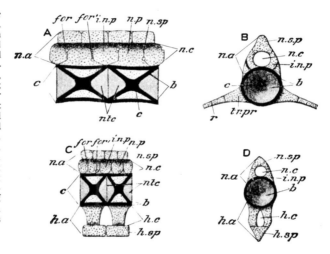

and posterior surfaces. Through the series of centra are found remnants of the notochord (*ntc.*). These are constricted in the centrum itself. In the large spaces formed by the apposition of the amphicœlous centra of adjoining vertebræ, a residual pulpy mass occurs. The concave anterior and posterior surfaces of the centra are covered by a dense calcified layer, and in *Squalus* eight radiating lamellæ of calcified tissue run longitudinally through the substance of the centrum itself. The centra, unlike those of the higher forms, are developed as chondrifications of the sheath of the notochord into which cells of the skeletogenous layer have migrated. On the dorsal side of the row of centra the spinal column is represented by the series of neural arches which support the walls of the spinal canal (*n. c.*). Owing to the presence of a series of intercalary cartilages the neural arches appear to be twice as numerous as the centra. Each neural arch consists on each side of a process, the *neural process* (given off from the centrum), and of a small cartilage, the *neural plate* (*basi-dorsal*), which becomes completely fused with the neural process in the adult.

Between successive neural plates (the width of each of which is only about half the length of the centrum) is interposed a series of plates of very similar shape, the *interdorsal* or *interneural plates* (*inp.*). Small median cartilages, the *neural spines*, fit in between both neural and interneural plates of opposite sides and form keystones completing the arches.

The transverse processes are very short. Connected with each of them is a rudimentary cartilaginous *rib* (*r.*) about half an inch in length.

The *cranium* (Fig. 157) is a cartilaginous case, the wall of which is continuous throughout, and not composed, like the skulls of higher vertebrates, of

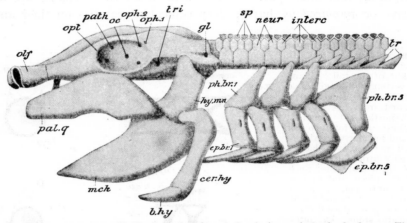

FIG. 157.—*Brachœlurus:* **Skull, visceral arches, and anterior part of spinal column.** The branchial rays are not represented. The skull and hyoid arch are somewhat drawn downwards, so that the hyoid and first branchial arch are not exactly in their natural relations. *cer. hy.* cerato-hyal; *ep. br.* 1. *ep. br.* 5, first and fifth epibranchials; *gl.* aperture for glossopharyngeal nerve; *b. hy.* basihyal; *hy. mn.* hyomandibular; *interc.* intercalary (interdorsal) plates; *mck.* Meckel's cartilage; *neur.* neural processes; *olf.* olfactory capsule; *oc.* foramen for oculomotor; *oph.* 1, foramen for ophthalmic division of facial nerve; *oph.* 2, foramen for ophthalmic division of trigeminal; *opt.* optic foramen; *pal. q.* palatoquadrate; *path.* foramen for 4th nerve; *ph. br.* 1 and *ph. br.* 5, first and fifth pharyngobranchial; *sp.* neural spines; *tr.* transverse processes and ribs; *tri.* foramen for trigeminal nerve.

a number of distinct bony elements fitting in together. At the anterior end is a *rostrum*, consisting in *Scyliorhinus* of three cartilaginous rods converging as they extend forwards and lateral ones meeting anteriorly. At the sides of the base of this are the *olfactory capsules* (*olf.*). These are thin rounded cartilaginous sacs opening widely below, the cavities of the two capsules being separated from one another by a thin septum. The part of the roof of the cranial cavity behind and between the olfactory capsules is formed not of cartilage, but of a tough fibrous membrane, and the space thus filled in is termed the *anterior fontanelle*. In contact with the lower surface of the membrane is the pineal body (p. 128). Each side-wall of this part of the skull presents a deep concavity —the *orbit*—over which is a ridge-like prominence, the *supraorbital crest*. This terminates anteriorly and posteriorly in obscure processes termed respectively the *preorbital* and *postorbital processes*.   Below the orbit is a longitudinal *infraorbital* ridge.

Behind the orbit is the *otic region* in which the parts of the membranous labyrinth of the internal ear are embedded.   On the upper surface of this posterior portion of the skull are two small apertures situated in a mesial depression.   These are the openings of the *endolymphatic ducts*, leading into the vestibule of the membranous labyrinth.   Behind this again is the *occipital region*, forming the posterior boundary of the cranial cavity, and having in the middle a large rounded aperture—the *foramen magnum*.   Through this the spinal cord, contained in the neural canal and protected by the neural arches of the vertebræ, becomes continuous with the brain.   Below this, on either side, is an articular surface—the *occipital condyle*—for articulation with the spinal column.   Between the two condyles is a concavity, like that of the vertebral centra, containing notochordal tissue.

A number of smaller apertures, or *foramina*, chiefly for the passage of nerves, perforate the wall of the skull.   Behind and to the outer side of the anterior fontanelle are apertures (*oph. 2, 1*) through which the ophthalmic branches of the fifth and seventh nerves leave the skull.   Piercing the inner wall of the orbit are foramina through which the optic or second pair of cerebral nerves (*opt.*), the oculomotor or third, (*oc.*), the trochlear, or fourth (*path.*), the trigeminal, or fifth (*tri.*), the abducens, or sixth, and the facial, or seventh, leave the interior of the cranial cavity.   Just behind the auditory region is the foramen for the glossopharyngeal (*gl.*).   In the posterior wall of the skull, near the foramen magnum, is the foramen for the vagus.

In close connection with the cranium are a number of cartilages composing the *visceral arches* (Figs. 157 and 158).   These are incomplete hoops of cartilage, mostly segmented, which lie in the sides and floor of the mouth-cavity or pharynx.   The first of these forms the upper and lower jaws.   The upper jaw, or *palatoquadrate* (*pal. q.*), consists of two stout rods of cartilage firmly bound together in the middle line and bearing the upper series of teeth.   The lower jaw, or *Meckel's cartilage* (*mck.*), likewise consists of two stout tooth-bearing cartilaginous rods firmly united together in the middle line.   This kind of union is a *symphysis*.   At their outer ends the upper and lower jaws articulate with one another by a movable joint.   In front the upper jaw is connected by a ligament with the base of the skull.

Immediately behind the lower jaw is the *hyoid arch*.   This consists of two cartilages on each side, and a mesial one below.   The uppermost cartilage is the *hyomandibular* (*hy. mn.*).   This articulates by its proximal end with a distinct articular facet on the auditory region of the skull.   Distally it is connected by ligamentous fibres with the outer ends of the palatoquadrate and Meckel's cartilage.   The lower lateral cartilage is the *ceratohyal* (*cer. hy.*).   Both the hyomandibular and ceratohyal bear a number of slender cartilaginous rods

—the branchial rays of the hyoid arch.   The mesial element, or *basihyal* (*b. hy.*), lies in the floor of the pharynx.   Behind the hyoid arch follow the *branchial arches*, which are five in number.   Each branchial arch, with exceptions to be presently noted, consists of four cartilages.   The uppermost of these— *pharyngobranchial* (*ph. br. 1–ph. br. 5*)—lie in the dorsal wall of the pharynx, not far from the spinal column.   The pharyngobranchials of the last two arches are fused together.   The next in order—the *epibranchials* (*ep. br.*)—with the exception of those of the last arch, bear a number of slender cartilaginous rods—

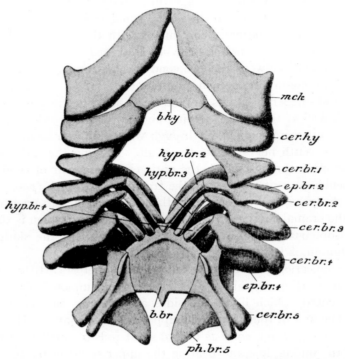

FIG. 158.—*Brachælurus:* **Visceral arches.**   Ventral view.   Letters as in preceding figure. In addition—*b. br.* basibranchial plate; *cer. br.* ceratobranchials; *hyp. br.* hypobranchials.

the *branchial rays*—which support the walls of the gill-sacs.   The next—the *ceratobranchials* (*cer. br.*)—are, with the same exception, similarly provided. The *hypobranchials* (*hyp. br.*), which succeed these, are absent in the case of the first and fifth arches.   In the middle line on the floor of the pharyngeal cavity is a mesial cartilage—the *basibranchial* (Fig. 158, *b.br.*)—which is connected with the ventral ends of the third, fourth, and fifth arches.   A series of slender curved rods—the *extrabranchials*—lie superficial to the branchial arches, along the borders of the corresponding external branchial clefts.   The branchial arches not only support the gills ; their jointed flexible structure also allows muscular pharyngeal movements which maintain the respiratory current of oxygenated sea-water. The pharyngeal walls expand, and the floor of the mouth is depressed. This causes water to flow into the buccal cavity. The mouth is now closed and the floor raised. This drives the imprisoned water out through the gill-slits. As it passes over the extensive capillary surface carbon dioxide is liberated and oxygen is taken up by the *hæmoglobin* carried in the red blood cells (pp. 70, 343).

The above movements are carried out by the lateral plate and myotomal hypoglossal muscles, the first innervated by vagus and glossopharyngeal nerves and the second by the hypoglossal (p. 130).

Two pairs of delicate *labial* cartilages are present at the sides of the mouth, and a couple at the margins of the openings of the olfactory capsules.

The skeleton of all the fins—paired and unpaired—presents a considerable degree of uniformity. The main part of the expanse of the fin is supported by a series of flattened segmented rods, the *pterygiophores* or cartilaginous fin-rays, which lie in close apposition. In the case of the dorsal fins these may be partly calcified. At the outer ends of these are one or more rows of polygonal plates of cartilage. On each side of the rays and polygonal cartilages are a number of slender 'horny' rays or *ceratotrichia* of dermal origin. On

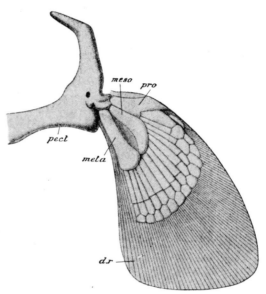

Fig. 159.—*Brachælurus*: Pectoral arch and fin. *d. r.* dermal horny rays; *meso.* mesopterygium; *meta.* metapterygium; *pect.* pectoral arch; *pro.* propterygium.

account of their appearance and horn-like consistency, these structures are commonly referred to as horny. They do not, however, consist of true horn, which is always epidermal in origin. They are composed of *elastin*, characteristic of elastic connective-tissue fibres.

In the smaller median fins there may be an elongated rod of cartilage constituting the skeleton, or cartilage may be entirely absent. In the pectoral fin (Fig. 159) the fin-rays are supported on three *basal cartilages* articulating with the *pectoral arch*. The latter (*pect.*) is a strong hoop of cartilage incomplete dorsally, situated immediately behind the last of the branchial arches. It consists of a dorsal, or *scapular*, and a ventral, or *coracoid* portion, the coracoid portions of opposite sides being completely continuous across the middle line, while the scapulas are separated by a wide gap in which the spinal column lies. Between the two portions are the three articular surfaces for the three basal cartilages. The coracoid portions are produced forwards in the middle line into a flattened process supporting the floor of the pericardial cavity in which the heart is lodged. The three basal cartilages of the fin are named, respectively, the anterior, *propterygium* (*pro.*), the middle, *mesopterygium* (*meso.*), and the posterior, *metapterygium* (*meta.*). Of these the first is the smallest and the last the largest. The first bears only one large ray; the other two bear twelve or more rays, differently arranged in the two genera.

The *pelvic fin* (Fig. 160) has only a single basal cartilage (*meta.*) articulating with the *pelvic arch*, with which also one or two of the fin-rays articulate directly. The pelvic arch (*pelv.*) is a nearly straight bar of cartilage which runs transversely across the ventral surface of the body, just in front of the cloacal opening.

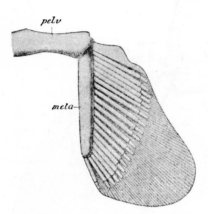

FIG. 160.—*Brachælurus:* **Pelvic arch and pelvic fin.** *meta.* metapterygium; *pelv.* pelvic arch.

Brief mention may be made of locomotion in elasmobranch fishes. The dogfish swims largely by means of the contraction of the muscle-fibres of its myotomes. Forward motion is carried out by alternate rhythmic waves of myotomal contraction passing posteriorly from the head and transverse thrusts of the tail. The first process depends partly on the presence of the vertebral column, which forms a resistant central axis. As Gray has shown, the muscle contractions undulate the streamlined body and thrust it ahead by transmitting a backward momentum to the surrounding water and pushing this back in a manner not essentially different from the operation of the man-made propeller (see also p. 86). The dogfish cannot move backwards. Lampreys (p. 176) and eels (p. 296) are able to do so because they can send contraction waves anteriorly. Most bony fishes can swim smoothly in reverse by fin-motion. In these, the evolution of the swim-bladder (p. 339), a hydrostatic organ, opened up all kinds of locomotory possibilities.

In the dogfish and in sharks generally the fins (including the caudal) are essentially stabilising and steering organs. Lacking a swim-bladder and lungs, cartilaginous fishes are heavier than sea-water. The specific gravity of a dogfish is about 1·06 compared with the 1·03 of sea-water, and so it must exert a lift with pectoral fins and the lower lobe of its tail in order to stay afloat. It is of great interest that all fishes that have developed an air-bladder or lungs seem to have at earlier stages of evolution possessed a shark-like tail, having only later developed the *outwardly* symmetrical caudal fin of familiar 'fish-tail' form (Figs. 204, 302).

Alimentary Canal and Associated Structures (Fig. 161). The mouth leads into a very wide cavity, the *pharynx*, into which open the lateral aspects of the internal apertures of the branchial clefts and the spiracle. From this runs backwards a short, wide, muscular-walled tube—the œsophagus (*œs.*)—which passes behind into the *stomach*. It will be recalled that no true stomach occurs in the Agnatha (p. 164). Among the Gnathostomata it is of almost universal occurrence. It exhibits great variation, however, and has been secondarily lost, in so far as histological structure is concerned, in certain highly specialised teleosts (p. 293), the Dipnoi (p. 361) and the Holocephali (p. 262). In the dog-fish it is of a peculiar U-shape with a long left limb continuous with the œso-phagus, and a short right one passing into the intestine.

The stomach is a capacious, muscular-walled, epithelium-lined bag in which the remains of fish, crabs, and other prey may be found. The acid secretion of the stomach prevents bacterial decomposition. The action of the powerful stomach-muscles helps to disintegrate the solid particles, thus providing a greater area for attack by proteolytic *pepsin* or a similar enzyme.

At the *pylorus* (*pyl.*)—the point where the stomach joins the intestine—is a slight constriction, followed by a thickening, the *pyloric sphincter*. This circular muscle ensures the retention of food in the stomach until stimuli cause it to relax and allow the particles to move through into the *small intestine*.

The small intestine is exceedingly short, measuring only an inch or two long. There next follows the *large* intestine, which is longer, much wider, and divisible into an anterior *colon* (*col.*) and a narrow *rectum* which terminates at the *cloaca*. Two prominent glands pour their secretions into the small intestine —the *liver* (*liv.*) and the *pancreas* (*pancr.*). The liver is a large bi-lobed gland. At the anterior end of the left lobe is embedded a rounded sac, the *gall-bladder* (*g. bl.*). Ducts connect each lobe of the liver with the gall-bladder and carry to it the bile or gall, which is subsequently passed down the *bile-duct* (*b. dct.*) into the small intestine near the beginning of the colon.

The pancreas is a pale, compressed gland consisting of two main lobes with a broad connecting isthmus. It lies in the angle between the right-hand limb of the stomach and the small intestine. Its duct, the *pancreatic duct*, carries digestive enzymes elaborated by the gland and enters the wall of the intestine, runs in it for about half an inch, and eventually opens at a point near the beginning of the colon.

Little is known of the digestive processes of the elasmobranch fishes. No doubt the bile acts primarily as an emulsifying agent upon ingested fats, separating them into minute droplets more readily accessible to the action of lipases. From the pancreas, and possibly also from the gut-wall, come other enzymes which hydrolyse carbohydrates and proteins. Absorption takes place largely in the colonic region, which is equipped with an anterior *spiral valve*. This begins at the end of the duodenum ; it is a richly glandular fold of tissue

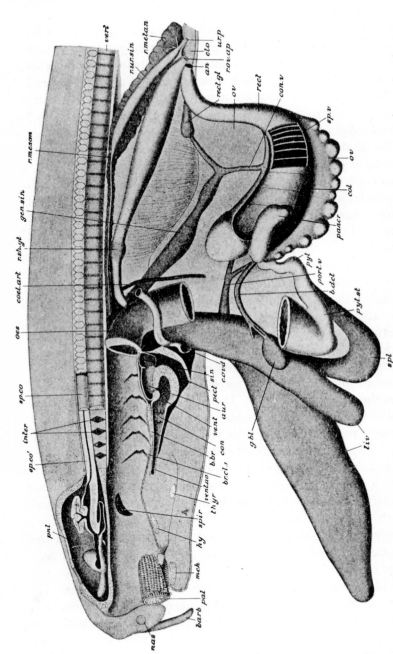

Fig. 161.—*Brachælurus:* **Visceral structure.** The head is represented in median vertical section. The left oviduct, kidney, and the stomach have been removed; the cloaca has been opened. The chambers of the heart have been opened. *an.* opening of rectum into cloaca; *aur.* atrium; *barb.* barbel; *b. br.* basi-branchial plate; *b. dct.* bile-duct; *br. cl.* internal branchial clefts; *clo.* cloaca; *cæl. art.* cœliac artery (cut short); *col.* colon; *con.* conus arteriosus; *con. v.* connecting vein between the genital (ovarian) sinus and the hepatic portal system; *c. ovd.* common cœlomic aperture of oviducts; *g. bl.* gall-bladder; *gen. sin.* genital sinus; *hy.* basi-branchial; *inter.* intervertebral substance; *liv.* liver; *mck.* Meckel's cartilage; *nas.* nasal cartilage; *œs.* œsophagus; *ov.* ovary; *pal.* palato-quadrate; *pancr.* pancreas; *pect.* pectoral arch; *pnl.* stalk of pineal body; *port. v.* hepatic portal vein; *pyl.* pylorus; *pyl. st.* pyloric portion of stomach; *rect.* rectum; *rect. gl.* rectal gland; *r. meson., r. metan.* anterior and posterior portions of kidney; *r. ov. ap.* aperture of right oviduct into cloaca; *r. sh. gl.* right shell-gland; *r. ur. sin.* right urinary sinus; *sin.* sinus venosus; *sp. co.* spinal cord; *sp. co'.* anterior part of spinal cord in median vertical section; *spir.* spiracle; *spl.* spleen; *sp. v.* spiral valve; *thyr.* thyroid; *ur. p.* urinary papilla; *vent. ao.* ventral aorta; *vert.* centra of vertebræ.

which runs spirally around the intestine and both retards the too rapid passage of food and affords a more extensive area for absorption of digested substances. The intestinal wall is invested with a ramification of capillaries which unite to form larger vessels which communicate with others from elsewhere (p. 112) as the hepatic portal vein and carry absorbed substances to the liver. There is little doubt that this gland is the site of manifold activities as in higher craniates. Apart from its role in the utilisation and transformation of absorbed substances, it probably also destroys effete red blood cells since *Kupffer cells* have been demonstrated in the liver of dogfish.

In addition to its exocrine activity, the pancreas has a second and *endocrine* function. In the pancreatic tissue (cf. *Petromyzon*, p. 185) *islets of Langerhans* occur in close association with blood capillaries, which carry away a hormone which probably has many of the same actions as insulin in higher vertebrates. There is some evidence that the islet-tissue is derived from intra-lobular ducts. Thus we may have another (see also p. 148) example of an older structure being converted to endocrine function.

The third gland opening into the alimentary tract, the *rectal* or *digitiform gland*, is small yet prominent. It is only about three-quarters of an inch long, and is of enigmatic function. It would seem, however, that it is by no means inactive. The gland has a central space lined with layers of cuboidal cells. Other cells of apparently secretory activity have what may be collecting ducts in their vicinity, and these ducts unite to form the short principal duct that empties into the rectum. At the same time the gland is highly vascular and conspicuously lymphoid. It is absent in actinopterygians, but appears to be present in the cœlacanth *Latimeria* (p. 360).

Morphologically associated with the alimentary canal is the *spleen* (*spl.*), a dark red body attached to the convexity of the U-shaped stomach. It sends a narrow lobe along the right-hand limb and is attached by means of a *gastrosplenic omentum* (see p. 74). The spleen is part of the blood-vascular system and in higher vertebrates has blood storage and other less obvious functions (p. 273).

FIG. 162.—*Brachœ-lurus*: Branchial sac. (Exposed from the exterior.)

Respiration.—The organs of respiration are the *gills*, situated in five *gill-sacs*. Each *branchial sac* (Fig. 162) is an antero-posteriorly compressed cavity opening internally into the pharynx and externally by the corresponding gill-slit. The walls of the pouches are supported by the branchial and hyoid arches with their rays, the first pouch being situated between the hyoid and first branchial arches, the last between the fourth and fifth branchial arches. On the anterior and posterior walls of the pouches are the *gills*, each hemibranch (p. 106) consisting of a series of close-set parallel folds of highly vascular membrane. Through this exceedingly thin membrane occur gaseous exchanges between the animal and the sea-water that is forced by buccal and pharyngeal musculature into the mouth and out through the gills (Fig. 73, p. 106). Carbon dioxide is given off by the blood and oxygen is taken up by its hæmoglobin. The re-oxygenated blood meanwhile continues its journey towards the *dorsal* aorta for re-distribution throughout the body (see below).

Separating adjoining gill-pouches, and supporting the gills, is a series of broad *interbranchial septa*, each containing the corresponding branchial arch with its connected branchial rays. The most anterior hemibranch is borne on the posterior surface of the hyoid arch. The last gill-pouch differs from the rest in having gill-folds on its anterior wall only. On the anterior wall of the spiracle is the *pseudobranch* (p. 320).

Blood-vascular System.—This follows the general vertebrate plan already observed in the Agnatha. The heart is situated in the pericardial cavity on the ventral aspect of the body, in front of the pectoral arch, and between the

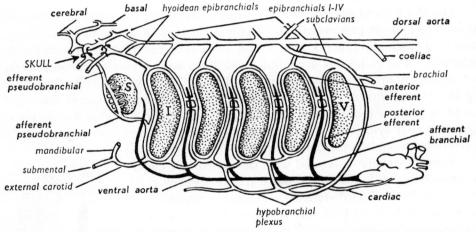

Fig. 163.—*Mustelus:* **Heart and branchial circulation.** (Redrawn after various authors.)

two series of branchial pouches. The dorsal wall of the pericardial cavity is supported by the basibranchial cartilage. Placing it in communication with the abdominal cavity is a canal—the *pericardio-peritoneal canal.* The heart (Fig. 161) consists of four chambers—*sinus venosus (sin.), atrium (aur.), ventricle (vent.),* and *conus arteriosus (con.)*—through which the blood passes in the order given. The *sinus venosus* is a thin-walled, transverse, tubular chamber, into the end of which the great veins open. It is here that the heart-beat originates (p. 109), and in it is an extensive nerve plexus connected with a branch of the vagus. Vagal stimulation slows the heart-rate. There is no 'antagonistic' accelerator branch from the sympathetic system such as occurs in higher forms (see p. 119).

The contractile sinus venosus communicates with the atrium by an aperture, the *sinu-atrial* aperture. The *atrium* is a large, three-cornered, thin-walled chamber. It is situated in front of the sinus venosus and dorsal to the ventricle. Its apex is directed forwards, and its lateral angles project at the sides of the ventricle; it communicates with the ventricle by a slit-like aperture guarded by a two-lipped valve. Contraction of the atrium drives blood into the ventricle. This is a thick-walled, globular chamber, forming the most conspicuous part of the heart when looked at from the ventral surface. The muscles of the ventricle contract and raise the blood pressure to fill the *conus arteriosus*, which runs forwards as a stout median tube to the anterior end of the pericardial cavity, where it gives off the *ventral aorta*. It contains two transverse rows of valves, anterior and posterior, the former consisting of three, the latter of three or four. The *ventral aorta* (Fig. 163) gives origin to a series of paired *afferent branchial arteries*, which carry deoxygenated blood to the branchial pouches. In *Scyliorhinus* the two most posterior arise close together near the beginning of the ventral aorta, the third pair a little further forwards. The ventral aorta then runs forwards and bifurcates to form the left and right common stem of the first and second afferent arteries, each of which in turn bifurcates to form the first and second afferent vessels of its side. In *Squalus* (Fig. 164 A, B) the arrangement is somewhat more primitive.

From the gills oxygenated blood passes by means of the *efferent branchial arteries*. These efferent vessels (Fig. 163) form a series of loops, one running around the margin of each of the first four internal branchial clefts. A single vessel runs along the anterior border of the fifth branchial cleft and opens into the fourth loop. The four main efferent branchial vessels (*epibranchials*) run inwards and backwards from the loops above the mucous membrane investing the roof of the pharynx to unite in a large median trunk—the *dorsal aorta* (*d. ao.*). From this thick-walled artery the blood is redistributed to tissues all over the body. A *dorsal carotid artery* is given off from the first efferent branchial. A branch (*hyoidean*) given off from the same efferent vessel supplies the pseudobranch (p. 230) and is then taken up by the *ventral carotid*. Both carotids run forwards to supply the head.

The large *dorsal aorta* (Fig. 163) runs backwards throughout the length of the body-cavity, giving off numerous branches, and is continued as the *caudal artery*, which runs in the canal enclosed by the inferior arches of the caudal vertebræ. The first pair of branches are the *subclavians*, for the supply of the pectoral fins. These are given off from between the third and fourth pairs of epibranchial arteries. The next branch is the unpaired *cœliac* (Fig. 161, *cœl.*). This runs in the mesentery and divides into branches for the supply of the stomach and liver, the first part of the intestine, and the pancreas. The *anterior mesenteric* artery, also median, supplies the rest of the intestine and gives off branches to the reproductive organs. The *lienogastric* supplies part of the stomach, the spleen, and part of the pancreas. The *posterior mesenteric* is a small vessel mainly supplying the rectal gland. Paired *renal* arteries carry

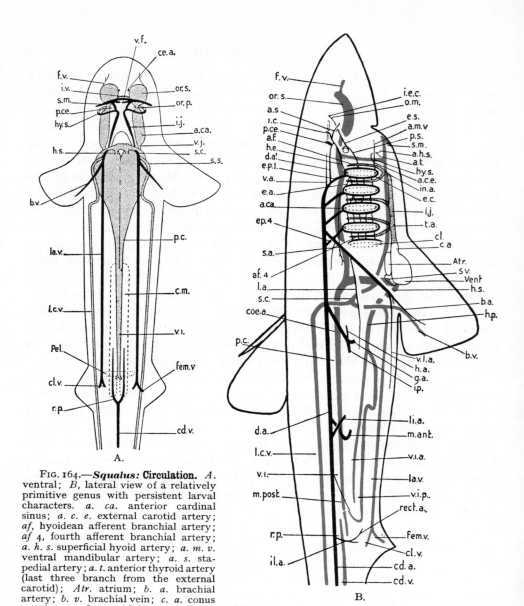

FIG. 164.—*Squalus:* **Circulation.** *A.* ventral; *B*, lateral view of a relatively primitive genus with persistent larval characters. *a. ca.* anterior cardinal sinus; *a. c. e.* external carotid artery; *af*, hyoidean afferent branchial artery; *af* 4, fourth afferent branchial artery; *a. h. s.* superficial hyoid artery; *a. m. v.* ventral mandibular artery; *a. s.* stapedial artery; *a. t.* anterior thyroid artery (last three branch from the external carotid); *Atr.* atrium; *b. a.* brachial artery; *b. v.* brachial vein; *c. a.* conus arteriosus; *cd. a.* caudal artery; *cd. v.* caudal vein; *ce. a.* anterior cerebral artery; *cl.* fifth gill slit; *cl. v.* cloacal vein; *c. m.* caudal mesonephros; *cœ. a.* cœliac artery; *d. a.* paired dorsal aorta; *e. a.* anastomosis between efferent collector loops; *e. c.* efferent collector loop; *ep.* 1–4, first and fourth epibranchial arteries; *e. s.* efferent pseudobranchial artery; *fem. v.* femoral ve˙n; *f. v.* anterior facial vein; *g. a.* gastric artery; *h. a.* hepatic artery; *h. e.* hyoidean epibranchial artery; *h. p.* hepatic portal vein; *h. s.* hepatic sinus; *hy. s.* hyoidean sinus; *i. c.* internal carotid artery; *i. e. c.* intracranial branch of the spiracular epibranchial artery; *i. f.* inferior jugular sinus; *il. a.* iliac artery; *in. a.* innominate artery; *i. p.* intestino-pyloric artery; *i. v.* interorbital vein; *l. a.* lateral artery; *la. v.* lateral abdominal vein; *l. c. v.* superior lateral cutaneous vein; *li. a.* lieno-gastric artery; *m. ant.* anterior mesenteric artery; *m. post.* posterior mesenteric artery; *o. m.* great ophthalmic artery; *or. p.* post-orbital sinus; *or. s.* orbital sinus; *p. c.* posterior cardinal sinus; *p. ce.* posterior cerebral vein; *Pel.* pelvic cartilage; *p. s.* afferent pseudobranchial artery; *r. p.* renal portal vein; *rect. a.* rectal artery; *s. a.* subclavian artery; *s. c.* subclavian vein; *s. m.* submental sinus; *s. s.* subscapular sinus; *s. v.* sinus venosus; *t. a.* ventral aorta; *v. a.* vertebral artery; *Vent.* ventricle; *v. f.* thyroid vein; *v. i.* inter-renal portion of posterior cardinal sinus; *v. i. a.* anterior intestinal vein; *v. i. p.* posterior intestinal vein; *v. j.* base of jugular vein; *v. l. a.* ventro-lateral artery. (After O'Donoghue and Abbot.)

a small quantity of arterial blood to the kidneys, and a pair of *iliac* arteries, likewise of small size, pass to the pelvic fins. In addition to these, a number of small *parietal* arteries, which supply the wall of the body, are given off throughout the length of the aorta.

The gills, as we have seen, stand between the heart and the dorsal aorta. Because of their resistance, the blood pressure in the dorsal aorta is much lower than in the ventral aorta. This is in great contrast to animals having a double circulation where the pressure lost in the passage through the respiratory capillaries is made up again when the blood returns to the left ventricle. In such animals distribution from the dorsal aorta is always at high pressure.

Venous return is probably partly assisted by the large and widespread *blood sinuses* that characterise the venous system of elasmobranchs. The veins have very thin walls, but the larger trunks are remarkable for sinusoidal dilatations, which are, of course, true vessels, and not to be confused with the blood sinuses found in invertebrates. Little knowledge concerning their precise mode of action is available but, as resistance is lowered by the widening of a vessel, it would seem that the sinuses may be adaptations that, along with the thin-walled sinus venosus, help to ensure that a supply of blood is constantly available to the muscular chambers of the heart. Little is known about the possible auxiliary action of somatic muscles of the kind that help squeeze the blood towards the heart in higher groups (see p. 78). There is evidence that a suction mechanism, made possible by the box-like cartilaginous framework (lined by the pericardium), considerably assists venous return. This structure is made up above by the basibranchial plate and below by the pectoral girdle. A *pericardio-peritoneal* canal penetrates from pericardium into the cœlom of the abdomen, where it narrows markedly. This canal may act as a valve that helps maintain a negative venous pressure by means of a one-way flow of fluid from pericardium to cœlom. Certainly when the atrium and ventricle powerfully contract, the pressure in the pericardium falls sharply and a compensatory flow of venous blood pours into the thin-walled sinus venosus in much the same way as the mammalian lung is filled with air.

An outline of the veins in *Scyliorhinus* is as follows. The blood comes back from the head region by a pair of *jugular* or *anterior cardinal sinuses*, and from the trunk by a pair of *posterior cardinal sinuses*. At the level of the sinus venosus the anterior and posterior cardinals of each side unite to form a short, nearly transverse sinus, the *precaval sinus* or *ductus Cuvieri*, which is continued into the lateral extremity of the sinus venosus. Into the precaval sinus, about its middle, opens an *inferior jugular sinus* which brings back the blood from the floor of the mouth and from the ventral surface of the branchial region. The two posterior cardinal sinuses extend backwards throughout the length of the body-cavity. In front these are enormously dilated; behind they lie between the kidneys. Anteriorly each receives the corresponding *subclavian vein* bringing the blood from the pectoral fin and adjacent parts of the body-wall. The *lateral vein* (*la. v.*), instead of joining with the subclavian, opens separately into the precaval. The *genital sinus* discharges into the posterior cardinal sinus.

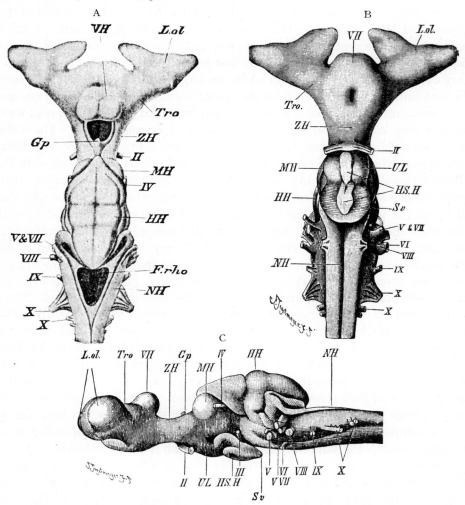

FIG. 165.—*Scyliorhinus:* **Brain.** *A*, dorsal view; *B*, ventral view; *C*, lateral view. *F.rho.* fossa rhomboidalis (fourth ventricle); *Gp*, epiphysis; *HH*, cerebellum; *HS. H*, hypophysis; *L. ol.* olfactory bulb; *MH*, mid-brain; *NH*, medulla oblongata; *Sv*, saccus vasculosus; *Tro,* olfactory peduncle; *UL*, lobi inferiores; *VH*, prosencephalon; *ZH*, diencephalon; *II*, optic nerves; *III*, oculomotor; *IV*, trochlear; *V*, trigeminal; *VI*, abducens; *VII*, facial; *VIII*, auditory; *IX*, glossopharyngeal; *X*, vagus. (After Wiedersheim.)

There are two *portal systems* of veins, the *renal* and the *hepatic portal*, by which the kidneys and liver, respectively, are supplied with venous blood. The *caudal vein*, which brings back the blood from the tail, runs along with the caudal artery, through the inferior arches of the vertebræ.

It divides on entering the abdominal cavity into right and left *renal portal* veins. These end in a number of afferent renal veins supplying the kidneys.

The *hepatic portal* vein (*h. p.*) is formed by the confluence of veins derived from the intestine, stomach, pancreas, and spleen, and carries blood and digested food-substances forwards to enter the liver to the right of the mid-line. The above does not apply to all species of dogfish (which fall into two sub-orders). Differences in *Squalus*, a less advanced form retaining certain larval characters in its blood vascular system, can be seen in Fig. 164.

Nervous System.—In the elasmobranch fishes the brain is large and highly organised and shows a considerable advance on that of the Cyclostomata. Anteriorly it consists of a rounded smooth telencephalon: both roof and floor are considerably thickened and meet internally in the mid-line, dividing the original median ventricle of the end brain into paired ventricles. It is probable that the end-brain in these animals serves principally as an apparatus for ana-lysing olfactory impulses. From its antero-lateral region each hemisphere gives off a thick cord, which dilates into large masses, the paired *olfactory bulbs* (*L. ol.*), each closely applied to the posterior surface of the corresponding olfactory organ. This structural arrangement is not inconsistent with the numerous accounts of naturalists and fishermen claiming high olfactory powers for selachians (p. 275).

The *diencephalon* (*ZH*) has a very thin roof. Its lateral walls are composed of two thickish masses, the *thalami*. Attached to the roof is a slender tube, the *epiphysis cerebri* or *pineal organ* (*Gp.*), which runs forwards and terminates in a slightly dilated extremity fixed to the membranous part of the roof of the skull. The pineal body does not appear to be secretory, nor does it retain any structure suggesting visual function (cf. *Petromyzon*, p. 189; Minnow, p. 345). The *hypothalamus* in the floor of the diencephalon is well-developed and may, as in 'higher' vertebrates, be concerned with the regulation of various uncondi-tioned reflexes and visceral functions. Two rounded bodies—the *lobi inferiores* —are prominent. These are dilated portions of the *infundibulum*. Behind, these give off a thin-walled, pigmented, vascular outgrowth—the *saccus vasculosus* (*Sv.*). We will see that this peculiar characteristic organ is highly developed in the bony fishes as well. It may be a pressure receptor centre.

Attached to the infundibulum and extending backwards from it is a thin-walled sac—the *pituitary body* or *hypophysis* (*HS.H*). In the pituitary, anterior, intermediate, tuberal, and neural (or posterior) 'lobes' occur. Probably a chromatophore-expanding hormone and gonadotrophic hormones occur. The thyroid gland (p. 151) is said not to be markedly influenced by hypophysectomy (cf. teleost fishes, p. 346).

In front of the infundibulum, and also on the lower surface of the dien-cephalon, is the *optic chiasma*, formed by the decussation of the fibres of the two optic tracts.

The mid-brain (*MH*) is large. It consists dorsally of a pair of oval *optic lobes* which form the tectum. These receive the optic tracts and, in addition, fibres which transmit a variety of afferent impulses unconnected with optical stimulation. There is, too, experimental evidence that efferent fibres from the mid-brain influence spinal centres. The floor of the mid-brain is almost continuous with the ventral surfaces of hind-brain and spinal cord.

The cerebellum (*HH*) is large and elongated in the antero-posterior direction. Its anterior portion overlaps the optic lobes, its posterior, the medulla oblongata. Its surface is marked with a few fine grooves. Into it lead sensory fibres from the ear and others from the facial, glossopharyngeal, and vagus nerves which carry afferent impulses from the lateral line system. The main part of the cerebellum (the *median body*) is disproportionately large in the biggest sharks and rays. The medulla oblongata (*NH*), broad in front, narrows posteriorly to pass into the spinal cord. The *fourth ventricle* (*F. rho.*) is a shallow cavity in the medulla oblongata covered dorsally only by a thin vascular membrane, the *choroid plexus*: it is wide in front and gradually narrows posteriorly. At the sides of the anterior part of the fourth ventricle are a pair of folded ear-shaped lobes, the *auricular lobes* of the cerebellum. These correspond with the flocculi of more advanced vertebrates. The medulla gives off a series of cranial nerves (p. 133). Of particular interest are those which are concerned with the control of branchial respiration and cardio-vascular activities. We have seen that in air-breathing vertebrates an important part of the mechanism for respiratory control is still located in the medulla in spite of the fact that the mode of respiration is radically different.

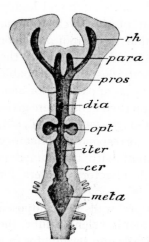

FIG. 166.—**Hemiscyllium: Relationship of brain ventricles.** *cer.* dilatation from which the epicœle is given off; *dia.* diacœle (third ventricle) pointing to the opening leading into the infundibulum; *iter.* iter or mesocœle; *meta.* metacœle (fourth ventricle); *opt.* optocœle; *para.* paracœle; *pros.* prosocœle; *rh.* rhinocœle.

The fourth ventricle (Fig. 166, *meta.*) is continuous behind with the central canal of the spinal cord. It extends into the cerebellum dorsally, and in front is continuous with a narrow passage, the aqueduct of the mid-brain, which opens anteriorly into a wider space, *third ventricle* (*dia.*) occupying the interior of the diencephalon. The third ventricle extends into the telencephalon and is prolonged into the cerebral hemispheres as the lateral ventricles on each side.

Cranial Nerves. From the anterior enlargements of the olfactory bulbs already mentioned spring numerous fibres which constitute the first pair of cranial nerves (*olfactorius*) and enter the olfactory capsules. Between the two olfactory lobes two small nerves, the *terminal* or *pre-olfactory*, arise from the telencephalon. These connect with the interior of the olfactory sacs. From the optic chiasma two tracts (see p. 130) (Figs. 92, p. 143; and 167) run outwards through the optic foramina into the orbits, each perforating the sclerotic of the corresponding eye and terminating in the retina. The third (*oculomotorius*), fourth (*trochlear*), and sixth (*abducens*) pairs of nerves have the general origin and distribution which have already been described as universal in the Craniata (p. 130).

The fifth nerve (*trigeminal*) (p. 131, Figs. 165, 167, 168) arises in close relation to the seventh (*facialis*). As it passes into the orbit it swells into a ganglion—the *Gasserian*. It has three chief branches. The first given off is the

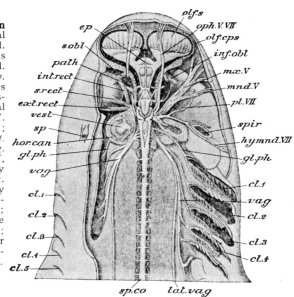

FIG. 167.—*Scyliorhinus:* **Brain and spinal nerves.** From the dorsal surface with the right eye removed. The cut surfaces of the cartilaginous skull and spinal column are dotted. *cl.1—cl.5*, branchial clefts; *ep.* epiphysis; *ext. rect.* posterior rectus muscle of the eye-ball; *gl. ph.* glossopharyngeal; *hor. can.* horizontal semicircular canal; *hy. mnd. VII.* hyomandibular portion of the facial; *inf. obl.* inferior oblique muscle; *int. rect.* anterior rectus muscle; *lat. vag.* lateral branch of vagus; *mnd. V*, *mx. V.* mandibular and maxillary divisions of the trigeminal; *olf. cps.* olfactory capsule; *olf. s.* olfactory sac; *oph. V. VII.* superficial ophthalmic branches of trigeminal and facial; *path.* fourth nerve; *pl. VII.* palatine branch of facial; *sp. co.* spinal cord; *sp.* and *spir.* spiracle; *s. rect.* superior rectus muscle; *s. obl.* superior oblique; *vag.* vagus; *vest.* vestibule. (After Marshall and Hurst.)

superficial ophthalmic (Fig. 167, *oph. V*; Fig. 168), a nerve which runs forwards through the orbit above the origin of the recti muscles, and in very close relation with the ophthalmic branch of the facial. Anteriorly it breaks up into branches distributed to the integument of the dorsal surface of the snout.[1] The main trunk of the nerve then runs forwards and outwards across the floor of the orbit, and divides into two branches, the *maxillary* and *mandibular*, or second and third divisions of the trigeminal. The former supplies the skin of the ventral surface of the snout, the latter the skin and muscles of the lower jaw.

[1] In most Chondrichthyes a nerve of considerable size—the *ophthalmicus profundus* (p. 131) —arises from the dorsal and anterior part of the Gasserian ganglion, and is usually regarded as a branch of the trigeminal. It runs forwards over the posterior rectus muscle and under the superior rectus, and perforates the pre-orbital process to end in the integument of the snout. Among other branches it gives off ciliary branches to the eyeball; these are joined by the ciliary branches of the oculomotor. The ophthalmicus profundus is not present in *Scyliorhinus* in the adult condition.

Of the branches of the seventh (facial), the *ophthalmic* runs through the orbit in close relation to the superficial ophthalmic branch of the trigeminal, and is distributed to the lateral line and ampullary canals of the snout (see p. 251). The *buccal* runs forwards in intimate relation with the maxillary division of the trigeminal, and breaks up into branches which are distributed to the sensory canals and ampullæ of the region of the snout. The *palatine* passes to the roof of the mouth. The main body of the nerve—*hyomandibular*—then runs outwards close to the edge of the hyomandibular cartilage and behind the spiracle, eventually becoming distributed to the muscles between the spiracle and the first branchial cleft. A small external mandibular branch comes off from it

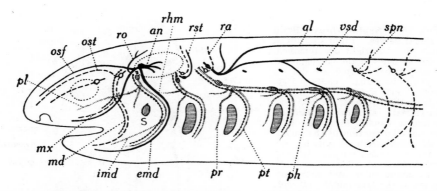

Fig. 168.—**Selachii: Components of dorsal root cranial nerves.** The ventral root nerves (somatic motor component) to eye muscles and hypoglossal muscles are omitted. The post-trematic branches of branchial nerves (as well as the hyomandibular and mandibular branches of the VIIth and Vth nerves respectively) include a visceral motor component absent from pre-trematic branches. These nerves supply visceral muscles which constrict the arch in question. The jaws and other arches are opened or expanded by the contraction of somatic muscles inner-vated by ventral branches of the anterior spinal nerves which are collected together to form a hypoglossal nerve emanating from the ventral aspect of the medulla. (See also Fig. 80, p. 129.) *al.* accessory line: *an.* auditory; *emd.* external mandibular; *imd.* internal mandibular; *md.* mandi-bular; *mx.* maxillary; *osf.* superior ophthalmic of facial; *ost.* superior ophthalmic of trigeminal; *ph.* pharyngeal; *pl.* palatine; *pr.* pretrematic; *pt.* post-trematic; *ra.* dorsal ramus; *rhm.* hyo-mandibular; *ro.* ramus oticus; *rst.* ramus supra-temporalis; *spn.* dorsal root of spinal nerve; *vsd.* vestigal dorsal root. Components: black line = lateral line; broken line = general cutaneous; beaded line = visceral motor; cross-hatched line = visceral sensory. (Redrawn after Goodrich.)

and goes to the lateral line and ampullary canals of the lower jaw. The eighth (*acousticus* or *auditory*) nerve passes directly into the internal ear, and breaks up into branches for the supply of its various parts. The ninth (*glossopharyn-geal*) perforates the posterior part of the auditory region of the skull, and, after it emerges, passes directly to the first branchial cleft, where it bifurcates. One branch now goes to the anterior, and the other to the posterior, wall of the cleft. The tenth and last nerve of the series—the *vagus* or *pneumogastric*—is a large nerve which emerges from the skull by an aperture situated between the auditory region and the foramen magnum. It first gives off a series of four *branchial* branches, each of which bifurcates to supply the anterior and posterior borders of the last four branchial clefts. The *lateralis* nerve is frequently referred to as a branch of the vagus, but it has a distinct origin in the medulla. After becoming separated from the vagus trunk it runs in the horizontal septum opposite the lateral line, which it supplies, to the posterior end of the body. The rest of the vagus runs backwards to divide into *cardiac* branches for the heart and *gastric* branches for the stomach. It will be observed that the system of neuromast organs (lateral line and ampullary organs) is supplied by nerve-fibres which pass out in various branches of the facial and in the lateralis branch of the vagus. All these fibres originate in a centre in the medulla, the *acousticolateral centre*, common to them and the fibres of the auditory nerve.

Spinal Cord. This is a cylindrical cord which extends from the foramen magnum, where it is continuous with the medulla oblongata, backwards throughout the length of the neural canal, enclosed by the neural arches of the vertebræ. As in the Craniata in general (see p. 124), it has dorsal and ventral longitudinal fissures and a narrow central canal, and gives origin to a large number of paired spinal nerves, each arising from it by two roots.

Autonomic Nervous System. The sympathetic chain of selachians, unlike that of the teleosts, and in fact uniquely among vertebrates, does not extend into the head (cf. Fig. 82, p. 119). Otherwise it occurs in the typical gnathostome pattern as a series of paired lateral ganglia approximately segmentally arranged, extending from about the level of the sinus venosus posteriorly over the kidneys to a little past the cloaca (Fig. 169). The prominent sympathetic ganglia, closely associated with adrenalin-chromaffin tissue (p. 152), contain motor nerve-cells (postganglionic) which send fibres to plain muscle (p. 76) variously investing the alimentary canal and other visceral organs and arterial walls. These motor-cells are in turn controlled *via* preganglionic fibres which originate in cells in the cord and emerge in the ventral spinal roots and pass to the *rami communicantes*.

Many of the fibres in the sympathetic chain are sensory. Postganglionic fibres, such as run in higher vertebrates (*e.g.* p. 119) from the sympathetic ganglia back to the spinal nerves to terminate in the skin, do not occur. Young found no evidence of the sympathetic control of chromatophores or other skin functions.

Although the vagus (Fig. 168) is massive and branched extensively to the heart, alimentary canal, and elsewhere there has been as yet no clear recognition of an antagonistic parasympathetic system (p. 121).

Organs of Special Sense.—The *olfactory organs* (Figs. 167; 89, p. 138) are rounded chambers enclosed by the cartilage of the olfactory capsules of the skull, and opening to the exterior by the nostrils on the ventral surface of the head. Water flows inwards and passes over chemoreceptors which lie in the epithelium covering a series of close-set ridges running out from a median septum.

Taste-buds, too, occur in the pharyngeal region.

The *eye* (Fig. 184, p. 273) has the general structure already described as characterising the Craniata in general (Figs. 90, 276, pp. 139, 413). The retina (except in *Mustelus* and the eagle-ray *Myliobatis aquila*) lacks cones: most selachians are apparently colour-blind. The lens is supported primarily by a dorsal thickening of a membrane that covers the ciliary body. Ventrally there is situated a papilla containing smooth muscle-fibres, the contraction of which moves the lens towards the cornea, achieving an accommodation (for nearer vision) which may be enhanced by the action of the protractor lentis muscle on the cornea itself. The primary apparatus of photo-adaptation in all species is, of course, the iris, which can contract into a narrow oblique slit in bright conditions.

The sclerotic is cartilaginous. The choroid has a silvery layer, the *tapetum lucidum*, beneath the photosensitive rods of the retina. This, an adaptation to life in dim light, reflects additional light on to the retinal cells (see also p. 140). The pigment epithelium is devoid of pigment cells in most species, but a few specialised forms which lack the *tapetum* have them (*e.g.* the Basking Shark *Cetorhinus* and the abyssal shark *Lœmargus*). There are the usual eye-muscles, the two *obliques* situated anteriorly, the four *recti* posteriorly, not embracing the optic nerve (Fig. 92, p. 143). The eyelids are represented by stiff folds.

The structures that make up the *ear* in vertebrates subserve three senses : 1. *orientation* (in regard to gravity) ; 2. *acceleration* (changes in speed and direction) ; and 3. *hearing* (the appreciation of air-, earth-, or water-borne sound waves). In the dogfish the apparatus consists only of the *membranous labyrinth* (Fig. 93, p. 144), equivalent to the internal ear of higher Craniata. The middle and outer ear are absent. The membranous labyrinth consists of a *utricle* and *saccule* (incompletely separated and forming a *vestibule*), and three *semicircular canals*. The vestibule communicates by a narrow passage—the *endolymphatic duct*—with the exterior, in the position already mentioned. Of the three semicircular canals, the anterior and posterior are vertical and the external horizontal, as in Craniata in general.

Each of the *endolymph*-containing semi-circular canals expands at one end to form an ampulla. At the other end each opens into the vestibule into which chamber the ampullæ also open, establishing a continuity of the fluid system. The actual receptors occur as sensory cristæ in the ampullæ with a neuro-epithelium made up of neuromast cells which are equipped with hair-like processes which are ensheathed in a gelatinous *cupola terminalis*. The detailed working of the six canals of this system in the maintenance of dynamic equilibrium is well discussed by Lowenstein (see references), but in general it can be said here that the fluid-filled apparatus rapidly perceives rotational changes and that each semi-circular canal is a bi-directional receptor.

In the endolymph of the utriculus and sacculus (and in the lagena of at least some elasmobranchs) are suspended, in a mass of gelatinous tissue, numerous minute calcareous *otoliths*, which give it a 'milky' character. These are gravity receptors of broadly the same function as those found in many invertebrate phyla. In the elasmobranchs studied the widest range of reception is found in the utriculus. It seems established, too, that all otolith organs respond not only to gravitational stimuli but to all other linear accelerations as well. The old functional concept which distinguished between dynamic receptors (canals) and the static receptors (otolith organs) must be abandoned.

It will be seen above that no cochlea (p. 145) occurs. The apparatus seems essentially concerned with the appraisal of position and the maintenance of equilibrium. There is, however, some evidence that selachians, with the nerve supply to skin and lateral line (see below) cut, can respond to low-frequency vibrations. Section of the auditory nerve drastically reduces the response.

Situated in the head are deep mucus-filled innervated canals called the *ampullæ of Lorenzini* (see also p. 359). There is some evidence that these are sense organs concerned with the appreciation of changes in water temperature. They appear to be part of the *lateral line system* which extends down each side of the body. This apparatus appreciates vibrations in the surrounding water. Specialised hair-like processes, tipped with a concretion of relatively heavy material, are sunk in minute pits and are connected with the lateral line nerves (see also p. 136). Thus, it is not easy to touch a fish, even if it cannot see the approaching objects. Blind species (*e.g.* the teleost *Anoptichthys*) catch minute animals that they never see. Pumphrey has shown that lateral line receptors act to some degree like the aerial of a direction-finder. Thus is the animal aware of vibrations set up in its neighbourhood and, then, apprised of the presence of predators or prey, it is able to take appropriate action (see below). At the same time it must be remembered that most fishes depend a good deal on their eyes (p. 273).

Endocrine Organs.—In addition to the pituitary (p. 150), pancreas (p. 152), and gonads (see below, p. 255), a *thyroid* gland (Fig. 161) and *adrenal* tissues (Fig. 169) also occur. We saw in *Petromyzon* (p. 176) the development of a simple, but seemingly typically craniate thyroid from the endostyle (pp. 196, 197) in the metamorphosis from ammocœte larva to adult, together with the secretion of an iodine-containing thyroxin, or a thyroxin-like substance, that will experimentally hasten anuran metamorphosis. In the dog-fishes we see the thyroid as a pharyngeal downgrowth sometimes still associated with a minute and an apparently functionless ciliated cavity that emphasises its endostylic origin. This is easily located just below the ventral aorta, where the vessel finally turns upward to branch and supply the first pair of branchial pouches. Evidence concerning thyroid function in selachians is confusing.

The *thymus* has often been considered, without proof, to be an endocrine organ. In dogfishes it can be found inconspicuously placed on each side of the thyroid and below the upper angles of the branchial clefts.

An adrenal gland (p. 152) does not occur as such, but there exist separately the homologues of both *medullary* and *cortical* tissues. The adrenalin-producing chromaffin tissue is distributed in a long segmental series of small glands (Fig. 169), some of them penetrating the roof of the posterior cardinal sinus. Anteriorly they are conjoined into elongated aggregations on each side of the œsophagus. Posteriorly, as Young has shown, they lie in kidney tissue. They are closely associated with the sympathetic ganglia (see also p. 249), and probably have broadly the same functions (p. 119) as in higher groups in which they, and the ganglia, share a common neural crest origin. The posterior elements are bigger in the male.

Inter-renal glands occur near the kidneys. Their position and form vary in different species—they may be single or diffuse. Essential to the life of the fish, they represent the adrenal cortex of mammals and the corresponding inter-digitating lipoidal cells found in the adrenals of reptiles, birds, and Amphibia (p. 152).

Excretion and Osmoregulation.—Each kidney consists of two parts, anterior and posterior. The former (Fig. 161, *r. meson.*, Fig. 170, k^1) is a long, narrow ribbon of soft reddish tissue, which runs along throughout a great part of the body-cavity at the side of the vertebral column. It is covered by peritoneum. The posterior portion is a compact, lobulated, dark red body, lying at the side of the cloaca, continuous with the anterior portion. It, too, is covered by peritoneum. Both portions possess ducts. Those of the anterior are narrow tubes, which run over its ventral surface and become dilated behind to form a pair of elongated chambers, the *urinary sinuses* (Fig. 171, *ur. sin.*). These unite behind into a median sinus (*med. ur. sin.*), which opens into the cloaca by a median aperture situated on a papilla, the *urinary papilla*. The ducts of the posterior portion, which are usually from four to six

FIG. 169.—*Scyllium:* **Medullary and cortical homologues of adrenal.** Aorta and kidneys with associated diffuse chromaffin tissue (black) and inter-renal gland (stippled) from ventral aspect. (Redrawn from Chester Jones, after Vincent.)

in number, open into the small urinary sinuses. These have the function of a bladder, but are derived from mesodermal tissue, and are therefore not strictly homologous with the urinary bladder in tetrapods. The kidneys of the male differ from those of the female. The posterior part of the male kidney has the same diameter as in the female. Its ducts, usually five in number on each side, open into the urinogenital sinus, some of the most anterior first uniting to form a common tube. The sinus has a median aperture into the general cavity of the cloaca situated on the summit of a prominent

FIG. 170.—*Scyliorhinus:* **Urinogenital system.** From ventral side. *A*, male and *B*, female. Only the anterior end of the gonad is represented in each figure, and except that in *B* both kidneys are shown, the organs of the right side only are drawn. In *A* the seminal vesicle and sperm-sac are dissected away from the kidneys and displaced outwards, and the ureters inwards. *ab. p.* depression into which the abdominal pore opens; *cl.* cloaca; *cls.* clasper; *ef. d.* efferent ducts of spermary; *k.* kidney; *k', k''.* anterior non-renal portion of the kidney, forming in the male the so-called 'Leydig's gland,' which, together with the coiled spermiduct, constitutes the epididymis; *lr.* anterior portion of liver; *m. d.* vestigial Müllerian duct in the male; *œs.* gullet; *ov.* ovary; *ovd.* oviduct; *ovd'.* its cœlomic aperture; *ovd''.* the common aperture of the oviducts into the cloaca; *r.* rectum; *sh. gl.* shell-gland; *spd.* spermiduct; *sp. s.* sperm-sac; *s. v.* seminal vesicle; *s. v'.* its aperture into the urinogenital sinus; *ts.* testis; *u. g. s.* urinogenital sinus; *ur.* posterior mesonephric ducts; *ur'.* their apertures into the urinogenital sinus; *u. s.* urinary sinus. (After T. J. Parker.)

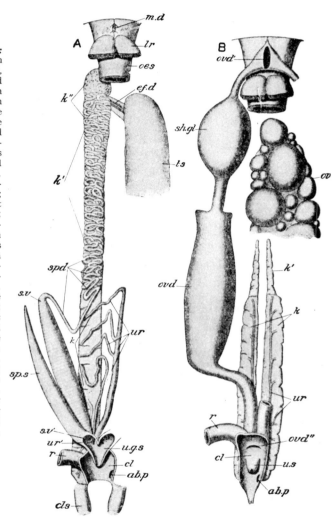

urinogenital papilla. The anterior non-renal part of the male kidney (*Leydig's gland*) is mentioned below (p. 255). The anterior part of the female kidney (Fig. 171) is degenerate and possibly functionless.

The urea concentration in the circulation of elasmobranchs—both sharks and rays—is uniquely high. Smith has shown that the blood of one of the dogfishes is more than 2 per cent. urea. The relative impermeability of the

gills to urea ensures an osmotic concentration a little above that of the surrounding sea. A complex renal mechanism ensures the reabsorption of urea through
part of the urinary tubules of the hind kidney. These
fishes tolerate a concentration of urea that is toxic
in other animals. The twenty-odd species of elasmobranchs living in fresh water to-day are probably re-
colonisers: they (e.g. *Trygon*, *Pristis*) still maintain
an exceedingly high urea level.

Elasmobranchs still convert some ammonia to
trimethylamine oxide. It has been suggested that
they solved both excretory and osmotic problems by
the development of the *ureotelic* mechanism that
allowed ancestral forms to colonise salt water. When
a habitually freshwater animal is put in salt-water
the osmotic pressure of its blood is far less than that
of the new medium. The gradual evolution of a
mechanism that secreted and retained a high level of
urea could counterbalance the
dangerously high (for a fresh-
water form) osmotic effects
of salt-water (pp. 156, 164).
Thus the urea-laden elasmobranch blood does not lose fluid
to the surrounding sea but, in
fact, achieves a modest intake
which is dealt with by the kidneys. Teleosts, as we shall see,
have solved the same problem in another way. Their
total salt concentration is much the same as in elasmobranchs. They carry no great amount of urea, but
maintain a balance by drinking sea-water and excreting
chloride at the gill-surfaces (p. 318).

All elasmobranch tissues except brain and blood can
synthesise urea. The animals are so perfectly adapted
to the high urea concentration that the heart will not beat
without it. Even the dogfish egg-case (the 'mermaid's
purse' (Fig. 172) contains a urea reserve. The embryo,
too, synthesises urea and stores it in the yolk.

Reproduction.—In the female there is a single large
elongated, lobulated, ovary (Figs. 161, 170, *ov.*) lying a little to the right of
the middle line of the abdominal cavity and attached by a fold of peritoneum,
the *mesovarium*. On its surface are rounded elevations or *follicles* of various

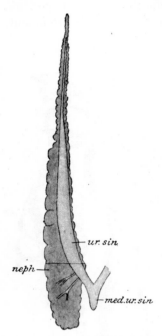

Fig. 171.—**Brachælurus:
Kidney and urinary sinus of
female** (Right). *med. ur.
sin*, median urinary sinus;
neph. kidney; *ur. sin*, right
urinary sinus.

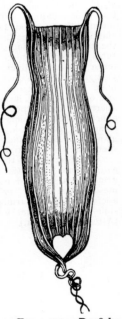

Fig. 172.—**Dogfish:
Egg-case with anchoring
elements.** (After Dean.)

sizes, each containing an ovum coloured bright yellow. As well as eggs, the ovary produces female sex hormones (œstrogen). There are two oviducts (Müllerian ducts) which are unconnected with the ovaries. These are represented in the male by vestiges at their anterior aspect (Fig. 170, *m.d.*). Each oviduct (Figs. 161 and 170, *ovd.*) is an elongated, thick-walled, muscular tube extending throughout the entire length of the abdominal cavity. Anteriorly, the two unite behind the pericardium to open into the abdominal cavity by a wide *oviducal aperture* (*ovd'.*). At about the point of junction of the middle and anterior thirds is a swelling marking the position of the *shell-gland* (*sh. gl.*). The posterior part dilates to form a wide *uterine chamber*. In *Scyliorhinus* the two unite to open into the cloaca by a common aperture situated immediately behind the opening of the rectum, while in *Squalus* they remain distinct and have separate cloacal openings. Each duct is guarded in the immature fish by a delicate membrane, the *hymen* (see also p. 894).

After the bursting of the follicles, and their extrusion from the ovary, the liberated ova—which are more than one centimetre in diameter—are propelled, often for comparatively long distances, by epithelial cilia into the oviducal aperture. There is evidence that the shell gland begins to secrete even before the eggs enter the oviduct. The eggs are driven by ciliary action down the oviducts, fertilised by spermatozoa stored in folds in the wall of the shell gland, and invested with a protective covering before entry into the uterus.

In the male (Fig. 170, A) the paired, soft, lobulated *testes* are each attached to the abdominal wall by a fold of peritoneum, the *mesorchium*. Each is composed essentially of convoluted seminiferous *tubules* which produce spermatozoa, and between these, *interstitial* or *Leydig cells* which secrete the male sex hormone (*testosterone* or its homologue) (Fig. 97, p. 152). Anteriorly, from each testis a small number of efferent ducts (*ef. d.*) pass to the anterior end of a long, narrow, strap-shaped body, which corresponds to the vestigial anterior portion of the kidney in the female. This is the *epididymis*. Its duct, the *vas deferens*, runs along the entire length of the non-renal part of the kidney (*Leydig's gland*). This structure, not to be confused with the hormone-producing *Leydig* (*interstitial*) *cells* of the testis, possibly adds a secretion that nourishes the spermatozoa (see also p. 889). Leaving the kidney, the vas deferens widens and opens into the *urinogenital sinus* (*u. g. s.*). This is a median chamber projecting into the cloaca. Posteriorly each spermiduct dilates to form a wide thin-walled sac, the *vesicula seminalis*. Closely applied to the latter is a thin-walled elongated *sperm-sac*, of uncertain function. Anteriorly the sperm-sac narrows to a blind extremity. Posteriorly the right and left sperm-sacs combine to form the urinogenital sinus. The posterior part of the kidney has the same character as in the female.

As mentioned previously, spermatozoa are transferred to the female through the agency of paired, grooved, and erectile *claspers* which are modified pelvic fins. These can be experimentally erected by means of adrenalin and electrical stimulation of appropriate spinal nerves. The claspers may be smooth, in others (e.g. *Squalus*, *Scyliorhinus*) they may be equipped with exoskeletal structures. These, analogous to the copulatory grapples of certain reptiles (p. 550) and mammals (p. 890), serve to maintain contact when inserted into the female cloaca, while the semen, with its cargo of spermatozoa, is probably forced along the grooves by the action of sea-water ejected from the capacious sac-like *siphon*. This lies beneath the skin of the ventral surface of the body and communicates with the claspers by means of paired ducts. In some species only one clasper is inserted at a time.

SUB-CLASS BRADYODONTI

These remarkable fishes, represented today only by *Chimæra* and its allies, emerged in the Upper Devonian. They may be divided into two orders. The first is composed of the more primitive Eubradyodonti, which, after a period of successful expansion, disappeared at about the end of the Palæozoic (p. 3). Extinct forms are known chiefly from their dentition. The principal teeth were essentially flattened crushing plates. A characteristic of the dentition was that there were available at any one time relatively few teeth which were successively replaced (e.g. *Helodus*). The second group is as follows:

Order Holocephali [1]

These arose in the Jurassic, or possibly Triassic and replaced the Eubradyo-donti (see above). Today a few survive as the remarkable mollusc-eating, generally deep-sea chimæras, ghost-sharks or rabbit-fishes (Fig. 173). They are seemingly elasmobranchian, as evidenced by the male claspers, the large egg-cases (and, when present, by the placoid scales) and by their general anatomical similarity to the Euselachii. In modern species the skin is naked except for a few such denticles restricted to the head-claspers.

Nevertheless, the group has a number of well-defined characters which some consider entitle its representatives to be placed in a separate sub-class. In the first place, the holostylic jaw suspension is characteristic (see p. 94) in that the upper jaws are immovably united with the cranium. Thus, support from the hyomandibular is not required and, in fact, neither jaws nor skull are attached to the hyoid arch. Characteristic, too, are the extra claspers on the head and in front of the ordinary pair on the abdomen. The presence of an operculum is a character which differentiates the Holocephali from the Euse-lachii. The dentition is also highly peculiar in the composition of the tooth-plates, as well as in their shape. There is no enamel, but, instead, a layer of *vitrodentine*, and the pulp cavity is much reduced. The teeth are in the form

[1] Ørvig (1960) suggests that the Holocephali are derived from coccosteomorphs (p. 211), implying that the elasmobranchs are at least diphyletic.

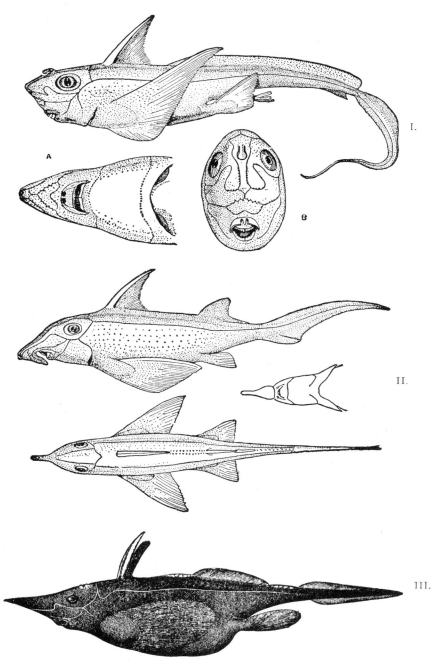

FIG. 173.—Sub-class **Bradyodonti,** Order **Holocephali: Representatives of constituent families.**
I. *Chimæra monstrosa*, male. *A*, ventral, *B*, front view of head. II. *Callorhynchus antarcticus*.
Dorsal, lateral, and ventral views. III. *Harriotta raleighana*.

of tritural plates formed, probably, by a fusion of originally separate denticles. Of these plates there are two pairs in the upper jaws, a small anterior and a larger posterior pair, and one large pair on the lower jaws. The arrangement of these plates, producing the 'parrot-like' beak, has contributed largely to the peculiar modification of the whole skull. The microscopic structure of the teeth is much like that of the Bradyodonti. An operculum covers the gills and there is no spiracle.

The earliest known representatives of the Holocephali differ very little in essential characters from the living forms. *Squaloraja* and *Myriacanthus* are representative and fairly completely known examples.

The relatively few existing representatives of the Holocephali form three families, the Callorhynchidæ (e.g. *Callorhynchus*), Chimæridæ (e.g. *Chimæra*), and Rhinochimæridæ (e.g. *Rhinochimæra*, *Harriotta*). *Chimæra*, the so-called ' King of the Herrings ' (Fig. 173, *I*) (a quaint name shared also with the bony fishes *Trachypterus* and *Regalecus*, p. 297), is found on the coasts of Europe, Japan, Australia and New Zealand, the west coast of North America, and off the Africa coast. *Callorhynchus* (Fig. 173, II) is tolerably abundant in the south temperate seas. *Harriotta* (Fig. 173, III) is a deep-sea form. These fishes are sometimes known as spook-fishes or ghost-sharks in Australian waters because of the pale ' ghostly ' iridescence that some of them emit.

External Characters.—The general form of the body is shark-like, but the large, compressed head and small mouth are strikingly different from the depressed, shovel-shaped head and wide mouth of most elasmobranchs. The mouth is bounded by lip-like folds, two of which, placed laterally and supported by labial cartilages, resemble the folds in which the premaxillæ and maxillæ of many bony fishes are enclosed. A third fold, external to and concentric with the mandible, is also supported by labial cartilages and has the appearance of a second or external lower jaw. In *Chimæra* the snout is blunt, in *Harriotta* long and pointed. In *Callorhynchus*, the so-called ' Elephant Shark ', it is produced into a rostrum, from the end of which depends a large cutaneous flap abundantly supplied with nerves and evidently serving as an important tactile organ.

A still more important difference from sharks and rays is the possession of only a single external branchial aperture, owing to the fact that a fold of skin, the *operculum*, extends backwards from the region of the hyoid arch. This covers the true gill-slits, which thus come to open into a common chamber situated beneath the operculum and communicate with the exterior by a single secondary branchial aperture placed just anterior to the shoulder-girdle : there is no spiracle. Equally characteristic is the fact that the urino-genital aperture is distinct from and behind the anus—there is no cloaca.

There are two large dorsal, and a small ventral fin. The caudal fin is of the ordinary *heterocercal* type in the adult *Callorhynchus*, but in the young (Fig.

179) the extremity of the tail proper is not upturned, and the fin-rays are arranged symmetrically above and below it, producing the *diphycercal* form. In *Chimæra* the tail may be produced into a long, whip-like filament. The pectoral and pelvic fins are both large, especially the former.

In the male there is a horizontal slit situated a little in front of the pelvic fins. This leads into a shallow glandular pouch, from which can be protruded a peculiar, and indeed unique, apparatus, the *anterior clasper*. This consists of a plate covered with recurved dermal teeth, to which is added, in *Callorhynchus*, a plate rolled upon itself to form an incomplete tube. The precise use of this apparatus is not known. A rudiment of the pouch occurs in the female, although the clasper itself is absent. The male possesses, in addition, a pair of the ordinary *myxopterygia* or posterior claspers, and is further distinguished by the presence of a little knocker-like structure, the *frontal clasper*, on the dorsal surface of the head. In *Harriotta* the paired claspers are poorly developed, and the frontal clasper is absent.

The lateral line is an open groove in *Chimæra*, a closed tube in *Callorhynchus*, and there are numerous sensory pits, arranged in curved lines, on the head. The skin is smooth and silvery, sometimes of an iridescent, but probably not luminescent, character. For the most part there are no exoskeletal structures. There are, however, delicate, recurved dermal teeth on the anterior and frontal claspers, and the first dorsal fin is supported by an immense bony spine or *dermal defence*. In the young,

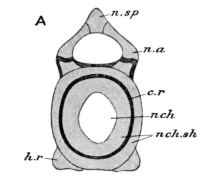

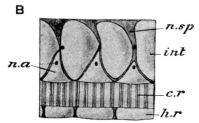

Fig. 174.—*Chimæra:* **Vertebra column.** *A*, transverse section, *B* lateral view. *c. r.* calcified ring; *h. r* hæmal ridge; *int.* intercalary piece; *n. a.* neural arch; *nch.* position of notochordal tissue; *nch. sh.* sheath of notochord *n. sp.* neural spine. (After Hasse.)

moreover, there is a double row of small dermal teeth along the back.

Endoskeleton.—The *vertebral column* consists of a persistent notochord with cartilaginous arches. In *Chimæra*, but not in *Callorhynchus*, there are calcified rings (Fig. 174, *c. r.*) embedded in the sheath of the notochord. The anterior neural arches are fused to form a high, compressed, vertical plate, to which the first dorsal fin is articulated. The *cranium* (Figs. 175 and 176) has a characteristic form, largely owing to the compression of the region between and in front of the large orbits, which are separated from the cranial cavity only by membrane in *Callorhynchus* (Fig. 176, *or.*). In *Chimæra* they lie above the level of the cranial cavity and are separated from one another by a median vertical partition of fibrous tissue (Fig. 175, *i. o. s.*). At first sight the palato-quadrate, or primary upper jaw, appears to be absent, but it is, in fact, represented by a triangular plate (*pal. qu.*) which extends downwards and outwards from each side of the cranium and presents at its apex a facet for the articulation of the mandible. The palatoquadrate is therefore fused with the cranium and furnishes the sole support for the lower jaw; the skull is *holostylic*. The pituitary fossa (Fig. 176, *s. t.*) is very deep and inclined backwards. On the ventral surface of the basis cranii is a pit (*pt.*) for the extra-cranial portion of the pituitary body. The posterior portion of the cranial cavity is very high. The anterior part—containing most of the fore-brain—is low and tunnel-like, and has above it a cavity of almost equal size (*Nv. 5 o'.*) for the ophthalmic branches of the fifth nerves. The greater part of the membranous labyrinth is lodged in a series of pits on the side-walls of the cranium (*a. s. c., p. s. c.*), and is separated from the brain by membrane only. The occipital region articulates with the vertebral column by a single saddle-shaped surface or *condyle* (*oc. cn.*). There is a great development of labial cartilages. Particularly noticeable

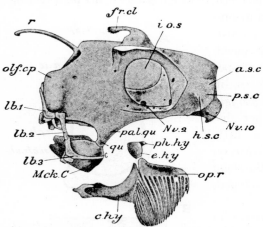

Fig. 175.—**Chimæra: Skull.** Lateral view of *C. monstrosa. a. s. c.* position of anterior semicircular canal; *c. hy.* ceratohyal; *e. hy.* epihyal; *fr. cl.* frontal clasper; *h. s. c.* position of horizontal semicircular canal; *i. o. s.* interorbital septum; *lb.* 1, *lb.* 2, *lb.* 3, labial cartilages; *Mck. C.* mandible; *Nv.* 2, optic foramen; *Nv.* 10, vagus foramen; *olf. cp.* olfactory capsule; *op. r.* opercular rays; *pal.qu.* palatoquadrate; *ph. hy.* pharyngohyal; *p. s. c.* position of posterior semicircular canal; *qu.* quadrate region; *r.* rostrum. (After Hubrecht.)

is a large plate which, in *Callorhynchus*, lies just externally to the mandible, nearly equalling it in size and having the appearance of a secondary or external jaw. In *Callorhynchus* the snout is supported by three cartilaginous rods growing forward from the cranium. The medial and dorsal rod represents the rostrum (*r*). These rods, as well as the great lower labial, are represented by comparatively small structures in *Chimæra* (Fig. 175, *lb. 3*).

The hyoid resembles the branchial arches in form and is little superior to them in size. Above the epihyal (Fig. 175, *e. hy*) is a small cartilage (*ph. hy.*), evidently serially homologous with the pharyngobranchials, and therefore to be considered as a *pharyngohyal*. It represents the hyomandibular of selachians, but, having no function to perform in the support of the jaws, it is no larger than the corresponding segments in the succeeding arches. Long cartilaginous rays (*op. r.*) for the support of the operculum are attached to the ceratohyal.

The first dorsal fin is remarkable for having all its pterygiophores fused in a single plate, which articulates with the coalesced neural arches already referred to. The remaining fins are formed quite on the selachian type, as is also the shoulder girdle. The right and left halves of the pelvic arch are separate from one another. They are united in the middle ventral line by ligament only. Each presents a narrow iliac region and a broad flat pubo-ischial region perforated by two apertures or fenestræ closed by membrane,

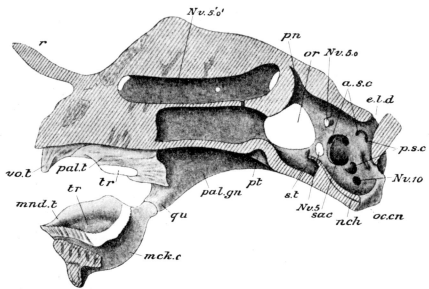

FIG. 176.—**Callorhynchus: Skull.** *C. antarcticus.* Sagittal section with labial cartilages removed. *a. s. c.* apertures through which the anterior semicircular canal passes from the cranial cavity into the auditory capsule; *e. l. d.* aperture for endolymphatic duct; *mck. c.* Meckel's cartilage; *mnd. t.* mandibular tooth; *nch.* notochord; *Nv.* 5, trigeminal foramen; *Nv.* 5. *o.* foramen for exit of ophthalmic nerves; *Nv.* 5.′*o*′, canal for ophthalmic nerves with apertures of entrance and exit; *Nv.* 10, vagus foramen; *oc. cn.* occipital condyle; *or.* fenestra separating cranial cavity from orbit; *pal. gn.* palatoquadrate; *pal. t.* palatine tooth; *pn.* position of pineal body; *pt.* pit for extra-cranial portion of pituitary body; *p. s. c.* apertures through which the posterior semicircular canal passes into the auditory capsule; *qu.* quadrate region of palatoquadrate; *r.* rostrum; *sac.* depression for sacculus; *s. t.* sella turcica; *tr.* tritor; *vo. t.* vomerine teeth.

one of them of great size in *Callorhynchus*. The skeleton of the anterior clasper articulates with the pubic region.

Alimentary Canal.—The *teeth* (Fig. 173, 176) are very characteristic, having the form of strong plates with an irregular surface and a sharp cutting edge. In the upper jaw there is a pair of small *vomerine teeth* (*vo. t.*) in front. Immediately behind them occurs a pair of large *palatine teeth* (*pal. t.*), and in the lower jaw a single pair of large *mandibular teeth* (*mnd. t.*). They are composed of vasodentine, and each palatine and mandibular tooth has its surface slightly raised into a rounded elevation of a specially hard substance, of whiter colour than the rest of the tooth, and known as a *tritor* (*tr.*). The *stomach* is absent as a

histological entity.   This probably represents a secondary loss as in the case
of numerous highly specialised teleosts (p. 336).   In the Holocephali the alimentary canal passes in a straight line from œsophagus to anus.   There is a well-
developed *spiral valve* in the intestine.

Respiratory Organs.—There are three pairs of *holobranchs* or complete gills
borne on the first three branchial arches, and two *hemibranchs* or half-gills,
one on the posterior face of the hyoid, the other on the anterior face of the
fourth branchial arch.   The fifth branchial arch is, as usual, gill-less, and
there is no cleft between it and its predecessor.

Blood-vascular System.—This resembles that of the dog-fishes in all essential respects.   The heart is formed of sinus venosus, atrium, ventricle, and
conus arteriosus, the last with three rows of valves.

Brain.—This (Fig. 177), on the other hand, is very unlike that of *Scyliorhinus*,
but presents a fairly close resemblance to that of *Scymnorhinus*.   The medulla

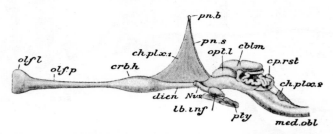

FIG. 177.—***Callorhynchus:* Brain.** *C. antarcticus. cblm.* cerebellum; *ch. plx* 1, choroid plexus of
fore-brain, and *ch. plx.* 2, of hind-brain; *cp. rst.* corpus restiforme; *crb. h.* cerebral hemisphere;
dien. diencephalon; *lb. inf.* lobus inferior; *med. obl.* medulla oblongata; *olf. l.* olfactory bulb;
olf. p. olfactory peduncle; *opt. l.* optic lobe; *pn. b.* pineal body; *pn. s.* pineal stalk; *pty.* pituitary
body.

oblongata (*med. obl.*) is produced laterally into large frill-like *restiform bodies*
(*cp. rst.*), which bound the hinder half of the cerebellum (*cblm.*).   The diencephalon (*dien.*) is long and trough-shaped.   The chief difference from the brain
of the dogfish is that the end-brain is greatly compressed and elongated by the
large orbits.   The combined diacœle and prosocœle are widely open above in a
brain from which the membranes have been removed, but in the entire organ
(Fig. 177) are roofed over by a conical, tent-like *choroid plexus* (*ch. plx.* 1).
The cavities of the small, spindle-shaped hemispheres (*crb. h.*), sometimes
regarded as corresponding to olfactory lobes only, communicate with the third
ventricle by wide *foramina of Monro,* partly blocked by up hemispherical
corpora striata.   Each hemisphere is continued in front into a slender, thin-
walled tube, the *olfactory peduncle* (*olf. p.*), bearing at its extremity a compressed olfactory bulb (*olf. l.*).

The optic nerves form a chiasma.   The *pineal body* (*pn. b.*) is a small
rounded vesicle borne on a hollow stalk (*pn. s.*) which runs just outside the

posterior wall of the tent-like choroid plexus. The *pituitary body* (*pty.*) consists of intra- and extra-cranial portions. In advanced embryos the two are united by a delicate strand of tissue.

Urinogenital Organs and Reproduction.—The *kidneys* (Fig. 178, *kd.*) are lobed, deep-red bodies, like those of dogfishes, but shorter and stouter. They are much longer in the male than in the female. The anterior portion is massive, and consists mainly of a mass of true renal tubules. It is indistinctly divided into segments. The posterior portion is narrower and also indistinctly segmented. From both parts arise a number of ducts (meso-nephric ducts) the majority of which open into the vas deferens, while the last six open into the urino-genital sinus. In the female the ducts all open into a rounded median *urinary bladder* or *urinary sinus*, situated between the two oviducal apertures. The female reproductive organs are also constructed on the general elasmobranch pattern, and are chiefly noticeable for the immense size of the shell-glands and uteri.

The male organs present certain unique characters. The *testes* (*ts.*) are large ovoid bodies the tubules of which apparently do not contain fully-developed sperms, but only immature sperm-cells. These latter are probably passed through vasa efferentia into the vas deferens, which is coiled in a highly complicated manner to form a body of considerable size, commonly termed the epididymis, closely applied to the surface of the anterior part of the kidney. In this the sperms become aggregated into *spermatophores* in the form of small ovoidal capsules surrounded by a resistant membrane and full of a gelatinous substance in which bundles of sperms are imbedded. The lower end of the vas deferens (*v. df.*) is dilated to form a large cylindrical *vesicula seminalis* (*vs. sem.*) imperfectly divided into compartments by transverse partitions (*B*) and filled with a greenish jelly. The spermato-

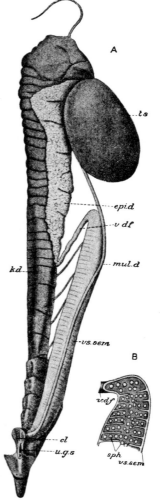

FIG. 178.—**Callorhynchus: Urinogenital System.** *C. antarcticus. A*, male urinogenital organs of left side, ventral aspect; *B*, anterior part of vesicula seminalis in section. *cl.* cloaca; *epid.* epididymis; *kd.* kidney; *mul. d.* Müllerian duct; *sph.* spermatophores; *ts.* testis; *u. g. s.* opening of urinogenital sinus; *v. df.* vas deferens; *vs. sem.* vesicula seminalis. (*A* after Redeke.)

phores (*sph.*) are passed into these compartments and finally make their way through the central passage into the urinogenital sinus (*u. g. s.*). The vestigial

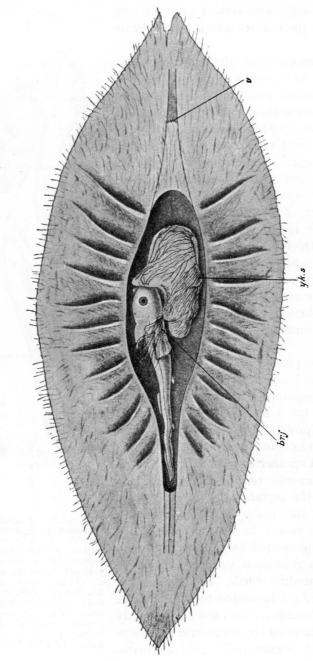

FIG. 179.—*Callorhynchus:* **Reproduction.** Egg-shell of *C. antarcticus* with embryonic chamber cut open to show the contained embryo. *br. f.* branchial filaments; *v.* valve through which young fish escapes; *yk. s.* yolk-sac.

Müllerian ducts (*mul. d.*) are much more fully developed than in dog-fishes. They are complete, though narrow, tubes which open in front by a large common aperture into the cœlom. Behind they are connected with the urinogenital sinus.

As in selachians, fertilisation is internal. The egg becomes surrounded, as in dog-fishes, by a horny egg-shell secreted by the shell-glands. The egg-shell of *Callorhynchus* (Fig. 179) is of extraordinary size—about 25 cm. in length, or fully five-sixths as long as the abdominal cavity—and the elongated chamber for the embryo is surrounded by a broad, flat expansion covered on one side with yellow hair-like processes. This gives the shell a close resemblance, doubtless protective, to a piece of kelp. The early development resembles that of selachians; but the yolk becomes divided into nucleated masses which divide into smaller segments, and the smallest break away and become dissolved in a milky nutrient liquid which fills the spaces of the shell. The advanced embryo has elongated gill-filaments (*br. f.*) projecting through the branchial aperture (and probably serving to absorb the nutriment derived from the yolk), a diphycercal tail, and a curiously lobed and nearly sessile yolk-sac (*yk. s.*). (For selachian development, see p. 279.)

GENERAL ORGANISATION OF ELASMOBRANCHII

External Characters.—Sharks (sub-order Pleurotremata) are usually somewhat fusiform and slightly compressed laterally. Rays occupy a separate sub-order (Hypotremata), but despite their radical dorso-ventral compression, the migration of the eyes to the dorsal surface, and their apparent dissimilarity from the sharks in other ways, the two groups have many features in common. The flattened form of the rays is an adaptation to a bottom-dwelling existence. They can commonly be seen gliding along the bottom of all relatively warm seas, and they extend into circumpolar regions as well. Although they are popularly supposed to be confined to shallow waters, some inhabit great depths and are blind. Their peculiar form and, in particular, their highly unpleasant and efficient weapons of defence have brought sting-rays and electric-rays to the attention of mankind from earliest historical times. That small withered curiosity, the 'Jenny Haniver', frequently sold on the water-fronts, is made from a skate (Family Rajidæ) that has been dried, and then cut and twisted into shape. Skates are fashioned into grotesque shapes and sold also as 'mermaids', 'sea-eagles', 'dragons', 'monkey-fishes', and 'basilisks' (see also p. 645). Rays appear on Etruscan mosaics and vases. Some attain great bulk. Among the true sting-rays, Captain Cook's Stingaree or Whai Repo (a Maori name) (*Bathytoshia*) of the Pacific reaches a length of 14 feet, a width of 6 to 7 feet, and a weight of 770 lbs. It is generally caught at from 20 to 60 fathoms, although sometimes speared in a few feet of water. Devil-rays ('Devil- or Diamond-fish') (Family Mobulidæ) may grow even bigger and are wider than the body is long (Fig. 154, p. 228). *Manta* (which uniquely has cephalic fins) reaches a width of 22 feet across its diamond-shaped body and 'wings' (pectoral fins). It may weigh more than 3,000 lbs.

The elasmobranch head is in many cases produced forwards into a long rostrum. This is of great length and bordered with triangular teeth in the sawsharks (*Pristiophorus*) and sawfishes (*Pristis*) (Fig. 154, p. 228). In the Hammerhead Shark (*Sphyrna = Zygæna*) the anterior part of the head is extended transversely and the eyes are carried at the lateral extremities.

There are well-developed median and paired fins. The caudal fin is large and, as a rule, strongly heterocercal in the sharks and shark-like rays. It is reduced in most of the latter group. The dorsal and anal fins are large in the sharks, the former completely divided into two. In the rays the dorsal fin is usually small, and the anal fin absent. The paired fins differ widely in the two groups. In the sharks both pairs are well developed, the pectoral being the larger. In the rays the pectoral fins are extremely large and much bigger than the pelvic fins. The pectoral fins fringe the greater part of the length of the flattened body, and are prolonged forwards on either side and even in front of the head. Thus, the animal presents the appearance of a broad, fleshy leaf. In all recent Chondrichthyes the male has, connected with the pelvic fins, a pair of grooved appendages—the *claspers* or *myxopterygia*—which subserve copulation (p. 255). It is of great interest that such organs, which make internal fertilisation possible, did not, except in the Devonian *Diademonus*, appear before the hybodont sharks (p. 224). The latter were equipped also with hook-like cephalic spines, which probably helped anchor the male during coupling, and some species of *Cladoselache* possessed a large head spine of perhaps similar function (Harris).

The mouth is situated on the ventral surface of the head, usually a considerable distance from the anterior extremity (cf., however, Fig. 151, p. 225). In front of each angle of the mouth is the opening of one of the olfactory sacs. Each of these is frequently connected by a groove—the naso-buccal groove—with the mouth-cavity. Behind the mouth, on the dorsal surface in the rays, and laterally in the sharks, is the spiracle. We saw (p. 106) that in sharks oxygenated water is taken in through the mouth, which is then closed, the buccal cavity contracted, and the water forced through the gill-slits. In the bottom-living rays the water is taken in through the spiracle. The water is driven across the respiratory surface by the closure of a special valve. Along each side of the neck in the sharks, and on the ventral surface in the rays, there is a row of slit-like apertures—the branchial slits or clefts. These are usually five in number on each side; but in *Pliotrema*, *Hexanchus*, and *Chlamydoselachus* there are six, and in *Heptranchias* seven. In *Chlamydoselachus* (Fig. 153) a fold comparable to a rudimentary operculum extends back over the first branchial cleft, and is continuous across the middle line ventrally. In the remainder of the sub-class no such structure is represented. A large cloacal opening is situated just in front of the root of the tail, and in most members of the sub-class a pair of small openings placed close to it—the *abdominal pores*—lead into the abdominal cavity.

When the **integument** develops any hard parts as is the case in the majority of the Chondrichthyes, they take the form, not of regular scales, as in most other fishes, but of numerous rough, hard *placoid scales*. These vary greatly in shape, are usually extremely minute, but are in some cases developed, in certain parts of the surface, into prominent tubercles or spines. When these hard bodies are small, and set closely together in the skin, they give the surface very much the character of a fine file. Such skin, known as 'shagreen', was formerly used for various polishing purposes in the arts, for armour, sword-hilts, and even as striking surfaces affixed to the sides of lucifer match-boxes. Each of the hard bodies has the same basic structure as a tooth (p. 103). Such denticles differ in superficial structure and arrangement in different groups and are of diagnostic significance. A highly specialised and dangerous integumentary structure—the so-called 'sting'—characterises the sting-arees, or dasyatid sting-rays (Family Dasyatidæ). One or several deciduous spines, capable of independent movement, are attached some distance up the

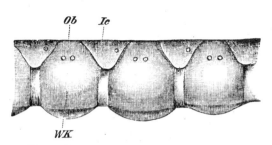

FIG. 180.—*Scymnorhinus:* **Spinal column.** *Ic.* intercalary cartilages; *Ob.* neural arches; *WK*, centra. (After Weidersheim.)

tail. Grooves in the spine carry toxic secretions from contiguous glands. Sting-rays produce agonising wounds and hideous scarring. A large ray may slash right down to the bone, and septicæmia often results. In 1938 a New Zealand girl aged eighteen was killed by stab-wounds from a fish that was almost certainly a sting-ray. In addition to inflicting three thigh wounds, the spine penetrated the thorax and both ventricles of the heart.

The **endoskeleton** is composed of cartilage, often with a deposition of calcareous matter in special places—notably in the jaws and the vertebral column. The entire spinal column may be almost completely cartilaginous (*Hexanchus* and *Heptranchias*). Usually the centra are strengthened by radiating or concentric lamellæ of calcified tissue ; or they may be completely calcified. They are deeply amphicœlous and the remains of the notochord persist in the large inter-central spaces. *Intercalary pieces* (Fig. 180, *Ic.*) are interposed between both superior and inferior arches. In the rays (Fig. 181) the anterior part of the spinal column becomes converted into a continuous solid cartilaginous and calcified mass—the *anterior vertebral plate* (*a. v. p.*).   As in fishes in general, two regions are distinguishable in the spinal column—the *precaudal* and the *caudal*, the latter being characterised by the possession of inferior or hæmal arches.   In the precaudal region short ribs may be developed, but these are sometimes rudimentary or entirely absent.   In the sharks pterygiophores, sometimes jointed, fused at their bases with the hæmal spines, support the ventral lobe of the caudal fin.   The dorsal lobe of the same fin is supported by a series of pterygiophores resembling produced neural spines, but only secondarily related to the spinal column,

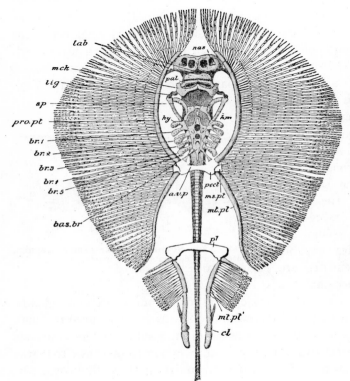

Fig. 181.—**Urolophus: Endoskeleton of sting-ray.** Ventral view. *a. v. p.* anterior vertebral plate; *bas. br.* basibranchial plate; *br.* 1—*br.*5 branchial arches. (The branchial rays are not represented, the round dots indicating their articulations with the arches.) *cl.* skeleton of clasper; *h. m.* hyomandibular; *hy.* hyoid arch; *lab.* labial cartilage; *lig.* ligament connecting the hyomandibular with the palatoquadrate and Meckel's cartilage; *mck.* Meckel's cartilage; *ms. pt.* mesopterygium, and *mt. pt.* metapterygium of pectoral fin; *mt. pt'.* metapterygium of pelvic fin; *nas.* nasal cartilage; *pal.* palatoquadrate; *pect.* pectoral arch; *pl.* pelvic arch; *pro. pt.* propterygium; *sp.* spiracular cartilage.

and sometimes also divided by joints.   The dorsal and ventral fins are sometimes supported by similar pterygiophores; but in many cases the cartilaginous supports of these fins consist, in whole or in part, of expanded plates of cartilage.   The marginal portions of the unpaired fins beyond the limits of the endoskeleton are supported by dermal fibre-like structures (*ceratotrichia*) composed of elastin.

The **skull** is an undivided mass of cartilage, hardened, in many cases, by deposition of calcareous matter, but not containing any true bony tissue.   It consists of a cartilaginous case which protects the brain and the organs of special sense.   The structure of this cartilaginous brain-case as it occurs in dogfishes has already been described. The main differences observable in the different families are connected with the size and form of the rostrum. In the rays the lower lip of the foramen magnum is deeply excavated for the reception of a short process, the so-called *odontoid process*, which projects forwards from the anterior vertebral plate, and on either side of this is an articular surface—the *occipital condyle*—for articulation with corresponding surfaces on that plate. In the sharks the skull is not so definitely marked off from the spinal column. The apertures of the endolymphatic ducts in the rays are not situated in a median depression, such as is observable in dogfishes and in all the sharks. The articular surface in the auditory region for the hyomandibular is sometimes borne on a projecting process, sometimes on the general level of the lateral surface. Sometimes in the rays there is a smaller articulation behind for the first branchial arch.

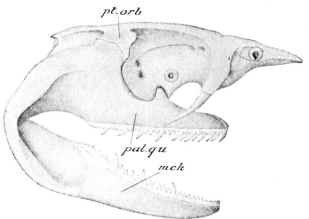

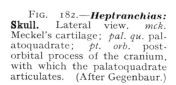

FIG. 182.—*Heptranchias:* **Skull.** Lateral view. *mck.* Meckel's cartilage; *pal. qu.* palatoquadrate; *pt. orb.* postorbital process of the cranium, with which the palatoquadrate articulates. (After Gegenbaur.)

The upper and lower jaws—the *palatoquadrate* and *Meckel's cartilage*—are connected with the skull through the intermediation of a *hyomandibular cartilage* (Fig. 157, *hy. mn.*; Fig. 181, *h. m.*). The skull is thus of the hyostylic type as regards the mode of suspension of the jaws. In sharks the palatoquadrate has a process (absent in rays) for articulation with the base of the skull in the pre-orbital region. In *Hexanchus* and *Heptranchias* (Fig. 182) there is, in addition to this, a prominent postorbital process of the palatoquadrate for articulation with the postorbital region of the skull (*amphistylic* arrangement). *Cestracion* is also in a sense amphistylic; the palatoquadrate is firmly united with the skull, articulating with a groove on the base, and the hyomandibular takes only a small share in the suspension of the jaws. At the sides of the mouth in all elasmobranchs is a series of *labial cartilages*, usually two pairs above and one pair below. Attached to the hyomandibular is a thin plate of the cartilage—the *spiracular* (Fig. 181, *sp.*)—which supports the anterior wall of the spiracle.

The hyoid arch proper is in most elasmobranchs connected at its dorsal end with the hyomandibular—sometimes at its distal extremity, sometimes near its articulation with the skull. In some rays, however, it is not so related, but articulates separately and independently with the skull behind the hyomandibular. In the genera *Hypnarce* and *Trygonorhina* it articulates with the dorsal portion of the first branchial arch. In sharks the hyoid is usually relatively massive. In rays it is smaller, and in most cases closely resembles the branchial arches, and bears similar cartilaginous *rays*. A larger or smaller median element, or basihyal, is present in all cases.

There are always five pairs of *branchial arches* except in *Hexanchus* and *Chlamydoselachus*, which have six, and *Heptranchias*, in which there are seven. Their dorsal ends are free in sharks, but in most rays they are articulated with the anterior vertebral plate of the spinal column. Externally they bear a series of slender cartilaginous *branchial rays*. The median ventral elements of the branchial arches are usually more or less reduced, and in some cases are represented by a single *basibranchial* plate (Fig. 158, *b. br.*). In the rays the fifth branchial arch articulates with the pectoral arch, a connection which is absent in sharks. A series of slender cartilages, the *extra-branchial cartilages*, support the branchial apertures. These are probably modified branchial rays.

The pectoral arch (Figs. 159, 181, *pect.*) consists of a single cartilage. In most sharks, a mesial flexible portion occurs by which it is divided into right and left halves. Each lateral half consists of a dorsal *scapular* and a ventral *coracoid* part, the two being separated by the surfaces on which articulate the basal cartilages of the fin. In rays, but not in sharks, the dorsal ends of the pectoral arch are connected with the spinal column (anterior vertebral plate) by a distinct articulation. The portion of the arch on which the articular surface is situated sometimes forms an independent *supra-scapula* cartilage.

The *basal pterygiophores* of the pectoral fin are typically three, *pro-*, *meso-*, and *meta-pterygium* (Figs. 159 and 181), but there are sometimes four, and the number may be reduced to two. The pro- and meta-pterygia are divided in the rays (Fig. 181) into several segments. The former articulates, through the intermediation of a cartilage termed the *antorbital*, with the olfactory region of the skull.

The *pelvic arch* (*pl.*), like the pectoral arch, is usually a single cartilage, but in some exceptional cases it consists of two lateral portions. In some cases a median *epipubic process* projects forwards from the pelvic arch, and frequently there is on each side a *prepubic* process. A lateral *iliac* process, which becomes highly developed in the Holocephali, is sometimes represented, and may attain considerable dimensions. The pelvic fin has usually two basal cartilages, representing the pro- and meta-pterygia, but the former is often absent. In the male special cartilages attached to the metapterygia support the claspers. With the basal cartilages of both pectoral and pelvic fins are connected a number of jointed cartilaginous fin-rays supporting the expanse of the fin.

The arrangement of the **muscles** is simple. The trunk-muscles are divided into a pair of dorsal and a pair of ventral divisions each, composed of many myomeres with intercalated myo-commata (Fig. 62, p. 86), following a metameric arrangement. The ventral part, where it forms the muscles of the wall of the abdominal cavity, is composed externally of obliquely running fibres, and represents one of the two *oblique* muscles of the abdomen of higher forms. Mesially this passes into a median band of longitudinally running fibres corresponding to a primitive *rectus*. The muscles of the limbs are distinguishable into two main sets— (1) those inserted into the limb-arch and (2) those inserted into the free part of the appendage. The latter, according to their insertion, act as elevators, depressors, or adductors. A series of circular muscles passes between the cartilages of the visceral arches and, when they contract, have the effect of contracting the pharynx and constricting the apertures. A set of muscles pass between the various arches and act so as to approximate them. A broad sheet

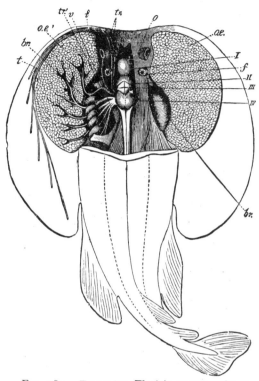

FIG. 183.—*Torpedo:* **Electric organs.** On the right the surface only of the electric organ (*O.E.*) is shown, on the left the nerves passing to the organ are shown. The roof of the skull is removed to bring the brain into view. *br.* gills; *f.* spiracle; *o.* eyes; *tr.* trigeminal; *tr'.* its electric branch; *v.* vagus; *I*, fore-brain; *II*, mid-brain; *III*, cerebellum; *IV*, electric lobe. (After Gegenbaur.)

of longitudinal fibres divided into myomeres extends forwards from the shoulder-girdle to the visceral arches.

Electric organs occur in several elasmobranchs. They are best developed in the electric-rays, numb-fishes, or torpedoes (Fig. 183), in which they form a pair of large masses running through the entire thickness of the body, between the head and the margin of the pectoral fin. A network of strands of fibrous tissue forms the support for a number of vertical prisms, each divided by transverse partitions into a large number of compartments or cells. Numerous nerve-fibres pass to the various parts of the organ. These are derived mainly from four nerves, which originate from an *electric lobe* of the medulla oblongata, with a branch from the trigeminal. Rays of this family often conceal themselves in the sand rather than retreat; they are sometimes trodden upon. *Torpedo* generates a greater potential than even the South American electric 'eel' (p. 334). Fishermen get electric shocks from captured torpedoes when hauling in nets or while standing with bare feet on a large catch of bony fishes under which a Numb-fish lies hidden. It will be seen that the electric organ can be a highly successful weapon of offence as well as defence. Electric-rays often eat bony fishes as large as is possible for them to swallow. In certain other rays electric organs are comparatively small and situated at the sides of the root of the tail. In all cases the cells are formed from specialised muscle-fibres.

Although no extant marine fish is known to use electrical discharges in direction finding (see p. 335), it is perhaps not impossible that the device originated for this purpose in shallow off-shore gulf-waters constantly flooded by muddy rivers. There is, of course, no direct comparison, but it is not without interest that extant teleosts of several families have suffered visual degeneracy in such situations.

Luminous organs occur on the surface of a few oceanic elasmobranchs. *Spinax molleri*, a small (20-inch) shark of Australian waters, gleams vivid greenish from its ventral surface. According to one early nineteenth-century author it imparts to itself 'a truly ghostly and terrific appearance'.

Alimentary Canal and Associated Structures.—*Teeth* are developed on the palatoquadrate and on Meckel's cartilage. They are arranged in several parallel rows, and are developed from a groove within the margin of the jaw. Successive rows come to the front, and, as they wear out, fall off and are replaced by others. In the sharks the teeth are usually large, and may be long, narrow, and pointed, or triangular with serrated edges (Fig. 147, p. 220), or made up of several sharp cusps. In the rays the teeth are more or less obtuse. Sometimes, as in the eagle-rays, they form a continuous pavement of smooth plates covered with enamel. Thus they are adapted to crushing food such as molluscs, crabs, and other animals. An exceptional shark is the large (up to 40 feet) Basking Shark (*Cetorhinus*), which lives on plankton. Water and *krill* are taken in through the mouth. The latter are strained and prevented from passing through the branchial clefts by elongated gill-rakers. There is recent evidence that during the winter these are lost and that *Cetorhinus* undergoes a quiescent demersal phase until the seasonal improvement of food supplies. Sharks generally have a prominent tongue supported by the median basihyal; this is entirely or almost entirely absent in the rays. The various divisions of the alimentary canal are similar in all the members of the class to those already described in dogfishes. A spiral valve is always present in the large intestine, though its arrangement varies considerably in the different families. In some cases (e.g. *Carcharinus*) the fold is not a spiral one, but, attached by one edge in a nearly longitudinal line to the intestinal wall, is rolled up in the shape of a scroll. A pair of pyloric cæca occur in *Somniosus*. Connected dorsally to the rectum is a median glandular cæcum, the *rectal gland*. The rectum always terminates in a *cloaca*, into which the urinary and genital ducts also lead. There is always a large liver and a prominent pancreas.

A *thyroid* can be found in the middle line behind the lower jaw. A representative of the *thymus* lies on either side, a little below the upper angles of the branchial clefts.

The **respiratory** and associated **organs** of the Chondrichthyes always have the general structure and arrangement already described in the case of the

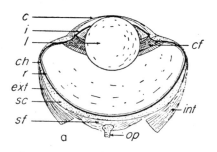
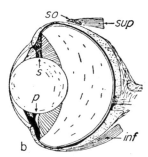

FIG. 184.—*Carcharodon*: **Eyes and mechanism of accommodation.** The left figure shows the peculiar prop-like optic pedicel (*op*) which is, however, absent (probably lost), in some elasmobranchs (*e.g.* Dogfish, *Scyliorhinus* and certain deep-sea forms) and not fully articulated in others. The eye is above represented in full accommodation. Were the protractor lentis muscle relaxed, the lens would be withdrawn from the cornea. *a*, horizontal section; *b*, vertical section (cf. teleost eye, p. 316); *c*. cornea; *ch*. chorioid; *cf*. ciliary folds, from which gelatinous zonule passes to lens equator; *ext*. external rectus; *i*. iris; *inf*. inferior rectus; *int*. internal rectus; *l*. lens; *op*. optic pedicel; *p*. papilla (bearing protractor lentis muscle); *r*. retina; *s*. suspensory 'ligament' (a thickening in the zonule); *sc*. scleral cartilage; *sf*. fibrous portion of sclera; *so*. superior oblique; *sup*. superior rectus. (After Walls.)

Dogfish. In the rays the water for respiration is taken in mainly through the spiracles; in the sharks through the mouth.

In addition to the gills supported on the hyoid and branchial arches there is also in the Notidanidæ a gill on the anterior side of the spiracular cleft—the *spiracular gill*—represented in many others by a *rete mirabile* or network of blood-vessels (*pseudobranch*, p. 230).

Blood-vascular System.—The *heart* has, in all essential respects, the same structure throughout the group. The conus arteriosus is always contractile, and contains several rows of valves. The general course of the circulation is the same in all (see pp. 240–245), with some variation in the precise arrangement of the vessels. In some of the rays the ventral aorta and the roots of the afferent vessels are partly enclosed in the cartilage of the basi-branchial plate.

Hæmatopoietic tissue occurs in the spleen. In addition, elasmobranchs of both sexes possess lymphoid *epigonal organs* (Fig. 185) that are concerned with the manufacture of both red and white cells. In *Cetorhinus*, unlike most selachians, the testis is almost completely surrounded by the epigonal organ (Matthews). In the female the organ is bilateral even though the left ovary is absent or rudimentary. The organ of Leydig, too, is said to produce granulocytes. As in the Agnatha, the lymphatic system has not been shown to be clearly distinct from the venous: blood is commonly found in lymph vessels (Mott).

Brain.—The fore-brain greatly exceeds the other divisions in size. In *Scymnorhinus* there are two widely-separated *cerebral hemispheres* containing large lateral ventricles. In other genera there is at most, as in dogfishes, a median depression of greater or less depth, indicating a division of the anterior end of the fore-brain into two lateral portions. In *Scyliorhinus*, as already pointed out, there is a median ventricle which gives rise anteriorly to two lateral ventricles, and the same holds good for *Squatina* and *Squalus*. In most rays there is only a very small median ventricle without anterior prolongations; in *Myliobatis* this is absent. The olfactory bulbs are of great size, in some cases with short and thick, in others longer and narrower, stalks. In *Scyliorhinus*, *Squatina*, and *Squalus*, as well as in *Scymnorhinus*, they contain ventricles (*rhinocœles*) forming part of the lateral ventricles. In the rays they are solid.

The *diencephalon* is of moderate extent. On its lower aspect are a pair of rounded *lobi inferiores*, which are of the nature of dilatations of the *infundibulum*, a part of the hypothalamus, and a *saccus vasculosus*, which is a diverticulum of the infundibulum. Directly below the saccus vasculosus lies the *hypophysis*. The *epiphysis* is long and narrow.

In the hind-brain the *cerebellum* is relatively greatly elongated and overlaps the tectum of the mid-brain and sometimes also the diencephalon in front, while behind it extends over the posterior part of the *medulla oblongata*. It usually contains a cerebellar ventricle. The medulla is elongated in the sharks, shorter and more triangular in the rays. The electric rays possess *electric lobes* which are rounded elevations of the floor of the fourth ventricle.

Organs of Special Sense.—Integumentary sense-organs (*neuromasts*, p. 137) are highly developed in the Chondrichthyes. They are supplied, as already mentioned, by branches of the nerves of the *lateral system*, comprising, in addition to the lateralis, nerves in relation with the facial and sometimes the glossopharyngeal. These integumentary sense-organs occur in the interior of a continuous system of closed tubes, the *sensory tubes*, more rarely of open grooves. The chief canals of this system are a *lateral-line canal*, running along the middle of each side of the body, which is continuous with certain canals in the head. These communicate with the exterior at intervals by small pores. In addition to the canals of the lateral-line system there are a number of isolated canals, the *ampullary canals*, with neuromasts contained in terminal enlargements or *ampullæ*. These, almost peculiar to the Chondrichthyes, are most numerous about the snout region. Of similar essential character are the *vesicles of Savi* which occur in the electric rays. (The teleost catfish *Plotosus* also possesses ampullæ.)

The *olfactory organs* are a pair of sacs opening on the lower surface of the head, a little distance in front of the mouth, and enclosed by the cartilaginous olfactory capsules of the skull. Their inner surface is raised up into a number of ridges on which the fibres of the olfactory nerves are distributed.

There is ample evidence that at least some sharks hunt primarily by scent. Collecting parties wading through shallows on the Great Barrier Reef have found that small sharks prefer to follow people whose legs have been gashed by coral. Commercial shark fishermen, who hunt Australian sharks for their hide and liver oils, sometimes throw overboard buckets of bullocks' blood obtained from abbatoirs, and find this a successful lure. Researches during the Second World War revealed that copper acetate repelled sharks to a certain extent.

The *eye* (Fig. 184) is usually big. It has a cartilaginous sclerotic, and is in most, but not all, cases attached to the inner wall of the orbit by means of a cartilaginous stalk or *optic pedicel* 'running prop-like from cranium to eyeball' (Walls). At the eyeball this is often expanded and cupped, and forms a socket joint for the rotation of the eye. In a few sharks and rays this pedicel is slender and sufficiently bent and elastic that its own tendency to straighten itself can proptose (protrude) the eyeball when the extra-ocular muscles act together. This action, with broadly the effect of a levator bulbi muscle (p. 413), may have been the original function of the apparatus. In the elasmobranchs studied, accommodation is brought about by smooth muscle-fibres that swing the whole lens towards the cornea. Thus the action is towards near vision, as in Man, and not towards distant vision, as in lampreys and bony fishes. The protractor lentis muscle may, in addition, cause the lens to bulge the cornea to some degree. A fold of the conjunctiva, resembling the *nictitating membrane* of higher vertebrates, occurs in some sharks (*e.g.* Carcharinidæ). One deep-sea electric ray, *Benthobatis moresbyi*, possesses degenerate eyes. Most elasmobranchs lack cones in the retina, but a few—e.g. *Mustelus* and particularly the eagle-ray (*Myliobatis*)—possess them, probably derived independently, in these animals, from rods (p. 140). The *tapetum* (p. 141) has been lost in at least two groups of unusual habit—the Basking Shark (*Cetorhinus*) and the abyssal shark *Læmargus*.

Audio-equilibration.—The *membranous labyrinth* consists of a utricle and saccule, incompletely separated, and together forming a *membranous vestibule* from which arise the three *semicircular canals* with their ampullæ, and also the *endolymphatic duct*. This retains its opening to the exterior on the dorsal surface of the head and represents the stalk of the embryonic otic vesicle. In the rays the semicircular canals form almost complete circles and open separately into the vestibule by narrow ducts.

Endocrine Organs.—Relatively little work has been done in this field in selachians. There is evidence that the pituitary exerts central governing influences (p. 149), but it would be unwise in the extreme to assume that elasmobranch endocrines exactly parallel functionally those of higher creatures. In some cases there is evidence that they do not.

The inter-renals are homologous with the adrenal cortex of higher animals, but differ in their position and, apparently, some of their functions. The selachian inter-renal can be single, median, and elongated (as in *Scyliorhinus*), paired, and diffuse (as in *Raja*), or single, asymmetrical, and condensed (as in *Torpedo*). Deprivation leads to death, but cortical extracts from a mammal (rat) will prolong life in *Torpedo* after removal of its inter-renal gland. Extracts from the skate inter-renal will likewise maintain life in adrenalectomised rats.

The medullary homologue has been dealt with above (p. 252). Little is known of the thyroid functions in selachians. Corpora lutea of a supposedly mammalian structure have been described, but these have not yet been proved to be true post-ovulatory, rather than pre-ovulatory, bodies. There is some evidence that extracts of dogfish pituitary will cause lactation in mammals, but nothing is known of the possible endocrine control of the so-called 'uterine-milk' of certain viviparous selachians (p. 278). Interstitial aggregations (*Leydig cells*) of the typical vertebrate kind (e.g. *Petromyzon*, Man) occur in the testes (see p. 152). There is evidence that testosterone increases clasper-length in young males (see p. 256 in regard to erection), and that œstrogens accelerate growth in the reproductive tract in young females.

The pancreas contains islets.

Urinogenital Organs and Reproduction.—The *kidneys* differ somewhat in the two sexes (p. 252). In the male the anterior portion persists in the epididymis, and its duct becomes the spermiduct, while the posterior portion, which is the functional kidney, has a duct or ducts of its own. In the female selachian there is no direct connection between the reproductive and renal organs; the anterior portion of the kidney may be functional, and its duct persists, opening along with those of the posterior portion. In the male the urinary ducts open into a median chamber—the *urinogenital sinus*—which extends into the cloaca, and receives also the spermiducts. It communicates with the general cavity of the cloaca by a median opening situated on a papilla—the *urinogenital* papilla. In the female there is a median *urinary sinus*, into which the urinary ducts open, or the latter may open separately into the cloaca (see Fig. 170, p. 253).

Save in certain exceptional cases (e.g. *Scyliorhinus*), there are two ovaries. These vary considerably in form, and towards the breeding are characterised by the great size of the follicles enclosing the mature ova. The oviducts

(Müllerian ducts) are separate from the ovaries. The right and left oviducts come into close relationship anteriorly, being united in the middle on the ventral surface of the œsophagus. Here each opens by a wide orifice into the abdominal cavity, or both open by a single median aperture. The following part of the oviduct is very narrow. At one point, however, it exhibits a thickening, due to the presence in its walls of the follicles of the *nidamentary gland*. Posteriorly, the oviduct gives rise to a dilated *uterus*, and this communicates with the cloaca through a wide *vagina*. In ovoviviparous elasmobranchs (p. 278) the shell-gland is small or vestigial.

The ova are very large, consisting of a mass of yolk-spherules held together by a network of protoplasmic threads, with, on one side, a disc of protoplasm—

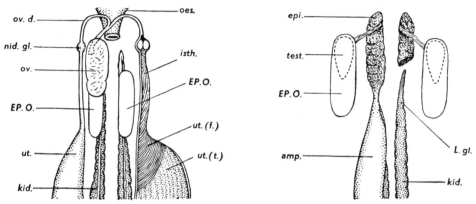

FIG. 185.—*Cetorhinus:* **Urinogenital and associated organs.** *Left:* of female (with œsophagus); *Right:* of male. *amp.* ampulla ductus deferentis; *epi.* epididymis; *E P. O.* epigonal organ (see p. 274); *isth.* isthmus; *kid.* kidney; *L. gl.* Leydig's gland; *nid. gl.* nidamentary ('shell') gland; *ov.* ovary; *ov. d.* oviduct; *œs.* œsophagus; *test.* testis; *ut.* uterus; *ut. (f.)* uterus (lined with folds); *ut. (t.)* uterus (lined with trophonemata). (Redrawn after Harrison Matthews.)

the *germinal disc*. The process of maturation is similar to that observable in holoblastic ova. One polar body is thrown off in the ovary, the other apparently at impregnation. The ripe ovum ruptures the wall of the enclosing follicle and so passes into the abdominal cavity to enter one of the oviducts through the wide abdominal opening. Impregnation takes place in the oviduct. The impregnated ovum in the oviparous forms becomes surrounded by a layer of semi-fluid albumen and enclosed in a shell of keratin secreted by the shell-gland. The shell varies in shape somewhat in the different groups. Most commonly, as in many dogfishes (Fig. 172), it is four-cornered, with twisted filamentous appendages at the angles, by means of which it becomes attached to sea-weeds and the like. In the skates the filaments are absent. In *Heterodontus* it is an ovoid body the wall of which presents a broad, spiral flange. In *Rhinobatus* and *Trygonorhina*, which are both viviparous, each shell encloses not one egg, but three or four.

Somniosus, formerly thought to differ from other Chondrichthyes in having the ova externally fertilised, produces remarkably small ova. The eggs of the Basking Shark, too, are relatively small.

Placentation.—It is among the elasmobranchs that we see the first development of a true *placentation* as distinct from the primitive arrangements that occur among arthropods (*e.g.* certain insects and *Peripatus*) and in *Salpa* among the Tunicata (p. 20). We will see that *vivipary* or internal gestation with the formation of a placenta (as apart from mere ovovivipary) has been developed independently also in teleosts (p. 351), and reptiles (p. 549), among poikilothermous animals. A placenta has been defined as 'any intimate apposition or fusion of the fœtal organs of the maternal (or paternal) tissues for physiological exchange' (Mossman), although, as Amoroso points out, people commonly restrict the expression to mean the *chorio-allantoic placenta* found in some reptiles and many mammals (see pp. 550, 904).

In a few sharks, snakes, lizards, and in most marsupials the chorion is vascularised from the allantois, and thus unites with the wall of the uterus or its equivalent structure. Selachians commonly nourish their internally developing young with material from the yolk-sac (*ovovivipary*), but in many of these, even though the egg-case is intact, the maternal epithelium secretes products that assist in the nutrition of the embryo. In some species there is a considerable development of new epithelium (*Acanthias*), or even villi (*Torpedo*, *Trygon*), but in others a so-called *uterine-milk* is produced without gross alteration of the maternal mucosa.

In the ovoviviparous elasmobranch *Lamna* the yolk is soon absorbed, but immature eggs or degenerating ovarian tissue pass into, and down, the oviducts to the uterine chamber, where the material is eaten by the embryos, which are said to remain within the parent for more than a year.

Among the truly viviparous selachians, placentation has been extensively investigated in *Mustelus*, *Scoliodon*, and other genera. The embryos of *Mustelus* each develop in separate compartments in which villi develop and fuse with grooves in the yolk-sac. This gives rise to a simple yolk-sac placenta, involving modification of both parental and embryonic tissues and the invasion of maternal capillaries to a degree that brings both circulations into an intimacy that allows efficient functional, including gaseous, exchange.

In several species of *Scoliodon* an almost complete union is formed between the yolk-sac of the embryos (again in compartments) and the maternal epithelium. The mucosa is raised, and then invaginated, into a series of small, highly vascular cups, and to each one of these a yolk-sac is joined. A *placental cord* is formed on which thread-like *appendicula* assist in the absorption of maternal secretions. The arrangement of the placenta differs in various species in the genus. In *S. sarrakowah* the placental cord is formed so that (as in higher mammals) a wholly vascular connection is obtained.

Development.—Except in one species of *Heterodontus*, cleavage is meroblastic. It is confined to the germinal disc. A segmentation cavity appears early between the blastoderm cells and the yolk; the floor of the blastocœle becomes

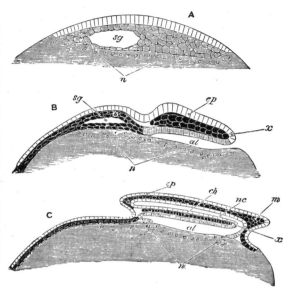

FIG. 186.—**Selachii: Development.** Embryo in longitudinal section. *A*, section of the young blastoderm with segmentation-cavity enclosed in the lower layer cells; *B*, older blastoderm with embryo in which endoderm and mesoderm are distinctly formed, and in which the alimentary slit has appeared. The segmentation-cavity is still represented as being present, though by this stage it has in reality disappeared. *C*, older blastoderm with embryo in which the neural canal has become formed and is continuous posteriorly with the alimentary canal. *Ectoderm* without shading; *mesoderm* and also *notochord* black with clear outlines to the cells; *endoderm* and lower layer cells with simple shading. *al.* alimentary cavity; *ch.* notochord; *ep.* ectoderm; *m.* mesoderm; *n.* nuclei of yolk; *nc.* neurocœle; *sg.* segmentation-cavity; *x.* point where ectoderm and endoderm become continuous at the posterior end of the embryo. (After Balfour.)

covered with a syncytium which probably plays a part in yolk digestion (Fig. 186, *n*). When cleavage is complete the blastoderm is a lens-shaped disc thicker at one end—the future caudal extremity.

Mass migrations of cells now take place round the *dorsal lip*, which is at the posterior edge of the blastodisc. An archenteron is formed (Fig. 186, *al.*). (An archenteron is not formed in the teleosts, but in most other respects gastrulation is similar in both groups; see p. 319.) The invaginated cells migrate forward forming mesodermal and endodermal structures and eliminating the blastocœle at the same time. It is possible that in addition to this forward migration some endodermal cells are derived in selachians by delamination from the early gastrula.

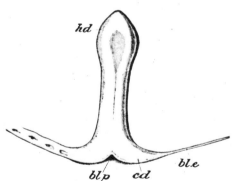

FIG. 187.—**Selachii: Development.** Embryo of *Scyliorhinus caniculus* with the tail-swellings well marked and the medullary groove just beginning. *bl. e.* edge of blastoderm; *bl. p.* blastopore; *cd.* caudal swellings; *hd.* head. (After Sedgwick.)

At the end of gastrulation the medullary groove begins to form in the same way as in other vertebrates. Similarly, somites, lateral plate, notochord, and intermediate cell mass become laid down. The archenteron becomes the alimentary canal.

As the blastoderm extends over the yolk, its posterior edge assumes the form of two prominent *caudal swellings* (Fig. 187, *cd.*). The medullary groove meanwhile deepens, and its edges grow over so as to form a canal (Fig. 186, *C*; Fig. 188). The union takes place first in the middle, the anterior and posterior parts (Fig. 188, *neur.*) remaining open for a time. When the posterior part closes, it does so in such a way that it encloses the blastopore, and there is thus formed a temporary passage of communication between the medullary canal and the archenteron—the *neurenteric passage.*

By degrees the body of the young fish becomes moulded on the blastoderm. This is effected by the formation of a system of anterior, posterior, and

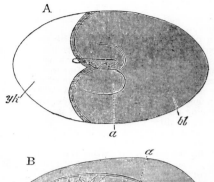
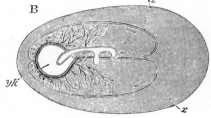
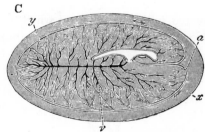

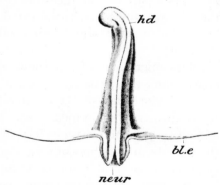

FIG. 188.—**Selachii: Development.** Embryo of a *Ray* with the medullary groove closed except at the hind end. The notched embryonic part of the blastoderm has grown faster than the rest and come to project over the surface of the yolk. *bl. e.* edge of blastoderm; *hd.* head; *neur.* unenclosed part of the neurocœle. (After Sedgwick.)

FIG. 189. — **Selachii: Development.** Three views of the developing egg, showing the embryo, the blastoderm, and the vessels of the yolk-sac. The shaded part (*bl.*) is the blastoderm, the white part the uncovered yolk. *A*, young stage with the embryo still attached at the edge of the blastoderm; *B*, older stage with the yolk not quite enclosed by the blastoderm; *C*, stage after the complete closure of the yolk. *a.* arterial trunks of yolk-sac; *bl.* blastoderm; *v.* venous trunks of yolk-sac; *y.* point of closure of the yolk-blastopore; *x.* portion of the blastoderm outside the arterial sinus terminalis. (After Balfour.)

lateral folds. These grow inwards and separate the body of the embryo from the rest of the blastoderm enclosing the yolk. As the folds approach one another in the middle, underneath the embryo, they form a constriction connecting the body of the embryo with the yolk enclosed in the extra-embryonic part of the blastoderm. The process may be illustrated by pinching off a portion of a ball of clay, leaving only a narrow neck connecting the pinched-off portion with the rest. The body of the embryo is thus gradually folded off from the *yolk-sac* and comes to be connected with it only by a narrow neck or yolk-stalk (Fig. 189). The head and tail of the young fish soon undergo differentiation, and a series of perforations at the sides of the neck form the branchial clefts and spiracle. A number of very delicate filaments (Fig. 190) grow out from these apertures and become greatly elongated. These are the provisional gills, which atrophy as development approaches completion, their bases alone persisting to give rise to the permanent gills. The great development of these gill-filaments in the embryos of some viviparous forms suggests that, in addition to their respiratory functions, they may also serve as organs for the absorption of nutrient fluids secreted by the villi of the uterine wall.

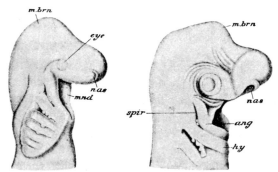

FIG. 190.—**Selachii: Development.** *Left:* Head of embryo of *Scyliorhinus caniculus*, with the rudiments of the gills on the first and second branchial arches. *Right:* at a somewhat later stage. The gill-filaments have increased in number and are present on the mandibular arch. *ang.* angle of the jaw; *hy.* hyoid; *m. brn.* mid-brain; *mnd.* mandible; *nas.* nasal sac; *spir.* spiracle. (After Sedgwick.)

The fins, both paired and unpaired, appear as longitudinal ridges of the ectoderm enclosing mesoderm. In some Chondrichthyes the paired fins are at first represented on each side by a continuous ridge or fold, which only subsequently becomes divided into anterior and posterior portions—the rudiments respectively of the pectoral and pelvic fins. Into these folds penetrates a series of buds from the somites. These, the *muscle-buds*, give rise to the fin-muscles. At first, from their mode of origin, these present a metameric arrangement, but this is in great measure lost during development.

While half the embryo is still in the yolk sac, and the body as yet 3 mm. long and possessed of only fifteen somites, its body-muscles contract rhythmically and cause a lateral bending of the head region. There is experimental evidence that such rhythmicity seems to be independent of neural control. Its function may be to keep the surrounding fluid moving and to assist oxygenation.

It is of interest that the ovoviviparous *Squalus acanthias* undergoes one of the longest gestation periods known. The 2 to 12 embryos may be held from 20 to 22 months (see also p. 907). During this period each is probably entirely dependant for nourishment on its extremely large yolk sac (Gilbert).

CLASS OSTEICHTHYES

Sub-Class Actinopterygii

INTRODUCTION

The ray-finned 'bony fishes' include all the commonest marine species of to-day (*e.g.* cod, sole, herring, eels) as well as the numerous forms that occur in freshwater lakes and streams of almost every country. They include also some of those peculiar and archaic survivals which used to be called 'ganoids' (pp. 287, 326)—*e.g.* the sturgeons, Garpike (*Lepisosteus*) [1] and the Bowfin (*Amia*) (p. 292). Other survivors of ancient lines, *Polypterus* and *Erpetoichthys* (p. 290), which were once placed with the crossopterygians—lung-fishes (p. 361) and cœlacanths (p. 356)—are now believed to be actinopterygians.

The earliest known actinopterygians came (as did the crossopterygians) from freshwaters of the mid-Devonian. The groups are undoubtedly older than the strata from which they were described. It is a curious fact that while only very few osteichthyian fragments of dubious early Devonian age have been discovered, great numbers of diverse species had appeared by the mid-Devonian and they actually dominated the freshwaters of the time.

Whether the Crossopterygii and the actinopterygians are of immediate common ancestry is uncertain. It is likely that some common progenitor did in fact exist in Upper Silurian or in very early Devonian waters. Each group had already diversified widely and characteristically by mid-Devonian, from which the earliest known indisputable examples come. The actinopterygians were at first much rarer than the crossopterygians, but to-day they are among the commonest vertebrates. The crossopterygians, on the other hand, have dwindled drastically, until to-day only four genera, including a mere handful of species, survive.

The Actinopterygii get their name from the structure of the paired fins, as seen in the more modern representatives of the group. The ancestral animals were more heavily scaled. Further, they were clumsier, and probably slower, than the more advanced and streamlined bony fishes of to-day. Unlike the paired fins of the Chondrichthyes (or the archipterygial fins of certain other

---

[1] This animal is usually called '*Lepidosteus*', but the original orthography is *Lepisosteus* and this is here used, with strong misgivings.

fishes which have cartilaginous or bony basal supports projecting outside the body-wall), the modern actinopterygian fin has these supports reduced almost to vanishing point. Further, the fin-web lying outside the body-wall is supported by the fin rays alone. The Polypterini and Chondrostei (sturgeons) (p. 288), and some of the early palæoniscoids (p. 285) which are somewhat more primitive as regards their fin structure, are exceptions.

The structure of the scales, being ganoid as opposed to cosmoid of early Crossopterygii (see p. 353), is an important diagnostic feature. The scales of most of the group, however, especially in the more recent forms, have gradually become modified by the loss of many elements, and may be reduced to thin horny structures, or may even be absent. The tail is at first heterocercal, *i.e.* the lower fin-lobe is disproportionately developed, and is supported only by the hypurals. It next becomes semi-heterocercal, and finally homocercal (Fig. 204, p. 302) or, more rarely, diphycercal (Fig. 251, p 365). The investing bones of the skull and jaws can be compared with those of the Crossopterygii, but show a certain amount of numerical reduction and modification in shape.

The earlier forms, judged by what we can see in the persisting species of the more primitive groups (such as the sturgeons, Polypterini, *Amia*, and *Lepisosteus*), possessed spiracles, abdominal pores, and a spiral valve in the gut. More advanced species have lost these structures. The respiratory arrangements have changed from a gill-condition near the laminar type to the fully filamentar (Fig. 73, p. 106). In exchange for a large valvular conus in the heart, a prominent elastic *bulbus arteriosus* has been evolved, the conus becoming reduced to one or, at most, two rows of valves. There is a gradual alteration of the genital ducts towards the specialised type of the teleosts (p. 293). The brain structure is characteristic in the large corpora striata, cerebellum, and medulla, presence of the valvula cerebelli, and in the absence of cerebral lobes.

The actinopterygians in general show no trace of internal nostrils. In the few forms that possess them (p. 339) such structures are not homologous with those of lung-fishes and tetrapods (p. 381). The more primitive actinopterygians, again unlike the lung-fishes, have only one dorsal fin (instead of two). Although no bony fish reaches a size rivalling that of the biggest sharks (p. 219), the chondrostean *Huso huso* (a sturgeon) grows to a length of about 24 feet and may weigh as much as 2,000 lbs. A few bony fishes are as ferocious as the most dangerous sharks. At least two kinds—the marine barracudas and the fresh-water Piranha (Caribe or Characin-fish) of South America—will attack Man without fear, or provocation. The barracudas (*Sphyræna*) are swift tropical and sub-tropical forms with dagger-like teeth. Some grow to a length of about eight feet and are much feared in West Indian and Central American waters. The river-dwelling Piranha (*Serrasalmus*) rarely exceeds two feet in length but hunts in large shoals. It possesses powerful jaws with cutting teeth that can inflict grievous injury.   Like sharks (p. 275) the Piranha is said to be acutely sensitive to the smell of blood.

A pineal aperture, common in early crossopterygians, rarely occurs.   Little muscle or other soft tissue extends into the paired fins.   These depend essentially on flexible dermal rays for their support.   The differences in scale structure have been mentioned above and elsewhere (p. 83).

As stated previously, the actinopterygians seem to have arisen in fresh water, as did other bony fishes.   There was some invasion by them of the sea as early as Palæozoic times, and in the Triassic a great marine radiation occurred, a trend that has been continued ever since.   The numerous freshwater teleosts of to-day have arisen as the result of former reinvasions of rivers and lakes.

As in most vertebrates, stories relating to the longevity of fishes are generally grossly exaggerated.   Pike and carp are traditionally claimed to live for as long as 150 to 200 years, but no reliable records are available.   Regan has suggested that pike of 60 or 70 lb. may be 'at least as many years old' (cited by Norman).

As usual, there is a variety of opinions concerning the most revealing classification within the group.   In the arrangement preferred below, the assembly is divided into three super-orders, for which are retained the old and familiar names Chondrostei, Holostei, and Teleostei.   At the same time we must remember that these names in no way truly reflect the history of actinopterygian—and osseous—development as was believed when they were first assigned.

SUB-CLASS ACTINOPTERYGII

Super-order Chondrostei
> **Orders Palæoniscoidea** (Devonian–Recent)
> **Acipenseroidei** (Jurassic–Recent)
> **Polypterini** (Eocene–Recent)

Super-order Holostei
> **Orders Semionotoidea** (Upper Permian–Recent)
> **Pycnodontoidea** (Upper Triassic–Eocene)
> **Aspidorhynchoidea** (Upper Jurassic–Cretaceous)
> **Amioidea** (Triassic–Recent)
> **Pholidophoroidea** (Triassic–Cretaceous)

Super-order Teleostei [1] (Lower Jurassic–Recent)
> **Orders Isospondyli** (= order Clupeiformes)
> **Haplomi** (= sub-order Esocoidei)
> **Iniomi** (= order Scopeliformes) ·

---

[1] This classification is essentially that of Regan.   The more modern arrangement of Berg is given in brackets.

Orders Miripinnati
  Giganturoidea (= order Giganturiformes)
  Lyomeri (= order Saccopharyngiformes)
  Ostariophysi (= order Cypriniformes)
  Apodes (= order Anguilliformes)

The above group is composed of 'soft-rayed' orders (e.g. Fig. 201).

Orders Heteromi (= orders Halosauriformes and Notocanthiformes)
  Synentognathi (= order Beloniformes)
  Salmopercæ (= order Percopsiformes)
  Microcyprini (= order Cyprinodontiformes)
  Solenichthyes (= order Syngnathiformes)
  Anacanthini (= orders Gadiformes and Macruriformes)
  Allotriognathi (= order Lampridiformes)

The above group is composed of 'intermediate' orders.

Orders Berycomorphi (= order Beryciformes)
  Zeomorphi (= order Zeiformes)
  Percomorphi (= order Perciformes)
  Gobiomorphi (= sub-order Gobioidei)
  Scleroparei (= sub-order Cottoidei)
  Thoracostei (= order Gasterosteiformes)
  Hypostomides (= order Pegasiformes)
  Heterosomata (= order Pleuronectiformes)
  Discocephali (= order Echeniformes)
  Plectognathi (= order Tetraodontiformes)
  Malacichthyes (= order Icosteiformes)
  Xenopterygii (= sub-order Gobiesocoidei)
  Haplodoci (= sub-order Batrachoidei)
  Pediculati (= order Lophiiformes)
  Opisthomi (= order Mastacembeliformes)
  Synbranchii (= order Synbranchiformes)

The above group is composed of 'spiny-rayed' (e.g. Fig. 202) and allied orders.

SUPER-ORDER CHONDROSTEI

ORDER PALÆONISCOIDEA

Palæoniscids and crossopterygians occur in the same Devonian deposits, but the former, although less numerous at first, quickly came to outnumber the cœlacanths and lung-fishes, and by Carboniferous times (p. 3) were already the dominant fresh-water vertebrates. The earliest known form is *Cheirolepis*, which, as with most of its late Palæozoic allies, was only 6 or 8 inches long.

The primitive ray-finned Palæoniscoidea probably arose from some ancestor common to themselves and the Crossopterygii. Palæoniscoids, however, had some points of difference from the osteolepids, cœlacanths, and Dipnoi on the one hand, and others, perhaps less deep-seated, distinguish them from later actinopterygians.

The main differences between the early actinopterygians and the crossopterygians can be seen by comparing two such forms as *Palæoniscus* and *Osteolepis*. The former had large eyes with no more than four sclerotic plates, as against the large eyes and many sclerotic plates of the latter. In *Palæoniscus*

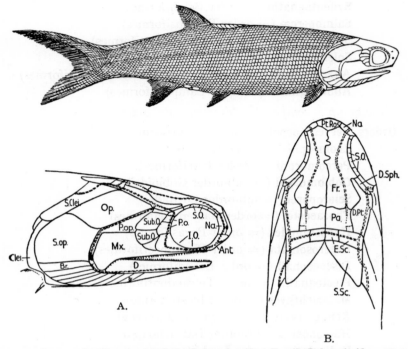

Fig. 191.—Super-order **Chondrostei,** Order **Palæoniscoidea,** Family **Palæoniscidæ.** *Palæoniscus.* Upper: Reconstruction (after Nicholson and Lydekker). Lower: A, lateral, and B, dorsal, aspect of head. *Ant.* antorbital; *Br.* branchiostegals; *Clei.* cleithrum; *D.* dentary; *D. Pt.* dermo-pterotic; *D. Sph.* dermo-sphenotic; *E. Sc.* extrascapulas; *Fr.* frontal; *I. O.* infraorbitals; *Mx.* maxilla; *Na.* nostril; *Op.* opercular; *P.A.* parietal; *P. op.* preopercular; *P. o.* postorbital; *Pt. Ros.* rostral; *S. O.* supraorbitals; *Sub. O.* suborbitals; *S. Clei.* supracleithrum; *S. op.* subopercular; *S. Sc.* suprascapular. (After Westoll.)

(Fig. 191) the maxilla had a wide postorbital extension which ran far backwards. This was firmly supported by a large preopercular, which functionally replaced the squamosal of *Osteolepis*. The cheek extended dorsally as far as the upper surface of the skull and helped to obliterate the spiracular cleft. In *Osteolepis* (Fig. 244, p. 355) the squamosal is a large bone. The preopercular was very small, and the maxilla itself was smaller. The osteolepid skull was further characterised by the internal nostril, the transverse meso-cranial joint (p. 358), and by peculiarities of dentition. All of these are entirely unrepresented in the actinopterygian skull. In the fins of palæoniscoids, while some of them had a series of divergent radials which formed a short, rounded lobe, there was no defined central axis. They were in no way archipterygial. The structure of the scales was ganoid, not cosmoid (p. 83). Their arrangement on the tail was characteristic : there was an apparent break of pattern in the lines of scales on the upper tail-lobe ; these appear to have to run in a different direction from those on the body. There was one dorsal fin only, compared with two in osteolepids.

The palæoniscoids were essentially, though not exclusively, Palæozoic fishes. They reached the peak of their development in the Carboniferous, and faded in the Triassic when they were being replaced by Mesozoic offshoots which

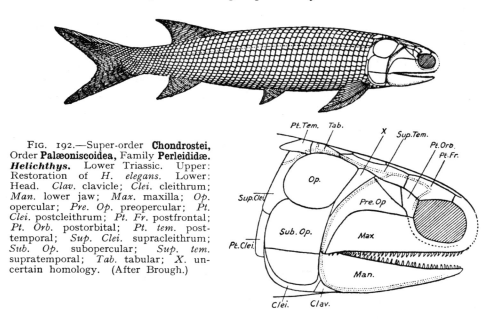

FIG. 192.—Super-order **Chondrostei**, Order **Palæoniscoidea**, Family **Perleididæ**. **Helichthys.** Lower Triassic. Upper: Restoration of *H. elegans*. Lower: Head. *Clav.* clavicle; *Clei.* cleithrum; *Man.* lower jaw; *Max.* maxilla; *Op.* opercular; *Pre. Op.* preopercular; *Pt. Clei.* postcleithrum; *Pt. Fr.* postfrontal; *Pt. Orb.* postorbital; *Pt. tem.* posttemporal; *Sup. Clei.* supracleithrum; *Sub. Op.* subopercular; *Sup. tem.* supratemporal; *Tab.* tabular; *X.* uncertain homology. (After Brough.)

specialised in various directions from the more primitive stock. Of these offshoots only a bare remnant has persisted in the four lines to-day represented by the sturgeons, *Polypterus, Lepisosteus,* and *Amia* (see pp. 290–293). There were, however, many other families evolved during the late Palæozoic and Mesozoic, all pursuing their own evolutionary lines, only to become extinct. Some primitive forms persisted until the Jurassic and early Cretaceous. All these may be placed in a rather loosely defined group, the Holostei (p. 291). However, such a group cannot be clearly defined from the earlier palæoniscoids on the one hand, nor their later representatives from the teleosts on the other. It is largely a matter of various trends of evolution, but all the Holostei show a general trend which is quite separable from that of the sturgeons (Chondrostei), in that there is no considerable loss of bone nor reduction of jaws. The fin structure and gradual loss of many primitive characters also differentiate them from *Polypterus*. The general trend of evolution away from their earlier palæoniscoid ancestors is shown by the forward movement of the point of suspension of the lower jaw and the greater freedom of movement of the maxilla so as to allow a wider gape. The fins become more definitely actinopterygian, and the tail more and more homocercal. The whole skeleton becomes more mechanically efficient.

The Palæoniscoidea therefore, for the present, must be regarded as a collection of families of separate lines of evolution whose actual relations one to another are still uncertain. Several lines had already become differentiated by the Devonian. These are so diverse that it is not possible to select one as absolutely typical of the whole group. *Cheirolepis*, although probably the earliest known species, was already specialised in several respects. The small scales were atypical in shape, the eyes unusually small, the skull had a very large posterior extension, and its dorsal surface was flat instead of rounded.

Families that may be placed in this order include the following: 1. Palæoniscidæ (e.g. *Palæoniscus* (Fig. 191), *Cheirolepis*, *Birgeria*). 2. Platysomidæ, deep-bodied fishes (e.g. *Cheirodus*, *Platysomus*). 3. Saurichthyiidæ, long-bodied fishes (e.g. *Saurichthys*, *Belonorhynchus*). 4. Catopteridæ (e.g. *Catopterus*). 5. Perleididæ (e.g. *Helichthys* (Fig. 192), *Perleidus*).

ORDER ACIPENSEROIDEI

This order is represented at the present time by the sturgeons—viz., *Acipenser* (Fig. 193), a genus of about twenty species living in the rivers of Europe, North America and Asia; *Scaphirhynchus*, the 'Shovel-nosed Sturgeon'

FIG. 193.—Super-order **Chondrostei**, Order **Acipenseroidei**, Family **Acipenseridæ**. *Acipenser*. One of the smaller sturgeons, the Sterlet (*A. ruthenus*) inhabits the Black and Caspian Seas. Sturgeons are mostly marine. They ascend rivers to breed and a few spend all their lives in fresh water. The tactile chin-barbels are a pointer towards the ground-feeding habits of the genus. Theoretically all sturgeons caught in English waters are the property of the Monarch (decree of Edward II, 1284–1327). *b*. barbels; *c. f.* caudal fin; *d. f.* dorsal fin; *pct. f.* pectoral fin; *pv. f.* pelvic fin; *sc.* scutes; *v. f.* ventral fin. (After Cuvier.)

of North America and Central Asia; *Polyodon*, the Spoonbill Sturgeon or Paddlefish of the Mississippi, and *Psephurus*, a spoonbill sturgeon from China.

The roe of various species of *Acipenser* is sieved, salted, and preserved for the market as caviar. Sturgeons have colonised both salt and fresh water. They stir up mud with the snout, and by means of variously modified buccal and pharyngeal arrangements are able to scoop up, or suck in and filter, various bottom-dwelling invertebrates.

The group as a whole shows a mixture of primitive and secondarily modified characters. In the first category are such features as the unconstricted notochord, the persistence of basi- and inter-dorsals and of basi- and inter-ventrals as separate elements in the vertebræ (Fig. 194), the retention of a clavicle in the shoulder-girdle, the primitive structure of the fins with their broad bases, the fulcral scales on the dorsal and caudal fin, the heterocercal tail, the open spiracle and spiracular pseudo-branch, the spiral valve and the arrangement of the urinogenital organs. In the second category are certain characters which are more developed in the earlier than in the later forms, and which are therefore known to have become degenerate or lost. These include the reduction of the jaws (owing to the suctorial method of feeding which has been acquired), the loss of ganoine on the scales and head bones, the reduction of the scales to a few rows on the sides of the body, and the irregularity and loss of some of the head bones and secondary multiplication of centres of ossification of others. There is also a general loss of ossification in the whole skeleton.

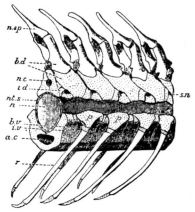

FIG. 194.—*Acipenser:* **Pre-caudal vertebræ.** *a. c.* aortic canal formed by the union of ingrowths from the basi- and interventrals of opposite sides; *b. d.* basidorsals; *b. v.* basiventrals; *i. d.* interdorsals; *i. v.* interventrals; *n.* notochord; *n. c.* neural canal; *n. sp.* neural spine; *nt. s.* sheath of notochord; *P.* parapophysis; *r.* rib; *s. n.* foramen for root of spinal nerve. (From *Cambridge Natural History.*)

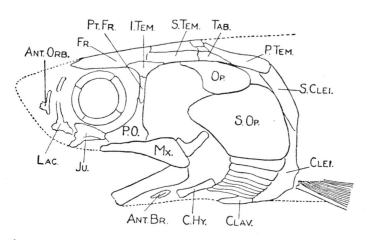

FIG. 195.—*Chondrosteus:* **Skull and pectoral girdle.** *C. acipenseroides. Ant. Br.* anterior branchiostegal; *Ant. Orb.* antorbital; *C. Hy.* ceratohyal; *Clav.* clavicles; *Clei.* cleithrum; *Fr.* frontal; *I. Tem.* intertemporal; *Ju.* jugal; *Lac.* lachrymal; *Mx.* maxilla; *Op.* opercular; *P. O.* postorbital; *P. Tem.* posttemporal; *Pt. Fr.* postfrontal; *S. Clei.* supracleithrum; *S. Op.* subopercular; *S. Tem.* supratemporal; *Tab.* tabular. (After Watson.)

A Jurassic species, *Chondrosteus acipenseroides* (Fig. 195), which reached a length of about 3 feet, was the earliest known true sturgeon. It was transitional in structure, and although degeneration had already set in, was probably of palæoniscoid origin through some such form as *Coccocephalus*.   Fishes of *Poly-odon* affinity occurred in the Cretaceous.   Their ancestry, however, is obscure.

ORDER POLYPTERINI (CLADISTIA)

Few fossils are known, but the Cladistia are obviously survivals from an ancient type.   *Polypterus* (Fig. 196) and *Erpetoichthys*, the only known members of the order, were once classed as crossopterygians largely be-cause of the appearance of the paired fins and of the arrangement of the paired ventral lung-like air bladder and its outlet into the pharynx.   This structure may have helped the survival of *Polypterus* in a periodically drought-stricken environment.   Spiracles persist and serve to expel excess water gulped in through the mouth.   In *Erpetoichthys* a pharyngeohypophysial duct remains open throughout life; in *Polypterus* it is closed in the adult.   The balance of

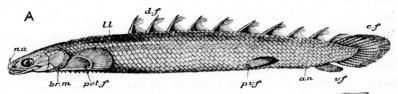

Fig. 196.—Super-order **Chondrostei**, Order **Polypterini**, Family **Poly-pteridæ.**   ***Polypterus bichir.***   The Central African *Polypterus* (and the closely related West African *Erpetoichthys*), together with the paddle-fishes (*Polyodon*) are aberrant freshwater 'chondrostean' survivors.   See also sturgeons (Fig. 193).   *A*, entire animal; *B*, ventral view of throat. *an.* anus; *br. m.* branchiostegal membrane; *c. f.* caudal fin; *d. f.* dorsal finlets; *jug. pl.* gular plates; *na.* nostril; *pct. f.* pectoral fin; *pv. f.* pelvic fin; *v. f.* ventral fin. (After Cuvier.)

evidence favours an origin from some palæoniscoid stock.   The thick scales, for instance, are of typically ganoid form.   The skull lacks the division into the orbito-ethmoidal and occipito-otic regions so characteristic of the crossoptery-gian skull (p. 368).   The position of the nostrils on the dorso-lateral surface of the snout is typically actinopterygian, as is the anatomy of the soft parts such as a pyloric cæcum in the gut and the teleostean-like character of the urino-genital organs.   The teeth are simple in structure, and are without the peculiar structure and method of replacement found in the Crossopterygii.   The structure of the paired fin is peculiar, with its long posterior axis and preaxial radials (Fig. 252, p. 367) and muscular lobe lying outside the body-wall.   The resemblance to the fin of the Chondrichthyes is superficial; and it is, however, quite unlike the archipterygial type of the Crossopterygii.   It can be interpreted as a modification of the basic actinopterygian pattern.   On the other hand, less modified form of the scales, the fin structure just mentioned, and various characters of the skull prevent any close association of these two fishes with other Actinopterygii and, for the present, they are best considered as represent-ing a persistent line of palæoniscoid affinity.

There are nine species of the genus *Polypterus* from the Congo, Nile, Niger, and Senegal river systems. The West African *Erpetoichthys* (= *Calamoichthys*) *calabaricus* is small and more elongated, but otherwise very similar. The most noticeable features are the rhomboid scales, the presence of a pair of gular plates between the rami of the lower jaws, the lobed pectoral fins, the absence of ventral fins, the abbreviated heterocercal tail, and the division of the dorsal fin into a series of repeated finlets ('sails'), each supported by an anterior spine.

SUPER-ORDER HOLOSTEI

As mentioned above this is an extensive, extremely varied and possibly very artificial group of ray-finned fishes that present features that seem to indicate a position between the Chondrostei (p. 285) and the teleosts (p. 293). Thus, the Holostei represent a fairly broad grade of development rather than a demonstrably related, however polymorphic, group. Such fishes possess an

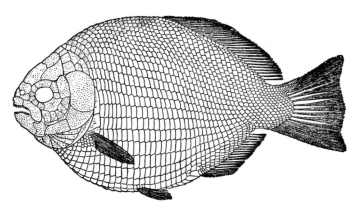

FIG. 197. — Super-order **Holostei**, Order **Semionotoidea**, Family **Semionotidæ**. *Dapedius politus*. This family, containing also *Lepidotus*, were common holosteans in Mesozoic seas. (After Smith Woodward.)

abbreviated heterocercal tail which sometimes superficially resembles the homo-cercal (Fig. 204, p. 302) appendage of later types; but the internal tail-structure remains unmistakably heterocercal. The scales are greatly modified, in that they have lost the middle layer of cosmine, yet the outer ganoine layer is retained in varying degree. There is a considerable loss of bony fin-rays. The spiracle has disappeared, and in most no trace remains of a clavicle. There is also a single dorsal swim-bladder (p. 339) principally of hydrostatic significance, but which is said to possess some slight respiratory function in modern representatives. The Holostei show a considerable degree of uniformity in the reduction, modification, and freedom of the maxilla, together with striking changes in the preopercular and orbital regions. These signalled the development of the more advanced teleost architecture with which we will become familiar later on (p. 304) and which achieved dominance in the Cretaceous (Table 1, p. 3).

The Holostei probably appeared first in the late Upper Permian and

Triassic (e.g. *Semionotus*) and became very plentiful in the Jurassic (e.g. *Lepidotus*, *Dapedius*) (Fig. 197). As far as is known, they ranged from a few inches to a few feet in length. Two restricted fresh-water genera, *Lepisosteus* and *Amia*, linger on to-day.

ORDER SEMIONOTOIDEA

This group arose (Family Semionotidæ) in the late Palæozoic and faded in the Cretaceous but still persists in a sole surviving genus of gar-pikes (*Lepisosteus*) of the fresh water of North and Central America. The second family (Lepisosteidæ) arose in the later Cretaceous or early Tertiary when the former was dying out.

Lepisosteus (Fig. 198) shows a number of primitive features, such as a long valvular conus to the heart and a corresponding absence of a bulbus arteriosus, a tail still hemi-heterocercal, an air bladder with cellular walls, and thick

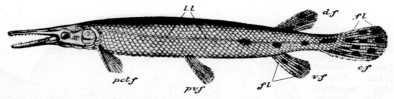

FIG. 198.—Super-order **Holostei**, Order **Semionotoidea**, Family **Lepisosteidæ**. *Lepisosteus*. The 'Bony Pike' or Garpike (*L. platystomus*) and the bowfins (*Amia*, Fig. 199); these swift, predaceous freshwater fishes are the only surviving holostean genera. *c. f.* caudal fin; *d. f.* dorsal fin; *fl.* fulcra; *l. l.* lateral line; *pct. f.* pectoral fin; *pv. f.* pelvic fin; *v. f.* ventral fin. (After Curvier.)

rhombic scales with a complete covering of ganoine. Fulcral scales are still retained, and traces of a clavicle are identifiable. On the other hand, the central jugal plate has been lost, and the spiracle is closed. The presence of pyloric cæca and the structure of the generative organs are teleostean features. Some specialised characters appear to be peculiar to the genus : the reduced maxilla and its functional replacement by a number of tooth-bearing infra-orbital elements ; the numerous small cheek plates and, above all, the opisthocœlous vertebræ as opposed to the much more common amphicœlous vertebræ of most actinopterygian fishes.

There are several living species of *Lepisosteus*, of which *L. tristœchus* is said to attain a length of 10 feet.

ORDER AMIOIDEA

This may be the typical holostean group. Mesozoic marine representatives of at least three families were extremely plentiful and a Tertiary fresh-water family (Amiidæ) persists to-day as a single North American species, the Bow-fin (*Amia*, Fig. 199). Like the gar-pikes, *Amia* shows a mixture of primitive and advanced characters. Of the former the lung is dorsal, but bilobed and cellular, so that a certain amount of air-breathing is still possible. A vestigial spiral valve is present in the intestine. A small valvular conus occurs in the heart, but there is also a considerable bulbus arteriosus. There is one large jugal plate between the rami of the lower jaws and well-developed branchiostegal rays as in teleosts. Unlike the teleost con-

dition, there are no pyloric cæca ; and the lower jaws still retain the full number of elements. Of progressive characters, the scales have become thin, cycloid, and have lost the ganoine layer ; the fins have lost all fulcra ; the tail is practically homocercal ; and the vertebræ solid and amphicœlous except in the tail region where separate basi-dorsals and basi-ventrals still occur.

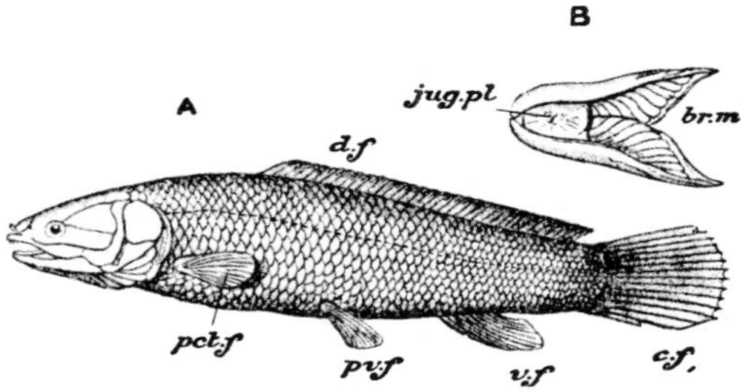

FIG. 199.—Super-order **Holostei**, Order **Amoidea**. Family **Amiidæ**. *Amia*. Bowfin (*A. calva*). The single surviving species inhabits North American freshwater lakes and rivers. The scales have lost their ganoine (p. 84). *A*, Entire animal; *B*, ventral view of throat. *br. m.* branchiostegal membrane; *c. f.* caudal fin; *d. f.* dorsal fin; *jug. pl.* jugular plate; *pct. f.* pectoral fin; *pv. f.* pelvic fin; *v. f.* ventral fin. (After Günther.)

In addition to the two orders, above mentioned, there were also the extinct Pycnodontoidea, Aspidorhynchoidea, and Pholidophoroidea. The last-named is perhaps the most interesting in that it gave rise to the Leptolepidæ (see below) which may have contained the ancestors of the teleosts. Although this family is generally considered to be teleostean, some authorities believe its members (e.g. *Leptolepis*) were no more than advanced examples of the Holostei.

SUPER-ORDER TELEOSTEI

The teleosts, of more than 25,000 living species, are an immensely successful group. They range through nearly all ocean depths and in the coldest polar seas and have colonised practically every freshwater habitat (including subterranean waters inhabited by relatively unpigmented, blind representatives) except those that freeze or are supplied by very hot thermal springs. The economies of whole tribes of mankind depend on them, and great industries have been established to exploit them. Teleosts present an almost bewildering —sometimes grotesque—diversity of form ; and an astonishing—and again sometimes grotesque—range of psycho-physiological adaptations (cf. Fig. 202, p. 297) that make those of most birds seem relatively unremarkable. Some teleosts regularly migrate between extremes of salt and fresh water. Some occur in inestimable numbers. Teleosts are of outstanding practical importance to mankind.

True teleosts probably appeared first in the lower Jurassic (e.g. *Leptolepis*, Fig. 200), and were certainly very abundant in the salt waters of the Cretaceous, in which they sometimes attained a length of more than 15 feet (e.g. *Portheus*). It is generally considered, but it has not been proved, that they were marine in origin. Certain it is that they are an offshoot of the holostean

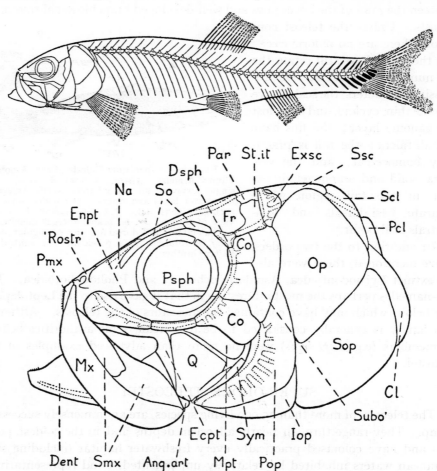

FIG. 200.—Super-order **Teleostei**, Order **Isospondyli**, Family **Leptolepidæ**. *Leptolepis*. *Leptolepis bronni*, was a small Jurassic fish that seems to be near the ancestral stem of the modern teleosts. Upper: restoration. In some genera hypurals were absent (see Berg). Lower: skull. *Ang. art.* angulo-articular; *Cl.* cleithrum; *Co.* circumorbital; *Dent.* dentary; *Dsph.* dermosphenotic; *Ecpt.* ectopterygoid; *Enpt.* entopterygoid; *Exsc.* extrascapular; *Fr.* frontal; *Iop.* interopercular; *Mpt.* metapterygoid; *Mx.* maxilla; *Na.* nasal; *Op.* opercular; *Par.* parietal; *Pcl.* postcleithrum; *Pmx.* premaxilla; *Pop.* preopercular; *Psph.* parasphenoid; *Q.* quadrate; *Rostr.* rostral bone; *Scl.* supracleithrum; *Smx.* supramaxilla; *So.* supraorbital; *Sop.* subopercular; *Ssc.* suprascapular; *St. it.* supratemporo-intertemporal; *Subo.* suborbital; *Sym.* symplectic. (After Rayner.)

phase of evolution, but the process of separation was gradual and a definite line of demarcation is not easy to make.

During the very early Tertiary the teleosts expanded enormously, and replaced the older phase of evolution so that at the present time they are, with the few exceptions already noted (p. 283), the only bony fishes in existence. The full tide of evolution has not yet been reached; new species are still in process of formation. Teleosts provide striking examples of adaptive radiation (p. 321).

The marks by which a teleost, whatever its shape and appearance, can be recognised are partly in the loss of certain characters that are still preserved by the more primitive actinopterygians, and partly the presence of a number of structures which are new or, at least, definite modifications of old ones. The diagnostic features of the teleosts essentially represent the 'further expression of evolutionary tendencies seen at work in the lower ray-finned fishes' (Romer).

The characters that are lost are: spiracle, spiral valve, conus arteriosus (reduced to one, or at most two, rows of valves; for this reduction the great enlargement of the bulbus arteriosus compensates). The swim-bladder (where retained) is essentially a hydrostatic organ but may be adapted to respiratory, or other functions such as sound production (p. 346). Ganoine disappears from the exoskeleton and scales. There are no longer fulcral scales on the fins. Gular bones, with very few exceptions where they are much reduced, have disappeared or, rather, have been replaced by branchiostegal rays (Fig. 304). Dermal bones tend more and more to sink beneath the skin, and to come into closer association with the endocranium than is the case with the more primitive palæoniscids and crossopterygians. The bones of the lower jaw are reduced to three elements only: the dentary, angular, and articular. The pectoral girdle has lost the clavicle.

Of new or highly modified characters, the gills are now fully filamentar (p. 299), the tail is externally (and in many cases internally) homocercal, or even gephyrocercal; but in a slight internal uptilting it still retains a hint of its heterocercal origin (p. 283). (In development too, it shows distinctly its origins from fishes with a heterocercal tail.) The endoskeleton has become almost wholly ossified. The skull, which shows an extreme range of variation in shape, nearly always has a single prevomer, and at the posterior dorsal surface a single supraoccipital bone. This element, sometimes stated to be formed by the fusion of the neural arches of some of the anterior vertebræ, is insignificant or absent in more primitive groups. Further drastic modifications appear in the shift of upper crushing teeth (when present) to the parasphenoid; the corresponding lower ones are attached to elements of the pharyngeal floor. The vertebræ are amphicœlous. There are additional 'ribs' known as the intermuscular bones. In the paired fins the radials are reduced to a few brachial ossicles, and the fin is completely fan-like, and without any trace of an axis. The urinogenital organs have become highly specialised in that both ovaries and testes have acquired new ducts. In the male there is no longer any connection between the testis and mesonephros. In the female in some cases there is still an open-mouthed oviduct leading from the cœlom, but usually the oviduct surrounds the ovary, so that the ova pass directly down to be discharged without being shed into the cœlom.

The brain is highly specialised. The upper walls of the cerebrum are very thin. (The enlarged corpora striata on the ventral surface show through and give a false impression of cerebral hemispheres.) The mid- and hind-brains, however, are often very large. There is a great development of the valvula cerebelli (Fig. 212), and the optic nerves cross over outside the brain without mixing (the absence of the so-called optic chiasma).

FIG. 201.—Super-order **Teleostei,** Order **Isospondyli,** Family **Salmonidæ.** *Salmo.* **Example from a 'soft-rayed' order.** Brook Trout (*S. trutta*). *a. l.* adipose lobe of pelvic fin; *an.* anus; *c. f.* caudal fin; *d. f.* 1, first dorsal fin; *d. f.* 2, second dorsal or adipose fin; *l. l.* lateral line; *op.* operculum; *pct. f.* pectoral fin; *pv. f.* pelvic fin; *v. f.* anal fin. (After Jardine.)

Teleosts fall essentially into three groups, (1) generalised *soft-rayed* orders, (2) *spiny-rayed* and related forms, and (3) a loose assembly of *intermediate* orders.

Soft-rayed orders:

These include the Isospondyli (e.g. *Salmo,* trout (Fig. 201); *Clupea,* herrings); Haplomi (freshwater fishes, e.g. *Esox,* pikes); Ostariophysi (= Cypriniformes) (mostly freshwater fishes, e.g. *Cyprinus,* carps; *Serrasalmus,* Piranha; *Electrophorus,* 'electric-eels,' *Clarias,* catfish; *Rhodeus,* bitterlings); and Apodes (= Anguilliformes) (*Anguilla,* eels) are the best known. Additionally there are the marine orders Iniomi (e.g. *Aulopus,* Australian Sergeant Baker), Miripinnati (a newly erected order, e.g. *Miripinna*), Giganturoidea (single genus *Gigantua*), and Lyomeri (of two families only, e.g. *Saccopharynx*).

Intermediate orders:

A group of orders, certain of which are sometimes placed in an 'Order' Mesichthyes, contains fishes that are distinct from the more primitive soft-rayed teleosts on the one hand, but have not attained the specialisation of the spiny-finned fishes on the other. These comprise the following: Heteromi (deep-sea oceanic fishes, e.g. *Lipogenys*); Synentognathi (e.g. *Exocœtus,* flying-fishes, or *Belone,* garfishes); Salmopercæ (three genera of North American freshwater fishes, e.g. *Percopsis*); Microcyprinæ (freshwater and marine fishes, *e.g.* cyprinodont *Fundulus* of North America), Solenichthyes (e.g. *Hippocampus*, sea-horses), Anacanthini (e.g. *Gadus*, cods; *Merluccius*, Hake), and Allotriognathi (e.g. *Regalecus*, Oar-fish).

Spiny-rayed and allied orders:

These comprise the following: marine Berycomorphi (e.g. *Trœichthodes*, Australian Nanygai) and Zeomorphi (e.g. *Zeus*, John Dory), marine and fresh-water Percomorphi (e.g. *Perca*, perch; Cichlidæ, e.g. *Tilapia* (Fig. 202)); Scombridæ, including tunny, mackerel, bonito; Sphyrænidæ, barracudas; Australian

FIG. 202.—Super-order **Teleostei**, Order **Percomorphi**, Family **Cichlidæ**. *Tilapia:* **Example from a 'spiny-rayed' order.** Most members of the genus *Tilapia* are mouth-brooders. For some days after hatching the young of *T. mossambica* still take refuge in the female buccal cavity in times of danger (p. 352). Redrawn from an F.A.O. photograph. (Some young have been eliminated for the sake of clarity.)

Murray Cod, *Moccullochella*; marine and sometimes freshwater Gobiomorphi (e.g. *Gobius*, gobies); Scleroparei (*e.g.* Triglidæ, gurnards; *Synanceja*, stone-fishes); Thoracostei (e.g. *Gasterosteus*, sticklebacks); the marine Hypostomides (toothless, bony-armoured Indo-Pacific fishes, e.g. *Pegasus*, *Acanthopegasus*); Heterosomata (e.g. *Psetta*, turbot and brill; *Solea*, soles and other flat-fishes); the marine Discocephali (e.g. *Echeneis* and *Remora*, sucker-fishes); the marine and fluviatile Plectognathi (e.g. *Balistes*, trigger-fish); the marine Malaci-chthyes (single family (Costeidæ)), Xenopterygii (*e.g.* Gobiesocidæ, cling-fishes), Haplodoci (e.g. *Porichthys*, toad-fishes) and Pediculati (angler-fishes); the freshwater Opisthomi (of Africa, e.g. *Mastacembelus*, and southern Asia);

and the superficially eel-like marine and freshwater Synbranchii (*e.g.* land-going *Amphipnous*).

It should be remembered that not all systematists approve of the representation set out above.

EXAMPLE OF A TELEOST FISH.—THE BROOK OR BROWN TROUT (SALMO TRUTTA)

The Brook Trout is common in the rivers and streams of Europe, and has been acclimatised in other parts of the world. It varies greatly in size according to its environment, but it may attain sexual maturity, and therefore be considered adult at a length of 18–20 cm. In large lakes it may grow to nearly a metre in length. Other allied species such as the Salmon (*S. salar*), the Char (*Salvelinus alpinus*), the American Brook Trout (*S. fontinalis*), are common in the Northern Hemisphere and of course differ from *S. trutta* only in detail.

External Characters.—The *body* (Fig. 201) is elongated, compressed, thickest in the middle and tapering both to the head and tail. The *mouth* is terminal and very large. The upper jaw is supported by two freely movable bones, the *premaxilla* (Fig. 205, p. 304) in front and the *maxilla* (*max.*) behind. Both bear sharp curved *teeth* arranged in a single row. When the mouth is opened a row of *palatine teeth* is seen internal and parallel to those of the maxilla, and in the mid-line of the roof of the mouth is a double row of *vomerine teeth*. The lower jaw is mainly supported by a *dentary* and bears a row of teeth. On the throat each ramus of the mandible is bounded mesially by a deep groove. The floor of the mouth is produced into a prominent *tongue* bearing a double row of teeth. In old males the apex of the lower jaw becomes curved upwards like a hook.

The large *eyes* have no eyelids. The flat cornea is covered by a transparent layer of skin. A short distance in front of each of the eyes is the double *nostril*. Each olfactory sac has two external apertures, the anterior one provided with a flap-like valve. There is no external indication of the ear.

On each side of the posterior region of the head is the *operculum* (Fig. 205, *op.*) or gill-cover, a large flap which, when raised, displays the gills. Between it and the flank is the large crescentic gill-opening from which the respiratory current emerges. The operculum is not a mere fold of skin, as in Holocephali, but is supported by three thin bones. The outlines of these can be seen through the skin. They are the *opercular* (Fig. 205, *op.*), *sub-opercular*, and *inter-opercular* (*inter. op.*); the last is attached to the angle of the mandible. The *pre-opercular* (*pre. op.*) is not an opercular support but is one of the cheek-bones following the outline of the hyomandibular. The ventral portion of the operculum is produced into a thin membranous extension, the *branchiostegal membrane*, which is supported by twelve flat, overlapping bones, the *branchi-*

ostegal rays. The narrow area on the ventral surface of the throat which separates the two gill-openings from one another is called the *isthmus*. The *gills*, seen by lifting up the operculum, are four red comb-like organs, each having a double row of free gill-filaments. Alternating with the gills are the five vertically elongated *gill-slits* which open into the pharynx.

The Trout breathes by drawing water in through the mouth and passing it outwards over the gills. *Inspiration* is effected by moving the gill-covers outward and depressing the floor of the mouth. The internal volume is thereby increased and the pressure decreased. With the buccal cavity thus widened, water flows in through the open mouth, compensating for the changed pressure. The *branchiostegal membrane* then extends and closes the posterior opening into the branchial chamber by filling the space between the free margin of the operculum and the body. This prevents any inflow of water from behind the head. This membrane is so arranged that water under pressure can nevertheless pass from the branchial chamber to the exterior. *Expiration* occurs when the gill-covers move inwards and the floor of the mouth is raised to force the water out of the branchial cavity and over the gills to the exterior. The action of a pair of transversely directed membranous folds, the *respiratory valves*, controls the direction of the respiratory current. One of these valves is attached to the roof, the other to the floor of the mouth. They can become expanded to block the passage when water presses on them from behind. Thus the water must pass over the gills (Fig. 73, p. 106).

On the ventral surface of the body, at about two-thirds of the distance from the snout to the end of the tail, is the *anus* (Fig. 201, *an.*). Behind it is the *urinogenital aperture* leading into the *urinogenital sinus*. Into this both urinary and genital products are discharged.

The region from the snout to the posterior edge of the operculum is the *head*. The *trunk* extends from the operculum to the anus. The post-anal region is the *tail*.

There are two *dorsal fins*. The *anterior dorsal* (Fig. 201, *d. f. 1*) is large and triangular, and is supported by thirteen bony fin-rays. The *adipose dorsal* (*d. f. 2*) is small and thick, and is devoid of bony supports : it is distinguished as an *adipose fin*, a structure that occurs in a very few families of teleosts. The *caudal fin* (*c. f.*) differs markedly from that of most Chondrichthyes in being, as far as its external appearance is concerned, quite symmetrical. It is supported by fin-rays which radiate regularly from the rounded end of the tail proper. Such outwardly symmetrical tail-fins are called *homocercal*. There is a single large *anal* fin (*v. f.*) supported by eleven rays. The *pectoral fin* (*pct. f.*) has fourteen rays and is situated, in the normal position, close behind the gill-opening, but the *pelvic fin* (*pv. f.*) has shifted its position and lies some distance in front of the vent. It is supported by ten rays, and has a small process or *adipose lobe* (*a. l.*) springing from its outer edge near the base

The body is covered by a soft, slimy skin through which, in the trunk and tail, the outlines of the *scales* can be seen. On the head and fins the skin is smooth and devoid of scales. A well-marked *lateral line* (*l. l.*) (p. 136) extends along each side from head to tail, and is continued into branching lines on the head. These run above and below each eye, along the lower jaw, and there is a well-marked line across the posterior aspect of the skull. The skin is grey above, shading into yellowish below. It is covered with minute black melanophores which, on the sides and back, are aggregated to form round spots two or three millimetres in diameter. In young specimens orange-coloured spots also occur.

Skin and Exoskeleton.—The *epidermis* is a squamous stratified epithelium and contains mucous glands and pigment cells (p. 82). Beneath the epidermis, the *scales* (Fig. 224, p. 329) are lodged in pouches of the dermis. They have the form of flat, nearly circular plates of bone. There are no Haversian canals, lacunæ or canaliculi (p. 73). This bone is laid down in concentric rings which represent the annual growth stages. Such rings represent differential seasonal growth-rates. Growth is faster in spring and summer and almost ceases during winter. An examination of the scale-rings, or similar ones in the otoliths (p. 317), reveals the age of a fish. The scales have an imbricating arrangement, overlapping one another from before backwards, like the tiles of a house, in such a way that a small three-sided portion of each scale comes to lie immediately beneath the epidermis, while the rest is hidden beneath the scales immediately anterior to it. It will be seen that such teleost scales are very distinct from the placoid scales of elasmobranch fishes which penetrate the epidermis and give rise to a 'shagreen' surface (p. 103). Besides the scales, the fin-rays belong to the exoskeleton, but will be considered below (pp. 307, 329).

Endoskeleton.—The *vertebral column* shows a great advance in being thoroughly differentiated into distinct bony *vertebræ*. It is divisible into an anterior or *trunk region* and a posterior or *caudal region*, each containing about twenty-eight vertebræ.

A typical trunk vertebra consists of a *centrum* (Fig. 203) (CN.) with deeply concave anterior and posterior faces, and perforated in the centre by a small hole. The edges of the centra are united by ligaments and the biconvex spaces between them are filled by the gelatinous remains of the notochord. Articulation between the arches is made by means of small bony processes, the *zygapophyses* (N. ZYG., H. ZYG.). To the dorsal surface of the centrum is attached, by ligaments in the anterior vertebræ, by *ankylosis* or actual bony union in the posterior, a low *neural arch* (N. A.). This consists in the anterior vertebræ of distinct right and left moieties, and is continued above into a long, slender, double *neural spine* (N. SP.), directed upwards and backwards. To the ventro-lateral region of the vertebra are attached by ligament a pair of long, slender *pleural ribs* (R.) with dilated heads. These curve downwards and backwards between the muscles and the peritoneum, thus encircling the abdominal cavity. In the first two vertebræ they are attached directly to the centrum. In the rest they are attached to short downwardly directed bones, the *parapophyses* (PA. PH.), immovably articulated by broad surfaces to the centrum. At the junction of the neural arch and centrum are attached, also by fibrous union, a pair of delicate *inter-muscular bones* (IM. B.). These extend outwards and backwards in the fibrous septa between the myomeres (p. 86). The first and second abdominal vertebræ bear no ribs. In the last three the neural spines (*B*, N. SP.) are single.

In the caudal vertebræ the outgrowths corresponding to the parapophyses are fused with the centrum and unite in the middle ventral line, forming a *hæmal* arch (*C*, H. A.), Through this run the caudal artery and vein. In the first six caudals each hæmal arch bears a pair of ribs (R.) ; in the rest the arch is produced downwards and backwards into a *hæmal spine* (*D*, H. SP.).

The centra as well as the arches of the vertebræ are formed entirely from the skeletogenous layer, and not from the sheath of the notochord as in elasmobranchs (pp. 231, and 90).

The posterior end of the caudal region is curiously modified for the support of the tailfin. The hindmost centra have their axes not horizontal, but deflected upwards and following the last undoubted centrum is a rod-like

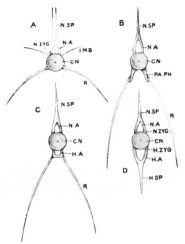

FIG. 203.—*Salmo :* **Vertebræ.** *A*, one of the anterior, and *B*, one of the posterior trunk vertebræ; *C*, one of the anterior, and *D*, one of the posterior caudal vertebræ. CN. centrum; IM. B. intermuscular bone; H. A. hæmal arch; H. SP. hæmal spine; H. ZYG. hæmal zygapophysis; N. A. neural arch; N. SP. neural spine; N. ZYG. neural zygapophysis; PA. PH. parapophysis; R. pleural rib.

structure, the *urostyle* (Fig. 204). This terminal structure consists of the partly ossified end of the notochord, which has thus precisely the same upward flexure as in dogfishes. The neural and hæmal spines of the last five vertebræ are very broad and closely connected with one another. They are more numerous than the centra ; and three or four hæmal arches are attached to the urostyle. In this way a firm vertical plate of bone is formed, to the edge of which the caudal fin-rays are attached fanwise in a symmetrical manner. It will be obvious, however, that this homocercal tail-fin is really quite as asymmetric as the heterocercal fin of dogfishes, since, as its morphological axis is constituted by the notochord, nearly the whole of its rays are, in strictness, ventral.

The *skull* (Fig. 205) is an extremely complex structure, composed of mingled bone and cartilage. The cartilage has no superficial mosaic of lime-salts such as we find in many Chondrichthyes, but certain portions of it are replaced by *cartilage (endochondral) bones*, and there are in addition numerous investing *membrane* or *dermal bones* developed in the surrounding connective-tissue. As in dogfishes, the skull is divided into cranium, upper and lower jaws, with their suspensory apparatus, and hyoid and branchial arches.

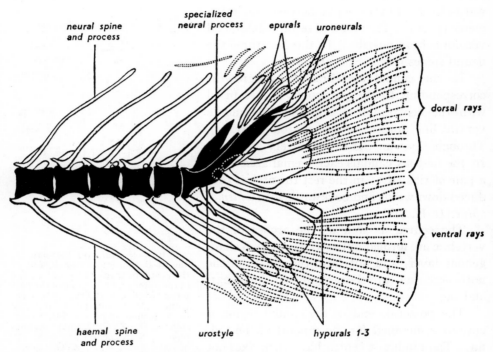

FIG. 204.—**Teleostei: Caudal skeleton.** The homocercal tail and its supports in a typical isospondylid. This form of tail is supported by uroneurals as well as hypurals (cf. p. 283). The number and arrangement of the skeletal elements are of great taxonomic significance. (Modified after Hollister.)

The *cranium* (Fig. 205) is a somewhat wedge-shaped structure, its apex being directed forwards. At first sight the distinction between replacing and investing bones is not obvious. After maceration or boiling, however, certain flat bones (the paired parietals, *par.*, frontals, *fron.*, and nasals, *nas.*, and the unpaired dermethmoid, *d. eth.*) can be easily removed from the dorsal surface as well as two unpaired bones (the parasphenoid, *par. sph.*, and vomer) from the ventral surface. The above are investing bones. They are simply attached to the cranium by fibrous tissue, and can readily be prised off when the latter is sufficiently softened by artificial means. We thus get a clear distinction between the cranium as a whole, or *secondary cranium* (complicated by the presence of investing bones), and the *primary cranium*, *neurocranium* or *chondrocranium* (left by the removal of these bones) which corresponds with the cranium of elasmobranchs.

The chondocranium (Fig. 206, p. 307) contains the same regions as that of *Scyliorhinus*. Posteriorly the *occipital region* surround the foramen magnum. Below that aperture is a single concave *occipital condyle* (for the first vertebra) produced above into an *occipital crest*. The *auditory capsules* project outwards from the occipital region. Between them, on the dorsal surface of the skull, are paired oval *fontanelles* (Fig. 206, *Fo.*). In the entire skull these are closed the frontal bones. The posterior region of the cranial floor is produced downwards into paired longitudinal ridges, enclosing between them a groove which is converted into a canal by the apposition of the parasphenoid bone and serves for the origin of the eye-muscles. In front of the auditory region the cranium is excavated on each side by a large *orbit*. A vertical plate or *interorbital septum* separates the two cavities from one another. In front of the orbital region the cranium broadens out to form the *olfactory capsules*, each excavated by a deep pit for the olfactory sac. Anterior to these is a blunt snout or *rostrum*. The occipital region is formed as usual from the parachordals of the embryonic skull, the auditory region from the auditory capsules, and the rest of the cranium from the trabeculæ.

The *replacing* or endochondral bones, formed as ossifications in the chondrocranium, correspond in essentials with the typical arrangement already described (pp. 95–97). In the occipital region are four bones. These are the *basi-occipital*, forming the greater part of the occipital condyle and the hinder region of the *basis cranii* or skull-floor ; the paired *ex-occipitals* (*ex. oc.*), placed one on each side of the foramen magnum and meeting both above and below it ; and the *supra-occipital* (*s. oc.*), forming the occipital crest already mentioned. Each auditory capsule is ossified by five bones—*i.e.* two more than the typical number (p. 96). These are 1. the *pro-otic* (*pr. ot.*), in the anterior region of the capsule, uniting with its fellow of the opposite side in the floor of the braincase, just in front of the basi-occipital ; 2. the *opisthotic*, in the posterior part of the capsule, external to the ex-occipital ; 3. the *sphenotic* (*sph. ot.*) (partly an investing bone), above the pro-otic and forming part of the boundary of the orbit ; 4. the *pterotic* (*pt. ot.*) (also partly an investing bone), above the ex-occipital and opisthotic, forming a distinct lateral ridge and produced behind into a prominent *pterotic process*; and 5. the *epiotic* (*epi. ot.*), a small bone, wedged in between the supra- and ex-occipitals and pterotic, and produced into a short *epiotic process*. On the external face of the auditory capsule, at the junction of the pro-, sphen-, and pter-otics, is an elongated facet (Fig. 205, *hyo. m.*). This is covered with cartilage and serves for the articulation of the hyomandibular.

The trabecular region of the cranium contains six bones. Immediately in front of the conjoined pro-otics, forming the anterior end of the basis cranii,

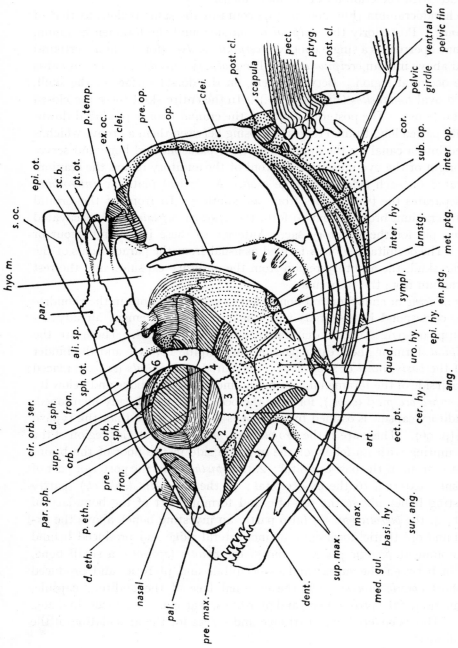

FIG. 205.—**Teleostei: Skull showing relationship with pectoral girdle.** This skull combines characters which would not be found together in any order. For example, the median gular is present only in the most primitive isospondylid fishes. In these the pelvic and pectoral girdles are not in contact; the anterior position of the pelvic girdle (as shown) being characteristic of more highly organised orders. It is unlikely that the bones of the circumorbital series are homologous with similarly named elements in higher vertebrates. Reading clockwise from snout: *pre. max.* premaxilla; *pal.* palatine; *nasal; d.eth.* dermethmoid; *p.eth.* parethmoid; *pre. fron.* prefrontal; *par. sph.* parasphenoid; *supr. orb.* supraorbitals; *orb. sph.* orbitosphenoid; *cir. orb. ser.* circumorbital series (see below); *d. sph.* dermos-

is a small unpaired Y-shaped bone, the *basisphenoid*. Above it, and forming the anterior parts of the side-walls of the brain-case, are the large paired *pterosphenoids* (*ali. sph.*). In the interorbital septum is a median vertical bone, representing fused *orbitosphenoids* (*orb. sph.*). Lastly, in the posterior region of each olfactory capsule, and forming part of the boundary of the orbit, is the *lateral-ethmoid* (*ec. eth.*), (not shown in Fig. 205).

The investing bones already referred to are closely applied to the roof and floor of the chondrocranium. They modify its form considerably by projecting beyond the cartilaginous part, and by concealing apertures and cavities. The great *frontals* (*fron.*) cover the greater part of the roof of the skull, concealing the fontanelles, and furnishing roofs to the orbits. Immediately behind the frontals is a pair of very small *parietals* (*par.*). In front of them is an unpaired *dermethmoid* (*d. eth.*). To the sides of this are attached a pair of small *nasals*. On the ventral surface is the large *parasphenoid* (*par. sph.*), which forms a kind of clamp to the whole cartilaginous skull-floor. In front of and below the parasphenoid is the toothed *vomer*. Encircling the orbit is a ring of scale-like bones, the *circumorbitals* (*c. orb. ser.*).

In the jaws, as in the cranium, we can see both primary and secondary structures. The primary upper jaw or *palatoquadrate* is homologous with the upper jaw of the dogfishes. However, instead of remaining cartilaginous, it is ossified by three replacing bones. The toothed *palatine* (*pal.*) is situated in front, articulating with the olfactory capsule. In the 'pterygoid' region the only replacing bone is the *metapterygoid* (*met. ptg.*) projecting upwards from the quadrate, but between the quadrate and the palatine are two investing bones, the *ectopterygoid* (*ect. pt.*) on the ventral, and the *entopterygoid* (*en. ptg.*) on the dorsal edge of the original cartilaginous bar. The *quadrate* (*quad.*), at the posterior end of the latter, furnishes a converse condyle for the articulation of the lower jaw.

These bones, do not, however, enter into the gape, and so do not constitute the actual upper jaw of the adult fish ; external to them are two large investing bones, the *premaxilla* (*pre. max.*) and the *maxilla* (*max.*), which together form the actual or secondary upper jaw. Both these bones bear many teeth. A

---

phenotic; *fron.* frontal; *sph. ot.* sphenotic; *ali. sp.* pterosphenoid ('alisphenoid'); *par.* parietal; *hyo. m.* hyomandibular; *s. oc.* supraoccipital; *epi. ot.* epiotic; *sc. b.* scale bone (supratemporal); *pt. ot.* pterotic (supratemporal in tetrapods); *p. temp.* post-temporal; *ex. oc.* exoccipital; *s. clei.* supracleithrum; *pre. op.* preopercular; *op.* opercular; *clei.* cleithrum; *post. cl.* postcleithrum; *scapula; pect.* pectoral fin; *ptryg.* pterygials; *ventral or pelvic fin*; *pelvic girdle*; *cor.* coracoid; *sub. op.* subopercular; *inter. op.* interopercular; *inter. hy.* interhyal; *brnstg.* branchiostegals; *met. ptg.* metapterygoid; *sympl.* symplectic; *en. ptg.* entopterygoid (true pterygoid); *epi. hy.* epihyal; *uro. hy.* urohyal; *quad.* quadrate; *ang.* angular; *cer. hy.* ceratohyal; *ect. pt.* ectopterygoid ('pterygoid'); *art.* articular; *sur. ang.* surangular; *basi. hy.* basihyal; *max.* maxilla; *med. gul.* median gular; *sup. max.* supramaxilla; *dent.* dentary.

The *circumorbital series* consists of lachrymal (1), jugal (2), suborbitals (3–5), dermosphenotic (6), postfrontal, supraorbital, and prefrontal. The *opercular series* consists of opercular, subopercular, interopercular, and branchiostegals. The vomer is not visible and the basioccipital is hidden by the opercular series. The alisphenoid is often called the pterosphenoid and the surangular is often called the supra-angular. (Modified after Gregory.)

small scale-like bone, the *supramaxilla*, is sometimes attached to the posterior end of the maxilla.

The lower jaw is similarly modified. Articulating with the quadrate is a large bone, the *articular (art.)*. This continued forwards by a narrow pointed rod of cartilage which is the unossified distal end of the primary lower jaw or Meckel's cartilage. The articular bone is its ossified proximal end. Therefore this bone is a replacing bone. Ensheathing Meckel's cartilage and forming the main part of the secondary lower jaw is a large toothed investing bone, the *dentary (dent.)*. A small investing bone, the *surangular (sur. ang.)*, is attached to the lower and hinder end of the articular.

The connection of the upper jaw with the cranium is effected partly by the articulation of the palatine with the olfactory region, partly by means of a *suspensorium* formed of two bones separated by a cartilaginous interval. The larger, usually called the *hyomandibular (hyo. m.)*, articulates with the auditory capsule by the facet already noticed. The small, pointed *symplectic (sympl.)* fits into a groove in the quadrate. Both bones are attached by fibrous tissue to the quadrate and metapterygoid (*met. ptg.*). In this way the suspensorium and palatoquadrate together form an inverted arch. This is freely articulated in front with the olfactory, and behind with the auditory capsule. The total result is an extremely mobile upper jaw. As its name implies, the hyomandibular (together with the symplectic) is commonly held to be the upper end of the hyoid arch and the homologue of the hyomandibular of Chondrichthyes. However, there is some reason for thinking that it really belongs to the mandibular arch, and corresponds with the dorsal and posterior part of the triangular palatoquadrate of Holocephali. A perforation in the latter would convert it into an inverted arch having the same general relations as the upper jaw *plus* suspensorium of the Trout, but fused, instead of articulated, with the cranium at either extremity.

The hyoid cornu is articulated to the cartilaginous interval between the hyomandibular and symplectic through the intermediation of a small rod-like bone, the *interhyal (int. hy.)*, which is an ossification in a ligament. It is ossified by three bones: an *epihyal (epi. hy.)* above, then a large *ceratohyal (cer. hy.)*, and below a small double *hypohyal*. The right and left hyoid bars are connected by a keystone-piece, the unpaired *basihyal (basi-hy.)*, which supports the tongue. This bone is toothed in *Salmo trutta*.

Connected with the hyomandibular and hyoid cornu are certain investing bones serving for the support of the operculum. The *opercular* (Fig. 205, *op.*) is articulated with a backward process of the hyomandibular. The *sub-opercular (sub. op.)* lies below and internal to the opercular. The *inter-opercular (inter. op.)* fits between the lower portions of the three preceding bones, and is attached by ligament to the angle of the mandible. The sabre-shaped *branchiostegal rays* are attached along the posterior border of the epi- and cerato-hyal.

Twelve such rays occur in *S. trutta*. Below the basihyal is an unpaired bone, the *urohyal* (*uro. hy.*).

There are five branchial arches, diminishing in size from before backwards. The first three present the same segments as in dogfishes: *pharyngobranchial* above, then *epibranchial*, then a large *ceratobranchial*, and a small *hypobranchial* below (Fig. 206; and Fig. 158, p. 234). The right and left hypobranchials of each arch are connected by an unpaired *basibranchial*. All these segments are ossified by replacing bones. The basibranchials are connected with one another and with the basihyal by cartilage so as to form a median ventral bar in the floor of the pharynx. In the fourth arch the pharyngobranchial is

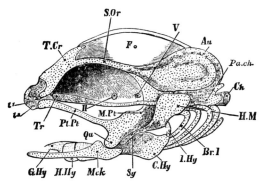

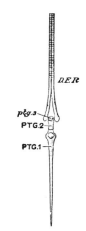

FIG. 206.—*Salmo*: **Skull of juvenile.** Second week after hatching with investing bones removed. *Au.* auditory capsule; *Br.* 1, first branchial arch; *Ch.* notochord; *C. Hy.* hyoid cornu; *Fo.* fontanelle; *G. Hy.* basihyal; *H. Hy.* hypohyal; *H. M.* hyomandibular; *1. Hy.* interhyal; *l*¹, *l*², labial cartilages; *Mck.* Meckel's cartilage; *M. Pt.* metapterygoid region of primary upper jaw; *Pa. ch.* parachordal; *Pl. Pt.* palatopterygoid region; *Qu.* quadrate region; *S.Or.* supraorbital region of cranium; *Sy.* symplectic region of suspensorium; *T. Cr.* cranial roof; *Tr.* trabecula; *II*, optic foramen; *V*, trigeminal foramen. (After Parker and Bettany.)

FIG. 207.—*Salmo*: **Dermal fin-ray and its supports.** *D. F. R.* Proximal part of dermal fin-ray minus distal tip; PTG. 1, proximal pterygiophore (interspinous bone) embedded in body muscle; PTG. 2, middle pterygiophore; *ptg. 3*, distal pterygiophore (cartilaginous.)

unossified and the hypobranchial absent. The fifth arch is reduced to a single bone on each side. Small spine-like ossifications are attached in a single or double row along the inner aspect of each of the first four arches. These are the *gill-rakers*. They serve as a sieve to prevent the escape of food through the gill-slits and to protect the gill filaments.

The comparison of this singularly complex skull with the comparatively simple one of a dogfish or sting-ray is made easier by the examination of the skull of a young trout or other bony fish. In the young salmon, for example, at about the second week after hatching, the only ossifications are a few investing bones. When these are removed we get a purely cartilaginous skull (Fig. 206), exactly comparable with that of a shark or ray. The cranium is devoid of replacing bones and divisible only into regions. The upper jaw is an unossified palatoquadrate (*Pl. Pt., M. Pt., Qu.*), and the lower jaw (*Mck.*) a large Meckel's cartilage. The suspensorium is an undivided hyomandibular (*H.M.*), and the hyoid and branchial arches are unsegmented.

The *first dorsal* and the *anal fins* are supported each by a triple set of pterygiophores, so that the fin-skeleton is multiserial, as in a dogfish. The proximal series consists of slender bony rays—the *interspinous bones* (Fig. 207, PTG. 1), lying in the median plane, between the muscles of the right and left sides. These are more numerous than the myomeres of the regions in which they occur. Their distal ends are broadened, and with them are connected the second series (PTG. 2) in the form of small dice box-shaped bones. To these, finally, are attached small nodules of cartilage (*ptg. 3*) forming the third series of radials. The *dermal fin-rays*, or *lepidotrichia* (*D.F.R.*), which lie in the substance of the fin itself, are slender bones, jointed together, and mostly branched in the sagittal plane. Each is formed of distinct right and left pieces, in close contact

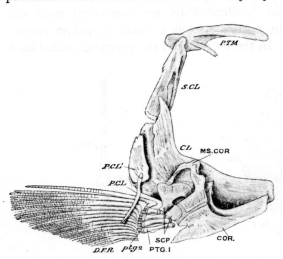

FIG. 208.—*Salmo* : **Pectoral girdle and fin.** *Left*, from inner aspect. *CL.* = cleithrum; COR. coracoid; *D.F.R.* dermal fin-rays; MS. COR. mesocoracoid; *P.CL., P.CL.',* postclavicles; PTG. 1, proximal, and *ptg. 2,* distal pterygiophores; *P.TM.* post-temporal; *S.CL.* supraclavicle; SCP. scapula.

for the most part, but diverging below to form a forked and dilated end, which fits over one of the cartilaginous nodules (*ptg. 3*). In the caudal fin (Fig. 204) the dermal rays are similarly seated on the broad hæmal arches of the posterior caudal vertebræ. The second dorsal or adipose fin (p. 299) has, as already noticed, no bony support.

The *shoulder-girdle* (Fig. 208), like the skull, consists of a *primary shoulder-girdle* (homologous with that of a dogfish), and, in addition, several investing bones. The primary shoulder-girdle in the young fish is formed of distinct right and left bars of cartilage, which do not unite with one another ventrally. In the adult each bar is ossified by three bones. These are 1. a *scapula* (*SCP.*), situated dorsally to the glenoid facets, and developed partly as a replacing, partly as an investing bone; 2. a *coracoid* (*COR.*), situated ventrally to the glenoid facet; and 3. a *mesocoracoid* (*MS. COR.*), situated above the coracoid and anterior to the scapula. Externally to these is a very large investing bone, the *cleithrum* (*CL.*). This extends downwards under the throat. Its dorsal end is connected by means of a *supra-clavicle* (*S. CL.*) to a forked bone, the *post-temporal* (*P.TM.*), one branch of which articulates with the epiotic, the other with the pterotic process. To the inner surface of the cleithrum are attached two flat scales of bone (*P. CL'.*), with a slender rod-like *post-clavicle* (*P. CL.*) passing backwards and downwards among the muscles.

The structure of the *pectoral fin* is very simple. Articulated to the posterior border of the scapula and coracoid are four dice box-shaped bones, the proximal pterygiophores or radials (PTG. 1), followed by a row of small nodules of cartilage (*ptg. 2*) representing distal pterygiophores. The main body of the fin is supported by dermal fin rays. These resemble those of the median fins and have their forked ends articulated with the distal pterygiophores. The first ray, however, is larger than the rest, and articulates directly with the scapula.

There is no pelvic girdle, its place being taken by a large, flat, triangular bone, the *basipterygium* (Fig. 209, B. PTG.). This probably represents fused proximal pterygiophores. To its posterior border are attached three partly ossified nodules, the distal pterygiophores (PTG.), and with these the dermal fin-rays are articulated. The adipose lobe of the pelvic fin is supported by a small scale-like bone.

The **muscles** of the trunk and tail are arranged, as in sharks, in zigzag myomeres (p. 86). There are small muscles for the fins, and the head has a complex musculature for the movement of the jaws, hyoid, operculum, and branchial arches.

FIG. 209.—*Salmo :* **Pelvic fin and skeleton.** Left, from dorsal aspect. B. PTG. basipterygium; D. F. R. dermal fin-rays; PTG. distal pterygiophores.

The **cœlom** is divisible into a large *abdomen* (Fig. 210) containing the chief viscera, and a small *pericardial cavity* (containing the heart) situated below the branchial arches.

Alimentary Canal and Associated Structures.—The large *mouth* (Figs. 205 and 210) has numerous small, recurved, conical teeth, borne, as already mentioned, on the premaxillæ, maxillæ, palatines, prevomer, dentaries, and basihyal. They obviously serve chiefly to prevent the escape of the slippery animals used as food. The food—small arthropods and fishes—is swallowed whole with the assistance of an enzyme-free mucus. The *pharynx* (*ph.*) is perforated on each side by four vertically elongated gill-slits, fringed by the bony tooth-like gill-rakers. Each gill-slit is >-shaped, the epihyal being bent upon the ceratohyal so that the dorsal and ventral moieties of the branchial arches touch one another when the mouth is closed.

The pharynx leads into a short *œsophagus* (*gul.*) which ends in a sphincter which probably prevents the entry of the respiratory water-current into the stomach. The U-shaped *stomach* (*st.*) consists of a wide cardiac, and a narrow

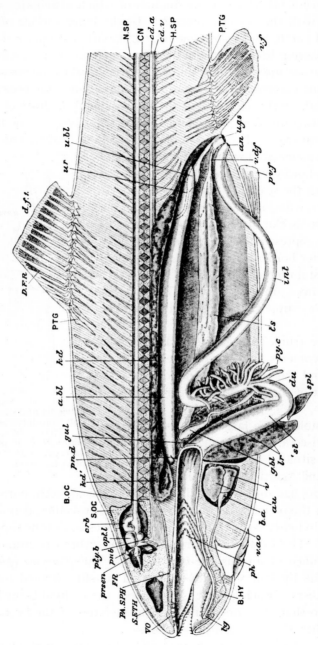

FIG. 210.—*Salmo*: **Skeletal and Visceral relationships.** *a. bl.* air-badder (opened); *an.* anus; *au.* atrium; *b. a.* bulbus arteriosus; B.HY. basihyal; B.OC. basi-occipital; *cd. a.* caudal artery; *cd. v.* caudal vein; CN. centrum; *crb.* cerebellum; *d. f.* I, first dorsal fin; *D. F. R.* dermal fin-rays; *du.* duodenum; *F.R.* frontal; *g. bl.* gall-bladder; *gul.* gullet; H. SP. hæmal spine; *int.* intestine; *kd.* kidney; *kd'.* degenerate portion of kidney; *lr.* liver; N. SP. neural spine; *opt. l.* optic lobes; *PA. SPH.* parasphenoid; *ph.* pharynx; *pn. b.* pineal body; *pn. d.* bristle passed into pneumatic duct; *prsen.* prosencephalon; *pty. b.* pituitary body; PTG. pterygiophores; *pv. f.* pelvic fin; *py. c.* pyloric cæca; S. *ETH.* supraethmoid; S. OC. supraoccipital; *spl.* spleen; *st.* stomach; *tg.* tongue; *ts.* testis; *u. bl.* urinary bladder; *u. g. s.* urinogenital sinus; *ur.* urinary duct; *v.* ventricle; *v. ao.* ventral aorta; *v. df.* vas deferens; *v. f.* ventral fin; *VO.* vomer.

pyloric, division. In the stomach true gastric digestion occurs. The entry from the pyloric division of the stomach to the anterior end of the intestine is guarded by a ring-shaped *pyloric valve*. The *intestine* passes at first forwards as the *duodenum* (*du.*), then becomes bent upon itself (*int.*) and passes backwards, without convolution, to the anus (*an.*). Its posterior portion has the mucous membrane raised into prominent annular ridges which increase its absorptive surface but do not constitute a spiral valve such as occurs in elasmobranchs. Opening into the duodenum are about forty blind glandular tubes, the pyloric cæca (*py. c.*).

The *liver* (*lr.*) is imperfectly divided into right and left lobes. There is a large *gall-bladder* (*g. bl.*). A diffuse and relatively inconspicuous *pancreas* occurs. This exhibits the compound structure and function remarked on in elasmobranchs (p. 239), producing both digestive enzymes and the hormone insulin or its homologue. Attached by peritoneum to the fundus of the stomach occurs a large *spleen* (*spl.*), a capacious sac of blood-storage, and other functions that is functionally associated not with the alimentary canal, but with the blood-vascular system (p. 312). The stomach, duodenum, and pyloric cæca are surrounded by loose folds of peritoneum loaded with fat. No rectal gland occurs.

Lying between alimentary canal and kidneys, and extending the whole length of the abdominal cavity, is the *swim-bladder* (*a. bl.*), a shiny thin-walled sac. This is essentially a hydrostatic organ (p. 339). It contains air of high oxygen content. In the trout it is *physostomatous* (as opposed to *physoclistous*)— it is 'open'. Thus, anteriorly, its ventral wall has a small aperture leading, by a short, thin *pneumatic duct* (*pn. d.*), into the œsophagus on the dorsal side somewhat to the right of the middle line.

Respiratory System.—There are four pairs of gills, each with a double row of branchial filaments, united proximally, but having their distal ends free : interbranchial septa are practically obsolete (Fig. 73, p. 106). The gills are borne on the first four branchial arches, the fifth arch bearing none. On the inner surface of the operculum is a comb-like body, the *pseudobranchia*, formed of a single row of branchial filaments, and representing either the vestigial gill (hemibranch) of the mandibular arch or the spiracular hemibranch. For the course of the respiratory current, See Fig. 76, p. 106.

Blood-vascular System.—Like that of the cartilaginous fishes, this consists of a 'single circulation'. The *heart* (Fig. 210) consists of *sinus venosus, atrium* (*au.*), and *ventricle* (*v.*). There is no conus arteriosus, but the proximal end of the ventral aorta is dilated to form a thin-walled, elastic *bulbus arteriosus* (*b. a.*), a structure which differs from a conus in being part of the aorta, and not the heart. Although itself not muscular, the teleost *bulbus* dilates and contracts as a response to the beat of the single ventricle, and by this means pressure through the short aorta to the gills is maintained. As in the elasmobranchs, the heart action is regulated by a depressor nerve of vagal origin. There is no corresponding sympathetic innervation.

In accordance with the atrophy of the hyoid gill, there is no afferent branchial artery to that arch, but a *hyoidean artery* springs from the ventral end of the first efferent branchial and passes to the pseudobranch (see p. 230), which thus only receives oxygenated blood. Despite its gill-like structure, the pseudobranch does not subserve any respiratory function. The right branch of the caudal vein is continued directly into the corresponding cardinal. The left breaks up in the kidney, forming a renal-portal system. There are no lateral veins, but the blood from the paired fins is returned to the cardinals. It will be seen that although the veins are wide, the elaborate system of venous sinuses seen in the elasmobranchs is lacking. The exact means—muscular or otherwise (p. 110)—by which venous return is achieved are imperfectly known. The red blood cells are, as in other fishes, oval nucleated discs carrying the red respiratory pigment hæmoglobin (see, however, p. 343).

In addition, nucleated reticulocytes and thrombocytes, as well as coarse and fine granulocytes and various lymphocytes, occur. No white cell, however, appears to exhibit the characteristics of mammalian monocytes. Coarse granulocytes commonly escape from the blood-vessels and are observed in large numbers in the intestinal mucosa and submucosa, gill epithelia and peritoneum. Hæmatopoiesis occurs chiefly in bony fishes in the kidney intertubular tissue and in the spleen. In some teleosts (*e.g.* Roach) this activity may be confined to the kidney, and in others (*e.g.* Perch) to the spleen. In the trout both organs are involved. In the maturation of the teleost erythrocyte there is a progressive enlargement of the cell; in birds and mammals its size decreases.

Nervous System.—The brain (Fig. 211), though in general not unlike that of elasmobranchs, is very different in detail and is in many respects of a distinctly more specialised type. The *cerebellum* (*HH.*) is very large and bent upon itself. The *optic lobes* (*MH.*) are also of great size. There is experimental evidence that this highly developed mid-brain region is of great importance in connection with learning, association, and the performance of relatively complex acts of behaviour. The *diencephalon* is much reduced and, indeed, is indicated dorsally only as the place of origin of the pineal body (*G.p.*). Ventrally occur large bean-shaped *lobi inferiores*. The infundibulum between the lobi inferiores gives attachment to the pituitary gland (*Hyp.*). Hence, seen from above, the small undivided *prosencephalon* (*VH.*) comes immediately in front of the mid-brain. The original roof, an *area* equivalent to the pallium of other vertebrates, has grown laterally, stretching the midline into a non-nervous structure. Frequently *olfactory bulbs* are situated in close apposition with the fore-brain, without intervening olfactory tracts such as are present in *Scyliorhinus*, but they are nearly as large as the corpora striata. Each contains a cavity (rhinocœle) communicating with the undivided ventricle of the fore-brain. Three transverse bands of fibres connect the right and left halves of the fore-brain, an *anterior commissure* joining the corpora striata, a *posterior commissure* situated just behind the origin of the pineal

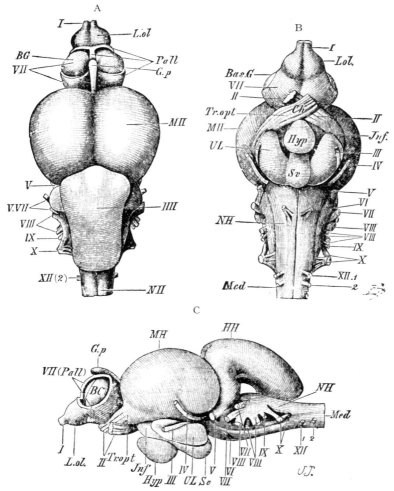

FIG. 211.—*Salmo:* **Brain and cranial nerves.** Dorsal (*A*), ventral (*B*), and lateral (*C*) views. *BG., Bas. G.* corpora striata; *ch.* crossing of optic nerves; *G. p.* pineal body; *HH.* cerebellum; *Hyp.* pituitary body; *Inf.* infundibulum; *L. ol.* olfactory bulbs; *Med.* spinal cord; *MH.* optic lobes; *NH.* medulla oblongata; *Pall.* non-nervous roof of prosencephalon (*not* equivalent to the pallium of other groups); *Sv.* saccus vasculosus; *Tr. opt.* optic tracts; *UL.* lobi inferiores; *VH.* prosencephalon; *I—X*, cerebral nerves; *XII.* 1, first spinal (hypoglossal) nerve; 2, second spinal nerve. (After Wiedersheim.)

body, and an *inferior commissure* in front of the infundibulum. The *pineal body* (*G. p.*) is rounded and placed at the end of a hollow stalk. No trace of any optic structure remains within. A shorter offshoot of the roof of the diencephalon may perhaps represent a rudimentary pineal eye. There is considerable evidence of a direct photo-receptive function in the diencephalon of certain fishes (p. 345). Behind the pituitary body is a *saccus vasculosus* (*s. v.*). This organ, as we have seen, is one of the cerebral specialisations that is pronounced in both cartilaginous and bony fishes. It may be a pressure receptor. The anterior part of the cerebellum (*HH.*) does not bulge outwards in the way it does in a dogfish. Instead, it pushes forwards under the roof of the mesencephalon to form the *valvula cerebelli* (Fig. 212), which is characteristic of teleost fishes. The hinder part of the cerebellum bulges outwards in the usual manner. The *optic nerves* do not form a chiasma, but simply cross one another, or decussate (*Ch.*), on leaving the brain, the right nerve going to the left, and the left nerve to the right eye.

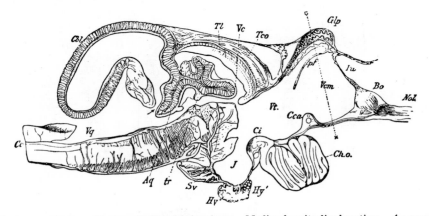

FIG. 212.—*Salmo:* **Brain and adjacent structures.** Median longitudinal section. *Aq.* aqueductus Sylvii; *Bo.* olfactory lobe; *Cbl.* cerebellum; *C. c.* canal of spinal cord; *Cca.* anterior commissure; *Ch. o.* optic nerve; *Ci.* inferior commissure; *Glp.* pineal body; *Hy. Hy'.* hypophysis; *J.* infundibulum; *Nol.* olfactory nerve; *Pa.* roof of telencephalon; *p. f.* velum transversum; *S. v.* saccus vasculosus; *Tl.* torus longitudinalis (of the cerebellum); *Tco.* pia mater; *tr.* crossing fibres of fourth nerve; *V. c.* valvula cerebelli; *V. cm.* ventricle of telencephalon; *V. q.* fourth ventricle; *Vt.* third ventricle. (From Goodrich, after Rabl-Rückhard.)

Autonomic Nervous System.—The autonomic nervous system is far more advanced than that of cartilaginous fishes, and is in some ways suggestive of the basic plan in tetrapods. It will be recalled that in elasmobranchs there is no sympathetic nervous system in the head. In teleosts paired symmetrical chains of *sympathetic ganglia* begin at the trigeminal level (Fig. 211) and run backwards to the end of the tail. A ganglion is connected with each cranial dorsal root, but these receive, not the pre-ganglionic fibres from adjacent segments, but others which emerge with the ventral roots in the trunk region, and therefore pass forwards in the sympathetic chain. The sympathetic trunk is connected with the mixed spinal nerves by *rami communicantes*. Young, who studied the autonomic nervous system of the Mediterranean Star-gazer (*Uranoscopus*), distinguished white and grey rami. (The latter do not occur in selachians.) Each ganglion receives a white ramus containing pre-ganglionic fibres from its spinal nerve and gives a grey ramus to the same nerve. The latter ramus carries post-ganglionic fibres, some of which are concerned with melanophore contraction.

Although there is a highly organised vagal arrangement, there is no apparent sacral parasympathetic system (p. 119), nor have any antagonistic fibres been demonstrated in other cranial nerves, although stimulation of oculomotor nerve-fibres seems to cause an effect opposite to that controlled by sympathetic fibres.

Apart from anatomical work there have been several physiological inquiries (involving electrical and pharmacological stimulation) into the autonomic organisation of teleosts. It would seem that in these fishes there has been developed the relatively clear-cut, and essentially antagonistic, sympathetic and para-sympathetic systems such as occur in the higher chordates (p. 119).

Organs of Special Sense.—The olfactory receptors are paired *olfactory pits*, each of which opens to the external by means of two apertures. Water flows into the anterior aperture, which is provided by a valve, and leaves by the other. The water passes over a series of sensory folds equipped with chemo-receptory cells. In bony fishes, unlike the elasmobranchs, the water current is of purely olfactory significance.

Another kind of chemoreceptor, the *taste buds*, is found in many parts of the body in various bony fishes. In *Trigla*, a gurnard, chemoreceptors, innervated by branches of spinal nerves, occur on their curiously modified pectoral fins, enabling the animal to test the bottom-mud and debris over which it slowly crawls. There is experimental and structural evidence that certain modern bony fishes (*e.g.* Minnow, *Phoxinus*) have taste-receptors located in their tails. The sense of *touch* is well-developed in bony fishes.

The *eye* (Fig. 213) has a very flat *cornea* with which the globular *lens* is almost in contact, so that the anterior chamber of the eye is extremely small. Between the cartilaginous *sclerotic* and the vascular *choroid* is a silvery layer or *argentea* (arg.), which owes its colour to minute crystals in the cells of which it is composed. There are no choroid processes. In the posterior part of the eye, between the choroid and the argentea, is a thickened ring-shaped structure, the *choroid gland*. This surrounds the optic nerve. It is not glandular, but is a complex network of blood-vessels, or *rete mirabile*. It is supplied with blood by the efferent artery of the pseudobranch. Close to the entrance of the optic nerve a vascular fold of the choroid, the *falciform process*, pierces the retina, and is continued to the back of the lens. Here it ends in a muscular knob, the *campanula Halleri* or retractor lentis. The falciform process with the campanula Halleri takes an important part in the process of *accommodation* by which the eye becomes adapted to forming and receiving images of objects at various distances. Accommodation in the trout is effected, not by an alteration in the curvature of the lens, as in higher vertebrates, but by

changes in its position, by which it becomes more approximated towards, or
further withdrawn from, the retina. In bringing about these changes of position the structures in question appear to play the principal part. In the trout,
and indeed in most bony fishes, the pupil size appears to alter very little or
not at all, but in others (as in the elasmobranchs) the iris is equipped with
muscles and is capable of considerable adjustment in aperture. In some

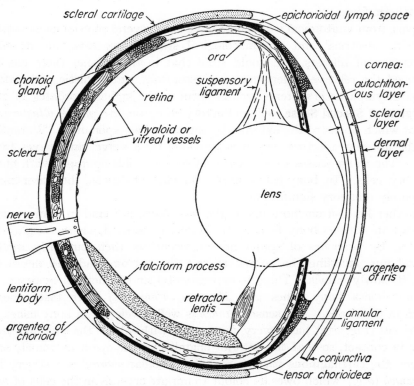

FIG. 213.—**Teleostei: Eye and optic nerve.** Generalised diagram of vertical section. The
argentea, shown in black, contains reflective and not absorptive pigment. Some structures shown
above may be absent in different species. Thus (for example) a falciform process and a system of
hyaloid vessels are never simultaneously present, and where the falciform process is lacking the
lentiform body is also absent (Walls). Cf. figures on pp. 191, 273, and 413. (After Walls.)

teleosts contraction of the iris sphincter is controlled by the sympathetic
nervous system, and dilation is brought about by impulses carried by oculomotor fibres. There is evidence that in eels iris adjustment may be under the
direct control of light.

The organ of *audio-equilibrium* (Fig. 214) possesses three *otoliths* (*ot.* 1–3),
of which one, the *sagitta* (*ot.* 1), is relatively large and may be as much as 6 mm.
in length. It almost fills the sacculus. Another otolith, the *asteriscus* (*ot.* 2), is
a small granule lying in the lagena or rudimentary cochlea. The third, the

lapillus (*ot.* 3), is placed in the utriculus close to the ampullæ of the anterior and horizontal canals. The above-described apparatus apparently shows a great advance on that of selachians. Bony fishes undoubtedly hear with great discrimination, despite the absence of the organ of Corti (p. 146). It would seem that in bony fishes the pars inferior (of the labyrinth) as a whole is probably the sound-receptor. In a relatively small bony fish it is not easy experimentally to assess the relative contributions of different auditory structures, but there is evidence that both lagena and sacculus are involved in normal performance. Destruction of either, however, still leaves considerable, though defective powers. There is some evidence, too, that in some fishes the utriculus plays a part in hearing, and it has been suggested that the air-bladder may be sometimes involved. *Weberian ossicles*, which are modified vertebral elements, connect the air-bladder with the auditory apparatus in some fishes (Ostariophysi).

The *lateral line system* is very well shown in *Salmo*, and indeed it reaches its highest development in actinopterygians. Each individual sensory organ lies in a pit. Pores communicate with the surrounding water. The pits are linked by canals and are innervated by the *lateral line* branch of the vagus. The head, including the lower jaw, is invested with shorter lines (p. 136). A considerable amount of experimental evidence suggests that a primary function of the lateral line system is to gauge pressure-waves, and so no doubt apprise

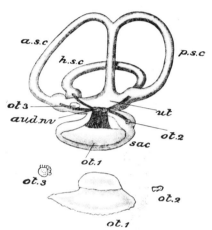

Fig. 214.—*Salmo:* **Audio-equilibration.** Right organs from inner side. The otoliths are shown separately below. *a. s. c.* anterior semi-circular canal; *aud. nv.* auditory nerve; *h. s. c.* horizontal canal; *ot.* 1—3, otoliths; *p. s. c.* posterior canal; *sac.* sacculus; *ut.* utriculus.

the fish of the presence of other individuals (see p. 346).

Osmoregulation and Excretion.—Many teleosts, including trout, can live in either marine or fresh water. There is much evidence that suggests that bony fishes were originally fresh-water animals. Certainly the amount of inorganic salts in the body-fluids of living forms is far less than that in the sea. The ability to change from salt to fresh, or even merely to a brackish-water habitat, imposes the necessity for physiological barriers to maintain the integrity of a fish's internal environment. We have already noted the presence of a largely non-vascular skin, mucous glands which secrete protective slime (p. 82), and a well-developed œsophageal sphincter which keeps the external medium away from the stomach and highly absorptive surface of the gut. The kidney tubules are equipped with a selective apparatus on the general craniate pattern (p. 157) which allows the reabsorption of body-salts essential for osmo-regulation.   Nitrogenous metabolites are excreted largely as ammonia (*ammonotelic* mechanism), though some urea is formed and discharged.   Much of the nitrogenous excretion of aquatic teleosts probably occurs through the gills.

Marine fishes, on the other hand, must keep their body-fluids at the appropriate concentration by swallowing sea-water (including that in their food), by the reabsorption and retention of fluid via the tubules, and by the elimination of salts by means of the gills, urine, and fæces. Glomeruli are fewer or may be entirely absent in some species (see p. 347).   This reduces the loss of fluid. Marine teleosts, as with freshwater forms, still excrete quantities of ammonia, some urea; and many rid themselves of nitrogenous waste in the form of soluble, non-toxic trimethylamine oxide (see also p. 253). Here too an additional excretory mechanism is present in the gills whereby chloride-secreting cells dispose of excess salts which are inevitably absorbed from the surrounding medium.   Hoar has shown that immature salmon (*Oncorhynchus*) go to sea only after the development of salt-secreting cells in their gills.

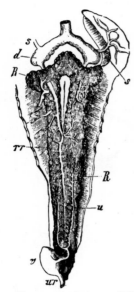

FIG. 215.—*Salmo:* **Kidney and adjacent structures.** *d*, precaval vein; *R* (to the right), kidney; *R* (to the left), degenerate anterior portion of kidney; *rr*, efferent renal vein; *s*. subclavian vein; *u*, *ur*, mesonephric duct; *v*. bladder.   (After Gegenbaur.)

The *kidneys* (Fig. 210, *kd.*, and Fig. 215, *R*) are of great size, extending the whole length of the dorsal wall of the abdomen, above the air-bladder, and partly fused together in the middle line.   They are derived from the mesonephros of the embryo.   Their anterior ends are much dilated and consist in the adult of lymphatic tissue, thus ceasing to discharge a renal function.   The mesonephric ducts (*ur.*) unite into a single tube, which is dilated to form a *urinary bladder* (Fig. 210, *u. bl.*, Fig. 215, *v.*), and discharges into the urinogenital sinus.   This, being mesodermal in origin, is not homologous with the endodermal bladder of higher forms.

Endocrine organs.—See p. 346.

Reproduction.—The *gonads* are of great size in the sexually mature fish.   The *testes* (Fig. 210, *ts.*) are paired, often convoluted, organs, sometimes extending the whole length of the abdominal cavity.   These are the 'soft roes' of commerce. Each is continued posteriorly into a *genital duct* (*v. df.*) which opens into the urinogenital sinus.   The homology of this with the ducts of the primitive nephridial system is uncertain.   The spermatozoa are shed into the external medium.   The ovaries—the 'hard roes'—also run the full length of the abdominal cavity.   They are much wider than the testes and are covered with peritoneum only on their inner or mesial faces.   The numerous ova, which are about 4 mm. in diameter, are discharged when ripe from their outer faces into the cœlom. The anterior wall of the urinogenital sinus is pierced by a pair of *genital pores* through which the ova make their way to the exterior where fertilisation occurs. It seems probable that these pores are degenerate oviducts and therefore in no way homologous with the abdominal pores of the Chondrichthyes (p. 230).

Development.—Fertilisation is external. The male sheds its milt or seminal fluid on the new-laid eggs. The ovum is covered by a thick membrane, the *zona radiata*. This is perforated by an aperture, the *micropyle*, through which a sperm finds access. A superficial layer of protoplasm surrounds a mass of transparent fluid yolk of a pale yellow colour. After fertilisation the protoplasm accumulates to form an elevated area or *germinal disc* at one pole. Here cleavage takes place (Fig. 216, *A, B*) in much the same way as in Chondrichthyes, except that, owing to the smaller proportion of yolk, the resulting blastoderm (*bl.*) and the embryo formed therefrom are proportionally much larger, and the yolk-sac (*y. s.*) correspondingly smaller, than in the two previous classes. Epiboly takes place as in Chondrichthyes, the blastoderm gradually growing

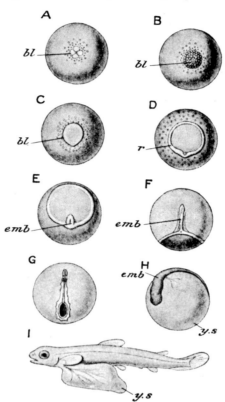

Fig. 216.—*Salmo:* **Development.** *A—H,* before hatching; *I,* shortly after hatching. *bl.* blastoderm; *emb.* embryo; *r.* thickened edge of blastoderm; *y. s.* yolk-sac. (*A—G* after Henneguy.)

round and enclosing the yolk (*C–F*). The embryo (*emb.*) arises as an elevation growing forwards from the thickened

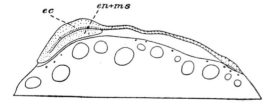

Fig. 217.—*Salmo:* **Development.** Blastoderm (in longitudinal section) at about the stage represented in *D* of Fig. 216. *ec.* ectoderm; *en + ms,* infolding giving rise to endoderm and mesoderm. (After Hertwig.)

edge of the blastoderm. As it increases in length it appears as a clear colourless band (*H, emb.*) winding round the yellow yolk. It is kept in close contact with the yolk by the enclosing zona radiata. There is no open medullary groove :

the nervous system is formed, as in lampreys, from a fold of ectoderm the walls of which are in apposition so as to form a keel-like ridge. The endoderm and mesoderm are formed as a result of a process of infolding of the posterior edge of the blastoderm (Fig. 217). Gradually the head and tail become free from the yolk. At the time of hatching, the yolk-sac (*I*, *y.s.*) is a shoe-shaped body sessile upon the ventral surface of the transparent embryo.

GENERAL ORGANISATION OF ACTINOPTERYGIANS

External Form.—Teleosts never reach the great bulk attained by many of the cartilaginous sharks and rays. They range in size from a tiny Philippine goby (*Mistichthys luzonensis*), about half an inch long, to the spear-fishes (see below) and the freshwater South American *Arapaima gigas*, which is said to attain a length of 15 feet and a weight of about 400 lb. On the other hand, the chondrostean *Huso huso* grows much bigger (p. 283).

A typical form of the bony fishes is represented by that of the Trout (Fig. 201)—a long, compressed body, nearly one third of which is formed by the tail, pointed anterior and posterior ends, a large vertical tail-fin, a head of moderate size, and a terminal mouth. Such a form is eminently fitted for rapid progression through the water. The speed of fishes, incidentally (as of most other animals, pp. 521, 559), is generally exaggerated. A goldfish's maximum speed seems to be about 3·8 m.p.h. and that of a trout 8·5 m.p.h. Salmon generally climb waterfalls by swimming up a more or less continuous stream of water, but they can in fact leap about 6 feet high and 12 feet forward and probably leave the water with a velocity of about 14 m.p.h. A barracuda can travel at some 27 m.p.h. (Gray). From the characteristic fish-form described above there are many striking deviations. The body may be greatly elongated and almost cylindrical, as in the eels, it may be lengthened and strongly flattened from side to side, as in the ribbon-fishes. The head may be of immense proportional size and strongly depressed, as in bottom-living fishes, like the 'Fishing-frog'. In the beautiful reef-fishes the body may be as high as it is long. The mouth sometimes has a ventral position, as in most chondrostei, with the snout prolonged over it. This is the case, for example, in the sturgeons (Fig. 193). In the allied *Polyodon* the snout takes the form of a horizontally flattened shovel-like structure, about one-fourth the length of the body. On the other hand, in the ground-feeding star-gazers and some other spiny-rayed fishes the lower jaw is underhung and the mouth is dorsal.

In the spear-, sword-, and sail-fishes (Istiophoridæ) the snout and upper jaw are forwardly prolonged into a sharp rostrum or beak. The British Museum possesses a fragment of ship's planking through which a transfixing 'spear' has been thrust for a distance of 22 inches. Spear-fishes (*Tetrapturus*) grow to a length of more than 14 feet and may weigh over 1,000 lb. Sword-fishes (*Xiphias*) may be even bigger. Sail-fishes (*Istiophorus*) grow to about 12 feet long; and their fin-rays support a tall, sail-like dorsal fin. In the tropical half-beaks (Hemirhamphidæ) the lower jaw projects and in the garfishes and garpikes both elements do so. Such a projection is different from the snout of sturgeons or *Polyodon*, for it is formed by the elongation of the bones of the jaws (premaxilla, maxilla, dentary, etc.), whereas in the above two chondrostean forms it is the anterior region of the cranium which is prolonged. Still another form of 'snout' is produced in many Teleostei by the great mobility of the jaws, allowing their protrusion as a short tube. In the wrasses or 'lip-fishes' the mouth is bounded by fleshy lips.

The bony fishes show many other interesting examples of structural and physiological *adaptation* to their various environments. The results of this adaptation can be viewed from two aspects. One result is to bring about a resemblance between animals of different phyletic origin that have taken up similar environments, a condition known as *convergent* adaptation. The other aspect, known as *divergent* adaptation, is when related animals have entered different environments and have come to differ superficially from one another, sometimes to a surprising degree.

An illustration of convergent evolution is the superficial resemblance between the extinct holostean *Thoracopterus* and the teleost 'flying fish', *Exocœtus*. By inference from its anatomy and morphology, *Thoracopterus* was a 'flying-fish'. Both this species and the living *Exocœtus* show in their exaggerated, wing-like pectoral fins and hypobatic tails, a striking similarity in general body form, while retaining, of course, the deeper-seated, fundamental osteological differences of their respective classes. Further examples of convergent evolutionary trends towards the 'flying' habit are found in two unrelated teleost genera, *Gasteropelecus*, a South American ostariophysian. and *Pantodon*, an African isospondylid. Here again the species exhibit hypertrophy of the pectoral fins, although the body-form of the two genera is different. Neither *Gasteropelecus* nor *Pantodon* can be considered such efficient gliders as *Exocœtus*, but both can skitter across the surface of the water for fairly considerable distances. Many fishes of very different families, or even classes, have acquired similar body-forms adapted to particular needs, such, for example, as the deep laterally compressed body shown by *Microdon*, an Upper Jurassic holostean, by the extant teleosts *Psettus sebæ* and *Pterophyllum* (the 'Angel-fish') amongst many others.

The teleosts, taken as a whole, in themselves afford an example of adaptive radiation. While retaining their well-defined and diagnostic characters, they have assumed an almost infinite variety of shape and construction in accordance with the many different environments into which they have migrated. Thus we may mention such forms as the flat-fishes, eels, pipe-fishes, porcupine-fishes, sun-fishes, the curious sea-horses, and so on, a small selection out of a vast range. On the other hand, the Ceratioidea ('angler-fishes'), give a good example of adaptive radiation over a small range of structure, and within the limits of a single group (p. 234). Here can be observed the evolution of the tentacle on the head in a diversified manner in various members of a family which otherwise retain a general resemblance to one another.

It is possible that no class of animals exhibit a greater variety of peculiar adaptations than the Actinopterygii. Almost anywhere we look—externally or internally—we will see in one family or other some bizarre or otherwise remarkable structural response to some special mode of life and environmental niche. Notable among these are various devices associated with the eyes. For example, in *Anableps tetrophthalmus* (Fig. 218), the 'Four-eyed Fish', each eye is divided into an upper and lower section for vision above and below water respectively. In *Periophthalmus*, the mud-skippers, or telescope-gobies, the bulbous, independently moving eyes project above the surface of the head.

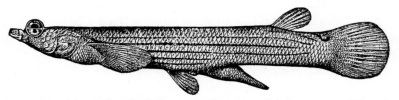

FIG. 218.—**Teleostei: Optic adaptation.** *Anableps tetrophthalmus*, a central and northern South American cyprinodont, is often called the 'Four-eyed Fish'. All three such 'top minnow' species possess two pupils in each eye. The upper (aerial) pupil is the larger and is generally out of the water. The lower (aquatic) pupil allows the animal to use the single ovoid lens to look *under* water. The retina is correspondingly modified. (From *Cambridge Natural History*.)

Tactile processes or *barbels* sometimes arise from the head (Figs. 193, 232). An *operculum* (Fig. 205) is always present. This is supported by a variable number of investing bones and is continued below into a *branchiostegal membrane*, which, except in Crossopterygii (p. 353) and the sturgeons, is supported by bony rays. In *Polypterus* a pair of bony *gular plates* (Fig. 196, B, *jug. pl.*, p. 209) are placed at the lower end of the branchiostegal membrane, between the rami of the mandible. *Amia* has a single plate in the same position. *Spiracles* are present only in *Polypterus* and some sturgeons.

Fins exhibit many modifications. This has been made possible because fishes equipped with a hydrostatic organ (the swim-bladder) can largely dispense with the more elaborate stabilising appendages (such as occur in the elasmobranchs) and so free the fins to subserve other functions. 'Concomitant with the loss of the heterocercal tail in evolution', Harris has explained, 'occurs a rapid and tremendous adaptive radiation of the pectoral fin in form and function.'

A common number of median fins is two dorsals, one caudal, and one anal, but the number of the dorsals may be increased, or there is sometimes a continuous median fin extending along the back and round the end of the tail to the vent. The dorsal fin may be partly or wholly represented by a series of small finlets (Fig. 196). The caudal fin may be diphycercal, heterocercal, or homocercal. In the sea-horses (Fig. 219) it is absent. In these, the tail is prehensile, and is used in the position of rest to coil, in the vertical plane, round seaweeds among which the grotesque form of the fish is very difficult to distinguish. Other fishes have exaggerated appendages which serve as camouflage. One such is the South American Angel-fish (*Pterophyllum*), the coloured streaming filaments of which enable harmonious merging with surrounding waterweeds. The brilliant reef-haunting so-called Butterfly-'cod' (*Pterois*) of the warmer parts of the Pacific and Indian Oceans have colourful and greatly

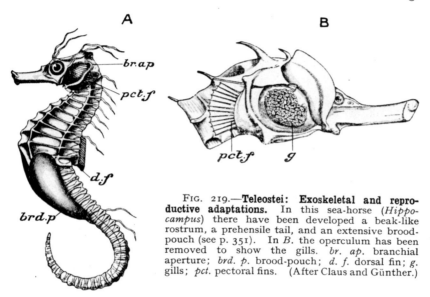

FIG. 219.—**Teleostei: Exoskeletal and reproductive adaptations.** In this sea-horse (*Hippocampus*) there have been developed a beak-like rostrum, a prehensile tail, and an extensive broodpouch (see p. 351). In *B*. the operculum has been removed to show the gills. *br. ap.* branchial aperture; *brd. p.* brood-pouch; *d. f.* dorsal fin; *g.* gills; *pct.* pectoral fins. (After Claus and Günther.)

lengthened fins and a head beset with tassel-like appendages of several vivid colours (p. 344). These trail through the water as the fish moves slowly along. The fin-membranes do not cover the spines, which are capable of producing a stinging wound. When approaching its victim, *Pterois* drifts almost imperceptibly forwards with its long fin-rays waving to and fro. There is evidence that instead of trying to escape, smaller fishes sometimes actually swim towards the predator, and are then engulfed with a single action of remarkable rapidity.

The *dermal rays* of the caudal fins of fishes are always jointed, as in the Trout. In the acanthopterygians more or fewer of the foremost rays of the dorsal, anal, and pelvic fins are unjointed, forming spines (Fig. 202, p. 297), sometimes large and strong enough to recall the dermal defences of Holocephali.

The anterior dorsal fin may attain an immense size, and is subject to curious variations. In the racquet-shaped Fishing-frog, Wide-gab, Allmouth, or Angler (*Lophius piscatorius*) the foremost rays are elongated, and bear lobes or

lures by which small fishes are attracted within reach of the jaws.   The Angler
gets some of its names from the inordinately wide, frog-like gape at the extreme
anterior aspect of its flattened body.   The outline of the lurking fish is partly
obliterated by a series of stumpy dermal appendages.   The pale buccal cavity
is camouflaged by a remarkable fold of pigmented skin on the lower jaw.

FIG. 220.—Teleostei: **Bioluminescence and angling mechanisms in deep-sea forms.**   Angler-
fishes (Ceratioidea).   The larger (nearly 19 inches long) has been referred to as *Galatheathauma
axeli*, the biggest angler yet caught.   It is highly unusual in possessing a large light organ suspended inside its jaws.   The jaws are fringed with powerful stabbing and holding teeth.
    The smaller animal is *Lasiognathus saccostoma*.   The elongated rod is possessed only by females,
which (in many species) carry the dwarf males attached to them (p. 350), at least during the
breeding season.   Some anglers are only ½ inch long.   Many can swallow prey bigger than themselves.   *Note*—The two animals shown above do not necessarily occur in the same environment.
(Redrawn after Bruun, N.B. Marshall.)

The Angler, aided by its weird specialisations, lies perfectly camouflaged and
motionless (except for the slowly-moving lure on its 'line') among weeds or
rock fragments.   The Angler has a formidable armoury of teeth and is able to
engulf fishes, including small sharks, about half its own length.   It also catches
surface-feeding gulls and other large birds.
    Some Angler-fishes (Ceratioidea, Fig. 220) have evolved a luminous lure on
a sometimes extensible rod and line that is probably the modification of a fin-

ray. The luminous organ is attached to the end of an *illicium*—the rod—which has a supporting basal bone and a musculature that raises and lowers it and the terminal light. The rod is usually short, but in a few species it may be several times longer than the fish that bears it. In some species (e.g. *Ceratias holbœlli*) the basal bone, ensheathed in anterior and posterior sockets of tissue, is mobile along a groove extending dorsally along head and body. Moved by a special musculature the basal bone and its lure can be projected back and forth. Bertelsen believes it possible that by such means prey may be lured into the fish's cavernous jaws. In the recently described *Galatheathauma* the forked luminous lure is dorsally situated *inside* the animal's gaping jaws.

In the remoras or sucking-fishes (*Echeneis* and other genera) the anterior dorsal fin is modified into an adhesive vacuum disk by means of which the fish attaches itself to the bodies of sharks, rays, sword-fishes, large bony fishes, turtles, whales, or even boats. Although good swimmers, remoras allow themselves to be carried for long distances, periodically leaving their chosen vehicle in order to capture smaller fishes. A remora is able to withstand the efforts of the host-fish to dislodge and devour it. The sucker of large species can resist a vertical pull of some 40 lb. The natives of some areas tie a line to a remora and then liberate it. When it attaches itself to a turtle they haul both animals to the boat. Occasionally small remoras have been found sheltering within the gills, or even in the buccal cavity of other fishes. An African remora has been seen to follow a man into the shallows in an attempt to fasten itself to his person.

Certain gobies, living in rock-pools from which they might be easily washed, have their pelvic fins modified into a suctorial apparatus. *Periophthalmus* can skip or waddle rapidly over sand and mud above the tide-mark by means of its pectoral fins, which, operated by a special musculature, act as levers and enable the fish to move at considerable speed. Its respiratory system is also remarkably modified (p. 339). Certain gurnards (Triglidæ) 'walk' along the sea-floor by means of elongated, innervated terminations to their pectoral fins which are probably also organs of special sense. In very calm and shallow waters gurnard tracks can be followed as easily as those of a tortoise on a beach.

The Australian hand-fishes (Brachionichthyidæ), related to the angler-fishes, exhibit remarkable specialisations in the same direction. These may occasionally startle novice fishermen by 'walking' along a trawler's deck on their superficially hand- or leg-like fins. These fishes retain the dorso-frontal 'angler' appendage and, in addition (as Gregory has pointed out), have modified the large and continuous pectoral fin (such as occurs in modern batrachoids or frog-fishes) into paired and jointed appendages upon which they progress across the sea-floor. The remarkable wing-like expansions of the pectoral fins in flying-fishes have already been noted. Some species, in favourable air-currents, can skim for several hundred yards over the wave-crests when menaced by larger hunting fishes.

In bony fishes the portion of the *paired fins* visible externally is usually very thin, and supported entirely by dermal rays.   But in the chondrostean *Polypterus* (Fig. 196, p. 290) the rays form a fringe round a thick basal lobe, which is supported by endoskeletal structures.   This condition is an approach to the structure met with in elasmobranchs and holocephalans.   The pectorals, as we have seen, vary considerably in size.   In many fishes the pelvics are reduced to filaments or scales.   The pectorals always retain their normal position, just behind the gill-clefts, but the pelvics often become more or less shifted forwards from beside the vent.   The change in position is least in the palæoniscoid derivatives [1] and in the Isospondyli and allied orders (p. 296), in

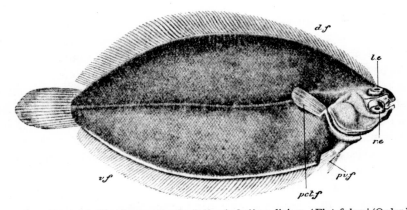

FIG.   221.—**Teleostei: Morphogenetic adaptation to bottom-living.** ' Flat-fishes' (Order Heterosomata) have the sighted upper surface obliteratively pigmented with chromatophores and the lower surface usually pallid.   Larvæ at first swim near the surface and possess bilaterally placed eyes.   Soon an area of cranial cartilage (supraorbital bar) is resorbed on one side and the adjacent eye migrates through a gap between the lateral ethmoid and the otic capsule over the dorsal surface to the opposite supraorbital bar, both eyes taking up the positions shown.   Ossification now occurs.   Other striking modifications occur.   The animal surveys the sandy bottom by raising its eyes slightly and moving them independently.   The species shown is *Glyptocephalus cynoglossus* (from right side). *d. f.* dorsal fin; *l. e.* left eye; *pct. f.* pectoral fin; *pv. f.* pelvic fin; *r. e.* right eye; *v. f.* ventral fin.   (After Cuvier.)

which these fins usually lie between the middle of the abdomen and the anus, and are *abdominal* in position.   In a large proportion of the fishes in the remaining teleost orders they come to be placed almost beneath the pectorals (Fig. 201, *pv. f.*), when their position is called *thoracic*, or on the throat, when they are said to be *jugular* in position.

A very remarkable deviation from the typical form occurs in the flat-fishes (Heterosomata).   The body (Fig. 221) is very deep and strongly compressed : the fish habitually rests on the bottom, in some species on the right, in others on the left side, partly covering itself with sand, and occasionally swimming with an undulating movement.   The under side is usually unpigmented, the

---

[1] The expression *palæoniscoid derivative* will be used in place of the archaic and misleading term 'ganoid'.   It should be remembered, of course, that all extant bony fishes (excluding crossopterygians, p. 353) are probably ultimately derived from the Palæoniscoidea (p. 285).

upper side dark and camouflaged. The eyes (*r. e., l. e.*) are both on the upper or dark-coloured side, and the skull is distorted so as to adapt the orbits to this change of position. The abdominal cavity is very small, the anus placed far forward, and the dorsal and anal fins are sometimes continuous.

Many shore-fishes exhibit protective characters, the tints and markings of the skin being harmonised with those of the rocks and sea-weeds, among which they live. The obliterative effect may be heightened by fringes and lobes of skin resembling seaweed. The colours are often adaptable. Trout, for instance, alter colour by the contraction or expansion of melanophores, according to whether the streams in which they live have a muddy or a sandy bottom. Teleost melanophores are innervated. Contraction of the pigment within the melanophores causes a paling of the skin. A body of experimental evidence suggests that darkening is caused by a secretion, from the posterior pituitary gland. The precise mechanism by which the internal neurohormonal mechanism is controlled by the environment is not understood (see however, p. 345).

In some shore-fishes, such as those of the coral reefs, the colours are of the most brilliant description. Vivid reds, blues, and yellows, spots or stripes of gold or silver, are common. It seems likely that the combination of colours produce a disruptive or obliterative effect and thus, although some fish adornments have threat or recognitional functions, it is by no means certain that coloured adornments appear to them as they do to higher vertebrates. But even if certain fishes do not appreciate colour as such, protection may still be gained if it produces an obliterative pattern. However, the female response to the seasonal appearance of a patch of bright red on the belly of the male Stickleback certainly suggests that, in some teleosts, at least one colour registers in a very positive manner.

In addition to chromatophores, fishes possess a second colour-producing apparatus—the *iridocytes* or reflecting cells. These cells, which contain *guanin* crystals, occur either immediately above or below the scales. Below the scales they are responsible for the silvery or white *argenteum layer*. When above the scales they alter light by interference and give rise to a characteristic iridescence. Some colours are produced by the combination of iridocytes and chromatophores.

Many deep-sea Teleostei are luminescent. In some species definite *luminous organs* (Fig. 222) are arranged in longitudinal rows along the body, each provided with a lens and other accessory parts, not unlike those of the eye, the whole organ having the character of a minute lantern. *Pachystomias* has a pair of relatively complex luminescent organs under each eye. An arrangement such as this occurs in several forms, giving the impression of a small searchlight. The Hatchet-fish (*Argyropelecus*) presents a dazzling spectacle, with much of its lateral surfaces illuminated by light from rows of photo-organs. The appearance of light can be stimulated by adrenalin injections, electric shocks, or other interference. Some fishes depend for the production of light on the presence of photogenic symbiotic bacteria in specialised areas. Most deep-sea angler-fishes possess luminescent lures (p. 314). There is some evidence that the luminous chin-barbels (Fig. 223) of some of the stomiatoid fishes are not only lures, but are also sensory—that by their means fishes may detect the precise

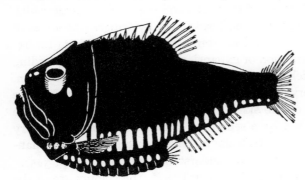

FIG. 222.—**Teleostei: Biolumi-nescence in deep-sea forms.** A hatchet-fish (*Argyropelecus gigas*) with light organs shown in white. Although only 3½ inches long, this is the largest member of the genus. Hatchet-fishes (Sternoptychidæ) are laterally compressed. (After N. B. Marshall.)

whereabouts of moving prey. Many fishes (stomiatoids and others) have, in addition, anterior luminous organs which act as flashing headlights and illuminate the copepods that the fishes engulf as food. The luminescence of some species is at least partly recognitional in function. In others, quick flashing may be defensive, and in yet others the function may be sexual. Teleost luminescence, although sometimes bacterial in origin, is more often produced

FIG. 223.—**Teleostei: Tactile, buccal, and luminal specialisations in deep-sea forms.** *Stomias*, a deep-sea form, possesses a barbel and can swallow prey larger than itself. The white spots are luminous organs. (From Hickson, after Filhol.)

by glandular cells (backed by black pigment and a silvery reflector), and passes through, and is altered by, a filter (*e.g.* red, violet, or green), finally emerging through a lens. A single fish may have thousands of tiny photo-spots. Photophores are richly vascular and there is evidence that some are under hormonal control. In some species innervation has been demonstrated.

Many species of fish possess poison-glands. The Stargazer (*Uranoscopus*) is equipped with poison spines on the operculum and dorsal fins, as is also its relative, the Weever (*Trachinus*). The anglers (*Lophius*) and the Trigger-fishes (*Balistidæ*) are other teleosts with a dorsal armament. Cat-fishes (*Siluroidea*), of wide distribution, possess a dangerous spine on each pectoral fin. The most formidable of all poisonous fishes is *Synanceja horrida*, the notorious Stone-fish of tropical reefs. This has inflicted a foot injury in Man causing total incapacity for months and necessitating an extensive skin graft.

Exoskeleton.—In many bony fishes, such as *Polyodon* (a chondrostean) and many eels, the skin is devoid of hard parts, but in most cases a dermal exoskeleton is present. In *Amia* (Fig. 199, p. 293) and in the majority of Teleostei this takes the form, as in the Trout, of *scales*, rounded plates of bone imbedded in pouches of the dermis and whose exposed areas overlap one another. When the free border of the scales presents an even curve, as in *Amia* and most physostomes and the cods (Anacanthini), they are called *cycloid* scales; when, as in most 'spiny-rayed' fishes, the free edge is produced into small spines (Fig. 224), they are distinguished as *ctenoid* scales. Usually the integument is continued as a thin layer over the surface of the

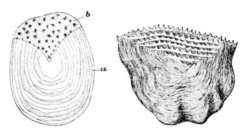

Fig. 224.—**Actinopterygii: Scales.** *Left:* Cycloid scale of *Salmo. a.* anterior portion covered by overlap of preceding scales; *b.* free portion covered only by pigmented epidermis. Such elements occur in some holosteans and most teleosts. *Right: Ctenoid* scale in which the free edge is armed with minute spines. Unlike the placoid scale of selachians (Fig. 59, p. 83) these are generally covered by epidermis. (For cosmoid and ganoid scales see Figs. 60 and 61.)

scales, but in a good many cases this investment is absent. In exceptional cases the scales by a redeposition of bone may be so large and strong as to form a rigid armour. In the sturgeons (Fig. 193) there is a strong armour, formed of stout bony plates, or *scutes*, produced into enamelled spines and articulating with one another by suture. Scutes are also found in many siluroids and in sea-horses and pipe-fishes (Fig. 219) and some Plectognathi; while in other Plectognathi the exoskeleton takes the form, as in globe-fishes (Diodontidæ), of long, outstanding, bony spines. In these so-called Needle-, Porcupine-, or Puffer-fishes, a thin-walled inflatable gastric diverticulum allows the whole body to be puffed up in globular shape, so that the remarkable armoury of dagger- or thorn-like spines can be defensively erected. Such spikes make it difficult for a fish to be swallowed.

Interesting experimental evidence is available on the relative vulnerability to predators of the Three-spined Stickleback (*Gasterosteus aculeatus*), with large spines, the Ten-spined Stickleback (*Pygosteus pungitius*), with small ones, and the Minnow (*Phoxinus phoxinus*), with none at all. *Phoxinus*, *Pygosteus*, and *Gasterosteus* were preferred by Perch and Pike in the order named, but if despined sticklebacks were offered, these were treated as minnows. Of the two sticklebacks, the more formidably armed *Gasterosteus* is the bolder, and nests in open situations (Morris).

In *Polypterus* and *Lepisosteus* are found *ganoid* scales in the form of thick, close-set, rhomboidal plates formed of bone, covered externally by a layer of enamel-like material (*ganoin*) and joined together by pegs and sockets. In some of the palæoniscoid derivatives the anterior fin-rays of both median and paired fins bear a row of spine-like scales called *fulcra* (Fig. 198, *fl.*). True dermal teeth similar to those of the Chondrichthyes occur scattered over the scales and lepidotrichia in some of the bony fishes (e.g. *Lepisosteus*, *Polypterus*).

Endoskeleton.—In the sturgeons the *vertebral column* (Figs. 194, 225) consists of a persistent notochord with cartilaginous arches, and is fused

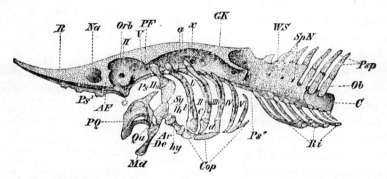

Fig. 225.—**Acipenseroidea: Skull.** Sturgeon. The investing bones have been removed. *a.* pharyngobranchials. *AF.* antorbital process; *AR.* articular; *b.* epibranchial; *c.* cerato-branchial; *C.* notochord; *Cop.* basibranchials; *d.* hypobranchial; *De.* dentary; *GK.* auditory capsule; *HM.* hyomandibular; *hy.* hyoid cornu; *Ih.* interhyal; *Md.* mandible; *Na.* nasal capsule; *Ob.* neural arches; *PF.* postorbital process; *PQ.* palatoquadrate; *Ps. Ps'. Ps''.* para-sphenoid; *Psp.* neural spines; *Qu.* quadrate; *R.* rostrum; *Ri.* ribs; *Sp. N.* foramina for spinal nerves; *Sy.* symplectic; *WS.* vertebral column; *x.* vagus foramen; *I—V,* branchial arches. (After Wiedersheim.)

anteriorly with the cranium. In the remaining orders bony vertebræ are present. The centra are biconcave, except in some eels, in which the anterior face is flat or even convex, and in *Lepisosteus*, in which the anterior face is distinctly convex. Vertebræ of this form, *i.e.* having the centrum convex in front and concave behind, are called *opisthocœlous*. Ribs are usually present : in *Polypterus* each vertebra has two pairs: a dorsal pair of considerable length, running between the dorsal and ventral muscles, and a short ventral pair be-tween the muscles and the peritoneum. The former answer to the ribs of elasmo-branchs, the latter to the ribs (*pleural ribs*) of the remaining bony fishes. There may be one or more sets of intermuscular bones, attached either to the neural arch (*epineurals*), or to the centrum (*epicentrals*), not preformed in cartilage, but developed as ossifications of the intermuscular septa. The posterior end of the vertebral column is turned up in the sturgeons, *Lepisosteus*, and *Amia*, resulting in a *heterocercal* tail-fin. In *Amia*, however, the fin-rays are so disposed that the fin appears almost symmetrical. Among Teleostei the tail-fin is very usually *homocercal*, as in the Trout, with a more or less disguised asymmetry: in many cases in the adult the development of the large, fan-shaped, posterior hæmal arches (hypurals) completely hide the upturned end of the notochord. In some, the spinal column ends simply in a somewhat compressed centrum around which the fin-rays are symmetrically disposed. Such truly symmetrical tail-fins are *diphycercal*.

In the structure of the *skull*, the cranium of the Acipenseroidea (Fig. 225) is an undivided mass of cartilage with a few isolated replacing bones. The roofing in-vesting bones lie in the dermis, so as to be practically superficial, and behind pass insensibly into the scutes covering the trunk ; the fact that these bones (parietals, frontals, etc.) are exoskeletal structures is here perfectly obvious. The same is the case in *Polypterus* (Fig. 226), in which, however, the replacing bones are better developed. In *Lepisosteus* and *Amia*, and especially the latter, the skull resembles that of the Trout in all essential respects, the main differences consisting in the absence of certain bones, such as the supra-occipital, and in the presence of additional investing bones. Among Isospondyli the investing bones remain separable from the chondrocranium in the adult. In most other orders (*e.g.* cod, haddock, or perch) they become grafted on to the chondro-cranium and so closely united with the replacing bones that they can be removed only by disintegrating the skull. Most of the original cartilage frequently disap-pears in the adult; the cranium becomes a bony mass in which replacing and investing bones are indistinguishable.

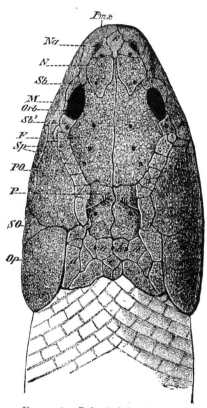

FIG. 226.—**Polypterini: Skull.** *Polypterus.* In dorsal view. *Pmx.* premaxilla; *Na.* external nostril; *N.* nasal; *Sb, Sb¹.* anterior and posterior suborbital; *Orb.* orbit; *M.* maxilla; *Sp.* spiracular bones; *PO.* preoperculum (?); *SO.* subopercu-lum; *Op.* operculum; *F.* frontal; *P.* parietal; *a, b, c, d,* supra-occipital shields. The two arrows pointing downwards under the spiracular shields show the position of the openings of the spiracles on to the outer surface of the skull. (After Wiedersheim.)

The varying size of the gape, which is so noticeable a feature in the fishes, depends on the inclination of the suspensorium. In wide-mouthed fishes the axis of the hyomandibular and suspensorium is nearly vertical or even inclined backwards. In small-mouthed forms it is strongly inclined forwards, and the length of the jaws is proportionately reduced. In the branchial arches the pharyngobranchials of each side are very commonly fused, and constitute what are called the *superior pharyngeal bones*. The reduced fifth branchial bars, or *inferior pharyngeal bones*, bite against them. Some percoid fishes are distinguished by having the inferior pharyngeal bones united into a single bony mass of characteristic form. The gill-rakers are often very highly developed, and may form a mesh capable of retaining even microscopic organisms.

Several species of teleosts are able to swallow prey much bigger than themselves. When certain deep-sea stomiatoid fishes do this they are aided by a

Fig. 227.—**Teleostei: Deglutition specialisations.** *Chauliodus* swallowing spiny prey (see text). Although this animal angles, it is a stomiatoid (see also Fig. 223), not a ceratoid angler-fish. (From N. B. Marshall, after Tchernavin.)

remarkable deglutition mechanism that enables the large struggling fish to be engulfed without damage to the hunter. Thus in *Chauliodus* (Fig. 227) the heart and ventral aorta are anteriorly placed between the lower jaw-bones. Parts of the fragile gill-arches, too, are directly adjacent. Tchernavin has shown, however, that when *Chauliodus* attacks, the powerful muscles extending from cranium to column contract and so swing the skull and anterior vertebræ upwards. At the same time the articulatory apparatus of the jaws is thrust forward. Concurrently, the wide gape is opened and sets of special muscles depress the pectoral girdle (and attached pericardium and heart) and the gill arches. Thus, each delicate and vital organ is pulled out of harm's way while the struggling, spiny catch is thrust by a 'stabbing' movement of sharp, elongated teeth down the pharynx into the widely distensible stomach. The deglutition process probably takes place very quickly and so respiration is only momentarily impeded.

In the *shoulder-girdle* of the Chondrostei there is a primary girdle consisting of large paired cartilages, not united in the middle ventral line, and unossified : each is covered externally by a large scute-like investing bone, the *cleithrum*. In *Polypterus* a clavicle and cleithrum are also present, but in the remaining palæoniscoid derivatives (p. 326) and in Teleostei the primary shoulder-girdle is reduced in size and is usually ossified as two bones, a dorsal *scapula* and a ventral *coracoid* : sometimes, as in the Trout, there may be an additional ossification, the *mesocoracoid*. Additional investing bones— *supracleithrum, 'postcleithrum*, etc.—are added, and one of them, the *post-temporal*, serves to articulate the shoulder-girdle with the skull (Fig. 208, p. 308). The skeleton of the *pectoral fin* of *Polypterus* (Fig. 228) differs substantially from that of other orders, including teleosts (Fig. 208) (see Daget).

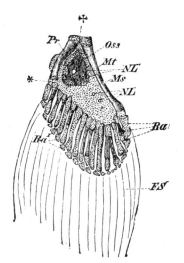

FIG. 228.—**Polypterini: Pectoral fin.** The presence in *Polypterus* of three elements—dorsal *Pr.* and ventral *Mt.* margins, and ossified media plaque *Oss.*—gives this fin a superficial resemblance to the pectoral fin of selachians (p. 235). There is no phylogenetic significance in this similarity. *F. S.* dermal rays; *N. L.* nerve foramina; *Ra.* first radials; *Ra*[1]. second radials; At * the bony marginal rays meet and shut off the middle region from the shoulder girdle. (After Wiedersheim.)

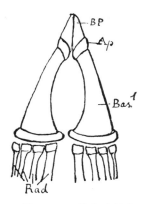

FIG. 229.—**Polypterini: Pelvic fin and cartilages.** Young *Polypterus*. *Ap.* part of basal; *Bas*[1]. basal; *BP.* pelvic cartilages (fused in adult); *Rad.* radials. (After Wiedersheim.)

In the Chondrostei (e.g. *Polypterus*) there occurs a vestigial *pelvic girdle* (Fig. 229, *BP*) in the form of a small rhomboidal cartilage to which the anterior ends of the basalia (*Bas* [1]) are attached. In all the remaining orders the pelvic girdle appears to be atrophied. The *pelvic fin* is supported by a single bone of variable form (Fig. 209, *B. PTG*) and apparently arising from the fusion of proximal pterygiophores. Between its posterior end and the dermal rays irregular nodules, representing radials, may be interposed.

The distinction between hard or unjointed fin-rays, or spines, and soft or jointed fin-rays has already been referred to. The major ray of the dorsal and pectoral fins sometimes, *e.g.* in trigger-fishes (Balistidæ), has the form of a very strong spine which can be 'locked' into its erected position, and only lowered by means of a complicated trigger mechanism derived from other bony elements of the fin (dorsal fin-spines), or by specially inserted muscles moving the spine base over an elaborate articular surface (pectoral spines in certain siluroids). In some cases the first dorsal spine springs from the skull.

The texture of the bones is subject to wide variation : in some 'spiny-rayed' fishes they are very thick and strong, in some places almost like ivory ; while in the Lump-fish (*Cyclopterus*), the huge Sunfish (*Mola*), and in many deep-sea forms, such as the ribbon-fishes (*Regalecus* and *Trachypterus*), the amount of mineral matter is so small that the bones are easily cut with a knife and weigh astonishingly little when dry.

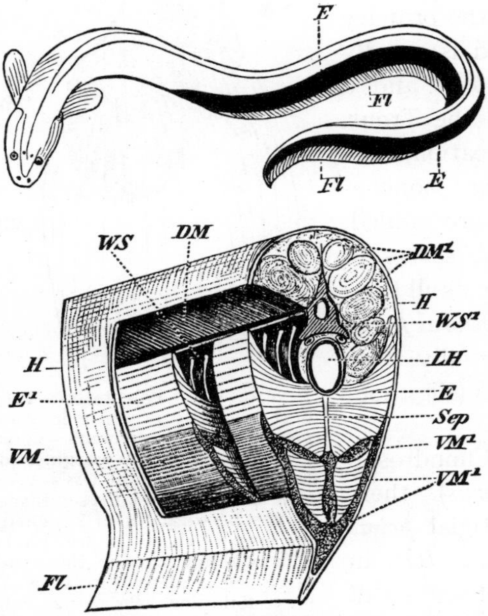

Electric Organs.—Members of four families of teleost fishes have independently developed organs which produce electricity. These are used for defence, the capture of prey, and perhaps as direction-finders. The best-known is the so-called Electric-'eel' (*Electrophorus* =*Gymnotus*) (Fig. 230)—a blind, superficially eel-like fish which grows to a length of about 8 feet, and is almost as thick as a man's thigh and lives in shallow muddy parts of the Amazon, Orinoco, and other South American rivers. On land *Electrophorus* can discharge about 500 volts. In water the charge is partly short-circuited and the shock (from an unexhausted fish) is about 250 volts, but still sufficiently strong to cause great discomfort to Man or to activate an electric buzzer or light

FIG. 230.—**Teleostei: Electric organs.** *Electrophorus electricus. Above:* showing the extent of the electric organ (*E*). *Fl*, ventral fin. *Below:* small portion of tail, in section. *DM, DM'*. dorsal muscles. *E, E'.* electric organ; *Fl*. ventral fin; *H*. skin; *LH*. caudal canal; *Sep*. fibrous septum; *VM, VM'*. ventral, muscles; *WS, WS'*. vertebral column, with spinal nerves. (After Wiedersheim.)

a neon sign (as one does in the New York Zoo). The electric organ consists of some seventy columns, each of which contains a series of about six hundred disc-shaped *syncytial electroplaxes* (electro-plate cells). The cells are probably formed from striated muscle-cells and together constitute a jelly-like mass located in the postero-ventral four-fifths of the body, and tail. This tissue is responsible for about half the total body-weight. Each electro-plate is innervated, and shocks are normally transmitted only when the fish is molested, or when it comes within range of its prey, which is stunned and then swallowed whole. The delaying mechanism which, after the reception of external stimuli, ensures the electric potential of all the widely separated electro-plates discharge at about the same time has not been satisfactorily explained.

Two star-gazers—the Mediterranean *Uranoscopus* and the American *Astroscopus*—also have muscle tissue modified into electric organs, but in each case these, innervated by the oculomotor nerves, are restricted to the region of the eyes. A third group of electric fishes is the African Mormyridæ, which produce weak shocks from modified caudal muscles (see below). A fourth family is represented by the African Cat-fish (*Malapterurus*).

Normal nerve-transmission is essentially an electrical phenomenon, but there has been for many years conjecture concerning the evolution of electric organs, since it was difficult to imagine what use they subserved until development had proceeded to a degree sufficient to generate power sufficiently high to deter an enemy or immobilise food. There is now evidence, however, that the African *Gymnarchus niloticus* gives out weak electrical impulses at a rate of about 300 per second throughout life and may detect changes in its electric field caused by obstacles or other animals in the surrounding murky river-water. If such a mechanism exists it might provide an explanation, as Lissman suggests, of the initial steps in the evolution of powerful electric organs.

If one picks up a wet individual *Mormyrus*, only a faint tingling can be detected. *M. kannume*, for example, discharges a continuous stream of weak impulses at a variable frequency. The discharge frequency is lowest when the fish is motionless. The rate increases rapidly to 80–100 impulses per minute if the animal is alarmed. The fish responds immediately any conductor enters its electromagnetic field. The precise means by which *Mormyrus* perceives its electrical disturbances is still unknown. *Mormyromasts*, which are neuro-glandular epidermal cells of a special kind, may be involved. It is perhaps significant that the cerebellar and acoustico-lateralis areas of the *Mormyrus* brain are remarkably developed, helping to make up a brain-weight between 1/52 and 1/82 of the total body-weight, 'a thing unparalleled among lower vertebrates' (Boulenger). It is not unlikely that this unusual development is somehow related to the co-ordination of impulses concerned with direction finding in this fish, which also lives in muddy waters providing poor visibility. Substantial electric potentials are also generated by certain elasmobranchs (p. 271) but (as in the case of star-gazers and *Malapterurus*) there is no evidence of their contemporary use in navigation (p. 272).

Alimentary Canal and Associated Structures.—Some fishes are toothless; but in most instances *teeth* are present, and may be developed on the pre-maxilla, maxilla, palatine, pterygoid, prevomer, parasphenoid, dentary, basihyal, and bones of the branchial arches. It is characteristic of most Teleostei, with the exception of Isospondyli, that the maxilla is edentulous and does not enter into the gape. The teeth may be either simply embedded in the mucous membrane and can be detached when the bones are macerated or boiled, or they may be implanted in sockets of the bone, or ankylosed to it.   They are formed of some variety of dentine, and are often capped with enamel.   Their succession is perpetual, *i.e.* injured or worn-out teeth are replaced at all ages.

In a very large majority of teleost species the teeth are small, conical, and recurved, suitable for preventing the struggling prey from slipping out of the mouth, but quite unfitted for either tearing or crushing.   In some fishes, such as the pike, the teeth are hinged backwards so as to offer no resistance to the passage of the prey towards the gullet, but effectually barring reverse movement.   In many deep-sea fishes (Fig. 227) the teeth are of immense size and constitute a very formidable armature to the jaws.   A number of instances occur in which there is a marked differentiation of the teeth, those in the front of the jaws (Fig. 231) being pointed or chisel-edged, and adapted for seizing, while the back teeth have spherical surfaces adapted for crushing.   In wrasses strong crushing teeth are developed on the pharyngeal bones.   In globe-fishes the teeth are apparently reduced to one or two in each jaw, but each 'tooth' in this case really consists of numerous calcified plates fused together.

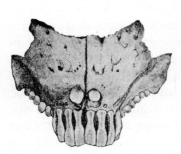

Fig. 231.—**Teleostei: Dental specialisation.** In *Sargus* (*Sparidæ*) premaxillary and maxillary elements are diversified in a manner reminiscent of tetrapods. (After Owen.)

Sniper-, rifle-, or archer-fishes (*Toxotes*) of Indo-Australian rivers exhibit remarkable modifications of the buccal cavity related to the propulsion of water at insects in foliage overhanging the river-banks.   These surface swimmers compress their opercula, sharply elevate the floor of the buccal cavity, and propel a jet of water through a nozzle-like groove in the dorsal aspect of the mouth.   This jet may travel, with startling accuracy, for several feet, knocking a fly into the water where it can be devoured.   Some species are about one foot in length ; young fishes only an inch long also have the shooting habit.

In some bony fishes the *alimentary canal* shows little differentiation into regions, but, as a rule, gullet, stomach, duodenum, ileum, and rectum are more or less clearly distinguishable at least histologically.   The *stomach* is generally V-shaped, but its cardiac region may be prolonged into a blind pouch.   This is often very distensible, allowing some of the deep-sea Teleostei to swallow fishes as large as themselves.   In many genera of several families the stomach is entirely absent (e.g. *Blennius, Cyprinus, Fundulus, Gambusia,* and *Labrus*). This is also the case in the Holocephali (p. 256) and is no doubt a secondary and adaptive condition.

Globe-fishes can inflate the gullet with air or water, as a result of which they can float upside down.   A *spiral valve* is very well developed in *Polypterus* and the sturgeons, vestigial in *Lepisosteus* and *Amia*.   It appears to be absent or vestigial in all Teleostei, except possibly in *Chirocentrus* (Isospondyli). A trace occurs in the herrings. The liver is usually large. A pancreas may be present as a compact gland, as in Chondrichthyes, or may be widely diffused between the layers of the mesentery, or in part surrounded by the liver. *Pyloric cæca* are commonly present, and vary in number from a single one to two hundred. The anus is always distinct from, and in front of, the urinogenital aperture.

Respiratory Organs.—The gills are usually comb-like, as in the Trout, the branchial filaments being free, owing to the atrophy of the interbranchial septa. In the sturgeons, however, the septa are fairly well developed, reaching half-way up the filaments, so that the latter are free only in their distal portions. This arrangement is obviously intermediate between the chondrichthyan and teleostean conditions. Perhaps the most striking deviation from the characteristic structure occurs in sea-horses, in which the gill-filaments are replaced by curious tufted processes (Fig. 219, *B*, *g*.). As a rule gills (holobranchs) are developed on the first four branchial arches, but the fourth is frequently reduced to a hemibranch, and further reduction takes places in some cases. The pseudobranch or vestigial mandibular gill may either retain the characteristic comb-like structure, as in the Trout (p. 311), or may be reduced, as in the Cod, to a gland-like organ formed of a plexus of blood-vessels and called a *vaso-ganglion* or *rete mirabile*. In most teleosts the mechanism of respiration is similar to that already described in the Trout, and respiratory valves are developed in the mouth-cavity. But there are considerable differences in details, more especially as regards the relative importance of the opercula and the branchiostegal membranes in carrying on the movements of inspiration and expiration.

A most complicated accessory respiratory device is the paired *suprabranchial organ* possessed by the catfish, *Clarias*. This is divided into two parts: (1) a highly branched arborescent structure associated with the second and fourth gill-arches on either side and (2) a heavily vascularised diverticulum of the branchial chamber which encloses it (Fig. 232). The epithelium of both the chamber and the arborescent organ has the same histological structure as gill-filaments, *i.e.*, thin outer epithelial layers and large intercellular spaces separated by 'pilaster' cells. Afferent and efferent blood-vessels, derived from those of the gill-arches, supply the intercellular spaces of the organ and its chamber. The entrance to the suprabranchial chamber is closed by a succession of fan-like structures developed from coalesced neighbouring gill-filaments on the dorsal aspect of the gill arches. These fans can seal the respiratory suprabranchial cavity. Air gulped through the mouth is then temporarily retained within. Greenwood reports that even before the arborescent organs arise, young *Clarias mossambicus* are able to survive in water of greatly reduced oxygen tension and, in fact, can live for as long as 18 hours when taken from the water, provided their environment is kept damp. Since the highly vascularised suprabranchial cavity is developed in fishes of this

size, it is presumed that it can function as a lung.   The early post-larval life is
spent in poorly oxygenated pools and swamps.   Adult *Clarias* are able to
progress from one swamp to another across damp grass-land.   In the neotenous
Clariallabes petricola the supra-branchial organ has almost disappeared.
Certain other probably neotenous clariid genera show various stages in the
reduction of this organ.

   In several fishes (*e.g.* Loach) respiration can take place through the epithelium
of the gut.   In *Amphipnous*, an Indian symbranchid, the gills are poorly

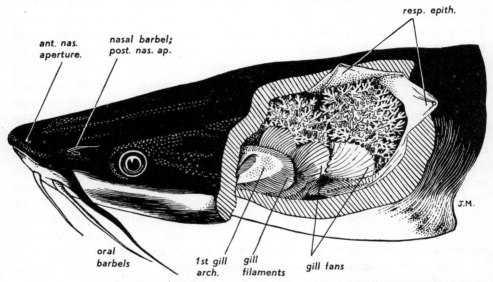

FIG. 232.—**Teleostei: Extra-branchial respiration.**   Supra-branchial organ of an air-breathing
freshwater catfish.   *Clarias mossambicus* gulps air at the surface in a manner not unlike that of
lung-fishes (Fig. 251, p. 365), but more swiftly.   The gill fans (derived from the upper gill filaments)
are mobile and probably control the flow of air or water into the supra-branchial cavity, but
exact details of the respiratory process are unknown.   Both aborescent organ and adjacent
epithelium (reflected) are respiratory in function.   There is no connection between nostrils and
either the branchial or pharyngeal cavity.   Nostrils are purely olfactory in function, allowing the
flow of water over the olfactory epithelium (Fig. 89, p. 138).   The barbels are tactile.   (From a
dissection by Greenwood and Marshall.)

developed and functionally replaced on each side of the body by a vascular sac
developed as a diverticulum from the pharynx and which opens anteriorly
into the first (hyobranchial) gill-cleft.   Such sacs are physiologically, though
not morphologically, lungs.   In the so-called Climbing Perch (*Anabas*) of Asia
(Fig. 233) folded plates (*B*) are developed from the first epibranchial bones and
covered with vascular mucous membrane.   The fish is able to progress on land,
holding on alternately by the spines of its pre-operculum and of its ventral
fins.   *Anabas* is so dependent on atmospheric oxygen that it is asphyxiated if
kept in water and denied access to the surface.   The widely held belief that
this species can climb trees is probably the result of faulty observation.   *Anabas*

are certainly found in the forked branches of trees. But they are dropped or placed there by kites which catch stranded fishes in drying pools (Das).

The Common Eel (*Anguilla anguilla*), which is notable for its overland journeys, is able to breathe cutaneously both in water and on land. Krogh long ago stressed that even in water more than half the total oxygen absorption is cutaneous, although carbon dioxide excretion is principally through the gills. Ashore, on the other hand, the eel excretes more than 90 per cent of its carbon dioxide through the skin. Oxygen uptake by the skin decreases sharply with a

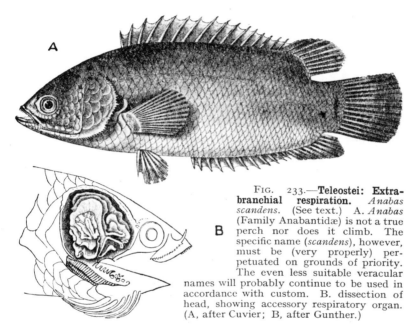

Fig. 233.—**Teleostei: Extra-branchial respiration.** *Anabas scandens*. (See text.) A. *Anabas* (Family Anabantidæ) is not a true perch nor does it climb. The specific name (*scandens*), however, must be (very properly) perpetuated on grounds of priority. The even less suitable veracular names will probably continue to be used in accordance with custom. B. dissection of head, showing accessory respiratory organ. (A, after Cuvier; B, after Gunther.)

rise in external temperature: perhaps a reason, as Carter suggests, why eels usually are found ashore only at night. In the mudskippers (*Periophthalmus*, p. 325) the oral and pharyngeal epithelium is highly vascular and subserves respiration.

In a few teleosts, notably the Stargazer, *Astroscopus*, there have arisen internal nares. Paired passages lead from the nasal capsules into the buccal cavity, perhaps facilitating aquatic respiration (and possibly olfaction), while the animal lies buried in the sand. The channels do not perforate any bony structure (Atz). They are absent in related genera; and are of course not homologous with comparable structures in lung-fishes and tetrapods (pp. 366, 383).

Swim-bladder.—It is now generally held that the swim-bladder arose from the primitive lung of ancient fishes (*e.g.* p. 108) and reached its present efficiency only when actinopterygian ancesters took to the sea. Swim-bladder and lung, then, are homologous. The swim-bladder (Figs. 234, 235) lies between the alimentary canal and the kidneys.   Although essentially a hydrostatic organ (see below), it may function also as an auxiliary respiratory device (see also p. 290), and is sometimes connected with the production or amplification of sound.   It may be single or multi-chambered, and is generally a tough sac overlain by a capillary network. Below the capillary system is a *tunica externa* of connective tissue.   Beneath this is a *tunica interna* consisting of smooth muscle-fibres with inner epithelial *gas-gland* (Fig. 235), which, in general, is specialised anteriorly for gas secretion and posteriorly for diffusion.   It may be open (*physostomatous*) or closed (*physoclistous*).   In the latter case the *pneumatic duct*, connecting the organ with œsophagus or pharynx, may be reduced to a mere thread or absent altogether. In *Polypterus* the swim-bladder consists of two lobes, the left one large, the right smaller (see Fig. 255, p. 371).   The swim-bladder in some species is divided into compartments, or may be produced into lateral diverticula.   In *Amia* and *Lepisosteus* (Fig. 234, *a. b*) its wall is sacculated or raised into anastomosing ridges, enclosing more or less well-marked chambers and thus resembling a primitive lung.   In *Polypterus* its lung-like character is enhanced by the ventral position of the opening and by the blood being conveyed to it (as is also the case in *Amia*) by a pair of *pulmonary arteries* given off from the last pair of epibranchial arteries, as in the Dipnoi (p. 372).   Even in some modern fishes the swim-bladder seems to be capable of acting as an accessory respiratory organ. It has been found that in a perch asphyxiated in stagnant water, the oxygen in the bladder, which normally amounts to 20 or 25 per cent., is entirely absorbed and replaced by nitrogen and carbon dioxide.   The primary function of the bladder, however, is hydrostatic, *i.e.* it serves to keep the fish at the same specific gravity as the water.   The specific gravity of the fish as a whole, rising or falling because of the increase or decrease of pressure at various depths as it descends or ascends, and causing greater or less compression of the gases in the swim-bladder, can be brought to approximately that of the surrounding water by increase or decrease in the quantity of the contained

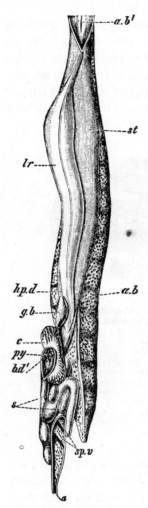

Fig.   234.—**Holostei: Swim-bladder and its general relationships.** *Lepisosteus. a.* anus; *a. b.* swim-bladder; *a. b'.* its aperture in the pharynx; *b. d'.* aperture of bileduct; *c.* pyloric cæca; *g. b.* gall-bladder; *hp. d.* hepatic duct; *lr.* liver; *py.* pyloric valve; *s.* spleen; *sp. v.* spiral valve; *st.* stomach. (From Wiedersheim, after Balfour and Parker.)

gas. Although physostomes (with 'open' swim-bladders) can replenish lost gas by swallowing at the surface, physoclists and some physostomes can transfer gas of high oxygen content direct from the blood-stream. In these animals, the epithelium of the bladder is differentiated into a *gas-gland* which is generally composed of many layers of specialised gas-producing cells which are supplied with blood-vessels from the *retia mirabilia* or *wundernetz* mentioned below (Fig. 236). Part of the arterial and venous system supplying the swim-bladder breaks up into minute vessels to form the retia mirabilia, and so comes into functional relationship with the cells of the gas-gland. Arterial capillaries bring in blood gases, and the gland secretes oxygen, carbon dioxide, and nitrogen into the lumen of the bladder, according to the needs of the moment. If gas is experimentally withdrawn, the gas-gland undergoes a compensatory hyper-secretion. Likewise, if the fish is experimentally burdened with a weight, it will at first sink, but later, with increased gas secretion, it recovers buoyancy by swim-bladder expansion. Gases can, on the other hand, diffuse *from* the swim-bladder into the capillaries and, in fact, some fishes (*e.g.* Myctophidæ, Gadidæ, Percidæ, Mugilidæ, etc.) possess an *oval* (Fig. 236), which is a thin-walled, richly vascular area of swim-bladder modified for the resorption of gases. The oval is equipped with an arrangement of circular and longitudinal muscles that can either expose the capillary area to, or mask it from, the internal surface of the swim-bladder and so reflexly control the gas pressure within. This secondary specialisation is no doubt of immense benefit to fishes that undergo relatively rapid vertical migrations to spend the night hours near the surface and to avoid daylight in the 'twilight' reaches of the depths. By altering the internal pressures and volume of its swim-bladder, the fish remains in hydrostatic equilibrium with the changing water-pressure, and so can move up or down with a

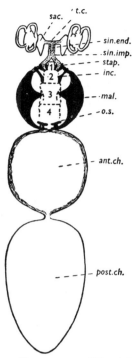

FIG. 235. — **Teleostei: Swim-bladder and its relationships with apparatus of audioequilibration.** (In a cyprinoid.) *ant. ch.* and *post. ch*: anterior and posterior chambers of swim-bladder; Weberian ossicles: *inc.* incus; *mal.* malleus and *stap.* stapes; *o. s.* os suspensorium; *sac.* sacculus; *sin. end.* sinus endolymphaticus; *sin. imp.* sinus impar; *t. c.* transverse canal. 1–4, vertebrae. (From Harden Jones and N. B. Marshall after Chranilov.)

minimum of muscular effort. The result of the sudden removal of pressure can be seen in the grotesque buccal protrusion of the swim-bladder from fishes suddenly hooked or trawled up from even moderate depths.

In some fishes with a functional pneumatic duct the gas glands are absent, but in the eels and others their place is taken by *red bodies* of similar appearance, but with non-glandular epithelium. In some forms with an enclosed swim-bladder the anterior end of the organ is forked, and each branch fits closely against a membranous space in the posterior wall of the auditory capsule, while laterally it extends outwards in the region of the shoulder-girdle, and comes to lie immediately beneath the skin. Any change in volume of the swim-bladder is thus communicated to the auditory organ. A more sensitive apparatus exists in the carps and siluroids (order Ostariophysi), in which a chain of bones connects the swim-bladder with the ear, forming the *Weberian apparatus* (Fig. 235). There is reason to believe that this apparatus, modified from processes of certain vertebræ, carries pressure stimuli anteriorly to the perilymph (p. 145).

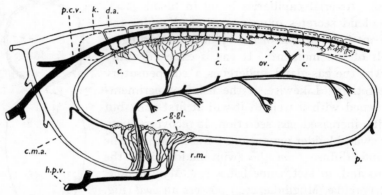

FIG. 236.—**Teleostei: Swim-bladder, its blood supply and intrinsic circulation.** The gas gland, oval and spatial relationship with the kidney are indicated. The arteries are shown white and the veins black. *c.* capillary layer; *c. m. a.* cœliaco-mesenteric artery; *d. a.* dorsal aorta; *g. gl.* gas gland; *h. p. v.* hepatic portal vein; *k.* kidney; *ov.* oval; *p.* peritoneum; *r. m.* retia mirabilia. (From Harden Jones and N. B. Marshall, after Saupe.)

The presence or absence of the swim-bladder is often closely correlated with the ecology of the animal (see Jones and N. B. Marshall). It may be lost in bottom-living, shallow-water fishes, and in those inhabiting the extreme ocean depths where it is sometimes converted into a fat-storage organ (see also p. 359). The efficient swim-bladder shown in so many modern teleosts is a relatively recent development. It has conferred upon them incalculable advantages.

Blood-Vascular System.—The structure of the heart forms one of the most striking differences between the palæoniscoid derivatives and the teleosts. In the former there is a muscular conus arteriosus with rows of valves, as in the Chondrichthyes. In teleosts a vestige of the conus containing two rows of valves has been found in *Albula* (Isospondyli), and similar vestiges occur in several other genera of the same order, but in all the rest of the teleosts it is entirely unrepresented. On the other hand, teleosts always have a large bulbus arteriosus—a fibrous non-contractile ring of tissue at the base of the ventral aorta.

The flesh of most fishes is pale, but in fast-swimming teleost tunnies (*Thunnus* and allied genera) and certain others there occurs highly pigmented, fat- and glycogen-containing *red muscle*, which, according to its anatomical situation, appears not to take part in the principal work of the body. In *Thunnus* and mackerel (*Scomber*) disproportionately large amounts of vitamins of the B-complex (excluding niacin) occur in red, compared with ordinary skeletal, muscle, leading to the view that it has functions somewhat comparable with certain of those of the liver. The circulatory arrangements of tunnies are of a complexity unique among fishes and these, in themselves, differ curiously between genera. The dorsal aorta gives off a series of cutaneous arteries which run laterally through the kidney tissue to emerge in the superficial musculature. Dorsal cutaneous arteries give off dorsal segmental arteries. The corresponding ventral vessels usually do likewise. The cutaneous arteries in turn lead to rows of arterioles. This arrangement is accompanied by a correspondingly rich venous vascularity. The visceral circulation, too, is noteworthy: certain branches of the cœliaco-mesenteric artery terminate in unusually rich and complicated vascular plexuses in the liver. The heat generated by metabolic activity raises the temperature of fishes generally to a level slightly in excess of that of the surrounding sea-water. In *Thunnus* the temperature may be as much as 10° C. more than that of the surrounding medium.

Bony fishes possess, as with all vertebrates, erythrocytes, and various kinds of leucocytes. The possession of red respiratory blood-cells (containing hæmoglobin) is a characteristic of vertebrates, although the *leptocephalus* larva of the eel does not acquire the pigment until it becomes an elver, and the pigment of *Petromyzon* (p. 176) is somewhat different from that of other vertebrates.

There is evidence, too, that Antarctic members of no less than three genera of marine teleosts (*Chænocephalus*, *Champsocephalus*, and *Pseudochænichthys*) possess colourless blood. They have yellowish-white gills, and Norwegian whalers call them *blodlaus-fisk* (Ruud). Investigation has shown that their blood is in fact essentially a transparent, yellowish-white plasma containing leucocytes as well as unknown principles that enable it to clot. No red cells whatever are found in *Chænocephalus* and no absorption bands can be discerned in the spectrum. The iron content of the plasma is relatively minute compared with that of other teleosts, and its oxygen capacity is correspondingly low. These probably comparatively sluggish fishes are relatively large; they sometimes attain a length of 60 cm. and a weight of more than 1 kg. Generally they are caught in water that is somewhat colder than 2° C.

Experimental evidence is available that carp, pike, and eels can remain alive, apparently little incommoded, after their blood is almost saturated with carbon monoxide bubbled through their tank. Such a state of carboxylation would kill quickly a mammal, and Fox has suggested that many fishes, including certainly the above Antarctic forms, probably carry adequate oxygen in their blood plasma for their needs while swimming quietly. The hæmoglobin in many teleosts is possibly used only in an emergency. On the other hand, it has been claimed that mackerel, for example, are unable to obtain sufficient oxygen unless they are swimming rapidly.

Brain.—The cerebellum and optic lobes are usually large. The diencephalon is well developed in palæoniscoid derivatives (p. 326). In the Teleostei the prosencephalon has the general features which have been described in the account of the brain of the Trout. It is not divided into hemispheres and has a roof which, except in *Amia*, is completely non-nervous. Its floor consists of a pair of massive corpora striata (Fig. 237, *prs.*, and Fig. 211, p. 313, *BG.*). In most instances the olfactory bulbs are in close apposition with the olfactory region of the prosencephalon without the intervention of olfactory stalks or tracts; but in some cases, as in cod (Fig. 238, *olf. p.*), they are borne on long *olfactory peduncles* or *olfactory tracts*. The palæoniscoid derivatives agree with Chondrichthyes in that the optic nerves form a chiasma, whereas in teleosts they simply cross one another or decussate. Here also, however, the distinction is not quite absolute, since in herrings and some other isospondylids one nerve passes through a slit in the other. In some plectognaths the spinal cord undergoes a remarkable shortening. In a sun-fish $2\frac{1}{2}$ metres in length and weighing a ton and a half, the cord is only 15 millimetres long. It is actually shorter than the brain.

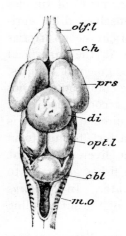

FIG. 237.—**Holostei: Brain.** *Lepisosteus* in dorsal view. *cbl.* cerebellum; *c. h.* olfactory part of prosencephalon; *di.* diencephalon; *m. o.* medulla oblongata; *olf. l.* olfactory bulbs; *opt. l.* optic lobes; *prs.* corpora striata. (After Balfour and Parker.)

Exteroception.—Walls is of the opinion that the *eyes* of deep-sea fishes are 'probably by far the most sensitive in existence'. It is certain that, like those of owls and other nocturnal land vertebrates, the eyes of certain deep-sea teleosts receive enough light in order to function in situations in which Man is completely blind. Certain deep-sea fishes have a retina containing up to 20,000,000 rods per square millimetre. Whole 'blocks' of rods are linked (*via* bipolar ganglion cells) to a single fibre of the optic nerve. Thus even though the infinitesimal amount of light impinging on a few rods may be insufficient to evoke a neural response, the combined (though withal weak) reaction of many may easily do so in an abyssal environment. Among fishes, large eyes are prevalent down to about 500 metres. Some species with wide pupils and big lenses—adaptations to marine twilight—live as deep as 1,000 metres. Below this depth the eye seems generally to become small, related essentially to the mere perception of light; and sometimes extremely degenerate, or merely vestigial, or even absent altogether. Light falling on the sea is absorbed and scattered: Beebe, in his bathysphere, found that under clear Bermuda waters a coloured book illustration showing bright red prawns appeared almost black at about 18 metres. Yellow light almost disappeared at about 100 metres and much of the green-blue was gone at 240 metres below. From 520 metres downwards the sea was black to the human eye.

A secondary photoreceptor mechanism exists in the pineal and adjacent areas of the diencephalon of some (and perhaps many) fishes (see also p. 196, and cf. p. 546). In *Phoxinus* (a cyprinid) it has long been known that chromato-

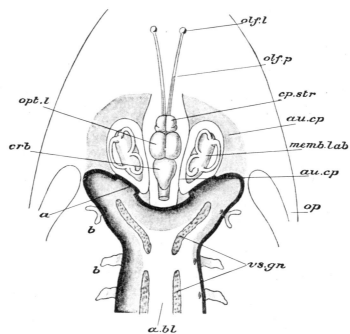

FIG. 238.—**Teleostei: Brain and membranous labyrinth.** *Physiculus bachus* (Moridae: cods). *a.* thickened portion of swim-bladder fitting into fenestra in posterior wall of auditory capsule; *a. bl.* swim-bladder; *au. cp.* outer wall of auditory capsule; *au. cp'.* inner (membranous) wall; *b.* hollow offshoots of air-bladder; *cp. str.* corpora striata; *crb.* cerebellum; *memb. lab.* membranous labyrinth; *olf. l.* olfactory bulbs; *olf. p.* olfactory penduncles (olfactory tracts); *op.* operculum; *opt. l.* optic lobes; *vs. gn.* vaso-ganglia.

phore responses are linked with the pineal region. There is evidence, too, that this area is light-sensitive in blind cave-fishes (*Anoptichthys*), as well as in other species with translucent tissue covering the diencephalon. Hoar has now shown that in the smolt of the Sockeye Salmon (*Oncorhynchus nerka*) light sensitivity is dependent on the pineal organ as well as the eyes. Destruction of the pineal area 'affects the distribution of pigment in the chromatophores and the phototactic response of the fish'.

An *auditory apparatus* (Fig. 93, p. 144; Fig. 214) occurs in all groups of fishes. It was for many years generally believed that fishes are relatively deaf and that few indeed are able to emit sounds. Water, of course, carries sound very efficiently. The speed of submarine sound is modifiable by density and hydrostatic pressure, but, as a general rule, it can be said that sound travels underwater at about 1,500 metres per second, compared with an average aerial speed of about 340 metres per second at sea-level.

By the use of sensitive hydrophonic apparatus developed during the 1939–1945 war much valuable information is becoming available concerning the *noises* made by bony fishes. Sound is produced by movements of various skeletal bones, spines, teeth, and the swim-bladder. The whistling 'song of the Sirens', which can be heard above the surface, is probably produced by members of the family Sciænidæ. Gurnards (Triglidæ) produce snoring noises by the muscular vibration of the swim-bladder, and because of this have been called 'crooners', 'pipers', and several onomatopœic names in various countries. Porcupine-fishes (*Diodon* and allies) produce grating sounds by movements of the jaws (and possibly palatal ridges), heightened perhaps by the resonatory capacity of the swim-bladder. On the other hand, some fishes are said to be deaf, and others incapable of making a noise. There is no reason to disbelieve that fish noises are important components of behaviour patterns concerned with threat, recognition, and courtship, as in other vertebrates.

The *lateral line organs* (pp. 136, 449) may be uncovered, but are usually canals which open to the environment by means of pores or tubules. Some abyssal fishes lack actual canals, but possess lateral line organs as sensory terminations of variously-shaped papillæ swinging free in the water. There is experimental evidence that when another fish swims by, the neural impulses from the lateral-line system are intensified. Such organs seem to respond only to low-frequency vibrations, and so apprise the fish of the approach of predators or prey, and probably help keep members of a shoal together. The disappearance of eyes in the deep-sea bottom-feeding brotulid fishes is accompanied by a remarkable compensatory development of the lateral-line system of the head. Brotulids inhabiting higher reaches have functional eyes, and less powerfully developed pressure receptors. In the scaleless *Miripinna* of the recently erected teleost order Miripinnati (Bertelsen and N. B. Marshall), the lateral-line organs are borne on projections. In one species (*M. esau*) the body is covered with branched, hair-like processes bearing glandular cells of uncertain function.

Endocrine organs.—These fall into the characteristic vertebrate pattern (p. 147). The pituitary varies considerably in structure from one group to another. 'Anterior' and neural lobes are readily recognised. There is some evidence that the *adenohypophysis* (Fig. 96, p. 150) in teleosts is itself made up of anterior, median, and posterior parts, the median section being homologous with the pars distalis, and the posterior, glandular portion with the pars intermedia of mammals. There is experimental evidence that the hypophysis produces growth, gonadotrophic, thyrotrophic, and adrenocorticotrophic hormones possibly from the median part of the adenohypophysis. Intermedin, of melanophore dispersing function, occurs and may come from the posterior part; and it has been claimed that an agent with an opposite effect is elaborated

at the anterior end of the gland.   The *pars nervosa* is believed to produce
vasopressin and oxytocin.   In some bony fishes the *thyroid* occurs in a compact organ, but in many others thyroid follicles are dispersed in the region of
the ventral aorta.   There is much evidence suggesting that thyroxin or its
homologue has at least a morphogenetic function.   Most investigators have
failed to find parathyroid tissue, but there is recent evidence that the *ultimobranchial cells* of the pharyngeal epithelium (Fig. 73 *A*, p. 106) may be significant
in this respect.   The adrenocortical homologue or *inter-renal tissue* is usually
confined to the generally lymphoid pronephros and may be congregated around
the posterior cardinals and their tributaries.   In many, if not all, groups
the *chromaffin tissue* lies in close association within the pronephros or in the
walls of the adjacent cardinals.   The function of neither tissue has been proved
in teleosts; but a relationship between the pituitary and inter-renal tissue
exists.   Much of the *islet tissue* may often occur outside the diffuse pancreas
in the region of pyloric cæca, spleen, and gall-bladder.   A hormone similar in
effect to insulin is discharged.   The bud-like *corpuscles of Stannius* (pronephric
region of Holostei and Teleostei) may be secretory.   In teleosts (*Lebistes*) the
pineal has possibly a secretory function related to growth.

Urinogenital Organs.—The *kidney* (Fig. 210, *kd.*) is formed from the mesonephros of the embryo.   The pronephros usually atrophies.   The urinary duct
(*ur.*) is the undivided pronephric duct : it unites with its fellow of the opposite
side before opening either directly on to the exterior or into a urinogenital
sinus.   A *urinary bladder* is formed as a single or double dilatation of the duct.
The right and left kidneys undergo more or less fusion, and their anterior ends
are usually converted into lymphatic tissue (*kd.'*), so that, while resembling the
rest of the organ in external appearance, they do not discharge a renal function.

In general, marine teleosts possess fewer glomeruli than fresh-water species.
Some, in fact, have become wholly aglomerular (*e.g.* the toadfish, *Opsanus tau*).
This specialisation was no doubt primarily associated with a constant osmotic
water-loss, which in turn reduces the amount of fluid traversing the glomeruli
and, in addition, the utility of urine-formation.   However, at least two
species of aglomerular fishes can live in fresh water: *O. tau* ascends streams,
and a tropical freshwater pipe-fish (*Microphis boaja*) breeds in them.

The *male organs* of *Lepisosteus* may be taken as an example of those of
palæoniscoid derivatives (p. 326).   The testis (Fig. 239, *ts.*) is a paired, lobulated
organ.   Spermatozoa from the seminiferous crypts (*lobules* or *tubules*) are
carried by a large number of vasa efferentia (*v. ef.*) into a longitudinal canal
(*l. c.*) lying alongside the urinary duct (*ur.*).   From this canal tubes are given
off which communicate with the urinary tubules of the kidney or open directly
into the duct, so that the seminal fluid has to traverse the latter in order to reach
the urinary bladder (*bl.*) and make its escape by the common urinogenital
aperture (*u.g. ap.*).   In teleosts there are no vasa efferentia.   However, the

posterior end of the testis is directly continued into a duct (Fig. 210, *v. d.*) which unites with its fellow of the opposite side and opens either into a urino-genital sinus, as in the Trout, or directly on the exterior, between the anus and the urinary aperture, as in cods. In eels the spermatozoa escape into the cœlom and are discharged by genital pores.

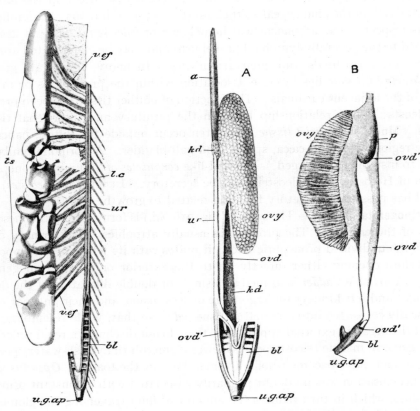

FIG. 239.—**Holostei: Urinogenital system in male.** *Lepisosteus.* *bl.* bladder; *l. c.* longitudinal canal; *ts.* testis; *u.g. ap.* urinogenital aperture; *ur.* urinary duct; *v. ef.* vasa efferentia. (After Balfour and Parker.)

FIG. 240.—**Holostei: Urinogenital system in female.** A. *Lepisosteus* and B. *Amia.* *a.* degenerate anterior portion of kidney; *bl.* bladder; *kd.* kidney; *ovd.* oviduct; *ovd'.* aperture of oviduct into bladder; *ovd''.* peritoneal aperture; *ovy.* ovary; *p.* peritoneum; *u.g. ap.* urinogenital aperture; *ur.* urinary duct. (A, after Balfour and Parker; B, after Huxley.)

The secretory elements of the testis of teleosts fall into two distinct types, the phylogenetic distribution of which is not yet determined. In many teleost fishes there are Leydig cells (p. 152) of the typical vertebrate type, such as we saw first in *Petromyzon* and which occur in selachians and in lung-fishes and *Latimeria* (p. 356). In others (e.g. *Esox*) there is no true interstitium. Instead, connective tissue cells of the lobule walls are seasonally modified to an apparently comparable function (Fig. 97). Such a phenomenon occurs also in certain urodeles (p. 452) but not in anurans.

In most palæoniscoid derivatives (p. 326) the *oviducts* (Fig. 240, *B*, *ovd.*) have funnel-like anterior ends (*ovd".*) opening into the cœlom, while posteriorly (*ovd'.*) they discharge into the dilated urinary duct (*bl.*). A similar arrangement occurs in the Smelt, one of the Salmonidæ, in which the eggs are discharged from the outer or lateral face of the ovary into the open end of the oviduct. But in most teleosts and in *Lepisosteus* (Fig. 240, *A*) the ovary (*ovy.*) is a hollow sac continued posteriorly into the oviduct (*ovd.*). The eggs are set free into its cavity from the folds into which its inner surface is produced, and so pass directly into the oviduct without previously entering the cœlom. The lumen of the ovary can be looked upon as a shut-off portion of the cœlom in *Lepisosteus* and the Teleostei. In the embryo a longitudinal fold grows from the ventral edge of the then solid ovary, and turns upwards along the lateral face of the organ. This is met by a descending fold of peritoneum from the dorsal wall of the abdomen. By the union of the two folds a cavity is enclosed and becomes the lumen of the ovary. The oviduct is developed as a backward continuation of these folds of peritoneum, and appears to be quite unconnected with the embryonic renal system, and therefore not to be homologous with the oviducts of selachians and Holocephali, which, as we have seen, are Müllerian ducts. In the Salmonidæ and the eels oviducts are absent. The ova are discharged by genital pores, which are probably to be looked upon as degenerate oviducts. True abdominal pores are present in palæoniscid derivatives and in some Isospondyli.

In two families, Sparidæ and Serranidæ, functional hermaphrodites are common: the gonads may contain both male and female elements. Such a condition is distinct from the occasional intersexuality that probably occurs in all vertebrate species. *Serranus* and *Lebistes* have been reported to be self-fertilising. *Seranellus subligarius* has been experimentally shown to be so (Clark).

Reproduction.—Most bony fishes are oviparous, the eggs being fertilised after they are laid. The eggs are always small by comparison with those of cartilaginous fishes, never exceeding 5–10 mm. in diameter. Usually they are much smaller. Externally shed eggs can be roughly arranged in two categories : (1) floating, *pelagic* eggs and (2) *demersal* eggs which sink to the bottom of the sea. Pelagic eggs generally contain an oil-globule which aids buoyancy. Their existence is hazardous and they are usually produced in stupendous numbers, *e.g.* a single turbot may shed over 9,000,000 eggs, and certain other species a great many more. Demersal eggs are usually covered with an adhesive substance and cling to each other and to weeds, rocks, and debris. Some species (*e.g.* sticklebacks) build nests. Some cat-fishes, and most members of the percomorph family Cichlidæ, carry eggs and young within their own buccal cavity (see below). The female Bitterling (*Rhodeus*) deposits its eggs in

the siphon of a mussel by means of a seasonally developed tube-like *ovipositor*.
Spermatozoa shed by the male are probably carried to the eggs in the siphon-
current.   The male Nursery-fish (*Kurtus*) possess a *cephalic hook* in the crook of
which is anchored and carried a grape-like aggregation of eggs deposited by the
female.   An even more bizarre nuptial specialisation is exhibited by certain
deep-sea angler-fishes.   Regan has shown that in *Edriolychnus* and *Ceratias* one
or several diminutive males are carried firmly attached to various parts of the
body of the female.   The blood-vascular system of each parasitic male and that
of the female host become joined.   The normal male mouth-parts are degenerate.   The teeth and much of the digestive apparatus are sacrificed, but at the
same time a vascular union of such intimacy is formed that it is often not easy

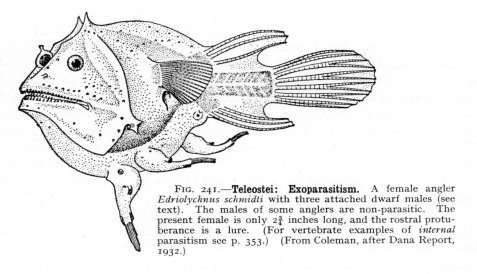

FIG. 241.—**Teleostei: Exoparasitism.** A female angler
Edriolychnus schmidti with three attached dwarf males (see
text).   The males of some anglers are non-parasitic.   The
present female is only $2\frac{3}{4}$ inches long, and the rostral protuberance is a lure.   (For vertebrate examples of *internal*
parasitism see p. 353.)   (From Coleman, after Dana Report,
1932.)

to see where male tissue begins and that of the female ends (Fig. 241).   Respiration in the male takes place through lateral slits.

In teleosts, as well as in elasmobranchs (p. 278), true vivipary, as opposed
to ovovivipary, has independently arisen.   It occurs in several orders, and
is widespread in the Microcyprini.   Families of this order show an extraordinary range of phenomena, exhibiting on the one hand the birth of living
young associated with little change from the typical oviparous structures (e.g.
Lebistes) and, on the other, vivipary associated with a degeneration of the yolk-
sac and the development of special structures that enable gaseous and nutritional
exchanges with the maternal tissues.

In the Pœciliidæ the fertilised eggs remain lodged in the single ovary, and
the embryos are held in the follicles until parturition.   The epithelium of each
follicle becomes a vascular syncytium.   The embryonic pericardial sac of each
embryo expands, becomes invested with capillaries, and, with the development

of epithelial folds, the two tissues come in contact as a *pseudo-placenta* not unlike the *epitheliochorial placenta* of certain mammals.

In the Anablepidæ (e.g. *Anableps*) a grotesque extension of this follicular pseudo-placentation occurs when the embryonic hind-gut temporarily expands and elongates. There are developed vascular bulbs on the tributaries of portal veins (Fig. 242). Turner suggests the possibility that additional nutriment can be absorbed through these structures from the parent to the gut of the embryo.

FIG. 242.—**Teleostei: Viviparity.** Partly dissected embryo of *Anableps dowei*, showing relationship of pericardial and cœlomic cavities, and expanded posterior intestine. The embryo is retained until parturition within one of the ovarian follicles, the epithelium of which is transformed into a *follicular pseudo-placenta* and an association between maternal and embryonic circulations comparable with the mammalian epitheliochorial placenta (p. 904) is formed. (From Amoroso, redrawn after Turner.)

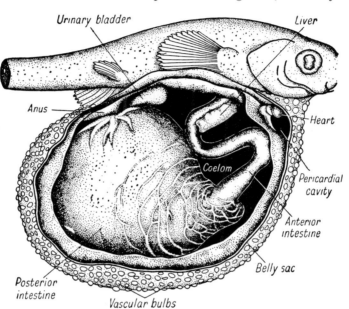

In one cyprinodont family—the Jenynsiidæ—the embryos are retained not in the follicles, but are ejected into the adjacent ovarian cavity. Here the epithelium becomes first secretory, and next sheds huge numbers of cells. The products of these, together with the remains of autolysed non-viable embryos, are ingested by the surviving young. As embryonic development proceeds, the ovarian tissues regress, and there are finally developed in the cavity a series of vascular folds which come in contact with the embryonic gills, and thereby allow a gaseous and nutritional exchange between ovary and the gills of the embryo.

Many instances of *parental care* of the young are known. A few species such as the Sea-horse (*Hippocampus*) and the pipe-fishes (Syngnathidæ), develop their young in a pouch (Fig. 219, *brd. p.*) on the abdomen of the male. In the siluroid *Aspredo* the eggs are pressed into the soft, spongy skin of the female (and thus carried about). Parental care is highly developed in the freshwater family Cichlidæ, of which *Tilapia*, an African genus, is an example.

When the breeding season approaches the male becomes aggressive and selects and defends a territory of lake-bottom. Next he excavates a small pit with his mouth. There now follows an active courtship, after which the eggs are laid in the nest and then fertilised by the extrusion of spermatozoa. Now occurs a most extraordinary thing in many, but not all, species of *Tilapia*. The female gathers up the eggs into her mouth, where they are brooded. When hatched, the very small young still take refuge in the mother's mouth, venturing out as they grow older, and retreating in times of danger. When they are about twenty days old, and still only a few millimetres long, they do not return and thereafter fend for themselves.

Tilapia nilotica, a fish that is common in the Sea of Galilee, is one of the mouth-brooding species of *Tilapia*. If a brooding female is picked up, the eggs often fall from her mouth. It is not impossible that this phenomenon inspired the command to St. Peter, attributed to Jesus: 'Go thou to the sea, and cast a hook, and take up the fish that first cometh up; and when thou hast opened his mouth, thou shalt find a piece of money: that take and give unto them for me and thee.' *T. nilotica* does in fact lay golden eggs. Those of *T. gallilea* and a few others lay green ones. All species of *Tilapia* possess, when young, a dark spot near the posterior end of the dorsal fin. This is often called the '*Tilapia*-mark'. It is sometimes called 'St. Peter's mark', allegedly left by the fisherman saint when he picked the animal up. In most species the St. Peter's mark disappears when the fish gets older.

Development.—In all palæoniscoid derivatives hitherto investigated, with the exception of *Lepisosteus*, cleavage is complete. In *Acipenser* and *Amia* it is very unequal, the macromeres being immense as compared with the micromeres. In *Polypterus* it is equal at first, becoming unequal later: the process may be said to be intermediate between the holoblastic and meroblastic types. In *Lepisosteus* the segmentation is meroblastic, the fissures not extending much beyond the equator of the egg. In Teleostei segmentation is always partial and discoidal. The general features of development are much the same as in the Trout, except that in sturgeons and *Polypterus*, as in craniates in general, there is an open medullary groove which becomes closed in to form a medullary canal. There is frequently a metamorphosis. In *Lepisosteus*, for instance, the newly-hatched young is provided with a sucking-disc, and the proportions of the head are quite different from those of the adult. In the larval sturgeon provisional teeth are present, and in many teleosts the young differ from the adult in the presence of large spines which by increasing the surface area probably aid in flotation. The pelagic larvæ of eels are strongly compressed, transparent, and have colourless blood (see p. 343). They are sometimes known as 'glass-fish', and until their real affinity became known were placed in the 'genus' *Leptocephalus*. One such leptocephalus larva, the adult of which is probably still unknown, is 184 cm. long. This, the biggest larva ever described, was taken by the Dana Expedition west of the Cape of Good Hope in 1930 (Taning).

The young of *Polypterus* possess external gills (Fig. 243; see also Fig. 262).

An especially remarkable developmental sequence occurs in Carapidæ or fierasfers. *Carapus acus*, for example, produces planktonic eggs, from which hatch *vexillifer larvæ*, each equipped with a long dorsal vexillum or banner. This degenerates, and the larva sinks to the sea-bed and enters the anus of a holothurian. The larva now metamorphoses into the *tenuis* stage, which feeds on the holothurian tissues and next changes into a *juvenile* and later into an adult.

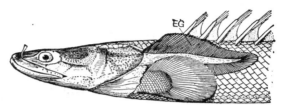

FIG. 243.—**Holostei: Development.** External gills (*E.G.*) in advanced larva of *Polypterus bichir*. (From Dean, after Steindachner.)

Internal parasitism.—The adult *Carapus* is capable of feeding both inside and away from the host. As many as seven parasites may occur in a single holothurian. A second group of internal (and external) parasites are the slender South American freshwater pygiidid *candiru* (e.g. *Vandellia* spp.) which enter the gill-cavities of bigger fishes and feed on the soft tissues within. *Vandellia* sometimes penetrates the urethra of Man and cow if they micturate while in the water.

SUB-CLASS CROSSOPTERYGII (CHOANICHTHYES)

INTRODUCTION

It is appropriate to deal with these, the crossopterygians (lung-fishes and allies), last and therefore immediately before the Amphibia. At the same time it must be clearly understood that even though they show certain undeniable features in common with tetrapods, they merely represent one branch of three widely different branches of piscine evolution and, in themselves, cannot be thought to be 'higher' in the scale of animal classification than either the elasmobranchs or actinopterygians. We will see, however, that the development by this stem of the aerial respiratory apparatus and other specialisations made possible the revolutionary movement of fish-like animals to dry land, and the consequent evolution of the tetrapods (p. 381). On grounds of microscopic anatomy as well as general morphology there is something to be said for separating the crossopterygians as a class by themselves.

It is probable that this sub-class, though once abundant in regard to individuals, has never been very extensive. To-day it is probably reduced to one recently discovered cœlacanth (p. 356) and to a few species of Dipnoi (p. 361), themselves aberrant members of an ancient side-line.

The earliest fossil appearance of the Crossopterygii is during the Middle Devonian period, by which time three separate groups, the Osteolepidoti, Cœlacanthini, and Dipnoi, were already clearly established. Westoll has provided good evidence that the early Dipnoi were closely related to contemporaneous Rhipidistia (see below). From the latter the Actinistia (= Cœlacanthini) are an ancient branch. The extant *Latimeria*, and lung-fishes as well, preserve many archaic characters. Because the Cœlacanthini and the Osteolepidoti are far more closely allied to each other than to the Dipnoi (lungfishes), Trewavas *et al.* have proposed the classification which is here adopted:

SUB-CLASS CROSSOPTERYGII

Order Rhipidistia

Sub-orders Osteolepidoti (Devonian–Permian)

Cœlacanthini (**Actinistia**) (Devonian–Recent)

Order Dipnoi (Devonian–Recent)

ORDER RHIPIDISTIA

Although the members of this group are in some respects too specialised to be themselves ancestral to the cœlacanths, lung-fishes, or tetrapods, the order may nevertheless be considered as the central one, from whose earlier, less specialised, roots the three above-mentioned branched off on their own lines of evolution. We shall see later (p. 382) that there is much reason to believe that the prototetrapod came from a generalised rhipidistian crossopterygian which was already well differentiated 'in earliest late Devonian times' (Westoll).

SUB-ORDER OSTEOLEPIDOTI

Osteolepis macrolepidotus (Fig. 244), the earliest well-known rhipidistian species, illustrates all the main features of the sub-class, as well as the particular features of its group. Compared with a primitive actinopterygian, such as *Palæoniscus* (p. 285), there were several points of variation in addition to such absolutely fundamental differences as the internal nostril and the cosmoid structure of the scales and head-bones. Among these were the two dorsal fins instead of one, the smaller eye with numerous sclerotic plates, as well as paired fins of the archipterygial type with a single basal element articulated with the shoulder-girdle. The dentition showed two peculiar features. The premaxilla, maxilla, and dentary were supplied with a number of small, sharp, conical teeth, such as occur in many fishes, but the prevomer, palatine, and ectopterygoid had, in addition, a series of larger teeth of a characteristic structure and method of replacement. The dentine was much folded, and replacement was alternate, a second tooth growing up beside the first, so that there was a large and a small socket side by side. Such an arrangement does not occur in other fishes. It is of high interest that both the above features have also been transmitted from some earlier ancestor to the tetrapods, as is shown by the 'labyrinthodont' teeth of the early Amphibia (p. 422). The arrangement of the jaws was *autostylic*. The suspension therefore resembled that of the earliest gnathostomes (p. 203), as well as that of the Amphibia.[1] Gills, guarded by opercula, were present.

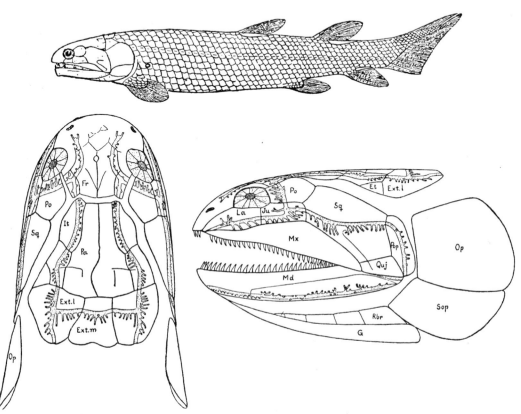

FIG. 244.—Order **Rhipidistia**, Sub-order **Osteolepidoti**, Family **Osteolepidæ**. *Osteolepis*. *Above:* Reconstruction of the Devonian *O. macrolepidotus* (after Traquair). Osteolepiform fish already possessed an interclavicle which is retained by primitive amphibians (see p. 425). The hinge between parietals and post-parietals was lost (Fig. 285, p. 427). *Below:* Skull, in dorsal and lateral views (modified after Säve-Söderbergh). *Ext. l.* and *Ext. m.* extra-scapulars; *Fr.* parietal; *G.* gular; *It.* supra-temporal; *La.* Lachrymal; *Md.* dentary; *Mx.* maxilla; *Op.* opercular; *Pa.* post-parietal; *Po.* post-orbital; *P. Op.* pre-opercular; *Qu. J.* quadratojugal; *S. op.* sub-opercular; *Sq.* squamosal. (After Säve-Söderbergh.)

The tail of the Rhipidistia, having a small epichordal lobe, was partly heterocercal. The composition of the ossified skull was, in general, not unlike that of a palæoniscid, but there was one important and characteristic point of difference : in all rhipidistians (Fig. 244) there is a line running transversely

---

[1] Jarvik's (1954) reconstruction of *Eusthenopteron* shows a hyoid arch which almost certainly bore a normal posterior hemibranch. There is also evidence of a vestigial prespiracular pouch.

across the skull between the parietal (*frontal* in older nomenclature) and postparietal (*parietal*) bones. This divides the skull into two portions. This feature alone would prevent any known form from being regarded as ancestral either to the dipnoan or tetrapod lines.

There is evidence that in early members of both orders there is an alternate deposition and resorption of the outer layer of cosmine in the skull-bones and scales during the life of the individual fish. This periodical absorption may have allowed the bones to grow and expand. As much of the detailed classification of extinct forms has been based on the structure of the scales, the recognition of this phenomenon may alter considerably the arrangement within the order (Westoll). Genera are as follows: *Osteolepis*, *Megalichthys*, *Thursius*, *Eusthenopteron*, *Rhizodus*.

SUB-ORDER CŒLACANTHINI (ACTINISTIA)

The Cœlacanthini, represented to-day by a single family, are a side line of the Crossopterygii which appear first in Upper Devonian deposits. Fossils occur both in fresh- and salt-water deposits. In the Carboniferous period (p. 3) *Cœlacanthus*, for example, was a fresh-water animal; whereas *Undina* (Fig. 245) and other Mesozoic cœlacanths were marine. No post-Mesozoic cœlacanth fossils have been found, and until 1939 it was thought that the Cœlacanthini had been extinct for some 50,000,000 years. Then a live specimen was trawled up off the east coast of South Africa. This fish, *Latimeria chalumnæ* (Fig. 246), was caught at about 40 fathoms and was some 5 feet long and weighed 127 lb. It was steel-blue in colour. Subsequent living specimens have been described as possessing eyes of a greenish-yellow luminescence. Unfortunately, before their extraordinary value was fully appreciated the viscera of the first specimen was destroyed; only the skin was preserved. J. L. B. Smith, who described *Latimeria*, now began an intensive effort to get further specimens with soft parts intact, and due to his initiative a second cœlacanth was recognised in a native fish-market on the remote island of Anjouan in the Comoro Archipelago late in 1952. This specimen, ironically enough, was caught with a fish-baited hook at about 8 fathoms some 200 metres off-shore. It was abnormal, having lost its dorsal fin and supplementary tail-lobe (no doubt in youth), and was described as a new genus and species. Subsequently, several more *Latimeria*, including one alive, have been captured and extensively studied by Millot and his associates. The new generic name proposed by Smith must be relegated to synonymy.

Fossil specimens (*Cœlacanthus*, *Macropoma*, *Undina*, etc.) had long revealed that the Cœlacanthini has the same general organisation of skull and scale structure as had the Osteolepidoti, together with some very definite specialisations of its own. It would seem that internal nostrils, if they ever existed, were lost very early in the evolution of the group (see Fig. 248). The structure

of the fins and tail, and the peculiar, calcified swim-bladder are highly characteristic.   The paired fins have the superficial appearance of those of an actinopterygian.   There is a short, blunt, and scale-covered lobe, around which the
fin-rays are attached as a fan.   The fins are pedunculate, their soft-parts
affording important information concerning the evolution of limbs, although
it must be emphasised that cœlacanths are off the main line of tetrapod
descent.   Such a narrow-based paddle, mechanically imperfect for aquatic
progression, was adapted for locomotion on a solid or semi-solid sub-stratum.
Observations by Millot on a captive cœlacanth have shown that it swims
by curious rotating movements of its pectoral fins, while the second dorsal
and anal fins, also highly mobile, serve together with the tail in steering.

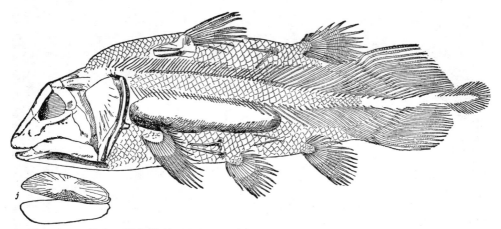

FIG. 245.—Order **Rhipidistia,** Sub-order **Cœlacanthini,** Family **Cœlacanthidæ.**   *Undina.*
U. penicillata.   (Triassic and Jurassic.)   *j,* gular plates.   (After Smith Woodward.)

Millot has shown, too, that a remarkable limb flexibility exists.   The orientation of these lobe-like fins varies greatly (by as much as 180°) even between the
two sides of one individual.   These data support the palæontological work of
Gregory, who emphasised the probable tetrapod descent from rhipidistian
ancestry involving the development of land-limbs from muscular, and hypothetically flexible, lobe-like paddles (Fig. 246).

The internal skeleton of the fins of *Latimeria* consists essentially of a single
basal plate.   This is attached to the shoulder-girdle in the case of the pectoral
fins.   Each basal plate is followed by a few axial pieces around which the fin-
rays are arranged, so that the fin appears to be essentially mesorhachic or
archipterygial.   The pelvic fin in extinct forms (*e.g.* the Triassic *Laugia* and
Jurassic *Coccoderma*) has come to be attached near and below a tiny true
pectoral fin.   This anterior migration was repeated in the unrelated actinopterygian teleosts 100 million years later.

Of the two dorsal fins, the anterior is supported by a bony plate, and the posterior by an osseous structure not unlike that of the pectoral fin.   The tail is diphycercal, with a small central projecting lobe.   The fin-rays are attached each one singly to a dorsal or ventral spine of a vertebra.   This is another point of convergence with the later teleosts.   The vertebral column, apart from the spines, is unossified.   There is a massive, unconstricted, and wholly cartilaginous notochord.   Neural and hæmal processes occur.

The skull, while showing a number of specialisations, is like that of the

FIG. 246.—Order **Rhipidistia,** Sub-order **Cœlacanthini,** Family **Latimeriidæ**. *Latimeria chalumnæ.*   For cephalic details, see Figs. 247, 248.   (Redrawn after Millot.)

Osteolepidoti in possessing a powerful and freely movable hinge on the dorsal surface between the parietals and post-parietals (p. 355).   This feature, together with the traces of cosmoid covering of the bones and scales, is further evidence of the common ancestry of the two sub-orders.

There are five gill-arches.   Four only of these are attached to the copula. The smallest and fifth gill-arch has no slit behind it.   The top of each arch bears a series of small plates which are covered with sharp spines of variable size. Two extensive sensory systems occur in the rostral region (Figs. 247, 248). They are quite distinct from each other.   One consists of a large, single-median chamber from which three paired *rostral tubes* communicate with the

exterior. Of these, the *postero-superior* and *postero-inferior rostral tubes*
emerge near the orbit and the *anterior rostral tube* near the point of the snout
(Fig. 247). There is no cir-
culation of water through
this apparatus, which is
permanently full of a jelly-
like material recalling that
of the ampullæ of Lorenzini
(p. 251). Its function is
uncertain. The second
apparatus is olfactory in
function. It is paired,
contains a nasal capsule,
and communicates with the
exterior by means of
typical nasal tubes. Each
anterior nasal canal emerges through one of the
paired rostral papillæ near

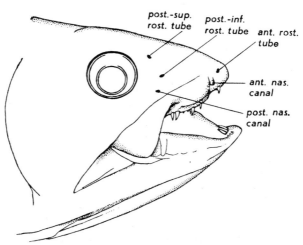

FIG. 247.—*Latimeria:* **Head and sensory organs.** (See
text and Fig. 248.) (Redrawn after Millot and Anthony.)

the extremity of the snout. Each *posterior nasal canal*, on the other hand,
opens to the cheek by a brief inconspicuous slit between the postero-inferior
rostral tube and the pseudo-
maxillary fold. In general, the
nasal apparatus resembles that
of *Polypterus*.

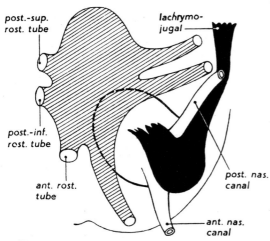

FIG. 248.—*Latimeria:* **Sensory organs.** (See text
and Fig. 247.) (Redrawn after Millot and Anthony.)

After the first (eviscerated)
specimen of *Latimeria* was described, there was much speculation concerning the probable
form of the swim-bladder.
Millot has now shown that the
organ is variable and sometimes
vestigial. A mere tube, two or
three inches long, extends from
the ventral aspect of the œsophagus, and is prolonged by a
long, fat-sheathed filament that
divides to an attachment with
the dorsal wall of the abdominal cavity. This reduction suggests that its original
function in *Latimeria* stock may have been more pulmonary than hydrostatic, as
might be expected. Further, no essentially pulmonary sac would be likely to
survive the retreat into relatively deep water and the assumption of wholly

aquatic respiration, but it has also to be remembered that the functional hydrostatic organ is at times most erratic in its distribution even within a genus.

Both the duct and its filament are surrounded by dense layers of homogeneous fat, constituting altogether a large fatty cord more than an inch in diameter. The flesh of *Latimeria*, too, is extremely oily, no doubt making for increased buoyancy (p. 349). The heart is exceedingly primitive—even more so than in the selachians (p. 240). The student is already familiar with the original simple longitudinal pump plan of the four chambers—bulbus cordis, ventricle, atrium, and sinus venosus—and how the characteristic S-flexure has become increasingly elaborate in tetrapod evolution. The cœlacanth heart remains relatively unfolded; in fact, the atrium has for the most part remained posterior to the ventricle. 'These fishes have thus retained up to the adult stage the mechanism most akin to the original vertebrate heart' (Millot).

From the buccal cavity, a remarkably wide, fluted, and muscular œsophagus leads imperceptibly into the long, spacious, double-limbed stomach, the posterior end of which is well behind the anus. Fish-prey can be swallowed whole. The transition between œsophagus and stomach can be determined only by its microscopic glandular structure; the long, tubular fundus glands are very well-developed. The gastric mucosa is dense. There is no cardia. A prominent annular sphincter allows ingress to a short chamber, probably an adumbration of the *bursa entiana* which occurs in many fishes and which opens into a 'sub-fusiform spiral intestine *en rouleaux* showing nearly a score of concentric turns' (Millot). This leads to a rectum and cloacal pouch—the latter bearing a single urinogenital papilla. The cloaca receives also secretions from a nearby encapsulated, median, nodular gland, which, though different from it, is possibly homologous with the digitiform (rectal) gland of selachians (p. 239).

The liver is bi-lobed, the left lobe being considerably the larger. A capacious gall-bladder occurs. The pancreas is prominent. The kidneys are fused into a single median organ which is applied to the *ventral* wall of the abdominal cavity. The ureters are symmetrical, and expand dorsally each into a voluminous bladder: thus the bladder is paired, and the kidney unpaired. The urethras are symmetrical as they enter the urinogenital papilla. The testes are paired, partly segmented, and held posterior to the anus. The large urinogenital aperture lies immediately behind and between the bases of the paired pelvic fins.

Despite profound changes in the swim-bladder (a notoriously adaptive organ), and the fact that only a bare outline of the anatomy is yet available, it is nevertheless obvious that in *Latimeria* we have an animal of extraordinary stability. The fish has persisted relatively unchanged from an era in which profound changes took place (p. 383), and became stabilised at a particularly instructive period of vertebrate history.

Order Dipnoi (Dipneusti, Dipneumones)

The peculiar lung-fishes are a Devonian offshoot from the crossopterygian stem. They still survive as three degenerate and specialised forms in widely separated tropical, or sub-tropical, fresh-water habitats of a special kind (Fig. 249). Lung-fishes appear first in mid-Devonian deposits, and were well

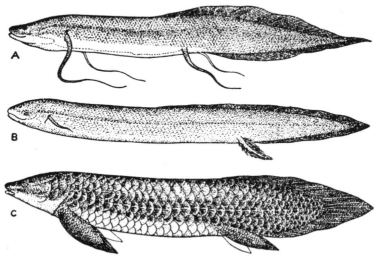

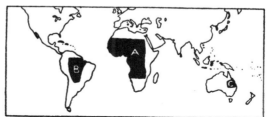

Fig. 249.—**Lung-fishes: Discontinuous distribution.** A. *Protopterus*, B. *Lepidosiren*, C. *Neoceratodus*. These dipnoan survivors are to-day confined to near-tropical (*Neoceratodus*) and tropical (*Protopterus, Lepidosiren*) freshwaters. *Neoceratodus* is restricted to two adjacent rivers: the black area shown is much too extensive. (After Norman.)

differentiated even then. They flourished moderately in the Permian and Triassic, and then became rare.

The living dipnoans are *Neoceratodus* of south-eastern (*not* tropical) Queensland (once called the 'Burnett Salmon'),[1] *Protopterus* of Africa, and *Lepidosiren*

---

[1] This singular fish was formerly casually eaten by people who were unaware of its interest. It is now rigidly protected by law. After Krefft in a newspaper of 1870 described what settlers called the 'amphibious fresh-water-salmon', he wrote some doggerel, probably for the amusement of his small son, from which the following is an extract :

> Lucullus ate Muræna rare,
> In Rome the daintiest dish,
> But Squatters on the Burnett dined,
> On geologic fish.

(A 'squatter' in the original early nineteenth-century Australian sense was usually, but not always, a reputable immigrant who took up vacant grazing-land, often under fee and licence. The term there has become respectable.)

of South America.   The name of the order, given before the structure of
the extinct types was fully known, refers to the two internal nostrils (choanæ)
which henceforth becomes a feature of the tetrapods.   A study of living lung-
fishes throws considerable light on the probable anatomy of the soft parts of the
extinct forms.   Each extant form not only breathes by means of gills but has a
highly-developed apparatus for the respiration of air—a lung (*Neoceratodus*)
or lungs (*Protopterus*, *Lepidosiren*)—with a co-ordinated arrangement of the
circulation.   Among other groups a comparable arrangement is found only in
Polypterus and *Amia*.   *Neoceratodus* is able to live in stagnant water that is
toxic to certain other species, but nevertheless dies if removed from water.
Protopterus and *Lepidosiren* can survive the drying of the environment by
æstivating in mud with a small aperture to allow respiration.   The former
secretes a slimy protective cocoon.   In both *Protopterus* and *Lepidosiren* an
epiglottis (p. 668) occurs.   The lung-fishes have bony scales which differ
among genera, but their relationship with the ancient cosmine scale (p. 83)
seems well established.   Dermal fin-rays occur.   The paired fins, however,
unlike those of any other fishes (with the exception of certain extinct Chondrichthyes and crossopterygians), are constructed on the biserial plan ('archipterygium', see pp. 99, 224).

   With special features of their own, the Dipnoi combine also characteristics in
which they resemble now one, now another, of the other groups of fishes.   The
notochord is persistent.   There are no vertebral centra, and the primary cranium persists with little ossification, but has added to it a number of investing
bones (p. 302).   There are four to six cartilaginous branchial arches.   The
dermal fin-rays are slender more or less ossified fibres and are supported by
numerous cartilaginous or ossified pterygiophores.   The caudal fin is often
apparently diphycercal.   The pectoral arch is a single cartilage with a pair of
superficial investing bones on each side.   The pelvic arch is well-developed and
cartilaginous.   The gills are covered by an operculum.   There is a dermal skeleton formed by over-lapping cycloid scales.   The heart is peculiar and to some
degree approaches that of the Amphibia.   The atrium and the sinus venosus are
each imperfectly divided into two parts.   The contractile conus arteriosus,
which has a spirally twisted form, is partly or completely divided by a longitudinal partition.   A pulmonary artery is given off from the efferent branchial
system on each side, and a pulmonary vein opens into the left division of the
atrium.   In *Lepidosiren* and *Protopterus* the larva possesses both suckers and
external gills.   In the latter genus, remains of these gills may persist in the
adults of some species.   The stomach has been secondarily lost in so far as
histological structure is concerned.

   The central nervous system is interesting in its undivided, or almost
undivided, mid-brain; and the pallium of the cerebral hemispheres, with its
layers of nerve-cells, has no parallel among the lower vertebrates so far con-

sidered. The paired oviducts open anteriorly into the cœlom, and male vasa efferentia carry sperms through the excretory part of the mesonephros (Fig. 260, p. 376).

The sub-class was never a very large one, but a succession of extinct genera is known that leads clearly to the modern species. A number of characters is common to all members of the order. The internal nostrils, cosmine covering of the bones and scales, and the mesorhachic fin all show that the Dipnoi evolved originally from an ancestor in common with the other crossopterygians. The jaw suspension is autostylic, the lower jaw articulating with a palatoquadrate process that is immovably fixed to each side of the skull. The characteristic pattern of the teeth is peculiar to the order. During the long history of the group its component members, while retaining all the essential anatomical features, show a gradual degeneration of certain parts. This can be seen in the bones of the skull, in a loss of cosmine, and in an alteration from the normal two dorsal fins and heterocercal tail to the almost eel-like body of *Lepidosiren*.

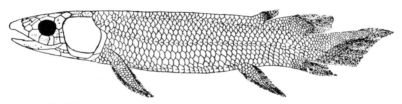

FIG. 250.—Order **Dipnoi** (*D. valenciennesi*), Family **Dipteridæ.** *Dipterus.* From something like this Middle Devonian form a 'line' is traceable through *Ceratodus* (Triassic) to *Neoceratodus* (Fig. 249). *Protopterus* and *Lepidosiren* represent an ancient side-line. (After Forster-Cooper.)

This fish has fused dorsal and anal fins, a gephyrocercal tail, thread-like paired limbs, and reduced scales (Fig. 249).

Dipterus valenciennesi (Fig. 250), the most primitive known form, had a body protected with stout cycloid scales covered, as were the bones of the head, with cosmine. The archipterygial paired fins were moderately long; there were two small dorsal fins, a heterocercal tail with a small epichordal lobe and an anal fin. The skull was completely roofed in by bones so numerous that their homologies, especially of those in the front region, with the head bones of other fishes are difficult to determine. There were no premaxillæ or maxillæ, and the bones of the palate were firmly fixed to the neurocranium and so produced the autostylic condition. There was a double series of gular bones between the rami of the lower jaws. The upper teeth were borne on the prevomers and palato-pterygoids, the former small, the latter a larger series of tubercles arranged as a pair of fans. These palatal teeth were in later forms fused into characteristic tooth-plates. A single pair of tooth-plates of corresponding pattern are carried on the lower jaws by the splenials.

Dipterus showed an interesting feature in the life-history of individual animals. Originally there were described two species of the genus, *D. platy-cephalus* and *D. valenciennesi*, both found preserved in the same horizons. The specific differences between the two lay in the fact that *D. platycephalus* had a completely bony snout, and the bones of the head and the scales are covered by a thick, smooth, and finely pitted outer layer of cosmine, which hid the underlying pattern of the scales, whereas *D. valenciennesi* had the front part of the snout without bone and the scales lack the outer layer, so that the pattern is clearly visible. It now appears that this apparent diversity may be explained as seasonal differences of a single species (*D. valenciennesi*). At recurring intervals during the life of the fish the outer layer of cosmine is resorbed to allow growth to take place. It is then re-deposited. Specimens have been found in the intermediate condition.

Representative genera of Dipnoi were *Dipterus* (Middle Devonian), *Pentlandia*, *Phaneropleuron*, *Scaumenacia*, and *Fleurantia* and *Rhynchodipterus* (long-snouted fishes) of the Upper Devonian. Others were *Uronemus* (Lower Carboniferous), *Conchopoma* (Lower Permian), *Ctenodus*, *Sagenodus* (Carboniferous and Permian). Of the living forms, *Protopterus* (Fig. 249) is known from the Miocene (with close allies from the Triassic onwards). *Neoceratodus* (Fig. 249) has apparently changed relatively little during the last 150 million years. Its widespread Mesozoic ancestor, *Ceratodus*, was described long before the extant Australian fish, dealt with below, was discovered.

Living Dipnoi belong to two sub-orders arranged as follows :

SUB-ORDER MONOPNEUMONA

Dipnoi in which the lung is single, and the lateral jointed rays of the 'archipterygium' are well developed. There survives only the Australian *Neoceratodus forsteri* (Fig. 249).[1]

---

[1] A brief note may be made concerning '*Ompax spatuloides*' (Jordan, D. S. (1919), *Genera of Fishes*, iii, 399), which was described by Count F. de Castelneau from drawings and other information in 1879. This interesting and perplexing specimen was described as 'a ganoid nearly allied to *Atractosteus*', and possibly to *Polyodon*, constituting a new species, genus, 'and probably a new family'. Very soon after its description there arose not inconsiderable doubt as to its authenticity, particularly as Count de Castelneau related that its discoverer, a museum director visiting the Burnett River, had been presented with the fish cooked, whereupon it had been consumed for breakfast. However, being impressed by its shape, the visitor had first had the animal drawn by a passing road-inspector. The sketches were despatched to the Count, together with field data suggesting that the specimen had been caught by aborigines in a water-hole where it lived with *Neoceratodus*. Many unsuccessful searches for further specimens were made. Not until half a century later, however, was the full story of '*Ompax*' revealed. A group of lung-fish conscious stockmen, hearing that a museum man was visiting the area, had determined that he should meet with a second 'living fossil'. They thereupon made him one: it was composed of several fishes, including perhaps *Neoceratodus*. From that time onwards, whenever anything peculiar in the locality was described, bushmen would say sardonically: 'It must be an *Ompax*.' (See Whitley.)

'*Ompax spatuloides*' arose out of the almost universal desire to make a fool of the expert. More such hoaxes (as distinct from serious frauds, pp. 454, 746) have found their way into zoological literature than is generally realised.

SUB-ORDER DIPNEUMONA

Dipnoi in which the lung is double, and the lateral rays of the 'archipterygium' are vestigial or absent. This group includes *Protopterus* (Fig. 251) of Africa and *Lepidosiren paradoxa* of South America (Fig. 249).

EXAMPLE OF THE SUB-CLASS.—PROTOPTERUS ÆTHIOPICUS

The genus *Protopterus* is confined to the fresh waters of tropical and subtropical Africa and is composed of the following four species: *P. æthiopicus* (Fig. 251), *P. annectens*, *P. amphibius*, and *P. dolloi*. The fossil history of the

FIG. 251.—Order **Dipnoi**, Sub-order **Dipneumona**, Family **Lepidosirenidæ**. *Protopterus æthiopicus*. Aerial respiration in the East African Lung-fish. Respiration is essentially pulmonary from a very early age. Degenerate internal gills are retained (Fig. 258) but the fish must surface periodically. It inhales for a few seconds, then flips its tail above the surface and plunges downward again.

genus, unlike that of *Neoceratodus*, is obscure. *P. æthiopicus* occurs in the tropical Lakes Victoria, Kyoga, Edward, and Albert and in the River Nile. Within the area of its present-day distribution, tooth-plates have been found in Miocene and Pleistocene deposits (p. 3).

P. æthiopicus attains a length of about seven feet and a weight of 90 lb., but a fish longer than five feet is exceptional. It is widely distributed within the lakes, occurring most abundantly in shallow water. It thrives in swamps where other fishes are not frequently found. It is able to rise to the surface and gulp air through the mouth into its lungs, thus obtaining enough oxygen to respire and so gain independence from dissolved oxygen in the water (Fig. 251). The West African *P. annectens* is able to spend long periods of æstivation under the mud in cocoons formed by dry mucus when the temporary swamps and rivers become periodically dry. The bulk of the population of *P. æthiopicus* is not compelled to æstivate and cocoons are not commonly found in nature. The species has been induced to æstivate under laboratory conditions (Homer Smith). As the water recedes, *Protopterus* burrows head-first into the ooze, and then reverses its position until the snout is just beneath the surface of water. As long as water remains, the fish surfaces regularly to breathe. When the mud-flat becomes exposed the fish coils upright in ooze, up to about 18 inches below the surface, with its tail covering the eyes. The epidermis secretes mucus, which hardens into a waterproof cocoon as the surrounding mud solidifies (Fig. 259). The cocoon is perforated by a breathing tube which connects the fish's mouth but not the nostrils with the exterior (see. p. 375). If exposed naked during this period, its skin shrivels and the fish dies within twenty-four hours. Inside its protective, fluid-retaining cocoon *P. æthiopicus* has lived for as long as three years in experimental æstivation.

The food of *P. æthiopicus* consists mainly of molluscs, although insects and small fishes are also eaten. Its movements are generally sluggish. The filamentous and highly mobile paired fins are well-supplied with receptor-organs which probably assist in the location of food. *Protopterus* moves in two different ways. Swimming is of an anguilliform type. In addition, it is able to ' walk ' along the bottom and through weeds by using its pectoral and pelvic fins as ' legs '.

External characters.—The eyes are small. The body is elongate and cylindrical, and covered with thin, bony imbricating cycloid scales. There is a continuous dorsal, anal, and caudal fin, supported by fibre-like, partly calcified dorsal rays (*camptotrichia*) which are more numerous than the endoskeletal radials. The limbs (pectoral and pelvic fins) are elongate and filamentous and are devoid of fin-rays.

The *external nares* differ from those of other vertebrates in being situated immediately outside the aperture of the mouth enclosed within the upper lip. A pair of *internal nares* open not far behind them into the anterior part of the mouth cavity, immediately in front of the upper tooth-plate. About two-thirds of the distance from the snout to the tail extremity there is a *cloacal aperture*. Two abdominal pores, opening into the cloaca, may be present, but usually they are confluent and have a single external opening.

There is an *operculum*, similar in appearance to that of other bony fishes, covering the branchial opening and bordering the single, slit-like branchial aperture of each side. No spiracles occur. The *lateral-line system* is well developed, especially on the head (Fig. 251).

Endoskeleton.—The *spinal column* is represented by a persistent notochord enclosed in a thick, fibrous sheath, together with cartilaginous neural and hæmal arches. The notochord—there are no vertebræ in modern Dipnoi—extends to near the pituitary region, and there is no distinct joint between the skull and vertebral column, which pass gradually into one another.

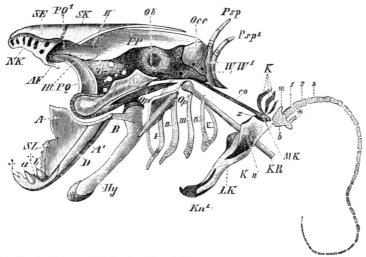

FIG. 252.—*Protopterus:* **Skull, shoulder girdle, and pectoral fin.** *A,A*[1]. splenial; *A,F.* preorbital process; *a* and *b* (on lower jaw), and *SL.* teeth; *b.* basal cartilage of pectoral fin; *B.* ligamentous band connecting the mandible with the hyoid; *co.* ligamentous band connecting the dorsal end of the pectoral arch with the skull; *D.* angular; *FP.* frontoparietal; *Ht.* membranous fenestra perforated by the foramen for the optic nerve (*II*); *Hy.* hyoid; *K.* external gills; *Kn.* *Kn*[1]. cartilage of the pectoral arch; *KR.* occipital rib; *LK* and *MK.* investing bones of the pectoral arch; *NK.* olfactory capsule; *Ob.* auditory capsule; *Occ.* supraoccipital; *Op.* and *Op*[1]. rudimentary opercular bones; *PQ.* palatoquadrate; *Psp. Psp*[1]. spinous processes of the anterior vertebræ; *SE.* supra-ethmoid bone; *SK.* roofing investing bones; *Tr.* palatoquadrate cartilage; *WW*[1]. anterior vertebræ coalescent with the skull; *I—V.* branchial arches (that marked *I* is forked and the anterior bar may represent the first, in which case there are six branchial arches); 1, 2, 3, segments of axis of pectoral fin; *, *, vestigial lateral rays of pectoral fin. †, †, projecting processes of free portion of Meckel's cartilage. (After Wiedersheim.)

A series of *neural* or *basidorsal cartilages* form the bases of the neural arches. These basidorsals extend upwards and form partly ossified neural arches which meet above the spinal cord. A longitudinal ligament runs along the top of the arches, and above it are a series of neural spines. The last-named fuse with the basidorsals in the posterior part of the column. This region is provided with hæmal or basiventral cartilages. Each neural and hæmal spine forms the proximal segment of a continuous, three-jointed, ossified rod. The two other segments of the rod are the radials. No centra are formed. Although the notochord is impressed by the basidorsal and basiventral cartilages, it is not constricted as in bony-fishes.

Pleural ribs are present, and extend downwards and somewhat posteriorly in the body-wall immediately outside the peritoneal membrane. The arrangement resembles that of the pleural ribs in other bony fishes. The first pair (the *occipital ribs*) are thicker and more massive than the others and are connected with the skull.

In the *skull* (Fig. 252) the cranial roof and walls, internal to the jaw muscles, are largely formed from the so-called parietal bones. Lying above and lateral to the parietals are the paired, posteriorly directed *frontals*. The cranial floor is formed by the expanded *parasphenoid*. The homologies of these investing bones are not understood: the terms employed above are used for the sake of convenience only. A system of letters and numbers is usually employed for their identification (Westoll). Two *exoccipitals* are present. A *palatopterygoid cartilage*, firmly fixed to the cranium, gives attachment to the mandible, so that the jaw suspension is autostylic (p. 94). *Hyomandibulæ* are absent. The upper tooth-plate is attached to the *prevomers* and to the *palatopterygoid*. Premaxillæ, maxillæ, and nasals are absent.

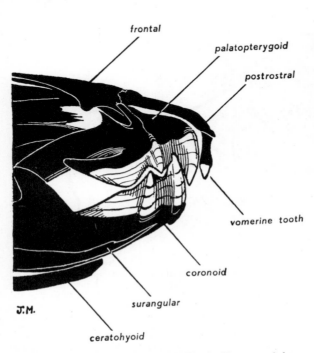

FIG. 253.—*Protopterus:* **Dentition.** Upper and lower tooth-plates in occlusion and their relationships with adjacent bones. The above clear-shown distinction between dental and osseous structures can be seen only in dry or fossil specimens. (Partly from a specimen in University College, London.)

The lower jaw consists of paired *Meckel's cartilages*, with large, tooth-bearing *coronoids* (= ' splenials ') situated on their medial aspects, and supra-angulars placed laterally. No true dentaries or splenials are developed. The mandible articulates with a large *intertemporal cartilage* (= pterotic, squamosal, of different authors). Fenestrated, cartilaginous *nasal capsules* are present, and small *opercular* and *interopercular* bones support the opercular fold.

The *hyoid* and *branchial arches* are cartilaginous. Only a *ceratohyal* is retained in the hyoid arch. There are five branchial arches and, in front of the first gill-slit, a rod, probably formed from the fused bases of the hyal rays.

There are no branchial rays, but all branchial arches bear a series of gill-rakers with cartilaginous supports.

The *pectoral girdle* (Fig. 252) is a stout cartilage overlain by a pair of investing bones. It is attached to the skull by a ligamentous band. The pelvic girdle is a single, lozenge-shaped, cartilaginous plate produced anteriorly into a long *epipubic process*. On each side of this projection are a pair of forwardly directed *prepubic processes*. The posterior aspect of the plate bears short processes for the basal cartilages of the pelvic fins.

The skeleton of the *pectoral fins* consists of an elongate basal cartilage followed by a central axis of small, cartilaginous rods. On one side (pre-axial face) of the central axis there is a row of jointed cartilaginous rays which support the somewhat expanded part of the fin. The *pelvic fin* skeleton is like that of the pectoral fin, except that preaxial radials are absent.

Alimentary Canal and Associated Structures.—The teeth (Fig. 253) consist of upper and lower *tooth-plates* derived during ontogeny from the coalescence of a number of small denticles. These become fixed to independently developed bony plates—the prevomer and palatopterygoids in the upper jaw and the coronoids in the lower.

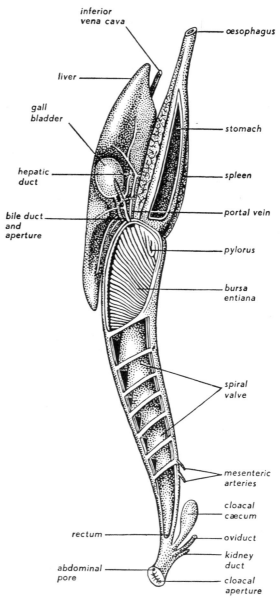

FIG. 254.—*Protopterus:* **Alimentary canal and associated structures.** The cystic ducts are not labelled. (Modified after W. N. Parker.)

The occlusal and labial surfaces of the tooth-plates are thrown into three major folds or cusps. In addition, there is a *lingual ridge* lying medially to the outer cusps.   The shape of the tooth-plates and the disposition of their cusps are essentially adaptations to crushing and shearing molluscs.   Paired *vomerine teeth* also occur.   A chief feature of the *alimentary canal* (Fig. 254) is the presence, throughout the length of the intestine, of a spiral valve.   It will be recalled that a spiral valve is present in elasmobranchs (p. 237), palæoniscoid derivatives (p. 326), and in *Latimeria* (Cœlacanthini, p. 360).   The rectum opens into a small cloaca.   The *liver* is large and unequally bilobed.   The gall-bladder lies between the small anterior lobe and the much larger posterior lobe.   A well-developed *pancreas* is embedded in the wall of the stomach and intestine, internal to the peritoneum. The pancreatic ductules unite and open into the bile-duct immediately before the latter enters the intestine.   Oesophageal, gastric, and intestinal epithelia are little different.   All are equipped with ciliated, columnar, and goblet cells.

Respiratory System.—The extent to which the adult *Protopterus* combines aquatic and aerial respiration has not been fully determined.   There are six *branchial arches*, with five open gill-clefts.   *Gill filaments* are developed only on the fourth and fifth branchial arches.   There is also an anterior *hyoidean hemibranch* and another *posterior hemibranch* associated with the sixth arch. Field and laboratory studies indicate that the adult *P. æthiopicus* is dependent on aerial respiration, since individuals prevented from breathing at the surface die of asphyxiation.   Doubtless the gill-filaments play some part in respiration, but their main function is probably associated with carbon-dioxide excretion. Four pairs of functional external gills occur in larval lung-fishes.   The external gills are atrophied or lost in the adult.

The lungs (Figs. 255, 256) are paired, elongate median dorsal sacs which open into a common pneumatic duct.   This duct is provided with a muscular chamber which opens into the ventral side of the œsophagus through a slit-like *glottis*.   The margins of the glottis are muscular, and there is an epiglottis-like *fibro-cartilaginous plate*.   Internally the cavity of each lung opens into a series of alveoli.   Each alveolus opens into lesser cavities, which in turn communicate with still smaller sacculi.   Hence, in structure the lungs basically resemble those of higher vertebrates (p. 107).   Phylogenetically, the lungs of *Protopterus* almost certainly correspond to the swim-bladder of bony fishes (p. 339).   They differ, however, in their blood supply (see below).   Blood reaches the lungs by a pair of pulmonary arteries which originate from the roots of the paired dorsal aortæ near the point of their junction to form the median dorsal aorta.

Blood-vascular System.—Correlated with the existence of lungs and a distinct pulmonary circulation (Fig. 256) there is a complication in cardiac structure.   The heart lies in a stiff-walled *pericardial cavity* (Fig. 257) situated below and somewhat behind the gills.   The sinus venosus is imperfectly divided into two parts, whilst the cavity of the atrium is divided by an almost complete septum.

Venous blood enters the right-hand division of the sinus venosus and passes through the right-hand chamber of the atrium to the partly divided ventricle. The pulmonary vein, by which oxygenated blood is returned to the heart from

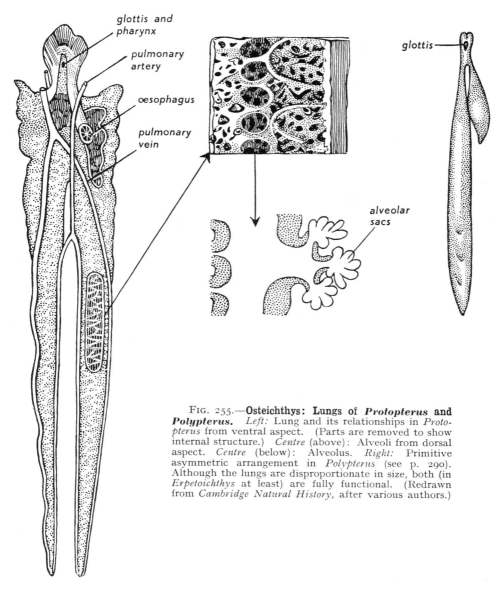

FIG. 255.—**Osteichthys: Lungs of *Protopterus* and *Polypterus*.** *Left:* Lung and its relationships in *Protopterus* from ventral aspect. (Parts are removed to show internal structure.) *Centre* (above): Alveoli from dorsal aspect. *Centre* (below): Alveolus. *Right:* Primitive asymmetric arrangement in *Polypterus* (see p. 290). Although the lungs are disproportionate in size, both (in *Erpetoichthys* at least) are fully functional. (Redrawn from *Cambridge Natural History*, after various authors.)

the lungs, passes through the sinus venosus and opens directly into the left side of the atrium. The large atrio-ventricular opening is fitted by a fibrous plug developed from the posterior margin of the opening. This characteristic structure, found only in the Dipnoi, can be raised or lowered to close or open the atrio-ventricular passage.   No true atrio-ventricular valves are developed.   A spirally twisted and weakly contractile conus arteriosus is present, but the ventral aorta is greatly reduced.   Internally, the conus is divided into two longitudinal channels.   This division is achieved by a longitudinal *compound valve* that abuts on one side of the conus against a longitudinal ridge on the

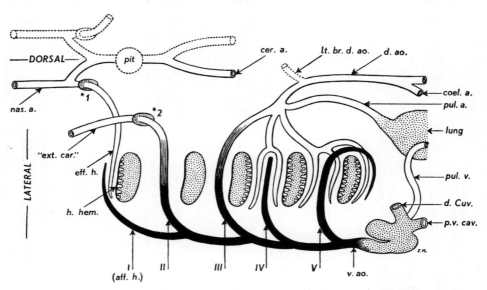

FIG. 256.—*Protopterus:* **Blood vascular and respiratory systems.** (From left side.) The blood from the lungs goes through the pulmonary veins into the left-hand division of the atrium. It is then directed by the valves of the heart into the ventral chamber of the short, horizontally-divided ventral aorta, thence probably proceeding direct to the anterior branchial vessels from which it is distributed to the brain and other cephalic structures.   (These, therefore, probably get the most highly oxygenated blood.)   The blood from the posterior vena cava is directed by the valve-system of the heart so as to pass into the upper channel of the ventral aorta, whence it is probably directed mainly into the more posterior branchial vessels.   Here some slight gas exchange may take place in the reduced gills.   Some of this blood probably returns to the lungs and some finds its way into the dorsal aorta to be distributed posteriorly (see Foxon).   I (*aff. hy.*), afferent hyoidean followed by afferent branchial arteries (II–V); *cer. a.*, cerebral artery; *cœl. a.*, cœliacomesenteric artery; *d. ao.*, dorsal aorta; *d. Cuv.*, ductus Cuvieri; *eff. h.*, efferent hyoidean artery; '*ext. car.*', 'external carotid' (continuous with branchial arch II); *h. hem.*, hyoidean hemibranch; *lt. br. d. ao.*, left branch of dorsal aorta; *nas. a.*, nasal artery; *pit.*, position of pituitary gland; *p. v. cav.*, posterior vena cava; *pul. a.*, pulmonary artery; *pul. v.*, pulmonary vein; *v. ao.*, ventral aorta; *1. marks point at which the nasal artery goes through the cranial wall; *2. point at which the 'external carotid' goes through squamosal area of the cranium to supply facial musculature and jaws.   (Greenwood and Marshall, unpubl.)

opposite side.   Oxygenated blood from the pulmonary vein flows almost directly into that division of the conus which is connected with the first two arches, and is thus carried into the carotid and cerebral circulation.   Venous blood, entering the right side of the heart, flows into the channel connected with the more posterior aortic arches, and is thus ultimately carried to the pulmonary circulation.

The four afferent branchial arteries originate close together, immediately in front of the conus, so that a ventral aorta scarcely exists. The afferent vessel to the hyoidean hemibranch arises from the first arch. A recurrent branch from the fourth arch supplies the posterior hemibranch.

In the two gill-less arches the aortic vessel is continuous, and not interrupted to form afferent and efferent vessels. In the hyoidean hemibranch, the posterior hemibranch, and in the two gill-bearing arches there are distinct afferent and efferent vessels. The *epibranchial arteries* from the gill-bearing arches are bifurcated and drain the hemibranchs of each arch. An efferent vessel from the posterior hemibranch joins that of the fifth (posterior gill-bearing arch). The four epibranchial arteries unite at about the same point to form a short common trunk on each side (the *paired dorsal aortæ*). In turn, these unite to form the *median dorsal aorta*. The pulmonary arteries arise from the paired aortæ slightly proximal to the union of the most posterior epibranchial; each divides into branches supplying the dorsal and ventral aspects of the lungs.

There are two *precavals* (*ductus Cuvieri*) (Fig. 257) as in dogfishes (p. 240). The right precaval is formed by the junction of the *inferior jugular, anterior cardinal,* and *subclavian* veins. The left precaval receives, in addition, the large posterior cardinal vein. There is no right posterior cardinal. The greater volume of blood from the posterior part of the

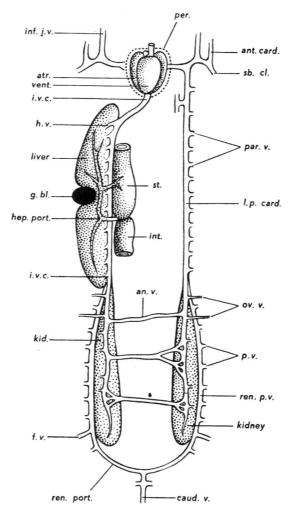

FIG. 257.—*Protopterus:* **Visceral relationships.** Diagrammatic. *ant. card.* anterior cardinal vein; *an. v.* anastomotic veins; *atr.* atrium; *caud. v.* caudal vein; *f. v.* femoral vein; *g. bl.* gall bladder; *hep. port.* hepatic portal vein; *h. v.* hepatic vein; *inf. j. v.* inferior jugular vein; *int.* intestine; *i. v. c.* inferior vena cava; *kid.* kidney; *l. p. card.* left posterior cardinal vein; *ov. v.* ovarian veins; *p. v.* parietal veins; *per.* pericardium; *ren. p. v.* renal portal veins; *sb. cl.* subclavian vein; *st.* stomach. (Modified after W. N. Parker.)

body is brought back to the heart by the inferior vena cava (Fig. 256), which discharges directly into the sinus venosus. Alone among fishes an inferior vena cava occurs in Dipnoi. It is invariably present in tetrapods (p. 404). The radicles of the inferior vena cava and the left posterior cardinal are formed by the *renal veins*; in their course to the heart both veins receive *genital* and *segmental veins*. Several *hepatic veins* open into the inferior vena cava during its passage through the liver. Posteriorly, the caudal vein divides into *left* and *right renal portal veins*, neither of which is, however, continuous with the inferior vena cava or the left post-cardinal vein. Each renal portal vein is joined by several *segmental veins* and by the *femoral veins*. There is an *intra-intestinal vein*. The *pulmonary veins* unite before discharging directly into the left auricle. It will be seen from the above that the plan of the blood-vascular system is in some respects intermediate between that of the Chondrichthyes (p. 219) and that of the Amphibia (p. 381).

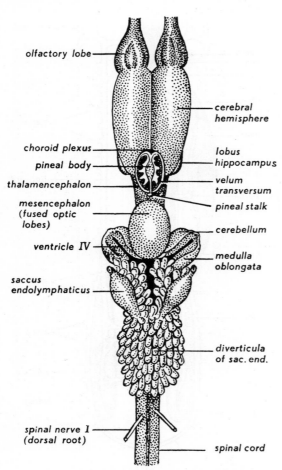

olfactory lobe

cerebral hemisphere

choroid plexus

lobus hippocampus

pineal body

thalamencephalon

velum transversum

mesencephalon (fused optic lobes)

pineal stalk

cerebellum

ventricle IV

medulla oblongata

saccus endolymphaticus

diverticula of sac. end.

spinal nerve 1 (dorsal root)

spinal cord

FIG. 258.—**Protopterus: Brain.** The significance of the peculiar saccus endolymphaticus, associated with the inner ear, is unknown. The central nervous system, like many other features, is reminiscent of the amphibian condition. (Modified after Burckhardt.)

A spleen is prominently present, producing both red cells and lymphocytes. The blood ' contains all the cellular varieties of higher forms ' (Downey).

Nervous System.—The brain (Fig. 258) is elongate and narrow, and shows great development of the cerebral hemispheres, which are distinct anteriorly but united behind. In their pronounced evagination the cerebral hemispheres recall those of amphibians, as does also the small size of the cerebellum. The olfactory lobes are sessile. The optic lobes form a single, oval body lying partly in front of the small cerebellum. A pineal body is present, and overlies a peculiar conical projection, the so-called *pineal pillow*, developed from the roof of the third ventricle. A *choroid plexus* covers the roof of the fourth ventricle, and an *anterior plexus*, in connection with the roof of the thalamencephalon, projects downwards into the third ventricle.

A *sympathetic system*, consisting of a very fine nerve-cord on each side of the dorsal aorta (below the notochord), has been described, associated with the vagus, in *P. annectens* by Giacomini.

General Metabolism and Excretion.—The elongated *kidneys* are separate anteriorly, but fused behind. They extend throughout the greater length of the visceral cavity. From each kidney a thick-walled duct opens separately into the cloaca. A cloacal *urinary bladder* is present.

Metabolism and excretion in *P. æthiopicus* have been studied extensively by Homer Smith. During the first week or so of æstivation (Fig. 259) the metabolic rate drops by about 50 per cent. It then decreases slowly until, after some three months, it is only about 10 or 15 per cent of that at the normal active feeding level. Under normal conditions the fish gulps air every ten or fifteen minutes; in æstivation it inspires at a minimum rate of once per hour and may, in fact, not breathe for several hours at a time. The cardiac rate slows to about three contractions per minute. The lung-fish may be relatively lean when it

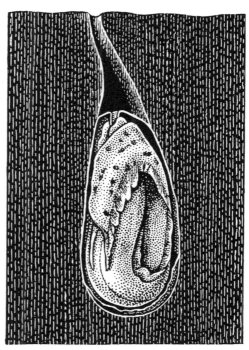

FIG. 259.—***Protopterus*: Aestivation.** While buried in mud *P. annectens* is curled inside a parchment-like, waterproof cocoon of dried mucus that is perforated only by a short respiratory funnel from mouth to tunnel. The cocoon prevents desiccation. Special excretory mechanisms prevent autointoxication (see text). (Modified after W. N. Parker.)

goes into æstivation, and after the first few days the reserve carbohydrate is exhausted, and it then metabolises fat and protein in about equal degree. The cloacal aperture is sealed by the cocoon, and nitrogenous metabolites are stored essentially as comparatively non-toxic urea, so that after about three years the urea may constitute as much as 3 per cent of the total body-weight. Inorganic sulphate, too, is stored, but there is no evidence of the formation of inorganic phosphate or the production of normal by-products such as creatine, creatinine, ketone bodies, uric acids, and ammonia. Active lung-fishes excrete between 30 and 70 per cent of their nitrogenous metabolites through the gills as ammonia (and the remainder mostly as urea). Ammonia, a highly toxic substance, is entirely absent in the buried fish, which thus avoids autointoxication. Upon its return to water the animal quickly discharges the stored urea through its gills, and after a brief period of osmotic inbalance (during which it appears somewhat waterlogged) normal excretory function is re-established.

Reproduction.—The paired ovaries are separate and in close proximity to the kidneys. The oviducts are paired tubes that open anteriorly into the

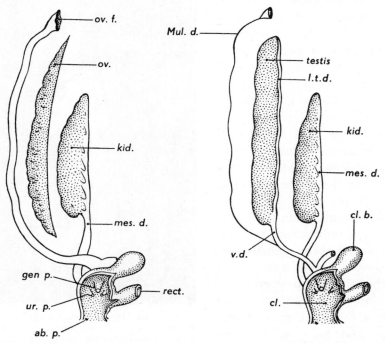

FIG. 260.—*Protopterus:* **Urinogenital system.** The similarity to the amphibian arrangement is striking. *Left:* Female. *ab. p.* abdominal pore; *gen. p.* genital papilla and pore; *kid.* kidney; *mes. d.* mesonephric duct; *ov.* ovary; *ov. f.* oviducal funnel; *rect.* rectum; *ur. p.* urinary papilla. (After Ayers and W. N. Parker.) *Right: cl.* cloaca; *cl. b.* cloacal bladder; *kid.* kidney; *l. t. d.* longitudinal testis duct; *Mul. d.* vestigial Müllerian duct; *v. d.* vas deferens. The association between gonad and kidney is much closer than shown in the present diagram. (After W. N. Parker.)

visceral cavity (Fig. 260). Posteriorly the oviducts coalesce before opening into the cloaca. A well-defined genital papilla and pore is present in the cloaca. At the approach of spawning the oviducts of a 'ripe' female may contain as many as 2,000 eggs. The ovaries in addition hold about 4,000 in an advanced stage of development (Greenwood).

The *testes* (Fig. 260) are elongate and, like the ovaries, are closely associated with the kidneys, lying along their lateral border. Each testis is differentiated into an anterior spermatogenic portion and a posterior tubular part which acts as a *vesicula seminalis*. There is a great reduction in the number of vasa efferentia, which are confined to the posterior part of testis and open into the kidney duct. Vestigial Müllerian ducts are present.

Development.—The following information refers to the West African *P. annectens*. In general, however, it covers also the embryology of *P. æthiopicus*,

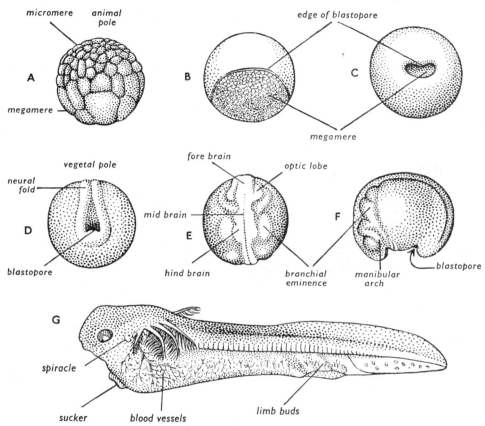

Fig. 261.—***Protopterus:* Development.** Note points of similarity (*e.g.* total cleavage and the formation of the yolk-plug) with the Amphibia. A. one day after fertilisation; B. two days, showing beginning of gastrulation; C. three days, showing late stage in closure of blastopore; D. four days; showing neural folds encircling blastopore; E. late on fourth day, showing differentiation of head region, branchial region, and pronephros; F. fifth day, showing early differentiation of external gills and sucker; G. larva 10 days after fertilisation and two days after hatching. (Modified after Budgett.)

except that the larvæ of the latter remain in the nest for about fifty days and breathe atmospheric air at an earlier stage. The slower rate of development in *P. æthiopicus* is perhaps related to the lower water temperatures at which the embryos develop (Greenwood). The eggs (Fig. 261) are about 3·5–4 mm. in diameter. Each egg becomes broken up during cleavage into large, pale green, yolky cells at the vegetal pole (megameres), and smaller, pink cells at the animal pole (micromeres) (Fig. 261 A). During gastrulation the yolky cells become invaginated through a blastopore, the pink cells gradually extending until they cover the whole egg (B and C). The blastopore is the place where the hind end of the embryo will be. The neural folds arise at the head end first, and then gradually develop along the trunk and tail regions until they eventually enclose the blastopore (D). The various regions of the brain and branchial arches are soon distinguishable externally (E and F).

The four pairs of external gills are well developed at hatching, and a tail has begun to form. An auditory capsule is present. The young larvæ are at first non-pigmented, and they remain in the nest for about three weeks (Bud-

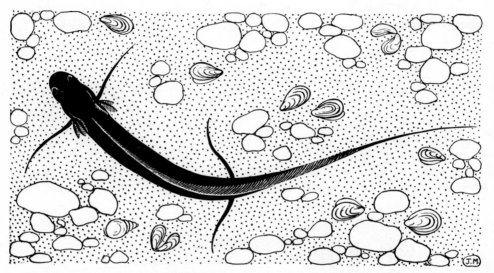

FIG. 262.—*Protopterus:* **Development.** Young *P. æthiopicus* with reduced external gills shortly after leaving the nest. They are found among the protective matted roots of papyrus and other lake-side plants where they feed on oligochætes and small bivalves. (From photograph and specimens.)

gett). They attach themselves to the walls of the nest with a ventral sucker (G). They probably do not feed, but obtain nourishment from their yolk stores. At this stage a network of blood-vessels is visible on the yolk-filled belly.

When the larvæ leave the nest they have become pigmented, have developed limbs, and are practically adult in form (Fig. 262). Their yolk supplies are almost gone and they soon start to feed on animal material. Their external gills become reduced and about a month after leaving the nest they begin to breathe air. The lung develops from a downgrowth in the floor of the pharynx. The rudiment grows backwards and eventually becomes bi-lobed. The lungs of *Protopterus* therefore have the same origin as those of terrestrial vertebrates, although they subsequently move around to the dorsal side of the alimentary canal and come to lie under the vertebral column. *Pinkus' organ* develops from the spiracular rudiment. This structure, of doubtful function, is known to occur only in *Protopterus* and *Lepidosiren*.

GENERAL ORGANISATION OF DIPNOI

The three genera of living Dipnoi are allied in all the essential features of their structure. Therefore it is only necessary to mention here the principal points in which *Neoceratodus* and *Lepidosiren* differ from *Protopterus*. *Protopterus* and *Lepidosiren* resemble one another more closely than either resembles *Neoceratodus* and are placed in the same family, the Lepidosirenidæ.

The *limbs* of *Lepidosiren* are similar to those of *Protopterus*, but in *Neoceratodus* they are broad and leaf-like, with a correspondingly modified skeleton. The tapering central axis is composed of a stout basal cartilage and a number of short, cartilaginous segments, with serially arranged rows of jointed, cartilaginous radialia projecting on either side. The *skull* of *Neoceratodus* differs somewhat from the lepidosirenid type, being an undivided mass, devoid of fontanelles. In many respects it resembles the skull of the fossil dipnoan *Ceratodus*, and is more primitive than that of lepidosirenids. Furthermore, true splenials and vestigial dentaries are present.

There are two lungs in *Protopterus* (Fig. 255) and *Lepidosiren*, but only one in *Neoceratodus*. The monopneumonous condition in *Neoceratodus* is possibly due to the suppression of the original left lobe (Goodrich). The internal structure of the lung, too, is simpler in this species. In *Neoceratodus* only four pairs of *gills* are developed, but each gill arch carries a double row of filaments. The hyoidean ' gill ' is a true pseudobranch. A peculiarity in this genus is that the branchial lamellæ of each gill arch extends on to the dorsal and ventral walls of the gill cleft, so that the hemibranchs of each cleft are continuous, both dorsally and ventrally. The fifth arch lacks gills.

Differences in the *branchial systems* of *Protopterus*, on the one hand, and *Neoceratodus*, on the other, are probably correlated with the more aquatic habitus of the latter. *Neoceratodus* does not æstivate, and is said to inhabit only permanent waters. It resorts to aerial respiration when the water becomes foul during the dry season. Although able to live in stagnant water that is toxic to other fishes, *Neoceratodus* dies if removed from water. It is not asphyxiated by prolonged immersion.

External gills are developed in the larvæ of *Lepidosiren* (Fig. 262), but not in *Neoceratodus*. Vestiges of the external gills persist in adult *Protopterus annectens* and *P. amphibius*. During the breeding season vascular filaments develop on the pelvic fins of male *Lepidosiren*. The function of these filaments is unknown, but it is thought that they may serve as accessory respiratory organs.

The *vascular system* of *Lepidosiren* closely resembles that of *Protopterus* (Fig. 256). In *Neoceratodus*, however, there are several points of difference. The heart in this genus is less specialised, in that the longitudinal septa of the conus are incomplete and represented by longitudinally arranged valves. Consequently there is more mixing of oxygenated and deoxygenated blood supplied to the anterior afferent vessels. Since there is a hyoidean pseudo-branch (as opposed to a hemibranch in *Protopterus* and *Lepidosiren*), the anterior afferent vascular system is different. The pseudobranch is supplied by a vessel from the efferent branchial artery of the first gill-arch. Anterior and posterior cerebral arteries originate from the pseudobranch.

The venous system in *Protopterus* and *Lepidosiren* is very similar, and represents in general a more advanced evolutionary stage than that of *Neoceratodus*. An abdominal vein, derived from the union of the pelvic veins, is present in *Neoceratodus*, but not in the other genera.

The *brain* of *Neoceratodus* differs from that of *Protopterus* (and *Lepidosiren*) in having paired optic lobes and a clearly demarcated bulbus and lobus in the olfactory tract. In each genus the alimentary canal is similar in most respects except for differences in dentition.

In the *urinogenital system* the kidneys are relatively more elongate in *Protopterus* and *Lepidosiren* than in *Neoceratodus*. In *Lepidosiren* the posterior aspects are unfused.

The testes of *Protopterus* and *Lepidosiren* are elongate, and divisible into an anterior, longer spermatogenic part and a posterior vesicula seminalis. In *Neoceratodus* and *Lepidosiren* about six vasa efferentia rise from the posterior region and enter the mesonephric tubule, the spermatozoa then passing through the mesonephric ducts. This arrangement shows considerable affinity with the Amphibia.

In *Protopterus* it has been demonstrated that the homologue of the adrenal medulla occurs in the walls of the intercostal branches of the dorsal aorta (Giacomini) and its chromaffin cells are innervated from the sympathetic chains (Holmes). It has been further suggested by Holmes that the cortical homo-logue may be widely distributed as diffuse specialised tissue identifiable in various organs throughout the body cavity.

CLASS AMPHIBIA

INTRODUCTION

The Amphibia, the first vertebrates to become adapted to life on land, may be distinguished from the choanate fishes, their predecessors, chiefly by their pentadactyle limbs, the absence of fin-rays in the unpaired fins (when these are present), and by the presence of a middle ear (see p. 144). The class falls into two main stems, one of which includes the frogs and toads (Anura) and the other the newts, salamanders (Urodela), and superficially worm-like Apoda (Gymnophiona). There were also a number of extinct orders, dating from the late Devonian, which were particularly numerous in Carboniferous and Permian times.

The earliest known anuran ancestor, *Protobatrachus*,[1] did not appear until the early Mesozoic. This animal, unquestionably frog-like, possessed a tail in the adult, but the skull was similar to those of modern frogs, except that an opisthotic was retained. The ribs were short, and the skin impression shows it had a frog-like waist. The presacral vertebræ were reduced in number, although there were more than eight. There were free caudal vertebræ. The animal was frog-like in having an elongate ilium and a fairly long femur, but the radius and ulna, and the tibia and fibula, were separate. The earliest true frog remains occur in the Upper Jurassic. The urodeles, too, have not been found before that period. No fossil Apoda has been discovered. To-day the most terrestrial Amphibia are the Anura. The Urodela have retreated once more to the water, and the degenerate Apoda into moist holes in the ground.

Typically, amphibians breathe by means of gills in the various larval stages, and by lungs when adult. The gills are retained by the adults of some urodeles, and the skin, which is usually naked, often plays an important part in respiration. The skull is *autostylic* (p. 94), and the free hyomandibula has been converted into a *columella auris*, which lies in the upper part of the spiracle between the inner ear and the *tympanic membrane* that is stretched on the outer part of the skull. In all but a few of the early forms there is an opening in the side of the ear capsule, the *fenestra ovalis*, through which the columella auris conveys sound-vibrations to the inner ear. The above elaboration is another

A number of equally important points should be briefly noted with regard

---

[1] Hecht (1962) believes that the resemblances between *Protobatrachus* and the Anura may be the result of convergence.

to skeleton and musculature.   The skull has become movably attached to the vertebral column by means of either one, or two, *condyles*.   An *interclavicle*, already present in osteolepiform fish, serves to brace the two halves of the shoulder-girdle together, and the pelvis became attached to the vertebral column, typically by a single sacral vertebra.   In modern forms only ten intra-cranial nerves occur; some of the Labyrinthodontia (p. 388) had twelve.

Although many of the old comparisons between the amphibian limb of to-day and the paired fins of selachians and *Polypterus* are of only historical interest, gross anatomical, and embryological, studies have shown that the complex system of tetrapod limb-muscles are arranged in two series that are derived from the simpler musculature of the upper and lower aspects of fins. Again, a comparison of the bony and skeletal structures of crossopterygians and

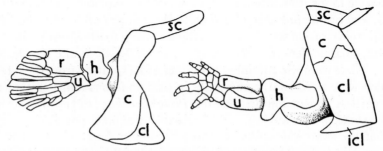

FIG. 263.—**The fish—amphibian transition: Shoulder girdle and fore-limb.** Comparison between a Devonian crossopterygian (*Sauripterus*) (left) and a primitive tetrapod.   *c.* cleithrum; *cl.* clavicle; *h.* humerus; *icl.* interclavicle; *r.* radius; *sc.* supracleithrum; *u.* ulna. (From Romer, partly after Gregory.)

early (fossil) amphibians shows how closely allied the two limbs really are (Fig. 263).   The earliest tetrapods were, in essence, highly specialised walking fishes with lungs.   This enormously interesting and important initial move-ment from water to land is now understood in broad outline.

There has been accumulated considerable evidence that suggests a mono-phyletic origin of all tetrapods from 'a single osteolepid type in the latter half of Devonian time' (Westoll).   The gradual colonisation of dry land depended not merely on the development of efficient lungs and walking legs.   Almost every part of the animal body was involved—the integument, skeleton, nervous system, special senses, blood vascular system, and so on.   Not only did animals require to breathe atmospheric oxygen and to walk : they had to withstand desiccation, rid themselves of the lateral line (in the adult), detect air-borne substances of a much greater dilution, and see and hear predators and prey at much greater distances—to mention only a few very obvious lines of adaptation. At the same time *no new organs were formed*.

Therefore it is possible that the changeover process may, under special environmental conditions that favoured the selection of special characteristics, have occurred relatively quickly in terms of geological time. It would seem that all the changes, however profound they appear at first sight if we compare, say, a cœlacanth and a frog, are readily explicable in terms of Darwinian–Mendelian inheritance. It is to-day a commonplace that genic segregation, recombination, and (rarely, but commonly enough) mutation constitute a mechanism which can generate, in conjunction with environmental selection pressure, changes and characters of a 'high degree of improbability' (Fisher). The state of the environment, and therefore natural selection, dictates probably the tempo and certainly the direction of subsequent events.

The Devonian period (p. 3), when fish were the dominant large animals, was an age of great climatic instability. There is evidence that the fresh-water streams and lagoons of that time were alternately filled and dried out in violent extremes of flood and drought. Such conditions of periodic desiccation theoretically should result in the extinction of numerous species, and at the same time favour the survival of the few possessed of physiological and structural adaptations suitable to function in the new conditions.

We have already seen that a bony supporting skeleton, osmotic homeostasis, internal nares, and lungs (to mention only three fundamental attributes) had been developed by ancient bony freshwater fishes. In the crossopterygians the appearance of two pairs of highly mobile, muscular, lobe-like lateral fins, supported by bones (Fig. 263), gave an indication of later possibilities in the development of walking legs as we know them in modern tetrapods. This is a classic example of *pre-adaptation*—the possession by an organism of characters that are conducive to its survival under altered conditions.

Buoyant progression in water, however, is a vastly different matter from terrestrial locomotion with its additional gravitational complications. The problems created by the gradual removal of the tetrapod body from the water were met by profound, but not radical, skeletal, muscular, and other changes in all parts of the body. Gross mechanical and structural adaptations (including new facets for the attachment of modified muscles) occurred particularly in the occiput, the central cantilever vertebral column, and the pectoral and pelvic girdles. The head, no longer largely supported by water, now required a more powerful musculature and corresponding elaboration of articular surfaces in the skull and adjacent endoskeleton. The lower jaws, no less than the neuro-cranium, required an elaborated musculature for their operation and support. The vertebral column had increasingly to support body weight : it gained in ossification and strength. It developed elaborate articulatory mechanisms, and serial apophyses for the anchorage of the modified musculature. The girdles had now simultaneously to provide support in locomotion and also to protect vital viscera from the injury threatened by the new upward thrusts involved. In fishes, each dermal girdle had constituted the posterior wall of the nearby gill-chamber and, in addition, had provided anterior anchorage for the locomotory myotomal muscles. With the advent of heavy upward pressures consequent upon walking, the dermal skeleton declined, and there arose anteriorly a powerful scapula (shoulder-blade) which became bound to the front ribs (of the thorax); and, posteriorly, there arose the triradiate pelvic apparatus, including the elaboration of the ilium with which we shall become familiar. In each girdle region arose supplementary modifications— such as endoskeletal processes for the firmer attachment of muscles, and (later on) the developed specialised limb-bones, including digits and other refinements.

Equally, the conquest of land depended on at least a primitive means of aerial respiration. It was formerly generally believed that the swim-bladder (p. 339) gave rise to the lung—a not unnatural conclusion, because the air-bladder at first sight appears as typical of bony fishes as is the lung of tetrapods. We now know that the primitive lung is a characteristic of ancient fishes; and it is usually held that it came first and that from it evolved the swim-bladder, an organ of specialised hydrostatic and other function found only in bony fishes. It seems certain that the swim-bladder reached its present efficiency only when the ancestors of the actinopterygians took to the sea. In the Devonian the development of a respiratory sac, however primitive, but at least capable of absorbing atmospheric oxygen, would be of immense importance to early fishes (as it is with some extant lung-fishes (p. 375)) that were compelled to live in water that became periodically low in level and clogged with rotting vegetation.

This periodic drying up of swamps placed a premium on the possession of the means to move up or downstream or across country from a drying locality to one that remained moist. Limbs thus paradoxically may have been a means of survival because they first allowed their possessors to remain in water, not to escape from it. Certainly some of the early tetrapods still retained the lateral line. So much granted, it is easy to imagine that types which possessed locomotory, respiratory, integumentary, excretory, and sensory specialisations related to drought survival would prosper and reproduce. Those whose adaptations were directed towards purely aquatic efficiency would fail.

More or less direct, and relatively unchanged, descendants of certain of the survivors are to be seen in the Dipnoi (lung-fishes) (p. 361). It should be emphasised, however, that there is no suggestion that the tetrapods are descended from even the most ancient Dipnoi. Both groups probably owe their ancestry either to ancient osteolepid, or to even earlier, rhipidistian freshwater fishes (p. 354) that flourished in the mid-Palæozoic (p. 3).

A comparison of the earliest Amphibia with Palæozoic fishes shows many resemblances between the embolomerous labyrinthodonts and the osteolepids of the Devonian. This is particularly marked in the general structure of the skulls (Fig. 285 B); in the similar 'labyrinthodont' pattern of the teeth (Fig. 280);

in the possession of large palatal 'tusks', and, to a less degree, in the pectoral and pelvic girdles. The comparison of the two types of archaic animals throws light on the probable mode of origin of certain tetrapod structures.

Along with the development of limbs, and increased efficiency of aerial respiration, the Amphibia suffered a remarkable *loss* of true biting, as apart from holding, teeth (though at least one genus, *Amphignathodon*, appears to have re-developed some). The earliest amphibians were probably piscivorous, but a drastic alteration in diet was compelled by their change from aquatic to terrestrial life. They were forced, by virtue of their imperfect adaptation, to confine their feeding to slow-moving prey such as snails, slugs, and later (some of them) to insects and other creatures that could be reached, and anchored, with a sudden flick of the muscular, protrusible, and sticky tongue which they later developed. The lateral line system, too, was soon lost in the early land-living adult amphibians, but was retained in the larvæ. Along with the loss of the lateral line in adults there have been remarkable modifications of other sensory organs, as will be seen later.

The amphibian skin became heavily keratinised. This assisted water retention, but at the same time allowed cutaneous respiration (p. 403). Yet, although certain toads inhabit relatively dry areas, amphibians in general cannot live away from moist situations. It is true that a very few anurans can survive in deserts but these (e.g. *Cyclorana* of Central Australia) do so by means of peculiar adaptations such as æstivation under dry caked mud, assisted by water storage allowed by the partial loss of kidney glomeruli. The water is held in the urinary bladder, peritoneal cavity, and subcutaneous tissues. If a lean *Cyclorana* is put into a beaker with two inches of water it resembles 'a somewhat knobbly tennis ball' within two minutes (Launcelot Harrison, cited by Buxton). Certain desert tribes of Australian aborigines know of this water storage and dig the toads out in times of extremity.

The permeability of the amphibian integument, then, has imposed serious limitations on the choice of habitat, as well as upon geographical distribution. A frog placed in sea-water dies very quickly—a moment's reflection will show the osmotic consequences of such a transfer.[1] This limitation reduces the possibilities of (but has not wholly prevented) the successful chance-transfer from island to island which has been an important factor in the geographical distribution of the higher groups (*e.g.* the migration on driftwood of rodents to Australia and to other islands). Again, the inevitable failure of the Amphibia to develop temperature control further limits their chances of land colonisation.

---

[1] Nevertheless, at least two euryhaline frogs have evolved. Both the mangrove-dwelling, crab-eating *Rana cancrivora* of Thailand, and the green toad (*Bufo viridis*) of Europe and the Middle East, can live in a highly salty environment. Adult *R. cancrivora* can tolerate salinity as high as 28%, and tadpoles 39%, at 30° C. For remarks on the striking physiological convergence between *R. cancrivora* and the ureotelic elasmobranchs see Gordon, *et al.* (1961); also Gordon (1962), in connection with *B. viridis*.

Fishes, although poikilothermous ('cold-blooded'),[1] can live in waters below the pack-ice of the coldest seas. Air is a much less efficient heat-conductor than water, and terrestrial animals are therefore subjected to violent fluctuations of temperature in deserts and, particularly, at high altitudes. Thus, although amphibians could exist comfortably in summer time in the high Arctic (as do insects), they could not survive winter there: they would be frozen hard for months.

Of the three surviving amphibian groups, the Anura (frogs and toads) are abundant in all the greater zoogeographical regions, but are represented by only one native genus in New Zealand and are absent from most oceanic islands. The Urodela (newts and salamanders) are almost exclusively Palæarctic and Nearctic forms, occurring in North America, Europe, Asia, and North Africa. A few species extend southwards into the Neotropical and Oriental regions. The Apoda (Gymnophiona, Cæcilia), on the other hand, are mainly tropical, occurring in the Neotropical, Ethiopian, and Oriental regions. They are absent from Madagascar, Australasia, and the Pacific Islands.

Dependence on relatively warm conditions affected the distribution of amphibians in past times as well as to-day. There is much fossil evidence that frogs, toads, and newts inhabited Britain before the last ice age. As the ice sheets swept over Europe the Amphibia perished, but during interglacial periods they gradually re-established themselves. Only a few species reached Britain before it was separated from the rest of the Continent. Fewer still reached Ireland, which was separated even earlier (see also p. 460).

Although amphibians were the dominant land-fauna in the Carboniferous, little more than 2,000 species live to-day, although some remain plentiful in appropriate areas. From the time of their emergence they have remained imperfectly adapted to terrestrial life : most land-going species remained dependent on fresh water for reproduction. The primitive tunnelling Apoda generally lay their eggs in damp burrows. Among the Anura, even the dry-skinned toads need water or damp earth to breed. Tree-frogs lay their eggs in water-filled notches and hollows. Others carry their eggs in pits and pouches in the skin, and another hatches its eggs in the damp vocal sacs of the male (p. 454). The male Obstetric Toad (*Alytes*) envelops his body and hind legs with strings of eggs, and thus keeps them moist. The Egg-pill Toadlet (*Metacrinia nichollsi*) of Western Australia lives under stones and logs, and in the galleries of the nests of a savage bull-ant (*Myrmecia regularis*) as a tolerated guest. Brooks found large eggs so coated in dust that they resemble pills covered with powdered cinnamon. This might retard evaporation. The tadpole stage passes before they hatch, and if put in water the young toadlets sink helplessly to the bottom. In another anuran genus, the African bufonid *Nectophrynoides* (p. 430), well-yolked eggs are developed but the young are retained within the

---

[1] The term 'cold-blooded' is not altogether desirable. The blood of a reptile in a desert in mid-summer is probably much warmer than that of warm-blooded mammals nearby.

oviduct, from which they emerge as perfect froglets. The elongated tadpole tails are highly vascular and effect respiratory transference from the maternal circulation. Up to 200 young may be borne by each female.

These and other bizarre adaptations (p. 453) are an expression of the amphibian inability successfully to colonise a wider, dryer world. The vast majority of Amphibia require a damp environment in which to breed because their eggs and embryos must extract oxygen and food from the surrounding water and at the same time excrete waste material directly into it. They have developed no protective shell, as have reptiles (p. 457), birds (p. 645), and primitive mammals (p. 693), and they lay down little yolk for the nourishment of the growing young. We will see later (p. 457) how the development of the amnion, allantois, yolk sac, and a horny or calcareous shell has enabled higher tetrapods to develop in a fluid environment untroubled by most of the hazards of dry land.

The need of a damp breeding environment, the permeability of the skin, and the imperfections of the blood vascular system rigidly limited the chances of survival away from water, and the development of amphibians as large terrestrial animals capable of effective competition with reptiles and birds. In the Carboniferous the Amphibia were able to flourish : to-day they are phylogenetically senile. It remained for the reptiles to escape completely from the water (though some have returned to it) and to give rise to the higher tetrapods which later came to dominate earth and air.

It is plain that the Permian amphibians had already become far too specialised to have been ancestral to the reptiles (traces of which are found in the Carboniferous), but the earliest reptiles are so similar to the Carboniferous labyrinthodonts that it is often hard to distinguish between them. A principal difference lies in the composition of the vertebræ, for, while amphibians tended to reduce the posterior pleurocentra, the reptiles reduced the anterior intercentra and evolved gastrocentrous vertebræ.

Although the Amphibia are, as mentioned above, a relatively unsuccessful class to-day, many individual species in special habitats achieve a considerable biomass, particularly in damp tropical regions. Even in temperate countries frogs can be extremely numerous. In one night alone 500 lb. of frogs' *legs* (*Rana pipiens*) were gathered in one half-mile stretch in the eastern United States (Noble). A few amphibians have become adapted to relatively severe climatic conditions—a species of *Bufo*, for example, lives on the Himalayas at 14,000 feet. As regards longevity, a salamander (*Megalobatrachus*) survived for fifty-two years in the Amsterdam Aquarium. The numerous stories of anurans living for centuries entombed in rocks are of course untrue. Such tales have currency in every country because eggs are occasionally washed into cavities and develop there ; and the adult sometimes survives for a time by means of food particles washed in by the same minute aperture that admitted the original egg.

A frog is generally used as an elementary type in the study of vertebrate morphology largely because of an almost universal availability and because many points of internal anatomy can be demonstrated merely by opening the body cavity. It need hardly be said that frogs (or *Necturus*, the urodele 'mud-puppy' used in many North American universities) cannot be considered truly typical of the Amphibia, as a glance at the condensed classification below will show.

This classification, while being 'vertical' and provisional, is at least 'an attempt to establish two major lines of descent each of which includes both older and younger elements' (Romer). These are, firstly, the Apsidospondyli, with several long-extinct labyrinthodont (p. 422) orders, including probably the Seymouriamorpha and the frogs; and secondly, the Lepospondyli (p. 430), including extinct orders as well as salamanders and the Apoda.

Some may regret the abandonment of the older classification involving the recognition of the Stegocephalia but this, as emphasised both by Watson and Romer, was an unnatural grouping. It mainly distinguished between geologically older and younger amphibians and had relatively little regard to their true relationships. Little virtue exists in perpetuating a useless and to some extent misleading concept merely on grounds of antiquity. It is now abundantly evident, for example, that *modern* amphibians are not a simple monophyletic assemblage but at least diphyletic. The many resemblances between the highly specialised frogs and salamanders of to-day are probably due to convergence as much as to their common origin perhaps nearly 300 million years ago.

CLASS AMPHIBIA

Sub-class Apsidospondyli
  Super-order Labyrinthodontia
    Orders Ichthyostegalia (Upper Devonian–Upper Carboniferous)
      Rhachitomi (Lower Carboniferous–Permian)
      Stereospondyli (Triassic)
      Embolomeri (Upper Carboniferous–Permian)
      Seymouriamorpha (Upper Carboniferous–Upper Permian)
  Super-order Salientia
    Orders Eoanura (Upper Carboniferous)
      Proanura (Lower Triassic)
      Anura (Salientia) (Upper Jurassic–Recent)
Sub-class Lepospondyli
  Orders Aistopoda (Carboniferous)
    Nectridia (Upper Carboniferous–Permian)
    Microsauria (Adelospondyli) (Lower Carboniferous–Permian)
    Urodela (Caudata) (Cretaceous–Recent)
    Apoda (Gymnophiona, Cæcilia) (? Recent)

EXAMPLE OF THE CLASS.—A FROG (RANA)

Rana temporaria is the most common British frog, and is found in ponds and damp situations all over the country. *R. esculenta* is the large green edible frog found on the continent of Europe, where its hind-legs, garnished with spices, are essentially a delicacy. It has been introduced into England. *R. pipiens* and *R. catesbiana* are common North American members of the genus. Other species of the same genus occur in all parts of the world except New Zealand, the southern part of South America, and various oceanic islands.

The Ranidæ, along with other anurans, are peculiarly specialised both in skeletal structure and muscular arrangement for the thrusting movements of the elongated hind-legs by which they jump and swim. In fishes, the vertebral column is essentially a pliable rod which is resistant to the tendency towards body-shortening caused by the serially contracting swimming muscles (p. 86). The new modes of locomotion, sometimes in a new environment—land—have given the vertebral rod a new task : it must now act as a central girder or ridge-pole for the support of the weight-bearing limbs. In conjunction with these are developed other structures in the pectoral and pelvic girdles to ensure the smooth articulation and functioning of the limbs. We shall see, equally allied to changed mode of locomotion, considerable departures in the arrangement of dorsal, lateral, and ventral muscles as well.

External Characters.—There is no exoskeleton. The *trunk* is short and stout, and is continued, without the intermediation of a neck, into the broad, depressed *head*. There is no trace of a tail, the *cloacal aperture* being terminal. The *mouth* also is terminal, and is characterised by its extraordinary width, the gape extending considerably behind the eye. On the dorsal surface of the snout are the small *nostrils*. The *eyes* are large and prominent, and each is provided with an *upper eyelid* in the form of a thick fold of skin and a *nictitating membrane*. This is a much thinner fold, which arises from the lower margin of the eye and can be drawn up over it. Close behind the eye is a circular area of tensely-stretched skin, the *tympanic membrane*, a structure not met with in any fish, and absent in the two other orders of *living* Amphibia. As we shall see, this is an accessory part of the auditory organ. There is no trace of branchial apertures.

The back has a peculiar bend or hump in the sitting posture which marks the position of the sacral vertebra. The limbs are of very unequal size. The *forelimbs* are short. Each consists of an *upper arm*, or *brachium*, which, in the ordinary position, is directed backwards and downwards from the shoulder-joint ; a *fore-arm*, or *antebrachium*, directed downwards and forwards from the elbow ; and a *hand*, or *manus*, ending in four short, tapering *digits*, directed forwards. The *hind-limb* is of great size. In the usual squatting posture the *thigh* or *femur* is directed downwards, outwards, and forwards from the thigh-joint, the *shank* or *crus*, inwards, backwards, and upwards from the knee.   The *foot* (*pes*) consists of two parts : a *tarsal region* directed downwards from the heel-joint, and five long, slender *digits* united by thin *webs*.   Thus the limbs are placed in such a way that the elbow and knee face one another.   The first digit of the frog's hand represents the *index finger* of Man.   That of the foot represents the *hallux* or great toe, and is turned inwards or towards the median plane of the body.

The *skin* is variable in colour (see below).   Generally it is greyish-brown in *R. temporaria*, greenish in *R. esculenta*, and is mottled, in both species, with dark brown or black.   In *R. temporaria* there is a large black patch over the tympanic region.   Sexual differences occur in both species.   In *R. temporaria* there is a large, black, glandular swelling on the inner side of the hand of the male.   This *nuptial pad*, which is less prominently developed in *R. esculenta*, facilitates the male's grip during amplexus (p. 418).   In *R. esculenta* and *R. ridibunda* the male has, at each angle of the mouth, a loose fold of skin, the *vocal sac*, which can be inflated from within the mouth into a globular form (Fig. 298, p. 443).

The skin is attached to the body-wall only at certain definitive points on ridges of connective tissue which are also the boundaries of subcutaneous lymph spaces (p. 115), of a semi-permeable character.   The skin is of great importance as a respiratory organ on land: there is evidence that lung respiration alone is insufficient to support life ashore and that the skin may excrete a greater amount of carbon dioxide than the lungs.   Further, during æstivation and hibernation the animal respires entirely by means of the skin.

The external respiratory surface is kept moist by the colourless secretions from mucous and serous glands.   The mucus makes the frog slimy and difficult for its enemies to hold and is also toxic in some species (p. 437).   The characteristic odours of frogs have their origin in glandular secretions.

Although the basic colour-pattern does not alter, the ground-colour of the skin of frogs can change slowly but completely as a result of environmental stimuli.   Placed in a dark, moist environment a frog darkens within a few hours and becomes black within a few days.   Removed to a dry, very light environment it pales within a few hours, and within a couple of days turns light yellow.   Unusually low temperatures cause darkening.   The neuro-endocrine basis of colour change, involving the *melanophores* of the skin, is discussed later (p. 450).   In addition, the melanophores can be directly influenced through the epidermis.   As well as the deeply situated black melanophores, the skin also contains layers of *guanophores*, enclosing almost colourless crystals of guanine, and yellow *lipophores* which lie close below the epidermis. The various colours of the skin of frogs are produced both by pigments and purely physical phenomena.   The melanophores are responsible for the appearance of black or dusky hues ; the lipophores produce yellow or gold.   When a frog's skin appears green it is because all other visible components of light are eliminated in one way or another. The melanophores absorb light of certain wavelengths; and the guanine crystals produce by diffraction a blue-green colour from which the blue or near blue are filtered by lipophores. *Rana temporaria* sometimes exhibits a certain amount of red which is thought to come from red pigment granules in the lipophores. Blue, which sometimes appears in *R. esculenta* (and in several tree-frogs), results from the absence of the yellow of lipophores which, in most species, screens it out.

Endoskeleton.—The *vertebral column* (Fig. 264) is remarkable for its extreme shortness, and, compared with fishes, its inflexibility. It consists of only nine vertebræ (*V. 1–V. 9*), the last followed by a slender, bony rod, the *urostyle* (*UST.*). The second to the seventh vertebræ have similar characters. The *centrum* (B. *cn.*) is somewhat depressed and has a concave anterior and a convex posterior face—a form known as *procœlous*. Each half of the *neural arch* consists of two parts: (1) a pillar-like *pedicle* (*pd.*) springing from the centrum and extending vertically upwards, and (2) a flat, nearly horizontal *lamina* (*lm.*), forming, with its fellow, the roof of the neural canal. When the vertebræ are in position, wide gaps are left between successive pedicles. These are the *intervertebral foramina*, and serve for the passage of the spinal nerves. The *zygapophyses* (*a. zyg.*) or yoking processes are far better developed than in any fish. They spring from the junction of pedicle and lamina, the anterior zygapophysis having a distinct articular facet on its dorsal, the posterior on its ventral surface. Thus when the vertebræ are in position the posterior zygapophyses of each overlap the anterior zygapophyses of its immediate successor. Laterally the neural arch gives off on each side a large outstanding *transverse process* (*tr. pr.*). Its crown is produced into a very small and inconspicuous *neural spine* (*n. sp.*).

The first or *cervical vertebra* (*V. 1*) has a very small centrum and no transverse processes. There are no anterior zygapophyses, but at the junction of centrum and arch there occurs on each side a large oval concave facet for articulation with one of the condyles of the skull (see below). The eighth vertebra has a biconcave centrum. That of the ninth or *sacral vertebra* (*V. 9*) is convex in front and presents posteriorly a double convexity articulating with a double concavity on the anterior end of the urostyle. The latter (*UST.*) is entirely hypochordal in nature and has nothing to do with the vertebral column or the perichordal tube.

The *skull* (Figs. 264 and 265) of modern Anura shows striking departures from the massively ossified early amphibian plan (Fig. 265), which has much in common with that of the rhipidistian fishes (see p. 354). In the Ranidæ it consists of a narrow *brain-case*, produced behind into great outstanding *auditory capsules*, and in front into large *olfactory capsules*. The whole of the bones of the *upper jaw* are immovably fixed to the cranium, so that the only free parts

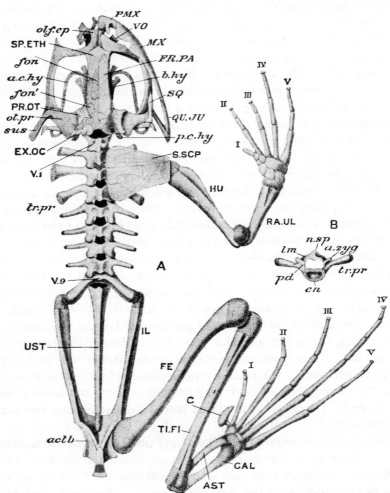

Fig. 264.—Class **Amphibia,** Order **Anura,** Family **Ranidæ.** *Rana:* Endoskeleton. *A.* from the dorsal aspect. The left half of the shoulder-girdle and the left fore- and hind-limbs are removed, as also are the investing bones on the left side of the skull. Cartilaginous parts dotted. Names of replacing bones in thick, those of investing bones in italic capitals, other references in small italics. *a. c. hy.* anterior cornu of hyoid; *actb.* acetabulum; AST. astragalus; *b. hy.* basi-hyal; C. calcar; CAL. calcaneum; EX.OC. exoccipital; FE. femur; *fon. fon'.* fontanelles; *FR.PA.* fronto-parietal; HU. humerus; IL. ilium; *MX.* maxilla; *olf. cp.* olfactory capsule; *ot. pr.* otic process; *p. c. hy.* posterior cornu of hyoid; *PMX.* premaxilla; PR.OT. pro-otic; *QU. JU.* quadrato-jugal; RA.UL. radio-ulna; SP.ETH. sphenethmoid; *SQ.* squamosal; S.SCP. supra-scapula; *sus.* suspensorium; TI.FI. tibio-fibula; *tr. pr.* transverse process; UST. urostyle; V.1, cervical vertebra; V.9, sacral vertebra; *VO.* vomer; *II—V,* digits of hand; *I,* the prepollex, a sesamoid bone; *I—V,* digits of hind foot. *B,* the fourth vertebra, anterior face. *a. zyg.* anterior zygapophysis; *cn.* centrum; *lm.* lamina; *n. sp.* neural spine; *pd.* pedicle; *tr. pr.* transverse process. (After Howes, slightly altered.)

are the *lower jaw* and a small plate of mingled bone and cartilage, the *hyoid apparatus.* This lies in the floor of the mouth and is the sole representative in the skull of the entire hyobranchial or gill-bearing skeleton of fishes.

As in teleosts, a number of investing bones can be removed from the skull without injury to the underlying chondrocranium. The latter, however, is not, as in the Trout (p. 298), the primary cranium alone, but, as in the Dipnoi (p. 361), the primary cranium *plus* the palatoquadrate or primary upper jaw. The cranium in the strict sense includes the brain-case and the auditory and olfactory capsules. The palatoquadrate (*pal. qu.*) is not a solid mass fused

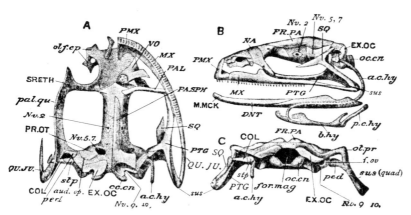

FIG. 265.—**Rana: Skull.** *A.* from beneath, with the investing bones removed on the right side (left of figure); *B.* from the left side, with mandible and hyoid; *C.* from behind, the investing bones removed at *sus. a. c. hy.* anterior cornu of hyoid; *aud. cp.* auditory capsule; *b. hy.* body of hyoid; COL. columella; *DNT.* dentary; EX.OC. exoccipital; *for. mag.* foramen magnum; *f. ov.* fenestra ovalis; *FR.PA.* fronto-parietal; M.MCK. mento-meckelian; *MX.* maxilla; *NA.* nasal; *Nv. 2,* optic foramen; *Nv. 5, 7,* foramen for fifth and seventh nerves; *Nv. 9, 10,* foramina for ninth and tenth nerves; *oc. cn.* occipital condyle; *olf. cp.* olfactory capsule; *ot. pr.* otic process; *PAL.* palatine; *pal. qu.* palato-quadrate; *PA.SPH.* parasphenoid; *p. c. hy.* posterior cornu of hyoid; *ped.* pedicle; *PMX.* premaxilla; PR.OT. pro-otic; *PTG.* pterygoid; QU.JU. quadrato-jugal; SP.ETH. sphenethmoid; *SQ.* squamosal; *stp.* stapes; *sus. (quad.)* suspensorium (quadrate); *VO.* vomer. A minute investing bone, the *septomaxillary,* which is present above the maxilla, close to the nostril, is not here shown. (See p. 424.) (After Howes, slightly altered.)

throughout its length with the cranium, as in the Dipnoi. Instead, it is a slender rod attached to the cranium at either end, but free in the middle. It is divisible into three regions : a posterior *quadrate region* or *suspensorium* (*sus.*), an intermediate *pterygoid region,* and an anterior *palatine region.* The suspensorium extends backwards, outwards, and downwards from the auditory region of the cranium. It is immovably united to the cranium by its forked proximal end. One branch of the fork—the *otic process* (Fig. 266, *ot. pr.*)—is fused with the auditory capsule. The other—the *pedicle* (*ped.*)—is fused with the trabecular region immediately anterior to the auditory capsule. Ventrally the suspensorium furnishes an articular facet for the mandible, and is connected with the delicate rod-like pterygoid region. This passes forwards and joins the palatine region, which is fused with a transverse bar, the *antorbital process*, the inner end of which is fused with the olfactory capsule.

The occipital region of the cranium contains only two bones. These are the *exoccipitals* (*EX. OC.*), which lie one on each side of the foramen magnum (*for. mag.*) and meet above and below it. There is no trace of supra- or basi-occipital. Below the foramen magnum are a pair of oval projections, the *occipital condyles* (*oc. cn.*), furnished by the exoccipitals and articulating with the cervical vertebra.

Each auditory capsule is ossified by a single bone, the *pro-otic* (*PR. OT.*). There are no other ossifications of the auditory region (p. 395). In the adult the pro-otic fuses with the exoccipital. It presents on its outer surface, behind the otic process of the suspensorium, a small aperture, the *fenestra ovalis*. This is closed by a membrane and cartilage. Beyond is the cavity of the auditory capsule, containing the membranous labyrinth.

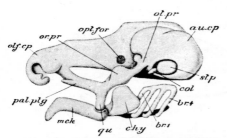

FIG. 266.—*Rana*: **Cartilaginous skull of tadpole.** In mid-metamorphosis. *au. cp.* auditory capsule; *br.* 1—4, branchial arches; *c. hy.* ceratohyal; *col.* columella; *mck.* Meckel's cartilage; *olf. cp.* olfactory capsule; *opt. for.* optic foramen; *or. pr.* orbital or muscular process of suspensorium; *ot. pr.* otic process; *pal. ptg.* palato-pterygoid bar; *qu.* quadrate; *stp.* 'operculum'. (After A. M. Marshall, slightly altered.)'

In front of the auditory capsules a considerable part of the cranial wall is formed of cartilage, and presents above a single large and a pair of small *fontanelles* (Fig. 264, *fon., fon.'*). Anteriorly it is ossified by the *sphenethmoid*, or *girdle-bone* (*SP. ETH.*), a short bony tube divided by a transverse partition into an anterior compartment which lodges the hinder ends of the olfactory sacs, and a posterior compartment which contains the olfactory bulbs.

The anterior compartment is again divided by a vertical partition which separates the olfactory sacs from one another, and the transverse partition is perforated for the transmission of the olfactory nerves.

The olfactory capsules (Figs. 265, 266, *olf. cp.*) have a delicate cartilaginous roof and floor produced into irregular processes which help to support the olfactory sac. They are separated from one another by a vertical plate of cartilage, continuous behind with the girdle-bone and representing the unossified part of the internal septum. The anterior wall of each is produced into a small, curved, rod-like *rhinal process*. The whole of the primary palatoquadrate arch is unossified in *Rana temporaria*; in certain other anurans, however, the quadrate appears as a distinct ossification.

To this partly ossified chondrocranium the usual investing bones are applied above and below. Covering the roof of the brain-case is a single pair of bones, the *fronto-parietals* (*FR. PA.*). In the majority of frogs no distinct frontal or parietal centres of development are visible at any stage. In the few where separate ossifications do occur, their independent existence is extremely transient and, at the most, lasts only about a day. Appearance and fusion have been demonstrated before the limb-paddle stage. (A supra-temporal bone exists in the skull of bufonid forms.) Over the olfactory capsules are paired triangular *nasals* (*NA*.), and applied to their ventral surfaces are small paired *vomers* (*VO*.). On the ventral surface of the skull is a large T-shaped *parasphenoid* (*PA. SPH*.). The stem of this structure underlies the basis cranii. Its two arms extend outwards beneath the auditory capsules.

In bony fishes, it will be remembered, the palatine and pterygoid are replacing bones, formed as ossifications of the palatoquadrate cartilage. In the frog this cartilage is, as we have seen, unossified, but to its ventral face two investing bones are applied. These are a small rod-like *palatine* (*PAL*.), and a three-rayed *pterygoid* (*PTG*.). The pterygoid has an anterior arm extending forwards to the palatine, an inner arm applied to the pedicle of the suspensorium, and an outer arm extending along the whole inner face of the suspensorium. It will thus be seen that bones originally preformed in cartilage may give place to investing bones, developed in corresponding situations, but altogether independent of the cartilage The latter remains unossified.

The suspensorium, as we have seen, is strengthened on its inner face by the outer arm of the pterygoid. Externally it is similarly supported by a hammershaped investing bone, the *squamosal* (*SQ*.). The upper jaw is formed by three investing bones: the small *premaxilla* (*PMX*.) in front, then the long, narrow *maxilla* (*MX*.), and finally the short *quadrato-jugal* (*QU. JU*.), which is connected posteriorly with the quadrate cartilage and squamosal (see also p. 467).

The mandible contains a persistent *Meckel's cartilage*, as a sort of core, outside which are formed two bones : a long *angulo-splenial* on its inner face, and a short *dentary* (*DNT*.) on the outer face of its distal half. The actual distal end of Meckel's cartilage is ossified as a small replacing bone, the *mentomeckelian* (*M. MCK*.), present in osteolepid fish (Jarvik).

The *hyoid apparatus* consists of a shield-shaped plate of cartilage, the *body of the hyoid* (*b. hy*.), This is produced at its anterior angles into slender rods, the *anterior cornua* (*a. c. hy*.), which curve upwards and are fused with the auditory capsules, and at its posterior angles into partly ossified rods, the *posterior cornua* (*p. c. hy*.), which extend backwards, embracing the glottis.

Two other cranial structures are noteworthy. External to the squamosal is a ring of cartilage, the *annulus tympani* (Fig. 93, p. 144), unique to Amphibia, which supports the tympanic membrane as the frame of a tambourine supports the parchment. Inserted into the fenestra ovalis is a nodule of cartilage, the *columella*, the middle of whose length is hammer-shaped and ossified, while its cartilaginous head, or *extra-columella*, is fixed to the inner surface of the tympanic membrane (see footnote, p. 414). Behind the columella, three quarters of the area of the fenestra ovalis is filled with membrane in which lies a large cartilaginous 'operculum' plate.

The comparison of the frog's skull with those of fishes is facilitated by a study of its development. In the tadpole, or larval frog, there is a cartilaginous cranium (Fig. 266) connected on each side with a stout inverted arch, like the subocular arch of the Lamprey or the palatoquadrate of *Chimæra* or *Neoceratodus*, and, like them, developed from the dorsal region of the mandibular arch. The quadrate region (*qu*). of this primary upper jaw is well in front of the eye, the axis of the suspensorium being inclined forwards and the mandible very short, in correspondence with the small size of the tadpole's mouth. The quadrate is fused by an ascending process with the trabecular region. An otic process (*ot. pr.*), unites it with the auditory capsule. Behind the suspensorium are distinct hyoid (*c. hy.*) and branchial (*br.* 1–4) arches supporting the gills by which the tadpole breathes. As development proceeds, the axis of the suspensorium is rotated backwards, producing the wide gape of the adult, and the stout palatopterygoid region of the subocular arch (*pal. ptg.*) gradually assumes the slender proportion it has in the adult. The greater part of the hyoid arch gives rise to the anterior cornua of the adult hyoid apparatus. The body of this is formed from the basihyal and basibranchials, and its posterior cornua is probably derived from the fourth branchial arch. The columella is developed independently, but may perhaps represent an epihyal or dorsal segment of the hyoid arch. Thus, with the assumption of aërial respiration, the complex branchial skeleton is reduced to a simple structure for the support of the tongue, larynx, and the muscles activating the floor of the mouth and throat.

The *pectoral girdle* has essentially the structure already described (p. 101) in general terms as characteristic of the pentadactyle Craniata, but it reflects the fact that the fore-limbs do relatively light work such as bracing the animal after each jump and occasionally transferring food to the buccal cavity (p. 400). To its various components are attached voluntary muscles which operate the forelegs and (a feature carried down from piscine ancestry) others which depress and elevate the lower jaw and pharyngeal floor. The depression of the pharyngeal floor causes an inrush of air through the nostril into the buccal cavity, after which the nostrils are closed and an elevation of the buccal floor forces the air through the glottis and into the paired *bronchi* to the lungs (see also *Respiration*, p. 403). The *scapula* (Fig. 267) is ossified, and is connected by its dorsal edge with a *suprascapula* (Fig. 264, *S. SCP.*) formed partly of bone, partly of calcified cartilage, and developed from the dorsal region of the embryonic shoulder-girdle. The *coracoid* is also ossified, but the *procoracoid* is represented by a bar of cartilage and has an investing bone, the *clavicle*, closely applied to it. These bones serve as struts to take the strains imposed on each side by the mobile humerus, the rounded head of which articulates with the *glenoid cavity* (Fig. 267). The suprascapula overlaps the anterior vertebræ. The coracoid and procoracoid are connected ventrally by a cartilage, the *epicoracoid*. This is in close contact with its fellow of the opposite side, so that the entire shoulder girdle, like that of a dogfish, forms a single inverted arch.

Passing forwards from the anterior ends of the united epicoracoids is a rod of bone, the *omosternum*, tipped by a rounded plate of cartilage, the *episternum*, and passing backwards from their posterior ends is a similar but larger bony rod, the *mesosternum*. This is also tipped by a cartilaginous plate, the *xiphisternum*. These two structures are the first indication of a sternum we have yet encountered, with the possible exception of the median ventral element of the shoulder-girdle of *Heptranchias*. The omosternum is developed as paired

FIG. 267.—*Rana:* **Pectoral girdle.** The cleithrum (Fig. 263, p. 382) is retained in anurans, alone among *extant* tetrapods. The procoracoid cartilage (in association with the clavicle) is not distinguished in the above drawing. The cartilaginous element anterior to the epicoracoid at the proximal end of the clavicle is the precoracoid (not arrowed). (From ventral aspect.)

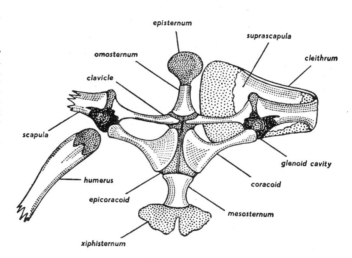

forward extensions of the epicoracoids which undergo fusion. The mesosternum and xiphisternum arise as two pairs of rods lying posterior to the epicoracoids, and subsequently one of each pair unites with the other. This sternal apparatus of the frog (and of the Amphibia in general) differs developmentally from the structures in the higher vertebrates to which the same name is applied. In the latter, the sternum is formed from detached portions of embryonic ribs (*costal sternum*).

The *fore-limbs* deviate from the typical structure (p. 100) chiefly in the fusion of the radius and ulna into a single *radio-ulna* (Fig. 264, *RA. UL.*), and in the presence of only four complete digits with a vestigial one, the *prepollex*, on the radial side. The last is well-developed as a copulatory aid in males. It represents a sesamoid bone. The complete digits are the second to the fifth of the typical hand. Six carpals only are present, the third, fourth, and fifth digits articulating with a single bone which has apparently risen by the fusion of the third, fourth, and fifth distalia and of at least one centrale.

The *pelvic girdle* is peculiarly modified. Although it contains the usual three principal units of tetrapods in general, these are in detail unlike those of any other group. The girdle consists of two long, curved bars articulating in front with the transverse processes of the sacral vertebra (Fig. 264) and unites posteriorly in an irregular vertical disc of mingled bone and cartilage which bears on each side a deep, hemispherical *acetabulum* (Fig. 268, *G*). Into this articulates the *femur* or thigh bone. The curved rods are the *ilia* (*Il. P.*). They expand posteriorly and unite with one another in the median plane to form the dorsal portion of the disc and about one-half of the acetabulum. The posterior portions of the disc and acetabulum are furnished by the *ischia* (*Is.*), fused with one another in the sagittal plane, their ventral portions by the similarly united *pubes* (*Kn.*). The ilium and ischium are formed of true bone, the pubis of calcified cartilage: the union of the elements in the median plane is the pubic *symphysis*.

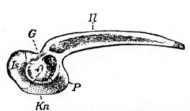

FIG. 268.—*Rana*: **Pelvic girdle.** From right. *G.* acetabulum; *Il. P.* ilium; *Is.* ischium; *Kn.* pubis. (After Wiedersheim.)

In the larva the ilium is vertical, but during development it becomes lengthened and at the same time rotated backwards, thus bringing the articulation of the hind-limbs as far back as possible.

In the adult the median pubic union, along with the bilateral iliac junction with the sacral vertebra (Fig. 264, V. 9), gives a rigidity to the apparatus as a whole. The ilia together form long jointed levers especially adapted for jumping. The hind-legs are flexed when each leaping movement begins. As the animal leaps, the legs simultaneously elongate with a backward transmission of force to the feet, which momentarily remain braced on the ground. The frog lacks a stabilising tail, and its centre of gravity is situated just behind the sacrum (Fig. 264). This latter fact, together with the position of each acetabulum and the length of the ilia, enables the relatively awkward animal to retain its equilibrium during forward propulsion. Frogs of several species are able to leap 3 or 4 feet under normal conditions. In a place called Angel's Camp, in Calaveras County, California, some thirty thousand gentlemen assemble each spring to bet at The Jumping Frog Jubilee. In May 1948 a frog called Heliotrope (of *Rana catesbiana*) leapt 11 feet 5 inches aided, doubtless, by not entirely natural stimuli. In 1953 South Africans entered the Californian contest with a frog named Leaping Lena (species not stated), which had *reputedly* leaped 24 feet 3½ inches. We are unable to report the result of the homeric international and interspecific contest that ensued.[1]

The muscles of the tetrapod limb are numerous and complex. Each seg-

---

[1] At a South African gathering termed the *Frogolympics* 'a single leap of fourteen feet [was] recorded for one of the species' (Rose). The species in the picture is *R. fasciata*.

ment has its own set by which the various movements are performed. There are muscles passing from the trunk to the limb-girdles ; from the trunk or the limb-girdles to the humerus and femur ; from the humerus and femur to the radio-ulna and tibio-fibula ; from the fore-arm or shank to the digits ; and from

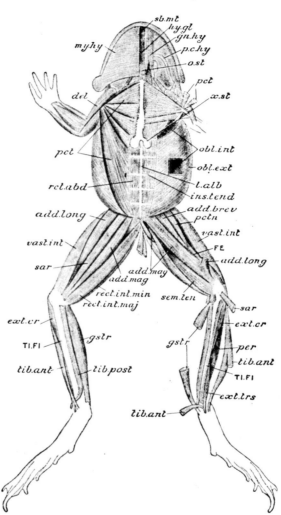

FIG. 269.—**Rana: Musculature.** Ventral aspect. On the left side (right of figure) many of the superficial muscles have been cut and reflected to show the deep layer. *add. brev.* adductor brevis; *add. long.* adductor longus; *add. mag.* adductor magnus; *del.* deltoid; *ext. cr.* extensor cruris; *ext. trs.* extensor tarsi; *FE.* femur; *gn. hy.* genio-hyoid; *gstr.* gastrocnemius; *hy. gl.* hyoglossus; *ins. ten.* inscriptio tendinea; *l. alb.* linea alba; *my. hy.* mylo-hyoid; *obl. int.* obliquus internus; *obl. ext.* obliquus externus; *o. st.* omosternum; *p. c. hy.* posterior cornu of hyoid; *pct.* pectoralis; *pctn.* pectineus; *per.* peronæus; *rct. abd.* rectus abdominis; *rect. int. maj.* rectus internus major; *rect. int. min.* rectus internus minor; *sar.* sartorius; *sb. mt.* sub-mentalis; *sem. ten.* semi-tendinosus; *tib. ant.* tibialis anticus; *tib. post.* tibialis posticus; *TI. FI.* tibiofibula; *vast. int.* vastus internus; *x. st.* xiphisternum.

one segment of a digit to another. For the most part, the limb-muscles are elongated and more or less spindle-shaped, presenting a muscular portion or *belly* which passes at either end into a *tendon* of strong fibrous tissue serving to fix the muscle to the bones upon which it acts (p. 74).

In the second segment of the *hind-limb* the tibia and fibula are fused to form a single *tibio-fibula* (Fig. 264, *TI. FI.*). The two bones in the proximal row of the tarsus—the tibiale or *astragalus* (*AST.*) and the fibulare or *calcaneum*

(*CAL.*)—are greatly elongated and provide the lever-like leg with an additional segment. There are three tarsals in the distal row, one of which appears to represent the *centrale*, another the *first distale*, and the third the fused *second* and *third distalia*. There are five well-developed digits. On the tibial side of the first there is an additional spur-like structure or *calcar* (*C.*). This is formed of three bones, a *metatarsal* and two *phalanges*. Such an additional digit is a *prehallux*.

All the bones of the limbs consist of the *shaft*, formed of true bone and of *extremities* of calcified cartilage (p. 73). Both in the freshly-prepared and in the dried skeleton the distinction is a very obvious one.

The musculature, as we have seen, has undergone great modifications in correspondence with the complex movements performed by the limbs. Likewise the abandonment (in the Anura but not in Urodela) of the sinuous mode of swimming is associated with considerable alterations. The dorsal muscles of the trunk are no longer divisible into myomeres (p. 86), but take the form of longitudinal or oblique bands lying partly above the vertebræ, partly between the transverse processes, and partly between the ilia and the urostyle. The *longissimus dorsi*, for example, extends from the head to the urostyle. The segmental origin of this muscle is suggested by numbers of narrow fibrous cross-bands. The urostyle is braced on the pelvic girdle by paired *coccygeo-sacralis* and *coccygeo-iliacus* muscles. The movement from water to land placed additional weight on the ventral musculature and differentiated a system of slings to support the abdominal viscera. There are a paired median band, the *rectus abdominus* (Fig. 269 *rct. abd.*) with longitudinal fibres and a double layer of oblique fibres—*obliquus externus* (*obl. ext.*) and *internus* (*obl. int.*)—extending from the vertebral column to the recti. Both the extensor dorsi and the rectus abdominis are traversed at intervals by transverse bands of fibrous tissue, the *inscriptiones tendineæ* (*ins. ten.*). The right and left recti are united by a longitudinal band of tendon, the *linea alba* (*l. alb.*).

Alimentary Canal and Associated Structures.—The wide mouth leads into a capacious *buccal cavity* which has in its roof the *internal* or *posterior nares* (Fig. 270, *p. na.*); these appear to be homologous with the oro-nasal grooves of fishes. A pair of projections, due to the downward bulging of the large eyes, invest the cavity in addition to the openings of the *Eustachian tubes* (*eus. t.*, see below). On its floor is the large *tongue* (*tng.*), attached in front and free posteriorly, where it ends in a double point. The tongue can be suddenly projected, point foremost, to capture and engulf insects. It is kept sticky by *intermaxillary glands*. Neither these, nor other mucous glands of the buccal cavity, produce digestive enzymes. A system of cilia also exists, and appears to circulate oral fluids over the surfaces of the buccal cavity. Immediately behind the tongue is a slit-like *glottis* (Fig. 270, *gl.*). *Teeth* are arranged in a single series round the edge of the upper jaw, attached to the premaxillæ and maxillæ. There is also a small patch of teeth (*vo. t.*) on each vomer just internal to the posterior nostril. The teeth are without pulp or nerve-tissue. They are small conical bodies, their bases ankylosed to the bones. They prevent smooth or slimy prey (millipedes, slugs, insects, and worms) from writhing out of the mouth. There are no teeth on the lower jaw.

The buccal cavity narrows towards the *pharynx*, which leads by a short *œsophagus* or gullet (*gul.*) into a *stomach* (*st.*) consisting of a wide *cardiac* and a

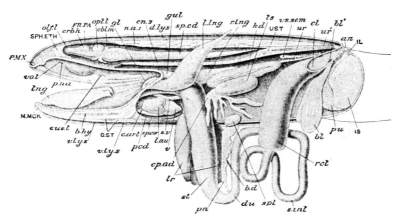

Fig. 270.—*Rana:* **Visceral relationships.** From left; the viscera somewhat displaced. *an.* anus; *b. d.* bile-duct; *b. hy.* body of hyoid; *bl.* urinary bladder; *bl'.* its opening into the cloaca; *c. art.* conus arteriosus; *cblm.* cerebellum; *cl.* cloaca; *cn.* 3, centrum of third vertebra; *cp. ad.* corpus adiposum; *crb. h.* cerebral hemisphere; *d. ly. s.* dorsal lymph sinus; *du.* duodenum; *ep. cor.* epicoracoid; *eus. t.* Eustachian tube; *FR. PA.* fronto-parietal; *gl.* glottis; *gul.* gullet; *IL.* ilium; *IS.* ischium; *kd.* kidney; *l. au.* left auricle; *l. lng.* left lung; *lr.* liver; M. MCK. mentomeckelian; *n. a* I, neural arch of first vertebra; *olf. l.* olfactory bulb; *opt. l.* optic lobe; O. ST. omosternum; *pcd.* pericardium; *PMX.* premaxilla; *pn.* pancreas; *p. na.* posterior naris; *pu.* pubis; *rct.* rectum; *r. lng.* right lung; *s. int.* ileum; *sp. cd.* spinal cord; SPH. ETH. sphenethmoid; *spl.* spleen; *st.* stomach; *s. v.* sinus venosus; *tng.* tongue; *ts.* testis; *ur.* mesonephric or urinary duct; *ur'.* its aperture into the cloaca; UST. urostyle; *v.* ventricle; *v. ly. s.* ventral lymph sinus; *vo. t.* vomerine teeth; *vs. sem.* vesicula seminalis.

short, narrow *pyloric* division. The stomach has a highly convoluted epithelium pitted with mucous cells, and, in the crypts, possesses tubular secretory glands which produce pepsin and hydrochloric acid. A pyloric *sphincter* guards the entrance to the *duodenum* (*du.*). This, the first portion of the small intestine, passes forwards parallel with the stomach. This part of the gut is richly supplied with *goblet-cells* which discharge mucus. Here digested food is absorbed into the *hepatic portal* system (p. 112). The rest of the small intestine (*ileum*) is coiled. The large intestine or *rectum* (*rct.*) is very wide and short, and passes without change of diameter into the cloaca, which possesses a cloacal aperture.

The *liver* (*lr.*) is composed of two large lateral, and one small median, lobes. The left lobe is itself partly divided. Between the right and left lobes lies a large *gall-bladder* (Fig. 271, G). The bile constantly secreted by the liver passes into the gall-bladder via *cystic ducts* (*D.cy.*) as well as directly into the *bile-duct* by way of minute *hepatic ducts* (*Dh*[1]). The bile-duct runs from the gall-bladder through the *pancreas* (P), a diffuse pale-coloured compound gland of exocrine and endocrine function (p. 152). The pancreas is held by mesentery between stomach and duodenum. Digestive juices elaborated by the exocrine (*acinous*) cells of the pancreas flow down the *pancreatic duct* which is bound to

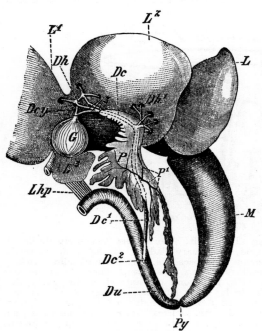

FIG. 271.—**Rana: Abdominal viscera.** *Dc.*, *Dc.*[1] common bile-duct; *Dc.*[2] its opening into the duodenum; *D. cy.* cystic ducts; *Dh.*, *Dh.*[1] hepatic ducts; *Du.* duodenum; *G.* gall-bladder; *L, L*[1], *O*[2], *L*[3], lobes of liver, turned forwards; *Lhp.* duodeno-hepatic omentum, a sheet of peritoneum connecting the liver with the duodenum; *M.* stomach; *P.* pancreas; *P*[1], pancreatic duct; *Py.* pylorus. (After Wiedersheim.)

the bile duct within a common sheath, and they empty into the duodenum through a common opening.

Morphologically associated with the alimentary tract is the *spleen* (Fig. 270, *spl.*), a small red globular blood reservoir attached by mesentery to the anterior end of the rectum. In the Salientia it is hæmatopœtic in function (see also p. 447).

In addition to the pancreas certain other glands can be examined during dissection of this area. The paired *thyroids* are small inconspicuous endocrine organs lying below the floor of the mouth in front of the glottis and lateral to the hyoid apparatus. Removal of the thyroids in tadpoles prevents full metamorphosis, although lungs and reproductive organs can still develop and growth may not be impaired. The administration of thyroid extracts will cause retardation of growth and sudden metamorphosis in various anurans.

The periodic *ecdysis*, or moult, of the keratinous epidermal layers of the skin is under the control of secretions of the *anterior pituitary* (Fig. 96, p. 150), and thyroid. If either gland is removed the old cornified layers remain unshed as a dark thick covering. Thyroid administration re-establishes moulting. *Parathyroids* (p. 152), which do not seem to have been demonstrated in fishes, occur in the Anura as paired ovoid bodies. There is evidence that, as in higher forms, they are concerned with calcium metabolism. The *thymus gland* is also paired. Situated behind and below the tympanic membrane, these bodies are of doubtful function. Certainly there is, up to the present, no acceptable evidence that they are endocrine organs.

On the ventral face of each *kidney* (Figs. 270 and 273) there occurs an elongated, yellow compound *adrenal* or *suprarenal gland* (p. 152). We have seen that in cylostomes and fishes the homologues of medullary and cortical tissue of the Mammalia occupy different situations (p. 152). In the Amphibia these dissimilar tissues have come together and interdigitate as in reptiles and birds.

Respiratory System.—The *lungs* (Fig. 270, *lng.*) are paired elastic sacs lying in the anterior part of the cœlom above the heart and liver. Their size and appearance vary greatly, according to their state of distension. Each contains a spacious cavity and has its walls raised into a complex network of ridges between which are *alveoli* (Fig. 74, p. 107). The septa between these are abundantly supplied with blood-vessels. The two lungs open anteriorly into a small *laryngo-tracheal chamber*, which communicates with the mouth by the narrow, slit-like *glottis*. The glottis and walls of the laryngo-tracheal chamber are supported by a framework provided by the *arytenoid* and *cricoid* cartilages. The mucous membrane of the laryngeal chambers is raised into a pair of horizontal folds, the *vocal cords*. These vibrate as air is forced back and forth between lungs and *vocal sacs*, which are buccal diverticula connected with the mouth by small slit-like apertures. The vocal sacs are resonators. Vocal chords occur in both sexes, but are much better developed in the male, which alone possesses vocal sacs (Fig. 298) and a voice. In breathing, the frog keeps its mouth closed, and by depressing the floor of the mouth, draws air into the buccal cavity through the nostrils. The floor of the mouth is then raised, the nostrils, which are valvular, are closed by a system of cartilaginous levers activated by the tight closure of the lower jaw, and the air is forced through the glottis into the lungs. Thus, inspiration is achieved by the activity of muscles arranged, and operating, essentially like those of fishes, from which the amphibian mechanism is clearly derived.

Within the lungs, the oxygen is taken up by the hæmoglobin of the erythrocytes which are coursing through the capillaries in the septa between the alveoli, and here, too, occurs the dissociation and excretion of carbon dioxide. In addition, frogs are capable of both *cutaneous* and *buccal* respiration. Gaseous exchanges cannot take place through a dry membrane: both skin and buccal surfaces are kept moist by special means. Buccopharyngeal respiration takes place at the same time as lung respiration: after the *glottis* is closed and traps air in the alveoli (p. 107), the nostrils are opened and a repeated raising and lowering of the buccal floor sucks air into, and forces it from the buccal cavity, the roof of which is invested with a respiratory capillary system.

Buccopharyngeal respiration is possibly less important than has been generally thought. Measurement of the capillary surface in the mouth of *Rana* and of *Bufo* has shown that they account for only 0·9 per cent., whereas those of the lung and skin account for almost 65 per cent. and 35 per cent. respectively of the total respiratory surfaces. Cutaneous breathing is probably continuous, and may be particularly important in species that periodically submerge in mud.

Blood-vascular System.—Fig. 272 shows some of the complexity of the anuran heart and ventral vessels, including devices which appear to keep the de-oxygenated and oxygenated blood-streams apart. There is no complete agreement as to how much mixing occurs. Certainly in the musculo-cutaneous vein there must be a mixing of the red cells oxygenated at the skin with (see below) those partly saturated with carbon dioxide at the muscles. A further mixing takes place in the right auricle.

A traditional view is that fairly complete separation of the main streams is achieved. It was later claimed that injected X-ray opaque material and cinephotography showed that, despite the trabeculæ and the differentiated pressures within the adjacent vessels, complete (or at least considerable) mixing of the two streams occurs in the ventricle. This view, too, has been challenged, and it now appears that the oxygenated and venous streams of blood are kept tolerably separate and selectively distributed to the arterial arches, although by a mechanism different from that envisaged in the traditional account (p. 406).

The heart lies in the *pericardial cavity* ventral to the œsophagus and in front of a *septum transversum* that completely separates the pericardial and cœlomic cavities. The heart is ensheathed by the *pericardium*, a double-walled sac. The inner wall (*epicardium*) is applied to the heart surface. The two walls unite at the base of the arterial arches but around the heart they are separated by a pericardial space containing serous fluid.

The *heart* consists of five chambers—a triangular sinus venosus (Figs. 272 and 273), right and left auricles (*r. au.*, *l. au.*), a muscular ventricle (*v.*, *ventr.*) and a conus arteriosus (*con. art.*). The thin-walled sinus venosus receives deoxygenated blood from the general circulation via three large vessels, the right and left pre-cavals (anterior venæ cavæ) and the post-caval (posterior vena cava) veins. From the sinus venosus the blood is delivered into the right auricle through sinu-auricular valves. (Here we see a striking advance on the Dipnoi in the greatly increased size of the left auricle, which is, however, only about half the volume of the right.) The two auricles are separated by the *inter-auricular septum* (Fig. 272), and into the left auricle runs a common pulmonary vein which has received oxygenated blood brought from each lung in the right and left pulmonary veins. The junction between pulmonary vein and left auricle is unguarded by valves. We see that one auricle contains deoxygenated blood (mixed with some oxygenated in the skin and buccal cavity), and the other auricle freshly oxygenated red cells. The auricles contract almost synchronously, and each squeezes its cargo of blood through a common auriculo-ventricular aperture, guarded by two pairs of valves (one pair

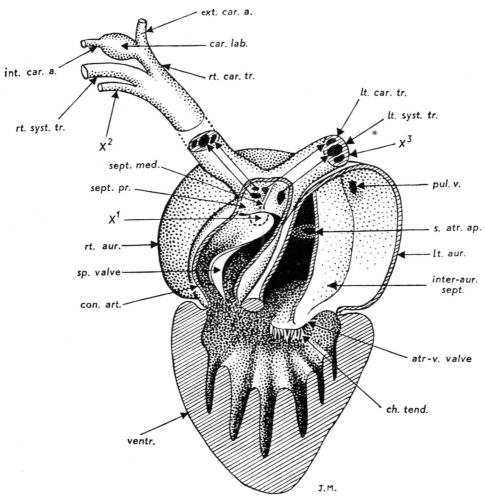

FIG. 272.—*Rana:* **Cardiac anatomy and circulation.** Ventral view. Simplified by the exclusion of the pylangial (ventriculo-conal) valves from near the base of the spiral valve (*sp. valve*). To the right of the spiral valve is (unmarked) the cavum aorticum, and to its left the cavum pulmo-cutaneum. The labelled structures are: *atr-v. valve.* atrioventricular valve; *car. lab.* carotid labyrinth; *ch. tend.* chordæ tendineæ; *con. art.* conus arteriosus; *ext. car. a.* external carotid artery; *inter-aur. sept.* inter-auricular septum; *int. car. a.* internal carotid artery; *lt. aur.* left auricle; *lt. car. tr.* left carotid trunk; *lt. syst. tr.* left systemic trunk; *pul. v.* pulmonary vein; *rt. aur.* right auricle; *rt. car. tr.* right carotid trunk; *rt. syst. tr.* right systemic trunk; *s. atr. ap.* sinu-atrial aperture; *sept. med.* septum mediale; *sept. pr.* septum principale; *sp. valve.* spiral valve; *ventr.* ventricle. X^1: Common entrance of pulmo-cutaneous arteries (below spiral valve); X^2: Right pulmo-cutaneous trunk; X^3: Left pulmo-cutaneous trunk. (Data from J. R. Simons.)

large and the other pair small) into the single ventricle. The latter has a transversely elongated cavity. Its dorsal and ventral walls are raised up into muscular ridges or *carneæ* with interstices between them. It is generally held that these help to prevent the mixing of the chemically dissimilar streams of blood. The contraction of the muscular ventricle follows auricular contraction immediately. Blood is driven into the thick-walled *conus arteriosus*, which springs from the right side of the base of the ventricle, and is expelled into the arterial arches. The conus arteriosus is incompletely divided by the spiral valve into two passages, the *cavum aorticum* leading to the carotid and systemic arches, and the *cavum pulmo-cutaneum* leading to the more dorsally placed entrance of the pulmo-cutaneous arches.

Traditionally it has been held that the blood first entering the conus from the ventricle passed into the cavum pulmo-cutaneum and its associated arches. It was believed that when the resistance to flow in these arches had risen, the blood next flowed into the systemic arches, and finally because the carotid labyrinths (see below) caused the carotid arches to exert the highest resistance the last blood to leave the ventricle flowed into the last-named vessels.

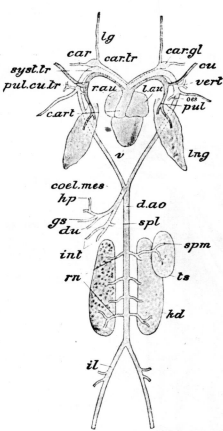

Fig. 273.—*Rana:* **Arterial system.** Relationship with the heart, lungs, kidneys, and left testis (from the ventral aspect). *car.* internal carotid artery; *car. gl.* carotid labyrinth; *c. art.* conus arteriosus; *car. tr.* carotid trunk; *cœl. mes.* cœliaco-mesenteric artery; *cu.* cutaneous artery; *d. ao.* dorsal aorta; *du.* duodenal artery; *gs.* gastric artery; *hp.* hepatic artery; *il.* iliac artery; *int.* intestinal arteries; *kd.* kidney; *l. au.* left auricle; *lg.* external carotid artery; *lng.* lung; *œs.* œsophageal artery; *pul.* pulmonary artery; *pul. cu. tr.* pulmo-cutaneous trunk; *r. au.* right auricle; *rn.* renal arteries; *scl.* subclavian artery; *spl.* splenic artery; *spm.* spermatic artery; *ts.* testis; *syst. ts.* systemic trunk; *v.* ventricle; *vert.* vertebral artery.

It has now been shown that while a selective distribution of the blood undoubtedly occurs, the mechanism which brings it about cannot operate as outlined above. In *Rana*, *Bufo*, *Hyla*, and *Xenopus* the movement of the blood in the three pairs of arches has been found to occur simultaneously. Furthermore, traces of the pressure waves recorded from the arches by optical and electronic manometers show that the patterns from all arches are similar and synchronous.

Despite this, a selective distribution does indeed take place, although this is rather less perfect than earlier authors believed. In general, more than half the blood ejected from the left auricle enters the carotid and systemic arches, while about the same proportion of that discharged from the right auricle enters the pulmo-cutaneous arches. The precise means by which this is achieved is still a matter of speculation.

The paired branches of the short ventral aortæ are each divided by two longitudinal partitions into three vessels. These are an inner or anterior (the *carotid trunk (car. tr.)*), a middle one (the *systemic trunk* or *aortic arch*), and an outer or posterior (the *pulmo-cutaneous trunk (pul. cu. tr.)*). The systemic trunks communicate separately with the conus at its distal end (sometimes described as the *bulbus arteriosus*) and the carotid trunks open slightly to the right of the junction of the two systemic trunks. The opening of the carotid trunks is guarded by a valve.

After being bound together in the way described for a short distance, the carotid, systemic, and pulmo-cutaneous trunks separate from one another. The carotid trunk divides into an *internal* (Figs. 272 and 273, *car.*) and *external carotid (lg.)* artery which supply the head. The former has at its base a small swelling, the *carotid labyrinth (car. gl.)*, which has a spongy interior containing numerous cavities and channels. This structure was sometimes called the carotid 'gland', but it is non-secretory. There is, however, evidence that the carotid labyrinth acts as a chemo- and baroceptor.

The systemic trunks curve round the œsophagus towards the dorsal midline. The right arch becomes the dorsal aorta as it passes posteriorly in the median position. The left arch touches the dorsal aorta briefly and communicates with it by a small aperture and is then continued as the *cœliaco-mesenteric* artery.

Apart from the arteries to the head, the lungs, and the skin, those supplying all parts of the body arise either from the dorsal aorta or from one of the systemic arches. The pulmo-cutaneous trunk divides into two: a *pulmonary artery (pul.)* to the lungs, and a *cutaneous artery (cu.)* to the skin.

In the tadpole there are four aortic arches, each consisting of an afferent and an efferent branchial artery connected by the capillaries of the gills. As the water-breathing larva undergoes metamorphosis into the air-breathing adult the gills disappear. The first aortic arch loses its connection with the dorsal aorta and becomes the carotid trunk. The second enlarges, retains its connection with the dorsal aorta, and becomes the systemic trunk. The third disappears. The fourth sends off branches to the lungs and skin, loses its connection with the dorsal aorta, and becomes the pulmo-cutaneous trunk.

Venous return. The blood from each side of the head is returned by *internal* (Fig. 274, *int. ju.*) and *external (ext. ju.) jugular veins* into the *precaval vein (pr. v.)*, which also receives the *brachial vein (br.)* from the fore-limb, and the *musculo-cutaneous vein (ms. cu.)* from the skin and muscles of the side and back, and part of the head : the two precavals open separately into the sinus venosus.

The course of the blood from the posterior part of the body is very different from that seen in fishes—the differences being due partly to the absence of a tail, partly to a peculiar modification of the lateral veins, and partly to the replacement of the cardinals by a *postcaval vein*, found among fishes only in the Dipnoi (p. 361).

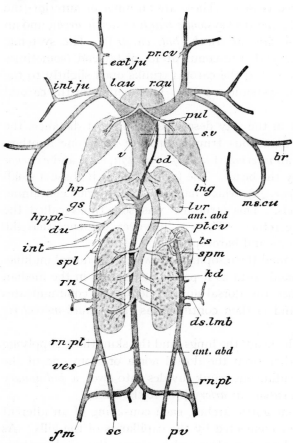

Fig. 274.—**Rana:** **Venous system.** Relationship with the heart, lungs, liver, kidneys, and right testis (from the dorsal aspect). *ant. abd.* anterior abdominal vein; *br.* brachial vein; *cd.* cardiac vein; *ds. lmb.* dorsolumbar vein; *du.* duodenal vein; *ext. ju.* external jugular vein; *fm.* femoral vein; *gs.* gastric vein; *hp.* hepatic vein; *hp. pt.* hepatic portal vein; *int.* intestinal veins; *int. ju.* internal jugular vein; *kd.* kidney; *l. au.* left auricle; *lng.* lung; *lvr.* liver; *ms. cu.* musculo-cutaneous vein; *pr. cv.* precaval vein; *pt. cv.* postcaval vein; *pul.* pulmonary vein; *pv.* pelvic vein; *r. au.* right auricle; *rn.* renal veins; *rn. pt.* renal portal vein; *sc.* sciatic vein; *spl.* splenic vein; *spm.* spermatic vein; *s. v.* sinus venosus; *ts.* testis; *ves.* vesical veins.

Two *portal systems* occur. The blood from the front part of the hind-leg is brought back by a *femoral vein (fm.)*, which, on reaching the cœlom, divides into two branches, a dorsal and a ventral. The dorsal branch is the *renal portal vein (rn. pt.)*. This receives the *sciatic vein (sc.)* from the back of the leg and passes to the kidney, in which it breaks up into capillaries. (It should be remembered, of course, that the minute vessels that form the kidney *glomeruli* (see p. 155) come from the renal *artery*.) The ventral branch is the *pelvic vein (pv.)*. This unites with its fellow on the opposite side to form the *anterior abdominal vein* (*ant. abd.*) which passes forwards in the ventral body-wall, between the linea alba and the peritoneum, to the level of the sternum, where it turns inwards and divides into two branches, both breaking up into capillaries in the liver.

Just as the anterior abdominal vein enters the liver it is joined by the *hepatic portal vein* (*hp. pt.*), bringing the blood from the stomach, intestine, spleen, and pancreas. The spleen (Fig. 270, *spl.*) is a small, red, globular body near the head of the rectum. The abdominal vein also receives *vesical veins* (*ves.*) from the urinary bladder, and a small *cardiac vein* (*cd.*) from the heart. It represents the lateral abdominal veins of Chondrichthyes united in the middle ventral line : the pelvic veins represent their posterior free portions.

The blood is collected from the kidneys by the *renal veins* (*rn.*), which unite to form the large unpaired *postcaval vein* (*pt. cv.*). This passes forward through the liver, receives the *hepatic veins* (*hp.*) from that organ, and finally opens into the sinus venosus. Thus the blood from the hind-limbs has to pass through one of the two portal systems on its way back to the heart. Part of it goes by the renal portal veins to the kidneys, and thence by the renal veins to the postcaval. The rest goes by the pelvic and abdominal veins to the liver, and thence by the hepatic veins to the postcaval. From here it enters the sinus venosus for re-distribution via the right auricle. Lastly, the blood which has been oxygenated in the lungs is returned by the *pulmonary veins* (*pul.*) directly to the left auricle.

It will be seen that there is no trace of cardinal veins in the frog. In the larva, however, both anterior and posterior cardinal veins are present. During metamorphosis, the ductus Cuvieri unite (as in fishes) and become converted to the precavals. The posterior portions of the posterior cardinals contribute to the formation of the postcaval. The anterior portions disappear.

Blood. As in other vertebrates, oxygen is transported by unstable association with the red respiratory pigment, hæmoglobin, carried in the erythocytes. Compared with that of the Mammalia, however, anuran hæmoglobin has a relatively low affinity for oxygen even when differential temperatures are taken into consideration. (There is evidence, too, that carbon dioxide transport is somewhat less efficient in the Amphibia.) As in fishes, birds, and reptiles, the erythocytes are nucleated throughout their life. They are relatively large oval discs, measuring about $20 \times 15\mu$, as compared with about 7μ in, for example, the rabbit. Erythrocytes are formed in the kidneys, and hæmatopetic tissue occurs also in the spleen and bone marrow, as in higher vertebrates. Destruction of effete cells occurs in the spleen and liver; some undergo fragmentation in the blood-stream. White cells consist of large phagocytic *macrophages*, *monocytes*, phagocytic *polymorpho-nuclear granulocytes* (of various kinds), and *lymphocytes* (p. 70). If a fine cannula filled with pathogenic bacteria is inserted into the peritoneal cavity of a frog and withdrawn after a few hours, it is found to be covered with 'wandering' phagocytic granulocytes, which have migrated to the source of infection to act in approximately the same manner as in higher tetrapods. *Thrombocytes*, probably essentially equal in function to blood-clotting *platelets* in the Mammalia, also occur.

Lymphatic System.—Vertebrates have a closed system of vessels, so that except in parts of special organs (such as liver, adrenal, and spleen) the materials carried in the capillaries do not come into direct contact with the general body-cells. The capillaries are separated from other body-tissues by fluid-filled *tissue-spaces*. These are filled with *tissue-fluid*, which is essentially blood plasma that has exuded through the walls of the capillaries. Across the fluid-filled tissue-spaces must pass oxygen and food substances brought by the blood. The passage of fluid from capillaries to tissue-spaces is carried out partly by pressure exerted by the heart-beat and partly by osmotic pressure of the blood and the adjacent tissue fluids.

As well as fluids and solutes, leucocytes can also pass from the blood-stream to the tissue-spaces. The tissue-spaces communicate with minute lymph-vessels which continue into larger vessels to make up a highly developed lymphatic system (p. 115). This, in the frog, is remarkable for the dilatation of many of its vessels into large *lymph-sinuses*. Between skin and muscle are spacious *subcutaneous sinuses* (Fig. 270, *v.ly.s.*), separated from one another by fibrous partitions. The presence of these sinuses allows the skin of the frog to slide back and forth across the underlying structures. The dorsal aorta of the frog is surrounded by a capacious *subvertebral sinus*. Lymph is driven through the above diffuse system of vessels into the venous system by means of anterior and posterior pairs of *lymph-hearts*. The anterior pair is situated beneath the supra-scapulæ. The other pair can be seen beside the posterior end of the urostyle. These lymph-hearts open into veins, and so the lymph fluid and its inclusions become once more mixed with the general circulation (see also *cœlomic fluid*, p. 415).

Nervous System.—The *brain* (Fig. 275) resembles, in pattern, that of the Dipnoi. There are large optic lobes, a well-developed diencephalon, and large fully evaginated hemispheres and olfactory bulbs, the last-named fused in the median plane. The corpora striata, or basal ganglia of the cerebral hemispheres, are connected together, as in all vertebrates, by an *anterior commissure* (Fig. 275, *D, Com.*, lower line), above which is another commissure (upper line) partly representing the *hippocampal commissure* of the brain of reptiles and mammals. The third ventricle is covered by a thick choroid plexus. The aqueduct of the mid-brain extends dorsolaterally into the optic lobes of the tectum. The lateral ventricles are large cavities in the cerebral hemispheres which extend into the olfactory bulbs. The hypothalamus is well developed, and to the infundibular stalk is attached the *hypophysis* or *pituitary gland*. This gland is of compound structure and great functional complexity and is connected to the hypothalamus by a portal system (p. 149). The pineal body is vestigial in the adult, being represented only by the stalk. The anterior choroid plexus (of the third ventricle) is found a little in front of the pineal. In the larva the pineal body occurs outside the skull and immediately

FIG. 275.—*Rana*: **Brain, pituitary, and cranial nerves.** *A*, dorsal; *B*, ventral; *C*, lateral; *D*, in longitudinal vertical, but not quite midline, section. *Cb.* cerebellum; *Cer. H.* cerebral hemispheres; *ch. plx¹.* anterior, and *ch. plx².* posterior choroid plexus (removed in *A*); *Com.* commissures, the two in front the *anterior* and *hippocampal*, the two above the *superior* or *habenular* and the *posterior*; *Cr. C.* crura cerebri; *Di.* diencephalon; *for. M.* foramen of Monro; *i.* iter, or aqueduct of Sylvius; *inf.* infundibulum; *Med. obl.* medulla oblongata; *Olf. l.* olfactory bulb; *opt. ch.* optic chiasma; *Opt. l.* optic lobe; *opt. v.* optic ventricle; *pin.* stalk of pineal body; *pit.* pituitary body; *Sp. cd.* spinal cord; *v³.* third ventricle; *v⁴.* fourth ventricle; *I—X*, cerebral nerves; *1Sp. 2Sp.* spinal nerves. (After Parker. *A—C*, after Gaupp; *D*, from Wiedersheim, after Osborn.)

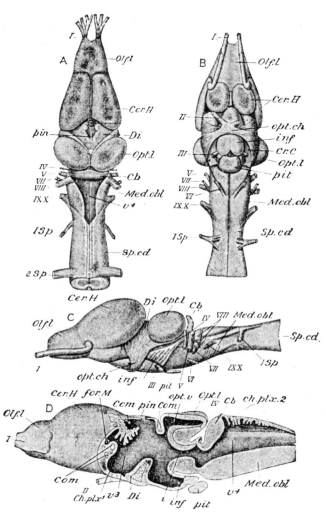

beneath the skin. The cerebellum is extremely small, as might be expected in a relatively inactive animal that moves principally in a single plane.

The cranial nerves are on much the same pattern as in the fishes, but the loss of gills in the adult has led to alterations in the course and significance of the ninth and tenth. The spinal nerves, too, have become modified in their arrangement and function along with the evolution of limbs. Corresponding with the number of vertebræ, there are only ten pairs of spinal nerves,

of which the second and third unite to form a *brachial plexus* giving off the nerves
to the fore-limb, while the seventh to the ninth and a branch of the tenth join
to form a *lumbo-sacral* or *sciatic plexus* giving off the nerves to the hind-limb.
Of the remainder, the first spinal nerve performs the function of the hypoglossal (Fig. 275, 1*Sp.*), supplying the muscles of the tongue: it passes out between the first and second vertebræ.   The minute fourth, fifth, and sixth spinal
nerves carry fibres to the muscles and skin of the body.   The cloaca and bladder
are supplied by a second branch of the tenth.   This nerve emerges from an
aperture near the anterior end of the urostyle.   The short spinal cord ends in
a delicate filament, the *filum terminale.*

Autonomic Nervous System.—The *sympathetic system* in *Rana* is represented
by a pair of sympathetic trunks which lie ventral to the vertebral column.
Each trunk consists of ten ganglia joined longitudinally by *connectives* ;   in
addition, each ganglion is connected to the corresponding spinal nerve by *rami
communicantes.*   Minute fibres may extend from ganglia of one chain to those of
the opposite side.   From the anterior cranial ganglion of the chain on each side,
nerve-fibres continue into the head to communicate with the vagus and other
cranial nerves.   The whole system, metamerically arranged, is divisible into
four regions—the *cephalic, cervico-branchial, abdominal,* and *sacro-coccygeal.*

Sympathetic fibres travel widely to innervate the dilator muscles of the iris
and muscles of the heart, aorta, arteries, arterioles, and the skin ; and other
organs, such as the lungs, stomach, intestine, liver, pancreas, spleen, kidneys,
adrenal tissues, gonads, bladder, cloaca, and rectum.   In addition, parasympathetic fibres from various cranial nerves, mainly the vagus, and from the
hinder part of the spinal cord (representing the *sacral parasympathetic outflow*)
supply most of the above structures.   The heart-beat is augmented by
sympathetic stimulation and depressed by vagal fibres.   The sympathetic has
a constrictor effect on arteries and arterioles.   Vaso-dilatation is also under
nervous control.   Although the evidence is often conflicting in detail, it is clear
that in the frog there is an autonomic nervous system essentially similar in basic
pattern to those found in homœothermous tetrapods.

Organs of Special Sense.—The *olfactory organs* show profound modifications
in accordance with assumption of terrestrial life and aerial respiration.   Each
olfactory chamber has two openings : the *anterior naris* or external nostril and
the *posterior naris* (Fig. 89, p. 138) or internal nostril.   The latter opens into
the mouth immediately lateral to the vomer.   It is probable that the internal
nostrils were formed by the modification of the oronasal groove of ancestral
forms.   The twin passages are separated by a *nasal septum.*   The olfactory
chambers within are lined with sensory epithelium, the fibres from which form
the olfactory nerves.   Across this epithelium passes air as it travels to and from
the lungs.   Further, a stream of water is circulated across the epithelium when
the frog is swimming, and so the animal can smell while submerged.   In addi-

tion, the *vomeronasal* (*Jacobson's*) *organ* has arisen in the Amphibia. This is formed by means of a naso-pharyngeal evagination. It is lined with sensory epithelium supplied by fibres from the olfactory and trigeminal cranial nerves. Jacobson's organ communicates with the olfactory chamber and the buccal cavity and enables the animal to smell substances taken into the mouth (p. 479).

Chemoreceptors for the appreciation of taste occur in the tongue and palate. The *eyes*, too, show adaptations to the terrestrial existence. *Lachrymal glands* produce a watery fluid (tears) which bathes the anterior eye surface and washes away injurious foreign bodies. *Eyelids* are developed : the upper lid is immobile; from the lower has developed the transparent *nictitating membrane*

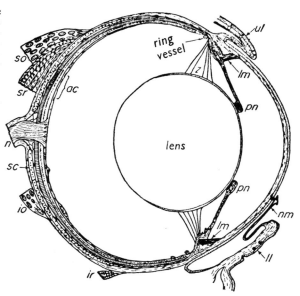

FIG. 276.—*Rana:* **Eye and optic tract.** During metamorphosis from the tadpole there develop 'terrestrial' features, such as the eyelids, nictitating membrane (see below), Harderian gland, and nasolachrymal (tear) duct. The six typical vertebrate eye muscles (p. 142) occur, together with a powerful *retractor bulbi* and a *levator bulbi.* The former (derived from part of the external rectus) is involved in swallowing as well as in the protection of the eyeball. The levator bulbi is derived from masticatory muscles. *ac.* area centralis (with local concentration of visual cells); *io.* inferior oblique; *ir.* inferior rectus; *ll.* lower lid; *lm.* lens muscles (protractors); *n.* optic nerve; *nm.* nictitating membrane (a transparent, independently movable part of the lower lid said *not to be homologous with that of higher tetrapods*); *pn.* pupillary nodules; *s.c.* scleral cartilage; *so.* superior oblique; *sr.* superior rectus; *ul.* upper lid; *z.* zonule (fibres are embedded in vitreous). (Modified after Walls.)

which flicks across the eyeball and assists in the cleansing process (Fig. 276). (In Man the remnants of a functionally similar reptilian structure are retained as a small pink fold, the *plica semilunaris*, between the medial ends of the eyelids.)

The arrangements within the nearly spherical eyeball also reflect the changed visual circumstances of tetrapods. The cornea is rounded, the lens is more flattened than in fishes, and the two structures are widely separated. This enables the *protractor lentis* muscles to move the whole lens forward (as homologous muscles move it slightly backwards in modern fishes). These muscles run in close association with the fibres that support the lens in its fluid bath; and radial muscle processes, the *musculus tensor chorioidea*, probably related to the ciliary muscles in higher forms, also occur. The above mechanism enables the terrestrial amphibian to focus on distant objects to an extent that would be impossible in animals living submerged in water. The iris is under the control of circular sphincter muscles and radial dilator muscles, which, although under nervous control (p. 119), are said also to be susceptible to response by direct illumination.   Both rods and cones occur in the retina.

In the ear, the organ of equilibration presents the same basic pattern from fishes to the Mammalia, but in the Amphibia we find accessory structures related to the reception, amplification, and conduction of vibrations from the external environment.   Thus, a *middle ear*, equipped with a *tympanic membrane* or *ear-drum*, appears.   Between this and the outer wall of the auditory capsule is a considerable space, the *tympanic cavity* (Fig. 93, p. 144).   This communicates with the pharynx by the short Eustachian tube already described (Fig. 270, *eus. t.*), so that a probe thrust through the tympanic membrane from outside passes directly into the pharynx.   In the roof of the tympanic cavity lies the columella (Fig. 265), its head, or extra-columella, attached to the inner surface of the tympanic membrane, its foot-plate or 'stapes'[1] fixed in the membrane of the fenestra ovalis.   Vibrations striking the tympanic membrane are communicated by the columella and stapes to the fenestra ovalis, thence to the perilymph, and next to the membranous labyrinth of the *inner ear*.   This is composed of the *utriculus* and *semi-circular canals*, and the *sacculus* with its diverticular *lagena* (Fig. 94,).   The *endolymphatic ducts* do not communicate with the exterior, but run dorso-anteriorly and fuse at the anterior end of the medulla oblongata.   Dissection of this region will reveal large aggregations of white calcareous particles. In some Anura these extend far down on each side of the vertebral column. These occur in paired sac-like organs which are connected with the inner ear; nevertheless their function is unknown.   The connection of the tympanic cavity with the pharynx (via the Eustachian tube) helps to maintain equality of pressure on each side of the tympanic membrane.   There seems little doubt that the tympano-eustachian passage is homologous with the first or hyomandibular gill-cleft, although, in anurans, it is formed independently of the clefts and never opens to the exterior.   From the consideration of their habits there can be no doubt that hearing in frogs is exceedingly important, more especially during the breeding season.   It is probable, too, that hearing is important in hunting and escape activity.   It has been experimentally shown that some anurans can appreciate auditory stimuli in the range between 50 and 10,000 vibrations per second.

Lateral line organs occur in the tadpole.   The lateral line cells are ciliated and are receptive to water-vibrations.   The organs along the body are innervated, as in the fishes, by the *ramus lateralis* from the vagus.   Those of the cephalic region are served by the vagus and, to a lesser degree, by branches from the facial and glossopharyngeal.   The whole system, in ranids, disappears during metamorphosis (see, however, Fig. 302, p. 449).

---

[1] The terminology of the structures of the columella is unsatisfactory.   The whole is homologous with the stapes of the Mammalia.

Endocrine Glands.—The compound pituitary gland is at the base of the hypothalamus (p. 127). Its various parts differ in their relationships from those in the higher tetrapods. Thus in the Anura the anterior lobe (*pars distalis*) is not anteriorly placed. The intermediate and neural parts and also the *pars tuberalis* of higher groups are represented, and the organ as a whole appears to show a considerable advance over those of fishes so far investigated. For the role of anterior and posterior lobes in colour change in *Xenopus*, see p. 450.

The anterior pituitary has powerful partial control of the primary sex organs. There is little doubt that its activity is considerably influenced by environmental changes through the intermediacy of the central nervous system, including the hypothalamus. Injections of macerated anterior pituitary material will cause unseasonal ovulation. The testes of frogs, too, are under partial control of the pars distalis. Other endocrine glands are the thyroid, paired parathyroids (p. 152), and paired adrenals and gonads (see below).

Urinogenital Organs.—The *kidneys* (Figs. 277 and 278, *N.*) are flat, somewhat oval bodies, of a dark red colour, lying in the posterior region of the cœlom. On the ventral face of each kidney is an elongated, yellow adrenal gland (p. 152). Considerable numbers of minute nephrostomes occur on the ventral kidney-surface and propel *cœlomic fluid* (almost identical with lymph) from the cœlom into the *renal veins*. It will be recalled that blood comes to the kidney from two entirely separate sources (p. 112). Branches of the *renal artery* run generally to the numerous *glomeruli* (p. 157). To the associated *uriniferous* or *renal* tubules run branches of the *renal portal* veins. Each glomerulus is composed of an arteriole (from the renal artery) which ends in a knot of capillaries whose outlet is a vessel connecting with the renal vein. The capillary knot is almost surrounded by an invagination of the end of a renal tubule which becomes a double-walled, delicate *Bowman's capsule*.

The vessel leaving the glomerulus is usually smaller than that entering it, and there is evidence that both blood and osmotic pressures are higher in the glomerulus than in the contiguous excretory capsule. A protein-free filtrate, containing waste nitrogenous products, passes over into the capsule and, helped by the beat of cilia, down the uriniferous tubule. At the same time there occurs a selective reabsorption of fluids and dissolved substances valuable to the animal, and these are transferred back into the general circulation. The urinary residue, including waste metabolites, passes down the tubule, and with the cargo from numerous others, is taken up by one of many *collecting tubules* which open into the mesonephric or *Wolffian duct*. Each of these (Fig. 277, *Ur.*) passes backwards from the outer border of the kidney and opens into the dorsal wall of the cloaca (*Cl.*). The kidney is developed from the mesonephros of the embryo, the urinary duct from the mesonephric duct. In the larva, a large pronephros is present and is, for a time, the functional kidney.

Opening into the cloaca on its ventral side is the *urinary bladder* (Fig. 270, *bl.*) (p. 401), an organ now encountered for the first time.   It is a bilobed, thin-walled, and very delicate sac into which the urine passes by gravitation from the cloaca when the vent is closed.   This sac is a *urinary bladder* and is quite different morphologically from the organ of the same name in fishes (which is a dilatation of the mesonephric duct) and is distinguished as an *allantoic bladder*.   From this urinary bladder, in the frog, further fluid can be reabsorbed into the circulatory system.

Because of its semi-permeable surface, the frog is in constant danger of being either waterlogged or dehydrated in extremes of climate.   It overcomes the former danger by the extraordinary efficiency of its glomerular system, which enables it to eliminate, when necessary, up to one-third of its body-weight in fluid per day.   However, as we have seen (p. 285), not even the auxiliary extra-renal water-absorbing mechanism of the bladder can enable the frog to withstand high temperatures (see also p. 385).

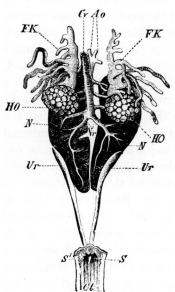

Fig. 277.—*Rana:* **Urino-genital system in male.** *Ao.* dorsal aorta; *Cl.* cloaca; *Cv.* postcaval vein; *FK,* fat-bodies; *HO,* testes; *N,* kidneys; *S, S',* apertures of mesonephric ducts into cloaca; *Ur.* mesonephric ducts. (After Wiedersheim.)

Reproduction.—In the male the *testes* (*HO*) are white ovoid bodies lying ventral to the anterior ends of the kidneys.   They are attached to the kidneys by folds of *mesorchium*, which are continuous with the peritoneal epithelium that cloaks the ventral face of each kidney and lines the entire body cavity.

The testes contain long, convoluted *seminiferous* (*spermatogenetic*) *tubules*, and in the interstices between are held numbers of *Leydig* or *interstitial cells* which produce male sex hormone under the stimulation of a pituitary gonadotrophin (p. 150).   The seasonal liberation of male testosterone in turn modifies the secondary sexual organs, including the *nuptial pad* (p. 390), and leads to appropriate changes in behaviour.   Seminiferous activity, too, is under the control of the anterior pituitary.   The spermatozoa are shed into *collecting tubules*, which lead to a number of delicate *vasa efferentia*.   These leave the inner edge of each testis, pass between the mesorchial folds, and enter the nearby kidney and become connected with the urinary tubules.   The spermatic fluid is thus passed into the urinary tubules and carried off by the *Wolffian* duct, which in the male frog is therefore a urinogenital duct.   This duct is attached to the lateral edge of the kidney.   The spermatozoa are carried down this towards a *vesicula seminalis* (Fig. 270, *vs. sem.*) or seminal vesicle, which is a dilation, of glandular appearance, near the cloaca. This vesicle receives spermatozoa through numerous small ducts in the outer side of the Wolffian duct. Storage occurs (in at least some species) before *amplexus* (see below). This mechanism has remained at a very primitive level, and is another indication that the parental amphibian stock separated very early in the evolutionary history of vertebrates.

Attached to each testis are lobed bodies of a bright yellow colour—the *fat-bodies* (*FK*) or *corpora adiposa*, which are food reserves during æstivation.

The *ovaries* (Fig. 278, *Ov.*) are large, folded, multi-lobed sacs, each of which is held in position by a peritoneal fold, the *mesovarium*, which also covers the ovary as a delicate membrane, on the surface of which the black-and-white ova project. A fat-body is attached to each ovary.

The ovary is under the control of the anterior pituitary, and in turn produces a female sex hormone, or hormones, which influences the secondary sexual organs and behaviour. It varies considerably in size according to season and reproductive condition. The ovaries of some of the Ranidæ may contain as many as 20,000 eggs, each measuring about 1·75 mm. in diameter. The Giant Toad (*Bufo marinus*) can produce 16,000 eggs in a single day. 'Ripe' ovaries usually give the whole body a puffed appearance. The ova are extruded through the ovarian wall directly into the cœlom.

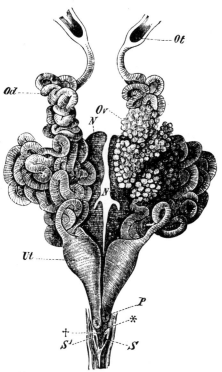

FIG. 278.—*Rana:* **Urinogenital system in female.** *N*, kidneys; *Od.* oviduct; *Ot.* its cœlomic aperture; *Ov.* left ovary (the right is removed); *P*, cloacal aperture of oviduct; *S*, *S'*, cloacal apertures of mesonephric ducts; *Ut.* posterior dilatation of oviduct. (After Wiedersheim.)

There is experimental evidence that, in *R. pipiens* at least, the eggs cannot yet be fertilised. Each *oviduct* (*od.*) is a greatly convoluted tube, the narrow anterior end of which opens into the cœlom by a slit-like aperture, the *ostium tubæ* (*ot.*). The paired oviducts open close to the roots of the lungs. Ova are driven into the oviducts by the action of peritoneal cilia. (Some species have cilia even on the surface of the lungs and pericardium.) Inside the oviducts, the eggs take on an albuminous covering and can thereafter be fertilised. As they are propelled down the tube by oviducal cilia they become progressively more gelatinous. Finally, they reach the wide, thin-walled posterior parts of the tubes (*ut.*), which become immensely dilated until the eggs are shed.

Fertilisation is external. In amplexus the male applies himself to the dorsal surface of the female, aided by a modified additional paired digit, the *prehallux*, and the nuptial-pad (pp. 390, 416). So tenacious is the grip that a male's fore-legs may sometimes be broken before it will release its hold. There is experimental evidence that this activity, once under way, involves essentially a simple reflex spinal arc, since it may continue after decapitation.

The male of *R. temporaria* has been known to clasp a fish or floating stick at the height of the sexual season, in the absence of a female. The swollen female may carry the male around for several days until the eggs are shed. As they are voided, the male pours spermatic fluid over them, achieving fertilisation. The process in the majority of species occurs in water.

Development.—The eggs are laid in water in gelatinous aggregations. The gelatinous material swells in water and protects the conspicuous eggs from small aquatic predators and buffers them against injury. Each egg has a black and a white hemisphere. The former is always directed upwards and surrounded by a sphere of jelly. The egg is telolecithal, the protoplasm being mainly accumulated in the pigmented hemisphere, while the white hemisphere is loaded with yolk. After the male sheds spermatic fluid over the eggs, the spermatozoa penetrate the albuminous jelly and vitelline membrane. In a short time the jelly swells and becomes thereafter impermeable to spermatozoa.

Segmentation begins by a vertical division of the fertilised egg into two cells (Fig. 279, *A*), and is soon followed by a second vertical furrow at right angles to the first (*B*), and then by an equatorial furrow placed nearer the black than the white pole (*C*). Thus the eight-celled embryo consists of four smaller black cells and four larger white cells. Further divisions take place (*D*), the black cells dividing rapidly into micromeres (*mi.*), the white, more slowly, into megameres (*mg.*). As in previous cases, the presence of yolk hinders the process of segmentation. The pigmented micromeres (*D–F, mi.*) give rise to the ectoderm, which is many-layered : the megameres (*mg.*) contribute to all three germ layers and are commonly called *yolk-cells*. During the process of segmentation a *blastocœle* (*E, bl. cœl.*) or segmentation-cavity appears in the upper hemisphere.

The black now begins to encroach on the white hemisphere until it covers the whole embryo except for a small patch, known as the *yolk-plug* (*G, H, yk. pl.*), at what will become the posterior end. This process is one of epiboly : the margin of cells surrounding the yolk-plug forms the lips of the blastopore.

The *archenteron* (*I, ent.*) arises by invagination of cells at the blastopore. The archenteron is at first a very narrow cleft, but soon widens considerably. For a long time it does not actually communicate with the exterior, since the blastopore is filled with the yolk-plug. As the archenteron extends forwards,

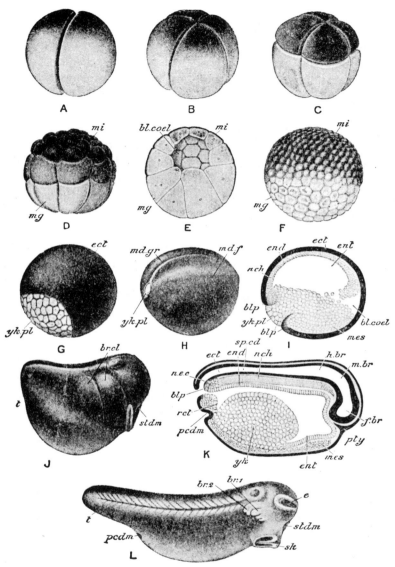

FIG. 279.—**Rana: Development.** *A—F*, segmentation; *G*, overgrowth of ectoderm; *H*, *I*, establishment of germinal layers; *J*, *K*, assumption of tadpole-form and establishment of nervous system and the notochord. The disputed enteric canal (see text) is also shown. *L*, newly-hatched tadpole. *bl. cœl.* blastocœle; *blp. blp′.* blastopore; *br.* 1, *br.* 2, gills; *br. cl.* branchial arches; *e.* eye; *ect.* ectoderm; *end.* endoderm; *ent.* enteron; *f. br.* fore-brain; *h. br.* hind-brain; *m. br.* mid-brain; *md. f.* medullary fold; *md. gr.* medullary groove; *mes.* mesoderm; *mg.* megameres; *mi.* micromeres; *nch.* notochord; *n. e. c.* neurenteric canal; *pcdm.* proctodæum; *pty.* pituitary invagination; *rct.* commencement of rectum; *sk.* sucker; *sp. cd.* spinal cord; *stdm.* stomodæum; *t.* tail; *yk.* yolk-cells; *yk. pl.* yolk-plug. (*A—D*, *F—H*, and *J* from Ziegler's models; *E*, *I*, *K*, and *L* after A. M. Marshall.)

the blastocœle gradually disappears. The walls of the archenteron are formed by endodermal cells, except for a strip of chordamesoderm lying along the antero-posterior axis of the archenteron roof. This separates off to form a notochord, whilst the endodermal cells form gut walls, the archenteron providing the lumen of the gut. Meanwhile mesodermal cells have invaginated ventrally and laterally to the yolk-plug and extended forwards and upwards between the ectoderm and endoderm layers. The mesoderm subsequently forms somites and lateral plate mesoderm.

The edges of the lower margin of the blastopore now begin to approach one another, and, uniting in the median plane, give rise to a vertical groove. In the meantime *medullary folds* (*H, md. f.*) appear and mark the dorsal surface. They are at first widely separated, but gradually approach one another and close over the medullary groove (*md. gr.*), thus giving rise to the central nervous system. Posteriorly they are continuous with the lips of the blastopore. The neurenteric groove becomes closed in behind. It has been claimed in the past that the archenteron communicates with the neurocœle by a neurenteric canal, but most recent workers doubt whether this actually exists, or if it does, that it persists for more than an hour.

The embryo soon begins to elongate. One end is broad, and, becoming separated by a slight constriction, is marked out as the *head*. The other end is bluntly pointed and is the rudiment of the *tail* (*t.*). On the ventral surface of the root of the tail a *proctodæum* (*pcdm.*) appears and communicates with the archenteron. The head and tail become more distinct. A pit—the *stomodæum* (*J, R, L, stdm.*)—appears on the antero-ventral surface of the head, and, immediately behind it (in *R. temporaria*), a semilunar area with raised edges, the *sucker* (*sk.*). The anatomical relationships of these structures vary among species. At each side of the head two branched processes appear. These are the *external gills* (*br. 1, br. 2*), and the regions from which they arise mark the positions of the first and second branchial arches.

The embryos are now hatched as *tadpoles*. They swim freely in the water or adhere to weeds by means of the sucker, which is really a glandular apparatus. They are still blind and mouthless; the stomodæum is not yet in communication with the archenteron. Soon a third pair of external gills appears on the third branchial arch, and the first two pairs increase greatly in size. The stomodæum joins the archenteron. Gill-slits (branchial clefts) are formed between the branchial arches, and eyes appear. The mouth is small, bounded by lips beset with horny papillæ and provided with a pair of horny jaws. This buccal rasp fragments the browsed food into minute particles which, in suspension, are gulped in by the action of the masticatory muscles and, entangled in mucus, are carried into the œsophagus by pharyngeal cilia. Strings of food-impregnated mucus thus reach the stomach. The food is passed into the intestine, which grows to a relatively great length and is coiled.

Soon the external gills show signs of shrivelling. At the same time *internal gills* not unlike those of fishes are developed in the branchial clefts. A fold of skin, the *operculum*, appears in front of the gills on each side. It grows from the region of the hyoid arch, and extends backwards until the gill-slits and external gills are covered. In *Rana*, the operculum on the right side soon unites with the body-wall so as to close the branchial aperture, but on the left side an opening (the spiracle) remains for a considerable time as the sole means of exit of water from the opercular chamber and therefore all visceral clefts. In other genera the opening is on the right side; and in yet others it is bilateral. At this stage the tadpole is strikingly fish-like. The lungs now appear, and the larva for a time becomes truly amphibious : it rises periodically to the surface to breathe air.

Meantime, limbs are developed. The hind-limbs appear as little rounded buds, one on each side of the root of the tail. The fore-limbs arise beneath the operculum and are therefore hidden at first. Soon, however, they emerge by forcing their way through the operculum on the right and the spiracle on the left. As the limbs increase in size the tail undergoes a progressive shrinking. The mouth widens by the backward rotation of the suspensorium. The intestine undergoes a relative diminution in length as vegetable is exchanged for animal diet. The small, tailed frog can now leave the water and hop about upon land. Its tail is soon completely absorbed. Metamorphosis is complete.

Partial neoteny has been recorded several times in *R. esculenta*. In this rare developmental abnormality metamorphosis is halted at the bud-stage in the hind-limb, yet the animal increases in overall size, becoming a bloated and gigantic tadpole 70 or 80 mm. long. Removal of the thyroid gland (p. 151) produces a very similar condition in the laboratory (see also pp. 2, 3).

INTERRELATIONSHIP OF AMPHIBIAN GROUPS

The classification of the Amphibia is uncertain. There are few known links between the various orders found in the late Palæozoic and early Mesozoic rocks (p. 3) and the three widely divergent tribes—frogs, salamanders, and cæcilians— that survive to-day (p. 388). The principal extinct groups are as follows :

SUB-CLASS APSIDOSPONDYLI

This great group is characterised by the possession of vertebræ which exhibit considerable variation, but which are probably a direct inheritance from crossopterygian ancestry. They have centra formed from cartilage blocks in units of two which are ossified, in varying degree, as anterior intercentra and posterior pleurocentra. We will see that such a basic pattern persists throughout the vertebrate series. The apsidospondylous amphibians fall into two superorders, the Labyrinthodontia and the Salientia (frogs, p. 428).

SUPER-ORDER LABYRINTHODONTIA

The name Labyrinthodontia is derived from the characteristic pattern of the teeth (Fig. 280). In cross-section the teeth show a prominent radiating

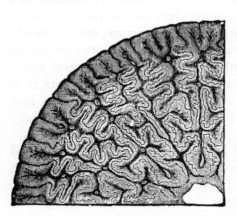

infolding of the enamel surface. Labyrinthodonts, arising from a fish ancestry in the Devonian, appear to exhibit at least two distinct evolutionary trends. From primitive aquatic forms there developed the extremely abundant Rhachitomi which were to become, in the Permian, markedly terrestrial. These in turn gave rise to the Stereospondyli, which became degenerate in many respects, and secondarily aquatic. Accompanying this general trend were progressive skeletal changes which were particularly impressive in skull and vertebræ (Fig. 281). This trend did not survive the Triassic (p. 3).

Fig. 280. — **Labyrinthodontia: Tooth structure.** The labyrinthine infolding is here shown in the stereospondylid *Mastodonsaurus*. (From B.M. (N.H.) Catalogue.)

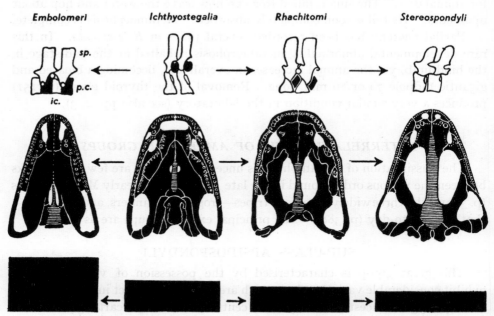

Fig. 281.—**Labyrinthodontia: Skulls and vertebræ.** The top series shows vertebræ in lateral view. *i. c.* intercentrum; *sp.* spinous process. Each pleurocentrum (*p. c.*) is black. The middle series shows skulls in palatal view, illustrating trends in vacuolation and variation in the parasphenoid (cross-hatched). The bottom series illustrates the proportions of height to width in each skull. The arrows indicate trends in labyrinthodont evolution according to Colbert. The skulls, drawn to the same length, are not to scale. (After Colbert.)

Probably stemming from primitive labyrinthodonts in another direction were the essentially aquatic Embolomeri. Some have suggested that these may have shared their ancestry with the Carboniferous stem-reptiles (pp. 458, 486).

ORDER ICHTHYOSTEGALIA

These are the earliest known Amphibia (Fig. 282). One, embedded in the Upper Devonian of Canada, was the remarkable *Elpistostege*, perhaps the nearest approach to a true prototetrapod yet described (p. 382). This animal

FIG. 282.—Super-order **Labyrinthodontia**, Order **Ichthyostegalia**, Family **Ichthyostegidæ**. *Ichthyostega*. Reconstruction. These late Devonian and Carboniferous amphibians existed in Greenland when the climate was rather different from now. They perhaps retained traces of their osteichthian ancestry in the possession of a tail supported by true fin-rays. The skulls were often more than 6 inches long. (See also Figs. 281 and 283.) (From B.M. (N.H.) Catalogue.)

was perhaps very close to the rhipidistian crossopterygians in its cranial structure, which in fact seemed to be intermediate between the crossopterygians and *Ichthyostega* to be dealt with below. It is unfortunate that few elements have been discovered. It is not known whether *Elpistostege* had fins or legs. Only a part of its dermal cranial roof is known from a single specimen.

Ichthyostega and *Ichthystegopsis*, which are found in Greenland fresh-water deposits of either Upper Devonian or Lower Carboniferous age, are now much better known. The skull of *Ichthyostega* was about 8 inches long and possessed three interesting features (Fig. 283). A pre-opercular and possibly a sub-opercular persisted on the back of the squamosal and quadratojugal bones as a relic of the fish opercular series, although no actual operculum has been shown.   The septomaxilla formed part of the dermal covering of the skull.   The nose consisted of a pit on the under side of the skull, which was bridged by a process of the maxilla and divided into anterior and posterior parts.   This last condition is reminiscent of that found in the Dipnoi and some of the early crossopterygians,

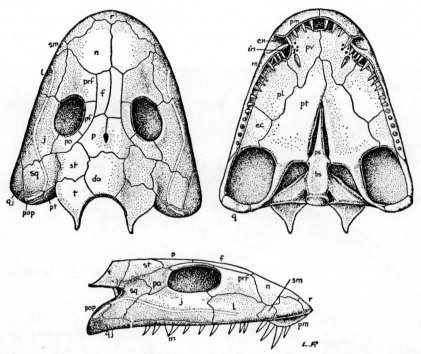

FIG. 283.—*Ichthyostega:* Cranium.   *bs.* basisphenoid; *do.* supraoccipital; *ec.* ectopterygoid; *en.* external nares; *f.* frontal; *in.* internal nares; *j.* jugal; *l.* lachrymal; *m.* maxilla; *n.* nasal; *p.* parietal; *pf.* postfrontal; *pl.* palatine; *pm.* premaxilla; *po.* postorbital; *pop.* preopercular; *prf.* prefrontal; *ps.* parasphenoid; *pt.* pterygoid; *pv.* prevomer; *q.* quadrate; *qj.* quadrato-jugal; *r.* rostral; *sm.* septomaxillary; *sq.* squamosal; *st.* supratemporal; *t.* tabular.   (After Romer.)

while in all tetrapods the anterior opening of the nasal pit has migrated to the upper surface of the skull and become completely closed off from the posterior opening, so as to form true internal and external nares (Fig. 89, p. 138).

ORDER RHACHITOMI

These (e.g. *Eryops*) were among the most plentiful and perhaps typical labyrinthodonts.   They flourished during the Permian and Triassic, but may have arisen much earlier.   Their rhachitomous vertebræ had a semi-lunar, wedge-like intercentrum and one or two (posterior) pleurocentra in addition to a vertical neural arch (Fig. 281).   *Eryops,* about 5 feet long, had short powerful legs and five toes.   The large depressed skull had large interpterygoid cavities.

An otic notch occurred.   Cranial and lower lateral elements were united.   In general, we have the impression of a superficially crocodilian animal which spent much time out of the water.

ORDER STEREOSPONDYLI

These (e.g. *Capitosaurus, Cyclotosaurus, Paracyclotosaurus* (Fig. 284), arose from rhachitome stock.   Transitional types lived in the early Triassic.

FIG. 284.—Super-order **Labyrinthodontia**, Order **Stereospondyli**, Family **Capitosauridæ.** *Paracyclotosaurus.*   This Upper Triassic form (*P. davidi*) was probably the largest labyrinthodont known.   It reached a length of about 11 feet and its skull, heavily armoured with sharp teeth, was some 3 feet in length.   This perhaps represents almost the end-phase of a labyrinthodont trend that led to the abandonment of land for a secondarily aquatic life.   The limbs were degenerate, and the great weight rested principally on the plate-like clavicles and interclavicle.   The upward-looking eyes reveal its bottom-hunting existence.   The fore-feet of many stereospondyls (unlike *Cyclotosaurus*) possessed only four toes.   *Paracyclotosaurus* was found in the Wianamatta fish-bed of St. Peter's, Sydney, alongside fishes closely related to *Palæoniscus* (p. 286) and *Semionotus* (p. 292).

These still labyrinthodont animals were undergoing a general degeneration and were returning to the water, and there is evidence that, at the same time, some had specialised to a degree that allowed the colonisation of the sea (*e.g.* the probably piscivorous, long-snouted *Trematosaurus*).   If this is indeed so, there is posed the fascinating problem of their larval development (p. 385).   The Stereospondyli had vertebræ in which the pleurocentra had vanished or almost so, the intercentra joining almost the whole structure. Skull ossification was much reduced except in the exoccipitals, which formed a double condyle. In the brain-floor region the basi-occipitals and basisphenoid had become unimportant compared with the hyper-development of the parasphenoid, which had apparently firm unions with the pterygoids. Large interpterygoid vacuities occurred.

These animals were large and heavy-headed. The skull of *Mastodonsaurus* was more than three feet long, though some forms (e.g. *Brachyops*) had short (though heavy) heads. The flattened skulls, dorsally placed eyes, and massive supporting pectoral plate (formed from clavicles and interclavicles) suggest a shallow-water, bottom-dwelling existence. It is certain that the weak limbs would have been inadequate efficiently to carry such a heavy, short body unsupported by water.

These curious creatures disappeared towards the end of the Triassic, possibly as a result of competition from the many aquatic reptiles which had then arisen.

ORDER EMBOLOMERI

Appearing first in the Carboniferous, the Embolomeri became abundant during the Permian, but did not survive beyond the Trias. Some of the early forms are very important, as they show features which are fish-like, yet at the same time they provided possible ancestors of the reptiles. Superficially some of the Carboniferous labyrinthodonts were rather like modern crocodiles, and some of them reached a length of more than 3 metres. *Palæogyrinus* (Fig. 285 B) had a long, cylindrical body with a powerful tail and poorly developed limbs. It has been claimed that the shoulder-girdle was attached to the back of the skull by a post-temporal bone, as in fishes. The build of the skull of these Carboniferous forms was very similar in general structure to that of the osteolepid fishes (Fig. 285 A), except that the specialised hinge (between the parietals and post-parietals) was missing. An important feature is seen in the structure of the teeth, which had the dentine infolded at the base into labyrinthine grooves, as in osteolepids. The vertebræ were *embolomerous*, consisting of a neural arch resting on two notochordal centra, an anterior intercentrum and a posterior pleurocentrum. The shoulder-girdle recalls that of the osteolepid fishes and the scapulocoracoid bone has increased in size. The pelvis was peculiar in being the only one known among tetrapods not directly attached to the vertebral column. It was held in place by ligaments.

The remarkable *Eogyrinus*, which lived during the Lower Carboniferous, and which is found particularly in coal-measure deposits, had double centra in which both (anterior) inter-centra and (posterior) pleuracentra formed complete discs. One or both of these were united with the neural arch. Both skull, roof, and palate were well-ossified and primitive in arrangement. The latter had vacuities between the pterygoids and the parasphenoid. There was on each side a mobile articulation between cranium and palate, a condition resembling that of bony fishes. A well-developed stapes (arising from the piscine hyomandibular) and an otic notch occurred. The body and tail were long and superficially crocodilian. The limbs were short with, possibly, fish-like girdles.

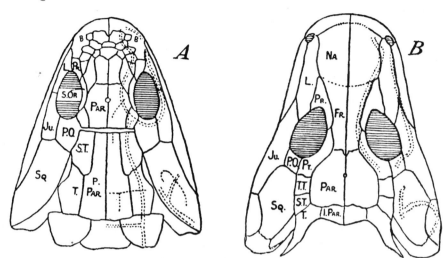

FIG. 285.—**Fish–amphibian relationships: Cranial bones.** *A. Osteolepis* (see p. 355), a Devonian fish from the Red Sandstone of Scotland, and *B. Palæogyrinus*, a Carboniferous amphibian (Embolomeri) from the Middle Coal Measures of Europe. The skull architecture of both animals shows considerable similarity. In the amphibian the remarkable hinge between parietals and post-parietals is missing. *Fr.* frontal; *I. Par.* interparietal; *Ju.* jugal; *L.* lachrymal; *Na.* nasal; *Par.* parietal; *P. par.* post-parietal; *P.O.* post-orbital; *Pr.* pre-frontal; *S. orb.* supra-orbital; *Sq.* squamosal; *S.T.* Supra-temporal; *T.* tabular; *T.T.* inter-temporal (modified after Watson).

Some of the Embolomeri were primitively aquatic, others apparently terrestrial and, in addition, others seem to have become re-adapted to lake-life. At the same time 'the fundamental morphology of the skeleton is strikingly uniform throughout the group' (Watson).

ORDER SEYMOURIAMORPHA

The Seymouriamorpha (e.g. *Seymouria*) (Fig. 286) is one of the most interesting known groups because it represents a stem apparently developed astride the transition line between the Amphibia and Reptilia. *Seymouria* exhibited, as Watson has shown, the phenomenon of *mosaic evolution*, which we shall see displayed with equal beauty in *Archæopteryx*, on the borderline between reptiles and birds (Fig. 414, p. 599), and in the ictidosaurs (p. 517), which likewise possess both typically reptilian and mammalian features.

Seymouria was about 2 feet long and was Lower Permian in age. It had a relatively small, pointed head, dorsal nostrils, a comparatively thick body, and short tail. All its limbs were pentadactyle, short, muscular, and thrust from the mid-line in an apparently reptilian manner. Further evidence of its affinity with the stem-reptiles (p. 458) is as follows: the atlas and axis were formed from anterior cervicals, and the basiventrals were reduced to form intercentra. There were a long interclavicle, and a ventral coracoid ossification in the shoulder girdles. The pelvic girdles were anchored by means of two sacral vertebræ. The ilium was dorsally expanded for the attachment of strong walking muscles. Had only fragmentary material, with merely the above characters apparent, been available for study there would be small argument against the inclusion of *Seymouria* among the Reptilia. But most of the remaining pieces of the mosaic, so to speak, could readily come from an embolomerous labyrinthodont amphibian. The skull was strongly ossified; and temporal fossæ were absent. An intertemporal bone, absent in reptiles, was retained. The palate, too, was primitive, and bore labyrinthodont-pattern teeth in pairs on vomers and palatines, as well as in pairs on the jaw. The tympanic membrane, bounded above by the supratemporal and below by the squamosal, stretched across an otic notch, which extended forward below the tabular and supratemporal so that the quadrate sloped forward. The fenestra ovalis was below the basal level of the brain. There was practically no neck; the shoulder-girdle lay beneath the jaw. The vertebræ showed little differentiation and the cervical elements bore ribs. Intercentra were present, and the ribs were large and double-headed, the knobs for attachment (to the intercentra) being retained. *Seymouria* perhaps lacked a cleithrum (present in most cotylosaurian reptiles); and some fossils show evidence of lateral line canals in the head region. If such canals did in fact exist they make certain its amphibian relationship.

It has been suggested that the Upper Permian *Kotlassia* exhibits erroneously changes typical of Amphibia that have reverted to the aquatic life. *Kotlassia*, incidentally, was erroneously reported to possess cosmine tissue (p. 83).

Despite their obvious labyrinthodont affinity, it would seem that the Seymouriamorpha appeared too late to constitute the basis for the main reptilian radiations. The earliest reptiles had already appeared in the Carboniferous. It would seem likely that both Seymouriamorpha and Cotylosauria shared a common labyrinthodont ancestry.

SUPER-ORDER SALIENTA (ANURA, BATRACHIA)

Frogs very like those of to-day occurred at least as early as the Jurassic (p. 3) and, like the Urodela (p. 432), are both degenerate and highly specialised in their anatomy. There is some fossil evidence that the Anura are descended from aberrant labyrinthodonts (p. 422). *Protobatrachus* (Order Proanura), an indubitable frog ancestor from the Triassic of Madagascar, had a skull not unlike that of extant forms. The trunk, however, was longer than that of modern frogs, and although the ilia were elongated, the post-cranial skeleton, including the caudal vertebræ, was not otherwise predominantly anuran. Other, more ancient, frog-like amphibians (*e.g.* the Upper Carboniferous *Amphibamus* and *Miobatrachus*) show cranial, vertebral, and other characters that suggest a labyrinthodont affinity. For these the Order Eoanura ('dawn frogs') has been erected. It should be remembered, nevertheless, that these animals have not been unquestionably proved to be ancestral to modern batrachians.

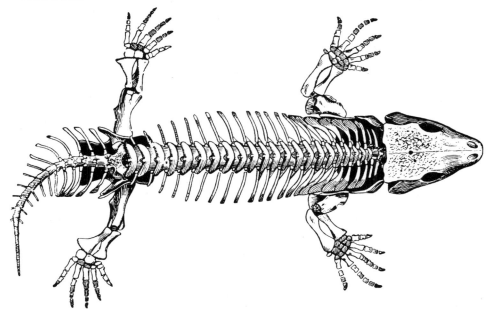

FIG. 286.—Order **Seymouriamorpha,** Family **Seymouridæ,** *Seymouria:* **Mosaic evolution.** *Seymouria* (Lower Permian of North America) possessed both amphibian and reptilian characters, but its sideline flourished after the stem-reptiles (p. 458) had arisen and *Seymouria* lived contemporaneously with them. It was about 2 feet long and is often placed with the reptiles, but it probably possessed lateralis organs (Fig. 302, p. 449). If so it is by definition an amphibian. (After Williston.)

All the modern frogs and toads are, in the adult, four-legged, squat-bodied, and without tails. They fall into the following families: Liopelmidæ (primitive frogs, with amphicœlous vertebræ, restricted to the New Zealand genus *Liopelma* and the North American *Ascaphus*; a remarkable example of discontinuous distribution. *Ascaphus* has a cloacal extension which apparently acts as an intromittent organ during internal insemination); Discoglossidæ (primitive Eurasian and Philippine frogs with opisthocœlus vertebræ, free sacral vertebræ with biconvex centre, and three pairs of ribs. Known from Upper Oligocene and Miocene and related to next family); Pipidæ (African and South American anurans lacking tongue and eyelids—except for *Pseudohymenochirus*, possessing lower eyelids. This group includes *Xenopus*); Pelobatidæ (ribless anurans from

Eurasia, East Indies, and Seychelles) ; Bufonidæ (widely distributed true toads with all vertebræ procœlus and a double condyle to the coccyx, and including both toothed and toothless genera which are sometimes placed in separate families ; common from the Miocene onwards) ; Brachycephalidæ (a poly-phyletic group of Neotropical forms, allied to the Bufonidæ ; with procœlus vertebræ and the pectoral girdles in partial or complete mid-line fusion) ; Hylidæ (widely distributed bufonids with an intercalary cartilage or bone between the last two phalanges of each digit : tree-frogs, usually with claw-shaped phalanges ; but some are terrestrial or fossorial ; a Miocene fossil is known) ; Ranidæ (true frogs of wide distribution except in South America and Australia, in each of which occurs only *Rana* ; Miocene) ; Rhacophoridæ (tropical Eurasian and African, Madagascan, East Indian ranid tree-frogs with cylindrical diapophyses and intercalary cartilages between the last two phalanges of each digit) ; Brevicipitidæ (narrow-mouthed toads of ranid affinity and cosmopolitan distribution which differ skeletally from ranids chiefly in their more dilated sacral diapophýses ; some advanced forms have become toothless and have lost all the ventral elements of the pectoral girdle except the coracoids).

SUB-CLASS LEPOSPONDYLI

The members of this side-line (which includes extant salamanders and cæcilians) are essentially characterised by relatively simple *lepospondylous* vertebræ.   It is held that the centrum of this type of vertebra was, unlike that of the Apsidospondyli, not pre-formed in cartilage, but instead arose by direct ossification around the embryonic notochord.   Each centrum sometimes retained an aperture housing part of a persistent notochord.

The Lepospondyli were small, late Palæozoic amphibians, ranging from a few inches to a couple of feet in size.   They flourished in the Carboniferous and disappeared in the Permian (p. 3).   They (e.g. *Diplocaulus*) had the neural arches and the centra of the vertebræ co-ossified.   Although the order includes forms of a generalised build, they were for the most part bizarre animals, with the posterior corners of the skull-roof enormously enlarged (Fig. 287).   A few were legless and superficially snake-like (Fig. 288).

Order Aistopoda

These small amphibians had long, snake-like bodies with as many as one hundred vertebræ and, often, curiously forked ribs (e.g. *Ophiderpeton*, Fig. 288). They are known only from Carboniferous deposits.

Order Nectridia

These bore symmetrically opposed neural and hæmal spines on their caudal vertebræ.   At least two distinct groups occurred in the Upper Carboniferous.

One type was superficially snake-like and almost, or entirely, limbless (e.g. *Sauropleura*), whilst the other possessed small limbs and a flattened skull with grotesque protuberances. Thus *Diplocaulus* (Fig. 287) was about 2 feet long and had a huge triangular head and small limbs. Its eyes looked upwards. The skull bore an extraordinary armament formed by the outgrowth of the tabulars. The cranium was largely unossified, and other degenerative changes were manifest. If we dismiss the all-important (from the diagnostic viewpoint) vertebræ, these could be mistaken for stem labyrinthodonts (p. 422).

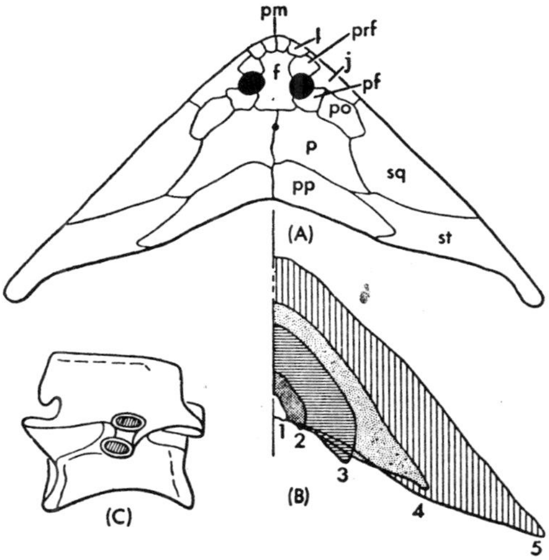

ORDER MICROSAURIA
(ADELOSPONDYLI)

Only a few microsaurians are known. In them the neural arches were loosely attached to single centra, which were excavated on each side. *Lysorophus* from the late

FIG. 287.—**Lepospondylid radiation: Skull of nectridian (with a vertebra characteristic of subclass).** *A.* 'Horned' skull of Lower Permian *Diplocaulus* in dorsal view (a little less than $\frac{1}{4}$ natural size). *B.* Growth stages from very young (1) to large adult (5). *C.* Lepospondyl vertebra in right lateral view ($\frac{5}{8}$ths natural size) (cf. Fig. 281, p. 422). *f.* frontal; *j.* jugal; *l.* lachrymal; *p.* parietal; *pf.* prefrontal; *pm.* premaxillary; *p. o.* postorbital; *pp.* post-parietal; *prf.* prefrontal; *sq.* squamosal; *st.* supratemporal. (After Colbert.)

Permian is known in some detail. It had an incompletely roofed skull, and showed much other evidence of cranial reduction, including the loss of circumorbital bones, which left the orbit open below. Its large branchial arches were ossified. This can lead only to the conclusion that gill-breathing was continued during adult life. These animals have been called Permian urodeles, but they retain too many labyrinthodont characters to be closely related to the Caudata, the earliest true examples of which were Cretaceous (p. 3).

FIG. 288.—**Lepospondylid radiation: Skeleton of aistopod.** Snake-like form of the Carboniferous *Ophiderpeton*. Certain nectridians (Fig. 287) became similarly elongated. (From Romer, after Fritschi.)

'ORDER PHYLLOSPONDYLI'

The amphibians believed to constitute the 'Order Phyllospondyli' may, in fact, have been small-gilled larval labyrinthodonts of rhachitome affinity.

Order Urodela (Caudata)

Although attempts have been made to derive the Urodela (newts and salamanders) from the Dipnoi, it is generally held that, however widely divergent are the three surviving lines, all amphibians come from the same stock (p. 282).

Salamanders and newts (Figs. 290, 291) are degenerate animals with a

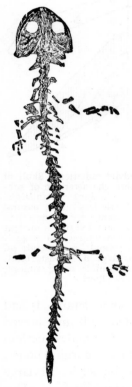

determinable ancestry from the Cretaceous (e.g. *Hemitrypus*). They show many similarities to the early Lepospondyli, but no Jurassic or Triassic links have been discovered. It is not without interest that one of the most celebrated of all fossils is that of a urodele. This is an Upper Miocene example of the cryptobranchid *Andrias* (Fig. 289) unearthed by the Swiss, Scheuchzer, in the early 18th century and illustrated and described as *Homo diluvii testis* ('Man, witness to the Deluge') in a contemporary treatise. Appended too was the following homily (tr.):

'Oh, sad remains of bone, frame of poor Man of sin,
Soften the heart and mind of recent sinful kin.'

It was left for Cuvier to show that the sinner was a salamander.

Modern urodeles (Figs. 290, 291) probably fall into eight families as follows: Hynobiidæ (Asiatic land salamanders); Cryptobranchidæ (large semi-larval Amphibia derived from the above which range through Asia and North America—known from the Miocene onwards); Amblystomidæ (American salamanders differing from the above in their fused angulars, long premaxillary spines and internal fertilisation and from the next family in their short prevomers and amphi-

Fig. 289.—**A witness of the Deluge** (see adjacent text). (From B.M. (N.H.) Catalogue.)

cœlous vertebræ); Salamandridæ (Eurasian and American Amphibia, including newts and terrestrial species —e.g. *Salamandra*—which have vomerine teeth on each side of the parasphenoid, and opisthocœlus vertebræ; Oligocene fossils are known); Amphiumidæ (Genus *Amphiuma* of North America, including the 'Conger-eel', a semi-larval creature of salamandrid derivation possessing lungs, a bony pterygoid, posterior prevomeral processes, and premaxillary spines separating the nasals); Plethodontidæ (American and European lung-less aquatic and terrestrial salamanders of salamandrid (see above) stock with a permanently cartilaginous pterygoid, vomerine teeth forming dentigerous patches over the parasphenoid, and a naso-labial groove); Proteidæ (permanently larval salamanders, with lungs and a distinctive long, anteriorly

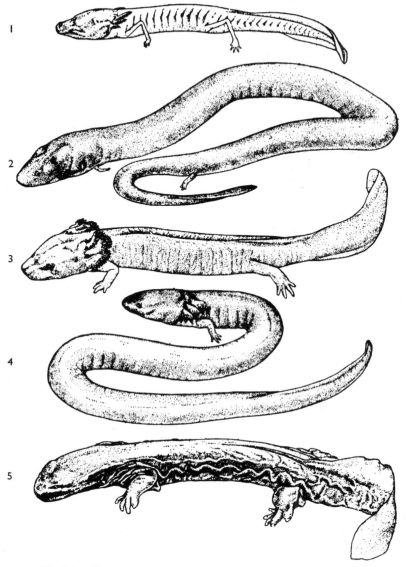

FIG. 290.—**Urodela: Permanent larvæ.** 1. *Typhlomolge rathbuni*, a blind plethodontid of North American caves (Sub-order Salamandroidea); 2. *Amphiumameans*, the Conger of North America (Salamandroidea); 3. *Necturus maculosus*, North American Mud-puppy (Proteida), of the same family as the unpigmented European Olm; 4. *Siren lacertina* (Meantes); 5. *Cryptobranchus alleganiensis* (Cryptobranchoidea). (After Noble.)

Although all extant sub-orders except one (Ambystomoidea) are represented above, it should be remembered it is only in the sub-orders Proteida and Meantes that *all* forms are permanently larval. The genic and dependent physiological factors controlling this varying condition (which represents further evidence of a retreat to the aquatic medium) have arisen independently several times.

directed pubo-ischium, including only the North American *Necturus* and the blind, unpigmented, cave-dwelling *Proteus* of Europe); Sirenidæ (American amphibians, e.g. *Siren* and *Pseudobranchus* of dubious affinities which, as adult forms, resemble the young of other families in possessing only forelimbs and an apparently 'juvenile' skull. At the same time they possess reduced pterygoids, a separately ossified coracoid, and a prominent vomeronasal organ).

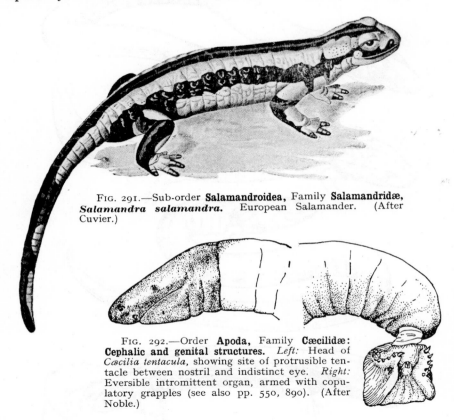

FIG. 291.—Sub-order **Salamandroidea**, Family **Salamandridæ**, *Salamandra salamandra.* European Salamander. (After Cuvier.)

FIG. 292.—Order **Apoda**, Family **Cæcilidæ**: **Cephalic and genital structures.** *Left:* Head of *Cæcilia tentacula*, showing site of protrusible tentacle between nostril and indistinct eye. *Right:* Eversible intromittent organ, armed with copulatory grapples (see also pp. 550, 890). (After Noble.)

ORDER APODA (GYMNOPHIONA, CÆCILIA)

This little-known group consists of aberrant blind, worm-like, limbless, tropical Amphibia with a very short tail and an intromittent organ in the male (Fig. 292). The body is usually grooved transversely, and in the grooves are often series of minute scales, a legacy from Carboniferous ancestors. The eyes are lidless and sometimes covered by cranial bones. A protrusible sensory tentacle occurs between nostril and orbit. The vent is almost terminal. Cranial elements and scales seem to be lost with progressive specialisation. The aquatic genus *Typhlonectes* has a flattened tail. Development of eggs may be internal (e.g. *Typhlonectes*) or external (from large-yolked eggs laid in burrows as in *Rhinatrema*). All cæcilians belong to a single family—the Cæcilidæ— which contains nineteen genera and about fifty-five species. Fossils are unknown, and the living animal is rarely seen.

Cæcilians are to-day restricted to damp, tropical areas, excluding Madagascar and Australasia. They are often extremely rare in regions that at first sight appear to provide for them eminently suitable habitats. Nevertheless they are unusually common in the Seychelles.

It has been suggested that the Apoda may be descended from the Carboniferous microsaurian Lepospondyli. These, as their name suggests, were once thought to be of reptilian affinity, but their amphibian relationship now seems well-established (p. 431).

GENERAL ORGANISATION OF THE AMPHIBIA

External Characters.—An example of Urodela with persistent gills and lateral line is afforded by the North American Water-newt, or Mud-puppy, *Necturus maculosus* (Fig. 290). The animal is sometimes more than a foot long. The elongated trunk is separated by a slight constriction from the depressed head, and passes imperceptibly into the compressed tail, which is bordered by a continuous median fin unsupported by fin-rays. The limbs are small and weak in proportion to the body, and in the ordinary swimming attitude are directed backwards, more or less parallel to the sagittal plane. The upper arm and thigh take a direction backwards and slightly upwards. The fore-arm, hand, and the shank and foot extend backwards and downwards. Each limb thus presents an external or dorsal and an internal or ventral surface, an anterior or *pre-axial* border (which terminates in the first digit) and a posterior or *postaxial* border (which terminates in the last digit). The eyes are small and have no eyelids. There is no tympanic membrane. The mouth is wide and bordered by thick lips. On each side of the neck are two gill-slits leading into the pharynx, the first between the first and second branchial arches, the other between the second and third. From the dorsal end of each of the three branchial arches springs a branched *external gill*. Very similar in its external characters is the blind, cave-dwelling, *Proteus* of Europe, which is, however, colourless. *Siren* (Fig. 290) differs mainly in its elongated eel-like body and in the absence of hind-limbs. All three genera are *perennibranchiate* or persistent-gilled.

The remaining Urodela are often called *caducibranchiate* or deciduous-gilled, and furnish a complete series of transitions from *derotrematous* forms which, while losing the gills, retain the gill-clefts, to *salamandrine* forms in which all trace of branchiate organisation disappears in the adult. In the American *Amphiuma* (Fig. 290) the body is eel-like and the limbs are extremely small. There are no gills in the adult, but two pairs of gill-openings are retained throughout life. In *Cryptobranchus* there is a single branchial aperture, sometimes present on the left side only ; but, as in the previously mentioned genera, four branchial arches are retained. In *Megalobatrachus*, the Giant Salamander of Japan and China, all trace of gill-slits disappears, but two branchial arches persist. This animal reaches a length of 5 feet. Lastly, in such species as the Spotted Salamander (*Salamandra maculosa*, Fig. 291) of Europe, and the common British newts (*Triturus*), the adult has no trace either of gills ŏr gill-slits, and the branchial arches are much reduced. The limbs in terrestrial salamanders stand out from the trunk, and are plantigrade. All trace of a median fin disappears, the tail becoming nearly cylindrical.

In the Anura the body is always characteristic in shape. The head is large and depressed with a wide mouth and large tympanic membranes in most genera. The snout in burrowing forms is often unusually sharp. It may be equipped with dermal ossifications, or it may remain blunt and be subcutaneously invaded with bone. The trunk is short and the tail absent, and the hind- much larger than the fore-limbs. In many species of *Hyla* an extraordinary arboreality is made possible by plate-like adhesive discs at the termination of the digits of all four legs. These discs are not suctorial in operation, but possess a moist, fibrous, corrugated anti-skid external layer which engages the leaf or stem. Capillary attraction is involved, as well as adhesion by means of mucus. The mucus is expressed by the action of collagen fibres which operate on the glands during the motions of climbing. A unique *intercalcary cartilage* developed between the terminal and penultimate joints facilitates adjustments of the adhesive disc in relation to the toe-hold. Some tree-frogs (e.g. *Chiromantis*) have opposable digits in the manner of reptilian chamæleons (p. 519) and many arboreal mammals.

In some toads (e.g. *Bufo bufo*), and most tree-frogs, the webs between the hind-toes are reduced or absent. In *Rhacophorus*, a genus of East African tree-frog, however, a web-surface greater than that of the ventral expanse of the body has been developed. Ventral surface and webbing of the elongated digits together produce a volplane mechanism functionally comparable with that of the reptile *Draco* (p. 518) and certain marsupials (p. 717) and rodents. Thus *R. malabaricus* can glide more than 30 feet from tree to ground. *Hyla venulosa* (of the Lower Amazon) can glide safely from a height of no less than 140 feet, even though its digits are unwebbed and not considerably enlarged (Cott).

In the Apoda (Fig. 292), the body is elongated and snake-like, the head is small and not depressed, and limbs are absent. There is hardly any tail. The vent (*an.*) occurs at the posterior end of the body on the ventral surface. These tropical animals mostly live in burrows. They are blind, or almost blind, but possess sensory tentacles lodged in pits.

The skin of Amphibia is soft and usually slimy, owing to the secretion of the cutaneous glands, which is sometimes poisonous. Thus when the European Natterjack (toad) (*Bufo calamita*) is frightened it exudes a protective white secretion of pungent odour. Many toads (and salamanders) have small poison-glands aggregated into a prominent swelling, the *parotoid* glands, on each side of the head. The Natterjack has an analogous gland on each hind-leg. The large and conspicuous dorsal warts of toads are each perforated by a pore that leads to a poison gland beneath. On gentle handling by Man the toad does not bring the glands into operation, but when seized by a predator it ejects poison from all over its body. The exudate contains two active toxins, *bufotalin* and *bufogin*, which, when swallowed, cause nausea, respiratory and muscular impairment, as well as a digitalis-like action on the heart. Large experimental doses of toad-venom cause the mammalian heart to slow and finally stop in systole. If attacked, the large Crested or Warty Newt (*Triturus cristatus*) of Europe discharges a secretion from its dorsal glands sufficiently venomous to cause a cat to foam at the mouth.

The colour of the skin is often brilliant : the Spotted Salamander is yellow and black, and many frogs are green and gold, scarlet and black, and so on. The green colour of tree-frogs is protective, serving to conceal them among the foliage of the plants on which they live. The beautiful and strongly contrasted hues of the Spotted Salamander and of some frogs may be instances of *warning colours* ; the animals are inedible owing to the acrid secretion of their cutaneous glands, and their conspicuous colours serve to warn off the birds and other animals which would otherwise devour them. Some tree-frogs are said to show no sign of fear of frog-eating birds, while the edible and more plainly coloured species are in constant danger.

The secretion of the conspicuous black and blue *Dendrobates tinctorius* of Central America is sufficiently venomous to be used by the ' Indians ' as an arrow poison. *Phyllomedusa* has a peculiar adaptation involving brilliant ' flashes ' that are visible only when the animal leaps. The sudden flash and sudden disappearance of colour may have confusion value. In many tree-frogs the brightness of the coloration varies with changes in light intensity in the forest. Quite apart from camouflage or warning, some colours are no doubt of sexual significance, but few experimental data are available on this, or any other point concerning the actual use, as apart from the physiological mechanisms, of colour.

In many toads the skin is dry, and covered with warts which assist in harmonising the animals with their surroundings. The development of a dry skin by anurans was a considerable step towards homœothermy, but as long as the anamniote egg was retained they had no chance of initiating a development similar to that which led to the emergence of the Reptilia (see p. 387).

Exoskeleton.—An exoskeleton is present in many burrowing Apoda in the form of small dermal scales. In some Anura bony exoskeletal plates occur beneath the skin of the back. In an Asiatic urodele, *Onychodactylus*, and in the African toad, *Xenopus*, small, horny claws are present on the digits. The South American frog *Leptodactylus pentadactylus* has horny chest grapples. With these and a few other exceptions the skin is devoid of hard parts. In the Australian *Limnodynastes* the endoskeletal long bone of the thumb perforates the surface and is an exoskeletal grappling aid during amplexus.

Endoskeleton.—The *vertebral column* is usually divisible into a *cervical region*, containing a single vertebra devoid of transverse processes; an *abdominal* or *thoracolumbar region*, containing a variable number of vertebræ with transverse processes and often with ribs; a *sacral region*, containing usually a single vertebra, the large transverse processes—or the ribs—of which give attachment to the ilia; and a *caudal region*, forming the skeleton of the tail. In the Apoda the caudal region is very short, and there is no sacrum. In the Anura the caudal region is represented by a single rod-shaped bone, the *urostyle*. The total number of vertebræ may reach 250 in Urodela and Apoda. In Anura there are commonly only nine vertebræ and a urostyle although ten occur in the primitive family Ascophidæ and nine in some advanced genera.

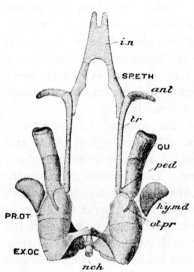

FIG. 293.—**Urodela: Chondrocranium.** *Proteus anguinus* in dorsal view. *ant* antorbital process; Ex.OC. exoccipital and epiotic; *hy. md.* hyomandibular; *i. n.* internasal plate; *nch.* notochord; *ot. pr.* otic process; *ped.* pedicle; PR.OT. pro-otic; QU. quadrate; SP.ETH. sphenethmoid. (After W. K. Parker.)

In the 'lower' Urodela (e.g. *Amblystoma*) the centra are biconcave, as in fishes. They are shaped like a dice-box and are lined at either end by cartilage which is continuous between adjacent vertebræ. The bony shell is developed before the cartilage appears, so that the vertebræ are, in fact, investing bones. The neural arches, on the other hand, are far better developed than in any fish, and have well-formed zygapophyses. These articulate by synovial joints.

The Apoda also have biconcave vertebræ, but in the 'higher' Urodela (e.g. *Salamandra* (Fig. 291)) and the Anura absorption of cartilage takes place between adjacent centra in such a way that the convex end of one fits into the concave end of the next, forming a cup-and-ball joint. In the 'higher' Urodela the convexity is on the anterior, the concavity on the posterior face of each centrum, and the vertebræ are said to be *opisthocœlous*. In the Anura they are usually, as in *Rana*, procœlous.

The first or cervical vertebra bears paired articular surfaces for the condyles of the skull, and between them the anterior face of the centrum gives off, in

Urodela, a projection called the *odontoid process*. The Urodela, moreover, have *ribs* articulating with the transverse processes of the abdominal and sacral vertebræ. These are short bones, forked proximally; and their compressed transverse processes are correspondingly divided. The sacral ribs of urodeles give attachment to the ilia, and the caudal vertebræ bear hæmal arches. In at least two genera the sharp free end of ribs penetrates the integument, apparently as a protective device (*Pleurodeles, Tylototriton*) (see also p. 739).

The *skull* of Urodela differs from that of the frog in many important

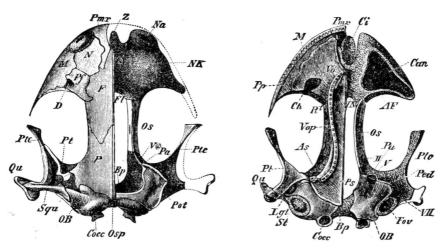

FIG. 294.—**Urodela: Skull.** *Salamandra atra.* *Left,* from above; *Right,* from below. In both the investing bones are removed on the right side of the figure. *Af,* antorbital process; *As,* alisphenoid region; *Bp,* basal plate; *Can,* nasal cavity; *Ch,* posterior nares; *Ci,* process of internasal plate; *Cocc.* occipital condyles; *F.* frontal; *Fl.* olfactory foramen; *Fov.* fenestra ovalis; *IN.* internasal plate; *Lgt.* ligament connecting stapes with suspensorium; *M.* maxilla; *N.* nasal; *Na.* nasal aperture; *NK.* olfactory capsule; *OB.* auditory capsule; *os.* sphenethmoid (orbitosphenoid); *Osp.* supraoccipital region; *P.* parietal; *Pa.* ascending process of suspensorium; *ped.* pedicle; *Pf.* prefrontal; *Pmx.* premaxilla; *Pot.* otic process of suspensorium; *Pp.* palatine process of maxilla; *Ps.* parasphenoid; *Pt.* pterygoid bones; *Ptc.* pterygoid cartilage; *Rt.* foramen for ophthalmic branch of trigeminal; *Qu.* quadrate; *Squ.* squamosal; *St.* stapes; *Vo.* vomer; *Vop.* vomero-palatine; *Z.* process of internasal plate; *II.* optic foramen; *V.* trigeminal foramen; *VII.* facial foramen. (After Wiedersheim.)

respects. Most strikingly, the trabeculæ do not meet either below the brain to form a basis cranii, or above it to form a cranial roof. Thus, when investing bones are removed, the cranium (Fig. 293) is completed above and below in the parachordal or occipital region only. Anterior to this it has side walls, but no roof or floor. There is, above, a huge superior cranial fontanelle, and below an equally large basicranial fontanelle. The former is covered, in the complete skull, by the parietals and frontals, the latter by the parasphenoid. In the perennibranchiate forms *Necturus* and *Proteus* the trabeculæ remain, even in the adult, as narrow cartilaginous bars. The chondrocranium is actually of a lower or more embryonic type than that of any other Craniata, with the possible exception of Petromyzontia and Myxinoidea (p. 175).

In the Urodela, moreover, the parietals (Fig. 294, *P.*) and frontals (*F.*) are separate.   The parasphenoid (*Ps.*) is not T-shaped.   The palatine and vomer are sometimes represented by a single bone, the vomeropalatine (*Vop.*), bearing teeth.   The suspensorium is inclined forwards, as in the tadpole, not backwards, as in the adult frog.   The hyoid arch is large, and its dorsal end may be separated as a hyomandibular.   There are three or four branchial arches.   These are large in the perennibranchiate forms, but undergo more or less reduction in caducibranch species, although they never form such a simple structure as that seen in the frog.   The stapes has no extra-columella attached to it, and, in correspondence with this, there is no tympanic cavity or membrane.

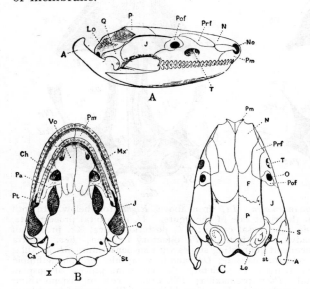

FIG. 295.—**Apoda: Skull.** *Ichthyophis glutinosa.*   × 3.   *A*, Lateral; *B*, Ventral; *C*, Dorsal view.   *A.* posterior process of the os articulare; *Ca.* carotid foramen; *Ch.* choana or posterior nasal opening; *F.* frontal; *J.* jugal; *LO.* exoccipital; *Mx.* maxilla; *N.* nasal; *No.* nostril; *O.* orbit; *P.* parietal; *Pa.* palatine; *Pm.* premaxilla; *Pof.* postfrontal; *Prf.* prefrontal; *Pt.* pterygoid; *Q.* quadrate; *S.* squamosal; *St.* stapes; *T.* tentacular groove; *Vo.* vomer; *X.* exit of vagus nerve. (After Sarasin.)

In the Anura there is a very wide range of variation in the skull.   Among the most important points are the presence, in a few species, of small supra- and basi-occipitals.   In others the roofing investing bones are curiously sculptured and so strongly developed as to give the skull a singularly robust appearance.

In the Apoda (Fig. 295) very little of the original cartilage remains in the adult state, but the investing bones are very large and form an extremely complete and substantial structure, especially remarkable for the way in which the small orbit (*O.*) is completely surrounded by bones.

The *shoulder-girdle* of Urodela (Fig. 296) is chiefly remarkable for the great size of the unossified coracoids (*A, Co., B, C*) which overlap one another on the ventral body-wall.   The procoracoid (*Cl.*) is also large, and there is no clavicle.   The *sternum* (*St.*) is usually a more or less rhomboid plate of cartilage between the posterior ends of the coracoids, and there is no omosternum.

In *Necturus*, however, the sternum presents a very interesting structure : it is a narrow, irregular, median bar, sending off branches right and left into the myocommas. This condition suggests an origin by the fusion of *abdominal ribs*, or supporting structures developed between the ventral portions of the myomeres, just as the true ribs are formed between their dorsal portions. In the Anura the epicoracoids either simply meet one another in the middle ventral line, as in *Rana*, or overlap, as in the Fire-toad (*Bombinator*) and the tree-frogs (*Hyla*). The overlapping of the coracoids, in Anura as in Urodela, is sometimes correlated with the absence of an omosternum. In the Labyrinthodontia there was a median ventral investing bone, the *inter-clavicle*, connected on each side with the clavicle and extended backwards to the sternum. There was also, on each side, a *cleithrum*, connected with the adjacent clavicle. This is retained in the extant Ascaphidæ.

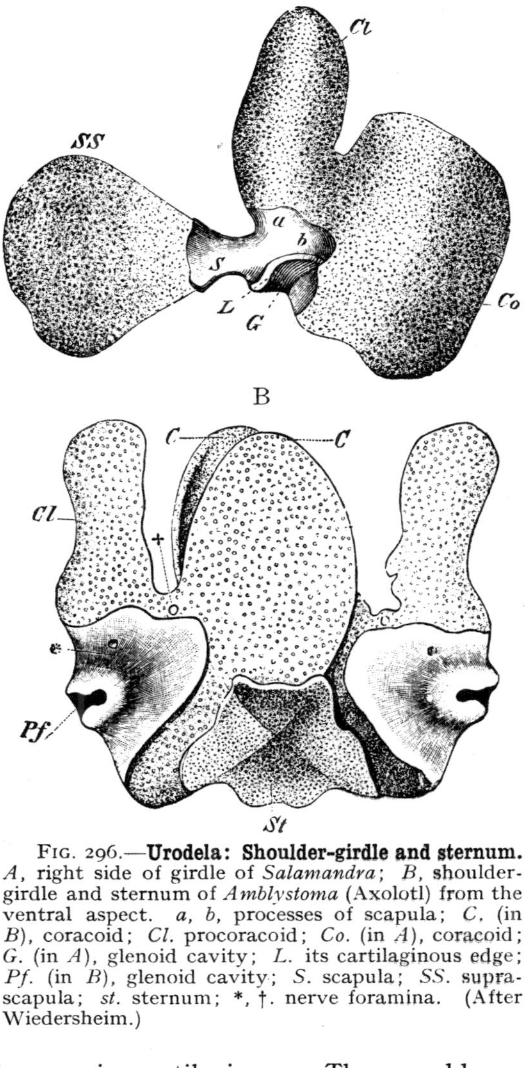

In the *pelvic girdle* of the Urodela the combined pubic and ischiatdic regions (Fig. 297, *P.*, *Is.*) of the right and left sides are united to form an elongated cartilaginous plate which gives off on each side, above the acetabulum (*G.*), a slender vertical rod, the ilium (*Il.*). Ossifications are formed in the iliac and

FIG. 296.—**Urodela: Shoulder-girdle and sternum.** *A*, right side of girdle of *Salamandra*; *B*, shoulder-girdle and sternum of *Amblystoma* (Axolotl) from the ventral aspect. *a*, *b*, processes of scapula; *C*. (in *B*), coracoid; *Cl*. procoracoid; *Co*. (in *A*), coracoid; *G*. (in *A*), glenoid cavity; *L*. its cartilaginous edge; *Pf*. (in *B*), glenoid cavity; *S*. scapula; *SS*. supra-scapula; *st*. sternum; *, †. nerve foramina. (After Wiedersheim.)

ischiatdic regions, but the pubic region remains cartilaginous. The resemblance of the pelvis of the lower Urodela, and especially of *Necturus*, to that of *Polypterus* (p. 290) and of the Dipnoi (p. 361) is noteworthy.

Attached to the anterior border of the pubic region there occurs in many Urodela and in *Xenopus* a rod of cartilage, forked in front, the *epipubis* (*Ep.*). It is developed independently of the pelvis and its relations to that structure are very similar to those of the sternum to the shoulder-girdle ; it has, in fact, been proposed to call it a *pelvi-sternum*.

The limbs of Urodela differ from the typical structure already described only in detail.　There are usually four digits in the fore-limb and five in the hind-limb.　In Anura the limbs are modified by the fusion of the radius and ulna and of the tibia and fibula, and by the great elongation of the two proximal tarsals. A prehallux is frequently present.

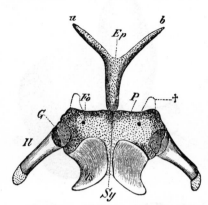

FIG. 297.—**Urodela: Pelvic girdle.** *Salamandra. a, b,* processes of epipubis; *Ep.* epipubis; *Fo.* obturator foramen; *G.* acetabulum; *Il.* ilium; *Is.* ischium; *P.* pubis; *Sy.* pubo-ischiatic symphysis; †, process of pubis present in some urodeles. (After Wiedersheim.)

Musculature.　In the 'lower' Urodela the muscles of the trunk and tail occur in the form of typical myomeres like those of fishes. Again, a newt (*Triturus*) swims essentially by the serial contraction of its myotomes, as do fishes.　When it wriggles quickly on dry land it employs much the same swimming mechanism.　When it moves quietly along it raises itself on its weak legs, which operate like those of Anura.　In the 'higher' urodeles the myomeres become converted into longitudinal dorsal bands (the *extensors of the back*), paired ventral bands (the *recti abdominis*), and a double layer of *oblique* muscles, covering the flanks.

Alimentary Canal and Associated Structures.　A few Amphibia (*Ceratophrys*, possibly *Amphignathodon*) bite, but in most the *teeth* are used to hold struggling prey before swallowing.　The teeth are always small and ankylosed to the bones : they may be singly or doubly pointed.　They occur most commonly on the premaxillæ, maxillæ, and vomers, but may also be developed on the dentaries, palatines, and, in one instance, on the parasphenoid.　In many Anura, such as the Common Toad, teeth are altogether absent.　A deciduous fœtal dentition occurs in ovoviviparous, but probably not in oviparous cæcilians. Although the teeth are somewhat rasp-like, they are apparently without function and are replaced by adult teeth at about the time of parturition (Parker). The *tongue* in many urodeles is fixed and immovable, like that of a fish.　In most Anura it is free behind, as in the frog, but in *Xenopus* and *Pipa* it is absent.

In some anurans the tongue is capable of swift and prolonged expansion for the capture of prey.　Its adhesive power in many frogs and some urodeles is enhanced by secretions from *lingual glands* (in the tongue itself) and from the *intermaxillary (internasal)* gland lying between the premaxillæ and the nasal capsule.　This opens into the buccal cavity.　The latter gland is less prominent in urodeles and is absent in cæcilians.　Anurans are additionally equipped with a *pharyngeal gland* that discharges into the internal nares. The buccal cavity and œsophagus of the Anura possess mucus-producing goblet cells. The œsophagus may be ciliated. Stomach-glands of anurans secrete both pepsin and hydrochloric acid. The stomach is enormously distensible, and together with the duodenum forms a U-shaped loop in which lies the pancreas. The small intestine is in all Amphibia a tube of almost uniform width. It is almost straight in Apoda, and is extremely long only in certain tadpoles (p. 420). A spiral valve does not occur: an increased absorption surface is obtained by great increase in length. Some tadpoles with a specialised protein diet lack the 'watch-spring' intestine of common herbivorous forms. There is some

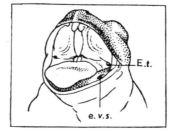

Fig. 298.—**Anura: Vocal apparatus.** *Left: Rana temporaria* (Brown or 'Common' Frog) croaking with distended *internal* vocal sacs. *Right: Rana ridibunda* (Marsh Frog) croaking with distended *external* sacs. (Redrawn after Malcolm Smith.) *Inset:* Buccal cavity of *Scaphiopus* showing entrance to left vocal sac (*e. v. s.*). The entrance to the Eustachian tube is marked *E. t.* (After Noble.)

evidence that the liver is of unusual importance in fat storage (in addition to the fat bodies). Certainly there is much evidence that amphibians can live for long periods without food. Axolotls, for example, have remained alive for 650 days under conditions of starvation, losing about 80 per cent. of the former body-weight.

Respiratory Organs and Voice.—Those of amphibians were the first true voices evolved, for, unlike fishes, frogs possess a larynx and tracheæ supported by a cartilaginous skeleton. In frogs the laryngeal chamber is divided into two parts by the vocal organs, which are lip-like continuations of the epithelium of the arytenoids. They call with the mouth closed. In many species air is forced from lungs across the larynx to inflate grotesquely the vocal sacs which, developed as buccal diverticula, serve as resonators (Fig. 298). Among the most characteristic sounds of tropical continental rain-forests are the calls of tree-frogs—the clear, bell-like note of *Hyla gratiosa* (the 'Smith '), which sounds like a blow on an anvil, the bird-like whistle of *H. avivoca*, and the cicada-like stridulation of *H. femoralis*: these are only a few frog sounds from the New World alone.

With very few exceptions Amphibia possess *external gills* in the larval state, but of course such delicate structures are not retained in adults of species which spend much time on dry land. In the perennibranchiate Urodela external gill organs are retained throughout life. They are branched, are abundantly supplied with blood, and spring from the dorsal ends of the first three branchial arches. The epithelium covering them is ectodermal, so that they are cutaneous and not pharyngeal gills. Therefore they may be of a different nature from the so-called external gills of the embryos of Elasmobranchii and Holocephali, which are the filaments of internal gills prolonged through the branchial apertures.

Internal gills are developed only in the larvæ of Anura. They appear as papillæ on the outer borders of the branchial arches below the external gills. They closely resemble the internal gills of fishes and appear to be homologous with them, although it seems probable that their epithelium is ectodermal.

In most adult Amphibia *lungs* are formed as outgrowths of the ventral wall of the pharynx. The right and left lungs communicate with a common *laryngo-tracheal chamber*, supported by the cartilages of the larynx and opening into the mouth by a longitudinal slit, the *glottis*. In the more elongated forms, such as *Siren*, *Amphiuma*, and the Apoda, the laryngo-tracheal chamber is prolonged into a distinct *trachea* or wind-pipe, supported by cartilages. In the Apoda, a *tracheal lung* may occur as in some snakes (p. 540); and the left lung is usually rudimentary. In some salamanders (*e.g.* all plethodontids) lungs are absent, and respiration is exclusively cutaneous and pharyngeal.

The salamander lung, when present, acts also as a hydrostatic organ. Species living in well-ærated mountain streams, where they must often lurk under rocks to avoid fast currents, have lungs that are reduced by comparison with those of pond-dwelling forms. A comparable reduction in the swim-bladder (p. 339) is seen in mountain teleost fishes.

The Amphibia display interesting supplementary adaptations to cutaneous respiration (p. 403). In *Cryptobranchus* there occur highly vascular folds in which capillaries penetrate almost to the epidermal surface; these folds are mobile in a manner that suggests the gill motion of other urodeles (e.g. *Necturus*). The so-called African Hairy Frog, *Astylosternus*, has extensive tracts of vascular papillæ investing the flanks and hind legs of the male during the breeding season. These probably compensate for its reduced lungs and the greater need for oxygen during periods of reproduction. The aquatic *Typhlonectes* (Apoda) has a richly vascular skin through which it respires.

Blood-vascular system.—The amphibian *heart* always consists of a sinus venosus, right and left auricles, a single ventricle, and a conus arteriosus. The sinus venosus opens into the right auricle. The pulmonary veins enter the left (p. 405). In *Rana* the interauricular septum is complete; in *Salamandra* it is perforated, and in some lungless urodeles it is fenestrated in a curious arrangement of muscular strands with intervening spaces.

The conus arteriosus of the anuran heart always possesses a well-developed longitudinal *spiral valve*, which incompletely divides the conus into two passages. One of these leads to the carotid and systemic arches; the other gives access to pulmo-cutaneous arches. In many urodeles the spiral valve is either greatly reduced or absent, as in Apoda. In all amphibians two sets of valves (which prevent back-flow of blood) are present. One such set is situated

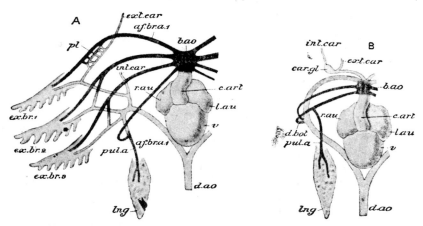

Fig. 299.—**Urodela: Circulation and respiration.** *Salamandra. A*, larva; *B*, adult. *af. br. a.* 1—4, afferent branchial arteries; *b. ao.* bulbus aortæ; *car. gl.* carotid labyrinth; *c. art.* conus arteriosus; *d. ao.* dorsal aorta; *d. bot.* ductûs Botalli; *ex. br.* 1—3, external gills; *ext. car.* external carotid; *int. car.* internal carotid; *l. au.* left auricle; *lng.* lung; *pl.* plexus, giving rise to carotid labyrinth; *pul. a.* pulmonary artery; *r. au.* right auricle; *v.* ventricle. (Altered from Boas.)

at the junction of the ventricle and conus; the other set lies between the conus arteriosus and the *bulbus aortæ*.

There is never any trace of an inter-ventricular partition such as has arisen in the Reptilia (p. 474). In the Dipnoi, too, we saw an almost completely divided ventricle (p. 370). Although there can be no suggestion that the tetrapods descended from lung-fishes, it is perhaps not impossible that the ventricles of ancestral tetrapods, too, were divided, and that there has been a secondary loss in the highly specialised, yet degenerate, Amphibia of to-day.

In the perennibranchiate Urodela, and in the larvæ of air-breathing forms, the circulation is essentially like that of a fish. The bulbus aortæ (Fig. 299, *A, b. ao.*), which represents an abbreviated ventral aorta, gives off four *afferent branchial arteries* (*af. br. a. 1–4*), three to the external gills, and a fourth which curves round the gullet and joins the dorsal aorta directly. From each gill an *efferent branchial artery* brings back the oxygenated blood, and the efferent arteries unite, in a somewhat irregular way, to form the dorsal aorta (*d. ao.*). Each afferent with the corresponding efferent artery constitutes an *aortic arch*. Short connecting branches unite the afferent and efferent arteries

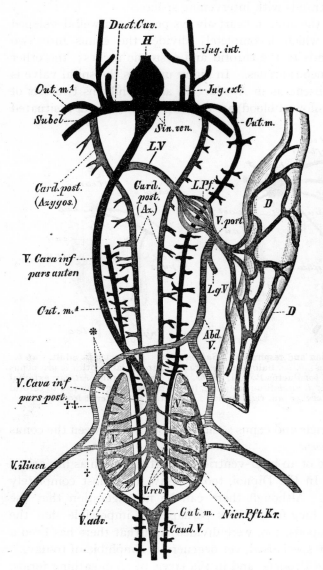

FIG. 300.—**Urodela: Venous system.** *Salamandra* (from ventral aspect). *Abd. V.* abdominal vein; *Card. post.* (*Az.*), azygos vein; *Caud. V.* caudal vein; *Cut. m.* left musculo-cutaneous vein; *Cut. m¹.* the same on the right side (partly removed); *D.* intestine; *Duct. Cuv.* precaval vein; *H.* heart; *Jug. ext.* external jugular; *Jug. int.* internal jugular; *Lg. V.* mesenteric vein; *L. Pf.* hepatic portal system; *L. V.* hepatic vein; *N,* kidney; *Nier. Pft. Kr.* renal portal system; *Sin. ven.* sinus venosus; *Subcl.* subclavian vein; *V. adv.* branches of renal portal vein; *V. Cava inf.* postcaval; *V. iliaca,* iliac vein; *V. port.* hepatic portal vein; *V. rev.* renal veins; *,* cloacal veins; †, branch of iliac to renal portal vein; ††, lateral vein. (After Wiedersheim.)

of each gill. Carotids (*ext. car., int. car.*) arise from the first efferent artery, and, when the lungs appear, a *pulmonary artery* (*pul. a.*) is given off from the dorsal portion of the fourth aortic arch of each side. When the gills atrophy (*B*) (in those Urodela which lack gills in the adult), the first aortic arch loses its connection with the dorsal aorta and becomes the carotid trunk. The second increases in size, forming the main factor of the dorsal aorta, and becomes the systemic trunk. The third undergoes varied reduction, and the fourth becomes the pulmonary artery, its dorsal portion retaining its connection with the systemic trunk in the form of a small connecting branch, the *ductus Botalli* (*d. bot.*). In the Anura, as we have seen, the third arch vanishes completely, and there is no ductus Botalli.

In the *venous system*, the Urodela exhibit very clearly the transition from the fish-type to the condition described in the frog (p. 272). The blood from the tail is returned by a *caudal vein* (Fig. 300, *Caud. V.*), which, on reaching the cœlom, divides into two *renal portal veins*, one going to each kidney. From the kidney the blood is taken, in the larva, into paired *cardinal veins*, each of which joins with the corresponding *jugular* to form a *ductus Cuvieri*. In the adult the anterior portions of the cardinals undergo partial atrophy, becoming reduced to two small *azygos veins* (*Card. post.*) which receive the blood from the region of the back. Their posterior portions unite and are continued forwards by a new unpaired vein, the *postcaval* (*V. Cava. inf.*). This, joined by the hepatic veins, pours its blood into the sinus venosus. The iliac vein from the hind-leg divides into two branches. One joins the renal portal. The other, representing the lateral vein of elasmobranchs, unites with its fellow in the middle ventral line to form the *anterior abdominal vein* (*Abd. V.*) and joins the hepatic portal (*V. port.*). Its blood, after traversing the capillaries of the liver, is returned by the hepatic vein into the postcaval.

The erythrocytes are oval and nucleated, and some are remarkable for their unusually large size. Those of the urodele *Amphiuma* are the largest erythrocytes known, being almost 80μ. in diameter. *Hyla arborea* has 700,000 red cells per cubic millimetre, whilst aquatic urodeles have a relatively low count (*e.g.* 36,000 in *Proteus*). Red cells seem to arise from a cell indistinguishable from lymphocytes in the kidney of some tadpoles and in the spleen of the adults of certain frogs. In other species they arise in the bone-marrow, as in the Mammalia. Thrombocytes of blood-clotting function occur.

Nervous System and Organs of Special Sense.—The *brain* of Urodela differs from that of the frog in its more elongated and slender form, in the comparatively small size of the optic lobes, and in the non-union of the olfactory bulbs. The *organ of Jacobson* is present except in *Proteus* and *Necturus*. The *olfactory sacs* always open into the mouth by *posterior nares* situated behind or external to the vomers. Apart from its importance in food gathering, the olfactory sense is probably vital in reproduction and other behaviour. Many frogs, as everybody knows, have a characteristic odour. Some (*e.g.* the Mink Frog, *Rana septentrionalis*) are said to smell like mink, others (e.g. *Pelodytes*) rather like onions and others (*e.g. Bufo vulgaris*) like vanilla. These odours, and those of certain salamanders (*e.g. Hydromantes*) come from granular or mucous glands on the skin.

The *eye*, consequent upon its emergence from the water and the necessity for a longer-sighted vision, exhibits important modifications (p. 413), and in the Urodela, which have retreated to the water, the lachrymal (tear) ducts are generally still retained. In at least some Apoda a single hypertrophied lachrymal gland has migrated and is found lodged in the sightless eye-socket; its tears probably lubricate the adjacent sensory tentacle (p. 434). The eyelids (including the nictitating membrane) were another response to the protection needed in terrestrial animals. In certain anuran tree-frogs the lids are transparent. In a few primitive forms lids are absent.

Urodeles. Apoda, and some Anura have no tympanic cavity or membrane, and no extra-columella. Occasionally (e.g. *Ascaphus*) even the 'stapes' (see p. 144) may be lost. In some genera one end of the 'stapes' (footplate

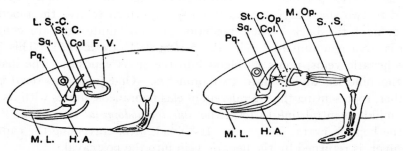

FIG. 301.—**Urodela: Exteroception.** Ground vibrations are transmitted via forelimbs and opercular muscles to the perilymph in the adult terrestrial salamander (*right*). This channel of communication remains incomplete in aquatic larval salamanders (*left*). *Col.* columella; *F. V.* fenestra vestibuli; *H. A.* hyoid arch; *L. S-C.* ligamentum squamoso-columellare; *M. L.* skeleton of the lower jaw; *M. Op.* musculus opercularis; *Op.* operculum; *Pq.* palatoquadratum; *Sq.* os squamosum; *S. S.* suprascapula; *St. C.* stilus columellæ. (From Noble, after Kingsbury and Reed.)

of columella) abuts on to the squamosal, from which it probably transmits vibrations to the jaw region. In some urodeles and anurans the stapes is greatly reduced and is associated with a nodule of cartilage inserted in the fenrestra ovalis. It is probable that this structure, the *operculum*, occurs only in amphibians and has no homologue in other vertebrates. Amphibia which have dispensed with a tympanic membrane have the operculum connected to the scapula by a minute *opercular muscle*. It is probable that vibrations from the forelimbs are conveyed on the tensed opercular muscle to the operculum and finally to the inner ear (Fig. 301).

In the perennibranchiate urodeles and in the larvæ of air-breathing forms *lateral line* organs occur. Among Anura these organs are generally lost during metamorphosis, but in a few strongly aquatic species they are found in the adults. Those of *Xenopus*, for example (Fig. 302), are superficial, being restricted to the epidermis. Groups of neuromast organs are arranged in small ridges or *plaques* distributed in rows that probably correspond with those of fishes (pp. 136, 137). Innervation is by two sets of cranial nerves. Of these, the *anterior lateralis* originates in a nucleus in the fourth ventricle. Its

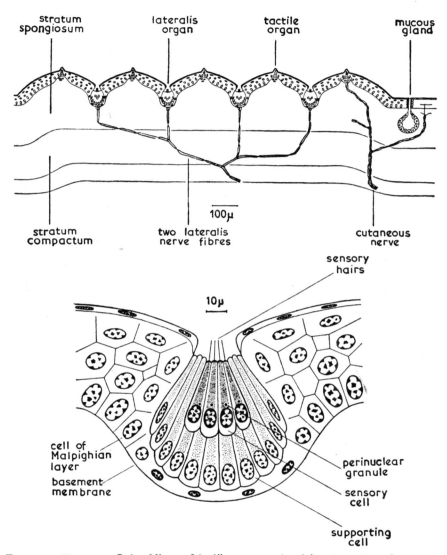

FIG. 302.—*Xenopus:* **Lateral line and tactile organs.** An elaborate system of organs occurs on the head, back, sides, throat, chest, and belly. *Above:* A lateralis plaque, showing arrangement of lateralis and tactile organs and their nerve-supply. *Below:* a single lateralis organ, showing its situation in the epidermis and the relationships of the sensory and supporting cells. (After Murray.)

ganglion fuses with that of the Vth and VIIth nerves, but most of its fibres separate to continue as the tractus supraorbitalis to the organs in head and snout. The mixed ramus of the VIIth nerve carries some fibres ventrally.

The *posterior lateralis* originates in a nucleus situated immediately behind that of the anterior lateralis and forms a mixed ganglion with the Xth; later again to become distinct and to run superficially to branch and supply the more posterior rows of neuromast organs. Each group of such organs is innervated by two big and one or two smaller fibres. The larger fibres branch extensively at the base of each individual organ, the smaller ones less so. The nerve-endings lie below or between the sensory cells which terminate in hair-like processes that are in contact with the surrounding water. The lateralis organs are probably sufficiently sensitive to detect disturbances made by minute aquatic organisms.

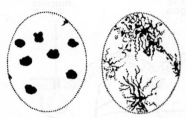

Fig. 303.—*Xenopus:* **Colour-change.** *Left:* Melanophores in wholly contracted condition, making for pallor. *Right:* Opposite condition. (Redrawn after Hogben and Slome.)

Endocrine System.—The general tetrapod pattern is fully established.

The *relative* non-specificity of hormones has led to the clinical use of *Xenopus* as a pregnancy indicator: its ovary responds rapidly to chorionic gonadotrophin (p. 905). Its utility in the laboratory is enhanced by the absence of any terrestrial phase in its life-cycle.

Colour change in anurans appears to be almost wholly under pituitary control and not directly influenced by the nervous system (cf. some fishes, reptiles). A posterior pituitary hormone (*intermedin* or ' B-substance ') causes the expansion of contracted melanophores (Fig. 303) and a general darkening of the integument. Pituitary extracts from other tetrapods produce a similar effect. Total hypophysectomy causes partial contraction and relative pallor. If the posterior lobe is ablated and the anterior part left intact, full contraction and paling result. Thus it has been suggested that a special W-substance, causing pallor, is elaborated by the adenohypophysis (see Hogben, Waring).

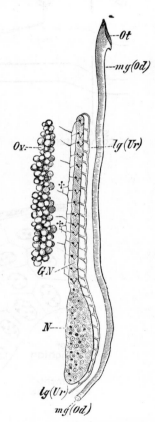

Fig. 304.—**Urodela: Urinogenital system in female.** *lg. (Ur.)* Wolffian duct (and collecting tubules); *mg. (Od.)* oviduct; *N.* kidney; *GN.* non-renal part of kidney; *Ot.* oviducal funnel; *Ov.* ovary; †, longitudinal canal. (From Wiedersheim, after Spengel.)

Urinogenital System and Osmoregulation.—Notwithstanding the many changes that accompanied the colonisation of land, the internal apparatus of the kidneys of extant amphibians retains a typical piscine appearance. Water loss ashore, however, is retarded by the reduction of glomerular filtration by means of a hormone from the pars neuralis (Fig. 96, p. 150) which constricts glomerular arterioles (cf. mammals, p. 889).

A second means of water conservation involves the changes in the permeability of the skin. Water, when available, seems to be passively absorbed through the skin of most Anura, but there is evidence that permeability, and therefore the absorption rate, is increased by a second pituitary principle. Sodium chloride, too, enters through the integument. During periodic moults the intake of both water and salts are considerably increased. It is not yet known whether a means of reducing skin permeability exists. Certain desert-dwelling frogs, which survive droughts by æstivating in dry subsurface mud, can absorb water with startling rapidity (p. 385). The kidneys of such frogs (*Cyclorana*, *Notaden*, and *Heleioporus*) possess venous sinuses into which drain peritoneal funnels. During æstivation, water stored in the peritoneal cavity is drawn through these channels into the general circulation. No amphibian, as far as is known, is aglomerular (cf. fishes, p. 347), but in *Cyclorana* the glomeruli are reduced in size and vascularity.

In the Urodela the kidneys (Figs. 304, 305) are much elongated and are clearly divided into two portions: a broad posterior part, the functional kidney (*N*), and a narrow anterior sexual part (*GN*.) connected in the male with the efferent ducts of the testis. Numerous ducts leave the kidney and open into the Wolffian (mesonephric) duct (*lg.* (*Ur.*)), which thus acts as a 'ureter' in the female, and as a urinogenital duct in the male. The oviduct (*mg.* (*Od.*)) is developed from the Müllerian duct, a rudiment of which (*mg.*, *mg¹.*) occurs in the male.

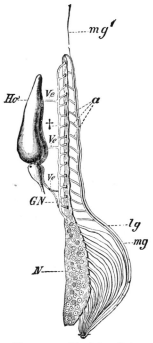

FIG. 305.—**Urodela: Urinogenital system in male.** *a.* collecting tubules (see also Fig. 304); *G. N.* non-renal part of kidney; *Ho.* testis; *lg.* Wolffian duct; *mg.* vestigial (in male) Müllerian duct; *N.* kidney; *Ve.* vasa efferentia; †, longitudinal canal. (From Wiedersheim, after Spengel.)

In the Apoda the kidneys extend the whole length of the cœlom, and in the young condition are formed of segmentally arranged portions, each with a nephrostome and a glomerulus, as in myxinoids (p. 197). A pronephros is present in the larva, but disappears in the adult. A urinary bladder is almost always present, opening into the cloaca and having no connection with the mesonephric ducts. In some Apoda the cloaca can be protruded and acts as an intromittent organ.

The testes of Amphibia show a great deal of variation. In the elongated

Apoda they are long bodies which look not unlike a string of beads. The expansions contain numerous seminiferous tubules. These discharge through paired ducts. Cæcilians with shorter bodies possess less diffuse organs. In *Taricha = Triturus* Leydig cells are lacking. These animals depart from the typical vertebrate interstitial pattern in that connective tissue cells of the tubule walls are seasonally converted to an endocrine function as in certain fishes (Fig. 97, p. 152).

The Bufonidæ and Atelopondinæ are perhaps unique in the possession of *Bidder's organ*. This structure occurs in males of all such species, and additionally in the females of some at the anterior end of the gonads. It is better developed in the male, but it is not always well defined even in adults (e.g. *Bufo carens*). In the females of some species it disappears with maturity. It would appear that Bidder's organ is a mesogonadic derivative which in certain circumstances (and after castration) can develop in either sex into a functional ovary. Broods of motherless toads have been raised from feminised males. It has been suggested, but not yet proved, that Bidder's organ is an endocrine gland.

Reproduction and Development.—External fertilisation takes place in most Amphibia. *Nectophyrnoides* (p. 386) produces well-yolked eggs, but the larvæ are retained in the oviduct until the completion of metamorphosis. Each surviving group contains such ovoviviparous individuals, *i.e.* those in which eggs are retained and development proceeds to some degree in the oviduct. The larvæ of at least one such ovoviviparous urodele, *Salamandra atra*, remain in the parent tract after the exhaustion of the egg-yolk. Only a few larvæ survive the ensuing competitive, intra-uterine cannibalism; these also ingest non-viable eggs, as well as red cells extruded by the hæmorrhaging oviducal wall. The larvæ of this urodele possess long, plume-like external gills during its oviducal existence; these are shed before birth. If, however, the unborn young are removed from the oviduct and placed in water, they swim about like ordinary aquatic larvæ until they lose the long gills and develop a shorter set.

In many Urodela the spermatozoa are aggregated into *spermatophores* by glands in the wall of the cloaca. These are deposited on the body of the female. They are then taken into her cloaca and so internal fertilisation occurs. Newts of the genus *Triturus* undergo elaborate courtship displays. A male follows a chosen female, stimulating her mouth-parts, flanks, and cloaca with pressure from his muzzle. He will impede her progress, and display with tremulously vibrating tail, and by other means. Finally he deposits one or more spermatophores, each containing hundreds of spermatozoa. The latter struggle violently, their heads projecting from the gelatinous secretion (from the male cloacal glands) that encloses them. If the female has been sufficiently stimulated she will press her cloaca over a spermatophore and enclose it. Once in the female tract, the sperms break free, and ascend to the *receptaculum seminis* or *spermatheca*, where they remain until the eggs are ready to be fertilised. Meanwhile, the gelatinous discarded spermatophore sheath is shed and the female will pick up no further spermatophores until the current batch of eggs are shed.

The eggs, which in some species are believed to be fertilised in the cloaca, are laid singly. They, too, are enclosed in a gelatinous material (secreted by

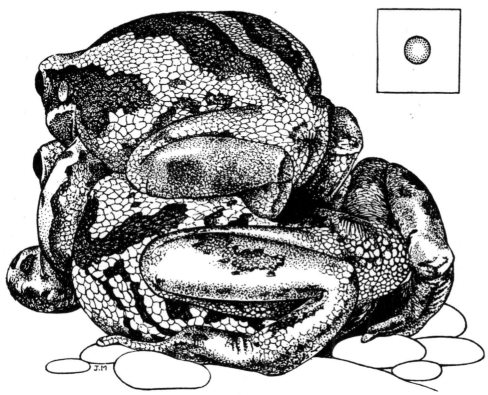

FIG. 306.—**Anura: Amplexus and parental care.** Marsupial Frog (*Gastrotheca marsupiata*) (X3). As the eggs (not shown *in situ*) are extruded from the female cloaca they are fertilised and swiftly thrust by the male's hind-legs into the damp environment of the incubation pouch on her dorsal surface. The period of development is from $2\frac{1}{2}$ (summer) to $3\frac{1}{2}$ months. The right top inset shows relative egg-size. (From photographs by Alan Goffin.)

oviducal glands), which enables them to be attached to leaves (often wrapped up by the female), floating community of algæ, or, where aquatic vegetation is lacking, to rotting leaves and other objects. It will be seen, therefore, that some amphibians (as with many bony fishes, pp. 297, 350) exhibit reflex behaviour patterns as complex and intriguing as those of the birds, excepting perhaps only the Ptilonorhynchidæ (p. 562).

Several remarkable instances of parental care are known among the Amphibia. A number of different species of frogs and toads construct nests or shelters of leaves or other materials in which the eggs are deposited and the young are developed. *Phyllomedusa*, a South American tree-frog, glues its eggs to foliage hanging over water, and, after hatching, the tadpoles drop straight into the appropriate environment. In the Obstetric Toad (*Alytes obstetricans*) of Europe, the male winds the strings of eggs—formed by adhesion of their gelatinous investment—round his body and hind-legs.[1] Here they are retained until the tadpoles are ready to be hatched. In *Rhinoderma darwini*, a small South American frog, the eggs are transferred by the male to the relatively immense vocal sacs that extend over its ventral surface: there they develop. The eggs of this species are much fewer and larger than in others.

Another anuran, *Pseudis paradoxa*, is remarkable in that the tadpole is many times larger than the adult. Still other fascinating larval—and parental—adaptations occur in the Anura. In *Gastrotheca* there occurs a special dorsal pouch in the female integument. This pouch, in which are carried fertilised eggs, opens a little (Fig. 305). In *G. marsupiata* anterior to the cloacal aperture the young are hatched as tadpoles, but in *G. oviferum* emergence is delayed until metamorphosis is complete.

Fig. 307.—**Anura: Ovoviviparity.** In the Surinam Toad (*Pipa dorsigera*) the eggs are lodged in lidded pits in the dorsal surface of the female. (After Mivart.)

In the Surinam Toad (*Pipa americana*) an even more astonishing arrangement is found (Figs. 307, 308). The dorsal skin of the female becomes soft and gelatinous, and here the male places and spaces the eggs. Each sinks into a small pouch, over which develops an operculum, which, it has been suggested, comes from a remnant of the egg envelope, reinforced by integumental secretions. Thus, the young develop moist and safe in maternal tissue. Between the invaginated pits arises a rich vascularisation. In each larva there develops

---

[1] The 'midwife Toad' figured in one of the most unhappy frauds in scientific history. Kammerer showed that this animal, which normally mates ashore (and which does not possess horny, pigmented nuptial pads, p. 390), can be induced experimentally to mate in relatively warm water. He asserted, with apparent sincerity, that his aquatic-mating males developed nuptial pads, and further, that subsequent generations of laboratory-bred toads inherited such acquired, pigmented pads in progressive degree. These conclusions were accepted by some, but disputed by Bateson and others. Kammerer's results could not be duplicated in repeat experiments. In 1926, when Noble examined histologically a museum specimen that had been previously exhibited by Kammerer, no nuptial pads were found, but, instead, a subcutaneous substance possessing properties indistinguishable from those of Indian ink. A few weeks later Kammerer shot himself on the Hochschneeberg. He left a letter admitting fraud but, it should be added, no confession of its authorship. He was aged 46.

a curiously broad and vascular tail : it is suspected that metabolic exchanges take place between maternal and embryonic tissues in the manner of a primitive placenta. The larva does not develop gills, and has been reported to be born as a tadpole about eighty days after egg-deposition.

Cæcilians are either oviparous and lay in burrows (e.g. *Ichthyophis* (Fig. 309), *Hypogeophis*) or ovoviparous (e.g. *Typhlonectes, Geotrypetes, Schistometopum, Chthonerpeton, Gymnopis*). In *Geotrypetes*, the large (about 4 mm.), yolky eggs migrate to the posterior end of the oviducts where they rest one closely behind another. When the yolk has almost gone, and the plumose external

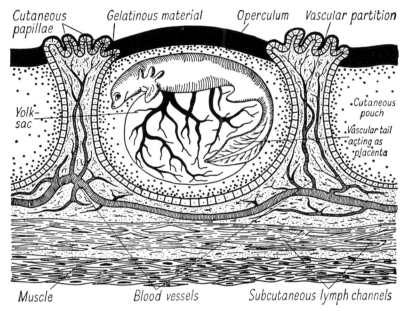

FIG. 308.—**Anura: Pseudo-placentation.** Gaseous exchanges occur between the maternal tissues and the expanded, leaf-like tail of the pouch larva of *Pipa dorsigera* (Fig. 307). (After Amoroso.)

gills are disappearing, the embryos (now about 25 mm. long) hatch and are next spaced throughout the length of the oviducts where they develop until they are about 75 mm. in length. Nutrition is now carried out by the oral absorption of uterine ' milk ' (see also p. 278). Both oviducal wall and fœtal epithelium are highly vascular, no doubt allowing gaseous exchanges. The neonatus appears to slough its corneal layer and to develop a relatively tough *stratum corneum* better adapted for its subsequent burrowing mode of existence. In some species the larvæ for a time lead an aquatic life. During this period they possess, like tadpoles, a tail with a tail-fin which is later absorbed. The larvæ of most Apoda have long external gills (Fig. 309).

Salamanders show many fascinating examples of physiological adaptation, including pædogenesis (p. 2).   Most of them undergo complete metamorphosis. Some come ashore as adults to live in damp situations, returning to water periodically to breed.   Others retain gills as well as lungs, and remain permanently in the water (*e.g.* the Northern American *Necturus*, 'Mud-puppy' or 'Water-dog').   Others have lost their lungs altogether.   Such creatures have lost one of the principal attributes that made the initial amphibian emergence possible and have returned to a life very roughly approximating that of their early ancestors.   A classical case of pædogenesis is furnished by the remarkable Mexican Axolotl, which frequently breeds in the gilled or larval state.   The experimental administration of thyroxin (p. 151), especially when the animal is very young, causes it to lose its gills, develop lungs, and emerge from the water in an adult form very like, if not identical with, the black-and-orange

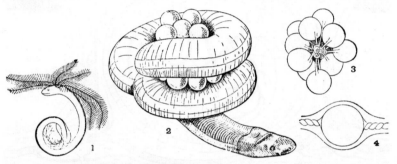

FIG. 309.—**Apoda: Reproduction and development.** *Ichthyophis glutinosa* (I). (× 1), a nearly ripe embryo, with gills, tail-fin, and still with a considerable amount of yolk; 2, female guarding her eggs, coiled up in a hole underground; 3, a bunch of newly-laid eggs; 4, a single egg, enlarged, schematised to show the twisted albuminous strings or chalazæ within the outer membrane, which surrounds the white of the egg.   (After P. and F. Sarasin.)

Tiger Salamander (*Amblystoma tigrinum*) of North America.   Metamorphosis can be induced also by reducing the water level in which the axolotl lives and thus making gill respiration difficult, whilst at the same time facilitating pulmonary respiration.   This was how metamorphosis in the animal was first discovered.   It is to the branchiate stage that the name Axolotl properly applies.

The Alpine Newt (*Triturus alpestris*) is of especial interest in that in the French and Italian lowlands complete metamorphosis occurs, whereas in the colder Lombardy lakes there has evolved a race that is often neotenous. Among the perennially larval forms no known experimental manipulation will induce metamorphosis.

Segmentation of the egg in the Anura and Urodela is always complete, but unequal.   In *Pipa* and *Alytes* there is a large quantity of food-yolk, and the developing embryo lies on the surface of a large yolk-sac.   In the Apoda the eggs are of large size, and segmentation is partial.   The formation of segments at the pole of the egg opposite that at which the formation of the embryo begins takes place only at the stage of gastrulation.   The embryo is coiled over the surface of the yolk, as in teleosts (p. 293).

CLASS REPTILIA

INTRODUCTION

It is difficult satisfactorily to define the Reptilia.   They form a hetero-geneous group and can be loosely described as amniotes which lack the diag-nostic characters of birds or mammals.   They (and consequently and ulti-mately birds and mammals) arose from a Carboniferous (p. 3) amphibian stock which had probably developed the shelled amniote egg.   By virtue of its complicated membrane structures, such an internally fertilised egg enabled the complete escape from the water that was impossible in allied amphibian groups.   Within the protective, yet permeable, horny or occasionally cal-careous egg-shell was developed the fluid-containing *amnion* which provided an aquatic environment for the developing land animal.   Respiration was carried out by means of the richly vascular *allantois* ;   and metabolites were excreted into, and stored in, the allantoic cavity.   The proteinous and other contents of the *yolk sac* allowed nourishment for the developing embryo during a prolonged embryonic life.   In some reptiles at least the albuminous ' egg-white ', accumulated during the journey down the oviduct, protected the yolk and other contents, while its watery nature allowed the dilution of yolk that would be used to feed the developing embryo.   (Possibly it provides vital mineral salts as well.)   Reptiles needed none of the bizarre reproductive devices evolved by the Anura (pp. 386, 452) in their attempts to colonise dry land.

In addition to the amnion and allantois, to be described presently (p. 649), reptiles have gastrocentrous vertebræ (p. 463) and a metanephric kidney (p. 153).   Although keratinous, horny scales are said to be absent in some reptiles, their occurrence as a complete covering of ectodermal origin is a character-istic of the group and almost peculiar to it.   In the Mesozoic these scales were often modified to form spectacular means of protection and adornment in the form of enormous horns (Fig. 342).   Although rarely petrified in themselves, they often left unmistakable impressions in the matrix, and so their form and extent can be determined.

The reptilian epidermis is always hardened and cornified, and sometimes forms substantial plates of horny material such as the scutes of ' tortoise-shell ' in turtles which protect the soft parts from injury and desiccation.   Underlying bony plates—osteoderms—frequently reinforce the exoskeleton, sometimes fused with the endoskeleton.   As the outer layer of scales and claws wear away, the horny tissue is replaced by proliferations from the epidermis below.

The term *Amniota* is used for the group formed by reptiles, birds, and mammals, the three 'highest' classes of vertebrates. Fishes and amphibians are referred to as the *Anamniota*. The division of the Amniota into the three classes mentioned above is kept because it is convenient.

Some of the earliest known reptiles, embedded in late Carboniferous deposits about 250 million years old, can be separated only with difficulty from the Amphibia on the examination of surviving parts. Permian representatives, however, were numerous, and admit of no such uncertainty. By the late Palæozoic (p. 3) the first great reptilian radiation was well under way with distinctive anapsid and synapsid forms predominating. These early reptiles were relatively short-legged, heavy, slow, and were rarely more than ten feet long (Fig. 310).

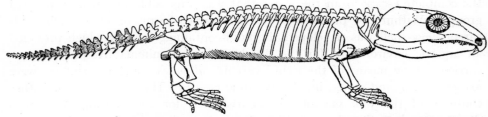

FIG. 310.—Sub-class **Anapsida,** Order **Cotylosauria,** Sub-order **Captorhinomorpha,** Family **Captorhinidæ.** *Labidosaurus.* This lower Permian American 'stem reptile' was a little over 2 feet long. The contemporary *Limnoscelis* (p. 406) was about 5 feet long, but most coltylosaurs were smaller. (From Romer, after Williston.)

The cotylosaurs ('stem reptiles') had disappeared by the late Triassic, but from them had arisen the material for a further reptilian radiation which produced, in the Mesozoic, one of the most spectacular and fascinating faunal groups that ever lived. By mid-Mesozoic, ancestors of each of to-day's reptilian orders had appeared, together with the forerunners of the birds (p. 507) and mammals (p. 513). More than fifteen orders, and dozens of families, arose. The individual animals ranged in size from swift, lizard-like creatures a few inches long up to lumbering semi-aquatic swamp-dwellers weighing more than 50 tons. The sea was likewise a centre of reptilian diversification ; and a few forms began to volplane through the air. It is as true as it is trite to say that the Mesozoic was the 'age of reptiles' and that then they 'dominated the earth'.

Most of these animals do not seem to have survived the Cretaceous or, at the latest, the early Cænozoic. It is not known what caused their disappearance. Certainly there is believed to have been a widespread elevation of the earth's surface together with changes in temperature and vegetation. This would, no doubt, affect a poikilothermous population. But most of the marine reptiles vanished as well. There is evidence of an increased aridity, which would certainly embarrass the gigantic swamp-dwelling dinosaurs. Doubtless climatic changes affected many successful reptiles by extinguishing the food upon which they were irrevocably adapted to feed. It has been suggested, too, that many of the small-brained (*e.g.* Fig. 342, p. 511) Mesozoic reptiles perhaps disappeared because they evolved no means of defending their eggs from predaceous ancestral mammals. This may have been a factor. Vague (in the current state of knowledge) notions concerning genetic instability leading to over-specialisation and phylogenetic senescence have also been put forward.

The smaller, swifter, more adaptable, warm-blooded ancestral mammals arose about the beginning of the Jurassic or even earlier and the marsupials and the eutherians became clearly diversified in the Cretaceous (p. 3). The best that can be said at present is that a combination of climatic and other factors, possibly including competition by the arising Mammalia, and perhaps by the birds as well, now caused the relatively sudden extinction of numerous hitherto highly successful types.

Excluding birds and mammals, the only animals of reptilian stock that have survived in considerable numbers are lizards and snakes. Lizards (Lacertilia) arose in the Triassic and have been common ever since. Snakes (Ophidia = Serpentes), the most recent reptilian development, arose from lizards (possibly related to the Platynota, p. 497) at some time in the Mesozoic, but did not become abundant until the Eocene. The more typical serpents did not appear in numbers until the Oligocene. Venomous snakes first appeared in well-established families as recently as the Miocene.

Of the multitude of reptiles that dominated the earth during the Mesozoic (p. 3), representatives of only four widely divergent orders are alive to-day. These are :

1. Lizards and snakes (Order Squamata), an example of which, the lizard *Lacerta*, will be dealt with in detail (p. 462).

2. The lizard-like Tuatara (*Sphenodon* = *Hatteria*)[1] of New Zealand (Order Rhynchocephalia).

3. Turtles and tortoises (Order Chelonia).

4. Crocodiles, gharials, alligators, and caimans (Order Crocodilia).

---

[1] There exists considerable confusion concerning the correct generic name of the Tuatara. In 1831, J. E. Gray described the skull of what he thought to be a new species of lizard. He conferred the name *Sphænodon* in allusion to its wedge-shaped teeth. Eleven years later he described the external appearance of an apparently new reptile in a collection from New Zealand and, not realising that it was, in fact, *Sphænodon*, called it *Hatteria punctata*, placing it in the agamid group of lizards. Quoting from the notes which accompanied the collection, he added that 'the natives called it "Tuatara"'. Little further attention was paid to the creature until in 1867 Albert Günther at the British Museum carefully studied the anatomy of several specimens and concluded that it was not a lizard at all. He referred it to a new order, the Rhynchocephalia ('beakheads'), which, it is now known, go back at least to early Mesozoic times. Animals almost identical with the Tuatara were in existence by the Jurassic (p. 3).

Strictly speaking, the Tuatara should be called neither *Sphenodon* nor *Hatteria*, but, in fact, *Sphænodon*. An application to the International Commission on Zoological Nomenclature has recently been made to validate the emendation to *Sphenodon* from *Sphænodon* and in anticipation of its success the more familiar spelling will be used hereafter in this volume.

Despite the retention of many primitive characteristics, and the drastic reduction in reptilian numbers and species after the Mesozoic, many families remain successful.   The Squamata are particularly diversified and numerous. Modern lizards number nearly 3,000 species (of some twenty families), many of which are common.   There are more than 2,500 species of snakes distributed among twelve families.   The Tuatara (*Sphenodon*), on the other hand, is the sole living representative of an order of lepidosaurian reptiles (p. 495) that was widespread during the Mesozoic.   It still survives on small islands off the coasts of islands (New Zealand), and probably only because its habitat was not colonised by terrestrial mammals, including Man, until relatively recently. The turtles and tortoises—slow, heavily-armoured, primitive creatures—still number more than 200 species.   Many forms, even the largest, remain plentiful in places where they are not too constantly molested by Man.   The Crocodilia, another ancient and once widespread group, now contains fewer than twenty-five species.   Many of these remain common where their numbers are not reduced by skin-hunters but very large examples are now extremely rare in most parts of the world.

Excluding only the circumpolar regions, land reptiles are spread all over the globe.   A few lizards extend southwards into the tip of South America and one lizard (*Lacerta vivipara*), and one snake (*Vipera berus*), cross the limit of the Arctic Circle.   The exclusion of reptiles from very cold regions is consequent on their failure to become homoiothermous, *i.e.* to regulate and retain heat generated by muscular activity.   The poikilothermy (p. 386) of reptiles probably caused them to disappear, for example, from what later became the British Isles, during the glacial epochs.   Ireland failed to get any snakes back (as distinct from the lizard, *L. vivipara*) because it was separated from the European Continent before Scotland and England, good St. Patrick notwithstanding.   Many of the smaller reptiles inhabiting temperate countries hibernate during the winter.   It is a sad and historical fact that the famous tortoise (*Testudo græca*) belonging to successive bishops of Peterborough, and reputedly 220 years old (*not* an historical fact, see also p. 489), died when left exposed in winter after being dug up by a gardener for 'a trifling wager' in the 18th century.

Yet reptiles flourish exceedingly in many temperate countries.   Thus, the mildly poisonous Common Adder or Viper (*Vipera berus*) is probably as common on the Kintyre Peninsula of Scotland as is any single species of snake in tropical Africa or New Guinea.   Although Reptilia are in general unquestionably more successful in hot countries, their inability to regulate their temperature causes some of them (e.g. *Lacerta vivipara*) to die if experimentally exposed to prolonged summer sunshine, even in northern latitudes.   Many desert reptiles lie in the shade of rocks, or in burrows, to escape the heat during the hottest time of day, and by constantly changing their position in relation to sources of external heat manage to keep their body temperature fairly stable.

It will have become obvious that *Lacerta*, the example chosen, is only broadly typical of the class as a whole of which an abbreviated, and provisional, classification is as follows :

CLASS REPTILIA

    Sub-class Anapsida
      Order Cotylosauria
        Sub-orders Captorhinomorpha (Upper Carboniferous–Permian)
                Diadectomorpha (Permian–Upper Triassic)
      Order Chelonia (Testudinata) (Middle Permian–Recent)
        Sub-orders Eunotosauria (Permian)
                Amphichelydia (Upper Triassic–Lower Cretaceous)
                Pleurodira (Upper Cretaceous–Recent)
                Cryptodira (Upper Jurassic–Recent)
    Sub-class Ichthyopterygia
      Orders Mesosauria (Lower Permian)
        Ichthyosauria (Middle Triassic–Upper Cretaceous)
    Sub-class Synaptosauria
      Orders Protorosauria (Permian–Triassic)
        Sauropterygia
      Sub-orders Nothosauria (Triassic)
                Plesiosauria (Triassic–Cretaceous)
                Placodontia (Triassic)
    Sub-class Lepidosauria
      Order Eosuchia
        Sub-orders Younginiformes (Upper Permian–Lower Triassic)
                Choristodera (Upper Cretaceous–Eocene)
                Acrosauria (Upper Jurassic)
      Orders Rhynchocephalia (Lower Triassic–Recent)
        Squamata
      Sub-orders Lacertilia (Sauria) (Triassic–Recent)
                Ophidia (Serpentes) (Lower Cretaceous–Recent)
    Sub-class Archosauria
      Order Thecodontia
        Sub-orders Pseudosuchia (Triassic)
                Phytosauria (Triassic)
      Order Crocodilia (Loricata)
        Sub-orders Protosuchia (Upper Triassic–Jurassic)
                Sebecosuchia (Cretaceous–Eocene)
                Mesosuchia (Jurassic–Eocene)
                Eusuchia (Cretaceous–Recent)

Order Pterosauria
  Sub-orders Rhamphorhynchoidea (Jurassic)
      Pterodactyloidea (Upper Jurassic–Upper Cretaceous)
Order Saurischia
  Sub-orders Theropoda (Middle Triassic–Upper Cretaceous)
      Sauropoda (Lower Jurassic–Upper Cretaceous)
Order Ornithischia
  Sub-orders Ornithopoda (Upper Jurassic–Upper Cretaceous)
      Stegosauria (Lower Jurassic–Lower Cretaceous)
      Ankylosauria (Cretaceous)
      Ceratopsia (Upper Cretaceous)
Sub-class Synapsida
  Order Pelycosauria
    Sub-orders Ophiacodontia (Permian)
       Sphenacodontia (Lower Permian–Lower Triassic)
       Edaphosauria (Permian)
  [1]**Order Therapsida**
    Sub-orders Dinocephalia (Middle Permian)
       Dicynodontia (Permian–Triassic)
       Theriodontia (Permian–Triassic)
Order Ictidosauria (Upper Triassic–Middle Jurassic)

EXAMPLE OF THE CLASS.—A LIZARD (LACERTA)

The most striking external differences between lizards (p. 389) and frogs are the covering of scales, the comparative smallness of the head, and the presence of a distinct neck, the great length of the caudal region, the shortness of the limbs, and the approximate equality in length of the anterior and posterior pairs. The anterior limbs are situated just behind the neck, springing from the trunk towards the ventral surface. The fore-limb, like that of anurans, is divided into three parts: the upper-arm or *brachium*, the fore-arm or *ante-brachium*, and the hand or *manus*. There are five digits provided with horny claws, the first digit or pollex being the smallest. The hind-limbs arise from the posterior end of the trunk towards the ventral aspect. Each, again like that of frogs, consists of three divisions—thigh or *femur*, shank or *crus*, and foot or *pes*. The pes, like the manus, terminates in five clawed digits, of which the first or hallux is the smallest. The head is somewhat pyramidal, slightly depressed: the openings of the external nares are situated above the anterior extremity. The mouth is a wide, slit-like aperture running round the anterior border of the head. At the sides are the eyes, each provided with upper and lower opaque, movable eyelids and with a transparent third

---

[1] A new and somewhat different classification has been recently suggested by Watson and Romer. See also Crompton for recent work on ictidosaurs.

eyelid or *nictitating membrane*, which, when withdrawn, lies in the anterior angle of the orbit. Behind the eye is a circular patch of skin—the *tympanic membrane*—corresponding closely to that of the frog, but somewhat sunk below the general level of the skin. The trunk is elongated, strongly convex dorsally, flatter at the sides and ventrally. At the root of the tail on the ventral surface is a slit-like transverse aperture—the *cloacal aperture*. The tail is cylindrical, thick in front, gradually tapering to a narrow posterior extremity; it is nearly twice as long as the head and trunk together.

There is an **exoskeleton** of horny *scales* covering all parts. These are formed from folds of the dermis, each covered with a thick horny epidermal layer. In size they differ in different positions. On the dorsal surface of the trunk they are small, hexagonal, and indistinctly keeled. On the ventral surface they are larger and are arranged in eight longitudinal rows. Immediately in front of the cloacal aperture is a large *pre-anal plate*. A collar-like ridge of larger scales surrounds the throat. On the tail the scales are elongated, keeled, and arranged in regular transverse (annular) rows, giving the tail a ringed appearance. On the surface of the limbs the scales of the pre-axial (radial or tibial) side are larger than those of the postaxial (ulnar or fibular). The scales on the upper surface of the head (*head-shields*) are large, partly bony in structure, and have regular and characteristic arrangement. The skin is periodically shed. The outer layers disintegrate into fragments instead of being sloughed off *in toto* as in many of the snakes and some lizards.

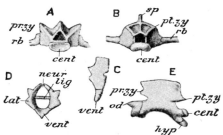

Fig. 311.—*Lacerta:* **Vertebræ.** *A*, anterior; *B*, posterior view of a thoracic vertebra; *C*, lateral, *D*, anterior view of atlas vertebra; *E*, lateral view of axis. *cent.* centrum; *hyp.* hypapophysis of axis; *lat.* lateral piece of atlas; *lig.* ligamentous band dividing the ring of the atlas into two; *neur.* neural arch of atlas; *od.* odontoid process; *pr. zy.* pre-zygapophysis; *pt. zy.* post-zygapophysis; *rb.* rib; *sp.* spine; *vent.* ventral piece of atlas.

Endoskeleton.—The *vertebral column* is of great length and composed of a large number of vertebræ. It is distinctly marked out into regions, a cervical of eight vertebræ, a thoraco-lumbar of twenty-two, a sacral of two, and a caudal of a considerable but indefinite number. A vertebra from the anterior thoracic region (Fig. 311, *A*, *B*) presents the following leading features. The centrum (*cent.*) is elongated and strongly *procœlous, i.e.* the anterior surface is concave, the posterior convex. The neural arch bears a short neural spine (*sp.*). There are pre- and post-zygapophyses (*pr. zy., pt. zy.*), the former with their articular surfaces directed upwards, the latter downwards. On each side at the junction of centrum and neural arch is a facet—the *capitular facet*—for the articulation of a rib. The cervical vertebræ in general are similar in essential respects to those of the trunk, but are somewhat shorter. The first two, however, differ greatly from the others. The first is the *atlas* (C, D). It has no distinct centrum, but is in the form of a ring. Ventrally on its anterior face it bears a smooth articular facet for the occipital condyle of the skull. It consists of three distinct ossifications, one ventral, the others dorso-lateral. The latter do not quite meet dorsally, being separated by a space bridged over by membrane. The second vertebra or *axis* (E) has a short conical process—the *odontoid process* (od.)—projecting forwards from its centrum. In the natural position of the parts the odontoid process (which is a part of the centrum of the atlas, and is not actually fused with, though firmly fixed to, the axis) lies in the lower or ventral part of the opening of the atlas. It is separated by a ligamentous band from the upper portion which corresponds to the neural arch, and lodges the anterior end of the spinal cord. On the ventral surface of the axis, and of each of the following five or six vertebræ, is a distinct bony nodule, sometimes termed the *intercentrum* or *hypapophysis* (hyp.). The sacral vertebræ have short centra and strong expanded processes—the *transverse processes*—which abut against the ilia. These are probably *sacral ribs*. The anterior caudal vertebræ are like the sacral, but have the centra longer, the transverse processes more slender, and the neural spines longer.

The posterior caudal vertebræ become gradually much smaller posteriorly, and the various processes reduced in prominence, until, at the end of the tail, the whole vertebra is represented merely by a rod-like centrum. Attached to the ventral faces of the centra of a number of the anterior caudal vertebræ are Y-shaped *chevron bones*—the upper limbs of the Y articulating with the vertebra, while the lower limb extends downwards and backwards. In nearly all the caudal vertebræ the centrum is crossed by a narrow transverse un-ossified zone through which the vertebra readily breaks. This singular adaptation, also found in *Sphenodon* and a few fossil reptiles, is widespread among lizards, and is a protective mechanism which enables the lizard to twist off its tail when the appendage is seized by an enemy. The severed tail jumps about by reflex action and presumably occupies the attention of the hunter while the lizard escapes. Such self-mutilation or *autotomy* is controlled by segmentally arranged caudal muscles which part near the point where the tail is grasped. The proximal part of the tail, near the reproduction organs, has no such power. Further, the organ can be regenerated. Occasionally *two* new tails develop, forking grotesquely.

The ribs are slender, curved rods, the vertebral ends of which articulate only with the capitular facets of the corresponding vertebræ. There is no direct articulation with the transverse processes. The ribs of the five anterior thoracic vertebræ are connected by means of cartilaginous *sternal ribs* with the sternum. The posterior thoracic ribs do not reach the sternum, the sternal ribs being very short, and free at their ventral ends. The *cervical ribs*, which are present on all the cervical vertebræ with the exception of the first three, are all shorter than the thoracic ribs, and none of them is connected with the sternum. Thus, as regards the structure of the vertebræ themselves, there is little to distinguish the posterior cervical from the anterior thoracic; but, for convenience of description, the first thoracic is defined as the first vertebra having ribs connected with the sternum.

The *sternum* (Fig. 312, *st.*) is a rhomboidal plate of cartilage with a small central space, or *fontanelle*, completed by membrane. Posteriorly it is produced into two slender flattened processes. On its antero-lateral borders are articular surfaces for the bones of the pectoral arch, and on its postero-lateral borders and the processes are small facets for the sternal ribs.

In the *skull* (Fig. 313) the chondrocranium, though persistent, is replaced by bones to a greater extent than in frogs, and the number of investing bones is more considerable. On the dorsal and lateral surface are a large number of dermal roofing bones. At the posterior end the rounded aperture of the foramen magnum (*for. mag.*) is surrounded by four bones—a *basioccipital* (*bas. oc.*) below, *exoccipitals* (*ex. oc.*) at the sides, and a *supraoccipital* (*supr. oc.*)

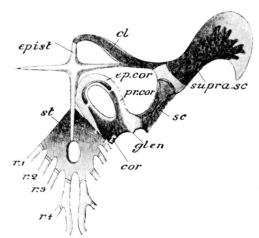

Fig. 312.—*Lacerta:* **Pectoral arch and sternum.** *cl.* clavicle; *cor.* coracoid; *ep. cor.* epicoracoid; *epist.* episternum; *glen.* glenoid cavity for head of humerus; *pr. cor.* procoracoid; *r.* 1—*r.* 4 first to fourth sternal ribs; *sc.* scapula; *st.* sternum; *supra. sc.* suprascapula. (After Hoffmann.)

above. The basioccipital forms the floor of the most posterior portion of the cranial cavity. Posteriorly it bears a rounded prominence, the *occipital condyle* (*oc. cond.*). In front of it, forming the middle portion of the floor of the cranial cavity, is the basisphenoid (*bas. sph.*), not represented in frogs. In front of this is an investing bone, the *parasphenoid* (*para.*), corresponding to the bone of the same name in the frog and trout, but here much reduced in size and importance and ankylosed with the basisphenoid. Compared with the skulls of other amniotes, it can be seen that those of reptiles in general retain relatively large areas of unossified cartilage in the adult, particularly in the anterior region. This arrangement allows considerable elasticity and aids the swallowing of large prey. Further, when a lizard opens its mouth it raises the upper as well as lower jaw. To enable this upper movement a special and remarkable hinge exists in the roof of the cranium. Here the supraoccipital and parietal elements are separated by an extensive *cartilaginous process*, which, attached to the occipital element, articulates loosely into a slot in the parietal and allows considerable play between the two areas and, in some reptiles, an astonishing widening of the gape (Fig. 332, p. 498). Skulls of

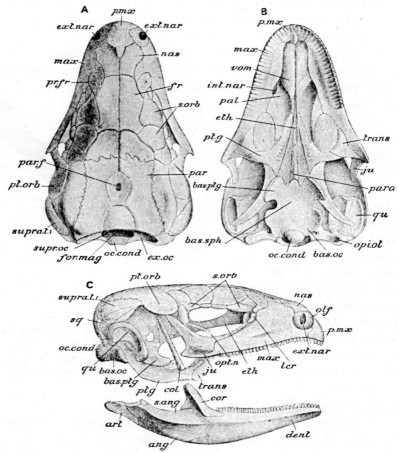

FIG. 313.—*Lacerta:* **Skull.** *A*, dorsal; *B*, ventral; *C*, lateral views. *ang.* angular; *art.* articular; *bas. oc.* basioccipital; *bas. ptg.* basipterygoid processes; *bas. sph.* basisphenoid; *col.* epipterygoid; *cor.* coronoid; *dent.* dentary; *eth.* ethmoid; *ex. oc.* exoccipital; *ext. nar.* external nares; *for. mag.* foramen magnum; *fr.* frontal; *int. nar.* internal nares; *ju.* jugal; *lcr.* lachrymal; *max.* maxilla; *nas.* nasal; *oc. cond.* occipital condyle; *olf.* olfactory capsule; *opi. ot.* opisthotic; *opt. n.* optic nerve; *pal.* palatine; *par.* parietal; *para.* parasphenoid; *par. f.* parietal foramen; *p. mx.* premaxillæ; *pr. fr.* pre-frontal; *ptg.* pterygoid; *pt. orb.* postorbital or lateral postfrontal; *qu.* quadrate; *s. ang.* supra-angular; *s. orb.* supraorbitals; *sq.* squamosal; *supra. t. 1.* supratemporal 1; *supr. oc.* supraoccipital; *trans.* transverse or ectopterygoid; *vom.* vomer. The unlettered bone internal to *pt. orb.* in *A* is the postfrontal. The transverse line behind *fr.* is a superficial mark, not a suture. (After W. K. Parker.)

this type, whenever movement between the upper jaw and brain-case occurs, are termed '*kinetic*'.

In the wall of the auditory capsule are three ossifications—*pro-otic, epiotic,* and *opisthotic (opi. ot.).* The first remains distinct, the second becomes merged in the supraoccipital, and the third in the exoccipital. The exoccipital and opisthotic are produced outwards as a pair of horizontal *parotic processes*.

The large orbits are closely approximated, being separated only by a thin vertical *interorbital septum*. The cranial cavity is roofed over by the *parietals (par.)* and *frontals (fr.)*. The former are united together. In the middle is a small rounded aperture—the *parietal foramen (par. f.)*. The frontals remain separated from one another by a median *frontal suture*. Between them and the united parietals is a transverse *coronal suture*. The nasal cavities are roofed over by a pair of *nasals (nas.)*. A small *prefrontal (pr. fr.)* lies in the front of the frontal, and helps to bound the orbit anteriorly. Another small bone—the *lachrymal (lcr.)*—perforated by an aperture for the lachrymal duct, lies at the anterior extremity of the orbit, just within its border. A row of small bones—the *supraorbitals (s. orb.)*—bounds the orbit above. Behind is a *postorbital* or *lateral postfrontal (pt. orb.)* articulating with the frontal. Just behind the postorbital is a *supra-temporal* bone (*supra t. 1*), in close relation to which is the *squamosal (sq.)*,[1] which bends forwards and upwards to form with the post-orbital the *superior temporal arch*. The superior temporal vacuity is obliterated in *Lacerta*. At the anterior extremity of the snout is a median bone formed by the coalescence of the two *premaxillæ (p. mx.)*. This bears the four anterior teeth of each side. On each side behind the premaxilla is the *maxilla (max.)*, consisting of two portions, an *alveolar* bearing all the rest of the teeth, and a *palatine* extending inwards on the roof of the mouth, together with an ascending process articulating with the nasal and pre-frontal above. Articulating behind with each maxilla is a *jugal (ju.)*, which forms the posterior half of the ventral boundary of the orbit. The *quadrate (qu.)* articulates movably with the parotic process, and bears at its distal end the articular surface for the mandible.

In the anterior portion of the roof of the mouth, articulating in front with the premaxillæ and maxillæ, are the vomers (*vom.*). Behind and embracing them posteriorly are the flat *palatines (pal.)*. The elongated *pterygoids (ptg.)* articulate in front with the posterior extremities of the palatines. Behind, each articulates with the corresponding *basipterygoid process (bas. ptg.)* of the basisphenoid, and sends back a process which becomes applied to the inner face of the quadrate. A stout bone, the *transverse bone* or *ectopterygoid (trans.)*, extends between the maxilla externally and the pterygoid internally. Extending nearly vertically downwards from the pro-otic to the pterygoid is a slender rod of bone, the *epipterygoid (col.)*.

The *columella* is a small rod partly composed of cartilage and partly of bone the outer end of which is fixed into the inner surface of the tympanic membrane.

---

[1] In early reptiles (e.g. *Limnoscelis*, p. 458; see also *Seymouria*, p. 429) the supra-temporal, squamosal and tabular may be borne on the posterior lateral wall of the skull. In extant reptiles these are generally reduced to one or two and their identities are not clear.

The inner end is attached to a small aperture, the *fenestra ovalis*, in the outer wall of the auditory capsule between the pro-otic and the opisthotic.

Certain depressions or fossæ and apertures or foramina are to be observed in the skull. The foramen magnum, the parietal foramen, and the orbits have already been mentioned. The *posterior temporal fossa* is situated on either side of and above the foramen magnum, bounded above and externally by the roofing bones, and on the inner side by the bones of the occipital region. The *inferior temporal fossa* is bounded internally by the pterygoid, and is separated from the palatine foramen by the transverse bone. The *lateral temporal fossa* is the wide space in the side wall of the skull behind the orbit. The bony bar which limits it above is the *superior temporal arch*; a bony *inferior temporal* or *quadratojugal arch* is here absent. The *tympano-eustachian fossa*, situated in the auditory region, is bounded by the bones of that region together with the quadrate. The *posterior* or *internal nares* are bounded posteriorly by the palatines. The *anterior* or *external nasal aperture* is situated at the anterior extremity of the skull bounded by the nasals and premaxillæ.

Each ramus of the *mandible* consists of six bony elements in addition to the slender persistent *Meckel's cartilage*. The proximal element, the *articular* (*art.*), bears the articular surface for the quadrate and is produced backwards into the *retro-articular process*. The *angular* (*ang.*) is a splint-like bone covering the ventral edge and the lower half of the outer surface of the articular. The *supra-angular* (*s. ang.*) overlies the dorsal edge and upper half of the outer surface of the same bone. The *dentary* (*dent.*) forms the main part of the distal portion of the mandible, and bears all the mandibular teeth. The *splenial* is a flat splint applied to the inner face of the dentary. The *coronoid* (*cor.*), a small, somewhat conical bone, forms the upwardly directed *coronoid process* immediately behind the last tooth. All these, with the exception of the articular, are investing bones.

The *hyoid apparatus* (see Fig. 318, *b. hy.*, p. 473; and p. 92) consists 1. of a median cartilaginous rod, the *basihyal*; 2. of the *anterior cornua*, elongated cartilaginous rods which, connected ventrally with the basihyal, curve round the œsophagus and end in close relation with the ventral surface of the auditory capsule; 3. of the *middle cornua*, rods of cartilage ossified at their proximal ends, and 4. of the *posterior cornua*, cartilaginous rods arising from the posterior edge of the basihyal and passing backwards and outwards. The middle cornua are vestiges of the first, the posterior of the second branchial arch.

In the *pectoral arch* (Fig. 312) the *coracoids* are flat bones articulating with the antero-lateral border of the sternum, and bearing the ventral half of the glenoid cavity (*glen.*) for the head of the humerus. A cartilaginous *epicoracoid* (*ep. cor.*) element lies on the inner side of the procoracoid and coracoid. A large gap or fenestra divides each coracoid into a narrow anterior portion—the *procoracoid* (*pr. cor.*), and a broader posterior portion, the *coracoid* proper (*cor.*).

The *scapulæ* (*sc.*) articulate with the outer ends of the coracoids, and each bears the dorsal half of the glenoid cavity. Dorsally, the scapulæ become expanded, and each has connected with it a thin plate of partly calcified cartilage—the *suprascapula* (*supra. sc.*). This extends inwards towards the spinal column on the dorsal aspect of the body. An element not hitherto met with, except in the Labyrinthodontia (p. 422), is the *interclavicle* or *episternum* (*epist.*). This is a cross-shaped investing bone, the stem of which is longitudinal. In the posterior portion of its extent it is closely applied to the ventral surface of the anterior part of the sternum, while the cross-piece is situated a little in front of the scapula. The *clavicles* (*cl.*) are flat curved bones articulating with one another in the middle line and also with the anterior end of the interclavicle. The bones of the fore-limb consist of a proximal bone or *humerus*, a middle division composed of two bones—the *radius* and *ulna*—and a distal division or *manus*. In the natural position of the parts the humerus is directed, from the glenoid cavity with which it articulates, backwards, upwards, and outwards. The radius and ulna pass from their articulation with the humerus downwards and slightly forwards. The manus has the digits directed forwards and outwards. When the limb is extended at right angles to the long axis of the trunk, it presents, like that of the frog, dorsal and ventral surfaces, and pre-axial and postaxial borders. In this the radius is seen to be pre-axial, the ulna post-axial. In the natural position the pre-axial border of the humerus is external. The distal end of the fore-arm is rotated in such a way that, while the pre-axial border faces forwards and outwards at the proximal end, it faces directly inwards at its distal end. The manus is rotated so that its pre-axial border faces inwards.

The *humerus* is a long bone consisting of a *shaft* and two *extremities*. Each extremity is formed of an *epiphysis* of calcified cartilage. The proximal extremity is rounded, the distal (*trochlea*) pulley-like with two articular surfaces, one for the radius and the other for the ulna. The *radius* is a slender bone consisting, like the humerus, of a shaft and two epiphyses. The distal extremity has a concave articular surface for the carpus, and is produced pre-axially into a *radial styloid process*. The proximal end of the *ulna* is produced into an upwardly directed process—the *olecranon* : the distal end bears a convex articular sur-

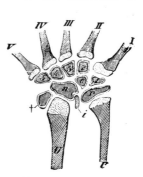

FIG. 314. — *Lacerta:* **Carpus.** Left, dorsal view. *R.* radius; *U.* ulna; *c* centrale; *i.* intermedium; *r.* radiale; *u.* ulnare; *1—5,* the five distal carpals; †, pisiform; *I—V,* the five metacarpals. (After Wiedersheim.)

face for the carpus. The *carpus* (Fig. 314) is composed of ten small polyhedral or rounded carpal bones. These consist of a proximal row containing three bones—the *radiale* (*r.*), *ulnare* (*u.*), and *intermedium* (*i.*), of a *centrale* (*c.*), and of a distal row of five (*1–5*) ; with an accessory or *pisiform* (†) bone attached to the distal epiphysis of the ulna on its postaxial side. The first digit or *pollex* consists of a metacarpal and two phalanges, the second of a metacarpal and three phalanges. The third digit consists of a metacarpal and four phalanges, the fourth of a metacarpal and five phalanges, and the fifth of a metacarpal and three phalanges. The number of phalanges in the first four digits is, therefore, one more than the serial number of the digit.

The *pelvic arch* (Fig. 315) consists of two triradiate bones, the *ossa innominata*, each ray being a separate bone. On the outer side at the point from which the rays diverge is a concave articular surface—the *acetabulum* (*Ac.*)—for the head of the femur. From the region of the acetabulum one of the rays,

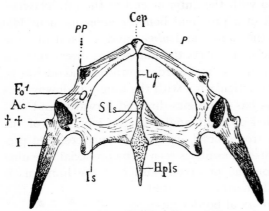

FIG. 315.—*Lacerta:* **Pelvis.** Ventral view. *Ac.* acetabulum; *Cep.* epipubis. *Fo′.* foramen for obturator nerve; *Hp. Is.* hypoischium; *I.* ilium; ††, process representing the pre-acetabular part of the ilium; *Lg.* ligament; *Is.* ischium; *p.* pubis; *pp.* prepubis; *S. Is.* ischiatic symphysis. (After Wiedersheim.)

the *ilium* (*I.*), a compressed rod, passes upwards and backwards to articulate with the sacral region of the spinal column. A second ray —the *pubis* (*p.*)—passes downwards and forwards to meet its fellow in the middle line. The articulation is termed the *pubic symphysis*. In the middle line in front, between the anterior ends of the pubes, is a small nodule of calcified cartilage, the *epipubis* (*Cep.*). The third ray or *ischium* (*Is.*) runs downwards and backwards, and articulates with its fellow in the *ischiatic symphysis*. The ventral ends of the two bones are separated by a plate of calcified cartilage (*S. Is.*). Between the pubes and ischia is a wide space, pulso-ischiac, divided by a median ligament (*lg.*) into a pair of apertures, the *pulso-ischiac foramena*. A smaller aperture in each pubis, the *obturator foramen* (*Fo.*), transmits the obturator nerve. A small rod of bone, the *os cloacæ*, or *hypo-ischium* (*Hp. Is.*), passes backwards from the ischiatic symphysis and supports the ventral wall of the cloaca.

The hind-limb consists, like the fore-limb, of three divisions. These are termed respectively the proximal or *femur*, the middle or *crus*, and the distal or *pes*. The proximal division consists of one bone, the *femur*; the middle division of two, the *tibia* and *fibula*; the distal of the *tarsal* and *metatarsal* bones and the *phalanges*. When the limb is extended at right angles with the trunk, the tibia is pre-axial and the fibula postaxial. In the natural position of the parts the pre-axial border is internal in all three divisions of the limb. The *femur* is a stout bone consisting of a shaft and two epiphyses. The proximal epiphysis develops a rounded *head* which fits into the acetabulum. Near it on the pre-axial side is a prominence, the *lesser trochanter*. A nearly obsolete prominence on the postaxial side represents the *greater trochanter*. The distal extremity is pulley-shaped, with internal and external prominences or *condyles* for articulation with the tibia. Immediately above the external condyle is a prominence or tuberosity for articulation with the fibula. The *tibia* is a stout, curved bone, along the anterior (dorsal) edge of which runs a longitudinal *cnemial ridge*. The proximal extremity presents two articular surfaces for the condyles of the femur. The *fibula* is slender, the proximal end articulating with the external tuberosity of the femur, the distal with the tarsus. The *tarsus* comprises only three bones in the adult, one large proximal *tibio-fibulare* (*tb. fb.*), and two smaller distal (*tars. dist.*). Each digit consists of a metatarsal and phalanges. The number of the latter is respectively, two, three, four, five, and three. The first and second metatarsals articulate with the tibial side of the tibiofibulare, the rest with the distal tarsals. In lizards the proximal head of the fifth metatarsal is hooked forwards and the fifth toe is peculiarly off-set backwards.

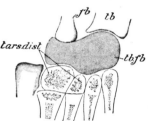

FIG. 316.—*Lacerta:* **Tarsus.** *fb.* fibula; *tb.* tibia; *tb. fb.* tibio-fibulare; *tars. dist.* distal tarsals. (After Gegenbaur.)

Alimentary Canal and Associated Structures.— The upper and lower jaws, forming the boundary of the aperture of the mouth, are each provided with a single row of small solid conical teeth, and there is in some species a patch of similar teeth on the pterygoid. The teeth are adapted to catching and holding, and not for chewing. On the floor of the mouth-cavity is the tongue, a narrow elongated fleshy organ, bifid in front. It is believed that, as with snakes, the bifid tongue of lizards is concerned with smell as well as taste. There is evidence that scent particles are picked up by the tongue tips and introduced into the *Organs of Jacobson*, which are accessory organs of smell (p . 481). *Mucous and salivary glands* occur. In the single genus of truly poisonous[1] lizards (*Heloderma*) salivary glands, as in many snakes, are specialised as venom-producing organs. The poison gland, however, is probably a modified *infra-labial* and therefore not homologous with that of snakes (p. 535).

The *œsophagus* leads into the *stomach* (Fig. 317, *stom.*), a muscular-walled cylindrical organ which, though expansible, is little wider than the œsophagus. Digestion begins in the stomach and is probably completed after the material passes through the *pyloric sphincter* into the *small intestine*, which is relatively abbreviated, as in most carnivorous animals. There is a *hepatic portal system*. At the point where the small intestine joins the wider *large intestine* or *rectum*,

---

[1] It is sometimes erroneously claimed that the Australian goannas (*Varanus* spp.) are venomous, but the poisoning from their bites is merely the result of bacterial infection such as might occur after attack by a dog.

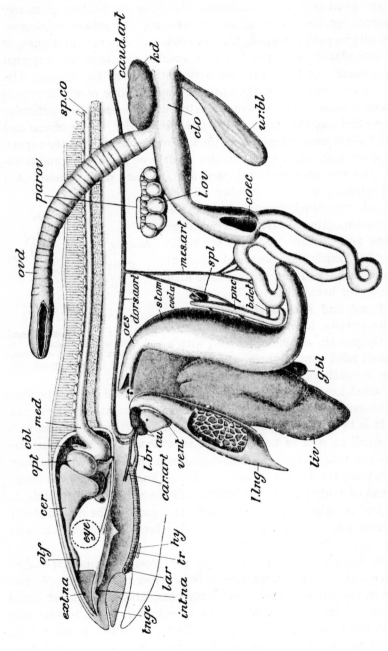

FIG. 317.—*Lacerta:* **Visceral relationships.** Lateral dissection of female (semi-diagrammatic). *au.* auricles; *b. dct.* bile-duct; *cav. art.* carotid artery; *caud. art.* caudal artery; *cbl.* cerebellum; *cer.* cerebral hemispheres; *clo.* cloaca; *cœc.* cæcum; *cœl. a.* cœliac artery; *dors. aort.* dorsal aorta; *ext. na.* external nares; *eye,* eye; *g. bl.* gall-bladder; *hy.* basi-hyal; *int. na.* internal nares; *kd.* kidney; *lar.* larynx; *l. br.* left bronchus; *liv.* liver; *l. lng.* left lung, opened to show internal structure; *l. ov.* left ovary; *med.* medulla oblongata; *mes. art.* mesenteric artery; *œs.* oesophagus; *olf.* olfactory bulb; *opt.* optic lobe; *ovd.* oviduct (turned aside); *parov.* parovarium; *pnc.* pancreas; *sp. co.* spinal cord; *spl.* spleen; *stom.* stomach; *tnge.* tongue; *tr.* trachea; *ur. bl.* urinary bladder; *vent.* ventricle.

the latter is produced into a short *cæcum* (Fig. 317, *cæc.*). The *liver* (*lr.*) is divided into right and left lobes, and a gall-bladder (*g.bl.*) lies in a cleft at the lower margin of the right lobe. The whitish *pancreas* (*pn.*), of compound structure and function (p. 152), is situated in the loop between the stomach and the duodenum, the anterior part of the small intestine. The *bile-duct* from the

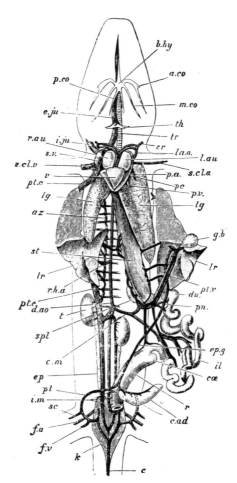

Fig. 318.—*Lacerta:* **Visceral relationships.** Ventral dissection of male showing the alimentary, circulatory, respiratory, and urinogenital organs. The liver (*lr.*) is divided longitudinally and its two halves are displaced outwards; the alimentary canal is drawn out to the animal's left; the cloaca with the urinary bladder and posterior ends of the vasa deferentia is removed, as also is the right adipose body. *a. co.* anterior cornu of hyoid; *az.* azygos or cardinal vein; *b. hy.* body of hyoid; *c.* caudal vein; *c. ad.* adipose body; *c. m.* cœliaco-mesenteric artery; *cæ.* cæcum; *cr.* carotid artery; *d. ao.* dorsal aorta; *du.* duodenum; *e. ju.* external jugular vein; *ep.* epididymis; *ep. g.* epigastric vein; *f. a.* femoral artery; *f. v.* femoral vein; *g. b.* gall-bladder; *i. ju.* internal jugular vein; *il.* ileum; *i. m.* posterior mesenteric arteries; *k.* kidney; *la. o.* left aortic arch; *l. au.* left auricle; *lg.* lungs; *lr.* liver; *m. co.* middle cornu of hyoid; *p. a.* pulmonary artery; *pc.* pericardium; *p. co.* posterior cornu of hyoid; *pl.* pelvic vein; *pn.* pancreas; *pt. c.* postcaval vein; *pt. v.* hepatic portal vein; *p. v.* pulmonary vein; *r.* rectum; *r. au.* right auricle; *r. h. a.* right hepatic artery; *sc.* sciatic vein; *scl. a.* subclavian artery; *scl. v.* subclavian vein; *spl.* spleen; *st.* stomach; *s. v.* sinus venosus; *th.* thyroid gland; *tr.* trachea; *t.* testis; *v.* ventricle. (After T. J. Parker.)

gall-bladder runs to, and through, the pancreatic tissue, where it receives *pancreatic juice* from several *pancreatic ducts*. Then it reaches the duodenum as a *hepato-pancreatic* duct. The stomach is attached to the body-wall by a fold of peritoneum, the *mesogaster*; the small intestine by a *mesentery*; and the rectum by a *mesorectum*. From the dorsal surface of the liver to the stomach there extends a thin fold, the *gastro-hepatic omentum*. This is continued backwards as the *duodeno-hepatic omentum*, connecting the liver with the first portion of the small intestine. The rectum leads into an extensive cloacal chamber which is subdivided into a *coprodæum* and *urodæum* and finally a *proctodæum* which terminates in a sphincter. The posterior, but not the anterior, peritoneum of the body cavity is pigmented black.

During the present dissection the following structures can be found :

1. The *thyroid gland*, a whitish, crescentic endocrine body on the ventral wall of the trachea a short distance in front of the heart.

2. Two pairs of thymus bodies (anterior and posterior) in close relationship with the origin of the paired carotid arteries. There is no evidence that they are of endocrine function.

3. The *spleen*, a sac of blood-storage and other functions, is held by mesentery near the pylorus (Fig. 317).

4. The paired endocrine *adrenal glands* (*suprarenals*), lying near the gonads (p. 152). The cortical and medullary homologues are interdigitated as in amphibians.

5. The *adipose bodies* (Fig. 318, *c. ad*), which are two masses of fat of somewhat semilunar shape in the posterior part of the abdominal cavity between the peritoneum and the muscles of the body-wall.

Blood-vascular System.—The *heart* shows an advance on that of the Amphibia even though the arterial and venous streams are probably not completely separate. The organ is enclosed in a thin transparent membrane, the *pericardium*, and is lined with *endocardium*. It consists of a *sinus venosus*, *right* and *left auricles*, and an incompletely divided *ventricle*. Fig. 319 shows the ventral and dorsal surfaces of the heart after removal of the pericardium.

The reptiles show a gradual absorption of the sinus venosus. Chelonians retain a large one, but in many it has disappeared, having been incorporated into the right atrium, where its remnants are identifiable as valve-like structures at the entrances of the great veins. In *Lacerta* three venæ cavæ empty independently into the sinus venosus. There are no valves. The sinus venosus lies dorsal to the right auricle, into which it empties through a slit-like *sinu-auricular aperture* (Fig. 320, *a. c. v.*) guarded by folds of the auricular wall. The left auricle is the smaller of the two and receives the single *pulmonary vein* on its dorsal wall near the *interauricular septum*. There is no valve. Although thin, the interauricular septum is complete. It runs on to a flap of the *atrioventricular valve* (*a. v. v.*), so that the blood passes from the two auricles to the ventricle through two openings (Foxon *et al.*). The auricles have their inner surfaces raised into a network of muscular ridges—the *musculi pectinati*. Removal of the ventral wall of the ventricle reveals an almost complete oblique *interventricular septum* (*i. v. s.*). Almost horizontal, this separates the right ventral part of the ventricle into a *cavum ventrale* (*c. v.*). Associated with the base of the *pulmonary artery*, this is sometimes termed the *cavum pulmonale.* The rest of the ventricle constitutes the *cavum dorsale*, which is in turn partly subdivided by *myocardial trabeculæ.* Some of these are fused, giving rise to a prominent ridge, or secondary septum, which partially divides the cavum dorsale as well. The resultant left cavity is the *cavum arteriosum*; the right the *cavum venosum.* The ventricle therefore consists of three incompletely separated cavities.

From this tripartite ventricle spring the three principal arteries (*aortæ*). From the right side (*cavum ventrale*) originates the pulmonary artery (Fig. 319, *p. a.*). Immediately dorsal arises the left systemic arch. Further dorsally,

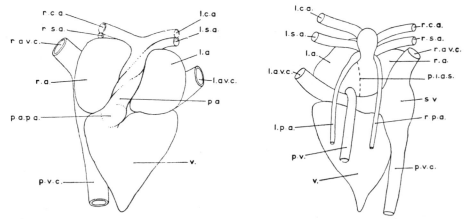

Fig. 319.—*Lacerta:* **Heart and large vessels.** Ventral (left) and dorsal views. *l. a.* left auricle; *l. a. v. c.* left anterior vena cava; *l. c. a.* left carotid arch; *l. p. a.* left pulmonary artery; *l. s. a.* left systemic arch; *p. a.* pulmonary artery; *p. a. p. a.* position of aperture of pulmonary artery; *p. i. a. s.* position of interauricular septum; *p. v.* pulmonary vein; *p. v. c.* posterior vena cava; *r. a.* right auricle; *r. a. v. c.* right anterior vena cava; *r. c. a.* right carotid arch; *r. p. a.* right pulmonary artery; *r. s. a.* right systemic arch; *s. v.* sinus venosus. (After Foxon, Griffith, and Price.)

and to the left, the right systemic arch takes origin. From this both carotid arteries arise. Each principal artery is guarded basally by a valve.

The course of blood distribution may be as follows : venous blood is emptied into the right auricle. Oxygenated blood from the lungs enters the left auricle. During ventricular *diastole* (relaxation) each auricle empties into the cavum dorsale of the ventricle. The blood which enters the cavum ventrale 'has to do so from the cavum dorsale over the edge of the incomplete septum' (arrow in Fig. 320). On ventricular *systole* (contraction) this blood will presumably pass into the pulmonary arteries ; for the septum is so aligned that when the ventricle contracts its free edge is brought against the opposite wall of the ventricle. Thus functional division of the ventricle is brought about in such a way as to connect the cavum ventrale with the base of the pulmonary arch. The opening into the left systemic arch remains connected with the cavum dorsale ' (Foxon *et al.*).   In the Chelonia, on the other hand, the left systemic arch opens to the right of the septum.

The substantial difference in size of the two auricles (see above) and the differential capacity of the cavum ventrale and the cavum dorsale make it impossible for equal quantities of blood to be sent to the lung and to the systemic circulation during each heart-beat, as occurs in the double circulation that has arisen in birds (p. 589) and mammals (p. 671).   Some mixture in the

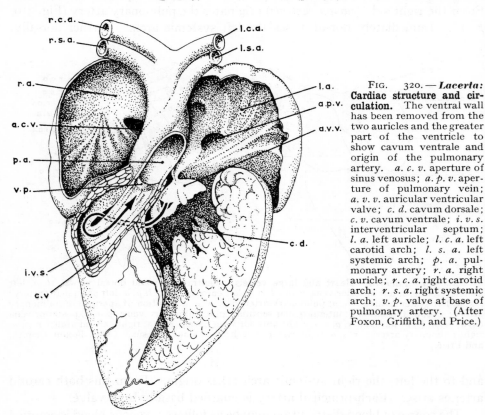

Fig.   320. — *Lacerta:* **Cardiac structure and circulation.**   The ventral wall has been removed from the two auricles and the greater part of the ventricle to show cavum ventrale and origin of the pulmonary artery.   *a. c. v.* aperture of sinus venosus; *a. p. v.* aperture of pulmonary vein; *a. v. v.* auricular ventricular valve; *c. d.* cavum dorsale; *c. v.* cavum ventrale; *i. v. s.* interventricular septum; *l. a.* left auricle; *l. c. a.* left carotid arch; *l. s. a.* left systemic arch; *p. a.* pulmonary artery; *r. a.* right auricle; *r. c. a.* right carotid arch; *r. s. a.* right systemic arch; *v. p.* valve at base of pulmonary artery.   (After Foxon, Griffith, and Price.)

Reptilia of arterial and venous blood must inevitably occur.   The most recent work suggests that oxygenated blood from the left auricle, entering the left part of the cavum dorsale, goes principally through both carotid arches, and the right systemic arch.   Some of the right systemic blood may be added via the *ductus caroticus* to that in the internal carotid.   De-oxygenated blood from the right auricle is emptied into the right portion of the cavum ventrale and passes into the pulmonary arteries for re-oxygenation at the lungs.   The blood in the right part of the cavum dorsale goes principally into the left systemic arch and probably passes through the ductus caroticus on that side into the carotid.

As regards circulation in general, the two aortic arches curve backwards round the œsophagus, one to the right and the other to the left. The two arches are non-equivalent and the right carries more highly oxygenated blood than the left. The right arch gives off two *subclavian arteries* as it passes to the mid-dorsal position, and then runs posteriorly as the median *dorsal aorta*. The left arch also passes to the mid-dorsal position, but it communicates with the dorsal aorta by a small aperture only and is continued mainly as the *cœliaco-mesenteric* artery (*c. m.*). This shortly divides into two trunks: a *cœliac* (Fig. 317, *cœl. a.*) supplying the stomach, spleen, pancreas, duodenum, and left lobe of the liver, and an *anterior mesenteric* supplying the posterior part of the small intestine. Three small *posterior mesenteric* arteries given off farther back supply the large intestine. Posteriorly, after giving off *renal* and *genital* branches, and a pair of large *iliacs* to the hind-limb, the dorsal aorta is continued along the tail as the *caudal artery* (Fig. 317, *caud. art.*). Throughout its length, in addition to the larger branches mentioned, the dorsal aorta gives origin to a regularly-arranged series of pairs of small vessels, the *inter-costal* and *lumbar* arteries. These give off branches that enter the neural canal, and others that supply the muscles and integument.

The venous blood from the tail is brought back by means of a *caudal vein* (Fig. 318, *c.*). This bifurcates at the base of the tail to form the two renal portal veins each of which carries blood to an adjacent kidney. Before entering the kidney each gives off a *pelvic* (*lateral*) *vein* (*pl.*) These are entered by the *femoral* and *sciatic* veins from the hind-limbs before they unite to form the median *epigastric* or *abdominal* (*ep. g.*), which eventually enters the left lobe of the liver. The *efferent renal veins*, carrying the blood from the kidneys, combine to form a pair of large trunks, which soon unite to form the median *postcaval*. The postcaval runs forwards towards the heart, and, after receiving the wide *hepatic vein* from the liver, enters the sinus venosus.

Two *precavals*, right and left, carry the blood from the anterior extremities and the head to the sinus venosus. The right precaval is formed by the union of the *internal* and *external jugular* and the *subclavian*. On the left side the precaval is formed by the union of *internal jugular* and *subclavian*, the left external jugular being absent. The liver is supplied, as in other vertebrates, by a *hepatic portal* system of vessels, blood being carried to it by a *portal vein*. This is formed by the union of gastric, pancreatic, splenic, and mesenteric veins. The *spleen* (Fig. 317 and 318, *spl.*) is a small red body lying in the mesogaster, near the posterior end of the stomach. The reptilian erythrocyte is nucleated and leucocytes of various kinds occur. The *lymphatic system* is highly developed. The main trunk divides and enters the precavals. Lymph-hearts occur.

Respiratory System.—Lizards, unlike frogs, have no auxiliary means of respiration. Although the *lungs* of *Sphenodon* and others are little more elaborate than those of anurans, those of most lizards, including *Lacerta*, show a considerable advance. Each organ (Fig. 317, *lg.*) is a fusiform sac, the inner lining of which is raised up into a network of delicate ridges giving the appearance of a honeycomb. These ridges are much closer and more numerous towards the anterior than towards the posterior end of the lung. In this arrangement we see what is probably a hint of the highly complex system later to be observed in birds in which *dead-space* air is almost eliminated by the circulation of the air-current across the anterior respiratory surface during both inspiration and expiration.

Air is drawn in from, and driven back to, the nostrils by means of a mechanism quite unlike that of fishes and Amphibia. Air is sucked into the elastic lungs as the trunk region in general is expanded by muscles which elevate the ribs. We shall see that this method of respiration is characteristic of the truly terrestrial vertebrates. In the Mammalia it is further complicated by the presence of the muscular diaphragm (Fig. 464, p. 676).

The structures lying between the nostrils and the lungs are a slit-like aperture, the *glottis* (situated behind the tongue), into which it leads, and a short chamber, the *larynx*. The larynx is less prominently developed than in many of the Amphibia. Its walls are supported by *cricoid* and *arytenoid* cartilages. From the larynx an elongated cylindrical tube, the *trachea*, passes backwards on the ventral side of the neck. Its wall is supported by a large number of small rings of cartilage, the *tracheal rings*. Posteriorly the trachea bifurcates to form two similar but narrower tubes, the *bronchi*, one of which enters each lung.

Brain.—The reptilian brain (Figs. 321, 322) lies quite loosely within the cranial cavity, surrounded by a tough fibrous membrane, the *dura mater*. It does not fill the cranium to nearly the same extent as does the brain of a mammal, a fact to be considered in the interpretation of endocranial casts of fossil forms. The hinder part of the brain is well protected by the bones of the back and base of the skull as well as those of the roof. The front of the brain, however, is more lightly covered, for, as we have seen, the side walls of the cranial cavity in the region between, and in front of, the eyes are often mainly cartilaginous or membranous.

The brain is small, both absolutely and relatively. In *Lacerta* it makes up only about 0·5 per cent of the body weight. In certain dinosaurs, whose bulk can be estimated at about 20 tons, the brain was only a few inches long. In general structure it falls into the typical vertebrate pattern of *fore-*, *mid-*, and *hind-brain*, the last-named being continuous with the spinal cord. In the fore-brain are paired ovoid *cerebral hemispheres* (relatively bigger than those of Amphibia) and their contained lateral ventricles. Anteriorly each hemisphere continues into an *olfactory stalk* that terminates bluntly in an *olfactory bulb* which received fibres from the olfactory epithelium of the nasal cavity. A *vomeronasal* nerve from the *organs of Jacobson* (p. 481 and Fig. 374, p. 544); entering an accessory olfactory bulb is prominent in many reptiles.

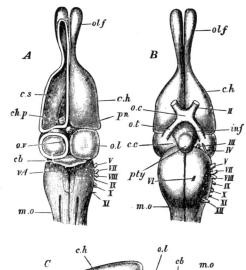

The extensive neopallium of the mammalian cerebral cortex (p. 678) probably has its homologue in a small dorsal area in each cerebral hemisphere which appears to be connected with the thalamus. Little information, however, is available concerning the significance of the reptilian cortex.

The most prominent part of the hemisphere is the *corpus striatum*, which occludes much of the lower and lateral aspects of each ventricle. This massive organ reaches an even greater development in birds (p. 593) in which it appears to be concerned with innate ('instinctive') patterns of behaviour. Behind and between the cerebral hemisphere and in close association with the corpora striata lies the small rounded *diencephalon* and enclosed *third ventricle* (Fig. 322). With the latter the *lateral ventricle* of each side communicates by means of the interventricular *foramina of Monro*. Each lateral ventricle contains a vascular, epithelial *choroid plexus* which secretes cerebrospinal fluid. A small *thalamus*, which appears to receive sensory impulses from the brain-stem and cord, occurs in the diencephalon. Below is the large unpaired *hypothalamus*, which is probably concerned with the integration of metabolic and visceral activities. The brain-floor is produced ventrally

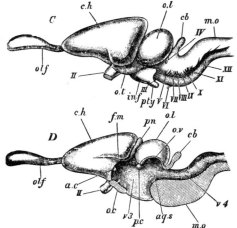

FIG. 321.—*Lacerta*: **Brain and cranial nerves.** *A*, dorsal, with the left hemisphere (*c. h.*) and optic lobe (*o. l.*) opened. *B*, ventral. *C*, from the left. *D*, in longitudinal vertical section. *a. c.* anterior commissure; *aq. s.* aqueduct of Sylvius; *cb.* cerebellum; *c. c.* crura cerebri; *c. h.* cerebral hemispheres; *ch. p.* choroid plexus; *c. s.* corpus striatum; *f. m.* foramen of Monro; *inf.* infundibulum; *m. o.* medulla oblongata; *o. c.* optic chiasma; *o. l.* optic lobes; *olf.* olfactory bulbs with their peduncles or tracts; *o. t.* optic tracts; *o. v.* aperture between aqueduct of Sylvius and optic ventricle; *p. c.* posterior commissure; *pn.* pineal apparatus; *pty.* pituitary body; *v. 3*, 3rd ventricle (diacœle); *v. 4*, 4th ventricle (metacœle); *I—XII*, cranial nerves. (After Parker.)

into a tubular process, the *infundibulum*, which ends in a compound *pituitary gland* or *hypophysis* of diverse endocrine function (see p. 149). There is a connecting *hypophysial portal system* (Fig. 95) between brain and gland. The roof of the diencephalon is produced into a median outgrowth, the *pineal apparatus* (Fig. 321, *D*, *pn*.; Fig. 322, *Z*), which is divided into two parts. One of these has connected with its distal extremity an eye-like structure, the *parietal organ* or *pineal eye* (Fig. 322, *pa*.), lying in the parietal foramen, while the other is the *pineal organ* or *epiphysis* (see p. 128).

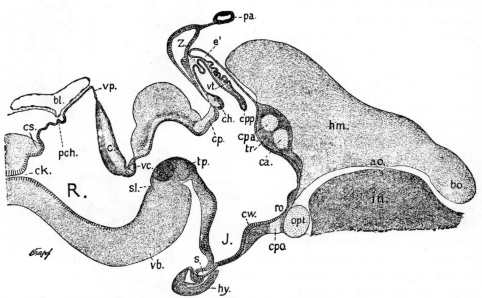

FIG. 322.—*Lacerta:* **Brain and hypophysis.** Longitudinal section in an embryo (× 26). *ao.* olfactory area; *bl.* blood-sinus; *bo.* olfactory bulb; *c.* cerebellar commissures; *ca.* anterior commissure; *ch.* superior (habenular) commissure; *ck.* central canal of spinal cord; *cp.* posterior commissure; *cpa.* anterior pallial (hippocampal) commissure; *cpo.* posterior optic commissure; *cpp.* posterior pallial (aberrant) commissure; *cs.* spinal commissure; *cw.* swelling of optic chiasma; *e¹.* paraphysis; *hm.* cerebral hemisphere; *hy.* hypophysis; *in.* cartilaginous inter-orbital septum; *J* (and *s*). ventricle of infundibulum; *opt.* optic chiasma; *pa.* parietal organ; *pch.* choroid plexus on medulla oblongata; *R.* 4th ventricle; *ro.* optic recess; *sl.* sulcus intraencephalicus posterior; *tp.* tuberculum posterior superius; *tr.* lamina terminalis; *vb.* ventral flexure of medulla oblongata; *vc.* valvula cerebelli; *vp.* posterior medullary velum; *vt.* velum transversum; *Z.* epiphysis. (From Wiedersheim, T. J. Parker, after K. von Kupffer.)

The mid-brain roof (*tectum*) is relatively elaborate. It has been established that its large paired *optic lobes* receive most of the fibres from the optic nerves. It is probable that the mid-brain is an important co-ordinating centre functioning in a manner somewhat comparable with the mammalian cerebral cortex (p. 678). The *cerebellum* (of the hind-brain) is small and lacks lateral lobes and is concerned primarily with equilibrium. It surmounts the *medulla oblongata* on the ventral surface of which there has not arisen any structure corresponding to the pons found in the Mammalia. Of the twelve cranial nerves that arise mainly from the mid- and hind-brains, the vagus (Xth) and the cranial root of the accessory (XIth) may be fused. From the medulla, the *spinal cord* is continued backwards throughout the length of the neural canal, becoming slightly dilated opposite the origins of the two pairs of limbs and tapering greatly towards the posterior end of the tail. For an outline of the autonomic nervous system see pp. 119, 412.

Endocrine glands.—These fall into the general vertebrate pattern (p. 147). The thyroid is single but may be paired in some species, the two organs sometimes being connected by a narrow band of tissue. Near the arterial arches, and some distance from the thyroid, occur bodies that are probably homologous with the mammalian parathyroids. The adrenals are situated close to the gonads; their medullary and cortical homologues are interdigitated. For the pituitary, see p. 149.

Organs of Special Sense.—The *olfactory organs* are more complex than those of the anura. The *nasal cavities* (Fig. 89, p. 138) open at the end of the snout by the external nares, and into the cavity of the mouth by a pair of slit-like *internal nares* situated near the middle line of the palate. The external aperture opens into a vestibule through which the air passes to the sensory epithelium of the nasal or olfactory cavity proper. This contains a convoluted *turbinal bone* over which the mucous membrane extends. Below each nasal cavity, and separated from them in the adult, is an *organ of Jacobson* or *vomero-nasal organ* (*J.J.*), a small sac with strongly pigmented

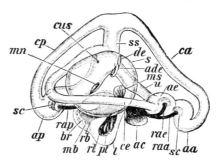

FIG. 323.—*Lacerta:* **Audioequilibration.** Lateral view of right membranous labyrinth. *aa.* anterior ampulla; *ac.* auditory nerve; *ade.* opening of the ductus endolymphaticus; *ae.* external ampulla; *ap.* posterior ampulla; *br.* basilar branch of nerve; *ca.* anterior semicircular canal; *ce.* external semicircular canal; *cp.* posterior semicircular canal; *cus.* canal connecting utriculus and sacculus; *de.* ductus endolymphaticus; *l.* lagena; *mb.* basilar membrane; *raa, rae, rap. rl.* branches of auditory nerve; *s.* sacculus; *ss.* common canal of communication between anterior and posterior semicircular canals and utricle; *u.* utriculus. (From Wiedersheim, after Retzius.)

walls supported by cartilage. Each opens into the mouth by a duct on either side at the front of the palate and is supplied by a separate *vomeronasal branch* of the olfactory nerve known as the *vomero-nasal nerve.* This sense-organ is important in most lizards and snakes and appreciates scent particles introduced into it by the tongue tips. There is experimental evidence that in some reptiles it plays a part in activities such as trailing prey and locating members of the opposite sex. Paired ducts communicate with the buccal cavity, probably enabling the olfactory appreciation of substances held in the mouth.

The *eye* (Fig. 375, p. 545) has a cartilaginous sclerotic with a ring of small bones supporting it externally. There is a cushion-like *pecten*, a vascular pigmented process similar to that occurring in birds (p. 596). This projects into the inner or vitreous chamber of the eye. Cones are proportionally very numerous in the retina. Accommodation is brought about by the ciliary muscles, which press the ciliary body against the periphery of the lens and deform into it a more rounded shape suitable for close vision. Two glands, the *lachrymal* and the *Harderian*, lie in the orbit and produce moistening and cleansing secretions. The eyes are protected also by lids. In addition, there is a third lid, the *nictitating membrane*, which slides across the moist cornea.

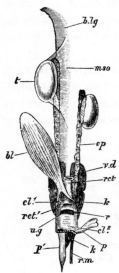

FIG. 324.—*Lacerta: Male urinogenital system.* The ventral wall of the cloaca is removed, the bladder turned to the right, and the peritoneal covering of the left testis and epididymis is dissected away. *bl.* urinary bladder; *b. lg.* fold of peritoneum supporting epididymis; *cl¹.* anterior and *cl².* posterior divisions of the cloaca; *ep.* epididymis; *k.* kidney; *mso.* mesorchium; *p.* copulatory organs, of which the right is shown retracted (*p'*) and the left everted (*p*); *r. m.* retractor muscle of latter; *r.* ridge separating anterior and posterior divisions of cloaca; *rct.* rectum; *rct'.* its opening into the cloaca; *t.* testis; *u. g.* urinogenital papilla and aperture; *v. d.* vas deferens. (After T. J. Parker.)

The *ear* consists of two principal parts, the *internal ear* or *membranous labyrinth*, and the *middle ear* or *tympanic cavity*. The latter is closed externally by the tympanic membrane (Fig. 93, p. 144). It communicates with the cavity of the mouth by the *Eustachian tube*, which is narrower and longer than in frogs. The inner wall of the tympanic cavity is formed by the bony wall of the auditory region of the skull, in which there are two fenestræ—the *fenestra ovalis* and the *fenestra rotunda*. The columella stretches across the cavity from the tympanic membrane, and is fixed internally into the membrane covering over the fenestra ovalis.

The parts of the membranous labyrinth (Fig. 323) are enclosed by the bones of the auditory region. Between the membranous wall of the labyrinth and the surrounding bone is a small space containing fluid, the *perilymph*. The labyrinth itself consists of the *utriculus* with the three semicircular canals and the *sacculus* with the *lagena*. The *utriculus* (*u.*) is a cylindrical tube, bent round at a sharp angle: the *semicircular canals* (*ca., ce., cp.*) are arranged as in vertebrates in general (p. 145). A narrow tube, the *ductus endolymphaticus*, leads upwards towards the roof of the skull and ends blindly in the dura mater. The *sacculus* is large and rounded. The *lagena* (*l.*) forms a flattened, not very prominent, lobe, and is of simple form. It contains what is probably a special organ of hearing, the *papilla basilaris*.

Urinogenital System.—The *kidneys* (Figs. 324 and 325, *k.*) are a pair of irregularly shaped, dark red bodies, each consisting of two lobes, anterior and posterior, situated in close contact with the dorsal wall of the posterior portion of the abdominal cavity, and covered with peritoneum on their ventral faces only. Their posterior portions, which are tapering, are in close contact with one another. Each has a delicate duct, the *ureter*, opening posteriorly into the *urodæum* of the cloaca. From here water is reabsorbed. A *urinary (allantoic) bladder (bl.)* (see also p. 159), a thin-walled sac, opens into the cloaca on its ventral side. To reach the bladder, from which fluid is probably reabsorbed, the urine must first pass into the cloaca and remain undischarged.

In the male the *testes* (Fig. 324, *t.*) are two oval white bodies. The right testis is situated just posterior to the right lobe of the liver ; the left organ is somewhat farther back. Their internal structure, and functions, follow the general craniate pattern (p. 152). Each testis is attached to the body-wall by a fold of the peritoneum, the *mesorchium (mso.)*. The *epididymis (ep.)* extends backwards from the inner side of each testis, and passes behind into a narrow convoluted tube, the *vas deferens* or spermiduct (*v. d.*), which opens into the terminal part of the corresponding ureter. Grooves guide the spermatozoa from the urodæum to twin penial structures ('*hemipenes*') (Fig. 324, *p.*[1]), which arise from the proctodæum as eversible folds. Vascular and erectile, these assume a cylindrical form when everted (Fig. 378, p. 550). Each has a dilated and bifid apex and is used singly and independently of the other for the discharge of spermatozoa into the female tract.

Fertilisation must, of course, be internal in truly terrestrial vertebrates and occurs in the anterior part of the oviduct before the enclosure of the egg by its protective coverings.

The *ovaries* (Fig. 325, *ov.*) are a pair of irregularly oval bodies with their surfaces raised up into rounded elevations which mark the position

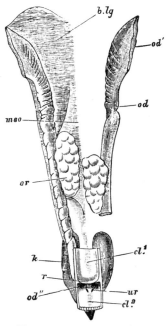

Fig. 325.—*Lacerta:* **Female urinogenital system.** The ventral wall of the cloaca, the urinary bladder, the posterior end of the left oviduct, and the peritoneal investment of the left ovary and oviduct are removed. *b. lg.* broad ligament; *cl*[1]. anterior and *cl*[2]. posterior divisions of the cloaca; *k.* kidney; *mso.* mesovarium; *od.* left oviduct; *od'.* its peritoneal aperture; *od".* aperture of right oviduct into the cloaca; *ov.* ovary; *ur.* aperture of ureter. (After T. J. Parker.)

of the oocytes. They are situated a little farther back than are the testes, and each is attached to the body-wall by a fold of the peritoneum, the *mesovarium (mso.)*. The eggs are extruded into the body cavity (*od'.*) and pass into the anterior ends of the oviducts (*od.*). These are thin-walled, wide tubes which communicate with the urodæum. Their opening (*od."*) is distinct from, and a little in front of, those of the ureters. A fold of the peritoneum, the *broad ligament (b. lg.)*, attaches the oviduct to the body-wall.

INTERRELATIONSHIP OF THE REPTILIAN GROUPS

One of the most noteworthy features of the reptiles is the evolution of the temporal region of their skulls.   The structure of this region has led to their classification into five principal groups, but it should be borne in mind that a considerable difference of opinion exists concerning the true affinities of many animals that are still known only by fragments of endo- or exoskeleton.

The basic classification of the Reptilia on temporal openings (Fig. 326) illustrates certain early evolutionary trends, but it is now generally believed

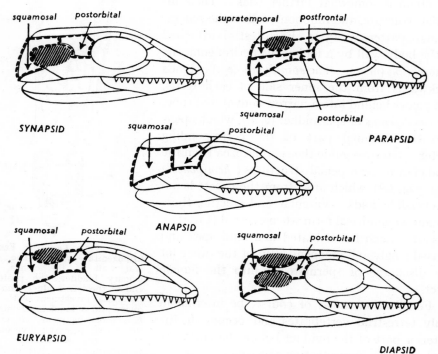

FIG. 326.—**Reptilia: Basic skull structure.**   For explanation, see Table 3, p. 485.   (After Colbert.)

that such a classification can also be very misleading.   For example, the ichthyopterygians (p. 490) and sauropterygians (p. 492), long classified together in the ' Parapsida ', are now thought to be only very distantly related.   The two immense assemblies, Lepidosauria (p. 495) and Archosauria (p. 498), both often believed to show the diapsid condition, have also diverged separately from the primitive reptilian stock.   An outline of the basic grouping is given in Table IV.

The most primitive forms, the Cotylosauria ('stem reptiles'), had a complete bony roofing in the temporal region—the anapsid condition—as did the early

Amphibia from which reptiles originated (see pp. 458, 486). According to most authorities, this is still found in living Chelonia (sometimes modified by emargination), which, together with the cotylosaurs, form the sub-class Anapsida (Fig. 484).

From this primitive skull may have evolved two principal types. The first of these has a single vacuity in each side, and is known as *synapsid*. The vacuity was bounded at first by the postorbital and squamosal bones above, and the squamosal and jugal bones below, but later the parietal appeared within the opening owing to the enlargement of the vacuity and reduction in

TABLE IV. Temporal Openings of Reptiles.

Condition.	Number and Arrangement.	Principal Groups.
Anapsid	None. Solid roof to skull	Cotylosaurs, chelonians * (turtles)
Synapsid	One. Low behind eye with postorbital and squamosal meeting above	Pelycosaurians and mammal-like reptiles
Parapsid	One. High behind eye usually with postfrontal and supratemporal meeting below	Mesosaurs and ichthyosaurs *
Euryapsid	One. Behind eye bordered below by postorbital and squamosal	Protorosaurs and sauropterygians
Diapsid	Two. Postorbital and squamosal usually meet between them	Eosuchians, Rhynchocephalia (*Sphenodon*), dinosaurs, pterosaurs, Crocodilia Squamata (lizards and snakes)

* Condition sometimes or always shown in modified form.

size of the postorbital. Reptiles having this type of skull—the Synapsida—are mammal-like and certainly include the ancestors of mammals which themselves possess the synapsid skull further modified by the loss of the postorbital and quadratojugal bones, and by the inclusion of the quadrate within the ear.

Another modification of the primitive type is known as *diapsid*. Here there are two vacuities in the temporal region, with the postorbital and squamosal meeting between them. This condition is found in many reptiles (*e.g.* Crocodilia, 'dinosaurs', pterosaurs). In a modified form it occurs in lizards, snakes, and persists also in birds. The lizards lost the quadratojugal, thus opening the lower vacuity below. The snakes, the most modern group of reptiles, carried this modification still further by reducing or losing the postorbital and losing the jugal. The birds lost the postorbital, with the result that the two vacuities and the orbital opening are confluent.

A few small reptiles (*e.g.* *Aræoscelis*) have a single temporal vacuity differing from the synapsid type in that the postorbital and squamosal meet below the opening. Some authorities believe this vacuity is homologous with the

upper vacuity of the diapsid skull, and that the vacuity of the synapsid skull
is homologous with the lower vacuity of the diapsid skull, and so have given it
another name—*parapsid*.   Often included in this sub-class are two aquatic
groups, the *Mesosauria* and *Ichthyosauria*, which have single temporal vacuities
in the skull.   Their skulls, however, are peculiar, and there is not a great deal
of evidence in the skeletons of these reptiles to ally them to the other orders.

It appears, therefore, that the primitive reptiles with a completely roofed,
or anapsid, skull gave rise to the Synapsida, and to the various diapsid and
parapsid groups.

SUB-CLASS ANAPSIDA

ORDER COTYLOSAURIA

The oldest reptiles, the cotylosaurs, range from the Upper Carboniferous
to the Upper Trias when they became extinct.   Many of them show little
advance on their ancestors, the labyrinthodont Amphibia.   The group is
probably mixed in origin.   The members composing it are held together
chiefly by two characters : the complete roofing of the skull, and the flattened,
plate-like pelvis.   These reptiles showed few specialisations, and varied in
size from about a foot to 10 feet in the case of the parasaurs.   Two sub-orders
are recognised as follows:

SUB-ORDER CAPTORHINOMORPHA

These (e.g. *Limnoscelis, Captorhinus, Labidosaurus* (Fig. 310, p. 358)) were
primitive Lower Permian cotylosaurians which varied considerably in structure.
They had high, narrow skulls contrasting with the typically flattened amphibian
form.   At the same time many of the characteristic cranial features of the
early Amphibia were retained.   The skull was completely roofed and strongly
ossified.   The amphibian otic notch was lost.   The position of the tympanic
membrane has not yet been certainly established.   These animals seem to
have been the forerunners of the Synapsida.

SUB-ORDER DIADECTOMORPHA

These (e.g. *Diadectes, Procolophon*) survived into the Triassic.   These
probably carried themselves clear of the ground, and some possessed remarkable teeth that suggest a herbivorous diet.   They developed a peculiar otic
notch and a short and heavy skull.   *Parasaurus* had a large skull studded
with protuberances and plate-like bones along its dorsal surface.   The sub-
order includes the majority of the cotylosaurs and has some features in common
with the Diapsida.

ORDER CHELONIA

The principal trend in amniote evolution involved, of course, adaptation to
terrestrial conditions but in all classes from Amphibia to Mammalia various

groups retreated to, or reconquered, the water.   The sea in particular, with its rich, unending harvest of food, has been repeatedly invaded by reptilian, avian, and mammalian lines.

The turtles (Fig. 327) including tortoises, probably represent an early off-shoot from the primitive cotylosaurs.   They retain certain unmistakable anapsid characteristics.   No convincing explanation has been forthcoming to account for the development of, and retreat into, their extraordinary, box-like exo-

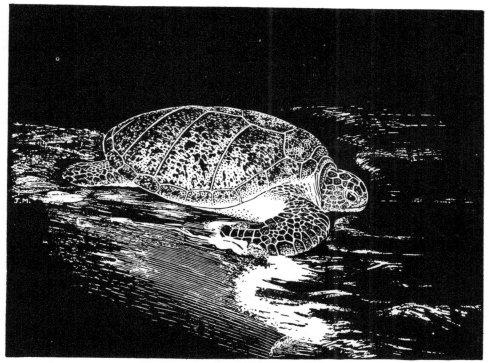

FIG. 327.—Sub-class **Anapsida,** Order **Chelonia,** Sub-order **Cryptodira,** Family **Chelonidæ.** *Chelonia.*   The Green (Edible) Turtle (*C. mydas*) re-entering sea after nocturnal egg-laying on a tropical beach.   (Partly after flash-light photograph: *Sarawak Museum Journal.*)

skeleton; and it is of high interest that, having established this peculiarly bizarre armour, they have, in many respects, remained stable and relatively unaltered since the Triassic some 160 million years ago (p. 3).

Living turtles—they are generally called tortoises when essentially terres-trial—range from a few inches to about 6 feet in length.   One turtle (*Dermo-chelys*) weighs considerably more than half a ton.   Both herbivorous and carnivorous forms exist.   There are more than two hundred living species, some of which have returned to an almost completely aquatic life.

Their early development is still obscure.   A good series of specimens is available from the Triassic onwards, but their pre-Mesozoic history is but sketchily discernible.   Permian specimens would tell palæontologists a great deal—but no undoubted chelonian has been found in these deposits.   Possibly *Eunotosaurus*, of mid-Permian age, is close to the main line of chelonian ancestry, but the skull roof of the specimen is damaged ; it is not known if it had a temporal aperture.   *Eunotosaurus* still possessed teeth (see below) ;   and although the limb-bones were badly preserved, the smaller number of vertebræ and broad ribs are suggestive, even though the animal had neither true carapace nor plastron (p. 527).   The plates of *Eunotosaurus* were almost spatulate rib-expansions, and it is now generally accepted that the characteristic plates of chelonians develop not from ribs, but from separate bony dermal plates which unite with each other and with supporting ribs and vertebræ.   The more restricted plastron of the turtles appears to have arisen from abdominal, and, anteriorly, from clavicle and interclavicle elements of the ancient dermal pectoral girdle.

In embryonic development the girdles, more or less inside the ribs in modern adults, do not change their position.   Instead, the adult condition arises by the radial expansion of the carapace (which becomes fused with the ribs early in development) and plastron until the margins of the developing armour extend over, enclose, and protect the girdles (Ruckes).   At the same time, however, there is no proof that phylogeny has duplicated ontogeny.

Once established, the turtles flourished both in numbers and, often, in individual size.   The Cretaceous *Archelon* was about 12 feet long with a similar approximate width across the flippers.   Protected by their grotesque armour and secure from too drastic competition in specialised ecological niches, some lines remained relatively abundant in the Cænozoic after most of their Mesozoic relatives had vanished.   Of the larger forms, a horned turtle *Meiolania* (a giant with a skull about 2 feet wide) survived in Australia until the Pleistocene.

The only considerable, but still relatively superficial, changes undergone by chelonians have been various reductions in armour and the modification of land-limbs into oar-like flippers.   In sea-going turtles the proximal limb-elements are compacted ; the distal ones are lengthened, and support the paddles with which the animal skulls swiftly along.   The retreat from the land and terrestrial predators has enabled certain marine forms (*e.g.* the modern *Dermochelys*) to reduce their weight by an enormous reduction in exoskeleton.   Most people believe all chelonians to be excessively slow-moving, but marine turtles, and *Dermochelys* in particular, are by far the fastest reptiles and, surprisingly, rival many large land tetrapods for speed. Terrestrial chelonians, though always slow, have often improved their agility by reduction of armour, particularly on islands free from predators.   Others have developed hinged armour (e.g. *Cinixys*) ; and the African *Testudo tornieri* has reduced its dermal armour to be sufficiently soft-bodied to squeeze between crevices in the rocky areas in which it lives.

Chelonians are said to live to a great age, but few authenticated data are available. The famous turtle with 'G. Washington, 1751' carved on its carapace is believed to have been a fraud, so to speak; and the Napoleonic giant of St. Helena, reputed to have lived more than 120 years, was probably 'composition of two animals whose period of residence . . . overlapped' (Loveridge, cited by Carr). Gilbert White is said to have kept a tortoise aged forty when acquired, for another fifteen years; and there is a famous tortoise, believed to have been left by Captain Cook in 1777, that still lives in Tonga. This scorched (by a bush fire) and battered veteran resides in the Palace grounds and bears the title of *Tui* (High Chief) *Malila* and is 'the greatest character, outside the Royal Family', in the islands (Snow). The animal is said to have been actually branded by Cook. In 1923 it was reported to be blind and that, when walking, it 'creaked like an ox-cart' (Flower). It was still alive in 1956. If, as seems probable, this venerable reptile (which is traditionally given a token portion of State banquets) is in fact one of the original pair left by Cook, it must be at least 180 years old.

The modern chelonian skull is without temporal vacuities (p. 484). The modern body is enclosed in a shell of bony plates, consisting of a dorsal carapace and a ventral plastron, partly of dermal and partly of endoskeletal origin. There is usually on the surface an epidermal exoskeleton of horny plates. The vertebræ and ribs of the thoracic region are firmly fused with the body carapace, into the composition of which they enter.

The limbs are sometimes terminated by clawed digits adapted for terrestrial locomotion, sometimes modified into the shape of flippers. There are no teeth, and the jaws have a horny investment. The lungs are compound sacs. In essentials the heart and brain resemble those of the Squamata (p. 496). There is a median penis differing in structure from that in Squamata, but essentially like that of crocodiles (p. 499).

The following *modern* groups are recognised:

Sub-order Pleurodira ('side-necked' turtles), of southern countries. These date from the Mesozoic, and generally curve the neck and draw the head sideways under the shell. Families: Pelomedusidæ, which are freshwater animals of Africa, Madagascar, and southern Australia. In these the skull is covered with horny shields, and the limbs are not paddle-shaped, and the neck is completely retractible. Chelidæ ('snake-neck' turtles) of South America and Australia. These are rather like the above, but the neck is long and not completely hidden when retracted. Kinosternidæ (musk terrapins of North and Central America).

Sub-order Cryptodira, the dominant and almost cosmopolitan chelonians of to-day and which date from the Cretaceous. These retract the head by means of an S-curvature of the neck. Families: Dermatemydidæ (Central American terrapins allied to the previous group). Platysternidæ (freshwater-dwellers of

Asia).   Emydidæ (almost cosmopolitan freshwater reptiles, but absent from Australia; they exhibit striking parallelism with the next family).   Testudinidæ (including most chelonians; cosmopolitan except for Australasia). These show gradations between terrestrial and aquatic extremes.   They include the diamond black terrapins (*Malaclemys*) of the epicure, the famous Giant Tortoises (*Testudo*) of the Galapagos, African and American gophers and many others).   Chelydridæ (snapping turtles of North and Central American freshwaters with large heads, long 'alligator-like' tails, rough shells, and projecting folds of skin on neck and limbs).   Chelonidæ (true sea-going turtles of which the

Fig. 328.—Sub-class **Ichthyopterygia**, Order **Ichthyosauria**, Family **Ophthalmosauriæ**. *Ophthalmosaurus*. The Mesozoic ichthyosaurs, bearing convergent resemblances to extant dolphins, seem to have been the most perfectly adapted of all aquatic reptiles. They could not lay ashore (cf. Chelonia and Crocodilia). Fossilised young have been found in the cloacal region of adults, suggesting an ovoviviparous mode of reproduction. (From B.M. (N.H.) catalogue.)

three best known are the essentially herbivorous Green or 'Soup' turtle (*Chelonia*), Hawksbill (*Eremochelys*) and Loggerhead (*Caretta*)).   Trionychidæ ('softshelled' turtles with reduced carapace and plastron covered with skin, fleshy lips and soft proboscis, and a flat and rounded form, from Africa, Asia, and North America).   Dermochelidæ (*Dermochelys* = *Sphargis*, the 'Leathery Turtle' with dermal skeleton consisting of a mosaic of bony plates embedded in the dorsal skin).

SUB-CLASS ICHTHYOPTERYGIA

ORDER MESOSAURIA

The true position of the mesosaurs (e.g. *Mesosaurus*) has not been established with certainty.   They occur in late Carboniferous or early Permian beds and were unquestionably reptiles that had become aquatic. They were freshwater lake-dwellers with slender bodies some 3 feet long. Their hind-legs were much the more powerful pair, and they had a long, laterally compressed tail. Their vertebræ had features not unlike those of the cotylosaurs from which they were possibly derived as an exceedingly ancient branch.

ORDER ICHTHYOSAURIA

These are fully marine, superficially fish-like, reptiles with a skull with a single lateral temporal vacuity (e.g. *Ichthyosaurus, Ophthalmosaurus* (Fig. 328)).

Some were of very large size (30 or 40 feet long), with a somewhat fish-like body and a large head produced into an elongated snout or beak. They had no neck but possessed an elongated tail and limbs in the form of swimming-paddles. The vertebræ were amphicœlous. A sacrum was absent, so that only pre-caudal and caudal regions are distinguishable. The ribs in the cervical region had two heads for articulation with the vertebræ. A sternum was absent, but there was a highly developed system of abdominal ribs. The skull was produced into an elongated rostrum, formed chiefly of the pre-maxillæ, and with small nostrils situated far back. The orbits were large and contained a ring of bones developed in the sclerotic. A colu-mella was present and articulated with the quadrate, and there was a large parietal foramen. The quad-rate was immovably fixed to the skull. The pterygoids met in the middle line and extended forwards to the vomers, and so separated the palatines, as in *Sphenodon*. The pectoral arch contained only cora-

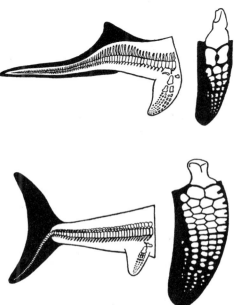

FIG. 329.—**Ichthyosauria: Locomotory speci-lisations.** The tetrapod limbs became paddles, and the tail scull-like. The more primitive forms (*e.g.* Mixosauridæ) of the Triassic still possessed tails of a fairly 'typical' reptilian form (top left figure). Advanced forms (*e.g.* Ichthyo-sauridæ of the Jurassic and Cretaceous) had evolved a homoceral tail superficially similar to that of many modern teleosts (bottom left). With this caudal development there was a re-duction in the size of the pelvic paddles. At the same time there occurred a marked increase in the size of the pectoral paddles (bottom right) which became stabilisers functionally similar to those of modern sharks. (Redrawn from Colbert, after various authors.)

coid, scapula, and clavicle. There was no precoracoid. The coracoids were broad bones which met ventrally for a short distance without overlapping. The bones of the pelvis were not strongly developed. There was no sacrum, *i.e.* the ilia had lost their connections with the spinal column. The pubes and ischia of opposite sides met in ventral symphyses. There was no obturator foramen. Humerus and femur were both short, and the rest of the bones of the limb were disc-like or polyhedral. The phalanges were numerous, and usually arranged in more, but sometimes in fewer, than the usual five series. The teeth were not in separate sockets, but set in a continuous groove. Some forms were toothless. The tail vertebræ in the middle forms had a characteristic downward bend which in later forms became almost a right angle. The body thus extended into the lower lobe of a large vertical caudal fin (Fig. 329).

The ichthyosaurs had become so fish-like that they would probably be helpless ashore. It is almost certain that ichthyosaurs were unable to lay their eggs ashore, and the presence of smaller, probably juvenile individuals within the ribs of adults suggests, but does not prove, that they were viviparous. The ancestry of the group is still in dispute. They appeared in the Triassic, flourished exceedingly in the Jurassic, and disappeared mysteriously in the Upper Cretaceous. Their distribution was almost world-wide.

SUB-CLASS SYNAPTOSAURIA

The synaptosaurians were late Palæozoic and Mesozoic aquatic reptiles possessing a single temporal ('parapsid') vacuity high in the skull. Many of them, however, had little else in common, and the present arrangement may not reflect their true affinities.

ORDER PROTOROSAURIA

This terrestrial group may represent the earliest synaptosaurians. The order was one of the few such found in the Lower Permian. *Aræoscelis* may have been an example, although recent evidence suggests that it was a cotylosaur (p. 486), and that the order Protorosauria may be more appropriately placed near the eosuchians (p. 495). *Aræoscelis* was an agile lizard-like reptile about a foot long with amphicœlous vertebræ and many other primitive features in skull and girdles. Protorosaurians ranged to several yards in length. Their affinities have not been established with certainty.

ORDER SAUROPTERYGIA

These were aquatic reptiles with a single temporal vacuity in the skull, which is bounded below by a postorbital-squamosal arch. The coracoids are single. There are three sub-orders:

SUB-ORDER NOTHOSAURIA

These were small and somewhat primitive Middle and Upper Triassic amphibious reptiles with webbed feet. They were probably close to the ancestry of the two following groups.

SUB-ORDER PLACODONTIA

The placodonts had long limb-bones and a specialised palate armed with massive crushing teeth on the palatine bones which were probably adapted to crushing molluscs. The vertebræ are deeply amphicœlous. The body was covered with heavy bony scutes. They were confined to the Middle Trias, e.g. *Placodus, Cyamodus.*

SUB-ORDER PLESIOSAURIA

These were aquatic reptiles, sometimes more than 40 feet long. They had flattened bodies. Their appearance was quite distinctive, and Dean Buckland, the celebrated 19th-century geologist (and divine), likened a plesiosaur to a

FIG. 330.—Sub-class **Synaptosauria**, Order **Sauropterygia**, Sub-order **Plesiosauria**. *Elasmosaurus.* Plesiosaurs sculled on, or near, the surface with paddles supported by numerous finger-bones that remained elongated and were never compressed like those of ichthyosaurs (Fig. 329). Hip and shoulder musculature was powerful. The teeth were many, sharp, and long; and were adapted to holding and swallowing struggling fish. Some plesiosaurs approached a length of 50 feet. The large flying reptile is *Pteranodon* (see p. 503).

snake threaded through a turtle's shell. This apt description, of course, refers only to the general shape, for the body was not heavily armoured (Fig. 330). The limbs were modified to form swimming-paddles. The vertebræ of plesiosaurs were usually amphicœlous. The sacrum consisted of one to five vertebræ.

There was no sternum. In the skull there were large premaxillæ. A bony secondary palate was absent and an ectopterygoid present. There was a well-marked parietal foramen. The ring of bony plates (developed in the sclerotic found in the orbit of some fossil reptiles) was not developed. The pectoral arch presented some remarkable features. The coracoids always met in a ventral symphysis, and the ventral portions (acromial processes) of the scapulæ often met. In front there was, in most cases, an arch of bone, consisting of a median and two lateral portions, which probably represent the interclavicle and the clavicles: in some forms this arch was reduced or absent. In the pelvis the broad pubes and ischia met in the mid-line. The two symphyses remained separate, or united and divided the space into two separate obturator foramina. The teeth were implanted in distinct sockets.

The ventral elements of each limb-girdle (scapulo-coracoid and pubo-ischium) were expanded and flattened and gave attachment to the large muscles operating the paddles which sculled the reptile through the water.

A divergent stem, represented by *Elasmosaurus*, had an enormously long neck containing nearly eighty vertebræ. At the other extreme was *Kronosaurus* with a short neck and a skull about eight feet long. The Plesiosauria dated from the Trias and extended to the Cretaceous.

The various reports of huge sea-serpents made from time to time have led some to believe that plesiosaurs may still exist, as do cœlacanth fishes (p. 356), in remote seas. For example, in 1809 an animal with a 'snake-like body' allegedly 56 feet long was washed ashore in the Orkneys and reported as a sea-serpent. Home identified the only parts preserved as belonging to the 'Great Basking Shark' (*Cetorhinus*) (p. 227). D'Arcy Thompson, however, believed the animal almost certainly to be a huge oar-fish (*Regalecus* (p. 297)). Again, in 1848 the captain and officers of H.M.S. *Dædalus* claimed that they saw a 'sea-serpent' about 60 feet long with a head 'without doubt that of a snake' off the African coast. As recently as 1917 officers and men of H.M.S. *Hilary* thought they saw a 'sea-serpent' with a black and glossy head near Iceland. It was sunk by anti-submarine fire, without surviving parts. Further, the numerous accounts of the Loch Ness 'monster' will be recalled.

In view of the discovery of living cœlacanths it would not be difficult to imagine that a plesiosaur or related form might still exist in remote waters except for one important fact—that sea-serpents must be lung-breathers and so spend much of their time on the surface. Therefore, they could not remain unobserved in these days of constant voyaging in all oceans, even including southern waters right to the Antarctic pack-ice. Porpoises swimming in line ahead are said to look very like a big undulating sea-serpent. 'Sea'-serpents have been reported from the Victoria Nyanza where the undulatory movements of three or four otters swimming in line conform closely to classic descriptions. Undulating flights of migratory sea-birds, large fishes moving in line ahead, attenuated masses of drifting seaweed and giant squids with trailing arms all assume shapes likely to influence the credulous. Certain eels reach a length of about 6 feet while still larvæ (p. 352). This has provoked the suggestion that some sea-serpent sightings may have referred to the occasional surface appearances of the (as yet undescribed) adult.

SUB-CLASS LEPIDOSAURIA

Representatives of this sub-class typically have two temporal vacuities (p. 484), though these have become reduced in the more specialised forms. The surviving lepidosaurs belong to the Orders Rhynchocephalia (e.g. the surviving *Sphenodon*) and Squamata (lizards and snakes).

ORDER EOSUCHIA

The eosuchians appeared in the Upper Permian. *Youngina*, the best-known specimen, had an interparietal, and tabular bones, in the skull and retained a parietal foramen. It had no antorbital foramen. There are adequate reasons for believing it was extremely primitive and sufficiently unspecialised possibly to have been ancestral to the Squamata (lizards, p. 496) and therefore ultimately also to the serpents. (Thalattosaurs, once thought to be eosuchians, are now believed to be aberrant marine lizards.)

ORDER RHYNCHOCEPHALIA

Members of this ancient order have lost the tabulars and interparietal of the Thecodontia while retaining the large parietal foramen, in which, in the living form, the non-functional median eye (p. 546) can still be made out. There is no antorbital foramen. The group, although apparently never very large, was once widespread. It is known from the Middle Trias (e.g. *Hyperodapedon, Rhynchosaurus*) of Africa, Europe, Asia, and the Americas. The sole living representative of this group, *Sphenodon* (Fig. 331), is the lizard-like Tuatara, which grows to about 2 feet long and has well-developed pentadactyle limbs adapted for walking. A nearly identical- animal, *Homœosaurus*, has been found in Jurassic rocks. The survival of *Sphenodon* in New Zealand is probably due to the absence of terrestrial mammals (including Man) until comparatively recent times. Today *Sphenodon* is restricted to coastal islands where it burrows into the soft soil, emerging particularly at night. It is rigidly protected by law. The anal opening of *Sphenodon* is transverse. There are no ' hemipenes ' (p. 550). The vertebræ are amphicœlous, and inter-centra are present. The ribs are single-headed and have uncinate processes. There is a sternum and abdominal ribs. The teeth are acrodont. The lungs, heart, and brain resemble those of Squamata.

ORDER SQUAMATA

The lizards (Lacertilia = Sauria) and snakes (Ophidia = Serpentes) are the most successful living reptiles. In addition, the order contains numerous extinct families. In general, Squamata are reptiles in which the skull has secondarily lost either one (Lacertilia) or both temporal vacuities (Ophidia).

FIG. 331.—Sub-class **Lepidosauria**, Order **Rhynchocephalia**, Family **Sphenodontidæ**. *Sphenodon*. The single surviving species of the entire order is the Tuatara, now confined to coastal islands of New Zealand. It grows to about 2 feet long. The skeleton retains features clearly suggestive of an eosuchian ancestry.

The surface is covered with horny epidermal scales, sometimes with the addition of dermal ossifications. The cloacal aperture is transverse. There is a pair of eversible penes in the male (Fig. 378, p. 550). The vertebræ are nearly always proccelous. When present, the sacrum usually consists of two vertebræ. The ribs have simple vertebral extremities. The quadrate is movably articulated with the skull, and there is no inferior temporal arch. The limbs, when present, are sometimes adapted for terrestrial locomotion and sometimes for swimming (mosasaurs). The teeth are acrodont or pleurodont (see below).

SUB-ORDER LACERTILIA

Modern opinion regards the lizards as derivatives of primitive Eosuchia (p. 495), an ancestry they probably share with *Sphenodon* (Fig. 331). The

Lacertilia are Squamata in which the limbs are often well developed. The mouth is capable of being opened to only a moderate extent. There are usually eyelids and a tympanum. A sternum and an episternum generally occur (Fig. 312).

Lizards appeared in the Triassic, and have been abundant ever since, They include the Gekkota (geckos); Iguania (not to be confused with Australian members of the Varanidæ, the goannas), which includes the true iguanas, agamas, and chameleons; Scincomorpha (a huge group, including our selected type *Lacerta*); Amphisbænia (burrowing, worm-like creatures superficially resembling the amphibian Apoda, and of broadly similar habits); Anguimorpha (*e.g.* slow-worms, *Anguis*, which possess, as do some other lizards, bony scales or osteoderms); and the Platynota including the living Varanidæ (of which the East Indian Komodo Dragon is about 12 feet long and the extinct Australian Pleistocene *Megalania* attained a length of more than 20 feet), and the Gila Monster and Mexican Bearded Lizard (*Heloderma*).

Of the above, the Iguania and Platynota are known from the Cretaceous, and the Ardeosauridæ, possibly allied to the geckos, occurred in the Upper Jurassic. It should be emphasised (as usual) that there is as yet no general agreement as to the best method of classifying the Lacertilia.

SUB-ORDER OPHIDIA (*SERPENTES*)

Snakes appear to have been derived from a lizard ancestry in Mesozoic times. They are Squamata with long, narrow bodies, typically devoid of limbs. The mouth is usually capable of forming a relatively wide gape by the divarication of the jaws (Fig. 332). The maxillæ, palatines, and pterygoids are freely movable. The rami of the mandible are connected together only by elastic fibres at the symphysis, and so they can be widely separated. There is no separate supra-temporal ossification. Sternum and episternum are absent. As in lizards, a lachrymal duct carries away the tears and opens into the mouth in close relationship with the duct of Jacobson's organ (p. 543). The middle ear is degenerate and the tympanum is absent (see also p. 144). As in some lizards, eyelids are replaced by transparent spectacles (p. 545).

Reptiles that were possibly snakes occurred in the Lower Cretaceous, but the Ophidia did not become abundant until the beginning of the Tertiary. Some apparently marine forms (e.g. *Palæophis*) occurred in the Eocene, and large constricting snakes like the modern boas and pythons are also found in deposits of this age. The Colubridæ (see below), containing the majority of smaller, harmless types (*e.g.* grass-snakes), did not expand until the Oligocene. The fanged, venomous types are only certainly identified from the Miocene onwards. The venomous Elapidæ and Viperidæ (including the rattlesnakes) are first seen as recently as the Miocene–Pleistocene.

As regards modern serpents, the sub-order Ophidia includes the Boidæ (often large, non-venomous, pythons and boas); Typhlopidæ (small, blind, non-venomous, worm-like burrowing reptiles); Leptotyphlopidæ (possibly allied to the above); Ilysiidæ (harmless, burrowing snakes); Uropeltidæ (harmless, burrowing snakes allied to the foregoing). (Most of the above have vestigial hind-limbs.) Xenopeltidæ (containing a single genus, *Xenopeltis*, from south-east Asia); Colubridæ (the great majority of living snakes divided into two groups—the harmless *Aglypha*, without grooved teeth, and the

FIG. 332.—Sub-class **Lepidosauria**, Order **Squamata**, Sub-order **Ophidia**, Family **Viperidæ.** *Crotalus.* Rattlesnake, showing wide divarication of jaws during a stabbing strike. Rapidity of attack (like their speed over the ground (p. 521) is grossly over-rated: the present species (*C. viridis*) was timed to strike at 7¼ feet per second. Note terminal caudal 'rattle' (see also Fig. 369, p. 534). (From a flashlight photograph by Van Riper.)

venomous Opisthoglypha, with one or two enlarged grooved poison fangs); Micruridæ = Elapidæ (sometimes thought to be Colubridæ and including the venomous cobras, true coral snakes, mambas, kraits, and the Australian black and tiger snakes, death-'adder', and many others); Hydrophidæ (venomous sea-snakes with valvular nostrils and vertically compressed, rudder-like tails); and Viperidæ (venomous vipers or true adders, and also rattlesnakes, with poison fangs in mobile maxillary bones which allow the teeth to swing, and lie parallel with the roof of the buccal cavity when not in use).

The affinities of the different families of snakes are not sufficiently well known to justify segregating them in larger groups of super-familial rank. The rattlesnakes are sometimes accorded sub-family rank (Crotalinæ), and the pythons are often separated from the boas as the Pythoninæ.

SUB-CLASS ARCHOSAURIA

The members of this group are diapsids (p. 484) without inter-parietal, tabular bones, or a parietal foramen. They are probably all descendants of Thecondontia (see below). The archosaurians form an assembly of reptiles which differ widely from the lepidosaurian Eosuchia, Rhynchocephalia, and Squamata already considered (p. 495). Some were bipedal and exhibited correspondingly striking modifications in the limb girdles. The hind legs were longer, and more powerful, than the others and were slung vertically below the body. The palatal teeth were lost in all but a few primitive forms. Some forms became toothless with the adoption of an almost certainly horny beak. There was a vacuity on the outside of the lower jaw between dentary, subangular and angular, and almost always an antorbital vacuity in front of the orbit.

Of this great and widely varying assembly of reptiles only the Crocodilia and the birds survive today. The osteology of modern crocodiles, together with Jurassic bones, leaves no doubt as to their relationships (p. 461).

Order Thecodontia

The thecodonts of the sub-order Pseudosuchia (e.g. *Ornithosuchus*, *Euparkeria*) arose in the Triassic. They were small carnivorous reptiles possessed of long, slim skulls and sharp teeth in sockets along the jaw-edges. The hind-legs were the longer pair, and possibly indicated the dawn of bipedal gait. Many pseudosuchians possessed a dorsal protection consisting of rows of curious bony plates (e.g. *Aëtosaurus*).

The Triassic thecodonts of the sub-order Phytosauria (e.g. *Phytosaurus*, *Mystriosuchus*) are of special interest in that they had become aquatic, and developed, before the true crocodiles evolved, many features characteristic of that group to-day. This convergent evolution is illustrated by the elongated skull, the formidable array of stabbing and holding teeth, and the general 'crocodilian' form. The external nostrils were sometimes set above the skull level, enabling the animal to breathe with nearly all of the body submerged, but, unlike in Crocodilia, they were posteriorly placed near the eyes.

After flourishing briefly, the phytosaurs were exterminated before the beginning of the Jurassic coincident with, and possibly in consequence of, the rise of the Crocodilia, a strikingly successful collateral amphibious line.

Order Crocodilia (Loricata)

The amphibious crocodiles, alligators, and their allies are the largest living reptiles and the only remnants of a once-widespread archosaurian stock that survived the Mesozoic. They seemed to be descended from Triassic thecodonts and, in fact, preserve a few primitive features relatively unchanged. Reptiles that were probably crocodiles have been found in Triassic deposits (Protosuchia) and unmistakable crocodiles, representing various side-lines, were common in the Cretaceous. The sub-order Eusuchia, in which modern forms (Fig. 333) are placed, dates from this period (p. 3).

The general features of modern Crocodilia are as follows : The dorsal surface, or both dorsal and ventral surfaces, are covered with rows of sculptured bony scutes. Epidermal scales are also present. The vertebral centra are either amphicœlous, flat at each end, or procœlous. The first caudal vertebra is unique in being convex at each end. The anterior thoracic vertebræ have elongated and bifid transverse processes, and to this transverse process the capitulum and tuberculum of the rib are both attached. The sacrum consists of two vertebræ. The ribs are bifid at their vertebral ends. The quadrate is immovable. There is a substantial lagena. The tympanic membrane is protected by two scaly flaps which are operated by special muscles and close the external meatus when the reptile dives. There is a

FIG. 333.—Sub-class **Archosauria,** Order **Crocodilia,** Sub-order **Eusuchia,** Family **Crocodilidæ.** *Crocodylus.* The Asiatic Marsh or Mugger Crocodile (*C. palustris*) in characteristic basking pose with jaws agape. Essentially freshwater, it also inhabits salt lagoons (in Ceylon). Growing to a length of 13 feet, it lives on fish and occasionally birds and small animals, only rarely attacking Man. It is said to be capable of æstivation. From fifteen to twenty eggs are buried in sandbanks and hatch in about fifty days. The newly emergent young are about 10 inches long and are at first relatively defenceless. (From a photograph by Lansler.)

complicated pressure-equalising Eustachian system. A sternum and abdominal ribs are present. The pelvis has the peculiarity of having the pubis excluded from the acetabulum. The limbs are adapted for walking and swimming. The teeth are lodged in sockets. The external nostrils occur on eminences at the end of the snout. These are opened by a longitudinal dilator muscle and closed by a constrictor muscle which completely encircles the dilator and squeezes it against the back of the nostril, closing the aperture during submersion. The fibres of both muscles are unstriped and innervated from the sympathetic system (Bellairs and Shute).

A horizontal partition, the secondary palate, is developed by shelves which grow out from the maxillæ, palatines, and, in the later crocodiles, the pterygoids. Thus the internal nares open into the throat (Fig. 138, p. 89). In life they are covered by a fleshy valve formed by two elements. The first is a muscular flap of tissue which projects downwards from the palate immediately anterior to the internal nostrils. The second is a flap-like extension of the tongue which is supported by a hyoid process. When in apposition, the two elements form a valve which seals the internal nares and enables the animal to breathe, with jaws open beneath the surface, so long as the tip of the nose is exposed to the air. This power to breathe through the relatively restricted surfaced part of the animal enables it to lurk almost completely hidden and to seize unsuspecting prey. Further, a crocodile can submerge with its jaws holding struggling prey without being in danger of flooding its nose or lungs.

The Salt-water or Estuarine Crocodile (*Crocodylus porosus*), common in the north-west Pacific, India, and Southern China, is especially deadly to Man. It grows to a length of 25 feet, and like other species, has a remarkable facility for suddenly thrusting the anterior third of its body swiftly up out of the water to seize an incautious man or beast.

The lungs of crocodiles are relatively complex. Further, the ventricle of the heart is completely divided in recent forms, but there are only two aortic arches. The pulmonary artery and left aortic arch come from the *right* ventricle into which venous blood flows from the cavals and right auricle. The right aortic arch arises from the *left* ventricle. The two aortæ are applied together and twisted ; but no mixing of blood occurs through a joint opening, the foramen of Panizzi (White). (We will see later that the pulmonary and systemic systems of birds have become completely separated by the abortion of the left arch (p. 589).)

The opening of the cloaca is elongated in the direction of the long axis of the body. There is a median erectile penis grooved for the passage of semen. A clitoris occurs in the female.

This order includes among living forms the true crocodiles, the gharials, as well as the alligators and caimans. Many extinct families have been recognised.

In some countries there is considerable, and often acrimonious, dispute as to whether the local animals are crocodiles (Fig. 333) or alligators. A key for generic identification (after Watson), based on characters of the head and skull, is given below.

I. Snout very long and slender ; the halves of the lower jaw fused in front as far back as the 15th tooth.

    (a) 27–29 teeth on each side of the upper jaw. *Gavialis* (the gharials of N. India).

    (b) 20–21 teeth on each side of the upper jaw. *Tomistoma* (the false gharials of Borneo and Sumatra).

II. Snout triangular or rounded; the halves of the lower jaw not fused farther back than the eighth tooth.

> (a) The fourth tooth of the lower jaw fits into a notch in the side of the upper jaw.   Crocodiles.
>
>> (1) Nasal bones dividing the nasal aperture into two.   *Crocodylus* (Africa to south China, northern Australia, New Guinea, and western Pacific; southern United States to Venezuela and Ecuador).
>> (2) Nasal bones not dividing the nasal aperture; snout turned up in front.   *Osteolæmus* (W. Africa).
>> (3) Nasal bones not dividing the nasal aperture; snout not turned up.   *Osteoblepharon* (Congo).
>
> (b) The fourth tooth of the lower jaw fits into a pit in the upper jaw. Alligators.
>
>> (1) Nasal bones dividing the nasal aperture.   *Alligator* (southern United States and south China).
>> (2) Nasal bones not dividing the nasal aperture.   *Caiman* (tropical South America).

Along with the tendency to assert that any dangerous crocodilian is a 'gator', there is an equally ridiculous belief among 'practical men' that in crocodiles the upper, and not the lower, jaw is hinged on the cranium.

As regards size, only the Salt-water (see above) American (*C. aculus*), Orinoco (*C. intermedius*), and Indian Gavial (*Gavialis gangeticus*) have been proved to exceed 20 feet.   The biggest Alligator (*Alligator mississippiensis*) is about 20 feet long, yet is harmless.   The Nilotic Crocodile (*C. niloticus*), like *C. porosus*, is known to kill Man.   The biggest scientifically recorded Nilotic Crocodile was only 16 feet long but more massive examples have undoubtedly been shot by hunters.   An American Alligator has lived to the age of fifty-six years.

ORDER PTEROSAURIA (PTERODACTYLA)

The Pterosauria were toothed and tailed flying reptiles in which the skeleton was modified in a manner analogous to that of the birds.   In some later forms the teeth were absent and seem to have been replaced by a beak. The bones were thin, light, pneumatic and cross-strutted like those of many birds (see Fig. 387, p. 572).   The fore-limb became a wing in which the fourth finger was greatly elongated and supported a membranous patagium.   The first three fingers were small and clawed, and the fifth was absent.   The carpus was reduced, but had a spur-like sesamoid bone added to it.   Though the sternum was large, keeled, and well ossified, clavicles and interclavicle were absent.   The pelvis had pubic bones which joined one another.   The hind-limbs were pentadactyle and rather weak, the fibula being reduced or absent. The skull was pointed and elongated, sometimes to an exaggerated degree. Brain-casts take a generally similar form to those of birds : the cerebellum was well-developed and the paired anterior parts associated with olfaction seem to have been reduced as in flying animals in general. The external nares were placed far back. The antorbital vacuity was large, and the eyes bordered with sclerotic plates. There was no parietal foramen. The head was supported at a right angle on a long neck of eight or nine procœlous vertebræ.

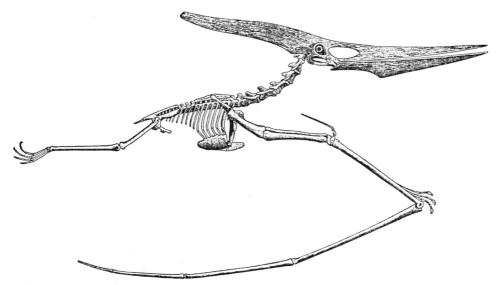

FIG. 334.—Sub-class **Archosauria,** Order **Pterosauria,** Sub-order **Pterodactyloidea,** Family **Pteranodontidæ.** *Pteranodon.* A toothless giant of the Cretaceous, with a wingspan of up to 27 feet (see also Fig. 330, p. 493). On the other hand, *Pterodactylus* and certain other genera were little bigger than sparrows. For a member of the second sub-order (Rhamphorhynchoidea) see Fig. 414, p. 599. (From Romer, after Eaton.)

There has been no general agreement concerning the origin of flight (p. 602). It has been suggested that these animals probably first volplaned from eminences or, on the other hand, may have made gliding leaps while running at speed on their powerful hind-legs. The spade-like sternum and pectoral girdles, though substantial, certainly do not convey the suggestion of a musculature sufficiently powerful to support flight, as developed in birds, or even the bats. It is probable that the pterosaurs were essentially gliders, and it is not impossible that many were marine animals which used air-currents to skim over the waves in a manner similar to that of the petrels. Their general structure makes it appear that they would have the greatest difficulty in becoming airborne after landing, but that they could hang efficiently to cliffs or trees by means of their fingers (Fig. 334), or perhaps upside down, like bats, by their toes.

The wing-membranes were supported essentially by one hugely elongated finger (Fig. 330). This suggests that they could not have existed efficiently among trees, for, if its poorly supported membrane were badly torn, a pterosaur would be unable to fly. A bird, on the other hand, can be severely battered and lose many feathers without being grounded; and the membranes of a bat, supported by several fingers, can be holed or even torn and yet the animal still can fly. Some pterosaurs (e.g. *Pteranodon*) had a wing-span of nearly 27 feet; others (e.g. *Pterodactylus*) were little larger than canaries. It is difficult to believe that these flying reptiles were not homœothermous to a fairly considerable degree, but in any case they faded, possibly as a result of competition with the emergent true birds, at the end of the Mesozoic.

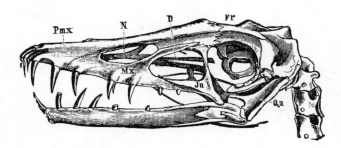

FIG. 335.—**Rhamphorhynchoidea: Skull and dentition.** *Scaphognathus.* *D.* pre-orbital aperture; *Fr.* frontal; *Ju.* jugal; *Mx.* maxilla; *N.* nasal opening; *Pmx.* premaxilla; *Qu.* quadrate. (After Zittel.)

The group flourished during the Jurassic and Cretaceous. There were two sub-orders: Rhamphorhynchoidea and Pterodactyloidea.

The Rhamphorhynchoidea were characterised by a long tail which was, in some species at least, terminally dilated by free caudal ribs; and by the possession of a fifth toe on the hind foot (examples: *Rhamphorhynchus* (Fig. 414, p. 599), *Dimorphodon*).

The Pterodactyloidea had an extremely reduced tail, no cervical ribs, and an incomplete fifth toe. Some forms were edentulous. Examples were: *Pterodactylus*, *Scaphognathus* (Fig. 335); *Pteranodon*, a toothless form with a curious balancing (or steering) backward prolongation of the head (Figs. 330, 334) and *Ornithodesmus*.

DINOSAURS

Among the archosaurians were also the fantastic Mesozoic creatures sometimes referred to as the 'Order' Dinosauria. These are readily divisible by a series of clearly marked characters into two groups, each of which ranks as an order. These are the Saurischia and the Ornithischia (Fig. 336).

Dinosaurs are often thought exclusively as immense animals, but some were no bigger than a hen. In each order existed both large and small reptiles. The biggest were the most massive animals ever to exist on land: the bulk of the largest dinosaurs has been exceeded only by the biggest modern whales. Both dinosaur groups showed great variation and extreme specialisation in many respects.

ORDER SAURISCHIA

Saurischians possessed a triradiate pelvis (broadly similar to that of the ancestral thecodonts) which was basically distinct from the bird-like arrangement (Fig. 337) that arose in the Ornithischia (p. 507). In the skull there

FIG. 336.—Sub-class **Archosauria:** (Orders **Saurischia** and **Ornithischia**). Left: *Tyrannosaurus*, a carnivorous saurischian from the North America Cretaceous which was about 18 feet high and some 50 feet long. Right: *Iguanodon*, a herbivorous ornithischian of the European Cretaceous which reached a height of about 14 feet. The two primary dinosaur stocks are widely divergent, a fundamental differentiating character being the structure of the pelvis (Fig. 337). Saurischians were primitively carnivorous, although some became quadrupedal and herbivorous (Fig. 339). Ornithischians were primarily herbivorous, and remained so until their extinction. Some became armoured quadrupeds in the Cretaceous. Other divergent archosaurian stocks are the pterosaurs (Fig. 334), crocodiles (Fig. 333), and birds (Fig. 414, p. 599). (Partly after various authors.)

were two, or one, antorbital vacuities, which were often very large. Teeth were present on the premaxillæ. There existed two saurischian sub-orders— the Theropoda and Sauropoda.

SUB-ORDER THEROPODA

Included in this group were the earliest true dinosaurs. Appearing in the Triassic, these were relatively small, slender, hollow-boned reptiles which (including the elongated tail) reached a length of not more than 10 feet. Ancestral theropods (e.g. *Ornitholestes*) were long-necked and bipedal, with the tail counterbalancing the body. The hands and small fore-limbs were used in

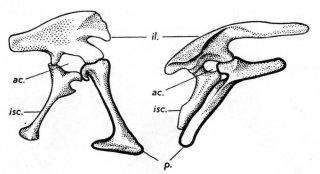

FIG. 337.—**Dinosaurs: Pelvic structure.** *Left:* Typical reptilian triradiate hip girdle of Saurischia. *Right:* Typical tetraradiate, bird-like, girdle of Ornithischia. *ac.* acetabulum; *il.* ilium; *isc.* ischium; *p.* pubis.

food-gathering: they were carnivorous, with gaping jaws and many sharp teeth.

From the above may have developed the *ornithominid* ostrich-dinosaurs (e.g. *Struthiomimus*) which appeared in the late Cretaceous. These swift, bipedal reptiles retained the hollow bone structure. They had enlarged fore-

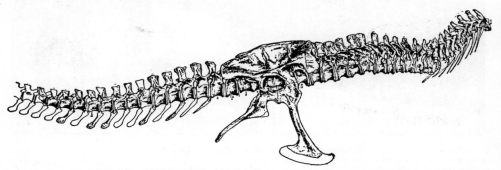

FIG. 338.—**Saurischia: Axial skeleton.** Vertebral column and pelvis of *Tyrannosaurus*. The massive vertebral column, pivoted at the open acetabula, was slung between the opposite halves of the pelvis. In the sitting pose the main weight (total up to 20 tons) was probably transmitted through the strong pubic column and its expanded 'shoe'. The cervical vertebræ are shortened, crowded, and curved upward, and so shorten the adverse leverage against the pelvis in carrying the huge head (Fig. 336). (From Gregory, after Osborn.)

limbs, but the reduction in both number and size of teeth, and the development of both jaws into a superficially beak-like structure, suggest a change to a less restricted diet.

Meanwhile there arose collaterally the great carnosaurian dinosaurs—big-headed, with wide gaping jaws equipped with long, stabbing, and tearing teeth which were sometimes recurved. These (e.g. *Tyrannosaurus*) (Fig. 338) finally reached a length of about 50 feet, stood perhaps 20 feet high, and fed on contemporary herbivorous dinosaurs. The disproportionally great size of the head (more than 4 feet long) was offset by the development in the skull of a remarkable fenestration which reduced weight and yet still provided anchorage for the powerful masticatory musculature essential to the animals' feeding habits. The carnosaurian neck was short, and the fore-limbs abbreviated and relatively minute. Those of *Gorgosaurus* (a reptile about 30 feet long) were unable to reach the mouth and were reduced to two digits that were probably useless for dealing with prey. The body was bulky and the tail elongated and of many vertebræ. The bones of the hind-legs were massive and obviously able to support several tons, and supplementary sacral vertebræ were attached to the pelvic girdle. These animals were extinguished at the end of the Cretaceous, possibly owing to the disappearance of their large herbivorous prey.

Meanwhile, yet another therapod group arose during the Triassic (e.g. *Yaleosaurus*, *Plateosaurus*) and ultimately, it is believed, gave rise to the next group.

SUB-ORDER SAUROPODA

These reptiles (e.g. *Apatosaurus*, *Diplodocus*, *Brachiosaurus* (Fig. 339)) were probably the largest and heaviest of all land animals. They grew to a length of more than 80 feet and weighed probably as much as 50 tons. The stock arose in the Jurassic. The sauropods were quadrupedal and herbivorous. They had small skulls and teeth, weak jaws, and elongated necks and tails. The brain was inordinately small; it would seem that the biggest dinosaur had a brain only 6 inches long. Spinal enlargements for the relay of impulses occurred often in the brachial region (between the shoulders) and always in the sacral region. The latter centre was many times bigger than the brain (see also Fig. 342). In these dinosaurs, too, temporal fenestræ lightened the cranium. In addition, the huge dorsal vertebræ were made less heavy by cavernous hollows in both centra and arches. These vertebræ were also produced into long spines to which supporting ligaments and tendons were presumably attached. The limb-bones were stout and non-pneumatic, but despite their strength there is much reason to believe that the biggest sauropods could not support their tremendous bulk on dry land.

It seems probable that the sauropods were swamp-feeders (Fig. 339). Little is known of their precise mode of grazing, but it is obvious that they needed a constant and tremendous harvest of lush pasture to support their prodigious bulk. They must have been highly vulnerable to any widespread climatic change towards aridity.

ORDER ORNITHISCHIA

The 'bird-like' dinosaurs possessed a pelvis (essentially like that retained in modern birds (p. 578)) in which the pubis lay parallel with an extended ischium

(Fig. 337). In the skull the antorbital vacuities were always small, and sometimes obliterated. One of their most noticeable characters was the possession of a ' predentary ' bone in the mandible that may have supported a horny beak. As a result, the teeth on the premaxillæ and on the front of the lower law

FIG. 339.—**Dinosaurs: Respiratory adaptations in unrelated bottom-feeders.** *Left:* The ornithopod *Parasaurolophus* (Family Hadrosauridæ = Trachodontidæ) of the North American Cretaceous. The grotesque crest, formed by an extension of nasal and premaxillary bones, contained an air-chamber of considerable capacity, perhaps enabling the animal to keep its head submerged for prolonged periods of bottom grazing. *Right:* The sauropod *Brachiosaurus* (Family Brachiosauridæ) of the African and North American Jurassic. An ally of *Apatosaurus* (= *Brontosaurus*), this is perhaps the biggest terrestrial animal that ever lived, reaching a probable bulk of some 50 tons. The nostrils had shifted to an eminence at the top of the head, enabling the animal to breathe with only a small portion of its bulk exposed. (Partly after Colbert.)

became suppressed. All the Ornithischia were herbivorous and they fall into the four following sub-orders:

SUB-ORDER ORNITHOPODA

These were bipedal, digitigrade forms with a complete and slender postpubis, and a small antorbital vacuity. Abundant in the Upper Jurassic and Lower Cretaceous (e.g. *Camptosaurus, Iguanodon* (Figs. 336, 340)) they grew to at least 30 feet long. An edentulous beak and broad (sometimes spatulate) teeth occurred in the very early types, suggesting that the ornithopods were herbivorous almost from their beginnings (Fig. 341). Despite their name, the early ornithopod foot was not nearly as bird-like (in the passerine sense) as that of the theropods (p. 505)—their feet had four toes, anteriorly directed. Another relatively primitive ornithopod was the Upper Cretaceous *Hypsilophodon*, a small, possibly partly arboreal, dinosaur about as big as a wallaby and superficially not unlike one in certain of its features.

The primitive ornithopods gave rise to two far more specialised types—the large hadrosaurs, or 'duck-billed dinosaurs', were one of these. The hadrosaurs became exceedingly common in the Upper Cretaceous by means of efficient aquatic specialisation. They are well known : many excellently

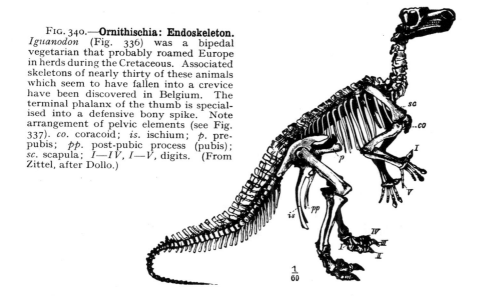

FIG. 340.—**Ornithischia: Endoskeleton.** *Iguanodon* (Fig. 336) was a bipedal vegetarian that probably roamed Europe in herds during the Cretaceous. Associated skeletons of nearly thirty of these animals which seem to have fallen into a crevice have been discovered in Belgium. The terminal phalanx of the thumb is specialised into a defensive bony spike. Note arrangement of pelvic elements (see Fig. 337). *co.* coracoid; *is.* ischium; *p.* pre-pubis; *pp.* post-pubic process (pubis); *sc.* scapula; *I—IV, I—V*, digits. (From Zittel, after Dollo.)

preserved remains have been found, including even 'mummies' in which petrified skin and foot-webbing is preserved. The hadrosaurs (e.g. *Anatosaurus = Trachodon, Edmontosaurus*) had long, toothless beaks, posteriorly placed nostrils, and crowded in the jaws, as many as 2,000 small, grinding teeth arranged in parallel rows. Certain genera (e.g. *Corythosaurus, Kritosaurus*) developed peculiar bony crests by alteration of the premaxillary and nasal elements above the nasal region.

The great spatulate beak and the enormous battery of grinding teeth suggest that the hadrosaurs obtained their food by grovelling in the mud for vegetable material. In several species it has been possible to follow the internal air passages from the external nostrils, and there are indications that they passed in a loop through the grotesque crest before reaching the internal nares. The by no means unplausible suggestion has been made that the dome-like osseous 'combs' may have been pneumatic in function and allowed their possessors to grovel underwater, and so exploit a special niche—the swamp-bottom—more fully than would be otherwise possible.

The troödonts, another specialised and aberrant, ornithopod stem, were, in wide distinction from the hadrosaurs, probably exclusively dry-land forms (e.g. *Troödon* of the Upper Cretaceous). They had an axial skeleton very similar to that of the camptosaurs (p. 508), but their skulls were extremely specialised in the possession of a solid dome of bone (much of it derived from the frontals and parietals) often produced into knobs and spikes. The most likely explanation for this bizarre armoury so far offered is that it may have been used as defensive, armoured battering ram against the often far larger,

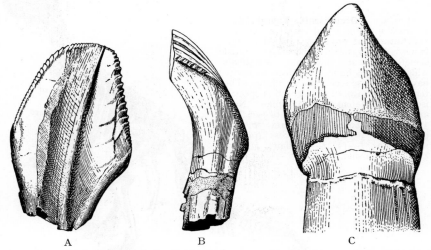

FIG. 341.—**Dinosaurs: Dentition of unrelated herbivores.** *A*, inner aspect of a crown from right lower jaw and *B*, hinder aspect of tooth from left lower jaw, of *Iguanodon*, an ornithopod (see Fig. 336). *C*, Tooth of *Cetiosaurus*, a sauropod (see Fig. 339). All natural size. (From B. M. (N.H.) Catalogue.)

contemporary, predatory dinosaurs with which the non-aquatic troödons had to contend. Perhaps it deterred aggressors with a sudden, intimidating charge such as is employed by the modern rhinoceroses.

SUB-ORDER STEGOSAURIA

The stegosaurs (e.g. *Stegosaurus* (Fig. 342)) were slow-moving, essentially Jurassic (including Liassic), reptiles which grew to a length of about 25 feet. They were quadrupedal, but the fore-limbs were the shorter pair. The skull was small, and the brain tiny and considerably smaller (as with the Sauropoda, p. 507), than the lumbar spinal enlargement. The back, neck, body, and tail were protected by a double series of huge, flattened, generally triangular and vertical spines and plates, particularly above the lumbar and pelvic regions. The tails of these extraordinary monsters were armed with two pairs of formidable spikes, serially and sub-terminally placed, apparently converting the appendage into a damaging, lashing weapon which may have protected the unarmoured flanks.

Other stegosaurs were *Scelidosaurus* of the early Jurassic, and *Kentrurosaurus* which flourished just before the Cretaceous.

SUB-ORDER ANKYLOSAURIA

These, too, were heavily armoured but quite differently and more extensively so ; in fact, only the chelonians (p. 486) have developed a more complete protection. They (e.g. *Ankylosaurus*, *Nodosaurus*) lived in the Cretaceous,

FIG. 342.—**Dinosaurs: Brain, spinal enlargements and hypophysis.** In the herbivorous ornithopod *Stegosaurus* the brain (arrowed) was small compared with the brachial enlargement of the cord and a mere 1/20th of the bulk of the sacral enlargement. The latter was involved in the control of the hind-limbs and the powerful armoured tail, which probably lashed defensively at contemporary carnivorous Sauropoda. The inset shows the relatively large size of the pituitary body (see p. 149) in relation to the brain of a troödont (Ornithopoda). Although *Stegosaurus* and similar types could exist with a brain about the size of that of a kitten, the pituitary, concerned with manifold body functions including growth, was large. (Modified after Colbert.)

and were slow-moving quadrupeds with short, broad skulls (with closed temporal regions) in which the basic elements were reinforced with an additional plating of polygonal bones. The dorsal surface of the body was protected by a mosaic of small osseous plates and the short, stout legs were guarded by projecting shoulder spines. The tail, too, was surrounded by bony rings, and sometimes armed with elongated spines. The analogy between these animals and the early, heavy, tanks of the First World War is inescapable.

SUB-ORDER CERATOPSIA

By the end of the Cretaceous, the so-called dinosaurian age was drawing to a close with the development of one of the most interesting groups of all, the ceratopsians or horned dinosaurs. These were quadrupedal forms with huge skulls, bony horns, and a great protective, sometimes solid, sometimes fenestrated, mantle of bone formed by grotesque prolongations of the parietals and squamosals over the neck. Among these was *Triceratops*, which grew to a length of about 20 feet. The skull may have accounted for almost one-third

FIG. 343.—Sub-class **Synapsida**, Order **Pelycosauria**, Family **Sphenacodontidæ**. *Dimetrodon.* Pelycosaurs represent a very early stage in the development of the mammal-like reptilian trend. *Dimetrodon* was about 11 feet long, and was perhaps one of the commonest Permian carnivores. The function of the grotesque 'sail' (supported by elongated vertebral spines, Fig. 344) is obscure. It probably occurred in both sexes. There have been suggestions that it was a thermoregulator; others have variously considered it to be 'protective', or a warning, device or merely 'a heredity maladjustment'. The persistence of the sail in two divergent, successful stocks argues in favour of function. The dagger-like anterior teeth were perhaps adapted to a fish diet. *Edaphosaurus*, about the same size, had an armoury of stubby teeth both in the jaws and on the flat upper and lower masticatory plates that lay within its buccal cavity.

of the total length of the animal. It was sometimes surmounted by paired horns (of a character curiously akin to that of to-day's ungulates, p. 841) and, in addition, a median nasal horn.

These animals were abundant about 60 million years ago when, excluding only the stegosaurs, each major dinosaur group still survived. All, however, apparently disappeared with a startling abruptness, geologically speaking, by the beginning of the succeeding Tertiary (p. 3).

SUB-CLASS SYNAPSIDA

The Synapsida were widespread, often mammal-like reptiles with a single lateral temporal vacuity primitively lying below the postorbital and squamosal. The brain-case was high and, as a result of the broad supraoccipital, the inner ear was placed low down. The teeth in the more advanced forms were usually heterodont. The lower jaw was flattened from side to side instead of being rounded in section, and, except in the most primitive members, the dentary was relatively large. There were always a coracoid and pre-coracoid in the shoulder-girdle. This condition has persisted in monotremes (p. 699), but in other extant mammals only the posterior of the two coracoids remains.

The synapsids dominated the land fauna of the Permian and much of the Trias. They are found abundantly in some deposits in North America and South Africa, and are known also from South America, East Africa, India, Central Asia, Russia, and Europe. Remains of the earlier types (pelycosaurs) (Fig. 343) occur mainly in America, and those of the more advanced forms (therapsids) in South Africa and Russia.

The group is especially interesting because it shows the various stages by which the mammals evolved from the earliest reptiles.

ORDER PELYCOSAURIA

The pelycosaurs, the most primitive members of the sub-class, occurred in the Upper Carboniferous, and especially in the Lower Permian. Some members, such as the small, long-tailed *Varanosaurus*, differed from the captorhinomorph cotylosaurs only in having the temporal vacuity. Others had become specialised. *Dimetrodon* had enormously elongated neural spines to its vertebræ (Fig. 344). These are believed to have been connected by skin and to have formed a huge 'sail'. *Dimetrodon* was more than 10 feet long and had dagger-shaped stabbing and holding teeth. Other pelycosaurs were adapted to a vegetarian diet (e.g. *Edaphosaurus*). The pelycosaurs, like the cotylosaurs, had relatively short limbs and a sprawling gait, but the remaining orders carried the body higher and were probably much more active.

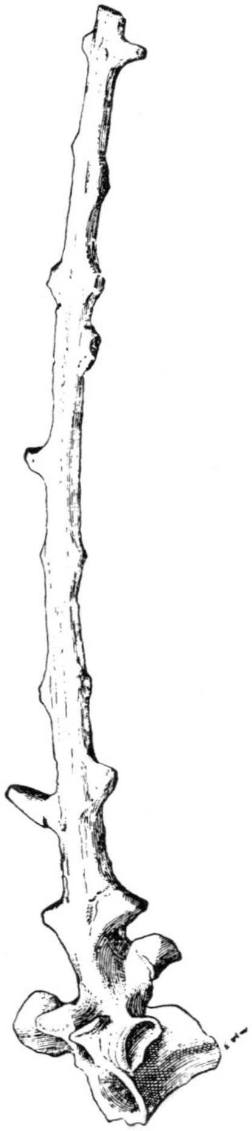

FIG. 344.—**Pelycosauria: Vertebral spine.** One of a series of 'sail' supports in *Edaphosaurus*. The short transverse 'yards' (of which only dorsal remnants remain) were lacking in *Dimetrodon* (Fig. 343). About one quarter natural size. (From B.M. (N.H.) Catalogue.)

ORDER THERAPSIDA

The therapsids were a varied and successful group of reptiles which have been claimed almost to bridge the 'entire evolutionary gap between a primitive reptile and a mammal' (Romer). The pelycosaurs showed relatively little advancement from the cotylosaurs (see above), but among the present group many mammalian diagnostic features (as far as hard parts are concerned) are present, even though the elements of the lower jaw had not been reduced to a typical dentary (p. 652). The teeth, however, were diversified into incisors, canines, and, in the later types, multi-cusped cheek teeth. In advanced types

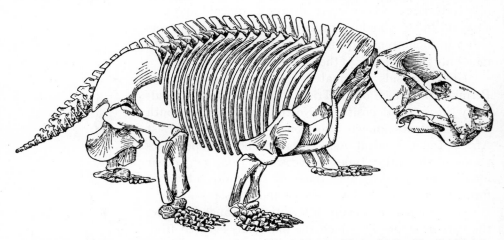

FIG. 345.—Sub-class **Synapsida,** Order **Therapsida,** Sub-order **Dicynodontia,** Family **Dicyno-dontidæ.** *Kannemeyeria.* A Lower Jurassic survivor of the dicynodont trend that appeared in the Middle Permian and became extremely widespread and plentiful at the end of the Palæozoic. In general, these creatures may have been herbivorous swamp-dwellers. *Kannemeyeria* was about 6 feet long. Others were much bigger (skull 3 feet long) and many were very small (skulls few inches big). This group (and the Pelycosaurs) represent two of the several mammal-like trends that appeared early, yet were extinguished. (After Pearson.)

the occipital condyle had become double. The pineal eye had disappeared, the temporal opening had grown bigger, and the quadrate and quadratojugal had been reduced. A secondary palate was sometimes present. The limbs in the higher forms were already suggestive of the mammalian pattern of the future. As will be seen below, there were other features that suggest that the mammals were derived from carnivorous reptiles of the therapsid stem.

Included among the order are the sub-orders Dicynodontia and Theriodontia. The former were for a time the most successful synapsid order, being found in extraordinary abundance from the Middle Permian to the Lower Trias and surviving until the Middle Trias. Typically they were of a heavy build, varying from 1 to 7 or 8 feet in length (Fig. 345). Their skull was very specialised, having huge temporal fossæ, T-shaped squamosals, and small quadrates. In the majority the dentition was reduced to a pair of canines (which were sometimes confined to the males) and the jaws were covered by a horny beak. The post-cranial skeleton was very mammal-like though clumsy. There was an acromion process on the scapula, the precoracoid was excluded from the glenoid cavity (Fig. 346), the ilium was considerably elongated, and the number of phalanges had been reduced from the reptilian number of 2 3 4 5 3 to the mammalian 2 3 3 3 3. *Dicynodon* was the commonest genus with about seventy species. *Lystrosaurus*, which occurred abundantly in the Lower Trias, had the snout elongated and turned down and was probably aquatic. Several genera, such as *Endothiodon* and *Esoterodon*, kept post-canine teeth and one form, *Eumantellia*, had incisors.

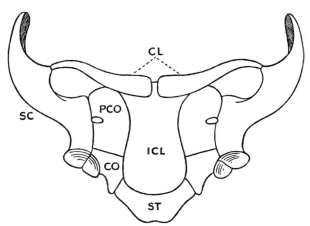

FIG. 346.—**Dicynodontia: Pectoral girdle.** Ventral aspect. *CL.* clavicle; *CO.* coracoid; *ICL.* interclavicle; *PCO.* precoracoid; *SC.* scapula; *ST.* sternum.

The third sub-order, the Theriodontia, were almost certainly ancestral to the mammals, those of the cynodont group, in particular, approaching the mammalian organisation. They are found from the Middle Permian to the Upper Trias, and are known from Africa, South America, and Russia. The group showed considerable variation in size. Some forms were less than a foot in length; others were the size of a lion. The majority were carnivorous or insectivorous, but some of the later members may have been herbivorous.

The evolutionary changes of the theriodonts show the gradual appearance of those characters which are typical of the mammals. In the skull (Figs. 347 and 348) the temporal vacuity was enlarged by the reduction and loss of the postfrontals. A secondary palate was formed by the outgrowth of a shelf from the maxillæ and palatines. The basioccipital was reduced and paired exoccipital condyles were formed. Also, the epipterygoid (columella cranii) expanded to form the mammalian alisphenoid. In the lower jaw the dentary increased steadily in size until the post-dentary bones were very small and almost hidden in outer view. At the same time, a distinctly mammal-like coronoid process was developed. The teeth of the early members were simple, though there were enlarged canines, which in some of the big gorgonopsians resembled the tusks of sabre-tooths (Fig. 568, p. 796). The post-canine teeth of the later members became specialised in a variety of ways, and were often very

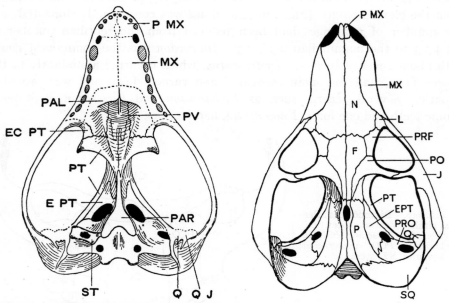

FIG. 347.—**Cynodontia: Skull.** *Thrinaxodon*, a Lower Triassic cynodont. *Left:* ventral, *Right:* dorsal view. *ECPT.* ectopterygoid; *EPT.* epipterygoid; *F.* frontal; *J.* jugal; *L.* lachrymal; *MX.* maxilla; *N.* nasal; *P.* parietal; *PAL.* palatine; *PAR.* parasphenoid; *PMX.* premaxilla; *PO.* postorbital; *PRF.* pre-frontal; *PRO.* pro-otic; *PT.* pterygoid; *PV.* vomer; *Q.* quadrate; *QJ.* quadrato-jugal; *ST.* stapes; *SQ.* squamosal. (After Parrington.)

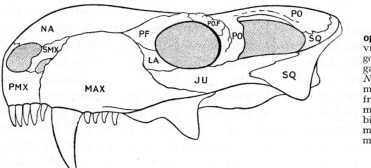

FIG. 348.—**Gorgonopsia: Skull.** Lateral view in a Permian gorgonopsid. *JU.* jugal; *LA.* lachrymal; *NA.* nasal; *MAX.* maxilla; *PF.* pre-frontal; *PMX.* pre-maxilla; *PO.* postorbital; *SMX.* septo-maxillary; *SQ.* squamosal.

mammal-like. The limb-girdles approached the mammalian condition in such characters as the formation of an acromion process on the scapula, the great expansion of the ilium, and the enlargement of the primitive pubic foramen to form the huge obturator foramen. The form of the limb-bones, too, approached the mammalian condition, and the number of phalanges in the feet was reduced to the mammalian number of 2 3 3 3 3 by the degeneration, and finally the loss, of one phalange in the third toe and two in the fourth.

FIG. 349.—Sub-class **Synapsida**, Order **Therapsida**, Sub-order **Theriodontia**, Infra-order **Gorgonopsia**, Family **Gorgonopsidæ.** *Lycænops.* Gorgonopsids were primitive carnivorous theriodonts that flourished as early as the Middle and Upper Permian and were already relatively mammal-like in appearance. (After Colbert.)

There were a number of different lines of evolution within the group, but those are not yet fully understood. The Permian Gorgonopsia (e.g. *Lycænops* (Fig. 349)) and Therocephalia (e.g. *Lycosaurus*) were on the whole more primitive anatomically than the (mainly) Triassic Cynodontia (Fig. 347) and bauriamorphs and may have been respectively ancestral to them.

The Upper Permian and Triassic Cyodontia (of the Theriodontia) were perhaps the most mammal-like of all, and interesting hypotheses, suggesting that they were already warm-blooded, hairy, and milk-producing, have been based on recently revealed structural details (see Watson). *Cynognathus* was a predaceous wolf-sized animal with large canines and cheek-teeth that bore accessory cusps: this dentition showed that the animal cut its food before swallowing. There was a secondary palate and an advancement towards the mammalian condition in anterior and posterior girdles and elsewhere.

ORDER ICTIDOSAURIA

The ictidosaurs (e.g. *Tritylodon, Bienotherium* (Fig. 350)) as a group ' closed the gap between mammals and reptiles ' (Colbert). They showed examples of the *mosaic evolution* already discussed in re-

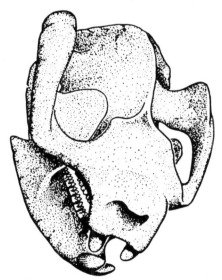

FIG. 350.—Sub-class **Synapsida**, Order **Ictidosauria**, Family **Tritylodontidæ.** *Bienotherium.* This Upper Triassic Chinese reptile had an unmistakably mammal-like cranium, jaws, and cusped dentition. The ictidosaurs, ranging from Triassic to the Middle Jurassic, appear to have been as intermediate between reptiles and mammals as were *Seymouria* (Fig. 286, p. 429), and *Archæopteryx* (Fig. 414, p. 599) between amphibians and reptiles, and reptiles and birds, respectively. Yet, like the above two 'mosaic' animals, the ictidosaurs could not possibly have been ancestral to the higher group whose characters they share. (After Colbert.)

lation to *Seymouria* (p. 427) and *Archæopteryx* (p. 600), but at the same time represented a specialised branch off the principal mammalian stem. They retained, though in a reduced condition, the typical reptilian quadrate and articular: the mammalian middle ear had not arisen. However, the temporal opening was large and confluent with the orbit, and in general the cranium, jaws, and dentition revealed an unmistakable trend towards a mammalian condition.

The ictidosaurs ranged from the Upper Triassic to the Middle Jurassic. The possibility has been suggested that the prototherians (p. 687) on the one hand, and the marsupials (p. 704) and the eutherians on the other, may have descended from separate, though collateral reptile stems.

GENERAL ORGANISATION OF RECENT REPTILIA

External Features.—In external form, as in some other respects, certain of the Lacertilia exhibit the least specialised condition to be observed among the living Reptilia. *Lacerta* is such a central type that the general account of that lizard (p. 462) applies in all the points of cardinal importance to a large proportion of the group. Modifications take place, however, in a variety of directions. The gape is generally wide and able to accommodate relatively large prey, but some lizards of specialised feeding habits have a small and atypical mouth. One such lizard is *Moloch horridus*, the Thorny Devil of Central Australia, which feeds on ants and has a small mouth placed beneath its remarkably ' thorny ' head. Some lizards possess erectile frills, and dorsal protuberances are common. The tail region is usually, as in the example, extremely long and tapering; but in some groups of lizards it is comparatively short and thick; and in others it is depressed and expanded into a leaf-like form. In the aboreal chamæleons (Fig. 351) the long and tapering tail is used as a prehensile organ, which is coiled around branches of trees and aids the animals in climbing. The flying-lizards (*Draco*) of the East Indies have an astonishing skeletal specialisation which enables them to make jumping glides from branch to branch. Ribs are laterally developed and adapted to the support of paired expansible membranes. Although *Draco* is called a ' flying-lizard ', it does not of course progress in the manner of a bird, bat, nor even a pterodactyl.

Among limbs, those of *Lacerta* are typical. In the chamæleons (Fig. 351) both fore- and hind-limbs become prehensile by a special modification in the arrangement, and mode of articulation, of the digits. The three innermost digits of the manus are joined together throughout their length by a web of skin, and the two outer members are similarly united. The two sets of digits are so articulated that they can be brought against one another with a grasping movement analogous to that of the foot of a parrot, or of the hand of Man. A similar arrangement prevails in the pes, the only difference being that the two innermost and three outermost digits are united. The lizards *Chlamydo-*

saurus and *Amphibolurus* have hind-limbs which enable them to run on their hind-feet with the forelegs entirely elevated from the ground. The tropical and sub-tropical geckos (Gekkota) are enabled by sucker-like discs on the ends of their toes to run readily over vertical or even overhanging smooth surfaces. These harmless, and indeed useful, little creatures can actually leap several

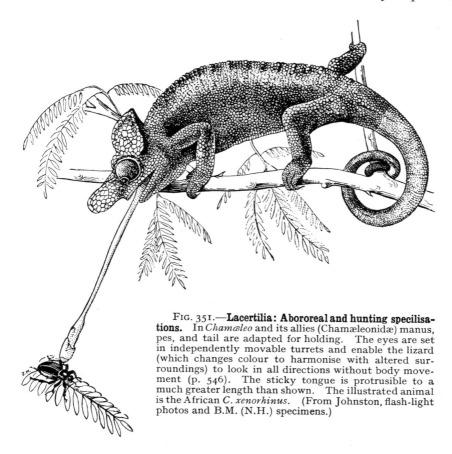

FIG. 351.—**Lacertilia: Abororeal and hunting specilisa-tions.** In *Chamœleo* and its allies (Chamæleonidæ) manus, pes, and tail are adapted for holding. The eyes are set in independently movable turrets and enable the lizard (which changes colour to harmonise with altered surroundings) to look in all directions without body movement (p. 546). The sticky tongue is protrusible to a much greater length than shown. The illustrated animal is the African *C. xenorhinus*. (From Johnston, flash-light photos and B.M. (N.H.) specimens.)

inches upside down, capture an insect on a ceiling, and still rarely fall to the floor.

On the other hand, in some groups of Lacertilia, such as the blind-'worm' (*Anguis*), limbs are entirely absent, or are represented merely by vestiges. Numerous intermediate gradations exist between these and forms (e.g *Lacerta*) with well-developed limbs. Limbless lizards (Fig. 352) bear a very close adaptive resemblance to snakes, not only in the absence of the limbs, but also in the general form of the body and the mode of locomotion. The largest living lizard, the Komodo Dragon (*Varanus*), reaches a length of 12 feet.

The body of a snake is elongated, narrow, and cylindrical, usually tapering towards the posterior end, and sometimes with, but more usually without, a constriction behind the head. In the absence of limbs, the beginning of the short caudal region is indicated only by the position of the cloacal opening. The fore-limbs are never represented even by vestiges, but in pythons and other snakes there are inconspicuous vestiges of hind-limbs in the form of small claw-like processes.

Lacking functional limbs, snakes move on land or in water by the movement of spinal column and muscles. This movement pushes the sinuous body horizontally against the resistant surrounding medium. Thus, most snakes can glide through a twisted glass tube, but not through a straight one of about their own diameter. A few thick-bodied snakes (*e.g.* boas, pythons, vipers)

Fig. 352.—**Lacertilia: Fossorial specialisations.** *Pygopus* and its allies (Pygopodidæ: the snake- or legless-lizards) live either in burrows or under rocks and vegetation. The body is serpentine. Fore-limbs have been lost and the hind-limbs reduced to scale-like vestiges. Some have lost the ear aperture and movable eyelids. The pupil is vertical (see Fig. 377, p. 547). About eighteen species, ranging up to 2 feet in length, occur in Australia and New Guinea. (After Brehm.)

sometimes progress slowly in a straight line essentially by means of contraction waves which pass along the costocutaneous musculature from head to tail. These specialised muscles are attached to the ventral scales which engage projections in the ground and so draw the animal along. The North American side-winders (*Crotalus*) and the Egyptian sand-vipers (*Cerastes*) move over loose sand by means of a series of horizontal double loops which engage the earth and propel the animal along sideways. One of the most interesting forms of reptilian progression is that of the various tropical and subtropical tree-snakes. These are thin and elongated, making for greater distribution of weight as they glide across leaves and twigs from one tree to another. The Asiatic *Chrysopelea* can ascend vertical walls and tree-trunks aided by laterally-keeled ventral scales which engage very tiny projections.

The thrusting serpentine movement of a frightened or angry snake gives a much greater impression of speed than is actually achieved. Few travel at more than four miles per hour. Meinertzhagen, however, reported that he 'timed' a speeding Black Mamba (*Dendroaspis angusticeps*) at 7 m.p.h.

The mouth of a snake is capable of being very widely opened by the free articulation of the lower jaw, and it is this which mainly distinguishes it from the snake-like lizard. Other points of distinction are the absence of movable eyelids in the snake and also the absence of a tympanum.

The largest living snakes are probably the Reticulated Python (*Python reticulatus*) of India and Malaya and the Anaconda (*Eunectes murinus*) of South America. The above python has been recorded to reach a length of 33 feet, but specimens more than 25 feet long are rare. Remarkable stories have been told of the alleged length of the Anaconda. This bulky boa is the heaviest of all snakes, but the biggest specimen yet recorded was 25 feet long, and weighed more than 300 lb. The biggest venomous snake is the Indo-Malayan King Cobra or Hamadryad (*Naia hannah*), which may grow to 18 feet. The Taipan (*Oxyuranus scutellatus*) of North Australia and Southern New Guinea is sometimes more than 10 feet long. Likewise, the giant South American pit-viper, the Bushmaster (*Lachesis muta* (Fig. 377)), and the green phase of the slender, semi-arboreal African Black or Green Mamba, both grow to about the same size. The longest sea-snakes (Hydrophidæ) grow to a length of 8 feet, which is scarcely long enough to have given rise to the repeated stories of sea-serpents (p. 494). Sea-snakes, exceedingly common in some tropical waters, are sometimes extremely poisonous. Some come ashore in sea-weed or bask on rocks but they cannot move efficiently out of water.

Sphenodon (= *Hatteria*), the New Zealand Tuatara (Fig. 331), the only living representative of the Rhynchocephalia, is a lizard-like reptile with a well-developed laterally-compressed tail, and pentadactyle extremities, very similar to those of a typical lizard. The upper surface is covered with small granular scales, and a crest of compressed spine-like scales runs along the middle of the dorsal surface. The lower surface is covered with transverse rows of large squarish plates (see also p 496.).

In the Chelonia (Fig. 327) the body is short and broad, enclosed in a hard armoured dorsal *carapace* and a ventral *plastron*. These are in most cases firmly united, apertures being left between them for the head and neck, the tail and the limbs. This armoury is formed by two components, firstly external horny scutes ('tortoise-shell' of turtles) which are modified scales and secondly curved underlying bony plates. The horny and bony elements do not coincide at their junctions, making for added strength. The neck is long and mobile ; the tail short. The limbs are fully developed though short. In some (land and fresh-water tortoises) they are provided each with five free digits terminating in curved horny claws. In the turtles the digits are closely united together, and the limb assumes the character of a 'flipper' or swimming-paddle. The cloacal aperture is longitudinal.

The Crocodilia (Fig. 333), the largest of living reptiles, have the trunk elongated and somewhat depressed, so that its breadth is much greater than its height.   The snout is prolonged, the neck short, the tail longer than the body and compressed laterally.   The limbs are relatively short and powerful, with five digits in the manus and four in the pes, those of the latter being partly or completely united by webs of skin.   The eyes are dorsally placed and the nostrils are situated near the end of the snout and capable of being closed by a sphincter muscle.   The cloacal aperture is a longitudinal slit.   The dorsal and ventral surfaces are covered with thick, squarish horny scales, often pitted or ridged, those of the dorsal surface of the tail developed into a longitudinal crest.

Integument and Exoskeleton.—Reptiles have no sweat-glands.   In the Chelonia there occur axillary inguinal scent-glands, but little is known of the function of their emanations.   The Kinosternidæ (musk-turtles) of North and Central America produce an especially pervasive odour and one species is known as the Stinkpot Terrapin (*Sternotherus odoratus*).   Crocodiles possess anal glands that give off a musky odour (into the cloaca) which is said to be significant in courtship.   Some reptiles are able to absorb water through their skin to some extent.   The scales of Squamata differ considerably in form and arrangement in different groups.   Sometimes they are smooth, sometimes sculptured or keeled.   Sometimes they are similar in character over all parts of the surface but usually there are specially developed scales—the *head-shields*—covering the upper surface of the head.   In the majority of snakes the ventral surface is covered with a row of large transversely elongated scales, the *ventral shields*.   In certain lizards (particularly the geckos) the scales are reduced and modified into the form of minute tubercles or granules.   In some lizards special developments of the scales occur in the form of large tubercles or spines.   Underlying the horny epidermal scales in some lizards (scincoids) are series of dermal bony plates.   In the integument of the geckos are numerous minute hard bodies which seem to be intermediate in character between cartilage and bone. The outer layers of the horny integument are non-nervous and non-vascular : they are dead, and gradually worn away (as are, for that matter, the outer cells of the human skin).   Keratin is continuously produced by cells in the deep epidermal layers just above the vascular dermis.   The keratinous cells may fall off piecemeal (as occurs whenever we wash our hands) or may slough off almost wholly or in segments, as when a snake discards its old skin.   The caudal rattle (Fig. 332) of the various American rattlesnakes (*Sistrurus, Crotalus*) arises as a succession of up to a dozen loose, unshed dermal constrictions: new-born snakes possess no rattle.   Its vibration, heard in some species at a distance of about 20 yards, may be a threat and warning device (see also p. 437).   In the snake-like amphisbænid lizards the scales are arranged in annular rings round the body and tail.

In addition to modification of the scales, the integument of the chamæleons is remarkable for the changes of colour which it undergoes. These changes are due to the presence in the dermis of pigment-cells which contract or expand under various influences. In chamæleons, the relatively quick changes in the chromatophores seem to be exclusively under the control of the autonomic nervous system. Nerve transection leads to a rapid darkening of the area previously innervated. The response in *Anolis* (which can change from bright green to dark brown) is more complex. In an illuminated bright container *Anolis* tends to become a vivid green, but goes brown in illuminated black surroundings. It can change from green to brown in from five to ten minutes; but the reverse change takes more than twice as long. Such quick changes do not occur in blinded animals, though there is evidence that a primary response operates extra-optically. There is experimental evidence that in several species hormones from the pituitary gland form an important intermediate link between exteroceptor organs and chromatophores. Hypophysectomised bright green *Anolis* cannot be changed to brown except by injections of pituitary extract. Transection of appropriate nerves, or even of the cord, does not inhibit colour responses. Further, skin-grafts quickly change in colour and likewise, the experimental exclusion of the blood supply from a part quickly results in its paling. Less conspicuous and rapid changes of colour take place in other lizards and snakes.

In the Chelonia, scales are confined to the head and neck, the limbs, and the tail. With the exception of the soft tortoises, and the Leathery Turtle (*Dermochelys*), both dorsal and ventral surfaces are covered by a system of large horny plates. A series of horny head-shields usually cover the dorsal surface of the head. Beneath the horny plates of the dorsal and ventral surfaces are the bony carapace and plastron, largely composed of dermal bones, but so intimately united with elements derived from the endoskeleton that the entire structure is best described in connection with the latter (p. 526). The curious arrangement of the bony plates, with their trinodal and equiangular seam junctions, is an interesting biological expression of the physical principal of conservation of border. Other biological examples are the shells of extinct eurypterids (Vol. I) and the comb-structure of honey-bees. The same principle is manifest in the directions taken by mud-cracks, and the hexagonal columns seen in basaltic lavas and other kinds of rocks, both volcanic and plutonic (D'Arcy Thompson).

In the Crocodilia the whole surface is covered with horny plates or scales, each usually marked with a pit-like depression about the centre, those on the dorsal surface being ridged longitudinally. Underlying each of these, which are of epidermal derivation, is a thick pad of dermal connective tissue which, in the case of the dorsal scales, is replaced by a bony scute. In the caimans (p. 502) thin scutes also occur under the ventral scales.

A periodical *ecdysis* or casting and renewal of the outer layers of the horny epidermis takes place in all the reptilia with the exception of the crocodiles. Sometimes this occurs in a fragmentary manner; but in snakes and many lizards the whole comes away as a continuous slough (see, however, p. 522).

Endoskeleton.—The vertebræ are always fully ossified. Among recent forms, the geckos and *Sphenodon* (Fig. 353) are exceptional in having the centra amphicœlous, with remnants of the notochord in the intercentral spaces. The rest of the recent groups for the most part have the centra procœlous. In many extinct forms, the neural arches were not directly attached to the centra by bone (*temnospondyly*): in recent forms there is a bony union (*Stereospondyli*) either through a suture or by fusion. Intercentra may be represented by intervertebral disks of fibrocartilage (Crocodilia) or by bony elements formed by ossification of the ventral portions of the disks (geckos, *Sphenodon*). In lizards in general, and in crocodiles, there are inferior processes (*hypapophyses*),

FIG. 353.—
Sphenodon:
Vertebra. The centrum is amphicœlous. (After Headley.)

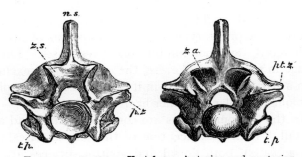

FIG. 354.—***Python:*** **Vertebræ.** Anterior and posterior views. *n. s.* neural spine; *p. z.* pre-zygapophysis; *pt. z.* post-zygapophysis; *t. p.* transverse processes; *z. a.* zygantrum; *z. s.* zygosphene. (After Huxley.)

perhaps representing intercentra, situated below the centra in the anterior cervical region. Chevron bones (inferior arches) occur in the caudal region of many reptiles (*Sphenodon*, Lacertilia, Crocodilia).

In snakes and iguanas, in addition to the ordinary articulating processes or zygapophyses, there are peculiar articular surfaces termed *zygosphenes* and *zygantra* (Fig. 354). The zygosphene is a wedge-like process projecting forwards from the anterior face of the neural arch of the vertebra. It fits, when the vertebræ are in their natural positions, into a depression of corresponding form—the zygantrum—on the posterior face of the neural arch of the vertebra in front. To this arrangement, as well as to the deeply concavo-convex centra, the extraordinary flexibility and strength of a snake's backbone are due.

The various regions of the spinal column are well marked in most of the lizards, in the Rhynchocephalia, in the Chelonia, and in the Crocodilia (Figs. 355, 356). In the snakes (some of which may have several hundred vertebræ) and many of the snake-like lizards only two regions are distinguishable—precaudal and caudal. In the others there is a sacral region comprising usually two vertebræ, both of which have strong processes (sacral ribs) for articulation with the ilia. The first and second vertebræ are always modified to form an atlas and axis : in the Lacertilia and Chelonia the latter has a distinct odontoid process. In chamæleons, *Sphenodon*, and the crocodiles there is a median bone, the *pro-atlas* (Fig. 357, *O*), intercalated between the atlas and the occipital region of the skull.

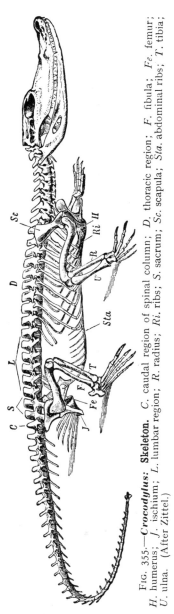

Fig. 355.—*Crocodylus*: Skeleton. *C.* caudal region of spinal column; *D.* thoracic region; *F.* fibula; *Fe.* femur; *H.* humerus; *J.* ischium; *L.* lumbar region; *R.* radius; *Ri.* ribs; *S.* sacrum; *Sc.* scapula; *Sta.* abdominal ribs; *T.* tibia; *U.* ulna. (After Zittel.)

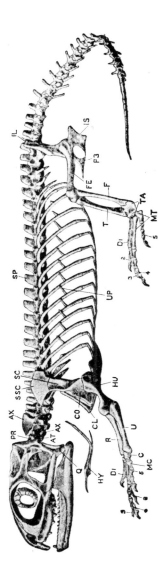

Fig. 356.—*Sphenodon*: Skeleton. AT. atlas; AX. axis; C. carpal bones; CL. clavicle; CO. coracoid; D. 1, 2, 3, 4, 5, digits; FE. femur; F. fibula; HU. humerus; HY. hyoid; IL. ilium; IS. ischium; MC. metacarpals; MT. metatarsals; PB. pubis; PR. pro-atlas; Q. quadrate; R. radius; SC. scapula; SP. spinal column (points to the spinous process of one of the thoracic vertebræ); SSC. supra-scapula; T. tibia; TA. tarsals; U. ulna; UP. uncinate process. (After Headley.)

Ribs are developed in connection with all the vertebræ of the pre-sacral or pre-caudal region. In the caudal region they are usually replaced by inferior arches; *Sphenodon*, Chelonians, Crocodilians, and snakes have caudal ribs which become fused with the vertebræ. In the Lacertilia only a small number (three or four) of the most anterior of the thoracic ribs are connected with the sternum by cartilaginous sternal ribs. The rest are free, or are connected together into continuous hoops across the middle line. In the so-called flying lizards (*Draco*) a number of the ribs are greatly produced, and support a pair of wide flaps of skin at the sides of the body, enabling the animals to glide. The widely expansible hood that is part of the intimidatory mechanism of the cobras (*Naia*) is controlled by the lateral spread of elongated anterior ribs. In *Sphenodon* (Fig. 356) and Crocodilia (Fig. 355) each rib has connected with it posteriorly a flattened curved cartilage, the *uncinate process* (see also Fig. 388, p. 572).

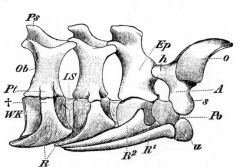

FIG. 357.—*Crocodylus:* **Vertebræ.** Anterior elements in young animal. *A.* atlas; *Ep.* axis; *h.* articulation of atlas with axis; *IS.* intervertebral discs; *o.* pro-atlas; *Ob.* neural arches; *Po.* odontoid bone; *Ps.* neural spines; *Pt.* transverse processes; *R, R¹, R².* ribs; *s.* arch of atlas; *u.* median piece of atlas; *WK.* centra. (After Wiedershiem.)

In Chelonia (Fig. 358) the total number of vertebræ is always smaller than in members of other orders. The cervical ribs are small and fused with the vertebræ. The cervical and the caudal are the only regions in which the vertebræ are movable upon one another. The vertebræ of the trunk, usually ten in number, are immovably united with one another by means of fibrocartilaginous intervertebral discs. Each of the neural spines, from the second to the ninth inclusively, is flattened and fused with a flat plate of dermal origin, the *neural plate* (Fig. 359), and the row of plates thus formed constitutes the median portion of the carapace. The ribs are likewise immovable. A short distance from its origin each passes into a large bony dermal *costal plate*, and the series of costal plates uniting by their edges form a large part of the carapace on either side of the row of neural plates. The carapace is made up of the neural and costal plates supplemented by a row of *marginal* plates (Figs. 358 and 359) running along the edge, and *nuchal* and *pygal* plates situated respectively in front of and behind the row of neural plates. In some cases the neural plates (*Chelodina*) and even the costal plates and ribs (*Testudo loveridgei*) are absent.

The bony elements of the plastron of the Chelonia are an anterior and median plate (*entoplastron*) and four pairs of plates which, in their order from before backwards, are termed *epiplastra, hyoplastra, hypoplastra,* and *xiphiplastra.* The median element probably corresponds to the interclavicle or episternum of other reptiles. The first pair (epiplastra) probably correspond to the clavicles. The others seem to be of the same character as the abdominal ribs of Crocodilia.

The carapace of the Luth or Leathery Turtle (*Dermochelys*) is distinguished from that of the rest of the order in being composed of numerous polygonal discs of bone, and in not being connected with the endo-skeleton. It has been sometimes suggested that this condition is the primitive one, but fossil evidence is to the contrary. In the plastron the median bone is absent. Carapace and plastron are firmly fixed together by bony union in most species, but sometimes the connection is ligamentous.

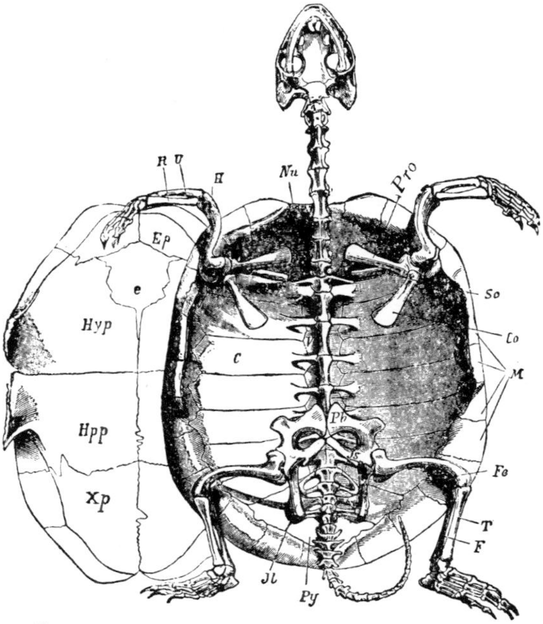

The *sternum* in the Lacertilia is a plate of cartilage with a simple or bifid posterior continuation formed by the fusion of five or six pairs of ribs. In the Ophidia and Chelonia it is absent. In the Crocodilia it is a broad plate bearing the cora-

FIG. 358.—**Chelonia: Exo- and endo-skeleton.** *Cistudo,* from below. The plastron has been removed and is represented on one side. *C.* costal plate; *Co.* coracoid; *e.* entoplastron (episternum); *Ep.* epiplastron (clavicle?); *F.* fibula; *Fe.* femur; *H.* humerus; *Hyp.* hyoplastron; *Hpp.* hypoplastron; *Jl.* ilium; *Js.* ischium; *M.* marginal plates; *Nu.* nuchal plate; *Pb.* pubis; *Pro.* procoracoid or process of scapula; *Py.* pygal plates; *R.* radius; *Sc.* scapula; *T.* tibia; *U.* ulna; *Xp.* xiphiplastron. (After Zittel.)

coids and two pairs of ribs with a posterior continuation which bifurcates behind.

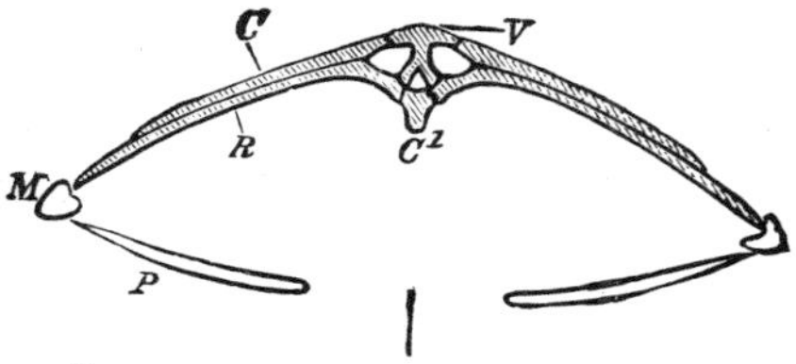

FIG. 359.—*Chelonia:* **Exo- and endo-skeleton.** In transverse section. *C.* costal plate; *C¹.* centrum; *M.* marginal plate; *P.* lateral element of plastron; *R.* rib; *V.* expanded neural plate. (After Huxley.)

A series of ossifications—the *abdominal ribs*—lies in the wall of the abdomen in the Crocodilia (Fig. 355, *Sta.*), and similar ossifications occur also in many lizards and in *Sphenodon*. As already noticed, the posterior elements of the plastron of the Chelonia are probably of a similar character.

In the *skull*, ossification is much more complete than in the Amphibia although the primary chondrocranium persists to a greater extent than in mammals. The number of bones is much greater. The parasphenoid is reduced, and its place is taken by the large basioccipital, basisphenoid, and presphenoid.

A fairly typical lacertilian skull has been described in the case of *Lacerta* (p. 446). Its principal characteristic features are the presence of an interorbital septum, the presence of the epipterygoid, and the mobility of the quadrate. The last of these features it shares with that of the Ophidia. The epipterygoid is absent in some lizards, such as chamæleons and many burrowing forms. The quadrate is not always movable. The skull of chamæleons has a remarkable helmet-like appearance owing to the development of processes of the squamosal and occipital regions, which unite above the posterior part of the cranial roof. The skull of the amphisbænians differs from that of other Lacertilia and approaches that of snakes in the absence of an interorbital septum.

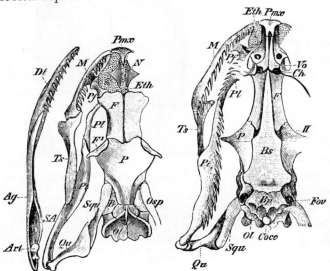

FIG. 360. — **Colubridæ: Skull.** *Natrix.* A, from above; B, from below. *Ag.* angular; *Art.* articular; *Bp.* basioccipital; *Bs.* basisphenoid; *Ch.* internal nares; *Cocc.* occipital condyle; *Dt.* dentary; *Eth.* nasal capsule or ethmoid cartilage; *F.* frontal; *F'.* postorbital; *Fov.* fenestra ovalis; *M.* maxilla; *N.* nasal; *Ol.* exoccipital; *Osp.* supraoccipital; *P.* parietal; *Pe.* periotic; *P. f.* prefrontal; *Pl.* palatine; *Pmx.* premaxilla; *Pt.* pterygoid; *Qu.* quadrate; *SA.* supraangular; *Squ.* squamosal; *Ts.* transverse; *Vo.* vomer; *II,* optic foramen. (After Wiedersheim.)

In the skull of Ophidia (Fig. 360) orbitosphenoid and pleurosphenoid or laterosphenoid elements are absent in the adult. Their places are taken by downward prolongations of the parietals and frontals. Along the base of the skull are two cartilaginous rods (Fig. 360, *B. T.*) which are the persistent trabeculæ of embryonic life. The interorbital septum is absent. Neither upper nor lower temporal arches are present. As in lizards, the palatines (*Pl.*) are widely separated from one another, and are usually slender. They are movably articulated behind with the pterygoids (*Pt.*), and the latter, through the intermediation of the slender transverse bones (*Ts.*), with the maxillæ. The premaxillæ are small, usually fused together and usually toothless. The maxillæ (*Mx.*), articulate with the conjoined lachrymal and prefrontal (*La.*), which, in turn, is connected with the frontal. In Viperidæ the maxillæ are short and freely movable, erecting the fangs. The long and slender quadrate (*Qu.*) is freely articulated with the posterior end of the elongated squamosal. The rami of the mandible, likewise long and slender, are not united anteriorly in a symphysis, but are connected together merely by elastic ligamentous tissue, so that when the mouth of the snake is opened to allow of the entry of relatively large prey (which it swallows whole) they are capable of being widely separated from one another. An African Rock

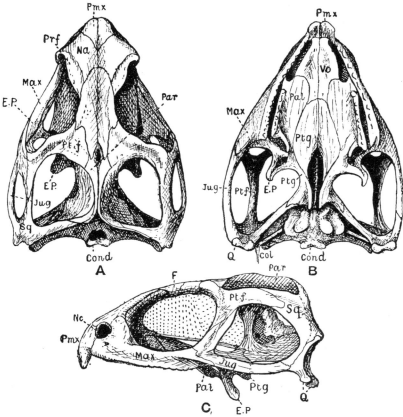

FIG. 361.—*Sphenodon:* Skull. *A*, dorsal; *B*, ventral; *C*, left-sided view of skull of *Sphenodon*, × ¾. *Col.* Columella auris; *Cond.* occipital condyle; *E. P.* ectopterygoid; *F.* frontal *Jug.* jugal; *Max.* maxilla; *Na.* nasal; *Nc.* anterior nasal opening; *Pal.* palatine; *Par.* parietal; *Pmx.* premaxilla; *Prf.* prefrontal; *Pt. f.* postfrontal and postorbital; *Ptg.* pterygoid or endopterygoid; *Q.* quadrate and quadrato-jugal; *Sq.* squamosal; *Vo.* vomer. (See also p. 467.) (From *Cambridge Natural History.*)

Python (*Python sebæ*) only 11 feet 9 inches long has been known to swallow a fully grown, horned Thomson's Gazelle (*Gazella thomsoni*). *Post-mortem* it was found that the gazelle's spine was fractured in four places. The pelvis and one thigh were also broken and the prey was so distorted that the ribs on one side protruded through the other side of the body. The swallowing process took 90 minutes (Pitman). Ditmars presented a freshly killed pig weighing 80 lb. to a python measuring 20 feet long and saw it swallowed whole.

In primitive burrowing snakes such as the Ilysiidæ, the jaw bones tend to be solidly united with the skull. The skull of *Sphenodon* is on the whole lizard-like, but there is a complete lower temporal arch. The quadrate (*Q.*) is immovably fixed, wedged in by the quadrato-jugal, squamosal, and ptery-goid. The premaxillæ (*Pmx.*) are not fused together, but separated by a suture. There is a broad palate formed by the plate-like vomers, palatines, and pterygoids (Fig. 361).

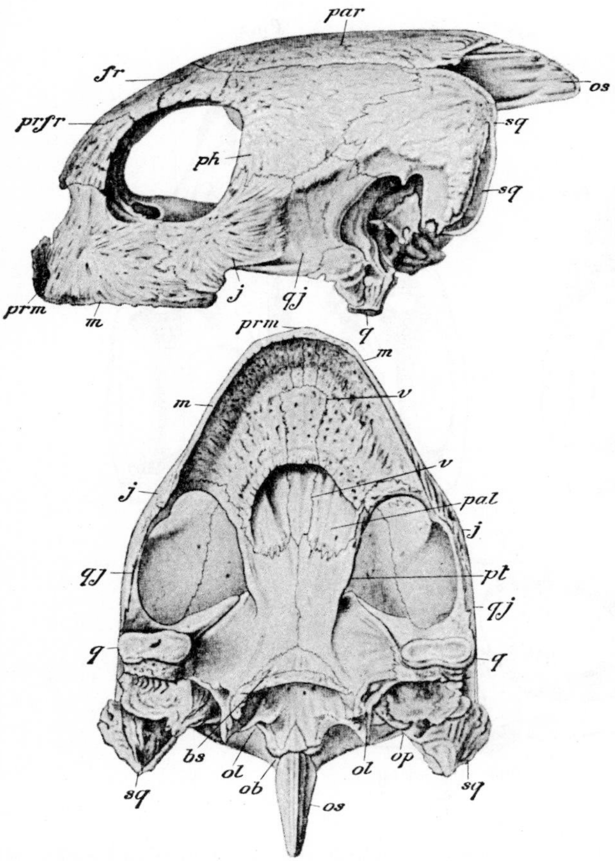

FIG. 362.—*Chelonia:* **Skull.** *bs.* basi-sphenoid; *fr.* frontal; *j.* jugal; *m.* maxilla; *ob.* basi-occipital; *ol.* exoccipital; *op.* opisthotic; *os.* supraoccipital; *pal.* pala-tine; *par.* parietal; *ph.* postfrontal; *prfr.* prefrontal; *pt.* pterygoid; *prm.* premaxilla; *q.* quadrate; *qj.* quadrato-jugal; *sq.* squamosal; *v.* vomer. (After Hoffmann.)

In the Chelonia (Fig. 362) all the bones, including the quadrate, are solidly con-nected together. Transverse bones (ectopterygoids), lachrymals, and orbitosphe-noids, and pleurosphenoids are absent. The place of the last named is taken to a certain extent by verti-cal downward plate-like ex-tensions of the parietals, the lower part of the plates per-haps representing the epi-pterygoids of lizards. There may be open temporal fossæ, the inferior boundary of which (*inferior temporal arch*) may be incomplete owing to the absence of the quadrato-jugal). In some chelonians (e.g. *Chelonia*, Fig. 362) the entire temporal region may be covered over by a sort of false roof formed of expan-sions of the postfrontals (*ph.*), parietals (*par.*), and squamo-sals (*sq.*) with the jugal (*j.*) and quadrato-jugal (*qj.*). The immovably fixed quadrates Fig. 362, *q.*) are modified to afford a part or the whole of the rim for the support of the tympanic membrane. The occipital condyle is sometimes trilobed. The vomer (*v.*) is unpaired. The palatines (*pa.*) are approximated and give off palatine plates, which for a short distance cut off a nasal passage from the cavity of the mouth. Nasals are usually absent as separate bones. The premaxillæ are very small. The rami of the mandibles are stout, and are firmly united together at the symphysis.

In the crocodiles (Figs. 363, 364), as in the Chelonia, the quadrate ($Qu.$) is firmly united with the other bones of the skull. There is a membranous and cartilaginous interorbital septum. There are no distinct bony orbitosphenoids, but pleurosphenoids are well developed. The orbit is separated from the lateral temporal fossa by a stout bar situated somewhat below the surface, and formed of processes from the postfrontal, jugal, and ectopterygoid. The lateral temporal fossa is bounded below, as in *Sphenodon*, by an inferior temporal arch composed of jugal and quadrato-jugal (paraquadrate). The frontals are early united into one,

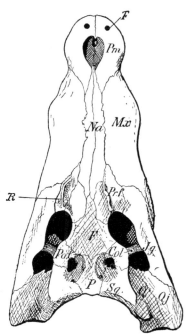

FIG. 363.—*Crocodylus:* **Skull.** Dorsal view in adult. *Col.* buttress connecting the postfrontal with the jugal and ectopterygoid; *F.* frontal; *Jg.* jugal; *Mx.* maxilla; *Na.* nasal; *P.* parietal; *Pm.* premaxilla; *Po.* postfrontal; *Pr. f.* prefrontal; *Q.* quadrate; *Qj.* quadratojugal; *R.* characteristic ridge on the prefrontal bone; *Sq.* squamosal; *T.* perforation in the premaxilla caused by a pair of lower incisor teeth. (After Gadow.)

and the same holds good of the parietals. Both palatine (*Pl.*) and pterygoid (*Pt.*), as well as maxillæ, develop palatine plates in the roof of the mouth, cutting off a nasal passage of great length from the cavity of the mouth, the posterior nares (*ch.*) being situated far back towards the posterior end of the cranial base. The nature of the articulation between the mandible and the quadrate is such that movement is restricted to the vertical plane, and lateral displacement is further provided against by the development of a broad process of the pterygoid against which the inner surface of the mandibular ramus plays, an arrangement which occurs also in most Lacertilia.

In accordance with their purely aerial mode of respiration, the *visceral arches* are much more reduced in the Reptilia than in the Amphibia in general. The only well-

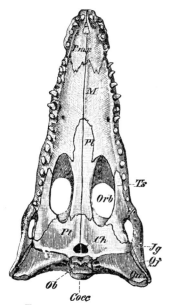

FIG. 364.—*Crocodylus:* **Skull.** Ventral view in young animal. *Ch,* posterior nares; *Cocc.* occipital condyle; *Jg.* jugal; *M.* maxilla (palatine process); *Ob.* basi-occipital; *Orb.* orbit; *Pl.* palatine; *Pmx.* premaxillæ; *Pt.* pterygoid; *Qj.* quadratojugal; *Qu.* quadrate. (After Wiedersheim.)

developed post-mandibular arch is the hyoid, and even this may undergo considerable reduction (Ophidia). The branchial arches are greatly reduced, or aborted, in the adult.

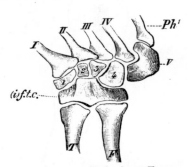

FIG. 365.—**Chelonia: Tarsus.** *Emys.* Right side from above. *F.* fibula; *T.* tibia; (*i.*) *f. t. c.* the united tarsals of the proximal row; *Ph'.* first phalanx of the fifth digit; 1—4, distal tarsals; *I—V*, metatarsals. (After Wiedersheim.)

There is little variation in the structure of the limb-arches and skeleton of the limbs in the different groups of Lacertilia. The pelvic arch is distinguished in the Lacertilia in general by its slender character. The pubes and ischia are (as is the case throughout the class) separated from one another by wide ischio-pubic foramina. This feature markedly distinguishes the reptilian pelvis from that of the Amphibia. In limbless forms the pectoral arch may be either present or absent.

In *Sphenodon* there is a foramen above the outer and one above the inner condyle of the humerus. There are eleven carpal elements, of which there are four, including a pisiform, in the proximal row, two centrals, and five in the distal row. The pubes are united in a symphysis, in front of which is a cartilaginous epipubis. A large oval foramen intervenes between the ischium and the pubis. A cartilaginous *hypoischium* is attached to the ischia behind. In the tarsus the tibial and fibular elements are distinct, though firmly united. The intermedium and the centrale are firmly fixed to the tibiale. There are three distal tarsal bones.

In the Chelonia (Fig. 358) the interclavicle (episternum) and clavicles are absent, unless, as is probable, the former be represented by the median element of the plastron and the latter by the first lateral pair. The entire pectoral arch is a tri-radiate structure of which the most ventral and posterior ray, ending in a free extremity, is the coracoid. The other two rays are the scapula and a process, sometimes regarded as representing the procoracoid, given off on the inner side of the scapula near its glenoid end. The bones of the carpus have nearly the typical arrangement, consisting, as in lizards, of a proximal row of three, a distal row of five, and a centrale between the two. The pelvis resembles

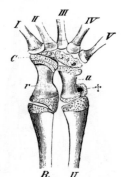

FIG. 366.—**Alligator: Carpus.** Young animal. *C.* centrale (?); *R.* radius; *U.* ulna; *r.* radiale; *u.* ulnare; 1—5, the five distal carpals (not yet ossified); 1 and 2 united into one, and also 3, 4, and 5; †, pisiform; *I—V*, the five metacarpals. (After Wiedersheim.)

that of Lacertilia, except that it is broader and shorter. Both pubes and ischia meet in ventral symphyses, and epipubic and hypoischial cartilages may be present. In the tarsus (Fig. 365) there is usually a single proximal bone and four distalia. There are never more than two phalanges in any of the digits.

In the Crocodilia also the clavicle is absent, but there is an episternum. The number of carpal elements is reduced, the largest being two proximal bones, the radiale and the ulnare (Fig. 366, *r*, *u*.). On the ulnar side of the latter is a small accessory bone (*pisiform*,†). The pelvic arch (Fig. 367) differs somewhat widely from that of other living reptiles, and the parts have been variously interpreted. Two bones (*P.*), which are usually regarded as the pubes, extend from the region of the acetabula forwards and inwards, but, though they become closely approximated anteriorly, do not meet in a symphysis. Between and in front of their anterior extremities, which are tipped with cartilage, extends a membrane (*M.*) with which are connected in front the last pair of abdominal ribs (*BR.*). The pos-terior ends of the pubes are cut off from the

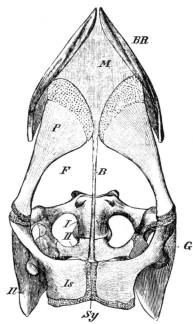

FIG. 367.—**Alligator: Pelvis.** Young animal in ventral view. *B.* fibrous band passing between the pubic and ischiatic symphyses; *BR.* last pair of abdominal ribs; *F.* obturator foramen; *G.* acetabulum; *Il.* ilium; *Is.* ischium; *M.* fibrous membrane between the anterior ends of the two innominate bones and the last pair of abdominal ribs; *P.* pubis; *Sy.* ischiatic symphysis; *I, II,* first and second sacral vertebræ. (After Wiedersheim.)

acetabulum by the in-terposition of a pair of bones which may be parts of the ilia, but are separately ossified. The ischia extend downwards and somewhat back-wards from the acetabula and are fixed together vent-rally (at *Sy.*), but there is no true symphysis, as their extremities remain cartilaginous. A hypoischium is not present. In the tarsus (Fig. 368) there is a probable astragalus, two proximal tarsal bones and a *calcaneum*—the latter having a prominent calcaneal process and two distal tarsal bones, together with a thin plate of cartilage supporting the first and second metatarsals. The missing fifth digit is represented by a rudimentary metatarsal.

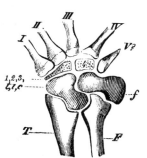

FIG. 368.—**Crocodylus: Tarsus.** Right, from above. *F.* fibula; *T.* tibia; *t.i.c.* pos-sibly the astragalus, formed of the united tibiale, inter-medium and centrale; *f.* fibulare (calcaneum); 1—3, united first, second and third distal tarsals; 4, fourth tarsal; *I—IV,* first to fourth metatarsals; *V?,* fifth distal tarsal and fifth meta-tarsal. (From Wieder-sheim.)

Alimentary Canal and Associated Structures.—Al-though buccal digestion does not occur, terrestrial reptiles, and particularly snakes, have active *supra-* and *infra-labial* salivary glands producing copious secretions which aid deglutition.   Contrary to popular belief, however, snakes do not 'slime' their victims before swallowing.   Many snakes can disgorge prey if frightened.

Reptilian teeth are generally thinly capped with an exceedingly hard, highly calcified, homogeneous layer of material that is superficially like the enamel found in mammals, but most of the tooth is made up of bone-like dentine.

The form and arrangement of the teeth already described in the account of *Lacerta* prevail in the majority of lizards.   In many of them the palatal teeth are absent.   The teeth are sometimes fixed by their bases to the summit of the ridge of the jaw (*acrodont* forms) and sometimes fixed by their sides to the lateral surface of the ridge (*pleurodont*).   They are never embedded in

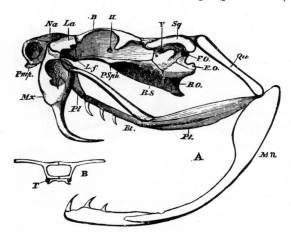

Fig. 369.—*Crotalus:* **Skull and fangs.**   Rattlesnake.   *A.*   lateral view.   *B. O.* basi-occipital; *B. S.* basi-sphenoid; *E. O.* exoccipital; *F. O.* fenestra ovalis; *La.* conjoined lachrymal and prefrontal; *L. f.* articulation between lacrymal and frontal; *Mn.* mandible; *Mx.* maxilla; *Na.* nasal *Pl.* palatine; *Pmp.* premaxilla; *P. Sph.* parasphenoid; *Pt.* pterygoid; *Qu.* quadrate; *Sq.* squamosal; *II, V,* foramina of exit of the second and fifth cranial nerves. *B.* transverse section at point lettered *B* in Fig. A: *T.* trabeculæ. (After Huxley.)

sockets in any recent form and are usually shed and replaced throughout the life of the individual.   Two remarkable Mexican lizards (*Heloderma*) are unique in having teeth that are grooved for the ducts of poison-glands.   In snakes (Figs. 360, 369) teeth are rarely developed on the premaxillæ, but are present on the maxillæ, palatines, and pterygoids, as well as the dentary of the mandible. Sometimes they may be of the same character throughout : solid, elongated, sharp-pointed, and usually strongly recurved, so that they have the character of sharp hooks.   The function of such teeth is to hold prey and prevent it from struggling free while it is being swallowed.   Non-venomous snakes possess teeth only of this character.   In venomous snakes some of the maxillary teeth become poison-fangs.   These are usually much larger than the ordinary teeth, and are either grooved or perforated by a canal for the passage of the duct of the poison-gland.   In the Viperidæ there is a single large, curved, poison-fang on the maxilla with small reserve-fangs at its base.   These are the only teeth borne by the maxilla, which is very short.   In the venomous colubrine snakes the poison-fangs are either the most anterior, or the most posterior, of a considerable range of maxillary teeth. In vipers the large poison-fang is capable of being rotated through a considerable angle, and moved from a nearly horizontal position (in which it lies along the roof of the mouth embedded in folds of the mucous membrane) to a nearly vertical one, when the snake opens its mouth to strike its prey. The rotation of the maxilla is brought about by the backward or forward movement of the lower end of the quadrate which imparts its movement to the pterygoid and thence to the other bones of the upper jaw.

The venom is ejected by the sudden contraction of a muscle often referred to as the temporal or masseter (Fig. 370). This muscle is probably not homologous with such mammalian elements, but is, in fact, the *capito-mandibularis superficialis* muscle (Colbert). The venom gland is a modified *superior labial* or 'parotid'. In *Naia naia* it is about the shape and size of an almond kernel and is thickly encapsulated with fibrous tissue. It is composed of a neck and a body through the long axis of which runs a duct. The capsule supports

FIG. 370.—*Crotalus:* **Poison apparatus.** Rattlesnake. *A*, eye; *Gc*, poison-duct entering the poison-fang at †; *Km*, muscles of mastication partly cut through at *; *Mc*. constrictor muscle; *Mc'*. continuation of the constrictor muscle to the lower jaw; *N*. nasal opening; *S*, fibrous poison sac; *z*, tongue; *za*, opening of the poison-duct; *zf*. pouch of mucous membrane enclosing the poison-fangs. (After Wiedersheim.)

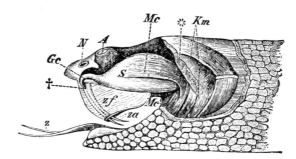

vascular fibrous septa which separate the glandular substance into secretory pockets, the *poison lakes of Bobeau*. The roughly fan-shaped capito-mandibularis superficialis muscle, originating on the post-frontal (post-orbital) bone and parietal ridges, embraces much of the body of the venom gland. Its contraction, which governs the biting movement, swiftly and synchronously expresses poison from the isolated poison lakes down the central duct into the neck of the gland and towards the adjacent fang. There is uncertainty concerning the precise means by which the poison canal joins the upper *intake aperture* (Fig. 371, *i. ap.*) of the fang, and especially how a new connection is established after the periodic spontaneous shedding of the operative fang or after (in some species) loss on impact with prey. In at least some species the duct bends inwards and ends in a cavity anterior to the bases of the fangs. Paired muscular cushions and a system of peridontal folds direct the venom into the basal intake aperture. The venom travels down the venom canal and is forced from the sub-terminal *discharge* aperture (*d. ap.*) at the moment of embedding. At the time of impact the jaws of rattlesnakes are widespread to the extent of nearly 180 degrees.

Snake venoms act in a variety of ways, so that it is possible to become immunised to the venom of one species and yet die from the bite of another. Venoms may 1. act on nerve cells and cause respiratory paralysis; 2. destroy the endothelium of smaller blood vessels and allow blood to seep into the tissues; 3. destroy erythrocytes, and 4. cause blood coagulation. The venom of the North Australian and New Guinea Taipan (*Oxyuranus*), discharged

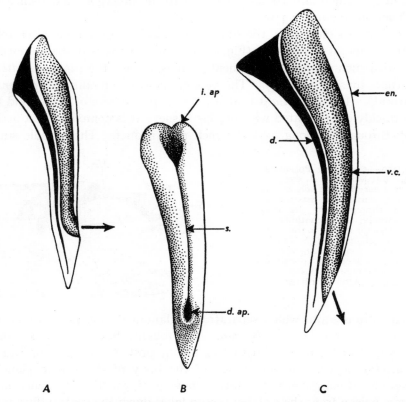

A　　　　　*B*　　　　　*C*

FIG. 371.—**Elapidæ: Dental specialisation.** Spitting (*A*, *B*) compared with a non-spitting (*C*) species. The venom enters the fang through an intake aperture (*i. ap.*), and is ejected through the discharge aperture (*d. ap.*). Thick arrows indicate direction of jet in each types. *d.* dentine; *en.* enamel; *s.* suture; *v. c.* venom canal. (Modified after Bogert.)

in great quantity and almost invariably fatal, acts in the first, third, and fourth ways outlined above. The neurotoxic venom of the Indo-Malayan King Cobra (*Naia hannah*) and Australian Death Adder (*Acanthophis*) leads to death chiefly from respiratory paralysis. The highly destructive venom of the Tiger Snake (*Notechis scutatus*) also primarily affects the nervous system, although it is a powerful coagulant as well. The hæmolysis and hæmorrhage caused by the venom of the South American Fer-de-lance (*Bothrops atrox = lanceolatus*) is so pronounced that bleeding occurs from the eyes, and renal and alimentary tract epithelium. A man bitten on one arm by a South African Boomslang (*Dispholidus typus*) suffered massive extravasation on the other as well.

The neurotoxic venom of the truculent African Black Mamba (*Dendraspis angusticeps*) has killed a man within twenty minutes. The venom of the less aggressive Gaboon Viper (*Bitis gabonica*) produces 'furious blood and tissue destruction' (Ditmars) as well as respiratory paralysis. This equatorial rain-forest reptile, of sinister beauty,[1] kills every time it bites in tropical Africa, reputedly within an hour. Only one bitten person is known to have recovered. This was a reptile curator at a North American menagerie who was struck on a finger by one fang only and was in a position immediately to receive treatment by incision, suction, intermittent torniquet, three kinds of antivenenes (none specific for *B. gabonica* is yet available), hot limb-baths and packs, injections of caffein, strychnine and novocaine, blood transfusion, and finally incisions to allow the escape of extravasated blood and lymph. Through these incisions tissue herniated. Voided urine consisted almost wholly of blood. Meanwhile, respiratory paralysis intervened, and after about an hour the agonised, pulseless patient became unconscious and appeared to be dying. He regained consciousness an hour later, and left hospital after three weeks. It is claimed that the congeneric horned West African River Jack or Rhinoceros Viper (*B. nasicornis*) is equally lethal. The loud-hissing Puff Adder (*B. arietans*), which often visits human habitation to feed on rodents, has a much less deadly hæmolytic, but to some degree neurotoxic, venom which nevertheless has occasionally been fatal within three hours.

In India, a country heavily populated by both snakes and Man, as many as 24,000 people have been killed by poisoning in a single year. This enormous death-rate is probably matched in no other country and is perhaps largely due to the presence of a mainly bare-footed population. The nocturnal kraits (*Bungarus spp.*), Russell's Viper (*Vipera russelli*), and the Cobra are chiefly responsible. In Australia and North America, on the other hand, the risk of snake-bite is negligible: in Australia an average of five people are killed each year. Most diurnal serpents are more wary of Man than he is of them and their columella/quadrate attachment (p. 448) enables them to disappear long before he comes in view. Vipers, however, are exceptional in that they tend to lie motionless, protected by their concealing coloration. The same is true of the viper-like Australian Death-adder (*Acanthophis antarcticus*), an elapid reptile that shows convergence in both form and habits in a country without vipers. Although apparently lethargic, vipers are capable of lightning attack if trodden on or when near their prey. A few snakes (*e.g.*

---

[1] This club-headed, thick-bodied, stub-tailed animal has a symmetrical carpet-like pattern of greenish-yellow, mauve, black, and buff. Inflation of the body during excitement brings the scale-edges into view. The scale colours have in life a delicate bloom, 'so that the whole design might have been painted on velvet' (Johnson).

Black or Green Mamba, King Cobra) are said to attack Man without positive provocation during the coupling season.

Chance of survival from snake-bite depends to a great degree on the amount of venom that the reptile habitually discharges, on its fang-length and the depth to which they are driven into the tissues. The essentially neurotoxic, but also coagulating, venom of the Australian Tiger Snake is drop for drop probably more potent than that of any terrestrial species, but its bite is fatal in only about 50 per cent of treated cases. The Tiger Snake has poison-glands of limited capacity and relatively short fangs. These are a mere 3·5 mm. long. Those of the Taipan are 12·5 mm. long and those of the full-sized (5 ft. 8 ins.) Gaboon Viper almost 2 inches in length if measured along the curve. It has been suggested that the neurotoxic venom of the Tiger Snake, Blue Krait of India (*Bungarus candidus*), and the Formosan *B. multicinctus*, are toxic to the mouse in a dosage of as little as 2–5/1,000 of a milligram and about 2 milligrams in the case of Man.

An interesting adaptation is shown in the fangs of the 'spitting' members of the cobra family and in the South African ringhals (*Hemachatus*) (Fig. 371). Here the suture (*s.*) line ends somewhat more proximally in a more restricted and relatively oval discharge aperture (*d. ap.*) through which, when the head is tilted at an exactly appropriate angle, the venom is explosively discharged at the victim's eyes. The attack of the Black-necked Cobra (*Naja nigricollis*) has been studied by Ditmars. It often takes the victim—Man or other animal—completely by surprise for the reptile will rear, and eject venom accurately into the victim's eyes at very slight provocation from a distance as great as six feet. A six-foot cobra has been known to eject at least some venom for a distance of 12 feet. Ditmars states that the term 'spitting' does not correctly indicate the manner of ejection since the jaws are slightly parted and the venom comes directly from the openings at the tips of the fangs. 'The snake rears. . . . Facing the object of anger it looks intently at one's face . . . if it seeks to direct the poison upwards it curves its rearing pose backwards, thus directing its head upwards. The ejection of the poison is an instantaneous operation. The jaws are slightly opened and closed so quickly as to appear like a snapping motion, and during this action the poison leaves the fangs. There is no dribbling or spilling of the fluid. It issues in twin jets. . . . There is every indication that, at the instant the snake prepares to eject the poison, it contracts the temporal muscle over each poison gland, thus producing pressure to force the toxic fluid a considerable distance. This flies with such force that its impact can be distinctly heard against ordinary glass five feet away. At the instant of ejection the snake emits a sharp hiss. This ejection of air might be an accompanying token of anger, or it may assist the travel of the poison.' As this type of poison is at once absorbed through the conjunctiva, the spray, if it reaches

its mark, 'throws the victim into a condition of pain and confusion, enabling the cobra to escape'. There is intense agony accompanied by acute
conjunctivitis and temporary blindness. 'Astonishing amounts of poison are
expended. After a vigorous demonstration, and the discharge of four to six
jets of poison, the glands rapidly refill . . . the new fluid is of much lighter
specific gravity than older storage.' Experimentally it has been shown that
the venom causes degeneration, and partial vascularisation of the cornea,
resulting in blindness if untreated.

Sphenodon (Fig. 361) possesses pointed, triangular, laterally-compressed
teeth arranged in two parallel rows, one along the maxilla, the other along the
palatine. The teeth of the lower jaw, which are of similar character, bite in
between these two upper rows, all the rows becoming worn down in the adult
in such a way as to form continuous ridges. Each premaxilla bears a prominent, chisel-shaped incisor represented in the young animal by two pointed
teeth. In the young *Sphenodon* a tooth has been found on each vomer—a
condition unusual among reptiles. In the Chelonia, teeth are entirely absent.
The jaws are invested in a horny layer in such a way as to form a structure
something like a bird's beak. The Crocodilia have numerous teeth which are
confined to the premaxillæ, the maxillæ, and the dentary. They are large,
conical, hollow teeth which are devoid of roots, each being lodged in its socket
or alveolus (thecodont), and each becoming replaced, when worn out, by a
successor developed on its inner side.

In some lizards the tongue is short and scarcely bifid; in others (e.g.
Lacerta) the forked part is of moderate length; and in others again, like the
monitors, the bifid tips are very long, as in snakes. The tongue of chamæleons
is an extraordinary organ. It is sub-cylindrical with an enlarged extremity,
and is so extensile that it is capable of being darted out to a distance sometimes
equalling, or even exceeding, the length of the trunk (Fig. 351). This protrusion is effected with great rapidity. In this way the animal catches insects
which constitute its food. The tongue in snakes is slender and bifid, capable
of being retracted into a basal sheath, and highly sensitive. It is used as a
tactile organ; and in conjunction with the organ of Jacobson (see p. 544). The
tongue of the Crocodilia is a thick, immobile mass extending between the rami
of the mandible. In some of the Chelonia the tongue is immobile; in others
it is protrusible, sometimes bifid.

In the alimentary canal of the reptiles special features are the muscular
gizzard-like stomach of the Crocodilia (sometimes containing *gastroliths*), the
presence of a rudimentary cæcum at the junction of small and large intestines
in most Lacertilia and in Ophidia, and the presence of numerous large cornified
papillæ in the œsophagus of the turtles.

Digestion begins in the stomach and is particularly rapid in snakes. When
a large animal is being slowly engulfed, the first part of the prey is partly

digested before the hind-parts have been swallowed. After taking in an especially large meal some reptiles (*e.g.* pythons) are able to do without another for more than a year.

There is a belief, common in most countries, that in times of danger snakes temporarily swallow their young as a protective measure. Many sober observers, from at least the 16th century onwards, have given currency to this belief, probably through optical illusion. When frightened, the tiny young of several species glide quickly *under* the mother's jaws and out of sight beneath her belly.

Respiratory System and Voice.—The reptiles all have an elongated trachea, the wall of which is supported by numerous cartilaginous rings. The anterior part of this is dilated to form the *larynx*, the wall of which is supported by *cricoid* and *arytenoid* cartilages. Although reptiles are on the whole not notable for their voices, many do communicate by sound. Geckos emit a peculiar little yapping bark when menaced. One is known as the Barking Lizard. It has been claimed, but not proved, that female crocodiles of some species are made aware of the hatching of their buried eggs by the squeaking of the young. The roar or bellow of an adult male *Crocodylus porosus* can be heard a mile away. Chelonians are said to 'bark' or 'grunt', but the evidence is conflicting. *Sphenodon* is said to emit a soft frog-like croak.

The reptilian trachea bifurcates posteriorly to form right and left *bronchi*, one passing to each lung. The *lungs* of the Lacertilia and Ophidia are of the relatively simple character already described in the lizard (p. 478). In some, the lung is incompletely divided internally into two portions—an anterior respiratory part with sacculated walls, and a posterior part with smooth, not highly vascular, walls, having mainly the function of a reservoir.

In snakes the lungs usually exhibit a striking asymmetry. The right lung is always very long and in marine species (in which it has a hydrostatic function) it may almost reach the level of the cloaca. The left lung is often rudimentary. In some snake-like lizards a similar asymmetry occurs, but in amphisbænids it is the right lung that may be reduced or aborted. In the more primitive snakes both lungs are functional and of almost equal size. In the Crocodilia and Chelonia the paired lungs are of a more complex character, being divided internally by septa into a number of chambers.

Some snakes possess a *tracheal 'lung'*. In these the incomplete tracheal rings allow the expansion of the tracheal membrane and the development of alveoli which sometimes extend from the head right down to those of the right lung proper. It has been suggested that this arrangement allows the snake to respire tracheally when the true lung is compressed by ingested prey. In the chamæleons (Fig. 351) a number of diverticula or *air-sacs* occur and are capable of inflation, causing an increase in the bulk of the animal which doubtless has an effect on assailants. The Australian Jew-lizard (*Amphibolurus*) is likewise capable of blowing itself up with air when confronted. The increased bulk makes it difficult for it to be swallowed by snakes and other enemies.

There has been considerable argument concerning respiration in chelonians. The thorax is relatively restricted in movement and it has been claimed that turtles achieve lung respiration essentially in the manner of frogs (p. 403). It is apparently true that there is a certain amount of hyoid movement, but it is possible that this is primarily concerned with the inflow of air for olfaction. Current opinion is that a series of special muscles, situated ventral to the viscera at the leg-pockets, alter cœlomic pressures and thus draw air into, and thrust it from, the paired bronchi and lungs. In addition, two other auxiliary respiratory devices have been reported in aquatic chelonians that spend periods below the surface. The pharyngeal cavity of many species is highly vascular, and it has been claimed that respiratory exchanges take place between pharyngeal wall and water taken in and expelled during submersion. The second auxiliary respiratory mechanism is located in paired cloacal diverticula which empty and fill through the vent of the submerged reptile.

Some soft-shelled turtles spend much of their time obliteratively concealed on, and partly in, the bottom mud of waters sufficiently still and shallow to allow the long neck to reach the surface like a periscope. The appropriately situated nostrils slightly emerge and take in atmospheric oxygen. Such animals, as mentioned above, can also breathe dissolved oxygen by means of pharyngeal and cloacal exchanges when the head is submerged during feeding and in times of danger.

Blood Vascular System.—In the reptilian heart (p. 474) the conus arteriosus, present as the most anterior chamber in the amphibian heart, is completely absorbed into the ventricle, from which therefore the arterial arches arise directly. Varying degrees of absorption of the sinus venosus into the right auricle are also to be observed throughout the class and thus, with the exception of *Sphenodon* (= *Hatteria*), it is not easily distinguished externally. Its aperture of communication with the right auricle is guarded by valves or foldings of the wall of the auricle.

There are, as in the Amphibia, always two quite distinct auricles, the right receiving the venous blood from the body, the left the oxygenated blood brought from the lungs by the pulmonary veins (Fig. 320). A vital point of difference between the heart of the reptile and that of the amphibian, however, is that in the former the ventricle is always more or less completely divided into right and left portions. In all the Lacertilia, Ophidia, and Chelonia the structure is essentially as has been described in *Lacerta*, the ventricular septum being well developed, but not completely closing off the left-hand portion of the cavity of the ventricle from the right (*cavum ventrale* = *pulmonale*).

This septum is more or less horizontal. The left-hand portion (which is much the larger) is further imperfectly divided into a *cavum venosum* to the right, and a *cavum arteriosum* to the left by a second septum formed by fused trabeculæ. The secondary septum is situated on the dorsal wall of the ventricle, approximately at a right angle to the primary septum. The separation is also helped by two elongated flaps of the auriculo-ventricular valve which project into the cavity of the cavum dorsale.

This secondary septum is probably homologous with the interventricular septum that has arisen in the crocodiles and which persists in birds (p. 589).

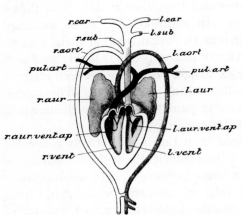

FIG. 372.—***Crocodylus*: Heart and great vessels.** Diagrammatic. The arrows show the direction of the arterial and venous currents. *l. aort.* left aortic arch; *l. aur.* left auricle; *l. aur. vent. ap.* left auriculo-ventricular aperture; *l. car.* left carotid; *l. sub.* left subclavian; *l. vent.* left ventricle; *pul. art.* pulmonary artery; *r. aort.* right aortic arch; *r. aur.* right auricle; *r. aur. vent. ap.* right auriculo-ventricular aperture; *r. car.* right carotid; *r. sub.* right subclavian; *r. vent.* right ventricle. (After Hertwig.)

From the cavum pulmonale arises the pulmonary artery and, from the cavum venosum, the right and left aortic arches. When the auricles contract, the cavum venosum becomes filled with venous blood from the right auricle, the cavum arteriosum with arterial blood from the left auricle; the cavum pulmonale becomes filled with venous blood which flows into it past the edges of the incomplete septum. When the ventricle contracts, its walls come in contact with the edge of the septum, and the cavum pulmonale is thus cut off from the rest of the ventricle. The further contraction consequently results in the venous blood of the cavum pulmonale being driven out through the pulmonary artery to the lungs, while the blood which remains in the ventricle (arterial and mixed) is compelled to pass out through the aorta. But in the Crocodilia (Fig. 501) the cavity is completely divided, so that there we may speak of distinct right and left ventricles. From the right arise the pulmonary artery and the left aortic arch : from the left the right aortic arch only. The right and left arches cross one another, and where their walls are in contact is an aperture—the *foramen Panizzæ*—placing their cavities in communication. Recent work indicates that during systole there is a considerable flow of blood from the right aorta to the left through this foramen.

Nervous System.—The *brain* of the lizard (p. 478) is fairly representative of that of modern Reptilia. It is in general more highly organised than the amphibian brain. The cerebral hemispheres exhibit a distinction into superficial grey layer or cortex containing pyramidal nerve-cells, and central white medulla, not observable in lower groups. The cerebral hemispheres are well-developed in all.

The most striking feature is the predominant development of the basal structures, the *corpus striatum*, the *septum*, and the *amygdaloid nuclei*. The cortex, dorsally situated in the pallial region of the hemisphere, is not extensive, but is clearly differentiated into three areas : medially the hippocampal, laterally the pyriform, and between them the dorsal or general cortex. The lateral or pyriform area is olfactory in function, but little is known of the function of the other two regions. There seems little doubt that from a functional point of view, the basal structures are by far the most important parts of the reptilian hemispheres. Their close connexion with the diencephalon (the thalamus and hypothalamus in particular) by the *basal fore-brain bundles* is evidence of this. Two *commissures* of the hemispheres are present : a dorsal or *hippocampal* and a ventral or *anterior* commissure. These appear to correspond, at least in part, with the commissures of the same name in mammals, but in general the reptilian brain shows a much closer resemblance to the brain of birds than to those of mammals.

The mid-brain consists dorsally usually of two closely-approximated oval optic lobes; rarely it is divided superficially into four. The cerebellum is always of small size, except in the Crocodilia (Fig. 373), in which it is comparatively highly developed, and consists of a median and two lateral lobes.

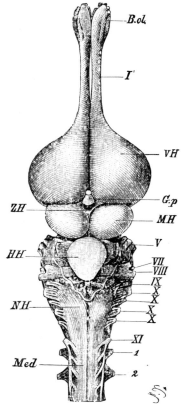

FIG. 373.—*Alligator:* **Brain and cranial nerves.** From dorsal aspect. *B. ol.* olfactory bulb; *G. p.* epiphysis; *HH*, cerebellum; *Med*, spinal cord; *MH*, optic lobes; *NH*, medulla oblongata; *VH*, cerebral hemispheres; *I—XI*, cranial nerves; 1, 2, first and second spinal nerves. (After Wiedersheim.)

Organs of Special Sense.—In most Lacertilia, but not in the Ophidia, the nasal cavity consists of two parts—an outer or vestibule, and an inner or olfactory chamber—the latter having the sense-cells in its walls, and containing a turbinal cartilage. In the turtles each nasal chamber is divided into two passages, an upper and a lower, and the same holds good of the hinder part of the elongated nasal chamber of the Crocodilia.

The *vomero-nasal* or *Jacobson's organ* (Fig. 374) is prominent in lizards (p. 481) and snakes. In each, the organ is separated from the olfactory cavity proper. It is best developed in snakes, and in lizards with a flicking, bifid tongue (e.g. *Varanus*). The tongue appears to pick up and convey scent particles towards the organ. Just as sight seems to be of great importance to most lizards (which are often sexually dimorphic), so is scent to snakes, which are not. Jacobson's organ is probably significant in courtship, enemy-recognition, and in tracking down prey. It has an extensive sensory area supplied by a large *vomero-nasal nerve*. In lizards and snakes most of the secretions from the *lachrymal* and *Harderian glands* find their way to the

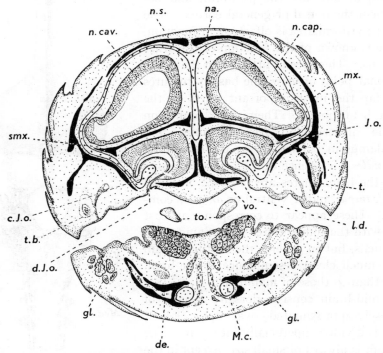

Fig. 374.—**Lacertilia: Vomeronasal organ.** Transverse section through snout of new-born *Anguis* (Slow worm). *c. J. o.* cartilage of Jacobson's organ; *de.* dentary; *d. J. o.* duct of Jacobson's organ; *gl.* salivary gland; *J. o.* Jacobson's organ; *l. d.* opening of lachrymal duct; *M. c.* Meckel's cartilage; *mx.* maxilla; *na.* nasal; *n. cap.* nasal capsule; *n. cav.* nasal cavity; *n. s.* nasal septum; *smx.* septomaxilla; *t.* tooth; *t. b.* tooth bud attached to dental lamina; *to.* tongue; *vo.* vomer. Drawn by A. d'A. Bellairs.

lachrymal duct which ends near the outlet of Jacobson's organ. These secretions may have some special property concerned with its function. In other amniotes excess tears are shed into the nose. Adult crocodiles have lost Jacobson's organ. It is present in *Sphenodon* in a rather primitive form, where it is not unlike the condition in mammals. In chelonians it is not separated from the nose.

The reptilian *eye* (Figs. 375) presents many specialisations. Lizards (excluding *Varanus*), but not chelonians, rely chiefly on monocular vision. The chamæleons, too, are exceptional and possess perhaps the most notable

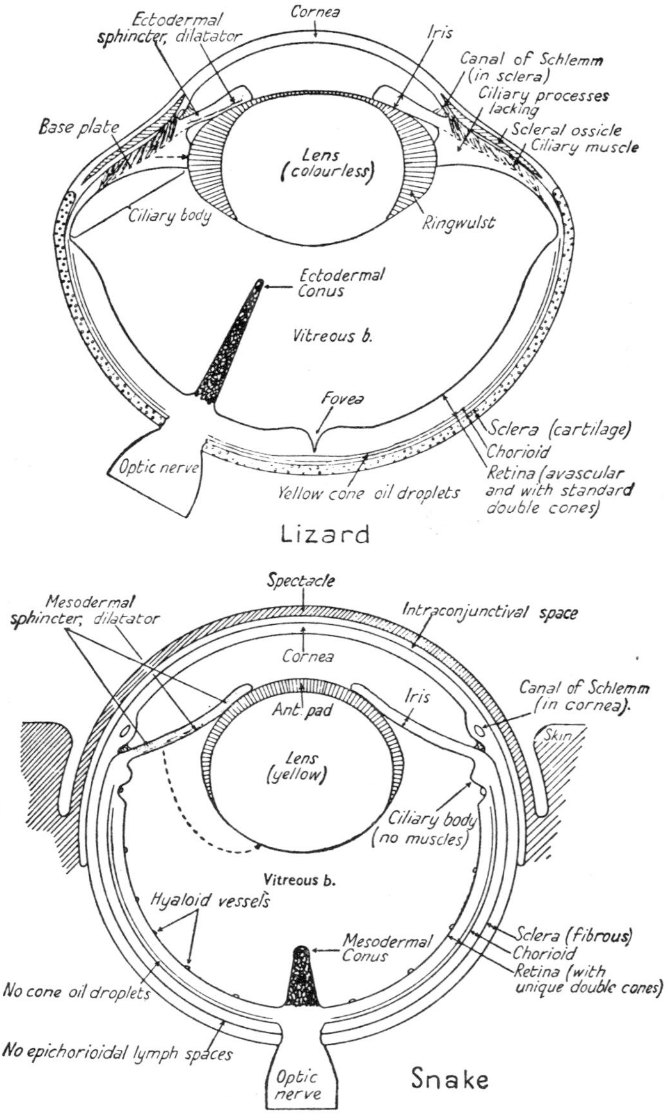

FIG. 375. — **Squamata: Comparison of lacertilian and ophidian eye.** It can be argued convincingly on ophthalmological grounds that the ancestors of snakes were fossorial. Walls postulates that in ancestral burrowing snakes the eye became a tiny spherical organ from which the scleral cartilage and ossicles had disappeared. The retina, apparatus of accommodation, and iris muscles (which contract and dilate the pupil) became degenerate. At the same time (as in many modern lizards), a protective spectacle had been evolved outside the cornea, probably derived from the fusion of the eyelids. Subsequently the snakes re-established themselves above ground and radiated successfully as a surface-dwelling group, though a few fossorial and generally rather primitive forms survived. The eyes of surface-dwelling snakes became efficient but retained the stamp of the fossorial phase in ophidian evolution. They were refurbished and transformed, and substitutions were found for many structures that were irretrievably lost. The spectacle remained useful in surface, as in fossorial life. The enlarged eyeball, having lost its stiffening scleral structures, remained spherical. A new method of accommodation was achieved by the invasion of the iris by the ciliary muscles, which now control both lens and pupil. A new sort of yellow filter, too, was developed: the lens itself became coloured (in compensation for the long-lost retinal droplets of lizards). In many diurnal forms the retina developed 'new and unique double cones', and there were great changes in the structure of the optic nerve and venous supply. A new type of conus papillaris (homologous with the avian pecten) arose (see p. 640). This vascular structure probably carries nutrient substances into the vitreous humour, whence they diffuse to the retina. The resultant eye 'presents substitutes for all the losses, remedies for all the defects, of the vestigial organ of the original snakes'. The dotted arrows show the direction of application of force during accommodation. (From J. Z. Young, after Walls.)

Lizard labels: Ectodermal sphincter, dilatator; Cornea; Iris; Canal of Schlemm (in sclera); Ciliary processes lacking; Scleral ossicle; Ciliary muscle; Base plate; Lens (colourless); Ciliary body; Ringwulst; Ectodermal Conus; Vitreous b.; Fovea; Sclera (cartilage); Chorioid; Retina (avascular and with standard double cones); Optic nerve; Yellow cone oil droplets

Snake labels: Spectacle; Mesodermal sphincter, dilatator; Intraconjunctival space; Cornea; Ant. pad; Iris; Canal of Schlemm (in cornea); Skin; Lens (yellow); Ciliary body (no muscles); Hyaloid vessels; Vitreous b.; Mesodermal Conus; Sclera (fibrous); Chorioid; Retina (with unique double cones); No cone oil droplets; No epichorioidal lymph spaces; Optic nerve eyes of all reptiles (Fig. 351, p. 519). These bulge turret-like, and each can be operated independently to a degree unknown in other animals. The eyes can be 'turned through 180° horizontally, 90° vertically, and one eye may be made to aim backwards while the other looks straight forward' (Walls). Thus, this heavily camouflaged, slow-moving lizard can look for prey in all directions at once and, although the lid-crater surrounding the small cornea restricts the visual field, the visual axis is long and the retinal image large. The remarkable power of convergence gives the centrally placed foveæ a common binocular point of aim and an uncommonly good judgment of distance for the astonishingly swift protrusion of the adhesive tongue. *Lacerta viridis*, by comparison, has only a 40° range of vision. The eyes of the sluggish Gila Monster (*Heloderma*) (p. 497) are fixed.

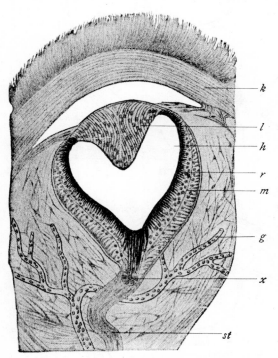

FIG. 376.—*Sphenodon:* **Pineal apparatus.** *g,* blood-vessels; *h,* cavity of the eye filled with fluid; *k,* capsule of connective-tissue; *l.* lens; *m.* molecular layer of the retina; *r.* retina; *st.* stalk of the pineal eye; *x,* cells in the stalk. (From Wiedersheim, after Baldwin Spencer.)

A *pecten* (pp. 481 and 595) is generally present. Internally the eyes of reptiles, other than snakes, are essentially like those of the lizard (p. 481). The eyes of snakes have many peculiarities, such as the absence of the scleral skeleton. In the chamæleons there is a single circular eyelid with a central aperture. In the greater number of geckos, some skinks and other lizards, and in all the snakes, movable eyelids have been replaced by a spectacle, probably developed from the eyelid rudiments. In such forms the nictitating membrane appears to have been lost. On the basis of the structural peculiarities of the ophidian eye, which differs in many ways from that of other reptiles, Walls has argued that the snakes originated as burrowing creatures, and later emerged above the surface of the ground (see Fig. 375).

Largely because of the profession of snake-charming there is perennial controversy concerning *hearing* in serpents. The middle ear cavity is virtually absent. A *columella auris* (p. 361) occurs embedded in muscular and fibrous tissue and attached externally to the quadrate. Thus, despite the piping of the charmer and the dancing of the cobra (or other species), it seems likely that the snake is insensitive to air-borne sound. Very probably it is optically influenced by the movements of the man and his instrument. There is suggestive evidence that a rattlesnake, for example, cannot hear its own rattling. On the other hand, the attachment of columella to quadrate undoubtedly makes the snake highly sensitive to earth-borne vibrations such as approaching feet (see also p. 448). Thus most snakes secrete themselves long before the approach of Man (see, however, p. 537).

Developed in close relation to the epiphysis there is in many lizards (*Lacerta, Varanus, Anguis, Amphibolurus,* and others), and particularly in *Sphenodon,* a remarkable organ—the *parietal organ* or *pineal eye* (Fig. 376). This is situated

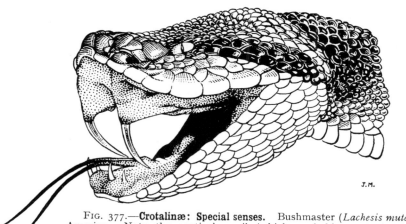

FIG. 377.—**Crotalinæ: Special senses.** Bushmaster (*Lachesis muta*) of tropical America. Note the vertical pupil (which probably protects dusk-sensitive retina from bright light) and the long forked tongue, which is functionally associated with the organ of Jacobson. (From photograph by Ditmars.)

in the parietal foramen of the cranial roof just under the integument, and covered in the young (e.g. *Scleropus*) by a transparent scale (Eakin, Quay and Westfall). The pineal eye is developed from a hollow outgrowth of the diencephalon in front of the epiphysis. The distal end of this becomes constricted off as a hollow sphere, while the remainder is converted into a nerve. The wall of the hollow sphere becomes divergently modified on opposite sides. The distal side gives rise to a lens-like thickening (*l.*). The proximal side forms a membrane several layers in thickness—the *retina* (*r.*). The whole is enclosed in a capsule of connective-tissue (*k.*). The nerve usually degenerates before the animal reaches maturity. It has been sometimes claimed, but not proved, that this organ retains a photo-receptor function in some modern reptiles. The paired *facial pits* that occur in pit-vipers (Crotalinæ) (Fig. 377), but which are absent in the Viperinæ, function as thermoreceptors (Bullock and Cowles). A pit occurs between eye and nostril and consists of two cavities separated by a membrane. These organs (and the pits in the marginal scales along the mouth of pythons and some boas) are supplied by branches of the trigeminal nerve. The apparatus perhaps helps the animals to locate precisely and attack warm-blooded prey.

Endocrine Glands.—These fall into the characteristic vertebrate pattern (p. 147), possibly including the formation of a post-ovulatory *corpus luteum* in viviparous and ovoviviparous snakes and lizards. A substance resembling progesterone has been extracted from the ovaries of ovoviviparous snakes and there is some evidence that, in at least one viviparous lizard (*Hoplodactylus*), progesterone or its homologue may be involved in pregestational changes in the female tract. The hypophysis is necessary for the maintenance of pregnancy in snakes. There is evidence, too, that in some species ovariectomy is followed by fœtal resorption in the early stages of development, but, at the same time, injection of progesterone does not prevent such effects as in mammals. It has been suggested, but not proved, that something not unlike the chorionic secretions of the Mammalia (p. 905) may take over in late pregnancy.

Excretion.—In common with the 'higher' amniotes, the metanephros takes on the function of excretion. With the elimination of gills, and the cutaneous permeability that accompanied the final conquest of land, the kidney in the Reptilia assumed additional importance. Life depended partly upon conservation of body-fluids. Glomeruli were reduced in size and vascularity. Excretion became *uricotelic* in at least some terrestrial stocks, including, apparently, that which gave rise to the birds. Such animals abandoned urea excretion, which involves considerable water loss. Uric acid, on the other hand, is comparatively non-toxic and insoluble, and is precipitated in the urodæum, the vital fluid being reabsorbed into the circulation and the now semi-solid or solid nitrogen compounds discharged as urates with the fæces. Among extant reptiles, the land snakes and lizards (to which water conservation is of great importance) retain drastically reduced glomeruli. Chelonians which have generally returned to water require no such protection and possess glomeruli very like those of typical anurans.

The Crocodilia, snakes, and some lizards (e.g. *Varanus*) lack a urinary bladder. Most lizards, *Sphenodon*, and the chelonians possess one. This opens into the urodæum. Aquatic reptiles, to whom water retention is less important, appear generally to excrete relatively large proportions of comparatively soluble, and therefore toxic, urea and ammonia, and little uric acid. Perhaps significantly, the land-living European tortoise *Testudo græca* excretes principally uric acid. In the North American Desert Gopher (*Gopherus agassizi*) the accessory bladders developed in other tortoises are reduced to tiny pouches which contain small amounts of urine. In this, the waste nitrogen is held, not as soluble urea but as uric acid, which can be retained for a considerable period without ill-effects. In the case of ovoviviparous lizards and snakes, which retain a relatively impermeable egg-'shell', it is advantageous to excrete embryonic nitrogenous waste principally as insoluble uric acid and not as the more toxic urea.

There is evidence that females of some species use bladder-fluid to moisten and firm the sand during nest-digging and possibly to moisten the eggs.

Reproduction.—The description already given of the reproductive organs of the lizard (p. 483) applies, so far as all the principal features are concerned, to all the Lacertilia and to the Ophidia.

In snakes and many lizards, however, a very distinct so-called *sexual segment* has been demonstrated in the male kidney. In *Vipera berus* the organ makes up almost half of the total kidney volume. The epithelium of the sub-terminal portion of each individual renal tubule (nephron) is sharply marked off into an area of columnar cells. No specific secretion has been demonstrated but the cells themselves are said to exhibit a cyclical activity that runs hand in hand with that of the secretory interstitial Leydig cells and the epididymis.

A feebly developed corresponding segment occurs also in the female. There is no evidence that the sexual segment in reptiles is homologous with the sexual component that has been described in the kidney of certain fishes and urodeles. It has not been shown in *Testudo*.

Anal glands are a characteristic of snakes. These lie at the base of the tail and discharge into the cloaca. There is some evidence that their odorous secretion enables the sexes to locate each other.

In the Crocodilia and Chelonia there is, instead of paired penes (Fig. 378), a median solid penis attached to the wall of the cloaca. A small process, the *clitoris*, occurs in a corresponding position in the female. Though fertilisation is always internal, most reptiles are oviparous, laying eggs enclosed in a tough, parchment-like or calcified shell. These are usually deposited in holes, and left to hatch by the heat of the sun. In the crocodiles they are laid in a rough nest. Turtles of various species lay from one to 300 eggs which they usually deposit in holes dug in the sand, often, in the case of marine species, on the beaches of remote tropical atolls after dark (Fig. 327).

Some lizards and snakes are ovoviviparous. Their eggs are enclosed in a thin membrane and retained in the oviduct during the developmental period. Diverse modes of parturition may have no taxonomic significance, for, within the genus *Lacerta*, one species, *L. agilis*, is oviparous and another, *L. vivipara*, is ovoviviparous. A few northern ovoviviparous or viviparous lizards and snakes are sometimes compelled to hibernate before the birth of their young, which are then retained in the oviduct until the following spring. Some lizards and snakes (as well as some fishes, p. 278) have developed yolk sac, and/or chorio-allantoic placentation. In such reptiles the eggs lie in expanded *incubating chambers* in the oviducts. A single large artery and vein runs dorsally along each oviducal wall, the artery giving off branches which pass around the incubating chambers. Where the arterioles break up into capillaries the vein is likewise joined by capillaries. Three types of primitive placentation have been described.

The first is a simple arrangement whereby change in the maternal and embryonic epithelium allows the capillaries of the two blood-streams to approach each other (the lizards *Lygosoma, Egernia, Tiliqua, Mabuya,* and probably *Chalcides* and the snake *Denisonia*). A second simple type involves the raising of the maternal capillaries into small ridges which are pressed against the chorionic ectoderm. Although some pseudopodial processes from the embryonic tissue penetrate the maternal epithelium, the union is superficial and without real interpenetration of parental and embryonic material (*Lygosoma*). In the third and most elaborate placentation, the oviducal wall is raised into a series of vascular folds in the form of an ellipse which is applied to a likewise elliptical area of thickened chorionic ectoderm (*Lygosoma, Chalcides*).

A remarkable post-partum function of the yolk sac (see below) has been recently suggested in the European Adder (*Vipera berus*)

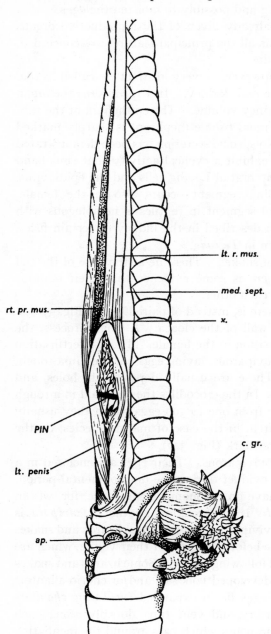

FIG. 378.—**Ophidia: Bilateral copulatory organs.** The penes (so-called 'hemipenes') of *Vipera berus* in ventral view with right organ artificially evaginated. On the left side the ventral caudal muscles have been removed and the invaginated penis exposed by retraction. *ap.* opening of left penial sac; *c. gr.* copulatory grapples on right penis; *lt. penis*, extending caudally under pin holding dissection flaps apart; *lt. r. mus.* large retractor muscle of left penis; *med. sept.* median septum; *pr. mus.* propulsor muscle; *x.* end of left penis and place of insertion of large retractor muscle. (Modified after Volsoe.)

(Bellairs, *et al*). The yolk-sac, which remains substantial at birth, is retracted into the juvenile body cavity and may provide a source of energy for the young snake for the first eight months of its life, including the period of winter hibernation.

The embryos of lizards and snakes possess a small *egg-tooth* which, when functional, is used to puncture and enlarge a hole in the egg-membrane. Two types of *egg-breaker* are known in amniotes. In lizards and snakes the egg-breaker is formed by a true tooth. This is composed of dentine and probably has an enamel cap. It projects forwards in the midline from the premaxilla. This structure—the egg-tooth—is present even in viviparous forms, though in these it may be degenerate. It is reduced, too, in ovoviviparous species, the young of which push through with the snout. The geckos are peculiar in having *paired* egg-teeth projecting side by side. In *Sphenodon*, chelonians, crocodiles, and birds there is no egg-tooth. In them its place is taken by a horny *caruncle* on the tip of the snout. Monotremes (p. 688) have both egg caruncle and egg-tooth though the latter may have little function. Among the marsupials rudiments of both structures have been found in the embryo.

Development.—In all Reptilia segmentation is meroblastic, being confined to a germinal disc of protoplasm situated on one side of the yolk. This divides to form a patch of cells which gradually extends as a two-layered sheet, the *blastoderm*, over the surface of the ovum. The upper of the two layers is the *ectoderm*, the lower the *yolk-endoderm*. The latter is comparable with the yolk-cells of the frog, and the shallow space between it and the yolk represents the *segmentation-cavity*. As the blastoderm extends (Fig. 379), it becomes distinguishable into a central clearer area (*area pellucida* (*a. pel.*)) and a peripheral whitish zone (*area opaca* (*a. op.*)). On the former now appears an elliptical thickened patch, the *embryonic shield* (*emb. s.*), which is formed by the ectoderm cells in this region assuming a cylindrical form while remaining flat elsewhere. Behind the embryonic shield appears a thickening, the so-called *blastoporal plate* or *primitive knot*. Cells invaginate through this region to form a *mesochordal canal* which runs in the direction of the long axis of the future embryo. The opening to the surface of the *mesochordal canal* is known as the blastopore (*bl. p.*). This subsequently takes the form of a narrow slit, the *notochordal canal*, running in the direction of the long axis. The cavity of the invagination corresponds to the archenteron of the frog, and the cells lining it are the notochord dorsally and the endoderm laterally and ventrally. The latter subsequently (Fig. 380) coalesces with the yolk-endoderm below the floor of the archenteron, and in this position an aperture is formed through which the archenteron opens freely into the shallow space that lies between the yolk-endoderm and the yolk. It is from the common cavity thus formed that the lumen of the enteric canal is derived. At a somewhat earlier stage a thickening (*pr. pl.*) has appeared in the yolk-endoderm in the region which will give rise to the head of the embryo. This is the *protochordal plate*. It enters into intimate relationship with the notochordal cells that roof over the archenteron and, when the floor of the latter becomes opened

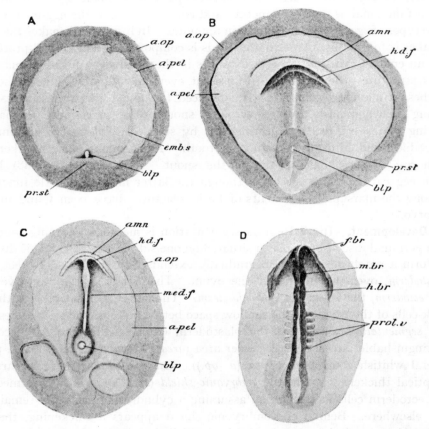

FIG. 379.—*Alligator:* **Development.** *A*, stage with embryonic shield, primitive knot and blastopore; *B*, considerably later stage in which the medullary groove has become formed, together with the head-fold of the embryo and the head-fold of the amnion; *C*, somewhat later stage with well-developed medullary folds and medullary groove; *D*, later stage in which the medullary groove has become partly closed in by the medullary folds and in which six pairs of protovertebræ have become developed. *amn.* amnion; *a. op.* area opaca; *a. pel.* area pellucida; *blp.* blastopore; *emb. s.* embryonic shield; *f. br.* fore-brain; *h. br.* hind-brain; *hd. f.* head-fold; *m. br.* mid-brain; *med. f.* medullary folds; *prot. v.* somites; *pr. st.* primitive knot. (After Clarke).

out, forms with them a continuous plate. In this, the notochord proper originates along the middle line. The mesoderm of all the region in front of the blastopore grows out from it at the sides. The aperture of invagination becomes narrowed, and is eventually closed by the approximation and coalescence of its edges. In the region in which the coalescence of the edges takes place there is for a time complete union of the layers, as in the region of the *primitive streak* of birds and mammals. The anterior part of the aperture, however, remains open for a time as the opening of the neurenteric canal.

In front of the blastopore a longitudinal depression, bounded by a pair of longitudinal folds (Fig. 379, *med. f.*), is the beginning of the medullary groove.

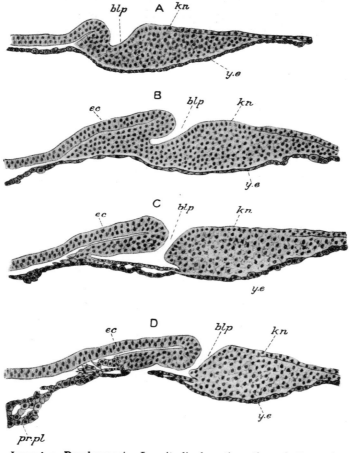

FIG. 380.—*Lacerta:* **Development.** Longitudinal sections through the embryonic area of blastoderms illustrating successive stages in the formation of the invagination-cavity (archenteron) and its communication with the segmentation-cavity. *blp.* blastopore; *ec.* ectoderm of embryonic shield; *kn.* primitive knot; *pr. pl.* protochordal plate; *y. e.* yolk-endoderm. In *D* the opening below and in front of *blp.* points to aperture of communication established between the invagination-cavity and the underlying space. (Modified after Wenckebach.)

As this becomes closed it encloses, in its posterior portion, the blastopore or dorsal opening of the neurenteric canal. At the sides of the medullary groove appear the somites (*prot. v.*). The general history of these parts has already been sketched in the section on the Craniata (p. 160), and further details will be given in the account of the development of birds (p. 645), which agrees with that of reptiles in most essential respects. In the section on avian embryology will also be found an account of the formation of the characteristic fœtal membranes, the *amnion* and the *allantois*, which applies in all essential respects to the Reptilia as well.

There are numerous accounts of the alleged great longevity of reptiles, especially chelonians (p. 489). There are apparently valid records of the survival in captivity of crocodiles and pythons for thirty years, of an Anaconda (*Eunectes*) to the age of twenty-nine, and of a *Sphenodon* to twenty-eight.

CLASS AVES

INTRODUCTION

In many respects birds are the most highly specialised craniate class. Almost every part of their organisation is modified in accordance with aerial life. All birds possess feathers, and only birds possess them. The fore-limbs are modified as wings. The sternum and shoulder-girdles are strikingly altered and serve as origins for the great wing-muscles and the mechanical framework to support their activity. The pelvic girdle and hind-limbs have changed to support the entire weight of the body on the ground. The perfection of the respiratory system, enabling a more complete absorption of oxygen and the production of a higher constant temperature than in other animals, has come hand in hand with the evolution of incomparable powers of flight. Important negative characteristics of modern birds are an absence of teeth and the left aortic arch. The right ovary and oviduct have generally disappeared. The brain is of a highly specialised character. The elevation of the group from near the ground has allowed the olfactory apparatus in most species to degenerate, and this has been accompanied by an extraordinary enlargement of the eye, and enhanced efficiency in vision. Despite the general validity of the old assertion that birds are essentially glorified reptiles, the above series of strongly-marked characteristics are hardly equalled in distinction in any other class. Moreover, the organisation of existing birds is, in its essential features, singularly uniform. Even taking flightless types into consideration, the entire class presents less diversity of structure than many single *orders* of fishes, amphibians, and reptiles.

Although fossil forms have been found that possessed teeth, feathers, the peculiarly avian synsacrum, and a long reptilian tail, the exact ancestry of birds is not yet known. Avian fossils are comparatively rare for mainly three reasons. In the first place, flight renders birds less likely to be bogged or drowned and embedded in silt. Secondly, birds that die on dry land or sea are usually eaten by predators, and have the hard parts scattered before inundation. Thirdly, the generally pneumatic bones of birds, though possessed of great tensile strength, are apparently less durable than those of other groups.

Probably the best that can be at present said with certainty is that the class is derived from a stock of Mesozoic archæosaurian bipedal reptiles (p. 498). The reptiles most closely allied to the birds appear to be the dinosaurs (p. 507) : certainly both groups had a common ancestry. The ancestral birds developed a feathery or feather-like covering probably first as a heat-conservation device (like the fur of mammals), and later as an aid to flight while gliding from trees or while volplaning off the ground at speed (p. 503).

The upper Jurassic genus *Archæopteryx* (? = *Archæornis*), by a lucky accident of petrifaction in fine-grained lithographic limestone, is available in fossil form, even including exquisitely preserved feather-structure. These small (crow-sized) birds provide, as does *Seymouria* (p. 427), splendid examples of *mosaic evolution*, *i.e.* the possession of well-developed characters thoroughly typical of both groups between which the animal is transitional.

Thus, *Archæopteryx* had the following reptilian characters : a long tail of many (20) free vertebræ, simple articulation between vertebral centra, short sacrum (of six vertebræ), separate metacarpals, clawed digits on the fore-limbs, separate metatarsals, simple ribs and gastralia, and simple brain with long, narrow cerebral hemispheres and small cerebellum behind the optic lobes. At the same time it had the following avian characters : feathers which were identical in structure with those of modern birds, arm-feathers arranged in an identical way, a furcula formed from fused clavicles, back-wardly projecting pubes, and an opposable hallux on each foot. There was no obvious trace of a sternum in the fossil specimen of either *Archæopteryx* or *Archæornis*. However, by means of X-ray examination, de Beer has now shown that in the former it was flat and bony, and that it therefore accords with other features revealing that in life *Archæopteryx* was incapable of flapping flight and must have used its wings to glide from the branches of trees (Fig. 414, p. 599).

The subsequent development of true flight, as distinct from the occasional gliding that is found among fishes, amphibians, reptiles, and mammals (excluding the true flight of bats), enabled birds successfully to exploit a new environment and to radiate rapidly into one of the most successful groups of modern animals.

Extant flightless birds are all descended from true fliers. However beneficial flight is in escaping enemies and for the exploitation of both sea and land, it has nevertheless been lost independently in a number of groups. The 'older' palæognathous birds (cassowaries, Emu, Ostrich, rheas, kiwis, moas, tinamous, and others) have all become flightless except the tinamous. The penguins (apparently an early offshoot from flying birds like petrels and albatrosses) have likewise become flightless. Among the more 'modern' Neognathæ many members of various groups have also, in special circumstances, lost the ability to fly. A classical case was the recently extinguished Great Auk or Garefowl (*Alca impennes*), a Razorbill-like auk whose wings became converted to paddles not unlike those of penguins: a striking example of convergent evolution. Several species of rails have become earth-bound, likewise gallinules (of which one flightless type, *Notornis mantelli*, still survives in southern New Zealand). There became flightless, too, at least one species of grebe (*Centropelina* of Lake Titicaca, in upland Peru) and a cormorant (*Nannopterum* of the Galapagos). Several ground-dwelling pigeons have ceased to fly, with a concomitant degeneration of wings and pectoral apparatus. Classical among these is a group of recently extinguished species which inhabited islands of the Indian Ocean. These were the awkward, swan-sized Dodo (*Didus ineptus*), which was common in Mauritius until the late 17th century, the Solitaire (*Pezophaps solitarius*) of nearby Rodriguez, and the White Dodo (*D. bonbonicus*) of Reunion. Representatives of other orders, including even parrots (*e.g. Strigops habroptilus* or Kakapo of New Zealand), also became flightless or almost so.

The reduction or complete loss of flight has often taken place in special circumstances in which the absence of predators has made flight no longer greatly beneficial. Oceanic islands, to which carnivorous mammals could not penetrate, have often been a nursery of flightless birds. The abandonment of flight allows a reduction in wing size, and often the assumption of a bulk greater than the muscle mass of any flying bird could possibly lift. Likewise, an increase in egg-size is possible. Once it becomes flightless, a bird must stay that way and remain at the mercy of later, more ferocious arrivals, including particularly predators introduced by Man. The flightless dodos, rails, Great Auk, and many others almost all vanished at the onslaught of Man and his domestic animals, although it is possible that some were already fading before the Europeans began to circumnavigate the world. A remarkable survival is the Tooth-billed Pigeon (*Didunculus*), which was in Samoa a ground-nester rapidly approaching extinction. It, however, still could fly. It began to nest in trees and has survived. Of the flightless 'ratite' (raft-breasted) species such as moas, kiwis, ostriches, rheas, etc., only those that are rigidly protected (*e.g.* kiwis) or large, powerful, and elusive (*e.g.* cassowaries, Emu, and the Ostrich) survive in considerable numbers.

As long as a bird remains a good flier it cannot become very large : it is probable that the size-limit for flying birds has been almost reached several times (*e.g.* pigeons, turkeys, birds-of-prey (p. 615)). Efficient flight requires a large surface-mass ratio. It is significant that the heaviest of the flying birds that are almost constantly on the wing (albatrosses, vultures, eagles) are soaring fliers which make very considerable use of long wings and rising air-currents. The heavy Mute Swan (*Cygnus olor*) is unable to take off from the surface of a frozen pond on a still day. A twelve-stone angel with pectoral muscles only as efficient as the very efficient muscles of birds would be faced with the gravest aerodynamical difficulties. Certainly there would be nowhere to house the relatively enormous muscle-mass required to get it airborne and to keep it so (p. 582).

Bird-flight, like any other, depends on the interaction of forces between the wings, the tail-rudder, and the atmosphere. Two principal forms of flight —gliding and flapping—exist. The first is relatively simple, yet still incompletely understood. All flapping birds (*e.g.* swallows) use gliding flight to some degree. Except when taking off and landing, the gliders ride almost exclusively on thermal air currents rising from the earth (*e.g.* birds-of-prey) or on perhaps more or less horizontal air-currents above the ocean (petrels, albatrosses).

The pectoralis major muscle (p. 580) is the chief motive force in the powerful down-beat of the flapping wing. This muscle is especially heavy, powerful, and copiously supplied with blood in flapping fliers. In this sort of flight not only streamlined wing-shape, and the principal up-and-down movements, but many essential subsidiary actions, involving individual groups of feathers and the tiny bastard-wing (p. 566), play a part. While a wing is actually beating, its shape, due both to muscle movement and to feather arrangement, is constantly changing. These influences, and postures, differ according to whether the bird is taking off, gliding, flapping, or landing. To a great degree, too, they differ according to the special modes of flight of individual genera. Thus, the heavy, though swift, flapping flight of swans; the delicate hovering of a Kestrel; and the alternative backwards-and-forwards flight of a humming-bird vibrating before a flower—all call into play different structural components. In humming-birds which can fly backwards a little, as well as hover for long periods, the up, as well as the down, strokes are powerful. (An analogy is a sculled boat compared with one that is rowed.) The supracoracoideus (so-called pectoralis minor) muscle of humming birds has almost as great a mass as the pectoralis major. The wings beat at a rate of more than 50 per second. The astonishing activity of these tiny creatures (some of which are less than 3 inches long and weigh only 3 grammes) involves a respiration rate of about 250 per minute (domestic fowl 30). The heart-beat of many small birds under stress or excitement exceeds 800 (domestic fowl 300). The temperature of passerines (p. 582) usually ranges from 102° to 111° F. (see also below).

The enormous surface in relation to the tiny mass of some humming-birds has made it necessary for them to evolve special behavioural and metabolic mechanisms to enable them to survive at night, since they are strictly diurnal feeders and therefore cannot replenish body-fuel after dark. By day, humming-birds have by far the highest metabolic rates (as measured by oxygen consumption in relation to mass) of all vertebrate animals. This metabolic rate, of course, goes hand in hand with a relatively enormous ingestion and combustion of fuel. One species, studied in a Californian laboratory, was observed to increase its feeding ratio about an hour before night-fall. Then the animal perched, and went into a state of torpidity in which its metabolic rate dropped sharply, and its temperature equalled that of the environment. A few humming-birds that inhabit cold places—*e.g.* the high Andes—are said to retreat at night into caves. A North American night-jar, the Poor-will (*Phalænoptilus nuttalli*), undergoes true hibernation involving a prolonged winter torpidity at reduced body temperature.

Under experimental conditions the Poor-will, Anna Humming bird (*Aeronautes saxatilis*), and the White-throated Swift (*Micropus apus*) will reduce their body temperature and become torpid (Bartholomew, *et al.*). A Poor-will became torpid at 3·5° C. and its body temperature fell to 4·8° C. The bird was aroused by gradually increasing the external temperature to 22° C. Several hours passed before the bird became fully active, but in a well-camouflaged species such slow recovery may not be disadvantageous. Humming-birds recovered rapidly. Reduced body temperature and torpor reduce energy consumption, and are associated with high metabolic rates during activity (humming-birds) or survival during long intervals of fasting (swifts and Poor-will).

The speed of birds, like their longevity (p. 562), has been greatly exaggerated, and few exact data are available on either. Most passerines (perching birds) of the size of a sparrow fly relatively slowly (15–35 miles per hour). Even the Carrier Pigeon averages no more than 50 miles per hour, but swifts (*Apus*) are believed to travel at between 60 and 90 miles per hour in short bursts.

The remarkable respiratory rate, oxygen consumption, and high temperatures of small flying birds result in a nervous and muscular efficiency that makes possible the seemingly tireless activity that is one of their most obvious characteristics. Heat generated by muscle activity is conserved principally by the relatively non-conducting plumage, which, in times of reduced temperature, can be erected by a mechanism essentially similar to that which achieves pilo-erection in mammals (p. 683). But even thickly plumaged birds must (like all animals with a large surface and a small volume) eat enormously in order to replace the body heat that is continuously flowing away. Thus, in countries with severe winter, birds that do not migrate die in great numbers. A few species such as swallows (*Hirundo*), bee-eaters (*Merops*), and Australian wood-'swallows' (*Artamus*) have developed a curious secondary conservation device—the 'clustering' habit of clinging perched together in dozens with only wing- and tail-tips exposed, to conserve heat for a few days until the probable advent of warmer weather. In recent severe winters swarming, sleeping swallows have been sent south over the European Alps by aeroplane in artificial migration to save their lives.

The colonisation by birds of areas too cold to support reptiles has been made possible partly by the development of their habit of *incubation* by which the embryo is kept at an appropriate temperature by heat from the brooding bird's body. In neognathous species a special adaptation in the form of bare, heavily vascular ventral *brood-patches* facilitates the transfer of parental heat to the eggs. The seasonal development of brood-patches is under hormonal control, and apparently involves a synergism between prolactin from the anterior pituitary gland (p. 150) and œstrogen from the ovary (p. 598). Several days before incubation begins, specific ventral areas shed their feathers and become richly vascularised. After the young fly the skin returns to the pre-nuptial condition.

A few tropical and sub-tropical species have reverted, with specialisations, to the reptilian habit of burying the eggs. Thus, the megapodes of Australia, New Guinea, and adjacent Pacific islands scratch together piles of decaying vegetation and therein lay their eggs. Some of these incubators, added to over the years, ultimately reach a height of 20 feet. The heat generated by the fermenting vegetation combined, in some species, with direct solar heat, incubates the eggs. The Australian Mallee Fowl, *Leipoa ocellata*, controls the temperature by altering the amount of covering material. In most species there is no such regulation by the parents. Some species lay their eggs in warm volcanic earth, while others depend on solar heat, burying their eggs in tropical beaches. Young megapodes are precocial, *i.e.* they are able to leave the nest and take care of themselves from the time they are hatched.

All small birds are perilously dependent on day-to-day food supplies, and a few species, including particularly the European Nuthatch (*Sitta*), gather stores for the winter as do certain mammals. Very young birds are particularly susceptible to low temperatures, being almost poikilothermous (p. 386) and in high, or even in temperate, latitudes are often in danger of freezing or starvation. The breeding season in non-tropical species is 'timed' to coincide with relatively high temperatures and abundant supplies of food for the young, although a few birds (*e.g.* Emperor Penguin, *Aptenodytes forsteri*) have evolved special anatomical and behavioural mechanisms that enable them to breed during mid-winter. Very young birds of some species are compelled to eat the equivalent of more than half their own weight in food per day in order to satisfy their metabolic requirements and keep warm. Not only must the food be sufficient in quantity, but it must also contain essential amino-acids. Thus, most vegetarian species give their young at least a partially insectivorous diet during the early stages of growth. Pigeons, which produce proteinous crop-'milk' (p. 583), are among the few species that can often successfully reproduce during autumn and winter.

Juvenile mortality in birds is extremely high, but once maturity is reached some species live to a considerable age. An Eagle-owl (*Bubo*) lived in captivity to the age of sixty-eight, and a Sulphur-crested Cockatoo (*Kakatöe*) to fifty-six. Eagles, pelicans, and condors (*Vultur*) have lived for more than fifty years and gulls, geese, and pigeons to between thirty and forty. A great

Fig. 381.—**Aves: Epigamic plumage.** The basic structure of the feather lends itself to diversification both in gross form and in microscopic structure, the latter sometimes producing weirdly beautiful 'interference' effects. Birds of widely different classes possess spectacular specialisations: *e.g.* the covert- (*not* tail-) feathers of the Indian peacock (*Pavo*), and the lyre-shaped feathers of Australian *Menura*; the racquet-tails of certain New Guinea Kingfishers (*Tanysiptera*); the trailing wing-plumes of the African nightjars *Macrodipteryx* and *Cosmetornis*, and so on. It is in the Paradiseidæ (New Guinea and Australian rain-forests) that epigamic specialisation (in males only) reaches its most astonishing extremes. Birds-of-paradise range in size between that of a thrush and a small pigeon. The selection of males above (not to scale) is as follows:

1. Ribbon-tail (*Tæniparadisea meyeri*). The white, dark-tipped tail-feathers, relatively the longest of any bird, were procured by Europeans from the head-dress of a stone-age Melanesian and were sent to the U.K., where they were found to be so characteristic that a new species could be described while the rest of the animal was still unknown. The bird is coloured green, purple, black, copper, brown, and white. 2. Superb (*Lophorina superba*). Principally metallic green and velvety black. 3. Twelve-wired (*Seleucidis melanoleucus*). Metallic green, dark glossed with purple, yellow flank-plumes (with shafts recurved), and brilliant red legs. (In the museum skin the yellow commonly fades to white.) 4. Sunset (*Paradisea apoda*). Chestnut, green and yellow, with golden plumes. This was probably the first species to reach Europe. No legs remained on the rough, native-preserved skins; hence Linnæus' specific name, and the sailors' legend (originating in the sixteenth century) of heavenly birds that came to earth only upon their death. 5. Blue-bird (*Paradisornis rudolphi*). Vivid blue, velvet black, and maroon. This, perhaps the loveliest of all, was acquired (but not collected) by Finsch and Meyer, who quickly named it after 'the high and mighty protector of ornithological researches over the whole world' who was later to finish his career at Mayerling. 6. Enamelled (*Pteridophora alberti*). The twin head-plumes have pale blue enamel-like 'flaps' projecting from the outer side of the shaft. The rest is velvet black, yellows, and brown. 7. King (*Cicinnurus regius*). During display the emerald-tipped pectoral fans are erected, the snowy ventral feathers are fluffed, and the 'metallic' green-tipped tail wires are swung forward over the crimson head. The apple-green gullet is meanwhile exposed; and the legs are blue. 8. Six-plumed (*Parotia sefilata*). Principally velvetblack, with a short glittering crest and a peculiar bronze-and-white tuft above the nostrils. Large erectile feathers form a breast-plate. The six head plumes are moved during display. 9. Republican (*Schlegelia wilsoni*), described by Prince Bonaparte. The face is black and the head is bare and blue; the nape is yellow, the back crimson, and there is a large emerald-coloured breast-plate. (Redrawn after Iredale and other authors.)

variety of birds have lived for thirty years in captivity. The greatest recorded age at liberty (determined by ringing) is that of a Black-headed gull (*Larus*) at twenty-five. The most controversial, and doubtless fictitious, age of any individual bird is the 120 years attributed to the celebrated sulphur-crested 'Cocky Bennett', for many years an institution at a public-house at Tom Ugly's

FIG. 382.—**Aves: Sexual and aggression display.** The scintillating blue-black male Satin Bower-bird (*Ptilonorhynchus violaceus*) of the forests of Eastern Australia builds an avenue-like display ground or bower which faces north and south. At one end he accumulates with great discrimination display objects broadly matching the colours of rival males. With these he performs a noisy flashing display that attracts a female and repels rivals. This is probably partly a displaced combat-drive. The male paints the inner walls of his bower with a mixture of charcoal ground up with saliva, or with pulped fruit, or other material. A special bark tool (see also Fig. 426, p. 621) is made for use in the plastering operation, which may be of the nature of displaced courtship feeding. After some weeks of male display, the watching female adopts a specific squatting position in or near the bower: this constitutes a sign-stimulus which leads to copulation. By now the forest has become seasonally full of the insect food on which the young will be fed.

Point, Sydney. Year after year pictures in avicultural and other journals showed this venerable bird with a grossly overgrown beak and a body almost completely devoid of feathers. He was extremely voluble, his favourite utterance being: 'One more bloody feather and I'll fly!' He came to a much-lamented end in 1916. Investigation showed his authentic history to cover a mere twenty-six years, although he was unquestionably somewhat older.

The behavioural activities of birds, however intelligent some species seem to be, are mostly reflex in character and essentially under the control of environmental events (including activities of the opposite sex) and the internal hormonal condition of the individual. For example, a parent passerine bird will work desperately to satisfy the squeaking, gaping maw of a young cuckoo and pass unheeding her own offspring, which, thrown from the nest by the parasite, lie dying in full sight a foot or so below. Her inherent urge is to feed a noisy coloured gape in the nest. The urge to seek, obtain, and defend *territory* is inherent and dependent upon the secretory condition of the testes. The same is true of *display*, which in birds reaches unparalleled beauty and complexity, and involves (*e.g.* in birds-of-paradise (Fig. 381)) the exhibition of epigamic plumes of sometimes almost indescribable beauty, and sometimes (in bowerbirds) the building of special structures which are enhanced with coloured and otherwise distinctive objects (Fig. 382). At the same time 'in some contexts it is doubtful whether birds are exceeded in learning ability by any organisms other than the highest mammals. . . . In their powers of coordinating their sense impressions for purposes of orientation . . . they appear supreme' (Thorpe).

DISTINCTIVE CHARACTERS AND CLASSIFICATION

Aves are Craniata in which the epidermal exoskeleton takes the form of feathers over the greater part of the body, of a *rhamphotheca* or horny sheath to the beak, and of claws on the digits of the foot and sometimes of the hand. In the standing position the body is entirely supported on the hind-limbs, the articulations of which are thrown forward. The fore-limbs are modified to form wings, usually provided with large feathers for the support of the body during flight. The cervical and free thoracic vertebræ are usually heterocœlous, but may be procœlous or amphicœlous. The sacral vertebræ are fused with the lumbar and with more or fewer of the posterior thoracic and anterior caudal to form a synsacrum for the support of the ilia. The posterior caudal vertebræ are usually fused to form a pygostyle around which the tail-quills are arranged in a semicircle. The bones of the skull undergo early ankylosis. There is a single, rounded, occipital condyle. The united premaxillæ form nearly the whole of the upper jaw. The lower jaw is composed originally of five or six bones in each ramus, and is supported by a freely articulated quadrate. The vertebral ribs are double-headed, provided with bony uncini, and articulate with the bony sternal ribs by synovial joints. The sternum is broad, and is typically produced into a longitudinal ventral keel, having a separate centre of ossification. The keel may be partially or completely aborted. The coracoid is usually more or less pillar-like, the scapula is sabre-shaped, and the clavicles and interclavicle unite to form a furcula.

Except in one extinct species the distal carpals and the metacarpals are united to form a carpo-metacarpus.   There are usually only three digits in the wing, which probably represent the first, second, and third of the typical hand. The ilium is of great size, having large pre- and post-acetabular portions. The acetabulum is perforated in the dry bone.   The pubis and ischium are directed backwards and, except in one case of each, there is neither pubic nor ischiatic symphysis.   The head of the femur is at right angles to the shaft. The proximal tarsals are fused with the tibia to form a tibio-tarsus.   The fibula is much reduced.   The distal tarsals are fused with the second, third, and fourth metatarsals to form a tarso-metatarsus ; the first metatarsal is free.   The fifth digit of the typical foot is absent.

In all Tertiary and Recent birds teeth are absent.   The œsophagus is frequently dilated into a crop and the stomach is usually divided into proventriculus and gizzard.   The junction between the large and small intestines is marked by a pair of cæca.   The lungs are spongy and non-distensible.   The bronchi give off branches which open on the surface of the lung into thin-walled air-sacs, and these in their turn usually communicate with pneumatic cavities in more or fewer of the bones.   The voice is produced in a syrinx situated at or near the junction of the trachea with the bronchi.   The heart is four-chambered, the right auriculo-ventricular valve is muscular, and the right aortic arch alone is present in the adult.   The renal portal system is reduced. The red blood-corpuscles are oval and nucleated.   The temperature of the blood is high (p. 558).   The optic lobes are displaced laterally owing to the meeting of the large cerebral hemispheres and cerebellum.   The lumbar region of the spinal cord has a sinus rhomboidalis.   The olfactory organ is usually poorly developed.   The eye is usually large, and has sclerotic plates and a relatively substantial pecten.   The ear has a large curved cochlea, and a columella.   The kidney is three-lobed, and is developed from the metanephros, the mesonephros undergoing atrophy.   There is no urinary bladder. The ovary and oviduct of the right side are more or less completely atrophied.

Birds are all oviparous, and the large ovum, containing much food-yolk, becomes invested with albumen, a double shell-membrane, and a calcareous shell, in its passage down the oviduct.   The embryo has an amnion, an allantois, and a large yolk-sac.   The newly-hatched young may be able to run or swim and to obtain their own food, in which case they are said to be *precocial* or *nidifugous* ;   or may be more or less naked and dependent for a time upon the parents for their food supply, when they are *altricial* or *nidicolous*.

There is no general agreement with regard to the classification of birds. Owing to the singular uniformity of the class in essential matters of structure, and its vast diversity in detail, avian classification is a matter of great difficulty. The following scheme is perhaps as good as any :

CLASS AVES

Sub-class Archæornithes
Order Archæopterygiformes (Jurassic)

Sub-class Neornithes

Super-order Odontognathæ
Orders Hesperornithiformes (Cretaceous)
Ichthyornithiformes (Cretaceous)

Super-order Palæognathæ
Orders Struthioniformes (Pliocene–Recent)
Rheiformes (Pliocene–Recent)
Casuariiformes (Pleistocene–Recent)
Apterygiformes (Pleistocene–Recent)
Dinornithiformes (Pleistocene–Recent)
Æpyornithiformes (Oligocene–Recent)
Tinamiformes (Pliocene–Recent)

Super-order Impennæ
Order Sphenisciformes (Oligocene–Recent)

Super-order Neognathæ (Cretaceous–Recent) [1]
Orders Gaviiformes, Podicipitiformes, Procellariiformes, Pelecaniformes, Ciconiiformes, Anseriformes, Falconiformes, Galliformes, Gruiformes, Charadriiformes, Diatrymiformes, Columbiformes, Psittaciformes, Cuculiformes, Strigiformes, Caprimulgiformes, Micropodiformes, Coliiformes, Trogoniformes, Coraciiformes, Piciformes, Passeriformes.

EXAMPLE OF THE CLASS.—THE COMMON PIGEON (COLUMBA LIVIA, *var.* DOMESTICA)

The Common, or Domestic Pigeon is known by many varieties, which differ from one another in size, proportions, coloration, and details in feather arrangement. The pouter, fantail, and tumbler illustrate extreme forms which have arisen by artificial selection. These quaint monsters have been produced by breeders who selected, generation after generation, individuals which most nearly attained to some arbitrary standard of perfection, bred from them alone, and killed off the 'inferior' strains. In the same way the Carrier Pigeon was bred for speed and stamina. It is probable that the wild ancestral species from which all these domestic breeds have arisen is the Rock Pigeon (*Columba livia*), which is widely distributed in the Palæarctic and Oriental regions. The following description refers especially to the common Dovecot

---

[1] For reasons mentioned on p. 555, relatively little is known of the fossil history of modern birds. Brief data are given under various orders, pp. 612–620.

Pigeon, which, although often feral, restricts itself to cities and so retains its association with its creator, Man.

External Characters.—The head (Fig. 383) is small, with a rounded cranium and prominent *beak* covered with a *rhamphotheca* or horny sheath.   The head, the long mobile neck, and trunk are invested in a close covering of *feathers*, all directed backwards and overlapping one another.

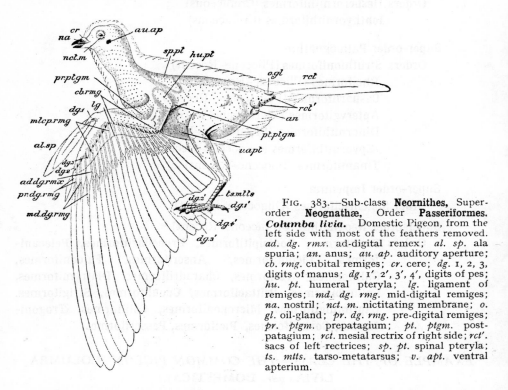

Fig. 383.—Sub-class **Neornithes,** Super-order **Neognathæ,** Order **Passeriformes.** **Columba livia.** Domestic Pigeon, from the left side with most of the feathers removed. *ad. dg. rmx.* ad-digital remex; *al. sp.* ala spuria; *an.* anus; *au. ap.* auditory aperture; *cb. rmg.* cubital remiges; *cr.* cere; *dg.* 1, 2, 3, digits of manus; *dg.* 1′, 2′, 3′, 4′, digits of pes; *hu. pt.* humeral pteryla; *lg.* ligament of remiges; *md. dg. rmg.* mid-digital remiges; *na.* nostril; *nct. m.* nictitating membrane; *o. gl.* oil-gland; *pr. dg. rmg.* pre-digital remiges; *pr. ptgm.* prepatagium; *pt. ptgm.* post-patagium; *rct.* mesial rectrix of right side; *rct′.* sacs of left rectrices; *sp. pt.* spinal pteryla; *ts. mtts.* tarso-metatarsus; *v. apt.* ventral apterium.

Upon removal of the feathers it can be seen that the true tail is a short, conical projection of the trunk, known as the *uropygium*, which gives origin to the series of large feathers—*rectrices*—(*rct.*) to which the word 'tail' is usually applied.   On the dorsal surface of the uropygium is a papilla bearing on its summit the opening of a *preen, coccygeal,* or *oil-gland* (*o. gl.*).   This is the only integumentary gland found in birds.   The skin is dry and no sweat-glands are present.   Thus, birds cannot cool themselves by the principal means available to the Mammalia.   In hot weather they do so by panting as do dogs, which also lack sweat-glands, except in specialised regions, *i.e.* the nose and the soles of the feet.

Connected with the lungs of birds are *air-spaces* which are widespread throughout the body (pp. 586, 589), and these are no doubt involved in the loss of body heat upon the operation of the panting reflex.   Probably, too, a

certain amount of heat is otherwise lost by radiation, convection, and conduction, by removal via the fæces, and by the evaporation of moisture from the
epithelial surfaces of the tongue, and the buccal cavity. A vasomotor nervous
system helps regulate heat loss. If the external temperature rises, the peripheral capillaries dilate, allowing the loss of heat. If it is depressed they
constrict, with the result that heat is conserved. An apparatus (p. 559)
probably broadly similar to the pilomotor mechanism of mammals also exists.
The skin contains nerve-endings and the papilla of each feather has its own
nerve-processes.

The wings show the three typical divisions of the fore-limb : upper arm,
fore-arm, and hand (p. 383); but the parts of the hand are closely bound
together by skin, and only three imperfectly-marked digits, the second (*dg. 2*)
much larger than the first (*dg. 1*) and third (*dg. 3*), can be distinguished. In
the position of rest the three divisions of the wing are bent upon one another
in the form of a *Z*; during flight they are straightened out and extended so
that the axis of the entire wing is at right angles to that of the trunk. On the
anterior or pre-axial border of the limb a fold of skin stretches between the
upper arm and the fore-arm ; this is the *alar membrane* or *pre-patagium* (*pr.
ptgm.*). A similar but much smaller fold extends, postaxially, between the
proximal portion of the upper arm and the trunk ; this is the *post-patagium*
(*pt. ptgm.*).

In the hind-limb the short thigh is closely bound to the trunk, not standing
well out as in a reptile, but directed downwards and forwards ; the long shank
extends from the knee downwards and backwards. The foot is clearly divisible
into a proximal portion, the *tarso-metatarsus* (*ts. mtts.*), and four digits, of
which one, the hallux (*dg. 1'*), is directed backwards, the others, the 2nd, 3rd,
and 4th of the typical foot, forwards. The entire hind-limb is in a plane
parallel with the sagittal plane of the trunk.

The mouth is terminal, and is guarded by the elongated upper and lower
beaks ; it has, therefore, a very wide gape. On each side of the base of the
upper beak is a swollen area of soft skin, the *cere* (*cr.*), surrounding the nostril
(*na.*), which has thus a remarkably backward position. It has been suggested
that the cere may be an exteroceptor organ, but there is no experimental
evidence that this is so. The *eyes* are very large, and each is guarded by an
upper and a lower eyelid and a transparent nictitating membrane (*nct. m.*). A
short distance behind the eye is the *auditory aperture* (*au. ap.*), concealed by
auricular feathers and leading into a short *external auditory meatus*, closed below
by the tympanic membrane. The *anus* or cloacal aperture (*an.*) is a large,
transversely-elongated aperture placed on the ventral surface at the junction
of the uropygium with the trunk.

Exoskeleton.—The exoskeleton (including the feathers) is purely epidermal,
like that of lizards, which also resemble birds in possessing protective horny

scales. These cover the tarso-metatarsus and the four digits of the foot. Each digit of the foot is terminated by a *claw*, which is also a horny product of the epidermis. The rhamphotheca is of the same nature.

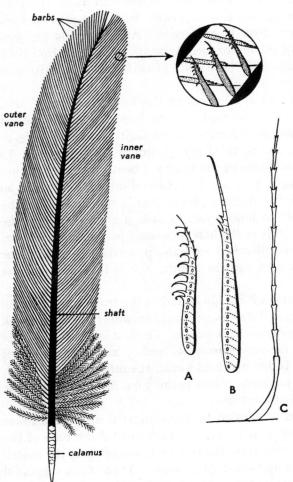

A feather (Fig. 384) consists of a hollow stalk, the *calamus* or quill, and an expanded distal portion, the *vexillum* or *vane*. At the proximal end of the quill is a small aperture, the *inferior umbilicus*, into which fits a small conical prolongation of the skin, the *feather papilla.* Here each feather has its own basal musculature which enables its erection in flight, in cold weather (avoiding heat loss) and at times of emotional excitement. A second, extremely minute aperture, the *superior umbilicus*, occurs at the junction of the quill with the vane on the inner or ventral face of the feather, *i.e.* the face adjacent to the body. A small tuft of down in the neighbourhood of the superior umbilicus represents the *aftershaft* of many birds—including some pigeons (see pp. 606, 627).

Fig. 384.—**Aves: Contour feather.** *Gallus domesticus.* The circular inset magnifies the interlocking mechanism between minute barbules and adjacent barbs (see text). *A.* distal barbule, *B.* proximal barbule, *C.* downy barbule from barb of basal, fluffy part of feather, lacking interlocking apparatus. (Redrawn after Rawles.)

The vane has a longitudinal axis or *rachis* continuous proximally with the quill, but differing from the latter in being solid. To each side of this shaft is attached a kind of membrane forming the expanded part of the feather and composed of *barbs*—delicate, thread-like structures which extend obliquely outwards from the rachis. In an uninjured feather the barbs are closely connected so as to form a continuous sheet. A moderate amount of force separates them, for they are bound together only by extremely delicate oblique filaments, the *barbules*, which have the same general relation to the barbs as the barbs themselves to the rachis.

The precise mode of interlocking of the barbs can be determined only by microscopic examination. Each barb (Fig. 384) is a very thin and long plate springing by a narrow base from the rachis, and pointed distally. From its upper edge (that furthest from the body) spring two sets of barbules, a *proximal set* directed towards the base of the feather, and a *distal set* towards its tip. Owing to their oblique disposition the distal barbules of a given barb cross the proximal barbules of the next, each distal barbule being in contact with several proximal barbules of the barb immediately distal to it. The lower edge of the distal barbule is produced into minute *hooklets* or *barbicels*. In the entire feather the hooklets of each distal barbule hook over prominent *flanges* of the proximal barbules with which it is in contact. In this way the parts of the feather are so bound together that the entire structure offers great resistance to the air.

Among the *contour* feathers which form the main covering of the bird and have the structure just described are *filoplumes*. These are delicate hair-like feathers with a long axis and a few barbs and devoid of locking apparatus at the distal end. The feathers of different parts of the body vary extremely in their individual structure in relation to function. Nestling pigeons are covered with a temporary investment of *down-feathers* in which also there is no interlocking of the barbs (Fig. 385).

Feathers, like scales, arise in the embryo from papillæ of the skin formed of derm with an epidermal covering (Fig. 385). The papilla becomes sunk in a sac, the *feather-follicle*, from which it subsequently protrudes as an elongated *feather-germ*. Its vascular dermal interior is the *feather-pulp*. The Malpighian layer of the distal part of the feather-germ proliferates in such a way as to form a number of vertical radiating ridges. Its proximal part becomes uniformly thickened. In this way is produced the rudiment of a down-feather which has a number of barbs springing, at the same level, from the distal end of the quill. The horny layer of the epidermis forms the temporary sheath which is thrown off as the feather grows and expands. The pulp of the permanent feather is formed from the lower or deep end of that of the down-feather. Its development is at first similar, but, instead of the ridges of the Malpighian layer remaining all of one size, two adjacent ones outgrow the rest and become the rachis. As the latter elongates it carries up with it the remaining ridges which become the barbs.

The feathers do not spring uniformly from the whole surface of the body, but from certain defined areas (Fig. 386), the *feather tracts* or *pterylæ* (*sp. pt.*, *hu. pt.*, etc.). These are separated from one another by featherless spaces or *apteria* (*v. apt.*), from which only a few filoplumes grow. The feathers are, however, long enough to cover the apteria by their overlap, and the body is

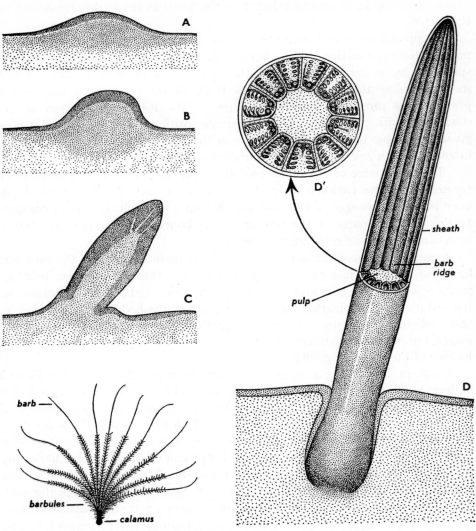

FIG. 385.—**Aves: Down-feather and its formation.** *Gallus domesticus*. *A*. Beginning of development, showing aggregation of mesodermal cells (primordium of dermal papilla) beneath ectoderm. *B*. Feather-germ rising above skin level due to increase in mesoderm and overlying ectoderm (epidermis). *C*. Later stage showing elongation of feather-germ. A thick cylindrical wall of epidermal cells encloses the central mesodermal pulp. At the apex of the feather (shown slightly at a tangent) epidermal cells are beginning to undergo rearrangement into longitudinal barb-ridges (see below). *D*. Feather near time of hatching, in tubular follicle lined with epidermis. The dermal papilla is now permanently located at the base of the follicle. The epidermal walls of the feather cylinder are divided into a series of longitudinal barb-ridges (primordia of barbs and barbules) surrounding the central pulp and protected by an external sheath. *D*. Transverse section, showing 11 barb-ridges, central pulp (with adjacent melanocytes) and external sheath. At bottom left is a mature down-feather of newly hatched chick. The sheath is split and the barbs and barbules are free. Note the absence of a shaft (cf. Fig. 384) and the circular arrangement of barbs around a short calamus. (Redrawn after Rawles.)

thus completely covered with a thick, very light, and non-conducting invest-ment.

In the wings and tail certain special arrangements of the feathers occur. When the wing is stretched out at right angles to the trunk, twenty-three large feathers (Fig. 383) are seen to spring from its hinder or postaxial border : these are the *remiges* or wing-quills. Twelve of them are connected with the ulna and are called *cubitals* or *secondaries* (*cb. rmg.*). The rest are known as *primaries*. Seven of these are attached to the metacarpal region, and are hence called *metacarpals* (*mtcp. rmg.*). The remaining four or *digitals* are attached to the phalanges of the second and third digits. These are again distinguished into a single *ad-digital* (*ad. dg. rmx.*), connected with the single phalanx of the third digit (Fig. 395, *ph. 3*, p. 577), two *mid-digitals* (*md. dg. rmg.*) with the

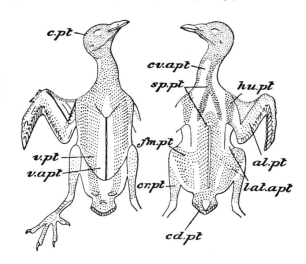

FIG. 386.—*Columba:* **Pterylosis.** *Left,* ventral; *Right,* dorsal. *al. pt.* alar pteryla or wing-tract; *c. pt.* cephalic pteryla or head-tract; *cd. pt.* caudal pteryla or tail-tract; *cr. pt.* crural pteryla; *cv. apt.* cervical apterium or neck-space; *fm. pt.* femoral pteryla; *hu. pt.* humeral pteryla; *lat. apt.* lateral apterium; *sp. pt.* spinal pteryla; *v. apt.* ventral apterium; *v. pt.* ventral pteryla. (After Nitzsch.)

proximal phalanx of the second digit, and two *pre-digitals* (*pr. dg. rmg.*) with its distal phalanx (Fig. 395, *ph. 2'*). A special tuft of feathers on the anterior border of the wing, arising from the pollex (Fig. 396, *ph. 1*), forms the *ala spuria* (*al. sp.*) or bastard wing. The spaces which would otherwise be left between the bases of the remiges are filled in, both above and below, by several rows of *upper* and *lower wing-coverts*. In the tail there are twelve long *rectrices* (Fig. 383, *rct.*) or tail-quills, springing in a semicircle from the uropy-gium. Their bases are covered, as in the wing, by *upper* and *lower tail-coverts*. The whole feather-arrangement is known as the *pterylosis*.

Endoskeleton.—Every part of the bird's skeleton presents characteristic and indeed unique features. The vertebral column, the skull, the sternum, the ribs, the limb-girdles, and the limbs themselves are all so highly specialised that there is hardly a bone, except the phalanges of the toes and the free caudal vertebræ, which could possibly be assigned to any other vertebrate class.

A further peculiarity is that many of the bones are light and contain no marrow. They are filled with air, and are *pneumatic* (p. 502). Large pneumatic bones are internally strutted (Fig. 387) in a manner known to engineers

FIG. 387.—**Neornithes: Internal strutting and pneumatism in bone.** Lightness is achieved without undue sacrifice of strength. The present example is from the metacarpal of a vulture. A comparable arrangement arose by convergence in the pterosaurs (p. 502). (Redrawn after Prochnow.)

as a Warren truss. This device is sometimes used in the wings of aeroplanes. The cavities of pneumatic bones open externally in the dried skeleton by apertures called *pneumatic foramina* (Fig. 395, *pn. for.*), by which, in life, they communicate with the air-sacs and ultimately the lungs (see p. 586). In the pigeon the bones of the fore-arm and hand, and of the leg, are non-pneumatic.

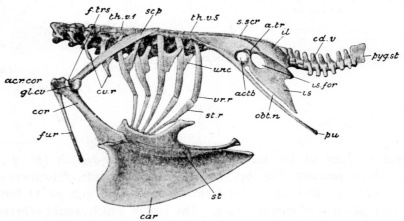

FIG. 388.—***Columba:* Endosketon.** *acr. cor.* acrocoracoid; *a. tr.* anti-trochanter; *actb.* acetabulum; *car.* carina sterni; *cd. v.* caudal vertebræ; *cor.* coracoid; *cv. r.* cervical ribs; *f. trs.* probe passed into foramen triosseum; *fur.* furcula; *gl. cv.* glenoid cavity; *il.* ilium; *is.* ischium; *is. for.* ischiadic foramen; *obt. n.* obturator notch; *pu.* pubis; *pyg. st.* pygostyle; *scp.* scapula; *s. scr.* syn sacrum; *st.* sternum; *st. r.* sternal ribs; *th. v.* 1, first, and *th. v.* 5, last thoracic vertebra; *unc.* uncinus; *vr. r.* vertebral ribs.

The *vertebral column* is distinguished from that of most other Craniata by the great length and extreme mobility of the neck, the rigidity of the trunk-region, and the shortness of the tail. As in Reptilia, the cervical passes almost imperceptibly into the thoracic region. Tne first vertebra with its ribs united with the sternum is conventionally considered as the first thoracic

(Fig. 388, *th. v.* I). There are fourteen cervical vertebræ. The last or last two of these have double-headed ribs (*cv. r.*), each having its proximal end divisible into the *head* proper articulating with the centrum of the vertebra, and a *tubercle* articulating with the transverse process. Their distal ends are free and do not unite with the sternum. In the third to the twelfth there are vestigial ribs (Fig. 389B, *rb.*), each having its head fused with the centrum, and its tubercle with the transverse process. The whole rib thus has the appearance of a short, backwardly-directed transverse process perforated at its base. The perforation transmits the vertebral artery, and is called the *vertebrarterial foramen* (*vrb. f.*).

The centra of the cervical vertebræ differ from those of all other Craniata in having saddle-shaped surfaces. The anterior face (Fig. 389, *A cn*) is concave from side to side and convex from above downwards. The posterior face (*B*) is convex from side to side and concave from above downwards. Thus the centrum in sagittal section appears opisthocœlous, in horizontal section procœlous. This peculiar and complicated form of vertebra is distinguished as *heterocœlous*. The centra articulate with one another by synovial capsules. Each of these is traversed by a vertical plate of cartilage, the *meniscus*, with a central perforation through which a *suspensory ligament* passes from one centrum to the other.

The first two vertebræ, the atlas and axis, resemble those of the lizard, but have their various elements completely fused. The ring-like atlas is small.

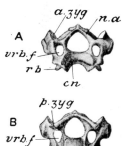

Fig. 389.—*Columba:* **Cervical vertebra.** *A*, anterior, *B*, posterior face. *a. zyg.* anterior zygapophysis; *cn.* centrum; *n. a.* neural arch; *p. zyg.* posterior zygapophysis; *rb.* rib; *vrb. f.* vertebrarterial foramen.

Between the last cervical vertebræ and the pelvic region come either four or five thoracic vertebræ (Fig. 388) fused into a rigid girder. When only four are present the first three are united. When there are five, the second, third, and fourth are joined, the last remaining free. The anterior thoracic as well as the posterior cervical vertebræ have the centrum produced below into a compressed plate, the *hypapophysis*, for the origin of the flexor muscles of the neck. They all bear ribs, each consisting of a vertebral (*vr. r.*) and a sternal (*st. r.*) portion, and articulating with the vertebra by a double head. The sternal, like the vertebral rib, is formed of true bone, not of calcified cartilage as in reptiles. It articulates with the vertebral rib by a synovial joint. Springing from the posterior edge of the vertebral rib is an *uncinus* (*unc.*), resembling that of *Sphenodon* and the Crocodilia, but formed of bone and ankylosed with the rib.

Following upon the fourth or fifth thoracic are about twelve vertebræ, all fused into another single mass (Fig. 388, *s. scr.*). This second rigid girder gives attachment laterally to the immense pelvic girdle. The whole of this group of vertebræ has, therefore, the function of a sacrum, differing from that of a reptile in the large number of vertebræ composing it. The first vertebra bears a pair of free ribs, and is, therefore, the fifth or sixth (last) thoracic (*th. v. 5*). The next five or six have no free ribs, and may be looked upon as lumbar vertebræ (Fig. 390, $l^1.$–$s^3.$). Their transverse processes arise high up on the neural arch. The ligament uniting them is ossified, so that the lumbar region presents dorsally a continuous plate of bone. Next come two sacral vertebræ ($c^1.$) homologous with those of lizards. Besides the transverse processes springing from the neural arch, one or both of them bears a second or ventral outgrowth (*c. r.*) which springs from each side of the centrum and abuts against the ilium just internal to the acetabulum. These distinctive processes are ossified independently and represent sacral ribs. The remaining five vertebræ of the pelvic region are caudal. Thus the mass of vertebræ supporting the pelvic girdle in the pigeon is a compound sacrum, or *synsacrum*, formed by the fusion of the posterior thoracic, all the lumbar and sacral, and the anterior caudal vertebræ.

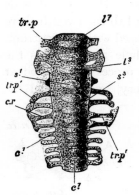

FIG. 390.—*Columba:* **Synsacrum.** Nestling (fourteen days old) in ventral aspect. $c^1.$ centrum of first sacral vertebra; $c^7.$ centrum of fifth caudal; *c. r.* first sacral rib; $l^1.$ centrum of first lumbar; $l^3.$ third lumbar; $s^1.$ of fourth lumbar; $s^3.$ of sixth lumbar; *tr. p.* transverse process of first lumbar; *tr. p'.* of fifth lumbar; *tr. p''.* of first sacral. (After T. J. Parker.)

The synsacrum is followed by six free caudals. The vertebral column ends posteriorly in an upturned, compressed bone, the *pygostyle* or ploughshare-bone (Fig. 388, *pyg. st.*). This is formed by the fusion of four or more of the hindmost caudal vertebræ.

Thus the composition of the vertebral column of the pigeon may be expressed in a *vertebral formula* as follows :

$$\overbrace{\text{Synsacrum.}}$$

Cerv. 14.   Thor. 4 or 5 + 1.   Lumb. 5 or 6.   Sacr. 2.   Caud. 5 + 6 + Pyg. 4 = 43.

The *skull* (Fig. 391) is distinguished at once by its rounded brain-case, immense orbits, and long, pointed beak. The *foramen magnum* (*f. m.*) is directed downwards as well as backwards, so as to be visible in a ventral view. On its anterior margin is a single, small, rounded occipital condyle (*o. c.*). Most of the bones, both of the cranial and facial regions, are firmly ankylosed in the adult, and can be distinguished only in the young birds.

The occipitals, parietals, frontals, and alisphenoids have the usual relations to the brain-case, the basi-occipital (*b. o.*), as in the lizard, bearing the occipital condyle. The basisphenoid (Fig. 392, *B. SPH.*) is a large bone forming the greater part of the basis cranii and continued forwards, as in the lizards, by a slender *rostrum* (Fig. 391, *pa.s.*, Fig. 392, *RST.*), which represents the anterior portion of the parasphenoid. On the ventral aspect of the basisphenoid paired membrane bones, the *basi-temporals* (Fig. 392, B. *TMP*), are developed. These become firmly ankylosed to it in the adult and probably represent the posterior portion of the parasphenoid. The tympanic cavity is bounded by

the squamosal (Fig. 391, *sq.*), which is firmly united to the other cranial bones. The main part of the auditory capsule is ossified by a large pro-otic (Fig. 392, *PR. OT.*). The small opisthotic of the embryo early unites with the exoccipital, the epiotic with the supra-occipital. The parasphenoid and mesethmoid together form the *interorbital septum* (Fig. 391, *i. o. s.*). This is a vertical partition, partly bony, partly cartilaginous, which separates the orbits from one another. The immense size of the eyes has produced a compression of this region of the skull. The ecto-ethmoids or turbinals are comparatively poorly developed, in correspondence with the small size of the olfactory organs. There are large lachrymals (Fig. 391, *lc.*, Fig. 392 *LCR.*), and the nasals (*na, na', na", NA*) are forked bones, each furnishing both an inner and an outer boundary to the corresponding nostril. The premaxillæ (*p.mx., PMX.*) are united into a large tri-radiate bone which forms practically the whole of the upper beak.

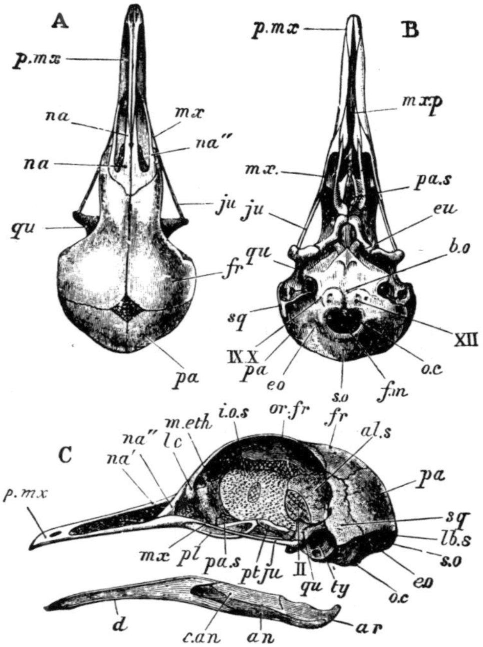

A cranio-facial hinge occurs (see p. 632). The maxillæ (*mx., MX.*),

FIG. 391.—*Columba:* **Skull.** Young bird, from *A*, dorsal; *B*, ventral; *C*, left view. *al. s.* alisphenoid; *an.* angular; *ar.* articular; *b. o.* basi-occipital; *d.* dentary; *e.o.* exoccipital; *eu.* aperture of Eustachian tube; *f. m.* foramen magnum; *fr.* frontal; *i. o. s.* interorbital septum; *ju.* jugal; *lc.* lachrymal; *lb. s.* lambdoidal suture; *m.eth.* mesethmoid; *mx.* maxilla; *mx. p.* maxillo-palatine process; *na. na'. na".* nasal; *o. c.* occipital condyle; *or. fr.* orbital plate of frontal; *pa.* parietal; *pa.s.* parasphenoid (rostrum); *pl.* palatine; *p.mx.* premaxilla; *pt.* pterygoid; *qu.* quadrate; *s. an.* supra-angular; *s. o.* supraoccipital; *sq.* squamosal; *ty.* tympanic cavity; *II—XII*, foramina for cranial nerves. (After Parker.)

on the other hand, are small, and have their anterior ends produced inwards into spongy *maxillo-palatine processes* (Fig. 391, *mx. p.*, Fig. 392, *mx. pal. pr*). The slender posterior end of the maxilla is continued backwards by an equally slender jugal (*ju., JU.*) and quadratojugal (*QU. JU.*) to the quadrate. The latter (*QU.*) is a stout, three-rayed bone articulating by two facets on its *otic process* with the roof of the tympanic cavity. It sends off an *orbital process* from its anterior margin, and presents below a *condyle* for

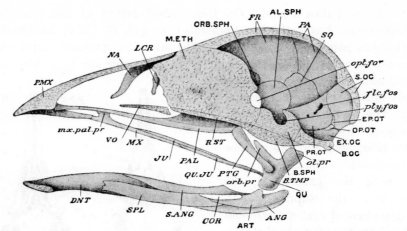

FIG. 392.—**Neornithes: Skull.** Diagrammatic, in sagittal section. *Replacing Bones*: AL.SPH. alisphenoid; ART. articular; B. OC. basi-occipital; B. SPH. basi-sphenoid; EP.OT. epiotic; EX.OC. exoccipital; M.ETH. mesethmoid; OP.OT. opisthotic; ORB. SPH. orbito-sphenoid; PR. OT. pro-otic; QU. quadrate; S. OC. supra-occipital. *Investing bones*: *ANG.* angular; *B. TMP.* basi-temporal; *COR.* coronary; *DNT.* dentary; *FR.* frontal; *JU.* jugal; *LCR.* lachrymal; *MX.* maxilla; *NA.* nasal; *PA.* parietal; *PAL.* palatine; *PMX.* premaxilla; *PTG.* pterygoid; *QU.JU.* quadratojugal; *RST.* rostrum; *S. ANG.* supra-angular; *SPL.* splenial; *SQ.* squamosal; *VO.* vomer; *flc. fos.* floccular fossa; *mx. pal. pr.* maxillo-palatine process, *opt. for.* optic foramen; *orb. pr.* orbital process; *ot. pr.* otic process; *pty. fos.* pituitary fossa.

articulation with the mandible. It is freely movable upon its tympanic articulation, so that the lower jaw has a double joint as in lizards and snakes.

The palatines (*pl., PAL.*) have their slender anterior ends ankylosed with the maxilla, their scroll-like posterior ends articulating with the pterygoids and the rostrum. The pterygoids (*pt., PTG.*) are rod-shaped and set obliquely. Each articulates behind with the quadrate, and, at about the middle of its length, with the *basipterygoid process*, a small faceted projection of the base of the rostrum. There is no vomer in the pigeon.

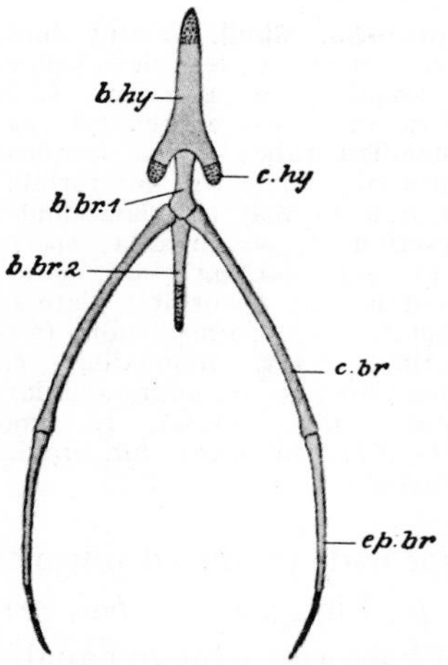

The *mandible* of the young bird consists of a replacing bone, the articular (*ar., ART.*), and four investing bones. These are the angular (*an., ANG.*), supra-angular (*s.an., S. ANG.*), dentary (*d., DNT.*), and splenial (*SPL.*). All have the same general relations as in lizards. The *hyoid apparatus* (Fig. 393) is of characteristic form, having an arrow-shaped body (*b. hy.*) with a short pair of anterior cornua (*c. hy.*) derived from the hyoid arch, and a long pair of posterior cornua (*c. br., ep. br.*) from the first branchial. The

FIG. 393.—**Columba: Hyoid apparatus.** The cartilaginous parts are dotted. *b. br.* 1, *b. br.* 2, basi-branchials; *b. hy.* basi-hyal; *c. br.* cerato-branchial; *c. hy.* hyoid cornu; *ep. br.* epi-branchial.

columella (Fig. 394) is a rod-shaped bone attached to the stapes, and bearing at its outer end a three-rayed cartilage, the *extra-columella* (*e. st., i. st., s. st.*), fixed to the tympanic membrane (p. 144).

The *sternum* (Fig. 388, *st.*) is one of the most characteristic parts of the skeleton. As in all modern flying birds, it is a broad plate of bone produced ventrally, in the sagittal plane, into a deep keel or *carina sterni* (*car.*), formed, in the young bird, from a separate centre of ossification. The posterior border of the sternum presents two pairs of notches covered by membrane. Its anterior edge bears a pair of deep grooves for the articulation of the coracoids. The broad keeled sternum gives insertion, both on the keel and on each side of it, to the massive pectoral muscles of flight. The keel serves also to strengthen the structure as a whole. On this broad ventral girder much of the weight of the bird is carried in flight.

The *shoulder* or *pectoral* girdle (Fig. 388) is unlike that of any other craniate. There is a pair of stout pillar-like struts, the *coracoids* (*cor.*), articulating with deep facets on the anterior border of the sternum, and directed upwards, forwards, and outwards. The dorsal end of each is produced into an *acro-coracoid process* (*acr. cor.*), and below this, to the posterior aspect of the bone, is attached by ligament a relatively flimsy sabre-shaped *scapula* (*scp.*). This extends backwards over the ribs, and makes an acute angle with the coracoid—the *coraco-scapular angle*. The glenoid cavity (*gl. cv.*) is formed in equal proportion by the two bones. Internal to it the scapula is produced into an *acromion process*. The scapula holds the wing up and out from the ribs. The coracoids, in conjunction with the anterior, slender V-shaped

FIG. 394.—*Columba:* **Columella.** Much magnified, with the cartilaginous parts dotted. *e. st.* extra-stapedial; *i. st.* infra-stapedial; *s. st.* suprastapedial; *st.* stapes. (After T. J. Parker.)

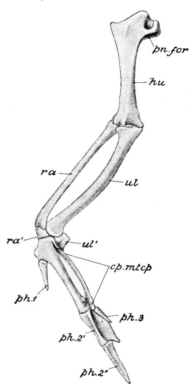

FIG. 395.—*Columba:* **Fore-limb.** Left (see also Fig. 417, p. 601). *cp. mtcp.* carpo-metacarpus; *hu.* humerus; *ph.* 1, phalanx of first digit; *ph.* 2′, *ph.* 2″, phalanges of second digit; *ph.* 3, phalanx of third digit; *pn. for.* pneumatic foramen; *ra.* radius; *ra′.* radiale; *ul.* ulna; *ul′.* ulnare.

furcula (*fur.*) or 'wish-bone', braces the mobile wing out from the sternum. The apex of the furcula nearly reaches the sternum. Each of its extremities is attached by ligament to the acromion and acro-coracoid processes of the corresponding side in such a way that a large aperture, the *foramen triosseum* (*f. trs.*), is left between the three bones of the shoulder-girdle. The furcula is an investing bone and represents fused clavicles and interclavicle.

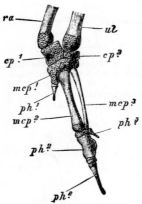

FIG. 396. — ***Columba: Manus.*** Left, in nestling, with the cartilaginous parts dotted. *cp.* 1, radiale; *cp.* 2, ulnare; *mcp.* 1, 2, 3, metacarpals; *ph.* 1, phalanx of first digit; *ph.* 2, *ph.* 2', phalanges of second digit; *ph.* 3, phalanx of third digit; *ra.* radius; *ul.* ulna. (After T. J. Parker.)

Equally characteristic is the skeleton of the fore-limb. The *humerus* (Fig. 395, *hu.*) is a large, strong bone, with a greatly expanded head and a prominent ridge for the insertion of the pectoral muscle. In it, as in all the other long bones, the extremities as well as the shaft are formed of true bone. The *radius* (*ra.*) is slender and nearly straight, the *ulna* stouter and gently curved. There are two large free carpals, a *radiale* (*ra'.*) and an *ulnare* (*ul'.*). Articulating with these is the *carpo-metacarpus* (*cp. mtcp.*) consisting of two rods. The rod on the pre-axial side is strong and nearly straight. That on the postaxial side is slender and curved. These elements are fused with one another at both their proximal and distal ends ; the proximal end is produced, pre-axially, into an out-standing step-like process. The carpo-metacarpus is formed by the union of the distal carpals with three metacarpals (Fig. 396), the second and third of which are the two rod-like portions of the bone, the first the step-like projection. Articulating with the first metacarpal is a single pointed phalanx (Fig. 395, *ph. 1*). The second metacarpal bears two phalanges, the proximal one (*ph. 2'*) produced postaxially into a flange, the distal one (*ph. 2''*) pointed. The third metacarpal bears a single pointed phalanx (*ph. 3*).

The *pelvic girdle* (Fig. 388) re-sembles that of no other vertebrate with the exception of certain dinosaurs (p. 506). In the walking or perching bird the centre of gravity is postero-ventral and the concentrated body weight is transferred by ribs and ab-dominal muscles to the massive *ilium* (*il.*) which is attached by fibrous union to the whole of the synsacrum and is ankylosed with it in the adult. It is divisible into *pre-acetabular* and *post-acetabular* portions of approximately equal size. As usual it furnishes the dorsal portion of the acetabulum, and on the

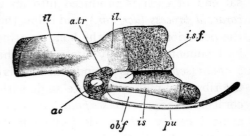

FIG. 397.—***Columba: Pelvic girdle.*** Left, in a nestling, with cartilaginous parts dotted. *Ac.* acetabulum; *a. tr.* anti-trochanter; *il.* pre-acetabular, and *il'.* postacetabular portion of ilium; *is.* ischium; *i. s. f.* ischiatic foramen; *ob. f.* obturator notch; *pu.* pubis. (After T. J. Parker.)

posterior edge of that cavity is produced into a process, the *anti-trochanter* (*a. tr.*). This works against the trochanter, a process of the femur. The ventral portion of the acetabulum is furnished in about equal proportions by the pubis and ischium (Fig. 397). It is not completely closed by bone, but is perforated by an aperture covered by membrane. Both pubis and ischium are directed sharply backwards from their dorsal or acetabular ends. The *ischium* (*is.*) is a broad bone, ankylosed posteriorly with the ilium, and separated from it in front by an *ischiatic foramen* (Fig. 388, *is. for.* ; Fig. 397, *i. s. f.*). The *pubis* (*pu.*) is a slender, curved rod, parallel with the ventral edge of the ischium, and separated from it by an *obturator notch* (Fig. 388, *obt. n.* ; Fig. 397, *ob. f.*). Neither ischium nor pubis unites ventrally: a pubic symphysis exists only in the Ostrich.

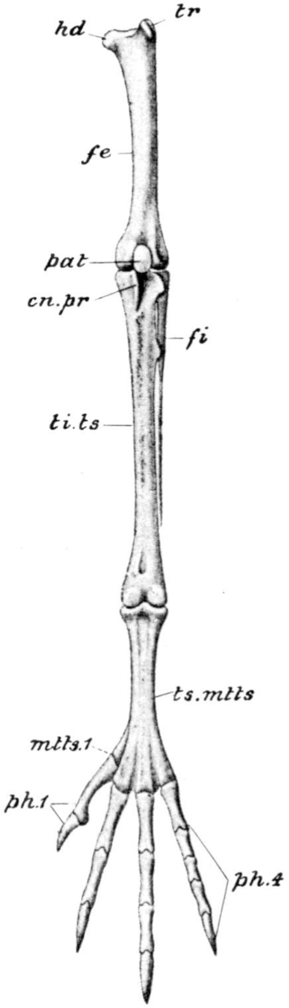

In the hind-limb the *femur* (Fig. 398, *fe.*) is a comparatively short bone. Its proximal extremity bears a prominent *trochanter* (*tr.*) and a rounded *head* (*hd.*). The axis of this is at right angles to the shaft of the bone. Thus the femur, and indeed the whole limb, lies in a plane parallel with the sagittal plane of the trunk. Movements of the legs are essentially antero-posterior in direction. The distal end of the femur is produced into pulley-like *condyles*. There is a small sesamoid bone (*i.e.* a bone developed in a tendon), the *patella* (*pat.*), on the extensor side of the knee-joint.

Articulating with the femur is a long bone, the *tibio-tarsus* (*ti. ts.*), produced on the anterior face of its proximal end into a large *cnemial process* (*cn. pr.*) Its proximal articular surface is slightly hollowed for the condyles of the femur. Its distal end is pulley-like, not concave like the corresponding extremity of the tibia of other Amniota. The pulley-like distal end of the bone (Fig. 399, *tl. 1*) consists of the proximal tarsals (astragalus and calcaneum) which at an early period unite with the tibia and give rise to the compound shank-bone of the adult. The *fibula* is very small, much shorter than the tibia, and tapers to a point at its distal end.

Following the tibio-tarsus is an elongated bone, the *tarso-metatarsus* (Fig.

FIG. 398. — *Columba:* **Hind-Limb.** Left. *cn. pr.* cnemial process; *fr.* femur; *fi.* fibula; *hd.* head of femur; *mtts.* 1, first metatarsal; *pat.* patella; *ph.* 1, phalanges of first digit; *ph.* 4, phalanges of fourth digit; *ti. ts.* tibiotarsus; *ts. mtts.* tarso-metatarsus; *tr.* trochanter.

398, *ts. mtts.*), presenting at its proximal end a concave surface for the tibio-tarsus, and at its distal end three distinct pulleys for the articulation of the three forwardly-directed toes. In the young bird the proximal end of this bone is a separate cartilage (Fig. 399, *tl. 2*), represent-ing the distal tarsals, and followed by three distinct metatarsals which belong respectively to the second, third, and fourth digits. Thus the ankle-joint of the bird is a *mesotarsal* joint, occurring, as in lizards, between the proximal and distal tarsals, and not, as in mammals (p. 665), between the tibia and the proxi-mal tarsals. To the inner or pre-axial side of the tarso-metatarsus, near its distal end, is attached by fibrous tissue a small irregular bone, the first metatar-sal (Fig. 398, *mtts. 1*). The digits have the same number of phalanges as in the lizard, the backwardly-directed hallux two, the second or inner toe three, the third or middle toe four, and the fourth or outer toe five. In all four digits the distal or ungual phalanx is pointed and curved, and serves for the support of the horny claw.

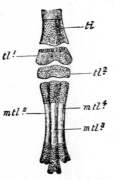

FIG. 399.—*Columba:* **Pes.** Part of left foot in embryo (highly magnified) with cartilaginous parts dotted. *mtl.* 2, second, *mtl.* 3, third, and *mtl.* 4, fourth metatarsal; *ti.* tibia; *tl.* 1, proximal tarsal cartilage; *tl.* 2, distal tarsal cartilage. (After Parker.)

Muscular System.—The toes are flexed by two sets of tendons. The deep tendons of the three forwardly-directed digits are formed by the trifurcation of the tendon of a single muscle, the *peroneus medius*. That of the hallux is derived from a separate muscle, the *flexor perforans*, which is joined by a slip from the peroneus medius. Thus a pull upon one tendon flexes all the toes. When the leg is bent, as the bird settles to roost, the flexion of the tarso-metatarsus on the shank puts the flexor tendons on the stretch as they pass over the mesotarsal joint, and by the pull thus exerted the toes are automatic-ally bent round the perch by the simple action of flexing the leg. They are kept in this position while the bird is asleep by the mere weight of the body. It has been thought that the action is assisted by a small but characteristic muscle, the *ambiens*, but this is now in dispute. The *ambiens* muscle arises from the pubis, and passes along the inner surface of the thigh. It continues into a long tendon which comes round to the outer side of the knee, enclosed in a special sheath, and continuing down the leg, joins the superficial flexors of the digits. This muscle, however, is absent in some species and its section in others does not affect perching ability.

As might be expected, the tetrapod musculature of the fore-limb is greatly modified. The powerful downstroke of the wing by which the bird rises and propels itself through the air is performed by the *pectoralis major* (Fig. 400, *pct.*), an immense muscle having about one-fifth the total weight of the body. This arises from the whole of the keel of the sternum (*car. st.*) and from the clavicle (*cl.*), filling nearly the whole of the wedge-shaped space between the body and the keel. This is the so-called 'breast' of the bird, the meat of which is highly vascularised and 'red' in the strongly flying pigeon, and white in the feebly flying Common fowl (*Gallus domesticus*). Its fibres converge to their insertion (*pct.''*) into the ventral aspect of the humerus (*hu.*, *hu'.*), which it depresses. The elevation of the wing is performed, not, as might be expected, by a dorsally-placed muscle, but by the *supracoracoideus* (*sb. clv.*) ('pectoralis minor'). This arises from the anterior part of the body of the sternum, dorsal to the pectoralis.

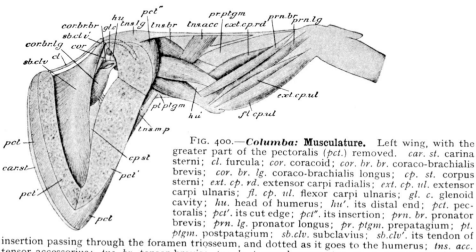

FIG. 400.—*Columba:* **Musculature.** Left wing, with the greater part of the pectoralis (*pct.*) removed. *car. st.* carina sterni; *cl.* furcula; *cor.* coracoid; *cor. br. br.* coraco-brachialis brevis; *cor. br. lg.* coraco-brachialis longus; *cp. st.* corpus sterni; *ext. cp. rd.* extensor carpi radialis; *ext. cp. ul.* extensor carpi ulnaris; *fl. cp. ul.* flexor carpi ulnaris; *gl. c.* glenoid cavity; *hu.* head of humerus; *hu'.* its distal end; *pct.* pectoralis; *pct'.* its cut edge; *pct''.* its insertion; *prn. br.* pronator brevis; *prn. lg.* pronator longus; *pr. ptgm.* prepatagium; *pt. ptgm.* postpatagium; *sb.clv.* subclavius; *sb.clv'.* its tendon of insertion passing through the foramen triosseum, and dotted as it goes to the humerus; *tns. acc.* tensor accessorius; *tns. br.* tensor brevis; *tns. lg.* tensor longus; *tns. m. p.* tensor membranæ posterioris alæ.

It sends its tendon through the *foramen triosseum* between furcula, scapula, and coracoid, to be inserted into the dorsal aspect of the humerus. Because the foramen acts like a pulley, the direction of action of the muscle is changed ; the backward pull of the tendon raises the humerus. Muscles concerned with rotational movements of the wing in the glenoid socket are the relatively small *scapulo-humerals* and *coraco-humerals*, which extend from girdle to humerus. The deltoid muscles are complex, each with three *tensores patagii* (*tns. lg.*, *tns. br.*, *tns. acc.*), the action of which is to keep the prepatagium tensely stretched when the wing is extended. A similar muscle (*tns. m. p.*) acts upon the postpatagium. The most important intrinsic muscles of the arm are the *biceps*, and the larger *triceps*, which operate the elbow and perform adjustments during flight. Fore-arm muscles such as the *extensor carpi radialis* and the *extensor carpi ulnaris* operate in conjunction with the two former, and are important in the stretching and folding of the wing. The radius is rotated medially by two *brachioradialis* muscles. Although the muscles of the digits are much reduced, they are nevertheless important in that they alter the disposition of individual parts of the wing—and even of individual feathers—during flight. The bastard wing (first digit) is independently movable by *policis* muscles ; it may help to control the leading edge of the wing, and to produce extra forward momentum during the take off. Much is still unknown about flapping, and even the simpler gliding, flight.

Locomotion.—Among vertebrates birds are uniquely adapted in their capacity for locomotion both in the air and on land. Many are expert swimmers as well. Upon the skeletal foundation briefly outlined are borne the feathers of flight and the individual muscle elements that allow simultaneous alterations in shape, size, angle, and, consequently, air permeability of the wings in response to the ever-changing requirements of different phases of flight. Although bird flight (including even the simpler soaring flight that depends primarily on rising air currents, or variations in air currents over waves) is still incompletely understood, certain of its features are relatively straightforward and closely analogous to the simpler flight of aircraft. The *leading edge* of each flight-feather is the narrower, and both fore and rear edges of most are relatively constant in width along its length. Depending on the characteristic mode of flight of the species, the terminal parts of some pinions, both forward and rear, are narrowed towards the central vein. Thus some feathers are terminally and subterminally *emarginated* and provide, as a whole, an effect not unlike that given by the slotting apparatus on the wings of an aeroplane.

Lift is achieved not only by the pressure of air-flow below the temporarily impermeable wing, but also by the semi-vacuum, producing a 'suction zone', caused by the swift rush of air cascading over the slightly convex dorsal surface of the wing. (This phenomenon can be crudely demonstrated by holding, and blowing hard over, a piece of curved cardboard which will then be slightly elevated.) The creation of the suction zone is assisted by the thin trailing edges which minimise the eddies behind the wings (*stream-lining*) and also by the convex upper surfaces (the *camber*). This all-important dorsal zone varies with the changing shape and movement of the wing in flight. If the angle to the direction of air-flow is increased, eddies (*trailing edge vortices*) spread from the downwardly directed trailing edge of the wing towards the suction zone, eliminating vacuum 'lift'. the animal begins to *stall*. The emargination of varying numbers of flight-feathers reduces the terminal eddies, and changes in the disposition of the small elements of the bastard wing (p. 566) perhaps further tend to reduce air turbulence, and tend also to allow a slower *stalling speed* while soaring. Habitually soaring birds are characterised by the pronounced emargination of their flight-feathers. There is, too, a broad relationship between wing-shape and slotting. Wings of *high aspect ratio, i.e.* those that are very long in comparison with breadth, are not as a rule markedly slotted. Wings of *low aspect ratio, i.e.* short and broad, are often notably so.

Most, if not all birds employ both flapping and soaring modes of flight. Flapping flight is infinitely the more complicated, involving constant changes in the relative positions of both distal and proximal parts of the wing. The intrinsic musculature and intimate structure (and even individual movements) of different feathers, together with movements of the pre- and postpatagia (Fig. 383), allow the wing to alter shape, so that the down-beat resembles a thrusting oar, impermeable to air, whilst in the up-beat it can be swiftly readjusted with a minimum of air resistance for the next powerful stroke. In addition, the rate of wing-beat varies widely from family to family. Types with a small wing-area in relation to mass flap quickly and have evolved special landing techniques. Those with a greater wing-area are able to progress quickly at a more leisurely rate of wing-beat. Generally speaking, fast-flying birds have, like fighter 'planes, relatively small wings. The bigger a flying bird becomes, the larger its wing must develop. Weight increases with the cube, while the expanse of the wing is related to the square of the linear dimensions. On the other hand, as the surface of the wing increases, so the edge losses decrease and a higher weight per unit area can be, and is, carried (*wing-loading*). At the same time, it has been shown experimentally that pigeons can fly when deprived of up to 45 per cent. of their wing-surface. Again, certain eagles (*e.g. Uroäetus*) are for short distances able to carry prey much heavier than themselves. Many, but not all, species fly well when the wings are in moult. Some birds, however (*e.g.* migratory shearwaters, *Puffinus*), delay the wing-moult, but not that of the body, until the completion of their long post-nuptial transequatorial migrations.

Alimentary Canal and Associated Structures.—The mouth (Fig. 401) is bounded above and below by the horny beak. The *tongue* (*tng.*) is large and pointed at the tip. It possesses what appear to be taste-buds and, in addition, mucous glands. Salivary glands—the median *sub-lingual* and paired *angle-glands* at the gape—produce saliva which moistens the food.

In some graminivorous species the saliva contains a diastatic enzyme. The pharynx leads into a wide and distensible œsophagus (*gul.*), which dilates into a large reservoir or *crop* (*crp.*) situated at the base of the neck, between the skin and the muscles, and immediately in front of the sternum. The crop enables the bird to ingest and store very quickly a large amount of food which it can later digest at leisure. The epithelium of the crop in both sexes sheds a white, slimy, proteinous, and fatty crop-'milk' during the breeding season (see p. 560). *Crop-gland* activity is controlled by *prolactin*, an anterior pituitary hormone.

The '*pigeon's milk*' is regurgitated to the young *squabs* which can double their hatching weight in only two days. A neonatal rabbit doubles its birth weight in six days and a cat in nine. 'Pigeon's milk', which is composed of from 65–81 per cent. water, 13·3–18·8 per cent. protein, 6·9–12·7 per cent.

fat, and 1·5 per cent. ash, is 'a very much more efficient nutriment than mammalian milk' (Needham); see, however, p. 790.

In the crop, the ingested food, consisting principally of grain, is macerated. From the crop the œsophagus is continued backwards into the *stomach*, which consists of two parts, the glandular *proventriculus* (*prvn.*) and the

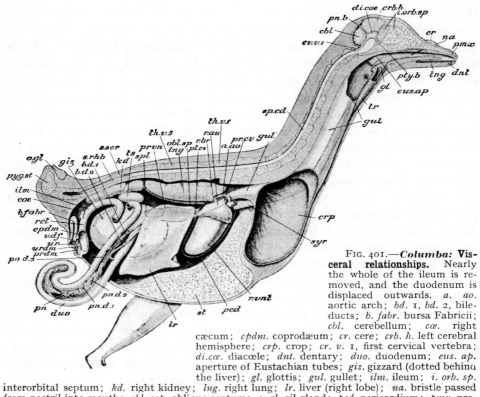

Fig. 401.—*Columba:* **Visceral relationships.** Nearly the whole of the ileum is removed, and the duodenum is displaced outwards. *a. ao.* aortic arch; *bd.* 1, *bd.* 2, bileducts; *b. fabr.* bursa Fabricii; *cbl.* cerebellum; *cœ.* right cæcum; *cpdm.* coprodæum; *cr.* cere; *crb. h.* left cerebral hemisphere; *crp.* crop; *cr. v.* 1, first cervical vertebra; *di.cœ.* diacœle; *duo.* duodenum; *eus. ap.* aperture of Eustachian tubes; *giz.* gizzard (dotted behind the liver); *gl.* glottis; *gul.* gullet; *ilm.* ileum; *i. orb. sp.* interorbital septum; *kd.* right kidney; *lng.* right lung; *lr.* liver (right lobe); *na.* bristle passed from nostril into mouth; *obl. sep.* oblique septum; *o. gl.* oil-gland; *pcd.* pericardium; *pmx.* premaxilla; *pn.* pancreas; *pn. b.* pineal body; *pn. d.* 1—3, pancreatic ducts; *pr. cv.* right precaval; *prdm.* proctodæum; *prvn.* proventriculus (dotted behind liver); *pt. cv.* postcaval; *pty. b.* pituitary body; *pyg.st.* pygostyle; *r. au.* right auricle; *r. br.* right bronchus; *rct.* rectum; *r. vnt.* right ventricle; *sp. cd.* spinal cord; *spl.* spleen (dotted behind liver); *s. rhb.* sinus rhomboidalis; *s. scr.* synsacrum; *st.* carina sterni; *syr.* syrinx; *th. v.* 1, first, and *th. v.* 5, fifth thoracic vertebra; *tng.* tongue; *tr.* trachea; *ts.* right testis; *ur.* aperture of left ureter; *urdm.* urodæum; *v. df.* aperture of left vas deferens.

muscular *gizzard* (*giz.*). The proventriculus appears externally like a slight dilatation of the œsophagus but it is a gastric structure, the walls of which contain numerous glandular pockets large enough to be visible to the naked eye. The gizzard has the shape of a biconvex lens. Its walls are very thick and its lumen is small. The thickening is due mainly to the immense development of the muscles which radiate from two tendons, one on each of the convex surfaces. In the epithelial lining of the gizzard are numerous minute tubular glands, which secrete a fluid which becomes thick, horny, and of a yellow or green colour and lines the gizzard. The cavity always contains small stones, which are swallowed by the bird and aid the gizzard in grinding up the food.

The *duodenum* (*duo.*) leaves the gizzard close to the entrance of the proventriculus and forms a distinct loop enclosing the *pancreas*. The duodenum is lined with villi and single or branched crypts of *Lieberkühn*. *Goblet cells* are also present. The pancreas (*pn.*) is a large reddish gland which discharges its exocrine products by three ducts (*pn.d. 1–3*) into the duodenum. The pancreas contains also endocrine *islets of Langerhans* which discharge into the blood-stream *insulin* or a hormone of similar function (p. 153). The hormone *secretin*, which in mammals influences the secretion of pancreatic juice, has been obtained from the walls of the pigeon's duodenum. Also opening into the duodenum are two *bile ducts* (*b.d. 1, b.d. 2*). These come direct from the right and left lobes of the large liver nearby. There is no gall-bladder in the pigeon, but one occurs in *Gallus* and many other species. The *ileum* (*ilm.*) presents first a single loop and then follows its greater part coiled into a sort of spiral and lastly comes a single loop which passes without change of diameter into the *rectum* (*rct.*). The junction between the two is marked only by a pair of small blind pouches or *cæca* (*cæ.*). These are much more capacious in many birds (e.g. *Gallus*) and are the site of a certain amount of digestion (of vegetable fibres) by enzymatic and bacterial action. There is some evidence too that they are concerned with the absorption of water. The *cloaca* is a large chamber divided into three compartments, the *coprodæum* (*cpdm.*), which receives the rectum, the *urodæum* (*urdm.*), into which the urinary and genital ducts open, and the *proctodæum* (*prdm.*), which opens externally by the vent. A thick-walled glandular pouch, the *bursa Fabricii* (*b. fabr.*), lies against the dorsal wall of the cloaca in young birds and opens into the proctodæum. It atrophies in the adult (see Fig. 413, p. 597).

Respiratory and Vocal Organs.—The *glottis* (Fig. 401, *gl.*) is situated just behind the root of the tongue, and leads into the *larynx*. This is supported by cartilages—a *cricoid* divided into four pieces, and paired *arytenoids*—but it is uncomplicated and does not, as in other vertebrates, function as a vocal organ. The anterior part of the trachea (*tr.*) has the usual position, ventral to the gullet. Further back, however, it is displaced to the left by the crop, becoming ventral once more as it enters the body-cavity, where it divides into the right (*r. br.*) and left *bronchi*. The rings supporting the trachea are not cartilaginous but bony, as also is the first ring of each bronchus. Those of the trachea completely surround the tube; those of the bronchi are incomplete mesially.

At the junction of the trachea with the paired bronchi occurs the characteristic vocal organ, the *syrinx* (*syr.*), found in no other class. The last three or four rings of the trachea (Fig. 402, *tr.*), and the first or bony half-ring of each bronchus (*br.*), are modified to form a slightly dilated chamber, the *tympanum*, the mucous membrane of which forms a cushion-like thickening on each side. At the junction of the bronchi a bar of cartilage, the *pessulus*, extends dorso-ventrally and supports an inconspicuous fold of mucous membrane, the *membrana semilunaris*. The membranous inner walls of the bronchi form the *internal tympaniform membranes*. A pair of *intrinsic syringeal muscles* arise from the sides of the trachea and are inserted into the syrinx, and a pair of *sterno-tracheal muscles* arise from the sternum and are inserted into the trachea. The voice is produced by the vibration of the semilunar membrane. Its pitch is altered by changes produced by the action of the muscles. The syringeal

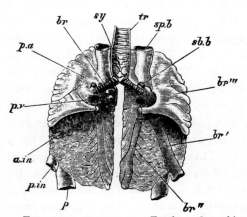

FIG. 402.—*Columba:* **Trachea, bronchi, and lungs.** Ventral aspect. *a. in.* aperture of anterior thoracic air-sac; *br.* principal bronchus; *br'. br'', br''',* secondary bronchi; *p.* aperture of abdominal air-sac; *p. a.* pulmonary artery entering lung; *p. in.* aperture of posterior thoracic air-sac; *p. v.* pulmonary vein leaving lung; *sb. b.* aperture of interclavicular air-sac; *sp. b.* aperture of cervical air-sac; *sy.* syrinx; *tr.* trachea. (After T. J. Parker.)

musculature (Fig. 444, p. 639) varies widely from group to group and is of diagnostic significance.

The paired primary bronchi do not immediately branch within the lungs in the manner characteristic of other tetrapods. Instead, each bronchus is continued through to the posterior end of the lung (Figs. 403, 404) and then divides into paired *secondary* or *lateral bronchi* which branch again and send tubes which give rise to a system of *tertiary* or *parabronchi*. This breaks up into an extensive ramification of fine branching and anastomising tubules or *air capillaries* which come into intimate contact with the red cells coursing through the *blood capillaries* of the lungs.

At the same time, each secondary bronchus continues and enters a bladder-like air-sac, formed as a dilation of the mucous membrane of the bronchus. One of these, the *abdominal air-sac*, lies among the coils of the intestine. The other, the *posterior thoracic air-sac*, is closely applied to the side-wall of the body. The bronchus also gives off, near its entrance into the lung, three short branches. One of these becomes connected with an *anterior thoracic air-sac*, situated just in front of the posterior thoracic. Another is connected with an *interclavicular air-sac*, which is median, unpaired, and connected with both lungs. The third enters a *cervical air-sac* placed at the root of the neck. Each side of the interclavicular gives off a diverticulum, or *axillary air-sac*, lying in the axilla. All these sacs are paired except the interclavicular, which is formed by the fusion of right and left moieties. The sacs communicate with the pneumatic cavities of the bones. Thus, some birds are able, with trachea blocked, to respire through the humerus and other bones if they are fractured and exposed.

There are several air-sac terminologies, but it seems generally agreed that there are four principal pairs and one unpaired (interclavicular) sac as above. Much of the inspired air, then, is drawn directly into the great system of air-sacs without contact with the respiratory surface. This air finally reaches the respiratory tissue by returning from the air-sacs via the secondary or lateral bronchi and in addition, via a system of *recurrent bronchi* which branch from the anterior ends of the air-sacs, excluding the cervicals. This highly specialised respiratory arrangement almost eliminates dead-space air (such as occurs in the Mammalia) and allows some birds (*e.g.* the Skylark, *Alauda*) to sing and fly for long periods without breathlessness.

The *lungs* (Figs. 401, 402) are very small in comparison with the size of the bird. They are only slightly distensible, being solid, spongy organs, not bags with sacculated walls as in amphibians and many reptiles. Their dorsal surfaces fit closely into the spaces between the ribs and have no peritoneal covering. Their ventral faces are covered by

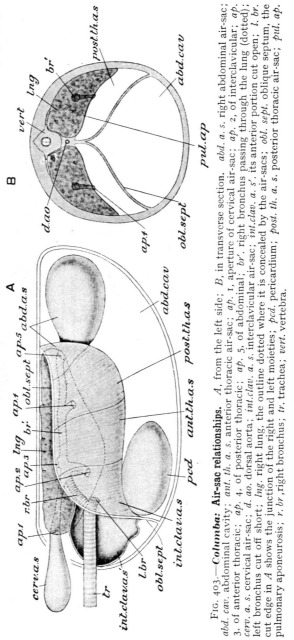

FIG. 403.—*Columba:* Air-sac relationships. *A*, from the left side; *B*, in transverse section. *abd. a. s.* right abdominal air-sac; *abd. cav.* abdominal cavity; *ant. th. a. s.* anterior thoracic air-sac; *ap.* 1, aperture of cervical air-sac; *ap.* 2, of interclavicular; *ap.* 3, of anterior thoracic; *ap.* 4, of posterior thoracic; *ap.* 5, of abdominal; *br'.* right bronchus passing through the lung (dotted); *cerv. a. s.* cervical air-sac; *d. ao.* dorsal aorta; *int. clav. a. s.* interclavicular air-sac; *int. clav. a. s'.* its anterior portion cut open; *l. br.* left bronchus cut off short; *lng.* right lung, the outline dotted where it is concealed by the air-sacs; *obl. sept.* oblique septum, the cut edge in *A* shows the junction of the right and left moieties; *pcd.* pericardium; *post. th. a. s.* posterior thoracic air-sac; *pul. ap.* pulmonary aponeurosis; *r. br.* right bronchus; *tr.* trachea; *vert.* vertebra.

a strong sheet of fibrous tissue, the *pulmonary aponeurosis* or *pleura* (Fig. 403, *B*, *pul. ap.*), a special development of the peritoneum. Into this membrane are inserted small fan-like *costopulmonary muscles*, which arise from the junction of the vertebral and sternal ribs.

The ventral or free walls of the thoracic air-sacs of each side are covered by a sheet of fibrous tissue, the *oblique septum* (*obl. sept.*). This is continued forwards to the pericardium, and is united with its fellow of the opposite side in the middle dorsal line. It divides the cœlom into two compartments—one containing the lungs with the interclavicular and thoracic air-sacs. The other (*abd. cav.*) contains the heart, liver, stomach, intestine, etc., with the abdominal

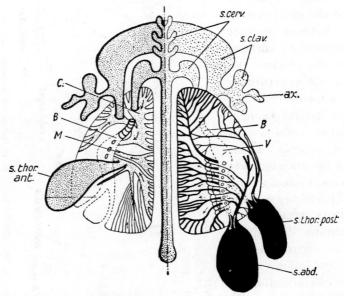

Fig. 404.—*Columba:* **Relationship between lungs and air-sacs.** From ventral (left) and dorsal (right) aspects. On the left side is shown only the ventral surface of the lungs, together with expiratory bronchi and air-sacs (dotted). On the right side the inspiratory bronchi and air-sacs are shown in black. *B.* main bronchus, *C.* cervical bronchus; *M.* mesobronchus; *s. abd.* abdominal air-sac; *s. cerv.* cervical air-sac; *s. clav.* inter-clavicular air-sac; with diverticulum (*ax.*) in axilla; *s. thor. ant.* and *post.* thoracic air-sacs. (From Young, after Brandes and Ihle.)

air-sacs. Unsuccessful attempts have been made to homologise the oblique septum with the mammalian diaphragm (p. 676). It has been sometimes thought to be an important part of the respiratory mechanism, but its experimental destruction does not appear to interfere with either inspiration or expiration.

Inspiration is brought about in the resting bird mainly by means of movements of the intercostal muscles, and expiration by the abdominal muscles which cause an alternate enlargement and diminution of the capacity of the cœlom, and thus pumps air in and out of the lungs. During flight the same effect seems to be produced by the movement of the pectoral muscles. In either case the inspired air rushes through the lungs into the air-sacs and thence by diffusion into the pneumatic cavities of the bones. Thus, while in other animals a certain amount of unchanged or residual 'dead space' air is always left in the lungs after each expiration, in birds this is confined to the air-sacs and to the smaller branches of the bronchi (Fig. 404). Respiratory movement forces a current of fresh tidal air through the lungs. As a result of this the aeration of the blood is very complete, and thus allows an unusually high degree of muscular efficiency and temperature (p. 558). There is evidence that birds resemble the Mammalia in having the respiratory centre in the medulla oblongata. A specific panting centre may occur in the dorsal part of the diencephalon. There is some evidence that one or both of these centres are sensitive to the carbon dioxide content of the blood-stream. Bilateral vagotomy and vagal stimulation have not led to consistent results.

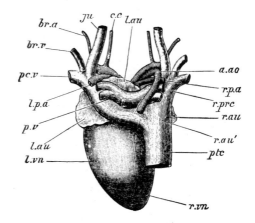

FIG. 405.—*Columba:* **Heart and large vessels.** Dorsal aspect. *a. ao.* arch of aorta; *br. a.* brachial artery; *br. v.* brachial vein; *c. c.* common carotid; *ju.* jugular; *l. au.* left auricle; *l. p. a.* left pulmonary artery; *l. vn.* left ventricle; *p. c. v.* left precaval; *ptc.* post-caval; *p. v.* pulmonary veins; *r. au, r. au',* right auricle; *r. p. a.* right pulmonary artery; *r. prc.* right precaval; *r. vn.* right ventricle. (After T. J. Parker.)

Thyroid, Parathyroid, and Thymus Glands.—Paired *thyroids* occur on each side of the trachea near its division into bronchi. They produce *thyroxin,* an iodine-containing hormone important in general metabolic function and said also to be especially concerned with the periodic moult. Thyroid activity is under the control of the anterior pituitary. Paired endocrine *parathyroids,* situated nearby, control calcium and phosphate metabolism. Paired elongated *thymus* glands are lodged on each side of the throat in the young bird. They involute at maturity, and in widely unrelated species show a marked enlargement at the end of the breeding season (Höhn). There is, nevertheless, no evidence of endocrine activity.

Blood-vascular System.—The *heart* (Fig. 405) is of great proportional size and, like that of crocodiles, consists of four chambers—right and left auricles and powerful right and left ventricles. These are lined with endocardium. There is no sinus venosus, that chamber being, as it were, absorbed into the right auricle (Fig. 405, *r. au.*). The right ventricle (Fig. 406) partly encircles the left, the former having a crescentic, the latter a circular cavity in

transverse sections.   The left auriculo-ventricular valve has the usual membranous structure, consisting of two flaps connected with the wall of the
ventricle by tendons, but the corresponding valve of the right side is a
large muscular fold, very characteristic of the class.   The pericardial sac con-

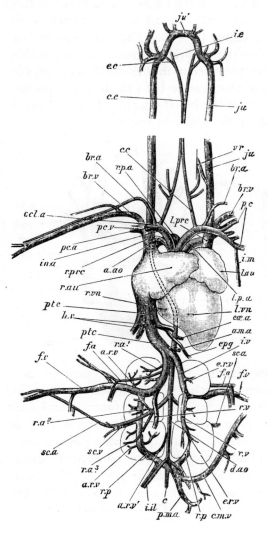

FIG. 406.—*Columba:* **Blood vascular
system.** Ventral aspect. *a. ao.* arch of
aorta; *a. m. a.* anterior mesenteric artery;
a. r. v. afferent renal veins; *a. r. v′.* vein
bringing blood from pelvis into renal portal
system; *br. a.* brachial artery; *br. v.*
brachial vein; *c.* caudal artery and vein;
c. c. common carotid artery; *c. m. v.*
coccygeo-mesenteric vein, displaced to the
right; *cœ. a.* cœliac artery; *d. ao.* dorsal
aorta; *e. c.* external carotid artery; *epg.*
epigastric vein; *e. r. v.* efferent renal vein;
f. a. femoral artery; *f. v.* femoral vein; *h. v.*
hepatic vein; *i. c.* internal carotid artery;
i. il. internal iliac artery and vein; *i. m.*
internal mammary artery and vein; *in. a.*
innominate artery; *i. v.* iliac vein; *ju.*
jugular vein; *ju′.* anastomosis of jugular
veins; *l. au.* left auricle; *l. p. a.* left
pulmonary artery; *l. prc.* left pre-caval
vein; *l. vn.* left ventricle; *pc.* left pectoral
arteries and veins; *pc. a.* right pectoral
artery; *pc. v.* right pectoral vein; *p. m. a.*
posterior mesenteric artery; *ptc.* post-caval
vein; *ra.¹, ra.², ra.³,* renal arteries; *r. a.u*
right auricle; *r. p.* renal portal vein, on the
left side of the figure, supposed to be
dissected so as to show its passage through
the right kidney; *r. p. a.* right pulmonary
artery; *r. prc.* right precaval vein; *r. v.*
renal vein; *r. vn.* right ventricle; *sc. a.*
sciatic artery; *sc. v.* sciatic vein; *scl. a.*
subclavian artery; *vr.* vertebral artery and
vein. (After T. J. Parker.)

tains serous fluid.   The right auricle receives the right and left precavals
(*r. prc., l. prc.*) and the postcaval (*ptc*) ; the left, four large pulmonary veins
(*p. v.*).   There is an elaborate coronary circulation (p. 115), the number of
arteries varying in different species of birds.   The intrinsic nervous system of
the heart includes a *sinu-auricular node* or *pace-maker* (in the wall of the right
auricle), an *auriculo-ventricular* node (in the atrial septum), and a right atrio-

ventricular ring of *Purkinje fibres* (p. 882). As in mammals, the contraction wave begins at the SA node, spreads through the atria to the AV node and thence by branches to the rest of the heart. Sympathetic stimulation accelerates heart action and parasympathetic (vagal) impulses slow it down.

The left ventricle (Fig. 406, *l. vn.*), as in crocodiles, gives origin to the right aortic arch (*a. ao.*), but the right ventricle (*r. vn*) gives off only one trunk, the pulmonary artery, which soon divides into two (*r. p. a., l. p. a.*). The left aortic arch is absent in the adult, and it is the right alone which is continued into the dorsal aorta. The result of this is that the systemic arteries receive oxygenated blood from the left side of the heart. The only mingling of oxygenated and non-oxygenated blood is in the capillaries. This is a tremendously important physiological advance made by birds over reptiles.

The aortic arch curves over the right bronchus to reach the dorsal body-wall, and then passes directly backwards as the dorsal aorta (*d. ao.*). Owing to the immense size of the pectoral muscles, the arteries supplying them are of corresponding dimensions. The right and left *innominate arteries* (*in. a.*), from which the carotids (*c. c.*), subclavians (*br. a.*), and pectorals (*pc. a.*) arise, are actually larger than the aorta itself beyond their origin. In correspondence with the position of the legs, the femoral (*f. a.*) and sciatic (*sc. a.*) arteries arise far forward. The caudal artery (*c.*) is small as would be expected.

The most characteristic feature in the disposition of the circulatory organs is the very considerable reduction of the *renal portal system*. There are two renal portal veins (*r.p.*) formed by the bifurcation of the caudal. Each, however, instead of breaking up into capillaries in the kidney, sends off only a few small branches (*a. r. v.*) which carry blood to that organ. The main vein passes forwards, through the substance of the kidney, and joins the femoral vein (*f. v.*) from the leg to form the iliac vein (*i. v.*). There occurs at the junction of the renal and iliac veins a valve which has been claimed to regulate blood-flow into the former vessel. The iliac unites with its fellow of the opposite side and forms the postcaval (*ptc.*). Thus the main part of the blood from the caudal and pelvic regions is taken directly to the heart, and not through the renal capillaries as in most fishes and all amphibians and reptiles.

At the point of bifurcation of the caudal veins a large *coccygeo-mesenteric vein* (*c. m. v.*) comes off, and, running parallel with the rectum (from which it receives tributaries) joins the portal vein. The abdominal vein of amphibians and reptiles appears to be represented, in part at least, by the *epigastric vein* (*epg.*), which returns the blood, not from the ventral body-wall, but from the *great omentum*. This fold of peritoneum, loaded with fat, lies ventral to the intestine and gizzard. The epigastric discharges into the hepatic vein.

The spleen (Fig. 401, *spl.*) is an ovoid red body of unusually small proportional size attached by peritoneum to the right side of the proventriculus.

The red blood cells are oval and nucleated. Leucocytes (lymphocytes, heterophils, polymorpho-nuclear-pseudo-eosinophilic granulocytes, basophils, eosinophils, and monocytes) occur. The blood of pigeons contains no platelets but it nevertheless clots quickly. Thrombocytes are present and may be involved in the general mechanism.

Lymphatic System.—This is extensive. It includes the lacteals coming away from the small intestine. The lymphatics unite eventually to form paired *thoracic ducts* which enter the precaval veins, thus achieving continuity with the general circulation (pp. 78, 115).

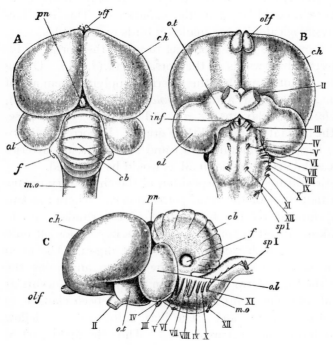

FIG. 407. — *Columba:* **Brain and cranial nerves.** *A*, from above; *B*, from below; *C*, from the left side. *cb.* cerebellum; *c. h.* cerebral hemispheres; *f.* flocculus; *inf.* infundibulum; *m. o.* medulla oblongata; *o. l.* optic lobes; *olf.* olfactory bulbs; *o. t.* optic tracts; *pn.* pineal body; *II—XII*, cranial nerves; *sp.* 1, first spinal nerve. (After T. J. Parker.)

Nervous System and Hypophysis.—The brain is remarkable for its short, broad, rounded form. Next to those of the Mammalia, the avian brain is relatively the largest. It retains several reptilian characteristics—the *medulla oblongata* (*m.o.*), for example, has a well-marked ventral flexure, as in lizards (p. 480). The *cerebellum* (*cb.*) is of great size, as might be expected in a flying animal in which control of equilibrium is of such importance. There are large spino-cerebellar tracts. The cerebellum has a large median portion and two small lateral lobes or *flocculi* (*f.*). The surface of the middle lobe is marked by transverse grooves, so that the superficial grey matter is greatly increased in extent. The fourth ventricle (Fig. 408, v^4) is completely hidden by the cerebellum, into which it does not extend. The *cerebral hemispheres* (*c. h.*) are large, but consist mainly of the massive and complex *corpora striata* : cortex (resembling that of the reptilian brain) is present in the pallial region of the hemisphere, but it is unconvoluted and not extensive. The backward growth of the hemispheres to meet the cerebellum has pressed the optic lobes of the mid-brain outwards so as to take up a lateral instead of the usual dorsal position. These are of large and rounded form. Each contains an extension from the aqueduct (Fig. 408, *o.v.*), a narrow passage which represents the original cavity of the mid-brain. A further result of the growth of the hemispheres and cerebellum (respectively back-wards and forwards) is that no part of the diencephalon (*thc.*) appears externally except on the ventral surface. Elsewhere it is seen only when the hemispheres are pressed aside. It contains a narrow vertical cavity, the third ventricle (*v³.*), bounded laterally by large thalami, and communi-cating on each side by the fora-mina of Monro (*f.m.*) (interven-tricular foramina) with the lateral ventricles or cavities of the hemi-spheres. The *optic nerves* and tracts are extremely prominent. The tracts are crossed, and termi-nate in the mid-brain (as in anurans) and in the thalami. The thalami receive sensory fibres of other kinds and are directly con-nected with the fore-brain (in-

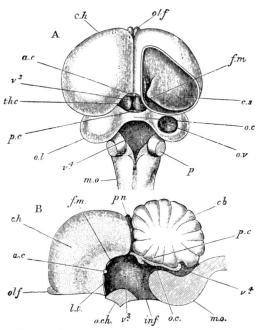

Fig. 408.—*Columba:* **Brain.** *A*, with the cavities opened from above; *B*, in sagittal section. *a. c.* anterior commissure; *cb.* cerebellum; *c. h.* cerebral hemispheres; *c. s.* corpus striatum; *f. m.* foramen of Monro; *inf.* infundibulum; *m. o.* medulla oblongata; *o. c.* optic commissure; *o. ch.* optic chiasma; *o. l.* optic lobes; *olf.* olfactory bulbs; *o. v.* optocœle; *p.* peduncles of cerebellum; *p. c.* posterior commissure; *pn.* pineal body; *thc.* diencephalon; *v³.*, diacœle; *v⁴.*, metacœle. (After T. J. Parker.)

cluding the *corpora striata* (*c. s.*)) and *spinal cord.* The *corpora striata* (*c. s.*) are of relatively immense size and form the greater part of the hemispheres. The remarkable development and differentiation of these organs is one of the most characteristic features of the avian brain. There is evidence that the relatively enormous corpora striata are concerned in the control of the reflex behaviourisms which largely govern the lives of birds.

From the *hypothalamus* there arises a *hypophysial* portal system that joins it with the well-developed *pars distalis* of the *anterior pituitary* gland. This compound endocrine structure lies protected in a bony pocket of the sphenoid, the *sella turcica*.   The *neural* lobe of the posterior pituitary is also well developed (Fig. 96, p. 150).

The anterior lobe is said to be bipartite. It produces hormones that influence at least the primary sex organs (*gonadotrophins*), the adrenal cortex (*adrenocorticotrophic* or *ACTH*), the thyroid (*thyrotrophic hormone*) and the crop-gland (*prolactin*) (p. 583).   The administration of prolactin also causes broodiness, and the collapse and metamorphosis of the testis that normally follows the completion of spermatogenesis in seasonal birds.   Although the avian pituitary gland has no recognisable intermediate lobe, there is evidence that the anterior lobe of the fowl produces a principle that exerts an intermedin-like effect : it expands the melanophores of hypophysectomised frogs and lizards.

The anterior pituitary, in its close relationship with the central nervous system and its exteroceptor organs, is ideally situated as a vital organ in the complex structural and functional chain by which environmental events (*external stimuli* of various kinds) partly control the reproductive and other processes.   The sight of another pigeon in a mirror, for example, will sometimes reflexly lead to enhanced follicle growth and ovulation.   Ventral stimulation by the normal clutch size appears to depress ovulation in many species.   Thus, if the female is prevented from completing the full clutch by the daily removal of an egg, she may continue laying, inhibiting broodiness for many weeks.

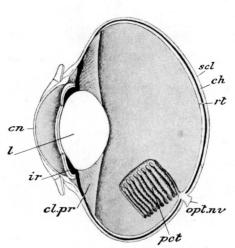

FIG. 409.—*Columba:* **Eye.** Sagittal section. *cn.* cornea; *ch.* choroid; *cl. pr.* ciliary processes; *ir.* iris; *l.* lens; *opt. nv.* optic nerve; *pct.* pecten; *rt.* retina; *scl.* sclerotic. (After Vogt and Jung.)

The *olfactory bulbs* (*olf.*) are extremely small, in correspondence with the poorly developed olfactory organ (see, however, p. 641).

The *spinal cord* (Fig. 401, *sp. cd.*) presents large brachial and lumbar enlargements from which the nerves of the fore- and hind-limbs respectively are given off.   In the lumbar enlargement there is a divergence of the dorsal columns of the cord converting the central canal into a wide, diamond-shaped cavity, the *sinus rhomboidalis* (*s. rhb.*), bounded above only by the membranes of the cord.   The *autonomic nervous system* is of essentially the same plan as in other tetrapods (pp. 119, 412).

Organs of Special Sense.—The *olfactory organs* are paired chambers at the base of the beak, separated from one another by the mesethmoid and bounded externally by the ecto-ethmoid.   The latter is produced inwards into three scroll-like processes, the *turbinals*, which greatly increase the surface of mucous membrane. The anterior portion of the cavity, including the anterior turbinal, is covered by laminated epithelium and serves as a vestibule. The posterior portion, including the middle and posterior turbinals, is invested by the one-layered epithelium of the Schneiderian membrane from which the fibres of the olfactory nerve arise. Most birds have a very poor sense of smell (cf. however, p. 641).

The *eye* (Fig. 409) is extremely large and has the form of a biconvex lens. Bony *sclerotic plates* help maintain its shape. A prominent *nictitating membrane* slides across the eyeball, as in reptiles. In many species of birds this is the only lid that blinks, although the other lids close in sleep. It has been suggested that the nictitating membrane closes and protects the cornea during flight. Certainly the sliding of the nictitating membrane helps keep the cornea clean, helped by the fluid (tears) from the lachrymal glands which supply each eyeball.

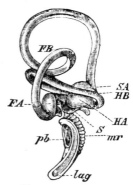

FIG. 410.—*Columba:* **Audio-equilibration.** Left, outer aspect of labyrinth. *FA*, ampulla of posterior canal; *FB*, posterior canal; *HA*, ampulla of horizontal canal; *HB*, horizontal canal; *lag.* lagena, at end of cochlea; *mr.* membrane of Reissner; *pb.* basilar part of cochlea; *S*, sacculus; *SA*, ampulla of anterior canal. (From Wiedersheim, after Hasse.)

Within the eye, the *iris* is controlled by striated fibres. Accommodation is achieved by the action of striated *ciliary muscles* (Crampton's and Brücke's), which alter the shape of the relatively soft lens. At the same time a special set of muscles alters the shape of the cornea. *Cones*, as well as *rods*, are present, and the retina bears a well-marked fovea (see also p. 639). Projecting into the cavity of the eye from the entrance of the optic nerve is a large *pecten* (*pct.*) in the form of a pleated and strongly pigmented membrane. The pecten, about the function of which there has been much controversy, first appears in the Reptilia (pp. 481 and 640).

The *ear* (Fig. 410) is divided into outer, middle, and inner sections, and is chiefly distinguished internally from that of reptiles by the greater development of the auditory apparatus. The cochlea is proportionately much shorter than in mammals and is straight, or almost so. It encloses a *basilar membrane* composed of numerous fibres bearing *hair-cells* which are believed to be sensitive to vibrations of high frequency. At the apical end of the cochlea there occurs another aggregation of hair-cells embedded in a mucoid *cupola* which, in addition, contains calcareous particles. A lagena occurs, which perhaps appreciates sounds of low pitch (see p. 642).

The *tympanic membrane*, cavity and the *columella* have the same essential arrangement as in lizards. The *fenestra ovalis* is almost occluded by the foot-plate of the columella (p. 146). This, and its extension, the *extra-columella*, conveys tympanic oscillations to the perilymph of the inner ear. *Eustachian tubes*, of pressure-equalising and drainage function, run from the middle ear and open by a special aperture (Fig. 401, *eus. ap.*) in the roof of the pharynx.

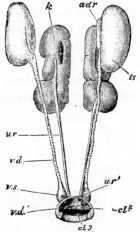

FIG. 411. — *Columba:* **Urinogenital organs in male.** During breeding season. *adr.* adrenal; *cl²*. urodæum; *cl³*. proctodæum; *k.* kidney; *ts.* testis, that of the right side displaced; *ur.* ureter; *ur′*. aperture of ureter; *vd.* vas deferens; *vd′*. its cloacal aperture; *v. s.* vesicula seminalis. (After T. J. Parker.)

There are prominent connexions between the cerebellum and the vestibular apparatus. The anterior canal (SB) is of great size, and the whole membranous labyrinth is closely invested by a layer of dense, ivory-like bone, the *bony labyrinth*. This can be isolated by cutting away the surrounding spongy bone.

Excretory and Reproductive Organs, and Adrenal Glands. The *kidneys* (Figs. 401, *kd.*, Figs. 411 and 412, *k.*) have a very characteristic form. Each is a flattened organ divided into three main lobes and fitted closely into the hollows of the pelvis. It is formed from the metanephros ; the large mesonephros or Wolffian body, which forms the embryonic kidney, atrophies. The glomeruli are supplied by branches of the renal artery.

A high degree of water-conservation is achieved by the addition of a long *loop of Henle* to each excretory tubule (Fig. 100, p. 155). Through this water is reabsorbed from the glomerular filtrate. There is left for excretion a concentration largely of uric acid precipitate, and sufficient fluid to carry it down the *ureter* (*ur.*), which is said in some species to be under sympathetic control and peristaltic in action. The *ureters* (*ur.*) are narrow tubes passing directly backwards to open into the urodæum, the middle compartment of the cloaca. There is a difference of opinion as to whether (as in the lizard) more fluid is reabsorbed from the cloaca. Finally, urine is discharged with the fæces. The fæces of seabirds, deposited in great quantities on certain coastal islands of Peru, South Africa and elsewhere, is

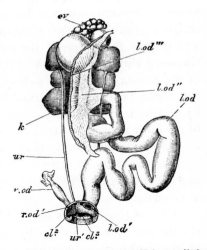

FIG. 412.—*Columba:* **Urinogenital organs in female.** During breeding season. *cl²*. urodæum; *cl³*. proctodæum; *k.* kidney; *l. od.* left oviduct; *l. od′*. its cloacal aperture; *l. od″*. its cœlomic funnel; *l. od‴*. its cœlomic aperture; *ov.* ovary; *r. od.* right oviduct; *r. od′*. its cloacal aperture; *ur.* ureter; *ur′*. its cloacal aperture. (After T. J. Parker.)

collected as *guano* (from : Peruvian *huano* or dung), since it is a valuable agricultural fertiliser.

The *adrenal* or *suprarenal* glands (Fig. 411, *adr.*) are prominent yellow bodies of irregular shape situated anterior to the kidneys and near the gonads. *Chromaffin tissue*, secreting *adrenalin* or its homologue, is inter-digitated (as in reptiles) with the lipoidal tissue that is homologous with the inter-renal gland of fishes (p. 252) and the adrenal cortex in the Mammalia (p. 152). Bilateral adrenalectomy generally results in death within twenty-four hours unless replacement therapy (cortical extracts) is provided. Adrenal tumours have caused virilism in fowls as also in mammals.

The *testes* (Figs. 401 and 411, *ts.*) are ovoid bodies, varying enormously in size according to the season. They are attached by peritoneum to the ventral

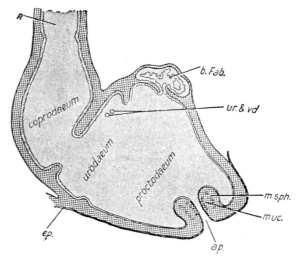

Fig. 413.—*Columba:* **Cloacal region.** The rectum discharges into the coprodæum; the urinary and genital ducts into the urodæum. Mixed fæcal and excretory materials are discharged from the proctodæum, but only after fluid has been conserved by reabsorption into the general circulation through the epithelium of all three cloacal chambers. The lymphoid bursa Fabricii (*b. fab.*) opens into the proctodæum and may possess a local protective function in the young. *ap.* vent; *ep.* epidermis; *m. sph.* cloacal sphincter; *muc.* mucous glands; *r.* rectum; *ur. & vd.* papillæ of ureter and vas deferens (or oviduct). (From Young, after Stresemann.)

surfaces of the anterior ends of the kidneys. Internally each testis is composed of convoluted *seminiferous (spermatogenetic) tubules* in which are elaborated spermatozoa. Between the tubules are aggregated *Leydig (interstitial) cells* which produce the sex hormone *testosterone*. Tubules are under the control of the gonadotrophic *tubule-stimulating* hormone (= *follicle-stimulating hormone* in female) and the interstitial cells are influenced by the *interstitial cell stimulating hormone* (= luteinising hormone) of the anterior pituitary. The testes are permanently retained within the body cavity—there is no temperature-regulating scrotum, such as occurs in most mammals (p. 889). It has been suggested that the abdominal air-sacs (p. 587), which extend into the testicular region, may reduce testis temperature and be concerned indirectly with spermatogenesis, but this is not proved (see also p. 644).

From its inner border each testis gives off a convoluted *vas deferens* (*v. d.*) which carries spermatozoa posteriorly, parallel with the ureter, to open into the urodæum on the extremity of a small papilla (Fig. 413). The posterior end of the sperm-duct is enlarged to form a *vesicula seminalis* (*v. s.*). There is no copulatory organ in pigeons.

The female organs (Fig. 412) are remarkable for the more or less complete atrophy of the right ovary and oviduct. The *left ovary* (*ov.*) is a large organ in the adult bird. Its surface is studded with follicles each containing a single ovum. The ovary is governed in its seasonal activity by *follicle-stimulating hormone* (= tubule-stimulating in male) and the *luteinising* hormone (= I.C.S.H. in male) of the anterior pituitary. It produces the female sex hormone, *œstrogen*, which modifies the accessory sexual organs and behaviour. Progesterone (p. 152) or a progesterone-like substance has been detected in the blood of both hens and cocks, but not from castrated birds.

The *left oviduct* (*l. od.*) is long and convoluted. Its anterior end is enlarged to form a wide membranous oviducal funnel (*l. od''.*) into which the ripe ova pass after extrusion from the follicles. The rest of the tube has thick muscular walls, lined with glandular epithelium, and opens into the urodæum. An obvious vestige of the right oviduct (*r. od.*) is found in connexion with the right side of the cloaca. A more or less extensive vestige of the right ovary is frequently present.

Insemination occurs when the proctodæa of male and female are everted and brought together. The sperms are shed into the female tract and travel up the oviduct, where fertilisation occurs. As the ova or 'yolks' pass down the oviduct they are invested with the secretions of its various glands Successive layers of *albumen* or 'white' are deposited first, next a parchment-like double *shell membrane*, and lastly a white calcareous *shell*. Two eggs are laid in a rough nest, and are *incubated* by the parents for fourteen days, the temperature being in this way kept at about 38° to 40° C. (100° to 103° F.). At the end of incubation the young bird is sufficiently developed to break the shell and begin free life. It is at first covered with fine down, and fed by both parents with the so-called 'pigeon's milk' (p. 583).

GENERAL ORGANISATION OF BIRDS

The range of structural variation in the entire class of birds hardly equals that of a single order of reptiles (*e.g.* pp. 496, 498). Among existing birds, the Emu and ravens, which stand nearly at opposite ends of the series, present nothing like the anatomical differences to be found (for example) between a common lizard and a chameleon. Hence, in dividing the class into orders, we find none of those strikingly distinctive characters which separate the orders of fishes, amphibians, and reptiles, but must be content with characters which in other groups would be considered insignificant. Such characters include details in the structure of the skull and sternum, in the arrangement of the muscles of the syrinx, wing and leg, in the form of the foot and in the peculiarities of the newly-hatched young. It is for this reason that in the classification (p. 606) few diagnostic details are given. To define each order adequately would involve a degree of taxonomic detail beyond the scope of the present work. The differences between the two avian sub-classes, the Archæornithes and the Neornithes are, however, of a fundamental nature.

SUB-CLASS ARCHÆORNITHES

ORDER ARCHÆOPTERYGIFORMES

These Mesozoic (p. 3) birds had no pygostyle (ploughshare bone). They possessed a long tail of many vertebræ, with the rectrices arranged in two lateral

FIG. 414.—Sub-class **Archæornithes**, Order **Archæopterygiformes**, Family **Archæopterygidæ**, *Archæopteryx*. Almost the first birds, these (left) were Jurassic contemporaries of the early pterosaurs ('pterodactyls') such as *Rhamphorhynchus* (right) (p. 504). The flying reptiles did not survive into Cenozoic times (p. 3) and left no descendants. Although the Archæopterygiformes (above), and also the Hesperornithiformes and Ichthyornithiformes (p. 603), seem to have died out in the Upper Cretaceous, at least one related line flourished and led to the modern birds. (Redrawn after B. M. catalogue, Heilmann and others.)

rows. The carpals and metacarpals were free, and the hand had three clawed digits. Enamelled-crowned teeth were present in both jaws. So far two genera have been described, each with a single species. These are *Archæopteryx lithographica* (Figs. 414, 415) and *Archæornis siemensi*, known only from two specimens [1] found in the Upper Jurassic limestone of Solenhofen in Bavaria. Each was about the size of a crow. They probably belong to the same genus or even species, in which case the name *Archæopteryx* has priority. In the fossils the impressions of many of the feathers are preserved. Had this not been so, it would not be easy to separate the fossils from those of certain small bipedal dinosaurs.

FIG. 415.—*Archæopteryx:* **Berlin specimen.** The feathered, yet tailed, toothed, and fingered (Fig. 416) *Archæopteryx* is an example of *mosaic evolution* like *Seymouria* (p. 427) and the pictidosaurs (p. 517). *c.* carpal; *cl.* furcula; *co.* coracoid; *h.* humerus; *r.* radius; *sc.* scapula; *u.* ulna; *I—IV*, digits.

A most striking feature in their organisation is the tail, which was composed of about twenty free caudal vertebræ gradually tapering to the distal end, as in most reptiles. The *rectrices* were arranged one on each side of the caudal vertebræ. The sacrum was made up of only about six vertebræ, as in the ornithopod dinosaurs (p. 508). These centra had amphiplatyan faces with no indication of the heterocœlous condition found in extant birds. In addition to cervical and thoracic ribs (which were apparently devoid of un-cinates), there were thin abdominal 'ribs', like those of *Sphenodon* and crocodiles. These *gastralia*, or so-called 'ventral ribs', are elements of dermal bone which lie in the ventral wall of the abdomen. There is no evidence that any of the true ribs were articulated with the small sternum.

The skull (Fig. 416) was proportionately large, with a rounded, bird-like brain-case and strong jaws, in each of which was a series of conical *teeth* lodged in sockets. The jaw-bones, however, were heavier than those of modern birds, and the teeth, though characteristically reptilian, were relatively small. The eyes were large and apparently avian.

[1] A third, very incomplete, fossil has now (1959) been found in the Langenaltheimer Haardt quarry, 6 metres lower than, and 97 years after, the London specimen.

The sternum, hidden in the limestone matrix, but revealed by the fluorescent quality of fossil bone under ultra-violet light, was flat without a keel (de Beer). The coracoids (*co.*) were small. The scapulæ (*sc.*) were slender, curved bones, and there was a U-shaped furcula (*cl.*) formed by the fusion of the clavicles. The bones were apparently without air-spaces (Fig. 387, p. 572). The vertebral articulation was simple and non-avian. The fore-limb skeleton was about the

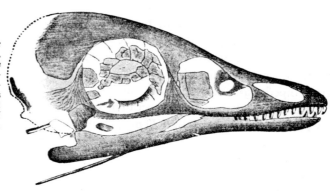

FIG. 416.—*Archæopteryx:* **Skull.** The toothed rostrum, sclerotic plates, and the large orbital and antorbital apertures are clearly shown. Enlargement of cranial bones reduced the two temporal apertures characteristic of archosaurian reptiles. (From Headley, after Dames.)

same size as the hind-limb. The shape of the humerus reveals that the biceps muscles were not powerfully developed. The radius and ulna were well developed. The metacarpals were free, as in reptiles, except for the third metacarpal, which was fixed with the carpal ossification—an indication of things to come. The number of phalanges followed the usual reptilian rule : two in the first digit, three in the second, and four in the third. The ungual phalanx of all three digits was claw-shaped, and doubtless supported a horny claw. Despite its feathers, the fore-limb was still essentially a foreleg (Figs. 415, 417).

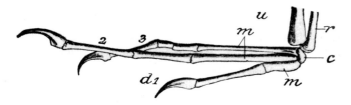

FIG. 417.—*Archæopt-eryx:* **Manus.** (Right). *c.* carpal; *d* 1, first digit; 2, second digit; 3, third digit; *m, m.* metacarpals; *r.* radius; *u.* ulna. (From Headley, after Dames.)

The *remiges* were divisible, as usual, into primaries (or *metacarpo-digitals*) and secondaries (or *cubitals*). The primaries were probably attached to the second, or to the second and third of the digits just described. The feathers were of the delicate structure shown in modern birds.

The pelvis and the *hind-limbs* combined both avian and reptilian characters. The elongated and backwardly directed *pubis* was bird-like. The separate *tibia* and *fibula* were of about the same length : there was no suggestion of fibula reduction, as in modern birds. The foot consisted of a slender *tarsometatarsus* and four digits. The *hallux* was small and opposable, as in many modern birds.

In addition to the wing and tail-quills there are remains of contour feathers at the base of the neck and wing-coverts. Moreover, the rectrices were continued forwards by a series of large feathers which extended for some distance along the sides of the body, and a row of similar but smaller feathers was attached along both anterior and posterior faces of the tibio-tarsus.

These birds could not fly efficiently. The small, flat sternum, relatively slight wing-spread and elongated, feathered, lizard-like tail make it clear that they merely volplaned from branches. The free, probably clawed, digits of the fore-limbs suggest a scrambling progression among branches. The evolution of true flight by arboreal *Archæopteryx*-like animals is more plausible than Nopcsa's surmise that avian flight was first developed in feathered terrestrial, bipedal animals that volplaned off the ground while running at speed.

Recent studies of an endocranial cast of *Archæopteryx* confirm Edinger's suggestion that the cerebral hemispheres were smooth, long, and narrow, and that the cerebellum was small. The latter lay behind the mid-brain instead of overlapping it from behind and pressing it down to a more ventral level, as in modern birds. For the purpose of its limited powers of flight, *Archæopteryx* did not require a high degree of cerebellar co-ordination (de Beer). Thus the brain was in certain important respects reptilian rather than avian. It seems almost certain, on the other hand, that the Archæornithes were homoiothermous.

There is every reason to believe that *Archæopteryx* was a forest bird, yet all three specimens (and an isolated feather) were embedded in marine beach deposits. It would seem that they were blown seawards (as are even expert fliers to-day), and so fortuitously came to rest in the fine-grained mud in which they were so wonderfully preserved.

SUB-CLASS NEORNITHES

This includes all other known birds (both extinct and living), which, according to some authorities, fall into four super-orders—1. Cretaceous Odontognathæ (e.g. *Hesperornis, Ichthyornis*); 2. Palæognathæ (*e.g.* Ostrich, Emu, etc.); 3. Impennæ (penguins), and 4. Neognathæ of more than a score of relatively modern orders. In all these groups the greatly shortened tail usually ends in a pygostyle, around which the rectrices, when present, are arranged in a semi-circle. Except in a few extinct forms there are no teeth. The metacarpals are fused with the distal carpals to form a carpo-metacarpus. Except in one instance, not more than two digits of the hand bear claws; in nearly all cases claws are absent in the manus. The sternum is well-developed and usually keeled or carinate (p. 577).

The Neornithes, as far as is known, first appeared in the Cretaceous. Cretaceous representatives were specialised water-birds that are preserved in chalky marine deposits in North America. These forms (e.g. *Ichthyornis, Hesperornis*) therefore probably give a no more characteristic impression of the late-Mesozoic avifauna than do divers (*Gavia*) or pelicans (*Pelecanus*) of that of to-day. Very little direct evidence is available concerning Cretaceous land-birds, although fragmentary fossils seem to make it clear that large flightless 'ratite' (p. 606) and other toothless birds already existed. Flying forest-birds in particular, are very rarely entombed in silt. Further, the relatively light bones of birds do not seem to preserve well, except in especially fortuitous

Fig. 418.—Sub-class **Neornithes,** Super-order **Odontognathæ,** Orders **Hesperornithiformes** and **Ichthyornithiformes,** *Hesperornis* and *Ichthyornis.* Birds attained their modern appearance in the Cretaceous but the flightless, superficially loon-like *Hesperornis* (below) nevertheless retained true teeth (Fig. 419). *Ichthyornis* (above) was a strongly-flying, keel-breasted, tern-like bird (Fig. 420) the head of which has not yet been found. (Redrawn from various sources.)

circumstances (*e.g.* p. 602). Fossils become more plentiful in Tertiary deposits, but these, too, are often fragmentary, and many of their relationships are highly speculative. By the Eocene and Oligocene, however, we find examples of most of the flying, swimming, and running types familiar today.

The Neornithes have been arranged as follows :

SUPER-ORDER ODONTOGNATHÆ

This Cretaceous (p. 3) group represents probably the first of the several successful avian attempts to exploit the prolific harvest of the sea. From the time of the initial emergence of amniotes (p. 457), various reptilian, avian, and mammalian stocks successively became partly, and occasionally wholly, marine. Although in regard to numbers birds may have become more successful seafarers than any other amniote class, none has ever become viviparous

FIG. 419.—*Hesperornis:* Skeleton. *H. regalis* was a marine Cretaceous bird that had become highly specialised to an aquatic life. The teeth, adapted for fishing, were in grooves and not in sockets like those of *Archæopteryx* (Fig. 414). Teeth were absent from the premaxilla: a horny beak was probably already present. *Hesperornis* seemingly possessed a strong convergent resemblance to modern divers (loons): the posture shown above is therefore much too erect and the feet should be more laterally placed. The occurrence of such widely divergent marine types as *Hesperornis* and *Ichthyornis* (Fig. 420) suggests that land-birds, too, must have radiated considerably in the late Cretaceous. Both the above-mentioned birds were preserved in Kansas chalk-deposits. The figure (right) is about 1/7 natural size. See also Fig. 418. (After Marsh.)

and entirely aquatic. The Odontognathæ are especially interesting in their retention of teeth—'so advantageous for catching fish' (Storer)—probably after teeth had been lost in the main stem of avian evolution. It was for many years believed that the Odontognathæ possessed a brain more reptilian than avian, but by the use of cranial casts Edinger has shown that the opposite is true.

ORDER HESPERORNITHIFORMES

Hesperornis (Fig. 419) was a powerful marine diving and swimming bird from the Cretaceous of North America which stood perhaps 3 feet high. Sharply pointed teeth were carried in grooves, not in distinct jaw sockets. The pre-maxillæ were without teeth. The neck was long, the body elongated ; and the sternum lacked a keel. The shoulder-girdle was much reduced, and the bird was almost certainly flightless (Fig. 419). The hind-limbs were powerful, and the toes probably webbed.

The order contains three families: Hesperornithidæ (e.g. *Hesperornis, Hargeria,* Upper Cretaceous of North America); Enaliornithidæ (e.g. *Enaliornis*

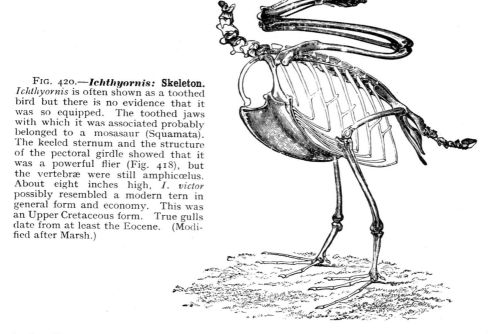

FIG. 420.—*Ichthyornis:* **Skeleton.**
Ichthyornis is often shown as a toothed bird but there is no evidence that it was so equipped. The toothed jaws with which it was associated probably belonged to a mosasaur (Squamata). The keeled sternum and the structure of the pectoral girdle showed that it was a powerful flier (Fig. 418), but the vertebræ were still amphicœlus. About eight inches high, *I. victor* possibly resembled a modern tern in general form and economy. This was an Upper Cretaceous form. True gulls date from at least the Eocene. (Modified after Marsh.)

of the European Lower Cretaceous; *Neogæornis* of the European Upper Cretaceous); and Baptornithidæ (e.g. *Baptornis,* North American Upper Cretaceous).

ORDER ICHTHYORNITHIFORMES

This order contains several species (*e.g. Ichthyornis* (Fig. 418) and *Apatornis*) found in the same deposits as *Hesperornis.* The brain of these somewhat tern-like marine flying birds was of the typically avian pattern. It was formerly believed that small, recurved and pointed teeth were set in sockets, but Gregory has shown that the toothed jaws attributed to *Ichthyornis* probably belonged to reptilian mosasaurs. It is not yet known whether these birds had teeth or not. The neck vertebrae were amphicœlous. The sternum had a well-developed keel, and the wings were not unlike those of modern flying birds (Fig. 420).

The order contains two families: Ichthyornithidæ (e.g. *Ichythyornis*) and

Apatornithidæ (e.g. *Apatornis*). All known specimens are from the Upper Cretaceous of North America.

SUPER-ORDER PALÆOGNATHÆ

These are almost always flightless and usually of large size. The substantial cerebellum is an indication that they are descended from volant ancestors. There is some evidence that the stock appeared at the end of the Mesozoic, and some (Emu, cassowaries, Ostrich, *Rhea*) are sufficiently powerful and adaptable to remain relatively plentiful to-day in the face of unprecedentedly savage competition by Man and his domesticated animals. One, the Ostrich, is farmed for its specialised filamentous plumage. Palæognathous birds, with a generally raft-like sternum, have been considered as a flightless 'Order Ratitæ', as distinct from an 'Order Carinatæ' of keel-breasted flying birds. Such an arrangement is untenable : several flying birds in specialised habitats have lost the carinate condition, and become raft-breasted in varying degree along with the abandonment of flying.

De Beer has now assembled evidence that the 'ratite' palate (see below) is not primitive, but neotenous. It probably represents an early stage 'through which the palate of many carinates passes during development'. In short, the so-called old palate (Fig. 434, p. 631) is probably an arrested development of the neognathous condition (see McDowell). Whether the flightless birds constitute a single natural group, or whether they are a heterogeneous assembly that have pursued more or less parallel lines consequent upon the loss of flight is at present unknown. The palæognathous palate varies greatly, as will be seen if the skull of an Ostrich, kiwi, cassowary, and tinamu are compared. Excepting only the Ostrich (which still exists commonly north of the equator), these birds live to-day only in southern continents and islands. It is important to remember, however, that ostriches were spread over much of the Eurasian landmass in the Tertiary, along with even larger ostrich-like forms.

The feathers of such birds are 'primitive', in that they have no hooked barbules, so that the barbs are free (Fig. 381, p. 561; Fig. 384, p. 568). Such feathers are a further neotenous character: they are essentially similar to down. Apteria are usually absent in the adult.

The rectrices are absent or irregularly arranged, and the pygostyle is small or undeveloped. The sternal keel is vestigial or absent. The coracoid and scapula are comparatively small and completely ankylosed. The acrocoracoid process is vestigial, and the coraco-scapular angle approaches two right angles. The wing is reduced in size and may be vestigial or absent. There are large basipterygoid processes developed from the basisphenoid. The vomer is large and broad, and separates the palatines, which do not come into contact with the cranium (cf. *neognathous* or so-called 'new jawed' condition,

p. 613). This condition occurs also in the toothed *odontognathous* forms (p. 603), and recalls to some degree that of archosaurian reptiles (p. 498). The quadrate articulates with the skull by a single or partially divided facet. Permanent sutures between the skull bones are another result of neoteny, *i.e.* 'the secondary retention of features which were juvenile in the ancestors of the ratites' (de Beer).

The males have an erectile penis and the females a clitoris. The young are precocious.

ORDER STRUTHIONIFORMES

The Ostrich (*Struthio camelo*) of Africa and Southern Asia (Arabia) is the largest living bird, standing nearly 8 feet high. Ostriches retain only two toes (the third and fourth), and the feathers lack an aftershaft. They extend their rudimentary wings while running at speed. The story that the Ostrich buries its head in the sand in order to conceal itself is untrue. A squatting bird, however, will often lower its head to a position parallel with the ground, and thus render itself less easy to see because of its obliterative coloration. Ostriches occurred in the Pliocene.

ORDER RHEIFORMES

These (genus *Rhea*) are two species of large running birds of the South American pampas which seem to occupy an ecological niche approximately similar to that of the surviving Australian Emu. Rheas retain three toes. The genus occurred in the Pliocene.

ORDER CASUARIIFORMES

Emus (*Dromæus*) and cassowaries (*Casuarius*) of Australia, New Guinea, and the East Indies. Of the vegetarian emus, which are known also from Australian Pleistocene deposits, only one species survives. This is a plain- and savannah-dwelling form, which is in no danger of extinction. It stands nearly 6 feet high. It is a swift runner and, in addition, has each inner toe (of the three) equipped with a powerful claw with which it can rip the belly of a dog. Next to the Ostrich, the Emu is the largest living bird. Its feather after-shafts are about the same length as the main quills.

The fruit-eating cassowaries are confined to the dense tropical rain-forests of Australia (one species only), New Guinea, and the East Indies. The wattled neck and brilliantly coloured head of each species are surmounted by a tall, horny casque, which probably helps the bird push through the thick 'jungle'. Cassowaries, too, can disembowel a dog with a single kick, and occasionally humans have been killed by the powerful, sharp inner toe. In both Emu and cassowaries the wings are reduced to vestiges supported by a single digit. The wing rudiments of cassowaries are distinguished by the possession of several spine-like, barbless feather-shafts some inches long. The dorsal feathers are long, and fall over the sides in a thick, almost hair-like protection against the spiky rain-forest tangles. Pre-Pleistocene fossils have yet to be found.

Order Apterygiformes

The kiwis (*Apteryx*, Figs. 421, 446) are confined to New Zealand and adjacent islands. They are relatively small, almost wingless birds, about the size of, or a little larger than, a domestic fowl. They run swiftly and defend

Fig. 421.—Sub-class **Neornithes**, Super-order **Palæognathæ**, Orders **Dinornithiformes** and **Apterygiformes**. *Dinornis* and *Apteryx*. Moas (left) became extinct in geologically recent times. They showed a degree of convergence with giraffes. The earth-probing kiwis (right) are protected by law, and some are not uncommon in many localities. Both groups originated in and are confined to the islands of New Zealand.

themselves with their claws. Kiwis are nocturnal, and live principally on worms and insects caught by a long probing beak, the nostrils of which are at the tip of the maxilla. The eyes are small (p. 640). The eggs are relatively the largest of all living birds (see also p. 609). The feathers have no after-shaft. Pre-Pleistocene fossils have yet to be found.

Order Dinornithiformes

The remarkable moas (families Dinornithidæ and Anomalopterygidæ) of New Zealand were of perhaps twenty species, ranging from the size of a turkey to the giant *Dinornis maximus* about 10 feet high (Fig. 421). In most species the wings and pectoral girdles had disappeared completely, and in no case was there any trace of a keel on the sternum. The beaks were short and the massive legs had four toes. They were probably vegetarian, some perhaps feeding in the manner of giraffes. Many Pleistocene fossils are available. Bones and even the loosely constructed feathers (without barbicels) have been preserved in middens. Moa bones were used by the Maoris as implements, and it has been generally thought that the birds were exterminated when New Zealand was colonised by them about the year A.D. 1350. This view is now subject to considerable doubt (Archey). Modern excavations show that moas were indeed killed in great numbers, but probably by a pre-Maori people who also buried moa-egg containers (holding about two quarts) with their dead. There is some evidence that moas disappeared less than a century before the arrival of the Maoris who in turn exterminated the earlier New Zealanders.

ORDER ÆPYORNITHIFORMES

The giant flightless Madagascan *Æpyornis* ('Elephant-birds') were extinguished in recent times, perhaps only a very few centuries ago and therefore rather later than the moas. They possessed relatively tiny wings, but had stout, powerful legs and four toes. Some were larger than ostriches: *Æ. titan* was about 10 feet high. Eggs have been found measuring 13 × 9·5 inches, with a probable capacity

FIG. 422.—Order **Tinamiformes**, Family **Tinamidæ**. *Eudromia.* *E. elegans* is, like many tinamus, extremely successful and widely distributed. In its various races it occurs from the valleys of the Andes to the Atlantic, and from Northern Argentine to Santa Cruz. Future research may shift the tinamus from the Palæognathæ to near the neognathous galliformes (p. 615). (Redrawn after Grasse.)

of about two gallons. It is not improbable that *Æpyornis* and its allies inspired the exaggerated stories (Marco Polo, *Arabian Nights*, etc.) of the giant Madagascan *Roc*, which was claimed to be big enough to carry off an elephant. Although it is possible that the egg of *Æpyornis* is the largest animal cell that has ever existed, it still falls rather below the size attributed to Roc's eggs— ('as big as a butt'). North African Pliocene fossils have been found. Madagascan fossils are Pleistocene.

ORDER TINAMIFORMES

The affinities of the superficially partridge-like, almost tail-less tinamus (Fig. 422) are uncertain. Traditionally they have been placed in the position given them here but there is much to be said for placing them near the Galli-formes (p. 615) in another super-order (Neognathæ) altogether.   Tinamus are essentially cursorial but they can fly clumsily over short distances: *the sternum is keeled*.   At the same time most authorities believe that their palatal struc-ture generally agrees with that of the palæognathous forms dealt with above.

There is but one family—the Tinamidæ—of more than fifty species which are confined to the mainland of southern Mexico, and Central and South America.   The various species have spread widely throughout open pampas, equatorial forests, and high into the barren uplands of the Andes.

When flushed, tinamus (which are cryptically coloured) usually run rapidly and may conceal themselves by squatting.   They do not perch.   They are essentially vegetarian.   Their eggs are remarkable: the shells are highly glossy and of a single, often intense, colour, according to the species.   Fossils are rare; some South American Pliocene and Pleistocene remains have been identified.

SUPER-ORDER IMPENNÆ

ORDER SPHENISCIFORMES

Although penguins (Fig. 423) are here placed in a separate super-order, it should be remembered that, despite their remarkably different appearance from all other birds, they undoubtedly exhibit fundamental similarities with the birds of the following super-order (Neognathæ), in which they are often included.   Some have suggested that penguins evolved from flightless raft-chested sea-birds but this view has little in its favour.   The balance of evidence, summarised by Simpson, suggests that the group evolved from a volant stock in which the wings were used both for flying and swimming (as, for example, by the extant auks).   With the loss of flight and increase in weight, the wing became increasingly efficient as a flipper which is nevertheless still used in exactly the same motion as that of a bird in flight.

Penguins have become wonderfully adapted to swimming and diving.   The bones, excluding certain skull-bones, are solid and there are no air-sacs within the body.   The closely packed plumage holds very little air.   The bones of the featherless wings have become flattened and united to form a powerful, resistant paddle or flipper which moves only at the shoulder-joint.   It seems probable that this flipper 'never ceased to be a functional wing, but only changed the medium in which it functioned' (Simpson).   The paddles are used also for fighting, and, in some species, for terrestrial locomotion.   The hind-limbs are strikingly modified for swimming.   The metatarsals, unlike those of other birds, are only partly fused and the feet are strongly webbed. The short, heavily packed plumage and subcutaneous fat deposits are insulat-ing in function.   The body is sleek and streamlined, and offers the least possible resistance to diving and submarine activities.

Although one species has followed the cold Humboldt current as far north as the Galapagos, penguins are typically Southern Hemisphere birds. They

FIG. 423.—Sub-class **Neornithes,** Super-order **Impennæ,** Order **Sphenisciformes,** Family **Spheniscidæ.** *Aptenodytes:* **Environment, development, and behaviour.** In its successful colonisation of the harsh Antarctic mainland, the Emperor Penguin, *A. forsteri,* has developed a series of remarkable, even bizarre, forms of behaviour. During blizzards the birds huddle tightly together in thousands, backs to the wind, with the chilled outer rank frequently changing places with warmer birds inside. The species establishes no territory and builds no nest. The female lays in the tempestuous darkness of winter and the single egg, and later the chick, is carried on the feet covered by a fold of tissue. The egg is early transferred to the male and the female goes off to the sea (often as far as 50 miles away) for approximately the whole incubation period of some 63 days. She returns laden with subcutaneous and peritoneal fat, and brings crustacean *krill* 'paste' to the male, whom she now relieves. Correlated with the mode of its transportation, and the time of its hatching, is the slow developmental rate of the Emperor chick. By comparison, the young Adelie Penguin (*Pygoscelis adelie*), which hatches in a nest in the same region in mid-summer, grows rapidly and is relatively large at the start of the next winter. Also correlated with the stringent environmental conditions is the development in the Emperor of a most exaggerated parental drive. Stray chicks are sometimes crushed to death—killed by kindness—by over-solicitous potential foster-parents. Levick says that chicks sometimes crawl under icy ledges to escape being cared for, and that even dead chicks may be carried about until the down is rubbed off their bodies. (From photographs by courtesy of F.I.D.S.)

occur in greatest numbers between the southern extremes of South America, South Africa, Australia, and the Antarctic continent (p. 612). They appear in mid-Tertiary deposits in South America and on Antarctic islands. Certain Miocene forms were about 5 feet high and weighed perhaps 200 lb.

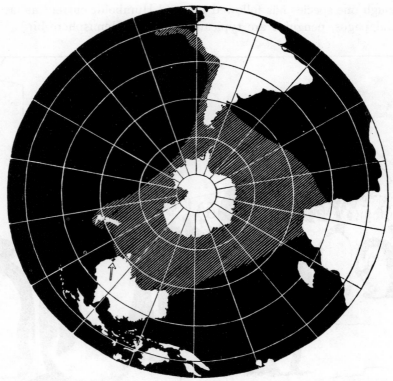

FIG. 424.—**Neornithes: Adaptation and geographical distribution.** *The minute spot* (arrowed) in eastern Australia roughly indicates the total distribution of the passerine Sydney Rock Warbler (*Origma rubricata*). *The vast cross-hatched ocean area* approximately covers the distribution of the penguins (Spheniscidæ).

In a restricted region of exposed Triassic sandstone, a small modern warbler has become essentially a rock-hopper. It wedges spider-web into a horizontal crevice in the roof of a dim cavern and to this it anchors its bulky moss and root-fibre pendent nest; its eggs have become white: it has become *Origma rubricata*. During the past 50 years odd deviant nests have been reported hanging in a *limestone* cave, culverts, a tent, an engine-room, a sewer shaft, a hollow log, and an artist's studio. The Rock Warbler is adapted to reproduction in spacious hollows. These are not found in quantity in surrounding geological formations; hence the restricted distribution.

Penguins no doubt evolved in the south, and became remarkably adapted (p. 611) to life in cold seas. They thrust out in all directions, colonising and speciating. One species—the Galapagos—is enabled by the cold Humboldt current to live on the equator; but none has been able to cross the warm seas to colonise the Arctic—as has, for example, the strong-flying Great Skua (*Catharacta skua*). Another species (the Humboldt) has spread along the colder western coast of South America, and the Gentoo and Rockhopper (both circum-polar in distribution) reach southern South America. Another (the African) lives in South Africa, and yet another (Fairy) in southern Australia and northern New Zealand. Four species inhabit the southern islands of New Zealand, where one breeds in woodland. Of the 17 species, only three (Chinstrap, Adelie, and Emperor) have successfully invaded the Antarctic continent.

SUPER-ORDER NEOGNATHÆ

This great group is characterised by the 'new jaw' arrangement as opposed to that of the palæognathous or 'old jawed' condition (p. 606). If the conclusion is accepted that the palæognathous condition is an arrested stage in the development of the neognathous palate, it follows that it is the so-called 'new palate' that is the primitive condition (unless one chooses to believe in the Theory of Recapitulation). In the neognathous condition the palatines extend posteriorly, make contact with the base of the cranium, and come into mobile articulation with the short pterygoid bones. The vomers, too, are brief. (In palæognathous birds this palato-cranial articulation is rigid.) Neognathous types arose in the Cretaceous (p. 3), radiated in the Tertiary, and became the dominant flying vertebrates. More than twenty orders (in the ornithological sense, p. 555) are represented, a few of which include the numerous species that occur on every city building and garden. They are as follows:

ORDER GAVIIFORMES

The long-necked loons or divers (*Gavia* = *Colymbus*) fall into a single family and genus of piscivorous sea- and lake-birds from North America, Europe, and the Arctic. In some characters (*e.g.* posterior position of legs) they have converged with *Hesperornis* (p. 604) but, on the other hand, they are powerful in flight. They lay their eggs in exposed places in nests made of piles of vegetation. Early Tertiary fossils are known. Some authorities include the divers with the next order.

ORDER PODICIPITIFORMES

The compact-bodied grebes (single family, Podicipitidæ) are also often called 'divers' because of their habits. They are freshwater birds of almost cosmo-politan distribution. They are almost completely aquatic and build floating nests. They are commonly said to be sufficiently agile to dive after a gun-flash, yet escape the bullet. This story has gained currency solely due to poor marksmanship. The toes are lobate and the legs are placed far back. Tertiary fossils occur.

ORDER PROCELLARIIFORMES

These are tube-nosed, long-winged sea-birds, of which the following families are recognised: Diomedeidæ (albatrosses), Procellariidæ (fulmars, shearwaters, etc), Hydrobatidæ (= Thalassidromidæ) (storm-petrels, etc.), Pelecanoididæ (diving petrels). Members of this order have penetrated the furthest limits of every ocean. The albatrosses, however, belong essentially to the Southern Hemisphere, although many cross the equator. Tube-nosed birds range in size from tiny storm-petrels (e.g. *Oceanites*) less than 7 inches long to the great soaring albatrosses (e.g. *Diomedea*) with a wing-spread of about $11\frac{1}{2}$ feet. Petrels got their name from St. Peter because they seem to walk on the water. They are called by sailors 'Mother Carey's Chickens'. ('Mother Carey' is a corruption of *Mater Cara*, the Blessed Virgin.) Procellariiformes breed general-ly on islands or cliffs, often in very high latitudes (e.g. *Fulmarus*). One shear-water, *Puffinus tenuirostris* (the fledgling of which is salted as 'mutton-bird'), breeds on islands off the Tasmanian coast and then makes an enormous circum-oceanic migration via New Zealand, Japan, Alaska, and California, arriving back in southern Australia about the same 12 days every year. All tube-nosed birds lay one large egg, sometimes in a burrow. Some eat plankton and fishes; others are scavengers. They are among the few birds with a well-developed olfactory apparatus (p. 641). They appear in Oligocene deposits.

ORDER PELECANIFORMES

A polymorphic assembly of voracious fish-eaters which occupy the following families: Phæthontidæ (Tropic- or Bos'un-birds), Pelecanidæ (pelicans), Balænicipitidæ (Shoebill), Pelagornithidæ (gannets and boobies), Phalacrocoracidæ (cormorants and shags), Anhingidæ (darters or snake-birds), and Fregatidæ (frigate-birds). They are generally colonial nesters and have four-toed webbed feet, bodies adapted for diving (some from heights of 60 feet), and long beaks with wide gapes for catching and swallowing struggling prey. Pelicans (*Pelecanus*) have buccal pouches for storage. Darters (*Anhinga*) first spear the fish, then toss, catch, and swallow. *Elopteryx*, which probably comes into this group, occurred in the Upper Cretaceous and may be one of the earliest known neognathous birds. The Tertiary *Odontopteryx* had a saw-edged beak.

ORDER CICONIIFORMES

This long-legged and correspondingly long-billed group is composed of the following: Ardeidæ (herons, egrets, and bitterns), Cochleariidæ (boat-billed herons), Scopidæ (hammer-heads), Ciconiidæ (storks, openbills, Jabiru), Threskiornithidæ (ibises, spoonbills, etc.), Phœnicopteridæ (flamingoes). The last-named alone have retained webbed feet, and have the middle toe relatively short. The egrets seasonally develop filamentous nuptial plumes which are marketed, generally illegally, as 'osprey plumes'. (Ospreys are fish-hawks.) All the above birds feed principally in marshes and mudflats, and this is probably responsible for the relative abundance of fossils from the Eocene onwards.

ORDER ANSERIFORMES

The swans, geese, and ducks are strong fliers and almost cosmopolitan: Anhimidæ (screamers, etc.), Anatidæ (all others). They may be vegetarian, mollusc- or fish-eaters, or filter-feeders with, in addition, special tactile organs on the beak. The feet are webbed, even in the tree-ducks. They are not uncommon from the Eocene onwards.

ORDER FALCONIFORMES

The diurnal birds-of-prey are grouped as follows: Cathartidæ (American vultures, condors), Sagittariidæ (Secretary-bird), Accipitridæ (harriers, kites, eagles, Old World vultures, and ospreys), Falconidæ (falcons and allies).

These powerful fliers have spread almost everywhere except Antarctica. They are notable for the spread of their sharp claws for catching and holding prey, and their hooked beaks for cutting and tearing. They generally eat living vertebrates, including fish (ospreys and sea-eagles), but some eat carrion and a few weak-billed forms devour insects. The Wedge-tailed Eagle (*Uro-cætus audax*) of Australia, which has in Tasmania a wing-span of from 6 to 10 feet (about 7 to 10 lb. weight), has been known to attack a seven-year-old girl when hungry after escape from captivity. An eagle of even greater size is *Pithecophaga*, the Monkey-eating Eagle of the Philippines. Two of the sea-eagles (*Haliætus pelagicus* and *H. albicilla*) may be even bigger.

The order is represented from the Eocene. The Pleistocene condor *Tera-tornis incredibilis* was the biggest flying-bird yet known and may have had a wing-span of 16 feet.

Order Galliformes

This heterogeneous group of game-birds is almost cosmopolitan. It in-cludes the Megapodidæ (incubator-birds, brush-'turkeys', etc.), Cracidæ (curassows, etc.), Tetraonidæ (grouse, ptarmigan), Phasianidæ (partridges, quail, true pheasants), Numididæ (guinea-fowl), Meleagrididæ (true turkeys), and the extraordinary sub-order Opisthocomi containing the single genus *Opisthocomus* (hoatzins) (Fig. 427). Notable for their palatability, massive scratching feet and short, powerful flight, galliform birds are largely gramini-vorous, but eat quantities of insects. They are essentially terrestrial. The palate is different from that of raft-breasted types (p. 606), and most modern groups as well, suggesting an ancient departure on an independent line. Pre-Eocene fossils, however, remain unknown.

Opisthocomus of South America is especially notable in that the nestling has, on the first two digits of the wing, claws used in clambering among branches. This character, however, is almost certainly of independent development, and not an inheritance from archæornithian (p. 599) ancestry.

Order Gruiformes

This is a polymorphic assembly including the Turnicidæ (bustard-quails), Pedionomidæ (collared hemipodes), Gruidæ (cranes, Brolga), Psophiidæ (trumpeters), Rallidæ (rails, gallinules and coots), Heliornithes (sun-grebes), Rhynochetidæ (kagus), Eurypigidæ (sun bitterns), Otidæ (bustards), and the Cariamidæ (cariamas).

Excluding polar regions, the order is almost universal. Many (*e.g.* rails) are laterally compressed reed-dwellers. The bustards have left the water and colonised grass-land and savannah. The order dates from the Eocene, and perhaps includes the South American Phororhacidæ and allies which, probably related to the cariamas, were common in the Miocene. These long-legged, heavy-beaked, flightless birds stood nearly 6 feet high (e.g. *Phororhacus*). They were carnivorous ground-nesters, and their temporary success was possibly related to the current absence of placental carnivores in South America.

ORDER DIATRYMIFORMES

These (Diatrymidæ, Gastornithidæ) were large, flightless European and North American forms which were common in the early Eocene and probably

FIG. 425.—Sub-class **Neornithes**, Super-order **Neognathæ**, Order **Diatrymiformes**, Family **Diatrymidæ**. **Diatryma**. *D. steini* was a North American Eocene cursorial form about 7 feet high which was nevertheless a 'modern' bird of an order perhaps allied to the Gruiformes (cranes, bitterns, bustards, etc.)   (Redrawn after Matthew and Grainger.)

related to the cariamas (see above). They had massive beaks, heads, and necks and, among them, *Diatryma* reached a height of about 7 feet (Fig. 425).

ORDER CHARADRIIFORMES

This universally distributed (excepting the ice-caps) polymorphic group contains the Jacanidæ (lotus-birds, Fig. 429, p. 624), Rostratulidæ (painted snipe), Hæmatopodidæ (oyster-catchers), Charadriidæ (lapwings, plovers), Scolopacidæ (woodcock, sandpipers, etc.), Recurvirostridæ (stilts, avocets), Phalaropodidæ (phalaropes), Dromadidæ (crab-plovers), Burhinidæ (thick-knees), Glareolidæ (coursers, pratincoles), Thinocoridæ (seed-snipe), Chionididæ (sheath-bills), Stercorariidæ (skuas, jaegers), Laridæ (gulls, terns), Rhynchopidæ (skimmers), and Alcidæ (auks, puffins). The above shore-dwelling groups, as well as their aquatic and sea-going derivatives, have become highly successful. Among the most interesting are the jacanas, which have developed slender, and enormously elongated, fore- and hind-toes adapted to progression over aquatic lily-leaves (p. 624). In *Phalaropus* the female is the more brilliant of the pair and also assumes at least some of the typically male pattern of behaviour, including territory selection. The male, on the other hand, incubates. Waders (Charadriidæ) occur in Tertiary deposits, gulls and auks in the Eocene.

Order Columbiformes

The pigeons and doves are universal, excluding polar regions. The order is often held to include the aberrant sand-grouse as follows: Pteroclididæ (sand-grouse), Raphidæ (extinct dodos, etc., p. 577), Columbidæ (all others). The last-named family are mostly graminivorous or frugivorous and produce 'pigeon's milk' (p. 583). The crested *Goura cristata* of New Guinea and adjacent isles may stand nearly 2 feet high. Pre-Miocene fossils are rare. The sand-grouse are ground-nesters which lack the characteristic raised hallux of the galliformes (p. 615), which they greatly resemble in several ways.

Order Psittaciformes

(Single Family Psittacidæ)

The parrots and cockatoos are common only in the tropics and sub-tropics, and reach their greatest number and diversification in the Australasian region. They have powerful hooked beaks (Fig. 436, p. 632) adapted to husking food and tearing dead timber in search of wood-boring insects, although many forms eat nectar or are almost entirely frugivorous. They possess a characteristic *zygodactylous* foot in which the 1st and 4th digits are backwardly directed, allowing for a pair of toes on each side of the branch. Their powers of mimicry, their longevity (p. 560) and vivid coloration are well known. They do not seem to mimic other species in the field, as do many passerines. The vivid coloration is obliterative amongst foliage, making them surprisingly difficult to see. At least one parrot (*Geopsittacus*) has become nocturnal. They occur in Miocene deposits.

Order Cuculiformes

The cuckoos (Cuculidæ), plantain-eaters, and turacos (Musophagidæ), possess a *zygodactylous* foot not unlike that of the parrots. Some species of cuckoos (e.g. *Centropus*) build their own nests. The eggs of parasitic species often match those of the host with remarkable fidelity. The Cuculidæ are widely distributed throughout tropical and sub-tropical regions and are common in temperate zones.   Musophagidæ occur in Africa and may not be truly referable to this group.   Cuckoos have been found in Oligocene deposits but fossils are rare.

ORDER STRIGIFORMES

The almost universally distributed owls occupy the ecological niche vacated at dusk by the diurnal birds-of-prey, with which they show notable convergence in beak and claw.   They are the Tytonidæ (barn-owls) and Strigidæ (all others). In texture, as well as in its 'loose' arrangement, the plumage is adapted to a relatively soundless approach, and the retina contains principally rods (p. 140). The eyes of owls are directed forwards (as are those of the nocturnal hunter *Podargus*, (p. 621)) and have become so large as to be almost immovable: the animal must rotate its neck to look sideways.   It is believed that some owls hunt largely by sound.   Prey (*e.g.* a rodent) is as a rule swallowed whole, much of the food residue being regurgitated as casts or pellets with the fur surrounding the sharp, broken bones.   Owls occur in Oligocene and later deposits.

ORDER CAPRIMULGIFORMES

The nightjars and allies are nocturnal insectivorous birds arranged as follows: Steatornithes (oil-birds), Podargidæ (frog-mouths), Nyctibiidæ (potoos), Ægothelidæ (owlet nightjars), and Caprimulgidæ ('night-hawks', 'goat-suckers').   These birds possess wide gapes, and 'loose' soft feathers recalling the plumage of owls (p. 643).   They have prominent, probably sensory, bristles around the gape, and are protectively camouflaged and difficult to see when at rest.   They are best developed in the tropics and sub-tropics but are not uncommon in temperate zones (e.g. *Caprimulgus, Podargus*). Fossils have been rarely found, but occur in Pliocene deposits.

ORDER APODIFORMES (MICROPODIFORMES)

The swifts and humming-birds—Apodidæ (swifts), Hemiprocnidæ (crested swifts), and Trochilidæ (humming-birds)—are a homogeneous group.   The swifts, however, have diverged sharply into fast-flying, wide-mouthed, large-eyed migratory insect-catchers, whilst the humming-birds have become generally tiny, protrusible-tongued, darting and hovering, relatively 'stationary', nectar (and insect) feeders.   Swifts are almost universal (excluding polar regions), whereas humming-birds are confined to the central zone of the Americas.   Many swifts, and particularly the edible-nest swiftlets (*Collocalia*), use a certain amount of saliva from sub-lingual glands (Fig. 442, p. 637) as nest cement.   Swifts are known from the Oligocene.

ORDER COLIIFORMES

The small distinct monogeneric group of mouse-birds or colies (Coliidæ) is confined to Africa.   Insectivorous and frugivorous, they creep through the branches of trees using their beaks, as well as peculiar feet on which the hallux can be brought forward. Some species of *Colius* have bodies little bigger than sparrows, but tails are as long as 10 inches. Fossils are unknown.

ORDER TROGONIFORMES

These fall into the single widespread family Trogonidæ of the tropical Americas, Africa, Asia (including the East Indies), and the Philippines. They range in size between that of thrush and crow, and have bristled gapes and invariably loose, beautiful plumage. They are known from the Miocene.

ORDER CORACIIFORMES

This is a widespread, colourful, and perhaps polyphyletic group as follows: Alcedinidæ (kingfishers), Todidæ (todies of the West Indies), Momotidæ (motmots of Central America), Meropidæ (bee-eaters), Leptosomatidæ (kirombos or Madagascan rollers), Coraciidæ (rollers), Upupidæ (hoopoes), Phœniculidæ (wood hoopoes), and Bucerotidæ (hornbills). The order is known from the Miocene.

ORDER PICIFORMES

The woodpeckers and their allies, absent only from Australasia and polar regions, are as follows: Galbulidæ (jacamars), Bucconidæ (puff-birds), Capitonidæ (barbets), Indicatoridæ (honey-guides), Picidæ (woodpeckers, wrynecks), Ramphastidæ (toucans). All have zygodactylous feet with the second and third digits directed forwards, and the first and fourth backwards. The honey-guides are especially noteworthy. The family is a predominantly African (south of the Sahara) group, although two of the 11 species are Asiatic. Certain species exhibit noisy excitement and appear purposefully to lead honey-badgers (*Mellivora capensis*) and Man to bees' nests. When the nest is broached the bird eats fragments of discarded comb. Friedmann describes the peculiar 'guiding' behaviour of *Indicator indicator* as a 'form of excitement reaction . . . when meeting with a potential foraging symbiont . . . that the bird associates with the act of opening bees' nests'. This meeting usually takes place near a bees' nest but ordinarily the bird does not in fact 'lead' in a direct route but noisily performs, often very circuitously, from tree to tree. It is not necessary for the bird to know in advance where the bees have built; the excitement fades, however, when a nest is reached. Then the bird sits quietly until it receives a meal of wax. These birds are the only vertebrates known to be capable of extracting nourishment from bees wax. Two micro-organisms of high lipolytic activity—a *Micrococcus* and a strain of the yeast *Candida albicans*—occur in the birds' fæces.

Several species of honey-guides resemble cuckoos in laying in the nests of other birds.

ORDER PASSERIFORMES

This—by far the largest avian order—is divided into four sub-orders: Eurylæmi (containing the single family Eurylæmidæ—broadbills of Indo-Malaya and Africa); Tyranni (a predominantly American assemblage including the tyrant-flycatchers (Tyrannidæ) and their allies, as well as the New Zealand 'wrens' (Xenicidæ)); Menuræ (the Australian lyrebirds (Menuridæ) and scrub-birds (Atrichornithidæ)); and Passeres or Oscines (all the remaining, and more familiar, song-birds). The more primitive sub-orders Eurylæmi and Tyranni were formerly brigaded as the Mesomyodi, and the Menuræ (also known as the Sub-oscines, Pseudoscines, Subclamatores, and *abnormal song-birds*) were grouped with the Passeres (the *normal song-birds* or Oscines) as the Acromyodi.

The sub-order Passeres (Oscines), numbering about 4,000 *normal song-birds*, includes the more familiar passerines such as (for example) larks (Alaudidæ), swallows (Hirundinidæ), bulbuls (Pycnonotidæ), 'flycatchers' (Muscicapidæ), dippers (Cinclidæ), shrikes (Laniidæ), true tree-creepers (Certhiidæ), tits (Paridæ), honey-eaters (Meliphagidæ), silver-eyes (Zosteropidæ), finches (Fringillidæ), weaver-finches, including sparrows (Ploceidæ), starlings (Sturnidæ), crows (Corvidæ), birds-of-paradise (Paradiseidæ), and bower-birds (Ptilonorhynchidæ).

There is some evidence that passerines occurred as long ago as the Eocene, but few fossil types have been found in deposits earlier than late Tertiary. Although the Oscines are unquestionably a relatively modern, and still expanding group, it is well to remember that their small, fragile bodies (and the habits of many) render them less likely to be fossilised.

Information in great detail concerning many Oscines and their complicated behaviour-patterns is available in numerous regional and other publications.

GENERAL ORGANIZATION OF THE NEORNITHES

External characters.—In the general build of the body the Neornithes differ from the Archæornithes chiefly in the shorter and stouter trunk, and in the point of articulation of the hind-limbs being thrown forward, so as to be almost directly below the centre of gravity of the body. The animal is thus enabled without effort to support itself on the legs alone. Birds are essentially bipedal. The only exception appears to be the young of the Hoatzin (*Opisthocomus*) (p. 615), which uses its wings in climbing (Fig. 427).

The *neck* is always well developed, and is often, as in the swan and flamingoes, of great proportional length. The cranial portion of the head is usually not large. The *beak* (Fig. 426) may attain a remarkable size, and exhibits a wide range of form. It may be extremely short and wide for catching moths and other flying insects, as in swifts and nightjars; short and conical for eating seed, as in finches; strongly hooked for tearing the bodies of animals, as in

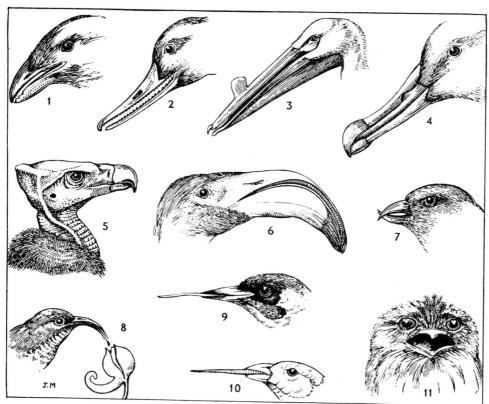

FIG. 426.—**Neognathæ: Rostral and associated specialisations.** Not to scale. 1. Beak serrations of the Australian Tooth-billed Catbird (*Scenopœtes dentirostris*) used for sawing through the petioles of leaves gathered for the daily decoration of its display-ground. 2. Fish-holding denticulations of the European Goosander (*Mergus merganser*). 3. Terminal hook and beak-pouch of the North American White Pelican (*Pelecanus erythrorhynchus*). The compressed horny beak adornment is seasonally developed and falls off without trace after reproduction. 4. Tube-nosed arrangement (in Wandering Albatross, *Diomedea exulans*) characteristic of ocean-going Procellariiformes (petrels and albatrosses). 5. Hooked beak of Egyptian vulture (*Trigoniceps occipitalis*) used for tearing dead flesh. The head and neck, often buried in suppurating material, are almost bare. 6. Marginal hooks and leaflets which, with a spiny tongue, form a filter-feeding mechanism in the old world Greater Flamingo (*Phœnicopterus antiquorum*). 7. Obliquely crossed mandibles of the passerine Palæarctic Crossbill (*Loxia curvirostra*). A special articulation and musculature enables a swift powerful movement that rips open fir-cones, after which the tongue scoops out the exposed seed. 8. The Pacific passerine *Neodrepanis coruscans*, illustrating convergence of beak form with that of a flower from which it brushes nectar and perhaps helps fertilise. 9. European Green Woodpecker (*Cecinus viridis*), which excavates with its beak, and then probes for organisms with its protrusible tongue (see also Fig. 440). 10. The Galapagos Woodpecker-finch (*Camarhynchus pallidus*) trenches with its beak and probes with a cactus spine; it is one of the few avian tool-makers (see also Fig. 382, p. 562). 11. Broad gape in Australian Tawny Frogmouth (*Podargus strigoides*), a nocturnal insectivorous species. The eyes are protected by tactile bristles and are directed forwards (see p. 643). A tuft of relatively filamentous, and probably tactile, feathers surmounts the beak. (After various authors.)

birds of prey, or for rending fruits of various kinds, as in parrots ; long, conical, and of great strength, as in storks ; slender and elongated, as in ibises and cur- lews ; broad and flattened for feeding in mud, as in ducks and geese; expanded at the end, as in spoonbills ; immensely enlarged, as in hornbills and toucans. It is most commonly bent downwards at the tip, but may be straight or curved upwards, as in the Avocet, or bent to one side, as in the New Zealand Wry- billed Plover. Among ducks and geese the beak has often a lateral straining device for the retention of food and the discharge of water. Mergansers have sharp horny tooth-like lateral projections with which to hold struggling fish. Tropical snake-birds (*Anhinga*) have stiletto-like beaks with which they spear fish, toss them up, and then swallow them head-first. The Tooth-billed Cat-

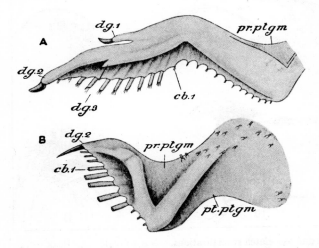

FIG. 427.—**Neornithes: Clawed wings.** *A*, Nestling *Opisthocomus* (with two clawed digits); *B*, Adult *Apteryx* (kiwi). Both from inner (ventral) aspect. *cb.* 1. first cubital remex; *dg.* 1, *dg.* 2, *dg.* 3, digits; *pr. ptgm.* prepatag- ium; *pt. ptgm.* postpatagium. (*A*, after Pycraft; *B*, after T. J. Parker.)

bird (*Scenopœtes*) has a serrated beak with which it saws through petioles in order to free green leaves for use on its display-ground.

The buccal arrangements of the flamingos (Phœnicopteri) deserve special mention: there has been developed a complicated filter-feeding mechanism, analogous to that of baleen whales, which enables them to subsist on organisms living in under-water mud. This apparatus varies in complexity among the six species (of three genera). The Lesser Flamingo (*Phœnicopterus minor*) has a filter sufficiently fine to permit the dredging of blue-green algæ and diatoms. The Greater Flamingo (*P. antiquorum*) (Fig. 426), on the other hand, eats chironomid larvæ and seeds: the two species can co-exist without direct com- petition. The filter-feeding apparatus involves both spiny tongue and lateral lamellæ that vary from species to species. Other vertebrate filter-feeders are ammocœte larvæ (p. 196), certain fishes, and the larvæ of the toad *Xenopus*.

The beak is sometimes, as in the toucans, brilliantly coloured, and there may also be bright coloration of the cere, as in the macaws, and of naked spaces on the head, as in the cassowaries. In the latter the head is produced into a great horny prominence or casque, supported by an elevation of the roof of the skull. The cere is frequently absent. The nostrils are placed at the base of the beak, except in *Apteryx*, in which they are at the tip.

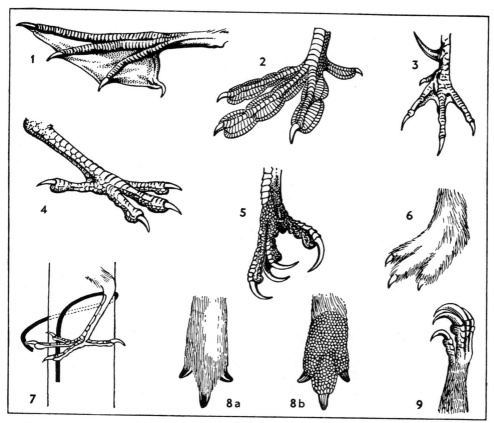

FIG. 428.—**Neognathæ: Pedal specialisations.** Not to scale. 1. Cormorant (*Phalacrocorax*), adapted to swimming and defence. 2. Grebe (*Podica* of African swamps), with laterally lobed toes adapted to diving, swimming and defence. 3. Jungle fowl (*Gallus* of India), running, scratch-ing and spurred for aggression and defence. 4. Megapode (*Megapodius* of New Guinea), heavy-limbed for incubator-building, as well as food-gathering, running and defence. 5. Hawk (*Accipi-ter*) grasping prey (note rough raised pads) and holding it while being torn with beak; also perching and defence. 6. Ptarmigan (*Lagopus* of Greenland tundras), running and defence, and feathered in relation to thermo-regulation. 7. Weaver (*Quelea* of African savannah), with 'typical' passerine foot adapted to perching, hopping and sometimes defence. In this and a few other genera the feet are used also to weave nesting material. 8. a,b. Sand-grouse (*Syrrhaptes* of Central Asian steppe), running, defence and thermo-regulation. 9. Swift (*Apus*). Pamprodactyle foot adapted for clinging to perpendicular surfaces. (For the unwebbed 'wader' foot see Fig. 445, p. 641, and for that of the lily-trotters, Fig. 429.) (Redrawn after Thompson, Grassé, Friedmann.)

The essential structure of the *wing*—apart from its feathers—is very uni-form. As a rule all three digits are devoid of claws, as in pigeons, but the ostriches have claws on all three digits. The rheas have claws on the first and sometimes on the second and third; and the cassowaries, Emu, and kiwis

(Fig. 608) on the second digit.   The Crested Screamer (*Chauna*) and two other species (and, as a rare abnormality, the Common Fowl and Goose) have them on the first digit.   With these exceptions, and that of the young of the Hoatzin (Fig. 427), the hand of the hatched bird has lost all the characters of the fore-

FIG. 429.—**Jacanidæ: Adaptation to the lily surface.**   The jacanas (lotus-birds, lily-trotters, or 'Christ-birds') are often imagined to 'walk on the water', but are in fact exquisitely adapted for life on floating leaves.   The negligible body-weight is distributed by elongated anterior digits and grossly hypertrophied hind-claws.   The eggs are laid in a shallow nest on leaves or floating debris and are stone-coloured and bear a disruptive pattern of 'hieroglyphic' markings.   The casque of *Irediparra gallinacea* (above) is yellow, like the centres of the surrounding lotus flowers.   The extreme specialisation of jacanas has resulted in a curiously *discontinuous distribution* among living forms (see also Fig. 424, p. 612).   Restricted to lily lagoons and lakesides in warm climates, three species inhabit Africa and Madagascar, one (of several races) the Americas, and three Asia–Australasia, of which only one (above) reaches the Australian continent.   (From photographs, and B. M. (N. H.) specimens.)

foot.   Besides the true claws, horny *spurs* are sometimes present on the carpo-metacarpus (plovers, etc.).   A recently extinguished pigeon, the Solitaire (p. 557), had a knob-like protuberance 'the size of a musket-ball' which is said to have made a rattling noise during the wing-whirring display.

There is almost every gradation in the proportional length of the *hind-limb*, from birds in which nothing but the foot projects beyond the contour feathers (and even the toes may be feathered), to the long-legged storks and cranes, in which the distal part of the tibio-tarsus is covered with scales as well as the foot (Fig. 428). In aquatic forms a *web* is stretched between the toes. This sometimes includes all four digits, as in cormorants. Sometimes it leaves the hallux free. Again, it may form a separate fringe or lobe to each digit, as in coots and grebes. As to the toes themselves, the commonest arrangement is for the hallux to be directed backwards, and Nos. 2, 3, and 4 forwards. Perhaps the most remarkable feet with this arrangement are those of the jacanas or parras (Jacanidæ), a widespread tropical and sub-tropical family of Charadriiformes (p. 616). In these all four unwebbed toes are grotesquely elongated and clawed, resulting in a distribution of weight that enables the 'Lotus-bird' to walk on the floating leaves of water-lilies (Fig. 429). Various species are known as Lily-trotters, or Christ-birds—because they apparently walk on the water. In owls No. 4 is reversible, *i.e.* can be turned in either direction. In the parrots, wood-peckers, etc., it, as well as the hallux, is permanently turned backwards in the zygodactylous condition. In swifts, on the other hand, all four toes turn forwards. The hallux is frequently vestigial or absent, and in the Ostrich No. 4 has also disappeared, producing the characteristic two-toed foot of that bird.

In some groups (*e.g.* nightjars, owls, and various aquatic or semi-aquatic birds such as bitterns, cormo-rants, gannets, and various waders) one claw on each foot of certain species may be *pectinated, i.e.* it has taken on a more or less comb-like structure. This varies greatly in complexity, perhaps reaching its highest ex-pression in bitterns (Fig. 430). Such feather-cleansing structures present an interesting analogy with the digital toilet implements of mammals.

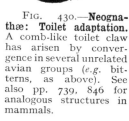

FIG. 430.—**Neogna-thæ: Toilet adaptation.** A comb-like toilet claw has arisen by conver-gence in several unrelated avian groups (*e.g.* bit-terns, as above). See also pp. 739, 846 for analogous structures in mammals.

Toilet-claws in birds are extremely erratic in their distribution. Thus, the Barn Owl (*Tyto alba*) possesses them, whereas many other owls do not. Among waders they are lacking in the Bar-tailed godwit (*Limosa lapponica*), yet present in the congeneric Black-tailed species (*L. limosa*).

It is probable that the possession of cleansing comb-claws is broadly related to diet: they appear to have arisen most often in species that feed on mucus-covered shore- or water-organisms. Certainly, in the Bittern (*Botaurus stellaris*) powder from the powder-down patches (see below) appears to reduce the viscosity of adherent mucus and thus make it more easily disposable by the toilet claws. It has been suggested, but not proved, that in moth-eating night-jars such specialised claws are used to clear moth scales from the hair-like tactile processes surrounding the gape.

Pterylosis.—With the exception of the penguins, most birds (excluding flightless 'ratites' (p. 606)) have the feathers arranged in distinct feather-tracts or *pterylæ*, separated by *apteria* or featherless spaces. These are commonly much more distinct than in the pigeon (Fig. 386), and their form and arrangement are of importance in classification. In the flightless birds apteria are usually found only in the young, the adult having a uniform covering of feathers. Such birds also have nothing more than the merest trace of hooklets on the barbules, so that the barbs do not interlock and the vanes of the feathers are downy or hair-like. In penguins (p. 610) the wing-feathers are degenerate. In nearly all neognathine birds except passerines (p. 620) there is an absence of the fifth secondary wing-quill: the condition of diastataxy or *aquintocubitalism*. The distribution of this phenomenon is erratic.

Many birds are naked when hatched, but in most cases the body is more or less completely covered by temporary feathers, the *nestling-down*. These are of various forms, but always have a short axis, soft loose barbs devoid of interlocking apparatus, and, except in the Emu, no after-shaft (Fig. 431). They are succeeded, as already described, by the *permanent feathers*.

Many birds, such as the swans, possess *down-feathers* or *plumulæ* throughout life, interspersed among and hidden by the contour feathers or *pennæ*. *Semi-plumes* are down with a well-developed axis. *Filoplumes* have an elongated axis and vestigial vexillum. A singularly specialised type of feather is the *powder-down*, well-developed in tracts or *powder-down patches* in herons, parrots and cockatoos, birds-of-prey, pigeons, and especially frog-mouths (*Podargus*). This down gives off a powder not unlike talc in its impermeability to water. The powder is not formed by the breakdown of a part of the fully developed feather, as has been sometimes claimed, but is a derivative of the innermost walls of the Malpighian layer of the feather papilla.

In many birds there springs from the under-side of the quill, near the superior umbilicus, a second vane, the *after-shaft* (Fig. 431), usually smaller than the main shaft, but sometimes of equal size. Both among flying and flightless birds there are genera with double-shafted feathers as well as allied forms in which the after-shaft is rudimentary or absent. Feathers are always shed or *moulted* at regular intervals, as a rule annually after the breeding season, though some species have a second lesser moult later on. During moult the old feathers drop out and new ones are formed from the same pulps.

Feathers may be anointed in some species with greasy secretion from the *coccygeal, uropygial, oil-* or *preen-gland*, a bilobular structure on the dorsal surface of the body above the base of the tail (p. 566). The function of the secretion is unknown. It has been variously suggested that it may waterproof the feathers, produce a specific recognition scent, and that it elaborates ergosterol, which, when exposed on the feathers, is transformed by sunlight to Vitamin D. It is assumed that the vitamin would be ingested during preening. Grassé suggests that birds which are addicted to excessive feather-eating may be suffering from Vitamin-D deficiency.

The *colours* of feathers present great variety. Black, brown, red, orange, yellow, and occasionally green are due to the presence of definite pigments, *i.e.* are absorption colours. The turacos possess the red copper-containing pigment *turacin* which is soluble in dilute alkali but not, as is often claimed, in ordinary rain-water! In this colourful group the green pigment *turacoverdin* also occurs. In avian plumage, white, and in some cases yellow, is produced by the total reflection of light from the spongy air-containing substance of the feather, there being, as in nearly all other natural objects, no such thing as a white pigment. Blue, violet, and in some cases green are produced by the light from a brown pigment becoming broken up as it passes through the superficial layer of the feathers in its passage to the eye. No blue or violet pigments occur in feathers, and green pigments are rare. The beautiful metallic tints of many birds are structural colours. In such feathers the colour changes according to the relative position of the bird and of the eye of the observer with regard to the source of light. The American flamingo (*Phœnicopterus ruber*) gets its pink and vermilion integumentary (skin, beak and feathers) colours from dietary carotenoids. The colours gradually fade in captivity unless the diet is carefully regulated. There is some evidence that crustacea are an important source of carotenoids in nature. Fox has evidence that the metabolic fractionation of dietary carotenoids seems to involve oxidative processes but that some astaxanthin may pass unchanged from crustacean to the avian integument.

There is also infinite variety in the colour pattern of birds. In many the colouring is concealing, harmonising with the environment. In the ptarmigan (*Lagopus mutus*) the colour changes with the moult from greyish-brown in summer to white in winter, the former

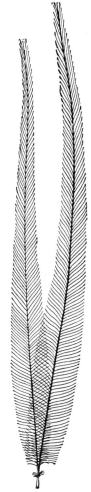

Fig. 431.—*Casuarius:* **Feather structure.** In cassowaries the aftershaft is almost as long as the primary shaft. The unconnected barbs are probably a neotenous feature (see text). (After Headley.)

plumage helping to conceal the bird among herbage, the latter on snow. Frequently, as in pheasants and birds-of-paradise, the female alone is protectively coloured, while the male presents the most varied and brilliant tints, enhanced by crests, plumes or tufts of feathers, lappets of skin, etc. (Fig. 381). The factors influencing sexual dimorphism differ from group to group and are sometimes complex. Comb-growth in the Domestic Fowl in both cock and hen is under the control of androgens from testis and ovary. The comb is smaller in ovariectomised females than in those left intact. Thyroxin (p. 151), as well as sex hormones, is influential in feather development and pattern. When the hens of certain breeds of fowl are unsexed the next growth of plumage is male-type, whereas that of the castrated cock is unchanged; the difference is controlled by œstrogen. There is evidence that in some species the female plumage is neutral, whereas the male colour is controlled by pituitary, not sex, hormones. In the Herring Gull (*Larus argentatus*) the cock-type plumage is under the influence of androgens. The plumage condition of some species (*e.g.* House Sparrow, *Passer domesticus*) appears to be under genetic control, in that in neither sex does castration cause change, nor does the administration of sex hormones. Parenthetically it may be mentioned that the colour of the beak and various soft parts also can be under either genetic or endocrine control. Witschi says that the change of bill colour from black to yellow in the Common Starling (*Sturnus vulgaris*) is a most delicate indicator for androgens: it 'heralds the start of the breeding season at a time when testicular changes are barely observable under the microscope and the deferent ducts still remain in the eclipse condition'. The colour reaction occurs about two weeks earlier in the males than the females.

Sexual dimorphism is common in monogamous as well as polygamous species. In conjunction with specific postures and calls, colours and erectile plumes become *sign stimuli* which evoke or *release* specific reactions, and indeed whole *patterns of behaviour* in rivals and mates. Such ornaments as the bars and spots on the wings and tail, fully exposed only during flight in many gregarious birds, and often widely different in closely allied species, are probably *recognition marks* which enable stragglers to distinguish between a flock of their own and other species.

Endoskeleton.—The vast majority of birds have saddle-shaped or heterocœlous cervical and thoracic vertebræ, but opisthocœlous thoracic vertebræ occur in the Impennæ (penguins), Laridæ (gulls), some Charadriiformes (*e.g.* stone-curlews and godwits), and some Pelecaniformes (*e.g.* cormorants and darters). In the Ichthyornithes alone they were biconcave.

The spaces between adjacent centra are traversed by a meniscus with a suspensory ligament, as in pigeons (p. 573). The number of vertebræ is very variable, especially in the cervical region, where it rises to twenty-five in swans and is reduced to nine in some song-birds. There is very commonly more or less fusion of the thoracic vertebræ, and the formation of a rigid synsacrum by the concrescence of the posterior thoracic, lumbar, sacral, and anterior caudal vertebræ is universal. The posterior cervical and anterior thoracic vertebræ commonly bear strong *hypapophyses* or inferior processes for the origin of the great flexor muscles of the neck. The number of true sacral vertebræ varies from one to five. A pygostyle, formed by the fusion of varying numbers of caudal vertebræ, is of general occurrence, but is small and insignificant or absent in certain 'ratites' (excluding, for example, the Ostrich).

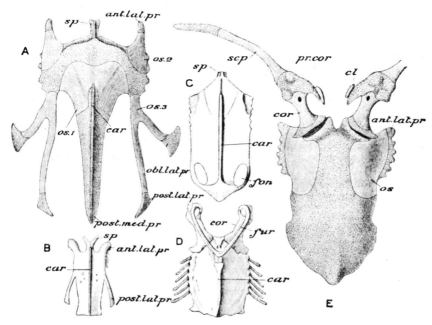

Fig. 432.—**Neornithes: Sternum and pectoral articulation.** Keel (carinate) and raft (ratite) types. A, *Gallus* (common Fowl, young); B, *Turdus* (Thrush); C, *Vultur* (Vulture); D, *Procellaria* (Petrel); E, *Casuarius* (Cassowary). *ant. lat. pr.* anterior lateral process; *car.* carina; *cl.* clavicle; *cor.* coracoid; *fon.* fontanelle; *fur.* furcula; *obl. lat. pr.* oblique lateral process; *os.* paired ossification of sternum in *E*; *os.* 1, carinal ossification in *A*; *os.* 2, *os.* 3, lateral ossifications; *post. med. pr.* posterior median process; *post. lat. pr.* posterior lateral process; *pr. cor.* pro-coracoid; *scp.* scapula; *sp.* spina sterni. (*A* and *E*, after W. K. Parker; *B, C,* and *D,* after Bronn.)

The *ribs* are always double-headed. The sternal ribs are ossified, not merely calcified, and are united with the vertebral ribs by synovial joints. Ossified uncini are nearly always present, and usually become ankylosed to the vertebral ribs.

The *sternum* of most flying birds is a broad plate, concave dorsally from side to side, and produced ventrally into an antero-posterior keel which is ossified from a distinct centre (Figs. 432, A, *os.* 1). The posterior edge of the bone is either entire (D), or presents on each side of the keel one or two more or less deep notches (A, B) or foramina (C). In the flightless genera (*E*) the keel is either absent or reduced to the merest vestige, and there is no trace of the carinal ossification in the young.   External to the coracoid grooves the anterior edge of the sternum is produced into larger or smaller antero-lateral processes (*ant. lat. pr.*).   In the Emu these are of great size and are closely applied to the pericardium.

It was upon the characters of the raft-like sternum that the group 'Ratitæ' was founded, but the difference between them and the keel-breasted 'Carinatæ' in this respect is not absolute, the ratite condition having been acquired by many 'Carinatæ' which have lost the power of flight.   The keel is very small in the flightless rails, *Gallirallus*, *Notornis*, and the extinct *Aptornis* from New Zealand.   It is practically absent in the Dodo (*Didus*) and Solitaire (*Pezo-*

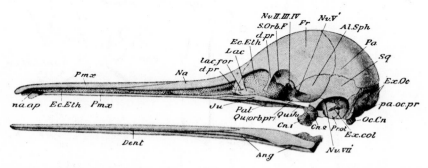

Fig. 433.—**Apteryx: Skull.**   Specimen from young kiwi in lateral view in which the cartilaginous parts are dotted.   *Al. Sph.* alisphenoid;   *Ang.* angular;   *Cn.* 1, *cn.* 2, condyle of quadrate;   *Dent.* dentary;   *d. pr., d. pr.* descending processes of nasal and frontal;   *Ec. Eth.* ecto-ethmoid;   *Ex. col.* extra-columella;   *Ex. Oc.* exoccipital;   *Fr.* frontal;   *Ju.* jugal;   *Lac.* lachrymal;   *lac. for.* lachrymal foramen;   *Na.* nasal;   *na. ap.* nasal aperture;   *Nv. II, III, IV,* optic foramen, transmitting also the 3rd and 4th nerves;   *Nv. V',* foramen for orbito-nasal nerve;   *Nv. VII',* for facial;   *Pa.* parietal;   *Pal.* palatine;   *pa. oc. pr.* par-occipital process;   *P. mx.* premaxilla;   *Pr. ot.* pro-otic;   *Qu. Ju.* quadratojugal;   *Qu. (orb. pr.)* orbital process of quadrate;   *S. Orb. F.* supraorbital foramen;   *Sq.* squamosal.   (After T. J. Parker.)

phaps), two gigantic extinct pigeons from Mauritius and Rodriguez.   It is likewise nearly absent in the Kakapo or Ground-parrot (*Strigops*) of New Zealand ; in the extinct Giant Goose (*Cnemiornis*) from the same country ; and in *Hesperornis*.   The absence of the carina must be considered as an adaptive modification of no phylogenetic significance.

The entire super-order of penguins (Impennæ) and the extinct Great Auk are also flightless, but their wings, instead of being functionless, are modified into powerful swimming paddles (Fig. 422).   There has therefore, in these cases, been no reduction either of the pectoral muscles or of the carina.

The *skull* of birds is generally remarkable for its huge orbits separated by a thin interorbital septum, and for the comparatively small size of the ethmoid bone and its turbinals.   A striking exception is afforded by the kiwis (*Apteryx*), in which the orbits (Fig. 433) are small, while the olfactory chambers (*Ec. Eth.*) extend backwards between the eyes.   The orbits are therefore separated from

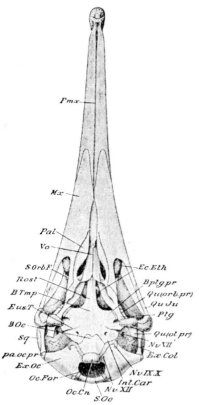

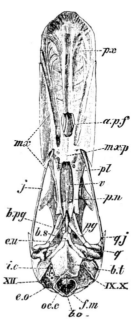

FIG. 434.—*Apteryx:* **Skull.** Specimen from juvenile kiwi, *Apteryx mantelli* (palatal aspect). The cartilaginous parts are dotted. *B. Oc.* basi-occipital; *B. ptg. pr.* basi-pterygoid process; *B. Tmp.* basi-temporal; *Ec. Eth.* ecto-ethmoid; *Eus. T.* Eustachian tube; *Ex. Col.* extra-columella; *Ex. Oc.* ex-occipital; *Int. Car.* carotid foramen; *Mx.* maxilla; *Nv. VII',* foramen for facial; *Nv. IX, X,* for glosso-pharyngeal and vagus; *Nv. XII,* for hypoglossal; *Oc. Cn.* occipital condyle; *Oc. For.* foramen magnum; *Pal.* palatine; *pa. oc. pr.* par-occipital process; *P. mx.* premaxilla; *Ptg.* pterygoid; *Qu. (orb. pr.)* orbital process of quadrate; *Qu. (ot. pr.)* otic process; *Rost.* rostrum; *S. Oc.* supra-occipital; *S. Orb. F.* supra-orbital foramen; *Sq.* squamosal; *Vo.* vomer. (After T. J. Parker.)

FIG. 435.—*Anas:* **Skull.** Duck, skull from palatal aspect. *a. p. f.* anterior palatine foramen; *b. o.* basi-occipital; *b. pg.* basi-pterygoid process; *b. s.* basi-sphenoid; *b. t.* basi-temporal; *e. o.* ex-occipital; *eu.* aperture of Eustachian tube; *f. m.* foramen magnum; *i. c.* internal carotid foramen; *j.* jugal; *mx.* maxilla; *mx. p.* maxillo-palatine process; *oc. c.* occipital condyle; *pl.* palatine; *p. n.* posterior nares; *px.* premaxilla; *q.* quadrate; *qj.* quadratojugal; *v.* vomer; *IX, X,* foramen for ninth and tenth nerves; *XII,* for twelfth nerve. (After Wiedersheim.)

one another by the whole width of the olfactory organ (see p. 641). The same thing occurs, to a less degree, in moas. In its essential features the skull is remarkably uniform throughout the class. The rounded form of the brain-case, more or less concealed externally by ridges for the attachment of muscles; the upper beak, composed mainly of great tri-radiate premaxillæ; the single, small rounded occipital condyle; the slender maxillo-jugal arch; the large para-sphenoidal rostrum; the freely articulated quadrate, with its otic, orbital, and articular processes; the absence of the reptilian post-frontals; and the early ankylosis of the bones—all these characters are universal among birds. There are, however, numerous differences in detail, some of which, connected with the bones of the palate, are of importance in classification.

In the large flightless forms and the tinamus there are large basipterygoid processes (Fig. 434, *B. ptg. pr.*) springing, as in lizards, from the basisphenoid, and articulating with the pterygoids near their posterior ends. The vomer (*Vo.*) is large and broad, and is usually connected posteriorly with the palatines (*Pal.*), which do not articulate with the rostrum. The maxillo-palatine pro-cesses are comparatively small, and do not unite with one another or with the prevomer. This arrangement of the bones of the palate is sometimes called *dromæo-gnathous*. In many birds, *e.g.* the pigeon and the fowl, the basi-pterygoid processes are either ab-sent or spring from the base of the rostrum. The vomer is small and pointed, or may be absent, and the palatines articulate pos-teriorly with the rostrum. The maxillo-palatines do not unite with one another. These peculiarities characterise the *schizognathous*

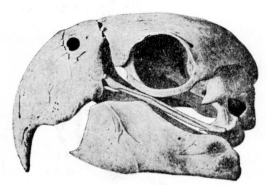

Fig. 436.—**Psittacidæ: Beak and skull articulation.** In parrots (e.g. *Ara*, Macaw, above) the hinge between beak and skull enables mastication movements of a unique character. (From a photograph by A. Hamilton.)

arrangement. In passerines a similar arrangement obtains, but the prevomer is broad and truncated instead of pointed in front. This gives the *ægitho-gnathous* arrangement. Lastly, in the storks, birds of prey, ducks, and geese, etc., the maxillo-palatines (Fig. 435, *mx. p.*) fuse with one another in the middle line, often giving rise to a flat, spongy palate and producing the *desmognathous* arrangement.

The most remarkably specialised form of skull is found in the parrots (Fig. 436). In many birds the nasals and the ascending process of the premaxillæ are very thin and elastic where they join the skull, and there is an unossified space in the mesethmoid, so that the upper beak is capable of a considerable amount of movement in the vertical plane. Thus there occurs a true cranio-facial joint or hinge between the upper beak and the skull. This gives the bird a 'sliding palate'. This mechanism is best developed in the parrots, allowing the curious upper beak movement that is so striking in the living bird. When the mandible is depressed, the contraction of the digastric muscle causes a forward movement of the lower end of the quadrate, which pushes forwards the maxillo-jugal bar and the palatines and pterygoids, the latter sliding upon the rostrum. Both the maxillæ and the palatines are articulated in front with the premaxilla, and together push it upwards. In this way depression of the lower produces an automatic raising of the upper jaw. The great size and strength of both premaxilla and mandible are remarkable, as also is the fact that the orbit is completely surrounded by bone, a backward process of the lachrymal being joined beneath it by a forward process of the frontal.

The *mandible* contains in the young bird the six bones on each side characteristic of reptiles. The coronoid is, however, often absent. As a rule the head of the *quadrate* articulates with the roof of the tympanic cavity by a single facet in the large flightless birds, by a double facet in the rest. The *hyoid* always agrees in essential respects with that of the pigeon. In woodpeckers the posterior cornua are curved round the head and attached to the skull in the neighbourhood of the right nostril, allowing the extreme protrusion of a long and flexible tongue (Fig. 441, p. 636).

The structure of the *shoulder-girdle* (Fig. 437) furnishes one of the most distinctive characters between ratite and non-ratite forms but, as with the sternum, the differences are adaptive and not of phylogenetic significance. In most of the latter both coracoid and scapula are large and united with one another by ligament. The coracoid has an acrocoracoid and the scapula an acromion process. The coraco-scapular angle is acute. A furcula occurs. In the large flightless forms the

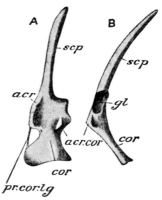

FIG. 437.—*Apteryx*: **Shoulder girdle.** (Left). *A*, anterior; *B*, lateral (outer) surface. *acr.* acromion; *acr. cor.* acrocoracoid; *cor.* coracoid; *gl.* glenoid cavity; *pr. cor. lg.* procoracoid, reduced to a ligament; *scp.* scapula. (After T. J. Parker.)

coracoid (Fig. 432, *cor.*) and scapula (*scp.*) are much reduced in proportional size and are ankylosed with one another. The acrocoracoid (*acr. cor.*) and acromion (*acr.*) processes are reduced or absent. The coraco-scapular angle approaches two right angles. There is no furcula, although separate vestiges of clavicles are present in the Emu and cassowaries. In the almost flightless song-bird *Atrichornis*, the clavicles are reduced to mere splints and the furcula has been lost altogether. At the same time, the absence of clavicles is not always associated with reduced powers of flight, as, for example, in some parrots. In some of the moas (*Pachyornis*, etc.) the shoulder-girdle is wholly absent. But, as in the case of the sternum, the distinction is not absolute. In *Hesperornis*, the Dodo, the Solitaire, *Aptornis*, *Notornis*, *Gallirallus* and *Cnemiornis* the bones of the shoulder-girdle are proportionally small. The coraco-scapular angle exceeds 90° and in some cases, such as certain parrakeets and owls, the furcula is slight, or represented by paired vestiges, or absent.

In most adult birds the procoracoid is reduced to a process on the dorsal end

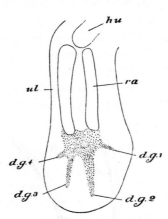

of the coracoid, but in the Ostrich and in the embryo of *Apteryx* it is well developed and separated by a fenestra from the coracoid. A small bone, the *accessory scapula*, is sometimes found on the outer side of the shoulder-joint.

The variations in the structure of the wing are mostly matters of proportion, but a remarkable flattening of all the bones is very characteristic of penguins, which are further distinguished by the presence of a sesamoid bone (p. 74), the *patella ulnaris*, in place of the olecranon process. In the Emu and kiwis the first and third digits of the normal wing have disappeared during development, the middle one alone remaining. In the moas (Fig. 431) no trace of a wing has been found, and in one species only is there even a trace of the glenoid cavity. In the embryos of several birds an additional digit has been found on the ulnar or postaxial side (Fig. 438, *dg. 4*). This

Fig. 438.—**Neornithes: Embryonic forelimb.** Tern (*Sterna*) showing pentadactyle hand in which the fifth digit does not develop. *dg.* 1—4, digits; *hu.* humerus; *ra.* radius; *ul.* ulna. (After Leighton.)

brings the total number of digits up to four, the fifth of the pentadactyle hand alone being unrepresented.

The simplest type of *pelvic girdle* is found in *Apteryx* (Fig. 439) and the

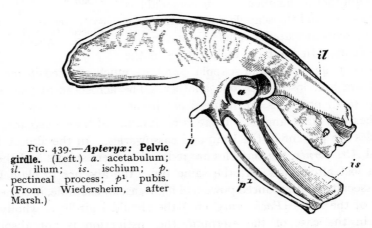

Fig. 439.—*Apteryx:* **Pelvic girdle.** (Left.) *a.* acetabulum; *il.* ilium; *is.* ischium; *p.* pectineal process; *p¹.* pubis. (From Wiedersheim, after Marsh.)

tinamous, in which both pubis and ischium are free along their whole length, as in dinosaurs. In the Emu and cassowaries the pubis and ischium unite by cartilage or bone at their posterior end with the ilium. In most birds the union between the two last is extensive. The deep ischiatic notch is replaced by a small foramen. In the embryonic condition the ilium has a very small pre-acetabular portion. The pubis and ischium are nearly vertical. There is a distinct pectineal process (*pp*) (retained in *Apteryx* (Fig. 439, *p*)) and the whole pubis is singularly like that of a dinosaur. In the Ostrich alone the pubes unite in the middle ventral line to form a symphysis. *Rhea* presents the unique peculiarity of a dorsal symphysis of the ischia, just below the vertebral column. In the Emu the posterior end of the pubis gives off a slender process, which extends forwards close to the ventral edge of that bone and probably represents the *epipubis* of reptiles.

In the sacral region of the larger running birds there occurs a spinal enlargement reminiscent, in very minor degree, of the remarkable condition found in certain dinosaurs (Fig. 342, p. 511).

The bones of the *hind-limb* are very uniform throughout the class, but the form of the tarsometatarsus of penguins is worthy of notice. It is short and wide. Its three constituent metatarsals, though fused, are clearly distinguishable throughout their whole length, and the resemblance to the homologous part in *Iguanodon* is very striking. In the embryo (Fig. 440) a vestige of the fifth digit (*mt. tsl.* 5) has been found in the form of a small rod of cartilage on the postaxial or fibular side. One or two free centralia may occur in the mesotarsal joint.

Except in certain diving birds (*e.g.* the puffins) the skeleton is always more or less pneumatic

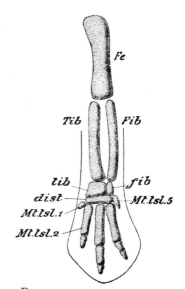

FIG. 440.—*Apteryx*: **Hind-limb and pes.** Embryo, in dorsal aspect. *dist.* distale; *Fe.* femur; *Fib.* fibula; *fib.* fibulare; *Mt.tsl.* 1—5, metatarsals; *Tib.* tibia; *tib.* tibiale. (After T. J. Parker.)

(Fig. 387). Often all the bones contain air except those of the fore-arm, hand, shank, and foot. In *Apteryx*, penguins, and some song-birds the skull alone is pneumatic. In the hornbills every bone in the body appears to contain air. As the passerine bird matures, an erosive process occurs, converting the cranium into a two-layered vacuolated structure in which innumerable little columns of osseous tissue separate a system of air-spaces. This pneumaticity of the skull is probably an adaptation towards keeping the head light and the centre of gravity well back during walking, swimming, and flying. The fragility of their skulls occasions great mortality from cerebral hæmorrhage among cage birds. Although there is no direct relationship between pneumaticity and flying power in specific groups, the typically avian bone structure undoubtedly greatly reduces weight without undue loss of strength. The dried skeleton of a large frigate-bird (*Fregata*), for example, weighs only about four ounces although the wing-span may be approximately seven feet. The bones, in fact, weigh less than the plummage (Murphy).

Alimentary Canal and Associated Structures.—In all existing Neornithes the jaws are covered by a horny beak and there are no *teeth*. That teeth were present in the more primitive birds, and have gradually been lost seems certain from the fact that the Cretaceous birds were toothed. In *Hesperornis* (Fig. 418) for example, there are long conical teeth in both jaws, set in continuous grooves. In *Gastornis* (Order Diatrymiformes) and in *Odontopteryx* (an extinct

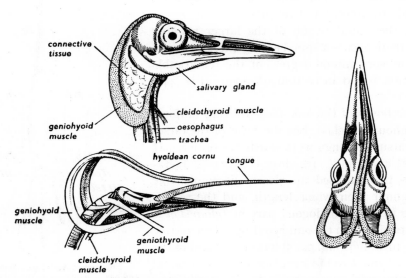

FIG. 441.—*Cecinus:* **Feeding specialisations.** The convulsive movement of the probing tongue of the European Green Woodpecker (*C. viridis*) is controlled principally by the massive genio-hyoid muscle which is closely bound to the hyoid cornua. These extend around and above the skull into the right moiety of the upper element of the beak. In the North American *Dryobates* the apparatus is not housed in the beak, but curves grotesquely around the right eye to the region of the ear. For the more typical hyoid apparatus see Fig. 393, p. 576. (Modified after Leiber.)

carinate form allied to the Anseriformes), the margins of the bony jaws are produced into strong, pointed, tooth-like prominences.

The young of many species possess bright yellow or otherwise coloured gapes. A few exhibit small light-reflecting areas which, along with head-movement and noisy squeaking, helps ensure that the parents will deposit the food. The *tongue* shows a great deal of variation. It may be relatively simple as in pigeons, horny as in parrots, brush-like as in honey-eaters, tube-like or brush-like as in humming-birds, or sticky at the tip as in ant-eating ground-woodpeckers. The tree-woodpeckers have an elongated barb-tipped tongue variously from two to five times the length of the powerful beak with which they enlarge the holes made by wood-boring organisms (Fig. 426, p. 621; Fig. 441).

Buccal glands, some at least of which produce *saliva*, occur. The sublingual glands of members of the Oriental, Indonesian, and Pacific genus *Collocalia* (Micropodidæ) become seasonally hypertrophied (Fig. 442) and produce a copious secretion of saliva that is used as nest-cement by the swiftlets, and as the basis for bird's-nest soup by the Chinese. European (*Micropus*), African (e.g. *Colletoptera*), and probably many other species of swifts also use saliva as nest-cement. The Palm-swift (*Cypsiurus*) of Africa is said also to glue its eggs to the nest with saliva. As a result, the palm leaves on which the nests are built can blow into any position without loss of eggs (Bannerman).

In the *alimentary canal* the chief variations concern the size of the crop, cæca, gizzard, and the extent of the intestine. In tubinarine birds (petrels, etc.) the proventriculus is especially large, and the surface of the secretory epithelium is increased by longitudinal ridges. The cells of the proventricular glands contain a concentration of lipids such as occur only sparingly in corresponding situations in other birds. It is possible that this material is the precursor of the oily substance that frightened petrels ejaculate at intruders. In grain-eating birds the gizzard has thick muscular walls and is lined by a thickened horny epithelium, as in pigeons (p. 584). In flesh-eaters, such as hawks and owls, it is thin-walled and lined with epithelium of a more usual

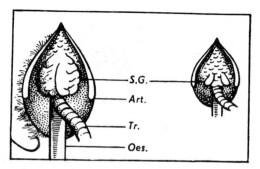

Fig. 442.—*Collocalia*: **Nest-cement production.** The sublingual salivary glands of Oriental and Pacific swiftlets (*Collocalia*) become seasonally hypertrophied as shown by *C. brevirostris* (left) which builds some weeks before *C. francica* (right). Both specimens were taken at the same time same date. *Art.* Articular bone; *Oes.* œsophagus; *S. G.* salivary gland; *Tr.* trachea. (Modified after Marshall and Folley.)

character. Nectar-eating birds possess relatively simple stomachs with extremely thin walls. In some birds, the indigestible hard parts of the prey are ejected from the throat. Owls swallow mice and small birds whole and eject the bones enclosed in a covering of fur and feathers. Piscivorous birds eject pellets of scales and bones and some insect-eaters likewise regurgitate indigestible chitinous exoskeletal structures.

In the Common Fowl and many other birds the cæca are of great length. A *gall-bladder* is usually present. The speed of digestion of course, varies according to the diet, but in general digestion seems to be more rapid than in most animals. In some frugivorous species the 'fleshless' stone of a berry may be voided less than fifteen minutes after it is swallowed. Small carnivorous birds are said to digest their prey within a few hours. Speedy digestion and absorption are essential in all animals of small volume, large surface, and high metabolic activity, and birds particularly fall into this category.[1]

Respiratory and Vocal Organs.—The rings of the *trachea* are always ossified. The respiratory tube is frequently deflected to one side by the crop, as in pigeons, and may undergo such an increase in length as to extend beneath the skin of the abdomen, or even into the keel of the sternum (Fig. 443). In the Whooper Swan (*Cygnus*) and certain cranes, the looped trachea probably functions as a resonator. An aberrant resonating chamber is found in the North American Heath Hen (*Tympanunchus cupido*). The anterior end of the œsophagus is enlarged into a vocal sac which can be inflated only by air that comes up from the respiratory system through the pharynx.

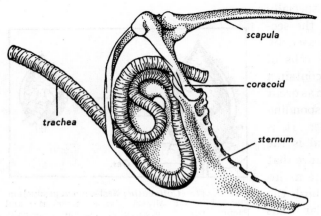

FIG. 443.—*Grus:* **Vocal specialisations.** The sternum in certain cranes (e.g. *G. antigone*) is excavated to accommodate the convoluted trachea. A convergent resonating arrangement has been evolved in swans. (Redrawn after Portmann.)

The *syrinx* is either *tracheo-bronchial*, as in the pigeon, *i.e.* formed by the distal end of the trachea and the proximal ends of the bronchi, or is exclusively *tracheal* (Fig. 444) or exclusively *bronchial*. In singing birds it is complex, provided with numerous muscles, and often more powerful in the male. In the mute Turkey Vulture (*Cathartes aura*) the syrinx is absent altogether.

The *lungs* are always firmly fixed to the dorsal body-wall by a pulmonary aponeurosis, and are only slightly distensible. The general arrangement of the air-sacs has been described in the pigeon (p. 586). In *Apteryx* the abdominal air-sacs are small, and are completely enclosed by the oblique septum, and do not extend into the abdominal cavity among the viscera. The bronchi send off branches at right angles.

---

[1] Several Australian and no doubt other species eat with impunity fruits that kill mammals. It might be expected that they detoxicate the poisonous principle in the liver, but apparently this is not so. If dogs or cats eat the *bones* of Bronze-wing Pigeons which have eaten the seeds of the heart-leaved poison (*Gastrolobium bilobum*), one of the Western Australian Leguminosæ, they die after convulsions and paralysis. The flesh of the pigeons is harmless to Man and dog. Here we may have a remarkable aspect of drought adaptation. It enables birds to take advantage of all possible foods in relatively unsustenable areas.

The **Circulatory Organs** agree in all essential respects with those of the pigeon. Their most characteristic features are the large size of the heart, the muscular right auriculo-ventricular valve, the atrophy of the left aortic arch, and the vestigial character of the renal portal system. The red blood-cells are always oval and nucleated.

Nervous System and Organs of Special Sense.—The *brain* is also very uniform in structure, being characterised by its short, rounded hemispheres, large folded cerebellum produced forwards to meet the hemispheres, and laterally placed optic lobes. In the embryo the optic lobes have the normal dorsal position, and the whole brain resembles that of a reptile. In *Apteryx* (see below) in correlation with the reduction of the eyes, the optic lobes are very small, and are situated on the under side of the brain. Above the anterior commissure is a small bundle of fibres which is probably the homologue of the *hippocampal commissure* of mammals.

A bird's *eyes* sometimes weigh more than its brain. A few relatively small hunting birds, such as certain hawks and owls, have larger eyes than Man. The avian eye contains no important structure absent in the Reptilia (taken as a whole), but it has reached a grade of efficiency higher than that of any other group. This is, of course, related to the flying habit ; and it is a commonplace that, alone of the major groups, the Aves contains no member that has lost the power of sight. Both the muscles of the iris and the ciliary muscles (of Crampton and Brücke), which procure accommodation by changing the shape of the unusually soft lens, are striated, and therefore relatively fast in their operation. The shape of the eyeball (comparatively flat to 'tubular'),

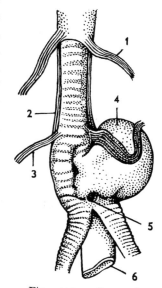

Fig. 444. — *Cyanochen:* **Vocal specialisation.** Male African Goose (*C. cyanopterus* with the additional syringeal elaboration of an osseous bulla (4) improving resonation. 1. ypsilotracheal, 2. tracheo-lateral, and 3. sternotracheal muscles, 5. inter-bronchial aperture, 6. œsophagus. (Redrawn after Grassé.)

and the corresponding arrangement of the internal structures, are related to the habits of the species. For example, in raptores the unusually long axial distance between lens and retina, and the broadening of the retinal area, probably allow a greater accuracy of vision in these diurnal hunters. The pit-like fovea, concerned probably with the detection of movement, is often exaggerated in birds. The retina of diurnal birds contain relatively few rods and a comparatively vast number of cones with coloured oil-droplets, the differential proportions of which help accentuate the appreciation of various colours in the environment. There is no truth in the repeated statement that diurnal birds are blue-blind, but it is probable that many of them are relatively insensitive to blue light rays. Such rays probably make distant small prey comparatively hazy and difficult to distinguish. A kestrel can see the movement of a field-mouse from a height at which most animals could probably detect nothing. In the eyes of most nocturnal birds cones are also present, but rods pre-dominate. There is also great variation in the number of cones from species to species. A sparrow possesses only about 400,000 per square millimetre of fovea, as against the 1,000,000 found in certain hawks, which have been claimed to possess a resolving power about eight times that of Man (Walls).

The most inefficient avian eye appears to be that of the nocturnal kiwis of New Zealand. Most night-hunting birds have eyes exceedingly well-adapted to take advantage of the small amount of light available to them, but the kiwis, on the other hand, have a powerfully developed olfactory sense (see below). In these, even though the orbit remains large, the eye has become reduced and myopic. The eyes of kiwis are probably unique in lacking the pecten (Fig. 409, p. 594), although a vestige of this enigmatic organ occurs in the embryo.

The pecten, the homologue of which is first obvious in fishes, occurs promi-nently as a pleated projection of highly vascular pigmented tissue from the optic nerve ('blind spot') into the vitreous humour. The blood vessels of which the pecten is largely composed are appreciably bigger than capillaries. The pecten is smallest in nocturnal birds and biggest in far-sighted diurnal hunters, in which it may extend from the retina almost to the lens. Although the pecten was observed in the 18th century, there is still no agreement con-cerning its function. Originally, and possibly still, it may have provided nourishment for the internal structures of the eye by the diffusion of blood solutes into the vitreous. Of the score or more other theories concerning its function, one of the most plausible is that it assists in movement-perception because, in strong illumination, the shadows of its pleats create numerous tem-porary blind-spots, and so increase the number of on and off photo-stimuli on the retina. Such may aid the detection, and continued observation of small, moving distant objects. It is a matter of common experience that the rapid blinking of the human eye may aid the perception of dimly seen objects by the production of discontinuous images.

The visual field of birds differs in relation to their habits and the position and shape of their eyes. Pigeons, *Gallus*, and passerines with laterally placed eyes (hunted birds) have a total visual field of sometimes more than 300 degrees, compared with a field of about 100 degrees in the predacious owls. In general the avian eyeball has a relatively restricted movement. Owls, which possess binocular vision, have increased the size of their eyes to an extent which makes it impossible for them to move in their sockets. In compensation there has been developed an extraordinary cervical mobility which allows the bird to rotate its head to such a degree that it can look backwards. Most birds move their heads when keeping a moving object under observation. Many shorebirds (*e.g.* snipe), however, have eyes placed in a relatively posterior position. This enables them to see behind with little adjustment. A most peculiar eye arrangement adapted to habit and habitat is found in the bitterns, which 'freeze' among rushes when they observe a predator. As the streaked throat is inclined upwards in line with the vertical rushes, the eyes focus downwards, enabling the motionless camouflaged bird to see anteriorly, and focus binocularly, below the tilted beak (Fig. 445).

All birds possess a functional nictitating membrane. In many species it is transparent. It has been suggested that this membrane is drawn protectively across the eye during long flights, but there is as yet no evidence that such is the case.

The *olfactory sense* in most birds is notoriously poor, but *Apteryx* is distinguished by the high development of the olfactory chamber, which extends from the tip of the beak to the level of the optic foramina. The turbinals are large and complex, and there is a vestige of the cartilage of Jacobson's organ. Also, sea-going Procellariiformes (petrels, albatrosses), which emit a characteristically strong and peculiar odour, possess remarkably developed olfactory organs. Nasal tubes open about midway along the beak and lead into thus protected capacious, paired, olfactory chambers, which are separated on the mid-line by an insubstantial septum. Extensive scroll-like turbinals invest the olfactory chambers and are supplied by the olfactory nerves (p. 130). The *olfactory bulbs* are extremely large.

Fig. 445.—*Botaurus:* **Adaptation to the reed-beds.** The European Bittern (*B. stellaris*) is disruptively patterned and 'freezes' on its nest when approached. The eyes are so situated that the bird can see under its elevated beak. This and the longitudinal ventral striping helps the sitting bittern to merge harmoniously with the perpendicular reeds. Nocturnal frogmouths (*Podargus*) of the Indo-Australian region 'freeze' when approached in daylight and look like the end of a fractured branch. In such species the head is moved almost imperceptibly so that the passing enemy can be kept in view. (From photographs.)

There is some evidence that these sea-scavengers locate their food *partly* by scent. It is possible (but not proved) that vultures, also possessed of a relatively complex olfactory apparatus, may do likewise. (For the function of the bilateral *nasal glands* see pp. 643–644.)

Taste-buds occur in birds, but not to the extent shown by the Mammalia. When present, they occur principally on the tongue or on the soft palate. It has been claimed that certain parrots are best equipped amongst birds. There is evidence that the contamination of food with relatively strong, and sometimes unpleasant, substances (*e.g.* anise, asafœtida, aloes, and camphor) does not deter turkeys, and that fowls and gulls, too, have an inefficient sense of taste.

The structure of the apparatus and *audition* and *equilibration* is very uniform throughout the class. Both elements are highly organised. The auditory apparatus has outer, middle, and inner parts like those of mammals (p. 144). A tympanic membrane separates the external meatus from the middle ear, which in turn communicates with the pharynx through the Eustachian tube, and with the inner ear through oval and circular apertures (*fenestræ*), which are covered by membranes. The fenestra ovalis is almost wholly occluded by the footplate of the *columella*, a cartilaginous extension (*extra-columella*) of which carries tympanic vibrations to the perilymph of the inner ear.

A *cochlea* (Fig. 410, p. 595) occurs as a relatively short, straight organ; although not 'snail-shaped', it is probably nonetheless homologous with the spiral-shaped mammalian structure. Cartilaginous shelves support the basilar membrane and divide the cochlea into two channels which communicate by means of an aperture near its apex, the *helicotrema*. One such channel is in communication with each fenestra. Agitation of the perilymph is reflected in movements of the basilar membrane, and its hair-like processes, which may be sound-receptors, the *hair-cells* being innervated by fibres from the cochlear ganglion. Contained in the basilar membrane are fibres which alter in length, and probably tension, and which as a whole may act as a frequency analyser.

The adjacent lagena contains additional hair-cells, the processes of which are sunk into a mucoid *cupola*, which is equipped with calcareous particles. (It is possible, but not unequivocally proved, that the 'lagenæ' of fishes and amphibians are homologous with each other and with that of reptiles, birds and monotremes.) It is surmised that in birds the lagena may respond to low, and the basilar membrane to high, frequency vibrations. Pumphrey has made the interesting suggestion that, on published evidence of vocal mimicry, Australian bower-birds (Fig. 382, p. 562) seem to have an auditory spectrum 'substantially wider than the pass-band of a broadcast receiver'. Birds vary a good deal in auditory power. The range of sounds audible to sparrows (*Passer*) is 675–11,500 frequencies per second, to the Canary (*Serinus*) 1,100–10,000, and to various parrots 40–14,000. These values are inferior by comparison with those recorded in some mammals. Even Man has a range of 20–20,000, whilst in their peculiar specialisation certain bats (p. 756) are claimed to have an upper range limit of 98,000 cycles per second.

The owls are of especial interest in that although they see very well by starlight (and by day), they appear to hunt largely by ear, and possess a skin-fold, hidden by feathers, that helps to direct sound towards the meatus. Some species have, in addition, a projecting feather formation, which probably helps to canalise sound in a manner analogous to the pinnæ of mammals (see p. 765). The plumage of owls, incidentally, is soft and fluffy, and makes the least possible warning sound during the approach to the prey.

FIG. 446. — **Neornithes : Tactile bristles.** Convergence in widely unrelated groups. Not to scale. Above: Nocturnal terrestrial forest-dwelling kiwi (*Apteryx*, Apterygiformes, p. 608). Below (left): Cave-haunting Guárcharo or Oil-bird (*Steatornis caripensis*, Caprimulgiformes, p. 618). (Right). Disposition of tactile bristles from ventral aspect. *Steatornis* now known to possesses an echo-location apparatus analogous to that of insectivorous bats (see p. 765). Flying in darkness the birds emit a stream of the 'sharpest imaginable clicks' (Griffin). Only when their ears were plugged did the clicking birds collide with the walls of a darkened room. The bristles shown above are probably used while alighting in the dark cavern and in nocturnal fruit-gathering outside. (Redrawn after Grassé, Ingram.)

Birds possess *tactile organs*. Light pressure on the plumage is appreciated, and it is probable that the bristly feathers near the mouth and eyes of many species are tactile in function. (Fig. 446.) 'Mud-feeders' (*e.g.* ducks and geese) have a considerable concentration of tactile corpuscles in the bill-tips, which apparently aid in the discrimination of food. There is evidence, too, that it is by means of *ventral tactile organs* that the sitting female becomes aware that her clutch is complete. Broodiness and inhibition of ovulation follow.

Excretion.—Birds retain a uricotelic excretory mechanism in the manner of reptiles (p. 548). Glomeruli are reduced in size and vascularity.

Whether marine birds drink sea-water, and by what means they maintain an appropriate salt balance, have been matters of discussion for many years. Until recently it was thought that the function of the bilateral *nasal glands* (which are relatively large in sea-birds) is to protect the nasal epithelium against sea-water. Schmidt-Neilsen and associates, however, have information suggesting that the glands are concerned with the extra-renal excretion of sodium chloride. They showed that cormorants (*Phalacrocorax*) excrete a high concentration of sodium chloride from these glands and confirmatory evidence has been obtained by work on penguins (*Spheniscus*) and other species. An adult penguin was not fed for 21 hours and was then given 5 gm. sodium chloride in 56 gm. of fish, the normal daily feed being about 800 gm. Within ten minutes, drops of clear fluid appeared at the beak-tip. This liquid was of high salt content; and two-thirds of the experimental dose was eliminated through the nostrils within four hours. Concurrent examination of cloacal matter suggested that 'the quantitative role of the kidney in sodium chloride excretion in this particular experiment was thus perhaps one-tenth of that of the salt-glands.'

It is clear that, in some species at least, the nasal gland is a far more efficient salt-excreting organ than the kidney. Even among plankton feeders it probably allows a net gain in drinking water. The liquid excreted in the beak is flung off with a characteristic head-shake that is a common sight to many who know sea-birds and which, in fact, has been described in ornithological literature without realisation of its significance (Matthews).

Reproduction.—In general, the avian urino-genital system resembles that described in the pigeon (p. 596), the most characteristic feature being the more or less complete atrophy of the right ovary and oviduct. In hawks, however, both ovaries are sometimes functional.

There is experimental evidence that in the Domestic Fowl spermatozoa must undergo some extra-gonadal maturation or other process. Spermatozoa taken experimentally from within the testes will not fertilise ova. Those taken from the epididymides will sometimes do so, whereas those from seminal vesicles are highly effective. In some species (*e.g.* many passerines) the sperm-filled seminal vesicles descend seasonally into cloacal protuberances, the interior of which are cooler than the body cavity. In birds (in which spermatogenesis occurs in abdominal organs of high temperature) spermatozoa can remain viable in the female tract for periods longer than that of most (but not all) mammals. Thus, a whole clutch of 20 or 30 eggs of the Domestic Turkey (laid at about daily intervals) can be fertilised as a result of a single copulation. In the Domestic Fowl eggs can be fertilised up to 20 days after insemination, but with less assurance after about the first week.

The 'ratites', Anseriformes, and some other large species possess a penis in the form of a thickening of the ventral wall of the cloaca : it has a groove on the dorsal surface serving as a sperm-channel, and its distal end is invaginated, in the position of rest, by an elastic ligament. In the Ostrich there is a solid penis, not unlike that of Chelonia and crocodiles : it can be retracted into a pouch of the cloaca. In the above groups a clitoris occurs in the female.

The rudimentary state of the right ovary in almost all species allows sex reversal from female to male to occur much more frequently than in most vertebrate animals. The traditional English couplet : '*A whistling maid, and a crowing hen, are fit for neither God nor Men*' has its counterpart in the French, German, and other languages. When the single functional ovary is obliterated by disease (or experimentally), the rudimentary tissue of the other often develops as an ovotestis, or even as a testis, and under the action of gonadotrophins (p. 150) pours its male secretions into the blood-stream, with characteristic results. It is claimed that occasionally hens have changed sex completely and fertilised other hens. From pre-Christian times, men have regarded a hen's assumption of male plumage,[1] and of an ability to crow, tread, and fight as a portent of disaster. The French said :

> *A hen that crows,*
> *A priest that dances,*
> *A woman who speaks Latin,*
> *Never come to a beautiful end.*

It would seem that after a hen assumes some male characters it may occasionally still lay a malformed egg. Ovarian function, it is thought, is not altogether inhibited, and on its way down the shrunken oviduct the so-called 'cock's egg' gets twisted and attenuated, so that the chalaza (Fig. 447) comes to assume roughly the form of a serpent. Such an egg has in the past often caused most awesome forebodings. An egg laid by a cock was alleged to hatch into a basilisk, regulus, or cockatrice, a creature mentioned in the Bible. A cockatrice was alleged to kill at a glance ; its fiery breath scorched all vegetation. It was part hen, part serpent, and the monarch of all the snakes and the dragons. It inspired in all a terrible dread. The cock alone was unaffected, and indeed in turn inspired the cockatrice to terror. Therefore, prudent mediæval travellers often took a cock with them. In Basel, as late as the 15th century, a cock was solemnly tried for witchcraft after laying an egg. The defence admitted the offence, but pointed out that the laying of the egg was unpremeditated and involuntary and, in fact, violated no law. But the prosecution asserted that the cock had been entered by the devil. They secured a conviction : and the cock and its egg were solemnly and legally burnt at the stake. Post-mortem examination showed that it contained no fewer than three more unlaid cock's eggs. The partial change from male to female probably occurs no more frequently in birds than in other groups.

[1] In *Gallus* the *male* plumage is the neutral (asexual) type and would appear at the next moult.

Development.—The process of development in birds has been most thoroughly worked out in the Domestic Fowl, but enough is known of the embryology of other birds to show that the differences are comparatively unimportant.

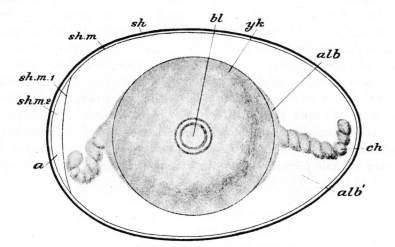

FIG. 447.—**Gallus: Structure of egg.** Semi-diagrammatic view of the egg of the Domestic Fowl at the time of laying. *a.* air-space; *alb.* dense layer of albumen; *alb'.* more fluid albumen; *bl.* blastoderm; *ch.* chalaza; *sh.* shell; *sh. m.* shell-membrane; *sh. m.* 1, *sh. m.* 2, its two layers separated to enclose air-cavity; *yk.* yolk. (After A. M. Marshall, slightly altered.)

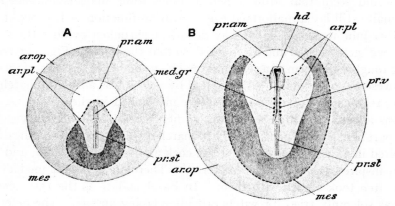

FIG. 448.—**Gallus: Development.** Blastoderm. Diagrammatic. *ar. op.* area opaca; *ar. pl.* area pellucida; *hd.* head; *med. gr.* medullary groove; *mes.* mesoderm, indicated by dotted outline and deeper shade; *pr. am.* pro-amnion; *pr. st.* primitive streak; *pr. v.* somites. (From A. M. Marshal, in part after Duval.)

Briefly, it can be said that the *ovum* is always large owing to the great quantity of food-yolk. The protoplasm forms a small *germinal disk* at the upper pole. Fertilisation is internal, and as the oosperm passes down the oviduct it is coated by successive secretions from the oviducal glands. It first receives a coat of thick, viscid *albumen* (Fig. 447, *alb.*), which, as the egg rotates during its passage, becomes coiled at either end into a twisted cord, the *chalaza* (*ch.*). Next, more fluid albumen (*alb'.*) is deposited layer by layer, then a tough, parchment-like *shell-membrane* (*sh. m.*), and finally a calcareous *shell* (*sh*). The shell-membrane is double, and at the broad end of the egg the two layers are separate and enclose an air-cavity (*a.*). The shell may be white or variously coloured by special pigments. It consists of three layers, and is traversed by vertical pore-canals. The calcareous material from which the shell is formed in at least some species (including pigeons), appears to be withdrawn from the substance of the bones. Thus females, but not males, form (possibly under the

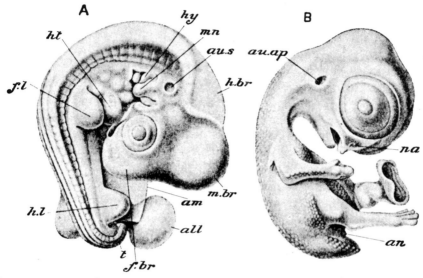

Fig. 449.—*Gallus:* **Development.** Late Stages. *all.* allantois; *am.* cut edge of amnion; *an.* anus; *au. ap.* auditory aperture; *au. s.* auditory sac; *f. br.* fore-brain; *f. l.* fore-limb; *h. br.* hind-brain; *h. l.* hind-limb; *ht.* heart; *hy.* hyoid arch; *m. br.* mid-brain; *mn.* mandibular arch; *na.* nostril; *t.* tail. (After Duval.)

seasonal influence of œstrogen) endosteal *medullary bone* which is later withdrawn and placed at the disposal of the shell-forming region of the reproductive tract.

Segmentation takes place during the passage of the egg down the oviduct, and results, as in reptiles, in the formation of a *blastoderm* (Fig. 448) occupying a small area on the upper pole of the yolk. In the newly-laid egg the blastoderm is divisible, as in reptiles, into two parts, a central, clear *area pellucida* (Fig. 448, *ar. pl.*) and a peripheral *area opaca* (*ar. op.*), and is usually two layers thick. The upper layer gives rise to the ectoderm and mesoderm, the lower layer is the developing endoderm. At first the endoderm is an irregular collection of cells, which is probably formed by a delamination from the upper layer; it soon becomes a continuous epithelium.

A grooved, longitudinal band, the *primitive streak* (*pr. st.*), now forms in the posterior three-quarters of the area pellucida. Through the primitive streak cells from the upper layer invaginate, and migrate laterally between the upper and lower layers to form the mesoderm. The primitive streak thus resembles the blastopore of amphibians, although no archenteron forms in birds.

When invagination has ceased, the *head process* forms by a forward migration of cells from the anterior tip of the primitive streak (*primitive knot* or Hensen's node). At almost the same time, the primitive knot migrates along the primitive streak toward the posterior end of the area pellucida, laying down a trail of notochord as it goes.

Immediately in front of the primitive streak the *medullary groove* (*med. gr.*) appears, and the *medullary folds* which bound it on the right and left diverge posteriorly, so as to embrace the anterior end of the primitive streak, in just the same way as they embrace the blastopore in Amphioxus.

The blastoderm gradually extends peripherally so as to cover the yolk. Thereby it becomes divisible into an *embryonic portion*, from which the embryo is formed, and an *extra-embryonic portion*, which invests the yolk-sac and takes no direct share in the formation of the embryo. The extension of the ectoderm and endoderm takes place regularly and symmetrically. The extra-embryonic mesoderm, while extending equally in the lateral and posterior regions, grows forwards in the form of paired extensions. These afterwards unite, but for a time there is an area of the blastoderm in front of the head of the embryo, formed of ectoderm and endoderm only. This is called the *proamnion* (*pr. am.*).

At an early period the mesoderm lying on either side of the medullary groove becomes segmented into somites (Fig. 448, *B, pr. v.*). The *lateral plate*, the extreme lateral part of the mesoderm, splits into somatic and splanchic layers with the cœlom between (Fig. 451, *B*).

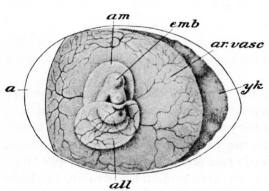

FIG. 450.—*Gallus:* **Relationship between embryonic and extra-embryonic structures.** *a.* air-space; *all.* allantois; *am.* amnion; *ar. vasc.* area vasculosa; *emb.* embryo; *yk.* yolk-sac. (After Duval.)

Gradually the embryo becomes folded off from the yolk-sac, as in other large-yolked eggs; but, owing apparently to the confined space in which it is enclosed, it soon turns over so as to lie with its left side against the yolk and its right side facing the shell (Fig. 450). The body (Fig. 449, *A*) becomes strongly flexed so as to bring the head and tail almost into contact, and the head soon acquires a proportionally immense size, with very large projecting eyes. At first the head is quite like that of one of the lower vertebrate embryos, with protuberant brain-swellings (*f. br., m. br., h. br.*), large square mouth, ventrally placed nostrils, connected by grooves with the mouth, and three or four pairs of gill-slits. As in reptiles, there is never any trace of gills. In the chick embryo as well as in most other birds, an opercular fold grows backwards from the hyoid arch, and covers the second and third branchial clefts. Soon the margins of the mouth grow out into a beak (Fig. 449, *B*). The clefts close, with the exception of the first, which gives rise to the tympano-eustachian passage. The head becomes characteristically avian. The limbs are at first alike in form and size (*A, f. l., h. l.*), and the hands and feet have the character of paws, the former with three, the latter with four digits. Gradually the second digit of the hand outgrows the first and third, producing the characteristic avian manus (*B*), while the metatarsal region elongates and gives rise to the equally characteristic foot. At the same time feather-papillæ make their appearance, arranged in narrow and well-defined pterylæ.

At an early period capillaries appear in the extra-embryonic blastoderm between the opaque and pellucid areas, and give rise to a well-defined *area vasculosa* (Fig. 450, *ar. vasc.*). They are supplied by *vitelline arteries* from the dorsal aorta, and their blood is returned by *vitelline veins* which join the portal vein and take the blood, through the liver, to the heart. The vascular area gradually extends, until it practically covers the whole of the yolk-sac: its vessels take an important share in the absorption of the yolk by the embryo.

Before the embryo has begun to be folded off from the yolk, the rudiment of one of the two characteristic *embryonic membranes*, the *amnion*, has appeared. A crescentic *amniotic fold* arises (Fig. 451, *A, am. f.*), in front of the head-end of the embryo, from the region of the pro-amnion. It consists at first of ectoderm only, the mesoderm not having yet spread into the pro-amnion. The fold is soon continued backwards along the sides of the body (*B*) and round the tail (*A*). In these regions (*am. f'.*), however, it consists from the first of ectoderm *plus* the somatic layer of mesoderm, *i.e.* it is a fold of what may be called the extra-embryonic body-wall. The cavity is a prolongation of the space between the somatic and splanchnic layers of mesoderm, *i.e.* is an extension of the extra-embryonic cœlom.

The entire amniotic fold gradually closes dorsally (*C*), forming a double-walled dome over the embryo. Its inner wall, formed of ectoderm internally and mesoderm externally, is the *amnion* (*am.*), the cavity of which becomes filled with a watery *amniotic fluid* serving as a protective water cushion to the enclosed embryo and to prevent desiccation. The outer wall, formed of ectoderm externally and mesoderm internally, is the *serous membrane* (*sr. m.*) or chorion. This comes to lie just beneath the vitelline membrane which subsequently disappears.

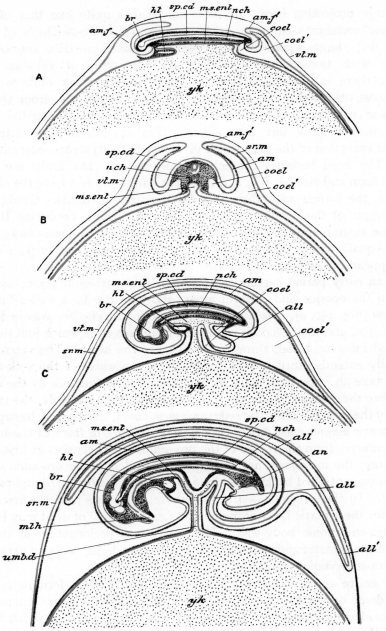

FIG. 451.—*Gallus:* **Development of fœtal membranes.** *A*, early stage in the formation of the amnion, sagittal section; *B*, slightly later stage, transverse section; *C*, sagittal section showing stage with completed amnion and commencing allantois; *D*, stage in which the allantois has begun to envelop the embryo and yolk-sac. The ectoderm is represented by a blue, the endoderm by a red line; the mesoderm is grey. *all.* allantois; *all'.* the same growing round the embryo and yolk-sac; *am.* amnion; *am. f., am. f'.* amniotic fold; *an.* anus; *br.* brain; *cœl.* cœlome; *cœl'.* extra-embryonic cœlom; *ht.* heart; *ms. ent.* mesenteron; *mth.* mouth; *nch.* notochord; *sp. cd.* spinal cord; *sr. m.* serous membrane; *umb. d.* umbilical duct; *vt. m.* vitelline membrane; *yk.* yolk-sac.

The second of the embryonic membranes, the *allantois*, is developed as an outpushing of the ventral wall of the mesenteron at its posterior end (*C*, *all.*), and consists, therefore, of a layer of splanchnic mesoderm lined by endoderm. It has at first the form of a small ovoid sac having the precise anatomical relations of the urinary bladder of Amphibia (Fig. 451, *A*, *all.*). It increases rapidly in size (Fig. 451, *all.*), and makes its way backwards and to the right, into the extra-embryonic cœlom, between the amnion and the serous membrane (Fig. 451, *C*, *D*). Arteries pass to it from the dorsal aorta. Its veins, joining with those from the yolk-sac, take the blood through the liver to the heart. Next, the distal end of the sac spreads itself out and extends all round the embryo and yolk-sac (*D*, *all'.*), fusing, as it does so, with the serous and vitelline membranes, and so coming to lie immediately beneath the shell-membrane. It finally encloses the whole embryo and yolk-sac together with the remains of the albumen, which has by this time been largely absorbed. The allantois serves as the embryonic respiratory organ, gaseous exchange readily taking place through the porous shell. Its cavity is an embryonic urinary bladder, excretory products being discharged into it from the kidneys.

Respiratory movements begin when the embryo pushes its beak into the air pocket that lies at one end of the egg. The shell is now punctured, usually by means of a little horny elevation, or *caruncle*, at the end of the beak. By this time the remainder of the yolk-sac has been drawn into the cœlom and the ventral body-walls have closed round it. The aperture in the shell is enlarged. The young bird hatches and begins a free life.

CLASS MAMMALIA

INTRODUCTION

All mammals possess dermal milk-glands, and only mammals possess them. All mammals are at least partially hairy. A single dentary, articulating with the squamosal, occurs on each side in the lower jaw. The skull has a double occipital condyle. The brain, and particularly the forebrain, is relatively large. The vertebræ are gastrocentrous (Fig. 452). Each vertebra consists of a centrum and a neural arch and, in addition, thin plate-like disks of bone—the epiphyses—at each end. On the cessation of growth these fuse with the body of the vertebra. The tympanic membrane or ear-drum is supported by a tympanic bone and there are three minute auditory ossicles (malleus, incus, and stapes) in the middle ear. A muscular diaphragm completely separates the thorax from the abdominal cavity. Excluding the Monotremata (p. 688) all mammals are viviparous, *i.e.* they produce their young alive. Most of them develop a filtering placenta between the maternal and embryonic tissues in the uterus and employ special means, both anatomical and behavioural, for the protection and nourishment of the newly born young. Like the birds, they are homœothermous with a four-chambered heart separating completely the oxygenated and deoxygenated blood. Birds and mammals are characterised also by the retention of a single aortic arch, in Mammalia the left one, in Aves the right.

The manifold physiological and behavioural advantages conferred by thermo-regulation and by the hyper-development of the cerebrum (as well as by the female's capacity to produce and carry in her body perfectly suitable food for the unborn young) have enabled eutherian mammals (p. 704) successfully to colonise most of the earth including some of its least hospitable parts. More than 8,500 extant mammalian species have been described.

Although prodigious gaps occur in our present understanding of mammalian evolution it is at least clear that they are derived from the Synapsida (p. 513), mammal-like reptiles of an ancient stem which appeared late in the Carboniferous (p. 3). The Synapsida prospered exceedingly in the Permian, yet were, surprisingly, seemingly on the wane before the great reptilian radiations came to fruition in the Mesozoic. The transition from primitive reptile to early mammal occurred between the Upper Carboniferous and the end of the Triassic. By the Lower Triassic there had appeared advanced theriodonts (e.g. *Cynognathus*) that were probably distinctly mammalian in appearance (p. 517). *Cynognathus* possessed a well-developed secondary palate, a feature that is characteristic of (though not peculiar to) sucking mammals. (A false palate occurs also in phytosaurs, crocodiles and one dinosaurian group.) In some advanced therapsids large infra-orbital foramina (which in mammals carry a rich nerve and blood supply to sensory whiskers and moist nasal mucosa) also occur. It must be emphasised, however, that these structures are no more than suggestive. There is, of course, no absolute evidence that any of these animals were homœothermous, had a four-chambered heart, were hairy or milk-producing. It seems possible, in fact, that many extinct animals not possessing the conventional squamosal-dentary articulation, and at present retained in the class Reptilia, might be called mammalian if their soft parts were available for study. In almost every fossil uncovered the bones alone are preserved or petrified, and although evidence can be got from endocranial casts, and further suggestive information obtained from other studies, it is inevitable that conventional definitions should be based wholly on osteological considerations.

After its successful radiation in the Permian the proto-mammalian stock suffered a set-back, and from the Triassic until the late Cretaceous (p. 3) it survived only as relatively inconspicuous, small animals that are very rarely found as fossils. Five groups—Multituberculata, Triconodonta, Symmetrodonta, Dryolestoidea and Docodonta have been recognised. Pre-Pleistocene monotreme fossils are unknown, but certain of the reptile-like skeletal components, the egg-laying habits, the imperfect thermoregulation and other primitive characters (p. 688) of the Monotremata suggest that they are survivors of some such early group. Specific cranial features argue that they are descended from triconodonts (p. 687).

No agreement has been reached as to the classification that most adequately expresses the relationships of these early mammals. Those particularly interested in mammalian palæontology should refer to works included in References (p. 909). It must be pointed out again that any phylogenetic arrangement adopted for animals of whose origins so little is known can only be provisional. For example, it was believed for many years that the Multituberculata were marsupials, but work done during the first half of this century has tended to disprove this and multituberculates are now placed in a sub-class of their own (see below). This arrangement indicates that they are mammals, but that they do not appear to be closely related to any other mammalian group.

The principal divisions are as follows : [1]

[1] Gregory (see p. 689) has proposed a new monotreme/marsupialian Sub-class Marsupionta involving a general arrangement as follows :

    Class Mammalia
        Sub-class Marsupionta
          Orders Marsupialia
             Monotremata
        Sub-class Monodelphia (Placentalia)

CLASS MAMMALIA
   Sub-class Prototheria
     Orders Triconodonta (Triassic–Cretaceous)
      [1] **Symmetrodonta** (Triassic–Cretaceous)
     Monotremata (Pleistocene-Recent)
   Sub-class Allotheria
     Order Multituberculata (Jurassic–Eocene)
   Sub-class Theria
     Infra-class Pantotheria (Trituberculata)
     Orders Dryolestoidea (Jurassic–Cretaceous)
      [2] **Docodonta** (Jurassic)
     Infra-class Metatheria
     Order Marsupialia (Cretaceous–Recent)
     Infra-class Eutheria (Placentalia)

EXAMPLE OF THE CLASS.—THE RABBIT (*Oryctolagus cuniculus*)

Oryctolagus cuniculus, along with other rabbits and the hares, belongs to the family Leporidæ of the Order Lagomorpha. They and the pikas of North America and Central Asia (Family Ochotonidæ) were originally placed with the Rodentia but modern work has shown that their many resemblances thereto are adaptive and superficial (p. 774).

External Characters.—The European Rabbit is a four-footed or *quadrupedal* animal. The whole surface of its body is covered with soft fur. Below the anterior extremity of the head the mouth is a transverse slit bounded by soft lips. The upper lip is divided by a longitudinal cleft, running backwards to the nostrils, and exposing the chisel-shaped *incisor teeth*. Behind the incisor teeth the hairy integument projects on each side into the cavity of the mouth. At the end of the snout, above the mouth, are two oblique slits, the nostrils. The large eyes, situated at the sides of the head, have each three eyelids, an upper and lower hairy lid, and an anterior hairless third eyelid or *nictitating membrane*, supported by a plate of cartilage. Tactile *vibrissæ*—very long, stiff hairs—are scattered above and below the eyes and on the snout. Behind the eyes, and a little nearer the summit of the head, are a pair of very long flexible and movable external ears or *pinnæ*. These are somewhat spout-shaped, expanding distally, and are usually placed vertically with the concavity directed laterally and some-

---

[1] *Incertae sedis.*

[2] Patterson removes the Docodonta from the Theria, and so limits the order Pantotheria to include only the dryolestids. He considers *Morganucodon* to be a docodont and not a triconodont, and places the symmetrodonts among the Theria, in the Infra-class Pantotheria. Kermack and Mussett have erected a Sub-class Eotheria including only the docodonts (mammals with a dual jaw articulation). They place the symmetrodonts in the Infra-class Pantotheria. The suggestion is again made (see also pp. 518, 688) that monotremes may have arisen independently; likewise the triconodonts, listed as an Order *incertae sedis*.

what forwards, leading to the external auditory opening. The *neck* is a distinct constriction, and the *trunk* is distinguishable into *thorax* in front and *abdomen* behind. On the ventral surface of the abdomen in the female are four or five pairs of *teats*. At its posterior end, below the root of the tail, is the *anus*. In front of this in the male is the *penis*, with a small terminal *urinogenital aperture*. The *testes* are enclosed in prominent *scrotal sacs* to right and left of the penis. In the female the genital opening is the *vulva*. In the space (*perinæum*) between anus and penis or vulva are two bare, depressed areas of skin into which open the ducts of the *perinæal glands* which secrete a product of strong and characteristic odour (p. 847). The *tail* is short and covered with a tuft of fur.

The *fore-* and *hind-limbs*, both of which take part in locomotion and in supporting the weight of the animal, differ considerably in size. The fore-limbs are much the shorter. Both have the same general divisions as in lizards. The upper arm is almost completely hidden by the skin, being applied closely against the side of the body. The *manus* is provided with five digits, each terminating in a horny claw. The thigh is also almost hidden by the skin. The *pes* has four digits only, all provided with claws.

Skeleton.—The *spinal column* of the Rabbit is divisible, like that of birds and lizards, into five regions—the cervical, thoracic, lumbar, sacral, and caudal. In the *cervical* region there are seven vertebræ, in the *thoracic* twelve (sometimes thirteen), in the *lumbar* seven (sometimes six) in the *sacral* four, and in the *caudal* about fifteen.

The centra of the vertebræ in a young rabbit consist of three parts—a middle part which is the thickest, and two thin disks of bone. The *epiphyses*, anterior and posterior, are applied respectively to the anterior and posterior faces of the middle part or centrum proper. Between successive centra in an unmacerated skeleton are plates of fibro-cartilage, the *intervertebral disks*.

The transverse processes of all the cervical vertebræ, except the seventh or last, are perforated by a canal, the *vertebrarterial canal*, through which runs the vertebral artery. The first vertebra or *atlas* (Fig. 452, *A*) resembles the corresponding vertebra of birds (p. 573) in being of the shape of a ring without any solid centrum like that of the rest. On the anterior face of its lateral portions are two concave articular surfaces for the two condyles of the skull. The second vertebra or *axis* (*A* and *B*) bears on the anterior face of its centrum a peg-like process, the *odontoid process* (*od.*), which fits into the ventral part of the ring of the atlas. It has a compressed spine (*sp.*), produced in the antero-posterior direction, and its transverse processes are short and perforated by a canal which carries the vertebral artery. All the cervical vertebræ except the last have their transverse process bifurcated into dorsal and ventral lamellæ. The seventh differs from the others in having a more elongated neural spine, in having its transverse processes simple and imperforate, and in the presence on the posterior edge of the centrum of a little concave semi-lunar facet.

The thoracic vertebræ (*C*) have elongated spines which are mostly directed backwards as well as upwards. The transverse processes are short and stout. Each bears near its extremity a small smooth articular surface or *tubercular facet* for the tubercle of a rib. On the anterior and posterior borders of each vertebra is a little semi-lunar facet, the *capitular facet* (*fac.*), situated at the junction of the centrum and the neural arch. The two contiguous semi-lunar facets of successive vertebræ form between them a little cup-like concavity into which the head or *capitulum* of a rib is received. The semi-lunar facet on the last cervical vertebra forms, with that on the anterior border of the first thoracic, the concavity for the head of the first rib.

In the lumbar region the spines are comparatively short, and both transverse processes and bodies are devoid of facets. From the centrum of each of the first two (or three) projects downwards a short flattened process—the

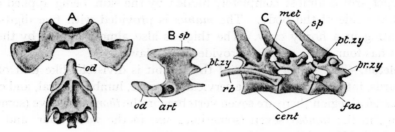

FIG. 452.—Class **Mammalia**, Infra-class **Eutheria**, Cohort **Glires**, Order **Lagomorpha**, Family **Leporidæ**, Sub-family **Leporinæ**, ***Oryctolagus:*** Vertebræ. *A*, atlas and axis, ventral aspect. *od.* odontoid process of axis. *B*, lateral view of axis. *art.* articular facet for atlas; *od.* odontoid process; *pt. zy.* post-zygapophysis; *sp.* neural spine. *C*, thoracic vertebræ, lateral view. *cent.* centrum; *fac.* facet for rib; *met.* metapophysis; *pr. zy.* pre-zygapophysis; *pt. zy.* post-zygapophysis; *rb.* rib; *sp.* spinous process.

hypapophysis. Certain accessory processes, the *metapophyses* (*met.*) and *anapophyses*, are well-developed, the former being extremely long in the posterior lumbar region. The metapophyses are situated in front, projecting forwards and outwards over the prezygapophyses. The anapophyses are situated below the postzygapophyses and project backwards. The transverse processes are long, and are directed forwards and outwards. That of the last lumbar is bifurcated. All bear short lumbar ribs at their tips.

The sacral vertebræ are firmly ankylosed together to form a single composite bone, the *sacrum.* The vertebræ bear a close resemblance to those of the lumbar region, but hypophyses and anapophyses are absent, and the metapophyses are comparatively small. The first and second bear great expanded lateral processes, or sacral ribs, with roughened external surfaces for articulation with the ilia. These are the only sacral vertebræ in the strict sense of the term, the following two being in reality anterior caudal.

Of the caudal vertebræ the more anterior resemble those of the sacral region, and have similar processes. Passing backwards in the caudal region all the processes gradually diminish in size. The most posterior vertebræ are represented merely by nearly cylindrical centra.

There are twelve pairs of *ribs*, of which the first seven are known as true ribs, *i.e.* are connected by their cartilaginous sternal parts with the sternum. The remaining five, the so-called false or floating ribs, are not directly connected with the sternum. All, except the last four, bear two articular facets. One of these is on the vertebral extremity or *capitulum*, and the other is on the neck of the rib (near the tubercle). The former is for articulation with the bodies, the latter the transverse processes of the vertebræ.

The sternum consists of six segments or *sternebræ*. The first, the *manubrium sterni* or *presternum*, is the largest and has a ventral keel. With the last is connected a rounded cartilaginous plate, the *xiphisternum*.

The *skull* (Figs. 453, 454), ignoring the jaws, is not very unlike that of birds in general shape. The length is great as compared with either the breadth or the depth. The maxillary region, or region of the snout (corresponding to the beak of birds (p. 575)), is long in proportion to the rest. The orbits are closely approximated, being separated only by a thin interorbital partition, and the optic foramina are confluent. But certain important differences are recognisable. One is the mode of union of the constituent bones. In the Pigeon, long before maturity is attained, the bony elements of the skull, originally distinct, become completely fused so that their limits are no longer distinguishable. In the Rabbit, on the other hand, such fusion between elements takes place in a few instances only, the majority of the bones remaining more or less distinct throughout life. The lines along which the edges of contiguous bones are united (the *sutures*) are sometimes straight, sometimes wavy and sometimes zigzagged serrations of the edges of the two bones interlocking. In some cases the edges of the bones are bevelled off and the bevelled edges overlap, forming a *squamous* suture.

Another conspicuous difference between the skull of the rabbit and that of the pigeon is in the mode of connexion of the lower jaw. In the rabbit it articulates directly with the cranium : the quadrate, through which the union is effected in the Pigeon, is apparently absent. Certain large apertures are readily identified with the large openings in the skull of birds. In the posterior wall of the skull is a large rounded opening, the *foramen magnum*, flanked with a pair of smooth rounded elevations or *condyles* for articulation with the first vertebra. These obviously correspond to the single condyle situated ventro-medially in the foramen in the pigeon. A large opening, situated at the end of the snout and looking forwards, obviously takes the place of the *external nares* of the Aves. A large opening in the roof of the mouth, leading forward to the external nasal opening, plainly represents, though much wider and situated farther back, the *internal* or *posterior nares* of birds. The rounded tubular opening (*aud. me.*) situated at the side of the posterior part

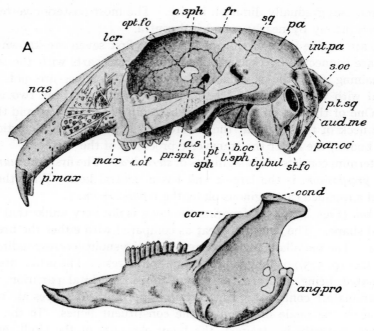

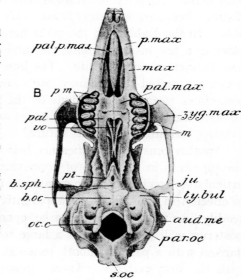

Fig. 453.—*Oryctolagus*: Skull. *A*, lateral view; *B*, ventral view. *ang. pro.* angular process of mandible; *a. s.* alisphenoid (external pterygoid process); *aud. me.* external auditory meatus; *b. oc.* basi-occipital; *b. sph.* basisphenoid; *cond.* condyle. *fr.* frontal; *int. pa.* interparietal; *i. o. f.* infra-orbital foramen; *ju.* jugal; *lcr.* lachrymal; *m.* molars; *max.* maxilla; *nas.* nasal; *opt. fo.* optic foramen; *o. sph.* orbito-sphenoid; *pa.* parietal; *pal.* palatine; *pal. max.* palatine plate of maxilla; *par. oc.* paroccipital process; *pal. p. max.* palatine process of premaxilla; *p.m.* premolars; *p. max.* pre-maxilla; *pr. sph.* pre-sphenoid; *pt.* pterygoid; *p. t. sq.* post-tympanic process of squamosal; *s. oc.* supra-occipital; *sph.* points to position of sphenoidal fissure, not clearly visible in a lateral view; *sq.* squamosal; *st. fo.* stylomastoid foramen; *ty. bul.* tympanic bulla; *vo.* vomer; *zyg. max.* zygomatic process of maxilla.

of the skull, some distance behind the orbit, is much the same as the *auditory aperture* of birds.

Surrounding the large opening of the foramen magnum are the bones of the *occipital* region of the skull, the *supra-*, *ex-*, and *basioccipitals*. The first of these (*s. oc.*) is a large plate of bone whose external surface is directed backwards and upwards, and elevated in the middle into a shield-shaped prominence. The *exoccipitals* lie at the sides of the opening, and each bears the greater part of the somewhat oval prominence or *condyle* with which the corresponding surface of the atlas or first vertebra articulates. Each is produced below into a process called the *paroccipital* (*par. oc.*), closely applied to the tympanic bulla. At the end of this, embedded in the tendon of a muscle (the *styloglossus*), is a small bony rod, the *stylohyal*. A small aperture, the *condylar foramen*, situated below the condyle, gives passage to one of the cranial nerves, the hypoglossal. The *basioccipital* is a median plate of bone, almost horizontal in position, which forms the floor of the most posterior part of the cranial cavity; it bears the ventral third of the occipital condyles. All these four bones of

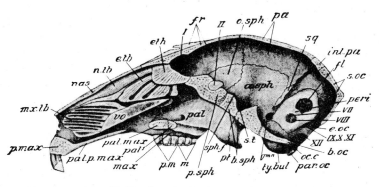

FIG. 454.—*Oryctolagus:* **Skull.** Longitudinal vertical section. The cartilaginous nasal septum is removed. *a. sph.* ali-sphenoid; *e.oc.* exoccipital; *e. tb.* ethmo-turbinal; *eth.* ethmoid; *fl.* fossa for flocculus of brain; *i.* incisors; *mx. tb.* maxillary turbinal; *n. tb.* naso-turbinal; *pal'.* palatine portion of the bony palate; *peri.* periotic (petrous portion); *p. sph.* pre-sphenoid; *sph. f.* sphenoidal fissure; *s. t.* sella turcica, or depression in which the pituitary body lies; *I.* point at which the olfactory nerves leave the skull; *II.* optic foramen; *V. mn.* foramen for mandibular division of trigeminal; *VII.* for facial nerve; *VIII.* for auditory nerve; *IX, X, XI,* for glossopharyngeal, vagus, and spinal accessory; *XII.* for hypoglossal. Other letters as in Fig. 453. (After T. J. Parker.)

the occipital region are in the adult rabbit united to form the single *occipital bone*. Articulating in front with the basioccipital, but separated from it by a plate of cartilage, is a plate of bone, also horizontal in position, which forms the middle part of the floor of the cranial cavity. This is the *basisphenoid*. It is perforated at about its middle by an oval foramen, the *pituitary foramen*, and on its upper surface is a depression, the *sella turcica*, or *pituitary fossa* (Fig. 453, *s. t.*), in which the pituitary body (hypophysis cerebri) rests. In front of it is another median bone of laterally compressed form, the *presphenoid*, with which it is connected by cartilage. The removal of this leaves a gap in the dried skull. The presphenoid forms the lower boundary of the single, large *optic foramen* (Fig. 453, *opt. fo.*). Connected laterally with the basisphenoid and presphenoid are two pairs of thin irregular plates, the *alisphenoids* (*a. s.*) behind and the *orbito-sphenoids* (*o. sph.*) in front. The alisphenoids are broad wing-like bones, each produced below into a bilaminate process, the *pterygoid process*. A large foramen, the *sphenoidal fissure* (*sph.*), situated between the orbitosphenoid and the alisphenoid of each side, transmits from the interior of the skull the third and fourth cranial nerves, the first and second divisions of the fifth, and the sixth nerves.

The boundary of the anterior part of the brain-case is completed by a narrow plate of bone, the *cribriform plate* of the *ethmoid* (Fig. 453, *eth.*), perforated by numerous small foramina for the passage of the olfactory nerves. This cribriform plate forms a part of a median vertical bone, the *mesethmoid*, the remainder of which (*lamina perpendicularis*) forms the bony part of the partition (completed by cartilage in the unmacerated skull) between the nasal cavities. Fused with the mesethmoid are two lateral, thin, twisted bones, the *ethmo-turbinals* (*e. tb.*). Articulating with the inferior edge of the mesethmoid is a long median bone, having a pair of delicate lateral wings, the *vomer* (*vo.*). None of these, save the cribriform plate, takes any share in the bounding of the cavity of the cranium. Roofing over that part of the cranial cavity, the walls and floor of which are formed by the sphenoidal elements, is a pair of investing bones, the *parietals* (Fig. 453, *pa.*). Farther forwards is another pair, the *frontals* (*fr.*). The parietals are plate-like bones, convex externally, concave internally, which articulate with the supra-occipital behind by a transverse serrated *lambdoidal suture*. The right and left parietals articulate mutually by means of a somewhat wavy *sagittal* suture. In front a transverse serrated suture, the *coronal*, connects them with the frontals. Between the supra-occipital and the parietals is a median ossification or *interparietal* (*int. pa.*). The frontals are intimately united in the median plane by means of the *frontal* suture. Laterally their orbital plates form an important part of the upper portion of the inner wall of the orbit. Above this, over each orbit, is a curved, somewhat crescentic process, the *supraorbital process*. Between the alisphenoid below, the parietal and frontal above, the frontal and orbitosphenoid in front, and the parietal behind, is the broad *squamosal* bone (*sq.*), whose superior margin is bevelled off. It is produced in front into a strong *zygomatic process*, which curves outwards, then downwards, and finally forwards, to unite, with the *jugal* in the formation of the *zygomatic arch*. Below the root of the process is a hollow, the *glenoid fossa*. Posteriorly the squamosal gives off a slender process, the *post-tympanic process* (*p. t. sq.*), which becomes applied to the outer surface of the *periotic*.

Between the occipital and parietal bones, below and behind the squamosal, are the *tympanic* and *periotic* bones. The tympanic forms the bony part of the wall of the external auditory meatus. Below it forms a dilated process, the *bulla tympani* (*ty. bul.*) projecting from the under surface of the skull. The periotic is a bone of irregular shape. Its internal (*petrous*) portion (Fig. 454, *peri.*) enclosing the membranous labyrinth of the internal ear. Externally it presents two small openings, the *fenestra ovalis* and *fenestra rotunda*, visible only when the tympanic is removed. Internally it bears a depression, the *floccular fossa*, for the lodgment of the flocculus of the cerebellum. Part of the periotic (*mastoid* portion) is seen on the exterior of the skull between the tympanic and exoccipital. The periotic and tympanic are not ankylosed together, but are loosely connected with the surrounding bones, and held in position by the post-tympanic processes of the squamosal. Between the tympanic and periotic are two foramina of importance—the *stylomastoid*, which transmits the seventh cranial nerve, and the *Eustachian aperture*, at which the Eustachian tube opens (Fig. 93, p. 144).

Roofing over the olfactory cavities are two flat bones, the *nasals* (*nas.*). Each has on its inner surface a very thin, hollow process, the *nasoturbinal*. In front of the nasals are the premaxillæ (*p.max.*) which are large bones forming the anterior part of the snout. They bear the upper incisor teeth and give off three processes—a nasal, a palatine (*pal. p.max.*), and a maxillary. The *maxillæ* (*max.*), which form the greater part of the upper jaw, and bear the premolar and molar teeth, are large, irregularly-shaped bones, the outer surfaces of which are spongy. They give off internally horizontal processes, the palatine processes (*pal. max.*), which unite to form the anterior part of the bony palate. Between the premaxillæ and maxillæ and the palatines on the lower surface of the skull is a large triangular opening divided into two *anterior palatine foramina* by the palatine processes of the premaxillæ. On the outer surface of each maxilla, above the first premolar tooth is the *infraorbital foramen* (*i. o. f.*), through which the second division of the fifth nerve emerges. A strong process given off from the outer face of each maxilla, and turning outwards, then backwards, to unite with the zygomatic process of the squamosal and thus to complete the zygomatic arch, is a separate bone in the young, the *malar* or *jugal* (*ju.*).

The maxillæ help to bound the nasal cavities externally, and each bears on its inner aspect a pair of thin scroll-like bones, the *maxillo-turbinals* (Fig. 454, *mx. tb.*). The rest of the narrow bony palate, forming the roof of the mouth and the floor of the nasal cavities, is formed by the *palatine plates* of the *palatine bones* (*pal.*). The so-called *pterygoids* (*pt.*) are small irregular bones, each of which articulates with the palatine in front and with the pterygoid process of the alisphenoid behind. These are probably equivalent to the fused pterygoids and ectopterygoids of reptiles (Parrington and Westoll). The *lachrymals* (*lcr.*) are small bones, each situated in the anterior wall of the orbit, perforated by a small aperture—the *lachrymal foramen*.

In the interior of the skull (Fig. 454) are three cavities, the right and left olfactory or nasal cavities in front, and the cranial cavity behind. The two first-named are separated from one another by a median partition or septum, partly cartilaginous, partly bony, formed, as above described, by the

mesethmoid. Each contains the *turbinals* or *turbinate bones* of its side. Each opens to the exterior by the large external nasal aperture and communicates behind with the cavity of the mouth by a posterior nasal aperture.

The cranial cavity has its walls moulded to a considerable extent on the surface of the contained brain, and, in consequence, concavities in the former correspond to the prominent portions of the latter. These concavities are termed the *fossæ*, and they consist of the *cerebellar fossa* behind and the *cerebral fossa* in front, with the inconspicuous *olfactory fossa* in the frontal region.

The *mandible*, or lower jaw, consists of two lateral halves or rami, connected with each other in front by a rough articular surface or *symphysis*. Behind they diverge like the limbs of a letter V. In each ramus is an anterior horizontal

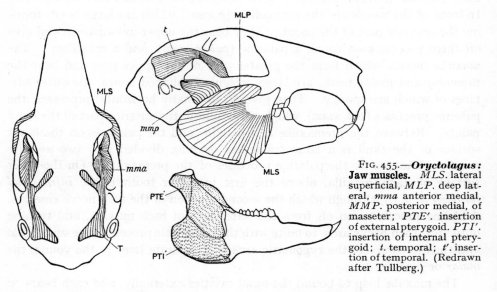

FIG. 455.—***Oryctolagus:*** **Jaw muscles.** *MLS.* lateral superficial, *MLP.* deep lateral, *mma* anterior medial, *MMP.* posterior medial, of masseter; *PTE'.* insertion of external pterygoid. *PTI'.* insertion of internal pterygoid; *t.* temporal; *t'.* insertion of temporal. (Redrawn after Tullberg.)

portion, which bears the teeth, and a posterior vertical or ascending portion, which carries the articular surface or *condyle (cond.)* for articulation with the glenoid cavity of the squamosal. In front of the condyle is the compressed *coronoid process.* The angle where the horizontal and ascending processes meet gives off an inward projection or *angular process (ang. pro.)* (Fig. 453).

The jaw-muscles in the Rabbit are specialised for the action of gnawing, though to a less extent than in many rodents (see Fig. 455). The muscles chiefly concerned are the *temporal, masseter, pterygoids,* and *digastric.* The temporal has its origin from a long, rather irregular area on the reduced temporal fossa, and is inserted on the medial side of the coronoid process of the lower jaw. The masseter is a large mass, and is divided into three sections, *deep* and *superficial lateral,* and *medial.* The origin is along the whole border of the jugal arch (the medial and deep lateral) and on the lower border of the maxilla (superficial lateral). The insertion of all three sections is on the outer face and border of the angle of the lower jaw. The *internal* and *external pterygoid* muscles arising from the pterygoid region are inserted on the inner side of the jaws at the angle and coronoid, respectively. The *digastric* muscles which open the jaws arise from the paroccipital process, and are inserted on the medial lower surface of the ramus. On the front part of the jaws are inserted other smaller muscles, such as the *buccinator*, which moves the lips, the *geniohyoglossus* for the tongue and so on.

The *hyoid* consists, in addition to the separate vestigial *stylohyals* already mentioned, of a stout thick body or *basihyal*, a pair of small anterior cornua or *ceratohyals*, and a pair of long, backwardly-directed cornua or *thyrohyals* (Fig. 612, p. 854).

The *auditory ossicles*, contained in the cavity of the middle ear and cut off from the exterior in the unmacerated skull by the tympanic membrane, are extremely small bones, which form a chain extending, like the columella auris of the pigeon, from the tympanic membrane externally to the fenestra ovalis internally. There are three of these auditory ossicles—the *stapes* (which corresponds to the columella of birds (p. 596)), the *incus*, and the *malleus*. The last-named has a slender process (*processus gracilis*). These are derived from the quadrate and articular elements (*q.v.*) of lower vertebrates. In addition there is a small disc-like *orbicular* bone which is attached to the incus.

The elements of the *pectoral arch* are fewer than in lizards (p. 486). There is a broad, thin, triangular scapula, the base or vertebral edge of which has a thin strip of cartilage (the *suprascapular* cartilage) continuous with it. Along the outer (dorsal) surface runs a ridge, the *spine* of which ends below in a long *acromion process*. From this a branch process or *metacromion* is given off posteriorly. The part of the outer surface of the scapula in front of the spine is the *prespinous* or *prescapular fossa*. The part behind is the *post-spinous* or *postscapular fossa*. At the narrow lower end of the scapula is a concave surface— the *glenoid cavity*—into which fits the head of the humerus. Immediately in front of this is a small inwardly curved process, the *coracoid process*, which is represented by two separate ossifications in the young Rabbit. A slender rod, the *clavicle*, lies obliquely in the region between the presternum and the scapula, but only extends a part of the distance between the two bones. In the adult it is connected with them only through the medium of fibrous tissue.

The skeleton of the fore-limb is more readily comparable with that of the lizard than that of the bird. There is, however, a difference in the position of the parts owing to the rotation backwards of the distal end of the humerus, all the segments being thus brought into a plane nearly parallel with the median vertical plane of the body, with the pre-axial border directed outwards, and the original dorsal surface backwards. The *radius* and *ulna* are fixed in the position of *pronation*, i.e. the distal end of the radius is rotated inwards, so that, while the proximal end is external to the ulna, the distal end becomes internal, and the digits of the manus are directed forwards.

At the proximal end of the humerus, are to be recognised 1. a rounded *head* for articulation with the glenoid cavity of the scapula ; 2. externally a *greater* and 3. internally a *lesser tuberosity* for the insertion of muscles ; 4. a groove, the *bicipital groove*, between the two tuberosities. On the anterior surface of the proximal portion of the shaft is a slight ridge, the *deltoid ridge*. At the distal end are two articular surfaces, the large and pulley-like *trochlea* for the ulna and the smaller *capitellum* for the radius. Laterally there is an internal, and an external, prominence or *epicondyle*.

The radius and ulna are firmly fixed together so as to be incapable of movement, but are not actually ankylosed. The radius articulates proximally with the humerus, distally with the *scaphoid* and *lunar* bones of the *carpus*. The ulna presents on the anterior aspect of its proximal end a deep fossa, the *greater sigmoid cavity*, for the trochlea of the humerus. The prominent process on the proximal side of this is the *olecranon* process. Distally it articulates with the *cuneiform*.

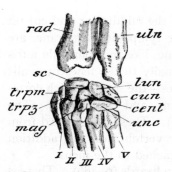

Fig. 456.—*Oryctolagus :* **Fore-arm and carpus.** Distal end, dorsal view, the bones bent towards the dorsal side so as to be partly separated. *cent.* centrale; *cun.* cuneiform; *lun.* lunar; *mag.* magnum; *rad.* radius; *sc.* scaphoid; *trpz.* trapezoid; *trpm.* trapezium; *uln.* ulna; *unc.* unciform; *I—V*, bases of metacarpals. (After Krause.)

The *carpal* bones (Fig. 456), nine in number, are all small bones of irregular shape. Eight of these are arranged in two rows—a proximal and a distal ; the ninth, *centrale* (*cent.*), lies between the two rows. The bones of the proximal row, taken in order from the inner to the outer side, are *scaphoid* (*sc.*), *lunar* (or *semi-lunar*) (*lun.*), *cuneiform* (*cun.*), and *pisiform*. Those of the distal row are likewise the *trapezium* (*trpm.*), *trapezoid* (*trpz.*), *magnum* (*mag.*), and *unciform* (*unc.*).[1]

The five *metacarpals* are all small but relatively narrow and elongated bones, the first being smaller than the rest. Each of the five digits has three *phalanges*, except the first, which has two only. The distal (*ungual*) phalanges are grooved dorsally for the attachment of the horny claw.

The pelvic arch (Fig. 457) contains the same elements as in the pigeon, but the union of the *ilium* with the sacrum is less intimate. The *acetabulum* is not perforated, and the *pubes* and *ischia* of opposite sides unite ventrally in a *symphysis* (*sy.*). The three bones of the pelvis—ilium, pubis, and ischium— are separate in the young Rabbit but are completely fused in the adult animal.

[1] The homologies of these bones are not quite certain, but are very probably as follows :— scaphoid = radiale ; lunar = intermedium ; cuneiform = ulnare ; pisiform = a sesamoid bone ; centrale = 1st and 2nd centralia ; trapezium = 1st distale ; trapezoid = 2nd distale ; magnum = 3rd distale ; unciform = 4th and 5th distalia.

The ilium and ischium meet in the acetabulum (to which they contribute), the articular cavity for the head of the femur. The remainder of the cavity is bounded, not by the pubis, but by a small intercalated ossification—the *cotyloid* bone. The ilium (*il.*) has a rough surface for articulation with the sacrum. Between the pubis (*pub.*) in front, and the ischium (*isch.*) behind, is a large aperture—the *obturator foramen* (*obt.*). The femur is rotated forwards when compared with that of the lizard, so that the limb is nearly in the same plane as the fore-limb, and the pre-axial border is internal and the originally dorsal surface is anterior. The femur has at its proximal end a prominent *head* for articulation with the acetabulum. External to this is a prominent process, the *great trochanter*. Internally there is a much smaller *lesser trochanter*, while a small process or *third trochanter* is situated on the outer border a little below the great trochanter. At the distal end of the femur are two prominences or *condyles*, with a depression between them. Two small sesamoids or *fabellæ* are situated opposite this distal end on its posterior aspect. Opposite the knee-joint, or articulation between the femur and the *tibia*, is a larger bone of similar character—the knee-cap or *patella*. The tibia has at its proximal end two articular surfaces for the condyles of the femur. Distally it has also two articular surfaces, one internal, for the *astragalus*, the other for the *calcaneum*. The *fibula* is a slender bone which becomes completely fused distally with the tibia.

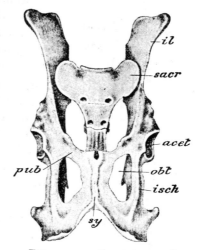

FIG. 457. — *Oryctolagus:* **Sacrum and innominate bones.** Ventral aspect. *acet.* acetabulum; *il.* ilium; *isch.* ischium; *obt.* obturator foramen; *pub.* pubis; *sacr.* sacrum; *sy.* symphysis.

The *tarsus* (Fig. 458) consists of six bones of irregular shape, arranged in two rows, one of the bones, the *navicular* (*nav.*), being intercalated between the rows. In the proximal row are two bones, the *astragalus* (*ast.*) and the *calcaneum* (*cal.*), both articulating with the tibia. The calcaneum presents behind a long *calcaneal process*. The distal row contains three bones, the *mesocuneiform*, *ectocuneiform*, and *cuboid* (*cub.*). The *entocuneiform*, which commonly forms the most internal member of this row in other mammals, is not present as a separate bone.[1]

There are four *metatarsals*, the *hallux* or first digit being vestigial and fused with the second metatarsal in the adult. The proximal end of the second is

[1] In all probability the homologies of these bones are as follows :—astragalus = intermedium + tibiale and proximal centralia; calcaneum = fibulare; navicular = 1st and 2nd centralia; entocuneiform = 1st distale; mesocuneiform = 2nd distale; ectocuneiform = 3rd distale; cuboid = 4th and 5th distalia and probably 3rd centralia.

produced into a process which articulates with the navicular. Each of the digits has three phalanges, which are similar in character to those of the manus.

The **cœlom** of the rabbit differs from that of birds and reptiles in being divided into two parts by a transverse muscular partition, the *diaphragm*. The anterior part, or *thorax*, contains the heart and the roots of the great vessels, the lungs and bronchi, and the posterior part of the œsophagus. The œsophagus perforates the diaphragm to enter the posterior part, or *abdomen* which contains the stomach and intestine, the liver and pancreas, the spleen, the kidneys, ureters and urinary bladder, and the organs of reproduction.

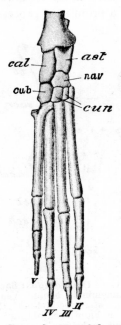

FIG. 458.—*Oryctolagus:* **Pes.** *ast.* astragalus; *cal.* calcaneum; *cub.* cuboid; *cun.* cuneiforms; *nav.* navicular.

Alimentary Canal and Associated Structures.—The teeth (Fig. 453) are lodged in sockets or *alveoli* in the premaxillæ, maxillæ, and mandible. In the premaxillæ are situated four teeth—the four *upper incisors*. Of these the two anterior are very long, curved, chisel-shaped teeth, devoid of roots and growing throughout life from persistent pulps. Enamel is present, and forms a thick layer on the anterior convex surface, which accounts for the bevelled-off character of the distal (occlusal) end. The layer of enamel is much harder than the rest of the tooth, which therefore wears away more quickly at its cutting extremity. Along the anterior surface is a longitudinal groove. The second pair of upper incisors are small teeth lodged just behind the larger pair. In the lower jaw are two incisors, which correspond in shape with the anterior pair of the upper jaw, but lacking any longitudinal groove. The remaining teeth of the upper jaw are lodged in the maxillæ. *Canines*, present in most mammals as a single tooth on each side, above and below, are here entirely absent, and there is a considerable space, or *diastema* between the incisors and the *premolars*, the teeth next in order. Of these there are three in the upper jaw and two in the lower. They are long and curved with persistent pulps like the incisors. The first upper premolar is smaller than the others and of simple shape. The rest have each a longitudinal groove on the outer side and a transverse ridge on the crown. The lower premolar has two grooves; the second is similar to those of the upper jaw. Behind the premolars are the *molars*, of which three occur on each side both in the upper and lower jaws.

Opening into the cavity of the mouth, or *buccal cavity*, are the ducts of four pairs of salivary glands. These are the *parotids* (situated below the pinnæ), the *infraorbitals* (below the eyes), the *submaxillaries* (Fig. 459, *s. mx. gl.*) (near the angles of the jaw) and the *sublinguals* (beneath the tongue). The saliva moistens and lubricates the food. On the floor of the mouth is the muscular *tongue*, covered with a mucous membrane beset with many papillæ, on certain of which the *taste-buds* (p. 137) are situated. The roof of the mouth is formed by the *hard palate*, which is crossed by a series of transverse ridges of its mucous membrane. Posteriorly the hard palate passes into the *soft palate*, which ends behind in a free pendulous flap, the *uvula*, in front of the opening of the *posterior nares*. When the animal propels food from the buccal cavity towards the œsophagus, the soft palate and uvula rise and block the flow of air from the

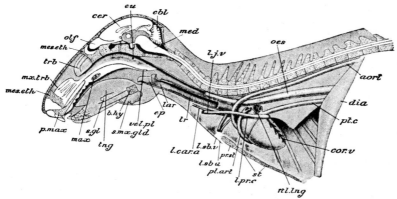

Fig. 459.—*Oryctolagus*: **Head, neck, and thorax.** Lateral view. The head and spinal column are represented in mesial vertical section. The left lung is removed. The greater part of the nasal septum is removed so as to show the right nasal cavity with its turbinals. *aort.* dorsal aorta; *b. hy.* basi-hyal; *cbl.* cerebellum; *cer.* cerebral hemispheres; *cor. v.* coronary vein; *dia.* diaphragm; *ep.* epiglottis; *eu.* opening of Eustachian tube into pharynx; *lar.* larynx; *l. j. v.* left jugular vein; *l. sb. a.* left subclavian artery; *l. sb. v.* subclavian vein; *max.* maxilla; *med.* medulla oblongata; *mes.eth.* mesethmoid; *mx. trb.* maxillo-turbinal; *œs.* œsophagus; *olf.* olfactory bulb; *pl. art.* pulmonary artery; *p.max.* premaxilla; *pr. st.* presternum; *pt. c.* post-caval vein; *rt. l. lng.* root of left lung with bronchus and pulmonary veins and artery cut across; *s. gl.* sub-lingual salivary glands; *s. mx. gld.* sub-maxillary salivary gland; *st.* sternebræ; *tng.* tongue; *tr.* trachea; *trb.* ethmo-turbinals; *vel. pl.* soft palate.

nostrils, and at the same time prevent food from entering the nares. At the anterior end of the palate a pair of openings, the *nasopalatine* or *anterior palatine canals*, lead into the nasal chambers, and into them open a pair of tubular structures, the *organs of Jacobson* (Fig. 460, *jcb.*). These are enclosed in cartilage and situated on the floor of the nasal cavities. Behind the mouth or buccal cavity proper is the *pharynx*, which in the rabbit is not sharply marked off from the buccal cavity, but begins where the hard palate ends. The pharynx is divided into two parts, an upper or *nasal* division (*nasopharynx*) and a lower or *buccal* division (*oro-pharynx*) by the soft palate. The aperture of the posterior nares is continuous with the nasal division, at the sides of which are the lower or pharyngeal openings of the *Eustachian tubes*. The nasopharynx is continuous with the oro-pharynx round the posterior free edge of the soft palate. From the oro-pharynx leads ventrally the slit-like opening of the glottis [1] into the *larynx* and *trachea*. Attached externally to larynx and trachea are the paired lobes of the endocrine *thyroid gland* (p. 151) and directly adjacent are the minute *parathyroid glands* (p. 152). These structures are endocrine glands and not of course part of the digestive system; nevertheless they are conveniently noted here. The thyroids secrete an iodine-containing hormone *thyroxin* which is important in general metabolism. If iodine is insufficient in the diet (as is often the case in certain mountain regions) the thyroid in turn receives insufficient quantities from the blood-stream and the pathological condition of goitre results in animals, including Man. The parathyroids secrete *parathormone* which controls aspects of calcium metabolism. Removal causes death. Overhanging the glottis is a leaf-like movable flap, the *epiglottis* (Fig. 459, *ep.*), formed of a plate of elastic cartilage covered with mucous membrane. Just as the uvula closes off the anterior part of the respiratory tract during deglutition or swallowing, the epiglottis closes off the latter part, thus protecting the bronchi and lungs from entrant and injurious food-particles. Accidentally aspirated particles are repelled by a defensive and explosive cough-reflex. Behind the pharynx comes the *œsophagus* or gullet (*œs.*) This is a narrow but dilatable muscular tube which runs backwards from the pharynx through the neck and thorax, enters the cavity

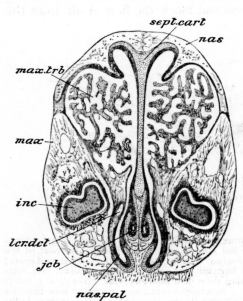

Fig. 460.—*Oryctolagus:* **Nasal region.** Vertical section through the anterior part of the head. *inc.* section of larger incisor tooth; *jcb.* lumen of Jacobson's organ, surrounded by cartilage; *lcr. dct.* lachrymal duct; *max.* maxilla; *max. trb.* maxillary turbinals; *nas.* nasal bone; *nas. pal.* naso-palatine canal; *sept. cart.* cartilaginous nasal septum. (After Krause.)

of the abdomen through an aperture in the diaphragm, and opens into the *stomach.* Food is propelled into the stomach by waves of peristaltic smooth muscle contraction under involuntary control.

The stomach (Fig. 461) is a capacious sac, much wider at the *cardiac* end, at which the œsophagus enters, than at the opposite or *pyloric* end, from which the comminuted food passes through a circular muscle, the *pyloric sphincter*, into the *duodenum* (*du.* and *du'*) the first part of the *small intestine.* The duodenum

---

[1] The term glottis is more strictly applied not to this slit, but to the slit-like aperture between two folds of the mucous membrane within the larynx—the *vocal cords*—which constitute the chief parts of the vocal apparatus.

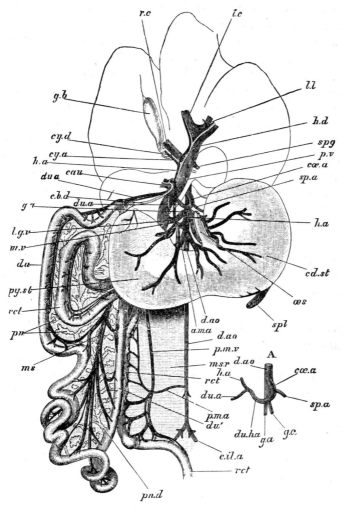

FIG. 461.—*Oryctolagus:* **Visceral relationships.** The stomach, duodenum, posterior portion of rectum and liver (in outline) with their arteries, veins, and ducts. *A*, the cœliac artery of another specimen (both × ⅔). The gullet is cut through and the stomach somewhat displaced backwards to show the ramifications of the cœliac artery (*cœ. a.*); the duodenum is spread out to the right of the subject to show the pancreas (*pn.*); the branches of the bile-duct (*c. b. d.*), portal vein (*p. v.*), and hepatic artery (*h. a.*) are supposed to be traced some distance into the various lobes of the liver. *a. m. a.* anterior mesenteric artery; *cau.* caudate lobe of liver with its artery, vein, and bile-duct; *c. b. d.* common bile-duct; *cd. st.* cardiac portion of stomach; *c. il. a.* common iliac artery; *cœ. a.* cœliac artery; *cy. a.* cystic artery; *cy. d.* cystic duct; *d. ao.* dorsal aorta; *du.* proximal, and *du'.* distal limbs of duodenum; *du. a.* duodenal artery; *du. h. a.* (in *A*), duodeno-hepatic artery; *g. a.* gastic artery and vein; *g. b.* gall-bladder; *h. a.* hepatic artery; *h. d.* left hepatic duct; *l. c.* left central lobe of liver, with its artery, vein, and bile-duct; *l. g. v.* lieno-gastic vein; *l. l.* lateral lobe of liver with its artery, vein, and bile-duct; *ms.* branch of mesenteric artery and vein to duodenum; *ms. r.* mesorectum; *m. v.* chief mesenteric vein; *œs.* œsophagus; *p. m. a.* posterior mesenteric artery; *p. m. v.* posterior mesenteric vein; *pn.* pancreas; *pn. d.* pancreatic duct; *p. v.* portal vein; *py. st.* pyloric portion of stomach; *rct.* rectum; *r. c.* right central lobe of liver, with artery, vein, and bile-duct; *spg.* Spigelian lobe of liver with its artery, vein, and bile-duct; *spl.* spleen; *sp. a.* splenic artery. (After T. J. Parker.)

is an elongated, narrow, greatly coiled tube curved into a U-shaped loop. It is succeeded by the coiled *ileum* which ends at an *ileo-colic sphincter* and a rounded expansion, the *sacculus rotundus*. At the junction of small and large intestine is the *cæcum*, a long, wide, capacious, thin-walled pouch which ends in a small blind *vermiform appendix*. The cæcum exhibits a spiral constriction which indicates the internal presence of a narrow *spiral valve*. In herbivorous animals (such as rabbits) the cæcum is an important organ of digestion and absorption. Leaving the cæcum close to the entrance of the ileum is the *colon*, a wide sacculated tube which is continued into a narrow, smooth-walled, posterior *rectum* (*rct.*), which opens to the exterior by an *anal orifice*. The intestine, like that of the pigeon, is attached throughout its length to the dorsal wall of the abdominal cavity by a *mesentery*, or double fold of peritoneum.

The *liver*, attached to the diaphragm by a fold of peritoneum, has its substance imperfectly divided by a series of fissures into five lobes. From each lobe arises a tiny *hepatic duct* and these unite mutually and with the *cystic duct* from the thin-walled *gall-bladder*, situate in a depression on the right posterior surface of the liver. The *common bile-duct* (*c. b. d.*), formed by the union of the cystic and hepatic ducts, opens into the dorsal aspect of the duodenum near the pylorus.

The *pancreas* (*pn.*) is a diffuse compound gland of combined exocrine and endocrine function lying in the fold of mesentery passing across the loop of the duodenum. Its single duct, the *pancreatic duct* (*pn. d.*), opens into the distal and ascending limb of the loop. In addition to the enzymes of the pancreatic fluid a further complement is secreted in the *succus entericus* produced by the glandular walls of the duodenum. From this region, too, arises the portion of the hepatic portal system which carries absorbed foodstuffs up to the liver (p. 112).

Rabbits share with the Common Hare, shrews, and probably other herbivores the habit of *refection* : they consume their own freshly voided fæces. It is probable that they thus obtain quantities of B complex vitamins that have been produced by bacterial action in the large intestine.

Blood Vascular System.—The *heart* (Fig. 462) is situated in the cavity of the thorax, a little to the left of the middle line and lies in a space, the *mediastinum*, between the two *pleural sacs* enclosing the *lungs*. The mediastinum is divisible into anterior, dorsal, median, and ventral parts. In the anterior part lie the posterior part of the trachea, the neighbouring parts of the œsophagus and of the thoracic duct of the lymphatic system, the roots of the great arteries and the veins of the *pre-caval* system, and the *phrenic, pneumogastric,* and other nerves. In the dorsal part are situated the posterior part of the œsophagus, the thoracic part of the dorsal aorta, the *pneumogastric* nerve, the *azygos* vein, and the *thoracic duct*. The middle part is the widest, and lodges the heart and roots of the aorta and pulmonary artery enclosed in the *pericardium*, the pos-

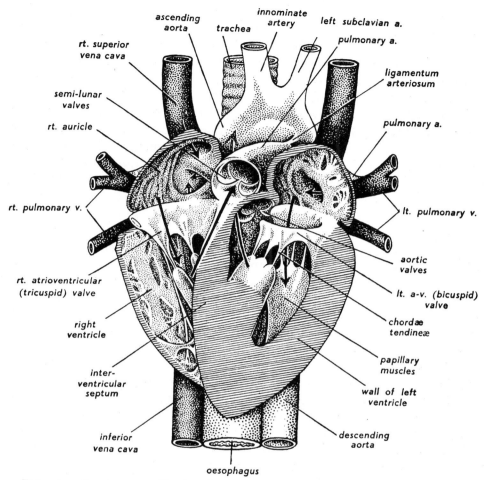

FIG. 462.—*Oryctolagus:* **Heart and associated structures.** Ventral aspect. The arrows indicate the general direction of blood-flow. On the left side oxygenated blood (received from both left and right pulmonary veins) empties into the left atrium, flows through the left atrioventricular (bicuspid, mitral) valve into the ventricle, and is propelled into the general circulation through the aortic valve. Into the right side comes deoxygenated blood (received from the general circulation via the right superior vena cava (top arrow) and left superior vena cava (lowest arrow). It flows into the ventricle through the right atrioventricular (tricuspid) valve (partly dissected out) and is propelled towards the semilunar valves into the pulmonary arteries and the lungs. The ligamentum arteriosum is a solid fibrous vestige of the ductus arteriosus that connects the pulmonary and systemic arches. It takes origin from the distal part of the left sixth arterial arch of the embryo. (Modified after Young.)

terior portion of the pre-caval veins, the phrenic nerves, the terminal part of the azygos vein, and the roots of the lungs. The ventral part contains only areolar tissue with the lobular lymphoid *thymus gland* of undetermined function. The pericardial membrane enclosing the heart consists of two layers, a *parietal,* forming the wall of the pericardial cavity, and a *visceral,* immediately investing the heart. Between the two is a narrow cavity containing a little lubricating *pericardial fluid*. In general shape the heart resembles that of birds—it has the apex directed backwards and slightly to the left, and the base forwards. Like that of the Pigeon, it comprises right and left auricles and right and left ventricles. The right and left sides of the heart have their cavities completely separated from one another by inter-auricular and inter-ventricular partitions.

Venous blood comes into the right auricle from the *right* and *left pre-caval* veins and the single *post-caval*. The first opens into the anterior part, the second into the left-hand side of the posterior portion, and the third into the dorsal surface (Fig. 462). In the wall of the right auricle is a small node of specialised tissue, the *sinu-auricular node* or pace-maker from which originates the heart-beat. The conduction apparatus of the *excitation wave*, involving the *auriculo-ventricular node*, *auriculo-ventricular bundle* and the *Purkinje network* of the Mammalian heart, is described on p. 882. From the inner surface of the auricle arise numerous cords of muscle fibres, the *musculi pectinati*.

A membranous fold, the remnant of the fœtal *Eustachian valve*, extends from the opening of the post-cava forwards towards the auricular septum. The opening of the left pre-cava is bounded behind by a crescentic fold, the *valve of Thebesius*. On the septum is an oval area, the *fossa ovalis*, where the partition is much thinner than elsewhere. This marks the position of an aperture, the *foramen ovale*, that occurs in the fœtus. The crescentic anterior rim of the aperture is known as the *annulus ovalis*. The cavity of the right auricle communicates with that of the right ventricle by the wide right auriculo-ventricular opening. This is guarded by a large valve, the *tricuspid*, composed of three membranous cusps. These are so arranged and attached that whilst they flap back against the walls of the ventricle to allow the passage of blood from the auricle to the ventricle, they meet together across the aperture so as to close the passage when the ventricle contracts. The cusps of the valve are attached to muscular processes of the wall of the ventricle, the *musculi papillares*, by means of tendinous threads called the *chordæ tendineæ*. The right ventricle, much thicker than the auricle, forms the right side of the conical apical portion, but does not extend quite to the apex. Its walls are raised up into muscular ridges called *columnæ carneæ*. It gives off in front, at its left anterior angle, the pulmonary artery, the entrance to which is guarded by three pouch-like *semilunar valves* (Fig. 462).

The left auricle receives oxygenated blood from the lungs. The right and left pulmonary veins open together into the cavity of this auricle on its dorsal aspect. A large left auriculo-ventricular opening leads from the cavity of the left auricle into that of the left ventricle. This is guarded by a *mitral valve* consisting of two membranous cusps with chordæ tendineæ and musculi papillares. In the walls of the ventricle are *columnæ carneæ*, rather more strongly developed than those in the right. At the basal (anterior) end of the left ventricle is the opening of the aorta, guarded by three *semilunar valves* similar to those at the entrance of the pulmonary artery. The *coronary* arteries, which supply the *cardiac muscle*, are given off from the aorta just beyond the semilunar valves. The corresponding vein opens into the terminal part of the left pre-cava. The pulmonary artery divides into right and left branches which carry venous blood to the corresponding lungs for oxygenation.

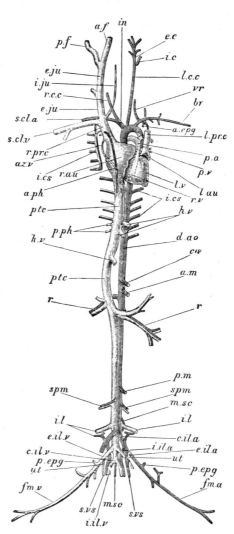

FIG. 463.—*Oryctolagus* : Blood vascular system. The heart is somewhat displaced towards the left of the subject; the arteries of the right and the veins of the left side are in great measure removed. *a. epg.* internal mammary or anterior epigastric artery; *a. f.* anterior facial vein; *a. m.* anterior mesenteric artery; *a. ph.* anterior phrenic vein; *az. v.* azygos vein; *br.* brachial artery; *c. il. a.* common iliac artery; *c. il. v.* hinder end of post-caval; *cœ.* cœliac artery; *d. ao.* dorsal aorta; *e. c.* external carotid artery; *e. il. a.* external iliac artery; *e. il. v.* external iliac vein; *e. ju.* external jugular vein; *fm. a.* femoral artery; *fm. v.* femoral vein; *h. v.* hepatic veins; *i. c.* internal carotid artery; *i. cs.* intercostal vessels; *i. ju.* internal jugular vein; *i. l.* ilio-lumbar artery and vein; *in.* innominate artery; *l. au.* left auricle; *l. c. c.* left common carotid artery; *l. pr. c.* left pre-caval vein; *l. v.* left ventricle; *m. sc.* median sacral artery; *p. a.* pulmonary artery; *p. epg.* posterior epigastric artery and vein; *p. f.* posterior facial vein; *p. m.* posterior mesenteric artery; *p. ph.* posterior phrenic veins; *pt. c.* post-caval vein; *p. v.* pulmonary vein; *r.* renal artery and vein; *r. au.* right auricle; *r. c. c.* right common carotid artery; *r. pr. c.* right pre-caval vein; *r. v.* right ventricle; *scl. a.* right subclavian artery; *scl. v.* subclavian vein; *spm.* spermatic artery and vein; *s. vs.* superior vesical artery and vein; *ut.* uterine artery and vein; *vr.* vertebral artery. (After T. J. Parker.)

From the base of the left ventricle the *aorta* takes oxygenated blood to a system of arterial vessels by which it is conveyed throughout the body. The aorta first runs forward, then bends round the left bronchus, forming the *arch* of the aorta (Figs. 462, 463), to run through the thorax and abdomen, in close contact with the spinal column, as the *dorsal aorta* (*d. ao.*). From the arch of the aorta are given off two large arteries, the *innominate* (*in.*) and the *left subclavian*. The innominate divides to form the *right subclavian* (*s.cl. a.*) and the *right* (*r. c. c.*) and *left* (*l. c. c.*) *common carotid* arteries. The subclavian passes to the fore-limb as the *brachial* artery, giving origin to the *vertebral* artery. After passing up through the vertebrarterial canal the vetebral artery supplies branches to the spinal cord, finally entering the cranial cavity and hind-brain. The subclavian also gives off the *anterior epigastric* or *internal mammary*, which supplies the thoracic parieties.[1]

The right carotid divides opposite the angle of the jaw into *internal* and *external carotids*. The left carotid and left subclavian correspond to the right carotid and right subclavian in their branches and distribution. If carefully looked for, the slight dilation of the *carotid sinus* can be seen at the origin of the internal carotid, the common carotid having been pulled to one side (the dissector going in through the neck). The carotid sinus contains receptors (*baroceptors*) that are sensitive to changes in blood pressure. These, originate reflexes that tend to stabilise blood pressure. Thus, nerve impulses are sent to cardiac and vasomotor centres in the medulla oblongata. A rise in arterial pressure causes a reflex slowing of the heart and vasodilation, thus restoring blood pressure to near its previous level. The reverse process also occurs.

Passing through the thorax the aorta gives off a series of small paired *intercostal* arteries (*i. cs.*). In the abdomen its first large branch is the *cœliac artery* (*cœ.*), which supplies the liver, stomach, and spleen (p. 105). Behind this it gives origin to the *anterior mesenteric* (*a. m.*), which supplies the intestine and the pancreas. Opposite the kidneys it gives off the two *renal* arteries (*r.*), and a good deal farther back the *spermatic* (*spm.*) or *ovarian* arteries as the case may be. Just in front of the origin of the spermatic arteries is given off a *posterior mesenteric* (*p. m.*), which supplies the hinder part of the rectum. A series of small *lumbar* arteries supply the side-walls of the abdominal cavity. Posteriorly the dorsal aorta divides to form the two common *iliac* arteries (*c. il. a.*) which supply the pelvic cavity and hind-limbs. A small *median sacral* (*caudal*) artery (*m. sc.*) passes backwards in the middle line to supply the caudal region.

The system of *caval* veins which bring venous blood to the right auricle consists of the *right* and *left pre-cavæ* and of the single *post-cava*. The right pre-cava is formed by the union of the *right jugular* (*e.ju.*) vein and *right subclavian* (*scl. v.*). The *azygos vein* (*az. v.*), the *right anterior intercostal* (*i.cs.*), and the *right anterior epigastric* or *internal mammary* also opens into it. The left pre-cava receives a series of veins similar to those forming the right, except that there is no azygos on the left side.

The post-caval vein (*pt. c.*) is formed in the hinder part of the abdominal cavity by the union of the *internal iliacs* (*i. il. v.*) which bring blood from the

---

[1] In any species there may be much variation in the mode of origin of the aortic arch branches.

back of the thighs. Shortly after its origin it receives the two *external iliacs* (*e. il. v.*) also coming from the hind-limbs. In front of this a pair of *ilio-lumbar* (*i.l.*) veins join it. A little farther forward the post-cava is joined by a pair of *spermatic* (*spm.*) or *ovarian* veins and opposite the kidneys by a pair of *renal* veins (*r.*). The post-cava ultimately also receives by means of the *hepatic* veins blood originally carried to the liver by the *hepatic portal system*, after the passage of such blood through the liver. The principal veins of the portal system are the *lieno-gastric, duodenal, anterior mesenteric*, and *posterior mesenteric* which unite to form a single, large *portal vein* (Fig. 461, *p. v.*). There is no trace of a renal portal system (pp. 112, 158).

The *red blood corpuscles* are circular, bi-concave, non-nucleated discs. The *spleen* is an elongated, compressed, dark-red body, situated in the abdominal cavity in close contact with the stomach to which it is bound by a fold of peritoneum, the *gastro-splenic mesentery*. The spleen is highly vascular and its functions include blood storage and the phagocytosis, by means of its reticulo-endothelial cells, of effete red cells. It has a fibrous capsule containing some smooth muscle from which anastomising trabeculæ extend inwards. In the resultant interstices lies the *splenic pulp* into which arterioles discharge into sinusoids and from which venules take up blood for venous return. The stored blood can be rapidly driven into the general circulation in emergency by the contraction of the capsule which is under sympathetic control (see p. 119).

Lymphatic System.—Although relatively difficult to demonstrate, the lymphatics, associated with the capillaries, ramify through almost every part of the body. Except in the spleen and parts of the liver, blood does not come in actual contact with the tissues—*tissue-spaces* lie between.

The capillary walls are highly permeable to all but the largest molecules, *i.e.* proteins. These are retained in the capillary, and exert an osmotic pressure *into* the capillary of about 25 mm. Hg. The *outward* movement is determined by the excess hydrostatic pressure over this osmotic pressure at the arteriolar end. At the venule end, the hydrostatic pressure is less than osmotic pressure and so water and its solutes (*e.g.* metabolites) move back in again.

The proportion of the tissue-fluid that passes into the *lymph capillaries* (*lymphatics*) as *lymph* is still almost identical with tissue fluid. Lymph contains much the same inorganic components as blood as well as some protein. It contains also *lymphocytes*, but lacks red cells and blood platelets which cannot penetrate the blood capillary walls. The lymph vessels are interrupted at various points by *lymph nodes* (containing *reticular cells*) which produce lymphocytes and macrophages which phagocytose bacteria and other invasive particulate matter.

Emulsified and partly digested fats are carried as *chyle* from the lymphatics of the small intestine. Lacking lymph-hearts (p. 116), but well-equipped with valves and so situated that muscle movement moves the fluid onwards, the immense mammalian lymphatic network finally canalises its contents into the blood-stream via the *thoracic duct* (Fig. 464). This passes anteriorly through the thorax and opens into the left external jugular vein near its junction with the subclavian. Lymphatics supplying the left side of the head, neck, and arm drain into the thoracic duct near its outlet. In some animals about three-quarters of each lung, and a large proportion of the peritoneum, drain into the *right lymph duct*, which enters the right external jugular directly.

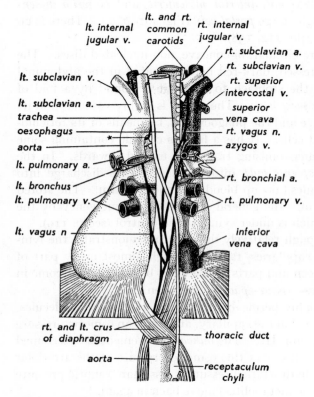

FIG. 464.—*Homo:* **Cardiac region and thoracic duct.** The pericardium has been dissected at its line of reflection from the vessels entering the heart. The descending thoracic aorta has been removed to reveal the course of the vagal nerves which form the œsophageal plexus and subsequently separate. The azygos vein has been cut near its entrance into the superior vena cava. The left recurrent pharyngeal nerve as shown (after leaving the vagus) hooking anteriorly (*) around the top of the descending aorta to the ligamentum arteriosus (ductus arteriosum) which is not shown. The receptaculum chyli is easily seen in the rabbit. (Modified after Boyd, *et al.*)

Respiratory System. The *larynx* (Fig. 465) is a chamber with walls supported by cartilage, lying below and somewhat behind the pharynx, with which it communicates through a slit-like aperture, the glottis. The cartilages of the larynx are, in addition to the *epiglottis* (p. 465), the large *thyroid* (*th.*), which forms the ventral and lateral walls, the ring-like *cricoid* (*cr.*), the two small *arytenoids* (*ary.*), and a pair of small nodules, the *cartilages of Santorini* (*sant.*), situated at the apices of the arytenoids. The *vocal cords* extend across the cavity from the thyroid below to the arytenoids above. The larynx is essentially a mechanical valve at the entrance to the air-way, capable of preventing or of regulating both the entrance and the exit of air from the bronchial passages and the lungs, in response to changing physiological requirements. Its permanent patency is ensured by the cricoid cartilage being completely ring-shaped, unlike the remaining laryngeal cartilages and the incomplete rings of trachea and bronchi.

Leading backwards from the larynx is the *trachea* or wind-pipe (Fig. 465, *tr.*), a long tube the wall of which is supported by cartilaginous rings which are incomplete dorsally. The trachea enters the cavity of the thorax, and there divides into the two *bronchi*, one passing to the root of each lung.

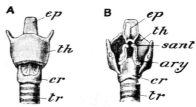

FIG. 465.—*Oryctolagus:* **Larynx.** *A*, ventral view; *B*, dorsal view. *ary.* arytenoid; *cr.* cricoid; *ep.* epiglottis; *sant.* cartilage of Santorini; *th.* thyroid cartilage; *tr.* trachea. (From Krause, after Schneider.)

The *lungs* (Fig. 466) are enclosed in the lateral parts of the cavity of the thorax. Each tri-lobed lung lies in a cavity, the *pleural sac*, lined by a *pleural membrane.* The right and left pleural sacs are separated by a considerable interval owing to the development in the partition between them (mediastinum) of the heart and other organs. The lung is attached to the mediastinum at its root only, and there the pleural membrane is reflected over it as a visceral layer (p. 107). In this respect the Rabbit's lung differs widely from that of birds. It differs also in its minute structure. The bronchus, entering at the root, divides and sub-divides to form a ramifying system of increasingly smaller tubes, each of the ultimate branches of which, or *terminal bronchioles*, opens into a minute chamber or *infundibulum*, consisting of a central passage giving off a number of thin-walled *alveoli*. Each alveolus is en-meshed externally by a dense network of capillaries, which in the total lung com-prise a relatively immense respiratory surface. As the blood flows through the capillaries, gaseous exchanges take place between it and the air entering and leaving the alveoli of the bronchial tract.

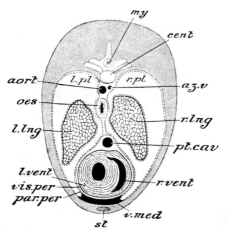

FIG. 466.—*Oryctolagus:* **Thoracic rela-tionships.** Transverse section in the region of the ventricles to show the relations of the pleuræ, mediastinum, etc. The lungs are contracted. *aort.* dorsal aorta; *az. v.* azygos vein; *cent.* centrum of thoracic vertebra; *l. lng.* left lung; *l. pl.* left pleural sac; *l. vent.* left ventricle; *my.* spinal cord; *œs.* œsophagus; *par. per.* parietal layer of pericardium; *pt. cav.* post-caval, close to its entrance into right auricle; *r. lng.* right lung; *r. pl.* right pleural cavity; *r. vent.* right ventricle; *st.* sternum; *v. med.* ventral mediastinum; *vis. per.* visceral peritoneum.

A group of infundibula (supplied by a single bronchiole, which divides therein to form the terminal bronchioles) is termed a *lobule* of the lung. In gross shape the lung is roughly conical, with the apex directed forwards. The base, which is concave, lies, when the lung is distended, in contact with the convex anterior surface of the diaphragm. The outer or costal surface is convex in adaptation to the form of the side-wall of the thorax; the internal or visceral surface is concave.

Nervous System. The *brain* (Figs. 467, 468) of the Rabbit displays the same principal parts as that of birds but with many differences in detail. The

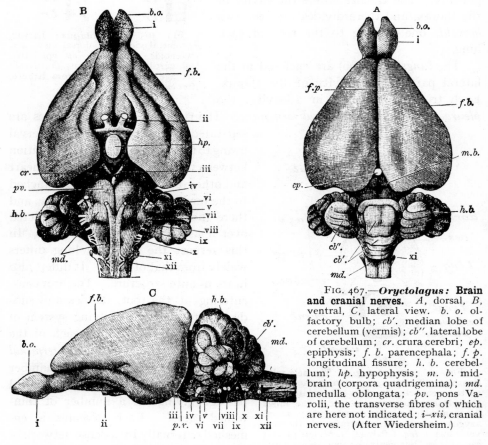

FIG. 467.—*Oryctolagus:* **Brain and cranial nerves.** *A,* dorsal, *B,* ventral, *C,* lateral view. *b. o.* olfactory bulb; *cb'.* median lobe of cerebellum (vermis); *cb''.* lateral lobe of cerebellum; *cr.* crura cerebri; *ep.* epiphysis; *f. b.* parencephala; *f. p.* longitudinal fissure; *h. b.* cerebellum; *hp.* hypophysis; *m. b.* midbrain (corpora quadrigemina); *md.* medulla oblongata; *pv.* pons Varolii, the transverse fibres of which are here not indicated; *i–xii,* cranial nerves. (After Wiedersheim.)

surface of the two relatively long and narrow cerebral hemispheres of the fore-brain (*prosencephalon*) present certain depressions or *sulci*, which, though few and indistinct, indicate surface lobes and convolutions (*gyri*) not distinguishable in the case of pigeon or lizard. The cerebral cortex is arbitrarily divided into paired *frontal, parietal, temporal,* and *occipital* lobes. Superficially the hemispheres comprise a *neopallium* of grey cortical tissue, several cell-layers thick, to which are carried impulses resulting from visual, auditory, tactile, and other forms of peripheral stimulation. From circumscribed cortical areas are initiated voluntary motor impulses which are carried via a bundle of motor axones, the *pyramidal tract*. Association pathways of considerable complexity link the various cortical areas, while the hemispheres are functionally united via the *commissural fibres* of the *corpus callosum* (Figs. 468, *cp. cl.*) and *anterior commissure*. Very large, club-shaped *olfactory bulbs* lie below the anterior extremities of the cerebral hemispheres; behind each, on the ven-

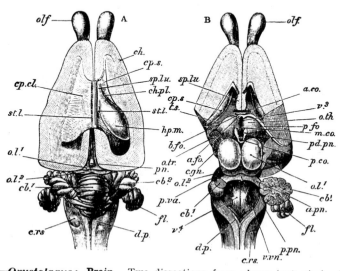

FIG. 468.—*Oryctolagus:* **Brain.** Two dissections from above (nat. size). In *A* the left parencephalon is dissected down to the level of the corpus callosum: on the right the lateral ventricle is exposed. In *B* the cerebral hemispheres are dissected to a little below the level of the genu of the corpus callosum; only the frontal lobe of the left hemisphere is retained; of the right a portion of the temporal lobe also is left; the velum interpositum and pineal body are removed, as well as the greater part of the body of the fornix, and the whole of the left posterior pillar; the cerebellum is removed with the exception of a part of its right lateral lobe. *a. co.* anterior commissure; *a. fo.* anterior pillar of fornix; *a. pn.* anterior peduncles of cerebellum; *b. fo.* body of fornix; *cb*[1]. superior vermis of cerebellum; *cb*[2]. its lateral lobe; *c. gn.* corpus geniculatum; *c. h.* cerebral hemisphere; *ch. pl.* choroid plexus; *cp. cl.* corpus callosum; *cp. s.* corpus striatum; *c. rs.* corpus restiforme; *d. p.* dorsal pyramid; *fl.* flocculus; *hp.m.* hippocampus; *m. co.* middle commissure; *o. l*[1]. anterior, and *o. l*[2]. posterior lobes of corpora quadrigemina; *olf.* olfactory bulb; *o. th.* optic thalamus; *o. tr.* optic tract; *p. co.* posterior commissure; *p. fo.* posterior pillar of fornix (tænia hippocampi); *pn.* pineal body; *pd. pn.* peduncle of pineal body; *p. pn.* posterior peduncles of cerebellum; *p. va.* fibres of pons Varolii forming middle peduncles of cerebellum; *sp. lu.* septum lucidum; *st. l.* stria longitudinalis; *t. s.* tænia semicircularis (narrow band of white matter between corpus striatum and optic thalamus); *v. vn.* valve of Vieussens; *v*[3], third ventricle; *v*[4], fourth ventricle. (After T. J. Parker.)

tral surface of the hemisphere, is the corresponding *olfactory tract* leading back to a slight rounded elevation, the *tuberculum olfactorium*. As mentioned above, the two hemispheres are connected by a commissural structure which occurs only in the Mammalia. This, the *corpus callosum*, runs transversely above the level of the lateral ventricles. Examined in transverse section, *i.e.* in a longitudinal section of the brain, the corpus callosum is seen to bend slightly downwards, forming the *genu*. Posteriorly it bends downwards and forwards, forming the *splenium*, which passes forwards and is united with the subjacent *fornix*—a commissural narrow median strand of longitudinal fibres, which bifurcates both anteriorly and posteriorly to form the so-called *pillars* of the fornix—anterior and posterior (Fig. 468, *p. fo.*).   Below the corpus callosum, between it and the fornix, the thin inner walls of the hemispheres (*septum lucidum, sp. lu.*) enclose a small, laterally compressed cavity, the so-called *fifth ventricle* or *pseudocœle*.   This is not a true brain-ventricle, but merely a space between the closely-apposed hemispheres.

The *lateral ventricles* of the cerebral hemispheres are much more extensively developed than in the brain of the pigeon.   They are of somewhat complex shape.   Each consists of a middle portion, or *body*, roofed over by the corpus callosum, a narrow anterior prolongation, or *anterior cornu*, a *posterior cornu* (which runs backwards and inwards) and a *descending cornu*.   This last passes at first almost directly outwards, then downwards, and finally inwards and forwards.   On the floor of the body of the ventricle, and continued along the whole extent of the descending cornu, is a prominent ridge of nearly semi-circular transverse section—the *hippocampus* (*hp. m.*).   This corresponds in position with a groove, the *hippocampal sulcus*, on the inner surface of the temporal lobe.   Internally the two hippocampi merge in a median commissural area—the *psalterium* or *lyra*.

Running along the anterior edge of the hippocampus is a ridge of fibres— the *tænia hippocampi* or *fimbria*—which passes down into the descending cornu. The union of the two tæniæ forms a median longitudinal strand, the *body of the fornix*, which, as already explained, lies below the corpus callosum, continuous with the splenium of the latter behind, but diverging from it anteriorly by dipping down towards the base of the brain.   In the angular space between the corpus callosum and the fornix below is the *septum lucidum*.   The tæniæ hippocampi are the *posterior pillars* of the fornix (Fig. 468, *p. fo.*).   The *anterior pillars* (*a. fo.*) are a pair of vertical bands which pass from the anterior end of the body downwards to the *corpus mammillare* (see below) at the base of the diencephalon.

Lying immediately in front of the hippocampus is a vascular membrane, the *choroid plexus* (*ch. pl.*) whose blood vessels secrete *cerebrospinal fluid*.   This passes inwards to join its fellow of the opposite side through a transverse passage, the *foramen of Monro*, which opens behind into the diacœle.   The floor of the anterior cornu is formed of an eminence of grey matter—the *corpus striatum* (*cp. s.*) which is, however, relatively restricted in mammals. The right and left corpora striata are connected together by a narrow transverse band of white fibres, the *anterior commissure* (*a. co.*), situated in front of the anterior pillars of the fornix.

In the diencephalon the *diacœle* (v^3), is a laterally compressed cavity, the roof of which is formed by a delicate vascular membrane, the *velum interpositum* (*vl. ip.*), in which there is a network of blood vessels (*choroid plexus* of the diacœle) continuous with the choroid plexuses of the lateral ventricles. From the posterior part of the roof of the diacœle arise the peduncles of the pineal body. Forming the lateral portions of the diencephalon are large masses of mixed grey and white matter, the *thalami* (*o. th.*). Various parts of these bodies are in communication with the cortex and in particular, with the areas concerned with olfactory, visual, auditory, visceral and other functions. The thalamus is probably an important centre of integration and activity and has intimate connexions with the underlying *hypothalamus* (see below) an ancient brain-floor structure concerned with the regulation of fundamental visceral and somatic activities. The thalami are connected by a mass of grey matter, the *middle* or *soft commissure* (*m. co.*) (not represented in lower vertebrates), which passes across the diacœle. A rounded elevation near the anterior end of the external surface of each thalamus is the *corpus geniculatum* (*c. gn.*). The anterior boundary of the diacœle is a thin vertical lamina, the *lamina terminalis*, of which the septum lucidum is a mesial anterior prolongation. Below, the floor of the hypo-thalamus is produced downward into a mesial process, the *tuber cinereum* or *infundibulum* (*inf.*). Down this tract runs a *hypophysial portal system* of vessels connecting the hypothalamus with the *pars distalis* or anterior 'lobe' of the compound pituitary gland (see Fig. 96, p. 150). Anteriorly, on the ventral aspect of the brain, is a thick transverse band of nerve-fibres, the united *optic tracts*, from the anterior border of which the optic nerves are given off. Behind the tuber cinereum, and formed as a thickening of its posterior wall, is a rounded elevation, the *corpus mammillare*.

In the mid-brain (*mesencephalon*) the dorsal part is remarkable for the fact that each *optic lobe* is divided into two by a transverse furrow, so that two pairs of lobes (*o.l¹.*, *o.l².*), the *corpora quadrigemina*, are produced. Between the anterior lobes passes the delicate *posterior commissure* (*p. co.*). On the ventral region of the mid-brain the *crura cerebri* are far more prominent than in the lower vertebrate groups. In the hind-brain (*rhombencephalon*) the *cerebellum* (Fig. 467, *cb'.*, *cb''.*) is large and complex. It is concerned with neuromuscular co-ordination and equilibrium. It consists of a *central lobe* or *vermis* and two *lateral lobes*, divided by very numerous fissures (or *sulci*) into a large number of small convolutions (or *gyri*). Each lateral lobe bears an irre-gularly-shaped prominence, the *flocculus*. On section (Fig. 468, *cb.*) the cere-bellum exhibits a tree-like pattern (*arbor vitæ*) from the arrangement of its white and grey matter. On the ventral aspect of the hind-brain a flat band of transverse fibres, the *pons Varolii*, connects together the lateral parts of the cerebellum. The cerebellum is attached to the other parts of the brain by three pairs of peduncles: the *anterior*, connecting it with the posterior optic lobes, the *middle*, passing on each side into the pons Varolii, and the *posterior*, connecting it with the dorsal portion of the *medulla oblongata*—a brain-stem segment containing ancient centres concerned with fundamental metabolic activities such as respiration and heart-beat.   Between the anterior peduncles extends a transverse band, the *valve of Vieussens* connected by its anterior edge with the corpora quadrigemina.   Behind this is a short tract of transverse fibres, the *corpus trapezoideum*, and behind this again is a slightly elevated area marking the position of the *olivary body*.   The floor of the fourth ventricle presents a median groove which ends posteriorly in a pointed depression, the *calamus scriptorius*, leading into the central canal of the spinal cord.

The Spinal Cord, Cranial, and Spinal Nerves.—As in reptiles and birds, there are twelve pairs of cranial nerves (p. 116) associated with specific cerebral regions, which, emerging through the several cranial foramina, convey afferent and/or efferent fibres to various muscles and sensory organs mainly in the head and neck although the Xth (vagus) and XIth (accessorius) nerves range more widely (p. 133).

The spinal nerves, too, are on much the same pattern as in reptiles and birds.   Each spinal nerve is attached to the cord by a sensory dorsal root and a motor ventral root.   From spinal nerves are given off *dorsal* and *ventral rami* to various tissues and a *ramus communicans* ('white' or *visceral ramus*), which is myelinated and in most cases communicates with a ganglion of the sympathetic nervous system (see below).

The spinal cord in mammals is, like the brain, ensheathed in three meningeal layers and consists of an outer *white* and an inner *grey matter* pierced by a *central canal* which, with ciliated lining, continuous with the brain ventricles, contains freely circulating *cerebrospinal fluid*.   The grey matter is arranged into paired *dorsal* and *ventral columns* which in cross-section appear as *horns* (p. 123).

Autonomic Nervous System.—This term covers two great functional components of the visceral nervous system—the *sympathetic* and *parasympathetic* —which involuntarily control many bodily activities and which are partly independent of the central nervous system.   When both sub-systems innervate a particular organ they usually act antagonistically.   Heart-beat, blood pressure (to a considerable degree), the activity of smooth (unstriated) muscle of numerous organs, secretion of certain endocrine and exocrine glands and many other important activities are partly or wholly under autonomic control.   The co-ordination and control of the majority of such functions are located in special centres in hypothalamus, medulla oblongata, and cord.   The autonomic system can be instantly stimulated to protective or stabilising reactions by environmental stimuli acting through the exteroceptors and the central nervous system, or by proprioceptive stimuli from within the organism.

The control of effector organs (glands, muscles, etc.) is not via single fibres from the central areas of control.   Instead, *preganglionic* fibres emerge from the central nervous system to effect synapses with other distinct nerve cells situated in sympathetic ganglia, the (*postganglionic*) fibres of which transmit impulses to the target-organs (Fig. 82, p. 119).

Sympathetic System (Fig. 82, p. 119).—Prominent chains of *sympathetic ganglia* extend from cervical to sacral regions on each side of the vertebral column. In the thoracic and lumbar regions these receive usually white myelinated *preganglionic* fibres from ventral nerve roots of the nearby cord ('thoracolumbar outflow'). In these ganglia the preganglionic fibres may establish synaptic relationship with cells giving rise to grey, unmyelinated *post-ganglionic fibres*, or they may traverse the ganglia uninterruptedly to synapse in more distant ganglia (*e.g.* cœliac, mesenteric ganglia). In either instance the efferent impulses are effectively transmitted to the relevant organs.

The anterior and posterior ends of each sympathetic chain also present ganglia, but these are not connected with the spinal cord. Like the other ganglia they each give off a grey ramus composed of postganglionic fibres which supply skin, the smooth muscle of blood vessels and other structures. From the large anterior ganglia also arise afferent fibres supplying the eyes, tear-glands, nasal mucosa, and salivary glands.

Sympathetic stimulation causes, among many other effects, increased heart-beat, rise in blood pressure, bronchial dilation, peripheral vascular contraction, sweat-gland activity, pupillary dilation, arrector pili contraction, salivary inhibition, contraction of certain sphincters, splenic contraction (with resultant increased volume of circulating blood), increased blood-sugar content—in short, the animal exhibits symptoms of fear or anger and is made ready for fight or flight. Increased output of *adrenalin*, the hormone from the medulla of the adrenal gland (p. 152), leads to such effects. 'Cold sweats , pallor, 'goose flesh' (and the related erection of hair in fear) are some equivalent phenomena familiar to timid or suddenly startled persons. Sympathetic fibres are *adrenergic* or sometimes (as in sweat-glands) *cholinergic* (see below).

Para-sympathetic System (Fig. 82, p. 119).—Preganglionic fibres of the broadly antagonistic parasympathetic system leave the central nervous system by two distinct routes—(1) in the vagus (Xth) and other (IIIth, VIIth, and IXth) cranial nerves and (2) through ventral spinal roots in the sacral region of the spinal cord ('craniosacral outflow'). The ganglia which receive parasympathetic fibres are situated close to, or even within, the organs supplied, hence their post-ganglionic fibres are short. This system is less extensive than the sympathetic because it does not extend to the skin or the limbs.

Parasympathetic stimulation leads to dilation of blood vessels (except the intrinsic coronary circulation of the heart), heightened salivary secretion, constriction of bronchi, increased peristalsis, sphincter relaxation, and pupillary constriction. In general the above states are relaxative and opposed to those induced by sympathetic stimulation. Parasympathetic fibres are *cholinergic* : their axone terminals secrete *acetylcholine* upon the arrival thereat of neural impulses. The acetylcholine is then quickly destroyed by an enzyme, *cholinesterase*.

Organs of Special Sense.—The more obvious sense-organs, eyes (p. 139), audio-equilibration (p. 143), olfaction (p. 138), taste (p. 137), as well as others (pp. 135, 137), have been mentioned elsewhere.

Urinogenital Organs.—The *kidneys* are of somewhat compressed oval shape, with a notch or *hilum* on the inner side. They are in close contact with the dorsal wall of the abdominal cavity, the right being somewhat in advance of the left. Towards the hilum, the tubules of the kidney converge to open into a wide chamber, the *pelvis*, which forms the dilated commencement of the ureter. When the kidney is cut across, its substance is seen to be divided into a central mass or *medulla* and a peripheral portion or *cortex* (see p. 154). The *ureter* (Fig. 469, *ur.*) runs backwards to open, not into a cloaca, but directly into the

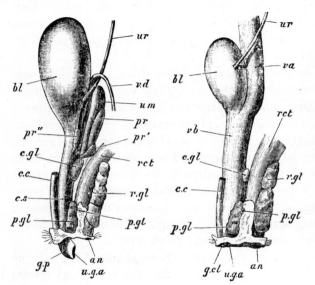

FIG. 469.—*Oryctolagus:* **Urinogenital system.** *Left,* Male; *Right,* Female; from the left side (half nat. size). The kidneys and proximal ends of the ureters, the testes, ovaries, Fallopian tubes and uteri are not shown. *an.* anus; *bl.* urinary bladder; *c. c.* corpus cavernosum; *c. s.* corpus spongiosum; *c. gl.* Cowper's gland; *g. cl.* apex of clitoris; *g. p.* apex of penis; *p. gl.* perineal gland; *p. gl'.* aperture of its duct on the perineal space; *pr.* anterior, *pr'.* posterior, and *pr''.* lateral lobes of prostate; *rct.* rectum; *r. gl.* rectal gland; *u. g. a.* urinogenital aperture; *u. m.* uterus masculinus; *ur.* ureter; *va.* vagina; *vb.* vestibule; *v. d.* vas deferens. (After T. J. Parker.)

urinary bladder (*bl.*). The latter is a pyriform sac with muscular walls which vary in thickness, according as the organ is dilated or contracted. In the male the openings of the ureters are situated nearer the posterior narrower end or neck than in the female. Adjacent to the anterior end of each kidney is a compound *adrenal (suprarenal) gland.*

In the male rabbit the *testes* are oval bodies, which, though in the young animal they occur in the body cavity, later pass backwards and downwards and come to lie each in a *scrotal sac* situated at the side of the urinogenital opening. The cavity of each scrotal sac is in free communication with the cavity of the abdomen by an opening—the *inguinal canal.* The testes each contain long, convoluted *seminiferous tubules* which elaborate *spermatozoa* and between the tubules lies an interstitium formed of *Leydig* cells which produce *testosterone,* the male sex hormone (see p. 152). The sperms are carried by a convoluted *epididymis*, closely adherent to the testis, which forms the proximal part of the *vas deferens*. The *vasa deferentia* (*v. d.*) terminate by opening into a urinogenital canal, or *urethra*, into which the neck of the urinary bladder is continued. A *prostate gland* (*pr.*), which contributes to the bulk of the seminal fluid, and which is influenced in its secretion by the male sex hormone, surrounds the commencement of the urethra, the neck of the bladder, and the terminal parts of the vasa deferentia. A dorsal diverticulum of the urethra, the *uterus masculinus* (*u. m.*), lies embedded in the prostate gland close to the neck of the bladder. A small pair of ovoid *Cowper's glands* (*c. gl.*), lie just behind the prostate close to the side of the urethra. These, sometimes called the *bulbo-urethral* glands, secrete a clear alkaline fluid which may neutralise urinary residues and, in addition, vaginal acidity.

The terminal part of the urethra traverses a cord of vascular tissue, the *corpus spongiosum* (*c. s.*), which forms the dorsal portion of the penis. The greater part of the penis is formed of two closely approximated firm cords of vascular tissue, the *corpora cavernosa* (*c. c.*). These are attached proximally to the ischia, and terminate in a pointed apex (*g. p.*). A loose fold of skin, the *prepuce*, encloses the penis. A pair of glands with an odorous secretion, the *perinæal glands* (*p. gl.*), open on the perinæal space at the base

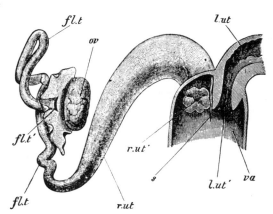

FIG. 470.—*Oryctolagus*: **Internal genitalia of female.** The anterior end of the vagina, with the right uterus, Fallopian tube and ovary (nat. size). Part of the ventral wall of the vagina is removed, and the proximal end of the left uterus is shown in longitudinal section. *fl. t.* Fallopian tube; *fl. t'.* its peritoneal aperture; *l. ut.* left uterus; *l. ut'.* left os uteri; *ov.* right ovary; *r. ut.* right uterus; *r. ut'.* right os uteri; *s.* vaginal septum; *va.* vagina. (After T. J. Parker.)

of the penis. Two other glands, the *rectal glands* (*r. gl.*), lie on either side of the rectum.

In the female the *ovaries* (Fig. 470 *ov.*) are small ovoid bodies attached to the dorsal wall of the abdomen behind the kidneys. These produce female sex hormones (*œstrogens*) and ova. The *Graafian follicles* enclosing the ova form extremely small rounded projections on their outer surface.

The eggs are shed into the abdominal cavity and enter the wide funnel-shaped openings ((*fl. t'.*), with fimbriated or fringed margins) of the paired *oviducts* or *Fallopian tubes* (*fl. t.*). Posteriorly each tube passes into a thick-walled *uterus* (*r. ut.*). The two uteri open separately into a median tube, the *vagina* (*va.*). The *vestibule* (Fig. 469 B, *vb.*), or *urinogenital canal*, is a wide median passage, into which the vagina and the bladder open. On its ventral wall is a small, hard, rod-like body, the *clitoris* (*c. c.*), with a pointed apex (*g. cl.*), corresponding to the penis of the male, and composed of two very short *corpora cavernosa* attached anteriorly to the ischia, and invested internally by a soft, grooved *corpus spongiosum*. The *vulva*, or external opening of the vestibule, is bounded laterally by two prominent folds—the *labia majora*.

Development.—The Rabbit is viviparous. After the minute ovum has escaped from its Graafian follicle it passes into the Fallopian tube, where it may become fertilised by one of the approximately 70 million spermatozoa produced at each ejaculation. (In the ram the number varies from 300 to 450 million, but there is great reduction after successive copulations.)

The fertilised egg undergoes cleavage to become a *morula* and reaches the uterus. In the endometrium *nidation* takes place and, now a *blastocyst*, it becomes a *fœtus*, or intra-uterine embryo. The young animal escapes from the uterus in a condition in which all the parts have become fully formed, except that the eyelids are closed and the hairy covering is not yet completed. As many as eight or ten young are produced at a birth, and the period of gestation, *i.e.* the time elapsing between the fertilisation of the ovum and the birth of the young animal, is thirty days. Fresh broods may be born once a month throughout a considerable part of the year, and the young rabbit may begin breeding at the age of three months.

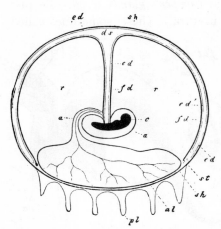

FIG. 471.—*Oryctolagus:* **Placentation.** Diagrammatic longitudinal section of embryo at an advanced stage of pregnancy. *a.* amnion; *a.* stalk of allantois; *al.* allantois with blood vessels; *c.* embryo; *ds.* cavity of yolk-sac (umbilical vesicle); *ed.* endodermal layer of yolk-sac; *ed'.* inner portion of endoderm; *ed''.* outer portion of endoderm lining the compressed cavity of the yolk-sac; *fd.* vascular layer of yolk-sac; *pl.* placental villi; *r.* space filled with fluid between the amnion, the allantois, and the yolk-sac; *sh.* subzonal membrane; *st.* sinus terminalis. (From Foster and Balfour, after Bischoff.)

Segmentation is of the holoblastic type. An amnion and an allantois are developed much as in the case of birds (p. 646). But the later history of these fœtal membranes is widely different in the Rabbit owing to the modifications which they undergo in order to take part in the formation of the *placenta*. Through the placenta (see p. 904) the fœtus receives its nourishment from the maternal circulation. The placenta is formed from the *serous membrane* or *chorion* in a limited disc-shaped area, in which the distal portion of the allantois coalesces with it (Fig. 471). The membrane thus formed develops vascular processes, the *chorionic villi*, which are received into depressions (the *uterine crypts*) in the mucous membrane of the uterus. The completed placenta with its villi is supplied with blood by the allantoic vessels. The placenta of the Rabbit is of the type termed *deciduate*, the villi of the placenta being intimately united with the uterine mucous membrane, and a part of the latter coming away with it at birth in the form of a *decidua*, or after-birth.

SUB-CLASS PROTOTHERIA (MONOTREMATA)

INTRODUCTION

It now appears to be reasonably certain that the Jurassic Triconodonta are ancestral to the extant prototherians or that the latter are derived from closely related unknown forms. From the early Cretaceous (triconodonts) to the Pleistocene (monotremes) nothing is known of the history of the group.

ORDER TRICONODONTA

Of the known groups of mammals, the Triconodonta are probably the most primitive. In the past they have been variously claimed to be monotremes, marsupials or to belong to an order with no close relationship to either. They are almost certainly prototherians. They (e.g. *Triconodon, Priacodon* (Fig. 472) *Amphilestes*) are found in deposits ranging from the Upper Trias to the Lower Cretaceous. They were probably carnivorous and ranged in size from a small shrew to a cat. The brain was small and probably primitive. Like the monotremes, but unlike all other mammals (and mammal-like reptiles), the lateral wall of the brain-case anterior to the ear is formed not by the alisphenoid but by the extension of the petrosal. There were three or four incisors in each jaw, well-developed canines,

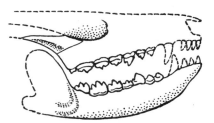

FIG. 472.—Sub-class **Prototheria,** Order **Triconodonta,** Family **Triconodontidæ.** *Priacodon.* These small creatures lived in North America during the Upper Jurassic and were perhaps the most primitive mammals yet known. The above restoration is about twice natural size. (Redrawn after Simpson.)

and up to nine cheek-teeth which cannot be separated into premolars and molars. The molar pattern was distinctive, with the three principal cusps arranged in an antero-posterior line.

Recent discoveries in South Wales (Kermack *et al*) have led to the collection of rich material of a triconodont related to *Morganucodon*. This makes available for the first time the almost complete osteological material of a Mesozoic mammal.

ORDER SYMMETRODONTA

This group (e.g. *Spalacotherium, Peralestes*) ranged from the beginning of the Jurassic to the Middle Cretaceous and is not unquestionably prototherian (see p. 654). Only jaws and teeth have been discovered. The molar teeth were triangular, the base of the triangle being on the inner (lingual) side in the lower jaw and on the outer (buccal) side in the upper jaw. The highest cusp was placed at the apex of the triangle, buccally in the lower jaw and lingually in the upper jaw. Cutting crests from the main cusp formed the anterior and posterior edges of the triangle. As the jaws closed, the triangular teeth formed an interlocking arrangement suited to the mastication of insects. The lower molars may be compared with the trigonids of trituberculo-sectorial teeth (p. 865), but there is no trace of a talonid. The lower jaw was without an angular process.

ORDER MONOTREMATA

The Platypus (Fig. 473) and the two echidnas (Fig. 474) are the only surviving prototherians. Their anatomy leaves no doubt of their great antiquity. The two families, the Ornithorhynchidæ and Tachyglossidæ, differ widely from each other in external appearance, and in relatively minor anatomical characters but they are bound together as a single order by the common possession of several deep-seated characters found in no other mammals.

Thus, while such essentially mammalian characters as milk-glands, hair, complete diaphragm, four cerebral optic lobes, etc., are all present, certain of their features indicate a wide cleft between them and all other mammals. Thus the monotremes lay eggs : there is no uterine gestation. The urinogenital organs are still not far from the reptilian condition (p. 482) : the erectile penis is composed of a corpus spongiosum, a corpus fibrosum, and bears a groove transmitting spermatozoa, but not urine. This last enters the cloaca through a special urinary canal (Fig. 488, p. 701). In the skeleton the shoulder-girdle not only retains well-developed coracoids (reduced to vestiges in other mammals) but also an interclavicle (Fig. 484). Though milk is produced, the mammary glands remain unspecialised, and devoid of nipples. The pouch which carries the eggs in the Tachyglossidæ is temporary.

The vertebræ are without epiphyses except in the tail region of *Ornithorhynchus*. The mode of exit of the spinal nerves—in the middle of the vertebra, instead of between adjacent vertebræ—is peculiar. The cervical vertebræ bear free ribs. The limbs are specialised for rapid swimming or digging.

The skull, though very different in shape in the two families, is in each constituted on the same general plan. The chondrocranium is typically mammalian, but differs in some respects from that of other mammals, *e.g.* in the absence of an alisphenoid bone and in the presence of a bone additional to the usual mammalian pterygoid (known as the '*Echidna pterygoid*') which homologises with the reptilian ectopterygoid.

The above brief osteological and physiological details make it seem that, although pre-Pleistocene monotreme fossils are still unknown, these and the triconodonts are extremely archaic mammals that have diverged from the main stock (if they do not represent a separate stem altogether) perhaps even before any of the Upper Jurassic mammals next to be described. Granting that the extant monotremes have become highly specialised in many of their features, their possession of such typically mammalian characters as milk-glands (probably derived from sweat-glands as in other mammals), hair (but only imperfect thermoregulation), and a large brain with a well-developed pallium (and convolutions in echidnas) carries the suggestion that such characters are

FIG. 473.—Sub-class **Prototheria**, Order **Monotremata**, Family **Ornithorhynchidæ**. *Ornitho-rhynchus*. The Platypus (*O. anatinus*) is one of the three species of living monotremes that are today confined to Australia and New Guinea. The Platypus lives in secluded fresh-water streams of Eastern Australia and Tasmania. Each pair digs two twisting burrows, each of which has two entrances (above the water-line) and may be from 20 to 50 feet long. Within one is built an incubating nest made of grass and leaves. While submerged the animal swims blind (see text and Fig. 475). (From photographs.)

primitive features of early mammals (see Figs. 643, 644, p. 886). Their presence in the monotremes leads particularly to speculation concerning the possible degree to which synapsid reptiles may have progressed towards lactation and homœothermy, and to speculation, moreover, that the monotremes represent an independent 'warm-blooded' line, derived from Triassic cynodonts (p. 517). It has also been suggested by Gregory that the monotremes are derived from archaic marsupial or pre-marsupial stock and that their peculiarities therefore, are essentially due to degeneration, neoteny, and specialisation, plus the retention of certain marsupialian characters.

The traditional, and probably correct view is that they derive from an early stock on the principal mammalian line of descent.

Today the Monotremata are confined to Australia and directly adjacent New Guinea. The Platypus[1] (*Ornithorhynchus anatinus*) (Fig. 473), the sole species of the genus and family, ranges widely from tropical Queensland along the east Australian seaboard to Tasmania where it lives in the pools of secluded

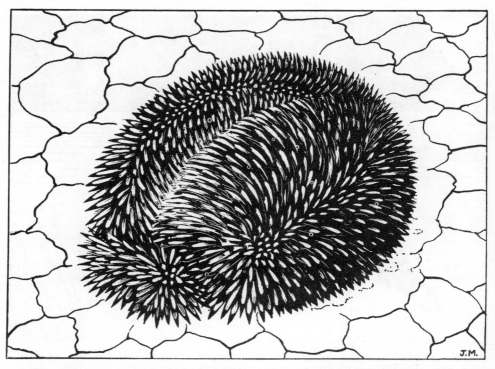

FIG. 474.—Sub-class **Prototheria**, Order **Monotremata**, Family **Tachyglossidæ.** *Tachyglossus.* Spiny Anteater (*T. aculeatus*). When the echidna is threatened its spatulate claws (Fig. 483) enable it to sink vertically and rapidly out of sight with a minimum of disturbance to the surrounding soil. A defensive echidna presents an unassailable bilateral barrier of spines that wholly conceals rostrum (Fig. 482) and legs. The short (half an inch long) tail is protected by a terminal tuft of spines. Even in rocky country, where burrowing is impeded, the claws and lateral spines engage the earth and make dislodgement almost impossible. *T. aculeatus* has a wide continental range: the illustration is from a photograph taken on a parched Queensland plain. *Zaglossus* (= *Proechidna*) is confined to New Guinea.

streams and rivers. Both it and *Tachyglossus* have been reported to undergo a limited hibernation (p. 883). In monotremes heat regulation is imperfect though of course far advanced over that of living reptiles. The temperature of *Tachyglossus* falls to 25° C. under an external temperature of 5° C., a condi-

---

[1] Outside Australia the 19th-century terms 'Duck-billed Platypus' or even 'Duckbill' are often used. Such names are undesirable. The muzzle of the Platypus bears only the most superficial convergent resemblance to the bill of a duck, and the avian appellation lends currency to the popular belief that the animal is a sort of non-missing link between birds and mammals.

tion frequently experienced in some parts of its range. In the absence of sweat-glands, panting mechanism (p. 708) or heat-reduction by vasodilation, the temperature of *Tachyglossus* rises with that of the environment above 30° C.: the animal dies of heat-stroke at about 37° C. if unable to cool itself by burrowing. The platypus has few sweat-glands but it lives mostly in the water or in a cool burrow and does not encounter the heat-hazards faced by spiny anteaters.

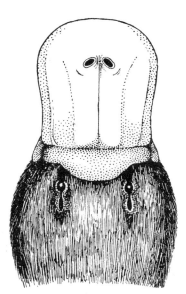

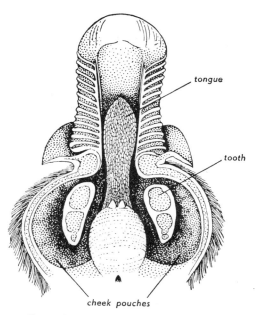

FIG. 475.—*Ornithorhynchus* : **Cephalic structures.** Like *Tachyglossus* (Fig. 482) the Platypus lacks vibrissae but its delicate flattened muzzle contains minute sensory pores. The muzzle extends backwards protectively over the face. The deeply set eyes and ears open into a facial furrow that is closed during submersion (Fig. 473); the animal hunts essentially by smell and touch. (Redrawn after Wood Jones.)

FIG. 476.—*Ornithorhynchus* : **Buccal apparatus.** The lower jaw has been exposed by cutting through the cheeks. Three pairs of teeth are fused together into a calcified mass. They have been largely replaced by horny material but in some specimens calcification remains evident. The cheek-pouches hold food gathered under water. The whole beak is a sense organ, for the animal swims with its eyes and ears enclosed in pouches (Fig. 475). (Redrawn after Wood Jones.)

The body of *Ornithorhynchus* is flattened and covered with a dense, soft under-fur protected by harsher outer fur. The upper jaw is produced into a depressed beak-like muzzle covered with soft, but tough skin (Fig. 475). In life the muzzle is moist and flexible and quite unlike the dry horny bill of a bird. The organ is pitted with tactile organs and bears also the nostrils. Nostrils and eyes face upwards. While feeding below the surface, both the small eyes and the ears (which lack pinnæ) are enclosed within a curious backward-directed facial-furrow. The inner ear remains primitive. The Platypus appears to find its way, and its prey, chiefly by olfaction and touch. Animal food, along with mud and sand, is sieved into the buccal cavity between serrations in the lower lips—an interesting convergence with the beaks of certain ducks and other animals. The sand assists in mastication, and the animal possesses storage cheek-pouches (Fig. 476).

The forelegs are short but powerful. The five digits end in strong claws which are set in a web which joins them together and then projects below and beyond the nails. This flap can be folded back so that the limb can be used for walking, digging, or swimming. The hind limb is less specialised. The proximal end of the fibula is prolonged in a manner analogous to the olecranon

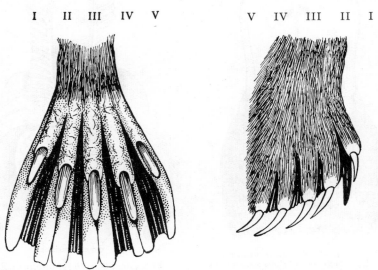

I   II III   IV V   V   IV III II   I

FIG. 477.—*Ornithorhynchus:* **Manus and pes:** *Left:* Left hand, from dorsal surface. The swim-webbing is carried beyond the extremities of the nails in a series of leathery extensions prolonging the line of the digits. The whole can be folded back to expose the tips of the burrowing (and defensive) claws. *Right:* Right foot, from dorsal surface. Beneath the first digit is a curious prolongation of the web membrane. This has nothing to do with the poison spur which is on the ankle (Fig. 478). (Redrawn after Wood Jones.)

process of the ulna, and in the male a hollow tarsal spur is connected with a small crural gland, the secretion of which is poisonous. In *Ornithorhynchus* this gland is well-developed: although not dangerous to Man its protein, including albuminous, secretion, can kill an experimental rabbit in 90 seconds. In *Tachyglossus* the apparatus is less developed (Figs. 478, 483). The tail is elongated, depressed, and is a powerful swimming-organ (Fig. 473).

Although the Platypus undergoes a courtship performance, and copulates in the water, it is in fact much less aquatic than is generally supposed. It spends most of its life in its burrow, and relatively few hours, generally in early morning and near dusk, in search of aquatic food. It spends considerable time performing its toilet beneath overhanging roots and rocks at the water's edge.

Two burrows are made and each has its concealed entrance above the water. One is inhabited by the pair ; the other, between 15 and 60 feet long, is the female's nesting chamber. This the brooding female blocks at intervals with barriers of earth moulded by the flat tail. The nest is made of grass, leaves or reeds and during the approximately 14 days' incubation of the two eggs, which tend to stick together (Fig. 479), the female does not leave the nesting chamber. When the burrow is broached, she makes no attempt to defend her young. The female is devoid of nipples—the milk exudes through relatively simple ducts and is licked up by the young (Fig. 480). Unlike *Tachyglossus*, the Platypus has a distinct voice—both growlings and whistling notes have been described from adults.

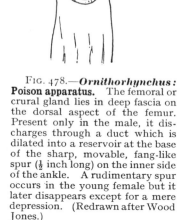

FIG. 478.—*Ornithorhynchus :* **Poison apparatus.** The femoral or crural gland lies in deep fascia on the dorsal aspect of the femur. Present only in the male, it discharges through a duct which is dilated into a reservoir at the base of the sharp, movable, fang-like spur ($\frac{1}{2}$ inch long) on the inner side of the ankle. A rudimentary spur occurs in the young female but it later disappears except for a mere depression. (Redrawn after Wood Jones.)

The teeth are remarkable (Figs. 476, 481). In the embryo calcified teeth arise in each half of the upper and lower jaws. They are very brittle, clearly degenerate, and are soon shed and replaced by underlying horny plates, in depressions of which the teeth were originally set. The teeth show some rather irregular tubercles arranged in a pattern that gave rise to a view that the Prototheria are descended from, or distantly related to, the Multituberculata. This view cannot be upheld on such evidence.

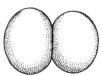

FIG. 479.—*Ornithorhynchus :* **Eggs.** About natural size. They are frequently superficially conjoined, and are of slightly variable size. Two, sometimes three, are laid. They are dirty white in colour and the largely keratinous shell can be dented like those of many reptiles. The egg-cell is about 6 mm. in diameter: some 30 times its size in Man. (Redrawn after Wood Jones.)

The dental formula is peculiar (Fig. 481). There appear to be no upper incisors formed, but there are five in the lower jaw. A canine is present in both jaws. The lower canine is followed by a problematic calcification which it is suggested is a second canine. The rest of the series consists of two premolars, of which the anterior is replaced, and three molars in both jaws. These teeth are not present together at any one time and most of them are non-functional and abort as mere calcifications. At 11 weeks old there remain only two teeth in the upper, and three in the lower, jaw.

All known fossils are Pleistocene in age and have been found only in Australia. The Platypus survived because of its highly secretive and specialised breeding- and feeding-habits, and because it possesses few natural enemies apart from pythons and goannas (*Varanus*).   It was still plentiful when Europeans arrived

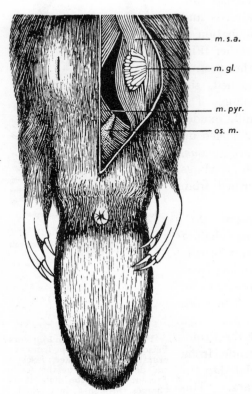

but rapidly became scarce because of the warmth and beauty of its fur. It is now rigidly protected and, al- though rare, can be seen in secluded streams a short distance from popu- lous cities.

The spiny ant-eaters (Tachy- glossidæ = Echidnidæ) (Figs. 474, 482) are represented by two closely allied genera *Zaglossus* (= *Proechid- na*), of New Guinea, and *Tachyglossus* (= *Echidna*), which ranges from New Guinea to Tasmania. These animals are land-living, insect-eat- ing burrowers of astonishing ability although they do not make tunnels. The body is covered above with strong pointed spines, between which are coarse hairs.   The lower surface of the body has hair only.   The weak jaws are produced into a sensitive pointed rostrum.   The long, sticky tongue is thrust through a buccal aperture on the ventral surface, and near the termination, of the muzzle and to this insects—mostly ants— adhere together with dirt which helps in mastication.   Teeth are absent in all stages of development.   The posterior aspect of the tongue is beset with horny serrations which grind the food against corresponding ridges on the palate.   Large submaxillary, parotid and sublingual glands are present, the secretions of which no doubt help neutralise formic acid discharged by their prey.

Fig.   480.—*Ornithorhynchus:* **Mammary glands, cloaca, and tail.**   The mammary glands are extremely simple: the young lick the milk from shallow longitudinal depressions.   The cloaca, into which discharge the rectum and the urinogenital sinus (Fig. 487), recalls the reptilian condition (Fig. 488A).   The body wall is reflected to show the *musculus subcutaneus abdominis*, mammary gland, *musculus pyramidalis* and *os marsupium* (marsupial   bone).   (Redrawn   after   various authors.)

The nasal passages open on the dorsal surface of the rostrum.   It would seem that along with its tactile muzzle, the animal is largely dependent on olfaction ; its repeated inspiratory 'sniffs' are a noticeable feature and variants of these, in the apparent absence of a true voice, may be used in communication. Like *Ornithorhynchus*, the eyes are small and the ears without a pinna. The tail is vestigial. The limbs are short and the feet provided with strong spade-like claws (Fig. 483). With these the spiny ant-eaters are able to burrow rapidly

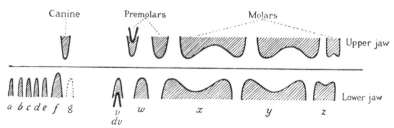

FIG. 481.—*Ornithorhynchus*: **Dentition.** The absence of upper incisors and the presence of an upper and lower replacing tooth should be noticed. *a—e* lower incisors; *f.* lower canine; *g.* ? second canine; *vw.* premolars; *dv.* replacing tooth; *x. y. z.* molars. (After Green.)

in a vertical direction, presenting to the attacker only its formidable armoury of stiff, sharp spines (Fig. 474). Once it begins to sink into the earth it is almost impossible to dislodge it alive. The second pedal digit is equipped with an elongated toilet-claw—an adaptation to the cleansing of its body—hair and armoury (Fig. 483).

FIG. 482.—*Tachyglossus*: **Cephalic structures.** The small ventral buccal aperture is just big enough for the protrusion of the sticky tongue to which insects adhere. The face is covered with bristle-like hair mixed with finer structures. Sometimes there is developed the suggestion of a pinna. The nostrils are dorsal. Nearly ¾ natural size. (Redrawn after Wood Jones.)

Oviposition in the spiny ant-eaters has not been observed. However, the female is able to curve her body sufficiently to lay the single egg directly into a ventral pouch (*incubatorium*) which develops during the sexual season. Here the egg hatches. The baby is fed by milk (from ducts which open into the pouch) until its spines become troublesome to the mother. It is then about 10 cm. long. This habit of carrying the egg, and carrying and feeding the young one in the pouch, together with the remarkable protection afforded by spines and special burrowing habit, has been a principal factor in the animal's survival. Today it is rigidly protected in Australia and is not rare in appropriate and very extensive habitats. As with the Platypus, fossils are known only from the Australian Pleistocene.

Skeleton of Prototheria.—In the Prototheria (Fig. 484) the epiphyses of the vertebræ are not well developed in *Ornithorhynchus*, being represented only in the caudal region, and they appear to be absent in *Tachyglossus*. In both genera there is the normal number of vertebræ in the cervical region. The odontoid process long remains separate from the centrum of the axis. The cervical transverse processes are separately ossified, and only completely unite with the vertebræ at a late period, sutures being traceable in all but very old animals. Zygapophyses are absent in the cervical region. There are

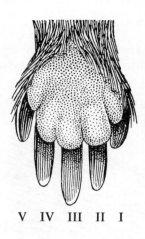

V IV III II I

I IV V

FIG. 483.—*Tachyglossus:* **Manus and pes.** *Left:* Left hand (of female) showing the spatulate claws adapted for rapid digging (Fig. 474). *Right:* Right foot (of male). The second pedal digit in both sexes becomes a curved elongated toilet-claw which enables the animals to scratch deep through hair and spines. The arrow indicates the poison spur which is lower down the leg than in the male Platypus (Fig. 478). It is relatively small and supplied by a pea-sized gland. (Partly after Wood Jones.)

nineteen thoraco-lumbar vertebræ in both genera. The transverse processes are short, and the ribs do not articulate with them, but only with the sides of the vertebral bodies. In the sacrum of *Tachyglossus* there are three or four, in that of *Ornithorhynchus* two, united vertebræ. The caudal region differs considerably in its development in the two genera. In *Tachyglossus* the tail is very short, the vertebræ depressed, with no inferior spines, but with about five subvertebral bones, which differ from ordinary chevron bones in being mere flat nodules. In *Ornithorhynchus* the tail is long, and the number of caudal vertebræ is twenty or twenty-one. Each has a distinct inferior spinous process (*infr. proc.*). The sternum consists of a presternum and three keeled sternebræ : in *Tachyglossus* but not in *Ornithorhynchus* there is a xiphisternum. The most remarkable feature of the sternal apparatus in the Prototheria is the presence of a T-shaped *interclavicle* (*epist.*) corresponding to that of reptiles. The sternal ribs are ossified, and are connected with the vertebral ribs by imperfectly ossified intermediate ribs (*int. rbs.*).

FIG. 484.—***Ornithorhynchus*:
Endoskeleton.** Male in ventral
view. The right fore-limb has
been separated and turned
round so as to bring into view
the dorsal surface of the manus;
the lower jaw is removed. *acc.
tars.* accessory tarsal bone supporting the spur; *ant. pal. for.*
anterior palatine foramen; *atl.*
atlas; *ast.* astragalus; *ax.* axis;
bs. oc. basi-occipital; *bs. sph.*
basisphenoid; *calc.* calcaneum;
cbd. cuboid; *cerv. rb.* cervical
rib; *clav.* clavicle; *cond. for.*
foramen above inner condyle
of humerus; *cor.* coracoid; *cun.*
cuneiform of carpus; *dent.* position of horny teeth; *ect. cun.*
ecto-cuneiform; *ent. cun.* ento-
cuneiform; *ep. cor.* epicoracoid; *epist.* interclavicle; *ep.
pb.* epipubis; *fb.* fibula; *fem.*
femur; *for. mag.* foramen magnum; *glen.* glenoid cavity of
shoulder-joint and glenoid
cavity for mandible; *hum.*
humerus; *in. cond.* inner condyle of humerus; *inf. orb. for.*
points to position of infra-
orbital foramen; *infr. proc.*
inferior processes of caudal
vertebræ; *int. rbs.* intermediate
ribs; *isch.* ischium; *mag.* magnum of carpus; *max.* maxilla;
max. for. maxillary foramen;
metat. I, first metatarsal;
metat. V, fifth metatarsal; *nas.
cart.* nasal cartilage; *obt.* obturator foramen; *ol.* olecranon;
out. cond. outer condyle of
humerus; *pal.* palatine; *pat.*
patella; *post. pal. for.* posterior
palatine foramen; *pr. max.* premaxilla; *pr. st.* presternum;
pter. pterygoid; *pub.* pubis;
rad. radius; *scap.* scapula;
scaph. scaphoid of tarsus;
scaph. lun. scapho-lunar; *ses.*
sesamoid bones of wrist and
ankle; *sp.* tarsal horny spur;
sq. squamosal; *tib.* tibia; *trd.*
trapezoid; *trm.* trapezium;
tym. c. tympanic cavity; *uln.*
ulna; *unc.* unciform; *vom.*
vomer; *x,* dumb-bell shaped
bone; *zyg.* zygomatic arch;
I—V, digits of manus.

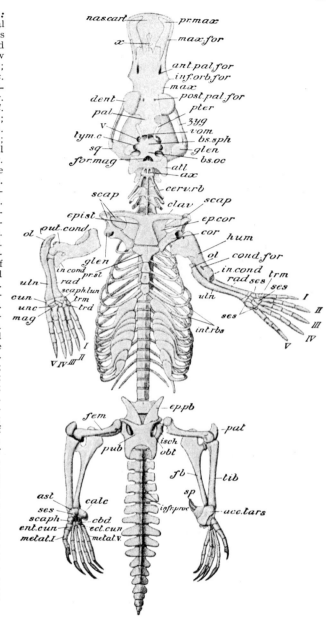

The *skull* of the monotremes differs widely from that of other mammals.
The bones early become fused together, so that it is difficult to trace their exact
boundaries. The brain-case is larger and much more rounded in *Tachyglossus*
than in *Ornithorhynchus*, in accordance with the larger size of the brain in the
former genus. In both genera there is a pterygoid (investing) bone not separ-

ately represented in higher mammals, corresponding to the pterygoid of lower vertebrates. The parasphenoid represents the lateral parts of the parasphenoid of lower vertebrates and the inner lamella of the pterygoid process (usually regarded as the pterygoid) of higher mammals. Perforating the posterior root of the zygomatic arch is a *temporal canal* which is comparatively wide in the

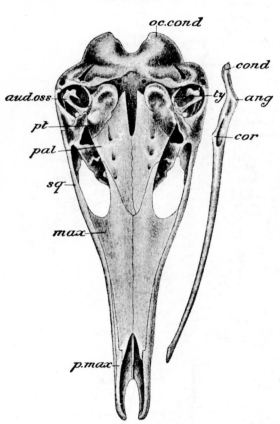

full-grown *Ornithorhynchus* and narrow in *Tachyglossus*. This structure is absent in higher mammals, and apparently represents the post-temporal fossa of reptiles.

In *Tachyglossus* (Fig. 485) the squamosal extends farther forwards and the posterior root of the zygomatic arch is more anterior than in mammals in general. The zygoma is very narrow, and there is no rudiment of postorbital processes : the jugal is absent as a separate ossification. The alveolar border of the maxilla (*max.*) is narrow and devoid of teeth. The nasal and premaxillary region of the skull is drawn out into a long, narrow rostrum. Near the anterior end of this is a rounded opening, the external nasal opening, which is entirely bounded by the premaxillæ—the nasals not extending so far forwards. An aperture in the nasal septum corresponds to an actual perforation by which the nasal cavities are in direct communication in the living animal. The pterygoids (*pt.*) are in the form of flat plates continuous with the bony palate ;

FIG. 485.—*Tachyglossus:* **Skull.** Ventral view, with right ramus of mandible. *ang.* angle of mandible; *aud. oss.* auditory ossicles; *cond.* condyle of mandible; *cor.* coronoid process; *max.* maxilla; *oc. cond.* occipital condyle; *pal.* palatine; *p.max.* premaxilla; *pt.* pterygoid; *sq.* squamosal; *ty.* tympanic ring.

they extend back so as to form a part of the walls of the tympanic cavities. The tympanic (*ty.*) is an imperfect ring which does not become united with the periotic. The mandible consists of very narrow styliform rami, loosely united at the symphysis. The condyle (*cond.*) is narrow, rather more elongated antero-posteriorly than transversely. There are very slight rudiments of the angle and of the coronoid process (*cor.*).

In *Ornithorhynchus* (Fig. 484) the zygoma is stouter than in *Tachyglossus*, and there is a postorbital process, formed by the jugal. The maxillary root of the zygoma develops a process which supports the horny tooth (*dent.*) of the upper jaw. The nasal and premaxillary are expanded into a rostrum which is much broader than in *Tachyglossus*. The premaxillæ (*pr. max.*) diverge from one another anteriorly, and then curve inwards again, partly enclosing a large space in which the nostrils are situated, and which is covered over in the recent state by the tough but sensitive hairless integument investing the cartilage of the rostrum, the latter being continuous with the nasal septum. In this space between the premaxillæ is situated a dumb-bell shaped bone (*x.*) which arises from palatal processes of the premaxilla. The pterygoid (*pter.*) is much smaller than in *Tachyglossus*, and does not extend as far back as the tympanic cavity. The mandible has its rami stouter than in *Tachyglossus*; they meet for a short distance anteriorly, and then again diverge slightly. The condyle is much larger than in *Tachyglossus*, and is transversely elongate. In front of it is a broad process bearing the horny tooth.

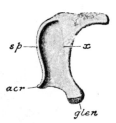

FIG. 486.—*Ornithorhynchus : Scapula.* Outer surface of left element. *acr.* process corresponding to acromion; *glen.* glenoid articular surface; *sp.* anterior border, corresponding to the spine; *x*, slight ridge which bounds the surface of origin of the sub-scapularis muscle anteriorly.

In the shoulder-girdle occur perhaps the most striking peculiarities of the prototherian skeleton. There is a T-shaped interclavicle (*epist.*), as already stated, similar to that of reptiles, the median limb articulating behind with the presternum and the cross-piece closely applied to the clavicles. There are two short and broad coracoids (*cor.*) (Fig. 484, p. 697). These articulate internally and behind with the presternum, and, externally, unite with the scapula to form the glenoid cavity. In front of the coracoid is a flat plate, the epicoracoid (*ep. cor.*). The scapula (Fig. 486) is unlike that of other mammals. It has a well-developed acromion process (*acr.*) with which the clavicle articulates and which terminates the anterior border, so that the latter would appear to correspond to the scapular spine of other mammals, an interpretation confirmed by the arrangement of the scapular muscles. The anterior part of the inner surface is in reality the pre-spinous fossa, the anterior portion of the outer surface is the post-spinous fossa and the part behind this, separated from it by a slight ridge, together with the posterior portion of the inner surface, is the sub-scapular fossa.

The humerus is of remarkable shape, with greatly expanded extremities (especially in *Tachyglossus*) and prominent tuberosities and condyles. In the carpus the scaphoid and lunar are united ; there is no separate centrale. There are a radial and two very large palmar sesamoids, which are sometimes united.

The pelvis presents a very long symphysis in which pubes and ischia take an almost equal share.   The acetabulum is perforated in *Tachyglossus*.   With the anterior border of the pubes are articulated a pair of large epipubic or 'marsupial' bones (Fig. 484, *ep. pb.*).   The femur has expanded extremities with prominent external and internal trochanters. There is a large ossified patella (*pat.*).   The fibula (*fb.*) has at its proximal end a remarkable compressed process which ossifies from a separate centre, and resembles the olecranon of the ulna.   In the tarsus there are the usual bones. In *Ornithorhynchus* the astragalus and calcaneum are firmly united, and an accessory ossification (*acc. tars.*) on the inner side in the male bears the tarsal spur.   The metatarsals are short and broad, as are all the phalanges except the last.

Visceral Anatomy.—The stomach of monotremes is almost globular.   Small and large intestines are differentiated and there occurs a cæcum of modest size. The large intestine enters the cloaca some distance posterior to the ureters and vasa deferentia (p. 488). The liver is large and prominent and there is a gall-bladder.   The bile-duct (in echidnas) traverses the pancreas (lying in the loop of the small intestine), where it is joined by a short pancreatic duct. There is a capacious spleen.   The lungs of the echidnas have been considered somewhat small in proportion to total body size.   The heart of monotremes is peculiar in that the tricuspid guards the *left* auriculo-ventricular aperture (cf. p. 671). The kidneys are large, and the ureters do not empty directly into the bladder

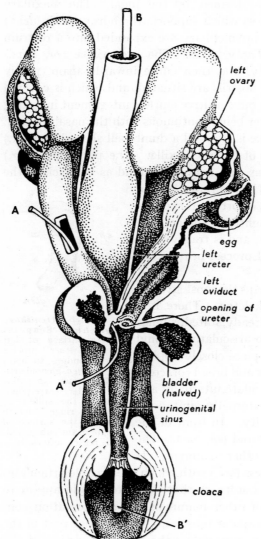

FIG. 487.—***Tachyglossus*: Female urinogenital system.** The echidna has been opened from the ventral surface. The bladder has been sectioned and the parts reflected to demonstrate its relationships. A bristle (A) shows the connexion between the right oviduct and the median urinogenital sinus. A rod (B) is passed through the intestine and its aperture into the cloaca. (Modified after Wood Jones.)

Figure labels: B, left ovary, A, egg, left ureter, left oviduct, opening of ureter, A', bladder (halved), urinogenital sinus, cloaca, B' but open into the urethra through a common aperture surmounted by a papilla (Fig. 487). The urine flows through a short *urinary* canal into the large urinogenital sinus: it does not, therefore, traverse the penis which carries only spermatozoa (Fig. 488). The glans is divided into four lobes and lies on the floor of the cloaca. The testes lie in depressions in the body wall. The urinogenital arrangements in female monotremes are shown in Fig. 487. To some extent the *adrenal* arrangement recalls that of the Reptilia: there is some

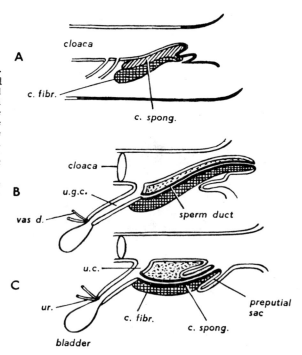

FIG. 488.—**Reptilian and monotreme affinities: Male urinogenital system.** The cloacal and penial arrangements of a chelonian (A) and monotreme (B, C) compared. The basic plan is the same, but in the monotremes spermatozoa from the vas deferens (*vas. d.*) are discharged through the urinogenital canal (*u.g.c.*) (see Fig. 487, A′) into a *sperm-duct* that traverses the penis. The urine, on the other hand, flows from the ureter (*ur.*) through the urinary canal (*u. c.*) and is discharged from the cloaca as in reptiles and birds. In B. the penis is erect; in C. withdrawn. For remarks on the corpus fibrosum (*c. fibr.*) and corpus spongiosum (*c. spong.*) see p. 890. (Modified after Ihle.)

intermingling of cortical and medullary tissues. There is however, an unmistakable aggregation of the two tissues towards the definite cortical and medullary zones that have become stabilised in the Metatheria and Eutheria.

SUB-CLASS ALLOTHERIA

INTRODUCTION

Under this sub-class is provisionally included the order Multituberculata, which ranged from the Jurassic until the Eocene (p. 3).

ORDER MULTITUBERCULATA

The affinities of the multituberculates (e.g. *Ctenacodon, Plagiaulax*) have been debated almost from the time of their initial description. At different times it has been held that they were ancestral to monotremes, or marsupials, or eutherians. It has also been suggested that they constituted an archaic, yet independent, branch of mammalian evolution; and this is the generally accepted view to-day. They were more highly specialised —and successful—than the triconodonts and flourished over the long period between Upper Jurassic and the Eocene. They existed, in fact, for as long a period as has been proved for any other known mammalian group—for rather more than 70 million years. They seem to have occupied an ecological position not unlike that of some extant rodents and to have been essentially vegetarian. Of unknown ancestry, they flourished in the late Cretaceous and were still common in the Tertiary and Palæocene, when occurred *Tæniolabis* (Fig. 489) with a heavy skull some six inches long.

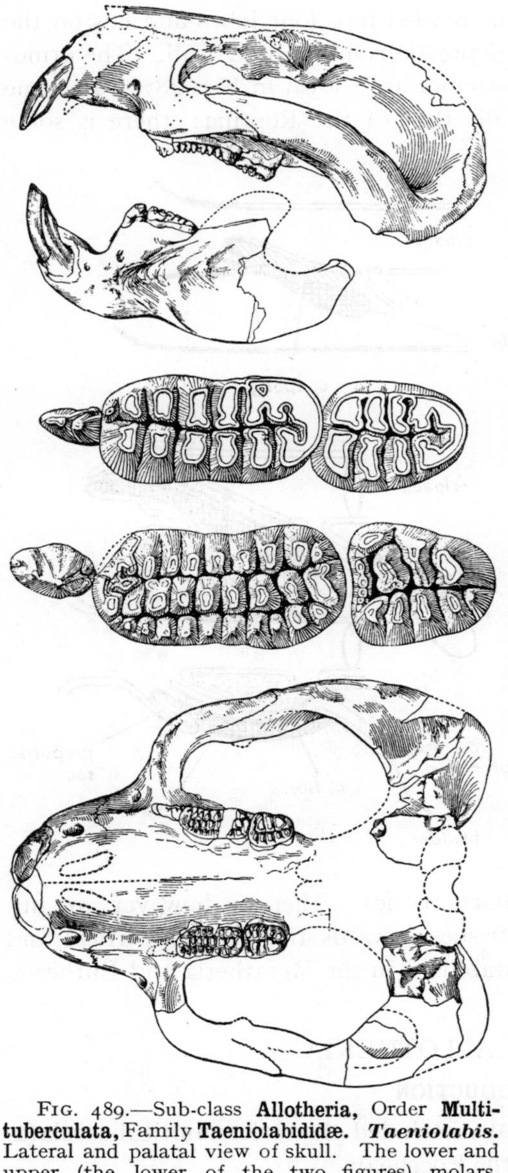

FIG. 489.—Sub-class **Allotheria,** Order **Multituberculata,** Family **Taeniolabididæ.** *Taeniolabis.* Lateral and palatal view of skull. The lower and upper (the lower of the two figures) molars. Lower Palaeocene of North America. (After Simpson.)

The most noticeable character, and the one from which the name of the sub-class is taken, is the structure of the molar teeth. These have from two to three longitudinal rows of tubercles with from two to five (or more) cusps in each row. There were only one lower, and three upper, incisors, the central one being much enlarged. Canines were absent. In many forms the anterior lower cheek-teeth were much enlarged and specialised, in a manner analogous to that of some living marsupials, *e.g.* the rat-kangaroo, *Bettongia*. The zygomatic arch arose far forward at the level of the anterior cheek-teeth, and extended back almost to the occiput. The lower jaw was stout, but without angular process, a character shared with the Triconodonta and Symmetrodonta.

SUB-CLASS THERIA

INTRODUCTION

These constitute the 'modern' mammals. The group has been split into three infra-classes, *viz.* 1. the probably ancestral Jurassic Pantotheria (= Trituberculata), including orders Dryolestoidea and Docodonta; 2. the marsupial Metatheria, and 3. the placental Eutheria, the most highly organised and advanced mammals; see, however, footnote on p. 654.

INFRA-CLASS PANTOTHERIA (TRITUBERCULATA)

This is an artificial assemblage of Mesozoic forms which are very imperfectly known and of uncertain affinities. They are of considerable interest, being possibly allied to the as yet unknown ancestors of the living non-monotreme mammals. All the Pantotheria were small; in the largest the jaw was only 4 cm. long. Their teeth are differentiated into incisors, canine, premolars and molars, but the number of molars is often as many as eight. Two orders may be distinguished.

ORDER DRYOLESTOIDEA

This group is known only from the Middle and Upper Jurassic. *Amphitherium* (Fig. 490) is the only known Middle Jurassic genus. Several genera occurred in the Upper Jurassic, e.g. *Amblotherium*, *Melanodon*, and *Paurodon*, but apart from the jaws and teeth hardly anything is known of their structure. The lower molar teeth consisted of an anterior triangle of cusps, the trigonid, and a posterior heel or talonid, which bit against the inner apex of the triangular upper molar. In the upper molar the highest cusp was internal

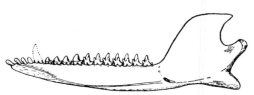

FIG. 490.—Sub-class **Theria**, Infra-class **Pantotheria**, Order **Dryolestoidea**, Family **Amphitheriidæ**. *Amphitherium*. Middle Jurassic of Europe. Inside lower jaw (over twice natural size). (Restoration after Simpson.)

(as in the symmetrodonts) but there was also a large cusp on the buccal side, and some additional smaller cusps. The trigonids of the lower molars bit between the triangular upper molars, and the diet was probably insectivorous. The contour of the lower jaw was not unlike that of a primitive 'insectivores', having a high coronoid and a well-marked angular process.

ORDER DOCODONTA

Usually united with the Dryolestoidea in an order Pantotheria, this small group (e.g. *Docodon*) from the Upper Jurassic differs from them markedly in the structure of the teeth and should probably be placed in a separate order. The molars do not have the form of interlocking triangles, though in the upper jaw they have three roots. The highest cusp of the upper molar is buccal in position, not lingual as in the Dryolestoidea; there is an inner cusp which however appears not to be homologous with that of Dryolestoidea, but shows much resemblance to the protocone of tritubercular teeth.

INFRA-CLASS METATHERIA (= MARSUPIALIA, DIDELPHIA)

INTRODUCTION

Marsupials (of which some lack a pouch, and a few possess a placenta) probably share a common Jurassic ancestry with the Eutheria or 'placentals' (p. 723). Certain isolated molar teeth of a pre-tritubercular pattern from the Middle Cretaceous of Texas could belong to marsupials or eutherians or to ancestors of both groups. In the Upper Cretaceous definite representatives of marsupials and eutherians are known. If one may judge from the small number of specimens, nearly all from one limited area, the marsupials appear to have been more numerous than the eutherians at that time, and it was not until the Cenozoic that the Eutheria (p. 703) gained ascendancy. It was possibly during the Cretaceous that marsupials entered New Guinea, Australia, and adjacent islands, which were isolated from Asia probably in the late Cretaceous (Fig. 492). Here they were able to survive free from competition with eutherians (except for bats and later rodent invaders, p. 709) and to radiate. It is probable that the basic stock was arboreal, though many have become terrestrial. Tree-kangaroos (*Dendrolagus* (Fig. 493)) have become secondarily arboreal from a fully terrestrial offshoot (see Macropodidæ, p. 716).

Marsupials are mammals basically similar to the Eutheria, but whose young are born in a rudimentary condition and are generally sheltered during their later development within an integumentary pouch, the *marsupium*. A pouch is lacking, however, in the Australian Numbat (marsupial ant-eater, *Myrmecobius fasciatus*, p. 713) in which the young are dragged along, clinging to the nipples. It is lacking also in the American *Chironectes* (Fig. 494), *Marmosa*, and *Monodelphis*. A common sphincter-muscle surrounds the anal and urinogenital apertures. The vaginæ are distinct, and each has a separate opening into the urinogenital canal (Fig. 648, p. 891). *In both sexes the ureters pass between the genital ducts: whereas in eutherians they pass outside the ducts.* The male has an erectile penis, which is sometimes bifid. In such species the clitoris is likewise double. An allantoic placenta is rarely developed (p. 904). When it occurs (*e.g.* in the Peramelidæ) it is of relatively simple structure, and functions for but a brief period. The brain lacks a corpus callosum and has large olfactory bulbs and small hemispheres which do not extend posteriorly over the cerebellum.

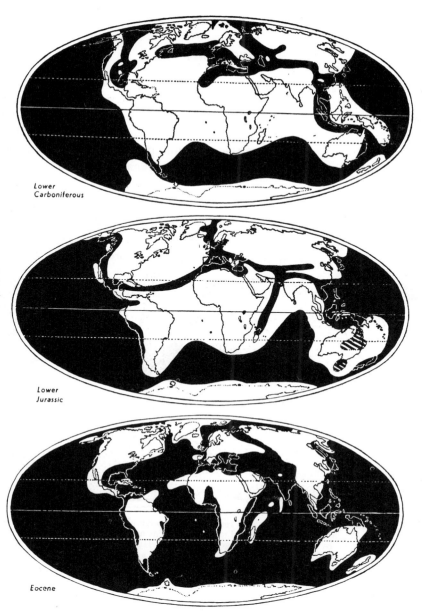

FIG. 491.—**Animal distribution: Continental connections.** The formation, destruction, and sometimes secondary emergence of inter-continental and other land-bridges (not necessarily complete at any one time) have been powerful moulding influences on the composition of the fauna of many areas. The disappearance of former land-bridges produced isolation which, together with climatic and resultant environmental changes, had a spectacular influence on, for example, the Marsupialia. Of northern origin, these radiated with enormous success in Australia and, to a less degree, in South America. Isolation and changed external conditions explains the present distribution of the relict Dipnoi (Fig. 249, p. 361), *Leiopelma* (p. 429) *Sphenodon* (p. 495), and many other groups. The dinosaurs (p. 504) were once almost universally distributed. Even flying birds (*e.g.* the Australasian avifauna) and marine fishes (*e.g.* slightly differing populations on each side of the Central American isthmus) have been affected. Many peculiar aspects of the composition of the fauna of Australia, New Zealand, North and South America and perhaps Madagascar can be broadly understood in terms of former land-bridges (see Fig. 597, p. 827, in relation to horses). At the same time it should be remembered that it is easy to postulate a land-bridge to account for phenomena that may have totally different, though less obvious, explanations such as chance dispersal from island to island (see Darlington). (The restricted striped areas above indicate extensive Jurassic lakes or inland seas.) (Modified after B. M. (N.H.) catalogue.)

The tympanic chamber of the skull is often open, with the tympanic ring exposed, a primitive feature shared with some eutherians: however, in a number of forms, the tympanic chamber is covered and the ring is hidden or 'ensnared'. In such instances, the cover is always formed by the alisphenoid bone, and not by an extension of the tympanic itself or by a combination of bones, as in various eutherians. The optic foramina are confluent from side

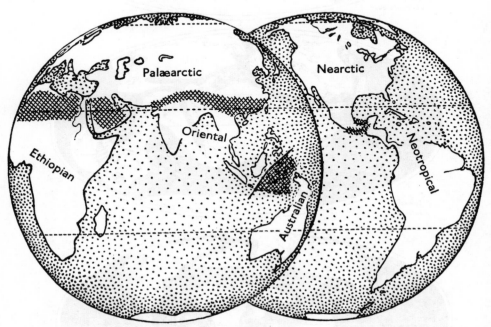

Fig. 492.—**Animal distribution: Faunal regions.** The boundaries between the six regions (of Sclater, and later Wallace) are indefinite. Transitional areas are cross-hatched. The line north of Australia was drawn by Wallace (and named after him by Huxley): it runs between Mindanao and Talaud, Borneo and Celebes, Bali and Lombok. Weber's Line, that of 'faunal balance', is somewhat to the east. The Sahara and Arabian deserts, the Himalayas and adjacent mountainous or arid regions, the high and cool Mexican Plateau: all constitute barriers to certain groups. New Zealand in particular (with its notable exclusions and its flightless birds, the frog *Leiopelma*, and *Sphenodon*) as well as Madagascar (with tenrecs and lemurs and notable absentees) also constitute definite faunal regions.

to side, and the internal carotid artery enters the skull through a foramen in the basisphenoid, and not through the foramen lacerum medium. The jugal bone extends far back, so as to participate in the formation of the glenoid cavity for articulation with the lower jaw, a feature universal in the Metatheria, but one of sporadic occurrence only in the Eutheria (*e.g.* Hyrax, many rodents). An inward inflection of the ventral posterior border of the lower jaw, the 'inflected angle', is to some degree a diagnostic feature, since it is not found elsewhere save in a few rodents. It occurs in all marsupials with the sole exception of the degenerate, thread-like jaw of the nectar-eating *Tarsipes* and is greatly reduced in the phalangerid genera *Dactylopsila* and *Dactylonax*. The seventh cervical vertebra in a large number of instances is pierced by a foramen for the vertebral artery, but this feature is also found occasionally in eutherians (some rodents, hyraxes, *Hippopotamus*, etc.). Well-developed epipubic bones are commonly, but not invariably, present.

FIG. 493.—Infra-class **Metatheria**, Order **Marsupialia**, Super-family **Phalangeroidea**, Family **Macropodidæ.** *Dendrolagus.* Tree-kangaroos (*e.g.* the Black-faced *D. lumholtzi*) are confined to the dense rain-forests of tropical Australasia. Secondarily arboreal, they have retained the remarkable leaping powers of the terrestrial kangaroos (which were themselves descended from a primitive arboreal marsupial stock). The tail of tree-kangaroos has become thinner, but has not re-developed prehensility. The feet have become shorter and broader. Some nails have become sharp and curved. The pads have become roughened and cushioned as a non-skid device. The hands have increased in size and power. The posture is less erect than in terrestrial forms. (From photographs.)

The dentition is curious in that there is only one set of teeth functional throughout life, with the exception of one tooth, a milk-molar, which is replaced by the last premolar. The pattern of the teeth varies according to function in much the same general directions as in the Eutheria, carnivorous, insectivorous, herbivorous and other adaptations being found.

In general it may be said that the marsupials represent a somewhat lower grade of vertebrate organisation than the Eutheria. They retain a number of primitive characters which they share with the more primitive eutherians (*e.g.*

many Insectivora) such as a small brain, occupying but a comparatively small portion of the skull and with its olfactory portion disproportionally large. The palate is incompletely ossified ('fenestrated'). A humeral entepicondylar foramen is very frequently present.

It has been pointed out that the monotremes are imperfectly homœothermous (p. 690). On the other hand, at least one marsupial, the Quokka Wallaby (*Setonix brachyurus*), 'possesses a capacity to control its body temperature . . . as great as, or greater than, that shown by most placental mammals of similar size' (Bartholomew). Further, marsupials employ the same general thermoregulatory mechanisms as eutherians—vasomotor changes, shivering, panting, copious salivation, and, presumably, changes in metabolic rate. (Salivation and licking is of particular importance in *Setonix* as well as other marsupials; it has also been observed in rodents and the Domestic Cat in which it seems to be essentially an emergency response.)

Although the terms 'placentals' and 'Placentalia' are frequently used to distinguish the Eutheria from the Metatheria, these are undesirable. It should be clearly understood that some marsupials have, seemingly independently, developed an efficiently vascularised allantoic placenta. *Perameles* (p. 715), in particular, has established a true chorio-allantoic placenta (p. 904), which is not deciduate, but is absorbed after the birth of the young. In *Phascolarctos* and *Phascolomys* (p. 716), too, there is allantoic vascularisation. All other marsupials studied in this respect have a comparatively small allantois and nourish the young through a yolk-sac placenta, which develops from the universally large yolk-sac during the brief period of gestation.

Metatheria were widely distributed over many parts of the world as recently as the Miocene period. They are now confined to the Australasian region (with the exception of New Zealand), to South America (where during the Tertiary period they had a wide expansion), and (a few species) to North America. The earliest known forms are from the Cretaceous of Canada.

This assemblage of marsupials and other primitive animals (*e.g.* Dipnoi, certain anurans, and flightless birds) in the southern hemisphere has suggested, very plausibly, that they, and their specific parasites, have been so distributed by means of long-vanished Antarctic land-bridges. On the balance of evidence, however, it is more probable that these archaic, isolated, southern survivors are remnants of formerly widespread stocks that have lingered on in 'species refuges' after their northern allies have been exterminated by ecological competition with later-evolved, more progressive forms.

The Australasian zoogeographical region (Fig. 492), excluding New Zealand, contains more than four times as many marsupials as occur in the Americas, where their congregation is chiefly in the southern continent. But at the same time it must be remembered that the Australasian region embraces also much of Indonesia and that marsupials occur (south-east of Wallace's Line) in the Celebes, Ceram, Amboyna, Timor, and New Guinea. In these countries, and particularly in the highly diversified Australian mainland environment, they prospered and now exhibit many beautiful examples of convergence with the more advanced, emergent, eutherians. Here marsupials developed variously running, leaping, burrowing, climbing, gliding, forms (see pp. 707, 717), but, as far as is known, no habitual swimmers. Such natatorial forms may have arisen and been later eliminated by rodent water-rats (see below). It has been suggested that pouched mammals would be unlikely to become successfully aquatic, but many marsupials became pouchless, including an aquatic opossum (*Chironectes*, Fig. 494) that developed in South America. No marsupial became truly a hooved animal, though *Chæropus*, the Pig-footed Bandicoot, exhibits modifications in that direction; and the numerous kangaroos, wallabies, wallaroos, rat-kangaroos, pademelons, and euros in any case dominated the plains and hills. Some marsupials became mouse- or rat-like, others somewhat sloth-like, others again cat- or wolf-like, while the marsupial-moles (*Notoryctes*) (Fig. 497) became fossorial and remarkably like the 'insectivoran' golden moles (Chrysochloridæ) in appearance and habit.

The isolated Australian marsupials suffered competition from only four types of eutherians. Into their habitat the bats flew, and the rodents probably drifted on debris. These rodents are myomorphs (p. 777) and probably invaded the region more than once. The invaders flourished and radiated, giving rise to peculiar Australian murid genera (e.g. *Pseudomys, Mastacomys, Mesembriomys, Conilurus, Leporillus, Notomys, Ascopharynx, Melomys, Uromys*) including also a distinct sub-family of water-rats, the Hydromyinæ. Some murids (*Notomys* and *Ascopharynx*) became jerboa-like. A later invasion by the genus *Rattus* gave rise to several species of this genus that are found only in Australia. These radiating rodents must have been severe competitors with the smaller marsupials but the effect of this impact is still unknown. About twenty genera of small terrestrial marsupials still exist to-day. Finally, the third type of competitor, Man, brought with him the fourth, a dog (*Canis dingo*) in his canoes. The Tasmanian Marsupial-wolf (*Thylacinus*) (Fig. 496), once widespread in the mainland was, by the time Europeans arrived, limited to Tasmania. The Tasmanian native (himself now extinct) had no dog. On this general question Storr has argued that animals (whether marsupial or eutherian) evolved in larger land-masses are able, when introduced into smaller countries, successfully to compete with either marsupials or eutherians that are native there.

No wholly satisfactory means of marsupial classification has been devised. Their taxonomy is usually based on the dentition, so that two groups are distinguishable: (1) the Polyprotodontia, with more than three incisors in each half of the upper jaw, (2) the Diprotodontia, with never more than three incisors in the upper, and one pair, in the lower jaw. Another method of classification is based on certain peculiarities of the foot-structure. Some marsupials have the second and third digits of the hind-foot united by a common sheath, while others have the toes all separate. These conditions are known respectively as *syndactyly* and *didactyly*. Most polyprotodonts are didactylous and all diprotodonts are syndactylous, but one super-family, the Perameloidea (bandicoots), are polyprotodont and syndactylous.

If the primitive condition be presumed to be polyprotodont and didactylous, it would appear that this stock evolved along two lines, of which one, the Didactyla, retained the simple foot-structure, and the other, the Syndactyla, acquired the peculiar modification of the second and third toes. If this be so, the second line may have undergone a further division in that some (the great majority, indeed) reduced the number of incisors and became diprotodont, while the Perameloidea, although becoming syndactylous, remained conservative as to their polyprotodont teeth.

With respect to dentition and foot-structure the marsupial groups arrange themselves as follows :

INCISORS		TOES	
Polyprotodontia	Didelphoidea Borhyænoidea Dasyuroidea Perameloidea	Didactyla	Didelphoidea Borhyænoidea Dasyuroidea Cænolestoidea
Diprotodontia	Cænolestoidea Phalangeroidea	Syndactyla	Perameloidea Phalangeroidea

There seems to be good evidence that the Didelphoidea (represented to-day in the Americas only) may be the most primitive marsupial stock known and that the remaining five groups (see below) arose from early representatives of this group and have been phylogenetically separate ever since the late Cretaceous or very early Palæocene. Past attempts to relate the widely (geographically and phylogenetically) separated stems have proved unsuccessful except in the case of borhyænoids and didelphoids (p. 711) where a fossil animal of intermediate structure (*Eobrasilia*) has been described from the Brazilian Palæocene.

It has often been stressed that any classification based on an extremely small number of characters in a large and diverse group is unlikely to be satisfactory. Hence in the present state of palæontological ignorance of ancestral Australian forms it is safest to adhere for the time being to a conservative classification of six groups 'each of which is, beyond serious doubt, a natural unit ' (Simpson).

ORDER MARSUPIALIA

Super-families Didelphoidea (Upper Cretaceous–Recent)
Borhyænoidea (Palæocene–Pliocene)

Dasyuroidea (Pleistocene–Recent)
Perameloidea (Pliocene–Recent)
Cænolestoidea (Paleocene–Recent)
Phalangeroidea (Pliocene–Recent)

SUPER-FAMILY DIDELPHOIDEA

These are the polyprotodont opossums [1] of North, Central, and South America *e.g. Didelphys, Marmosa, Chironectes*) (Fig. 494). They are small, arboreal,

FIG. 494.—Order **Marsupialia,** Super-family **Didelphoidea,** Family **Didelphidæ.** *Chironectes.* The Water Opossum or Yapok (*C. minimus*) is a cat-sized South American forest-dweller that has become web-footed, semi-aquatic, and pouchless. It lives in bank-burrows and feeds largely on fish and crayfish. The single species of *Chironectes* belongs to the same sub-family (Didelphinæ) as the originally-named opossums (*Didelphys*) of North and South America. (From B.M. (N.H.) specimens.)

generally insectivorous animals with an elongated, naked muzzle, a well-developed (though nailless) opposable hallux and long prehensile tail. A pouch is sometimes present, but it is incomplete or absent in most living

---

[1] There is evidence that the North American opossum was really called by the 'Indians' by the name *possum*, preceded by a grunt, hence 'o-possum' (Hartman). The opossum-like phalangers of Australia were called opossums as early as the 18th century by naturalists who realised the similarity, and not by 19-century gold-diggers from California as is often asserted. The name phalanger was probably first applied (by Buffon) to the American and not the Australian animals.

forms.   One species, the Water Opossum (*Chironectes*) of Central and South
America, has webbed toes.   Some American opossums have the remarkable
habit, rare among mammals, of feigning death on capture—hence the expression
'playing possum'.   Australian so-called opossums (phalangers, p. 716)
incidentally, do not 'play possum'.   The Didelphoidea are early represented by
Eodelphis, *Didelphodon*, and several others in the Upper Cretaceous, *Pera-
therium*, found in both Europe and America from the Eocene to the Miocene,
hardly differ (as far as can be told from fragments) from small living didelphids.

SUPER-FAMILY BORHYÆNOIDEA

This super-family is represented by a South American group of polyprotodont
carnivorous animals of dubious affinity, which became extinct in the Pliocene.
They (*e.g.* the Oligocene–Miocene *Borhyæna*, the Miocene *Prothylacinus*) were
large-headed, rather short-legged terrestrial animals, as big as bears, with
powerful claws and a small hallux.   The Pliocene *Thylacosmilus*, a late survivor,
had long stabbing teeth not unlike those of the sabre-toothed 'tiger' (p. 796).
These animals have been claimed to show affinity with the Australian thylacines
(Fig. 496) and to constitute evidence for the existence of an Antarctic land-
bridge but any resemblance is probably due to convergent evolution.

The carnivorous Borhyænoidea probably radiated in seclusion after the
separation of South America early in the Eocene (Fig. 491).   Although a few
eutherians (p. 723) had already reached that continent, these did not include
carnivores.

SUPER-FAMILY DASYUROIDEA

This Australasian group contains a large number of forms exhibiting an
astonishing range of adaptive radiation.   The carnivorous, essentially terrestrial Dasyuridæ (native-'cats', Tasmanian Devil, Thylacine, etc.) generally
have the pollex rudimentary, the foot four-toed, the hallux, when present, small
and clawless, and the tail non-prehensile.   The marsupium is well-developed
(but generally shallow) and the tail long.   Body-length may be as great as two
feet, although many are smaller than a domestic cat.   The early settlers called
the first-encountered species the 'spotted marten' (Fig. 495).   The predaceous
Tasmanian Devil (*Sarcophilus*) is larger, with a more thick-set body.   Its bones
have been found in aboriginal middens on the Australian mainland, although
good evidence is wanting of its occurrence there since European settlement.
The large carnivorous Tasmanian Marsupial-'wolf' (*Thylacinus*) (Fig. 496)
is to-day extremely rare.   It was formerly widespread on the Australian
continent, where it was exterminated before the advent of white settlement.
It bears a remarkable resemblance both in appearance and size to the true wolf.
Its skull too, is wolf-like in general outline, and its dentition is as dog-like as is
possible for a marsupial.   *Thylacinus* is prominently barred across the dorsal

surface, making for concealment in the heavy timber where it lives. It is inoffensive to Man, despite the vernacular, 'Tasmanian Tiger'.

Also included in the present super-family is the semi-arboreal genus *Phascogale*, containing three slender, graceful, but ferocious brush-tailed animals, each about the size of a small rat. Now rare, *Phascogale* raids poultry farms, killing far in excess of its hunger. Allied to the above are several

FIG. 495.—Order **Marsupialia**, Super-family **Dasyuroidea**, Family **Dasyuridæ**, Sub-family **Dasyurinæ. Dasyurops.** The Tiger-cat or 'Spotted Marten' (*D. maculatus*) of the early British colonists in Australia is a fearless hunter with which the Felidæ, in some respects, converged. The Tiger-cat sometimes kills wallabies, and has been known to keep a couple of Irish terriers at bay. The body is about two feet long. *Dasyurops* differs from *Dasyurus* in the possession of a hallux, serrated foot-pads, and a spotted tail. The pouch is shallow and reversed—a crescentic fold encloses only the front and sides of the mammary area which supports six nipples arranged in two rows. 'Dasyures' easily hold their own against imported eutherians but have been decimated in populous areas because of their blood-thirsty raids on domestic poultry. (From photographs.)

genera of pouched rats and mice (e.g. *Dasycercus, Dasyuroides, Sminthopsis*) as well as long-tailed, hopping, pouchless (or almost pouchless) Jerboa-like marsupials (*Antechinomys*). Some of the first-named accumulate fat stores in their tails.

Two further genera of great interest are the curious numbats or banded ant-eaters (*Myrmecobius*), and the Marsupial Mole (*Notoryctes*). Two species of the former occur : these are rat-sized, and banded across the lumbar and sacral regions. The female is pouchless, and so the small young are carried

attached to the nipples.   Numbats are very specialised gentle creatures, not
fast on the ground, not deep burrowers and not climbers.   Probably they could
not have survived anywhere outside the isolation provided by Australia.
Although not persecuted by Man, they have become rare owing, possibly, to
the destruction of their native habitat by settlement and by feral domestic cats.

FIG. 496.—Order **Marsupialia,** Super-families **Dasyuroidea and Perameloidea.** The banded
Tasmanian-wolf (*Thylacinus cynocephalus*) (Family **Dasyuridæ,** sub-family **Thylacininæ**) inhabits
hilly heavily-timbered country.   Although harmless to Man it has been known to tear open the
skull of a bull-terrier with a single bite.   The four young are carried in the pouch for about three
months.   The thylacine is shown holding a bandicoot (*Thylacis*) (Family Peramelidæ.)   The
single species is extremely rare.   (From photographs.)

Notoryctes, the Marsupial-mole (Fig. 497), is a small, burrowing, desert
animal which bears a superficial resemblance to the African golden moles
(Chrysochloridæ, p. 729).   It has short, powerful, furred limbs, each with five
toes.   The third and fourth toes of the fore-foot are provided with remarkable,
large, flat, triangular claws.   The rhinarium is covered with a horny shield
and the dorsal aspect of the head is also protected by a hard shield.   The tail
is short and covered with bare, horny skin.   An auditory pinna is absent, the
eyes are vestigial and the fur is silky and almost plush-like.   A well-developed
pouch opens backwards.   Pleistocene fossil examples have been found.

SUPER-FAMILY PERAMELOIDEA

The bandicoots (Fig. 496) are inoffensive Australasian terrestrial grass- and forest dwellers (e.g. *Perameles, Thylacis, Macrotis, Chæropus*) usually of burrowing habit. They range in size from that of a large rat to that of a rabbit and subsist on a mixed diet. Although rarer than formerly, they are still plentiful in the outer suburbs of Australian capital cities. They have an elongated, pointed muzzle, and, in some cases, large auditory pinnæ. The tail is usually short but sometimes long. The first and fifth digits of the fore-feet are vestigial or absent, the remaining three being nearly equally developed. In the hind-foot the fourth toe is longer and stouter than the others, while the

FIG. 497.—Order **Marsupialia,** Super-family **Dasyuroidea,** Family **Notoryctidæ. *Notoryctes.*** The xerophilous Marsupial Mole (*N. typhlops*), with which the African golden moles (Fig. 510, p. 729) show extraordinary convergence. There are two species. See also Figs. 495, 496 for dog- and cat-like forms within the same super-family. (From *Cambridge Natural History*.)

second and third are small and slender, and united together by a web of skin: the first is vestigial or absent. The marsupium opening is directed backwards. Allied to the true bandicoots are the beautiful bilbies or rabbit-bandicoots (*Thylacomys*). These are more carnivorous; and have long silky fur and long rabbit-like ears. Fossil bandicoots have been found in Pliocene and Pleistocene deposits.

SUPER-FAMILY CÆNOLESTOIDEA

These South American marsupials do not fall into either of the main assemblages outlined above. They are represented to-day only by *Cæno- lestes, Orolestes,* and *Rhyncholestes,* small rodent-like forms which, with the true opossums (p. 711), represent the two marsupial types that survived the late-Tertiary placental invasion from the north. The Cænolestoidea is ob- viously of considerable antiquity and Palæocene fossils are known. *Cænolestes* is a small, superficially very mouse-like animal with a polyprotodont upper dentition and with the median pair of lower incisors enlarged as in the con- ventional Australian diprotodont condition (p. 709). The toes have not become syndactylous. The most likely explanation of their 'aberrant' form is that they and the Australian diprotodonts were separated in the late Mesozoic when still in the polyprotodont condition and that, in isolation, the Australian forms became fully diprotodont, the Cænolestoidea partly so. *Polydolops*

(Palæocene–Eocene), *Abderites* (Oligocene–Miocene) and other forms pursued this tendency much further than did *Cænolestes*.

SUPER-FAMILY PHALANGEROIDEA

Into this Australasian group fall the arboreal phalangers or possums (e.g. *Trichosurus*, *Pseudocheirus*) and flying-phalangers (marsupial gliders) (e.g. *Petaurus*); the arboreal, clinging, superficially somewhat sloth-like Koala (*Phascolarctos*); the aberrant, burrowing wombats (*Phascolomys*); and the great assembly of kangaroos and their allies (Macropodidæ) (Fig. 493, p. 707).

The phalangers have both fore- and hind-feet prehensile. The second and third toes of the hind-foot are slender and united by a web, but the hallux, which is nailless, is opposable to them. The fourth and fifth toes are nearly equal. The tail is well developed and may be prehensile. The flying phalangers are provided with lateral folds of skin extending from the fore- to the hind-limbs and, acting as a parachute, enable the animal (as in the true flying-squirrels), to make leaping descending glides from tree to tree. Phalangers are often of great beauty and were hunted extensively for their fur but they are now generally protected and are not uncommon in the gardens of inner suburbs of capital cities. The group contains also minute pigmy possums (*Cercaërtus*), pigmy 'feather-tailed' gliders (*Acrobates*) (Fig. 498) as well as the large slower-moving cuscuses (*Spilocuscus*) of tropical Australasia. Remarkably specialised, too, is the tiny, dorsal-striped, arboreal, monospecific, Honey-possum (*Tarsipes*) which occupies a sub-family by itself. It has an extensile tongue, degenerate cheek-teeth, and a long prehensile tail.

The wombats (Phascolomyidæ) are large, heavy, thick-bodied vegetarian animals that live in burrows, emerging at night. They have short, flattened heads and short thick limbs, provided with strong claws on all the digits except the hallux. The second and third toes of the hind-foot are partly skin-connected. The tail is very short.

The rare arboreal Koala is the sole living representative of the family Phascolarctidæ. It is an inoffensive, sluggish, and extremely beautiful marsupial. Once slaughtered for its pelt, it is now rigidly protected. It has a thick body, vestigial tail, cheek-pouches, and an extremely capacious cæcum. The Koala's feeding habits are inordinately specialised. It will eat the leaves of about a dozen species only of *Eucalyptus*. It never drinks but licks up earth containing, no doubt, essential mineral factors. The pouch of this animal is peculiar in that its lateral recesses extend to the flanks. The gestation period is said to be only 35 days. One young is produced every second year. Although the adult is about 30 inches long the neonatus is only about $\frac{3}{4}$ inch in length and weighs about $5\frac{1}{2}$ grams. At birth the fore-limbs are relatively powerfully developed. It is primarily by means of these that the blind, helpless young one makes unaided a wriggling two-inch journey to the backwardly directed pouch (see also p. 908). Therein it fixes itself unaided to one of the two nipples. At about six months the baby is some six inches long, but it does not outgrow the pouch until two months later, after which it is carried about on the female's back, or held in her arms as she sleeps in a tree-fork.

The kangaroos and their allies (Macropodidæ), are remarkably adapted for

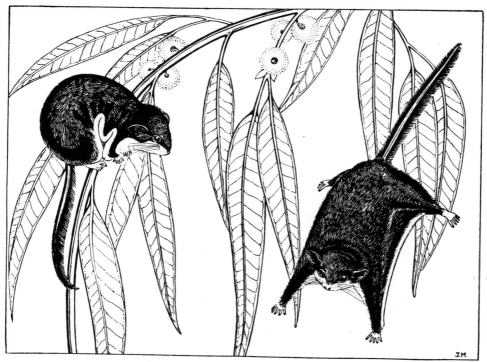

FIG. 498.—Order **Marsupialia**, Super-family **Phalangeroidea**, Family **Phalangeridæ**, *Acrobates*. The Australian possums (phalangers) belong to the same super-family as the kangaroos, the Koala and the burrowing wombats and are therefore only distantly related to the American opossums (Fig. 494). The Feather-tailed, or Pygmy, Glider (*A. pygmæus*) inhabits the eucalyptus forests of Eastern Australia and still survives in the suburbs of capital cities. About the size of a mouse, it spends the daylight hours in hollow limbs, emerging at dusk to feed on insects and nectar. The tail-structure has no interlocking device such as occurs in true feathers. Larger gliders have fluffy tails: in the cat-sized *Schoinobates volans* the tail is about 20 inches long and steers the animal from high branches to lower ones in glides of up to 120 yards. (Partly after Gould, and B.M. (N.H.) specimens.)

swift terrestrial locomotion. They have a relatively small head and neck. The forelimbs are small, and each is provided with five digits. The hind-legs are long and powerful. Rapid progression is effected by great springing leaps (as long as 26 feet) with the body inclined forwards and the fore-limbs clear of the ground. The foot is narrow and provided with four toes, a hallux being absent. The two inner (second and third) toes are small and united by integument. The middle toe is very long and powerful, and is a formidable

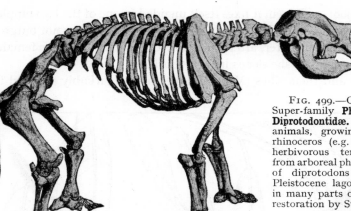

FIG. 499.—Order **Marsupialia,**
Super-family **Phalangeroidea,** Family
Diprotodontidæ. Diprotodon. These
animals, growing to the size of a
rhinoceros (e.g. *D. australis*) were a
herbivorous terrestrial development
from arboreal phalanger stock. Fossils
of diprotodons bogged in receding
Pleistocene lagoons have been found
in many parts of Australia. (From a
restoration by Stirling.)

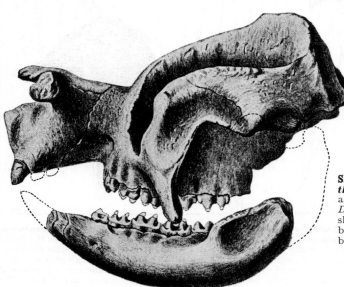

FIG. 500.—**Diprodontidæ:
Skull and dentition of *Nototherium*.** This Pleistocene
animal was smaller than
Diprodoton (Fig. 499) but
shared its general resem-
blance to the extant wom-
bats. (After Owen.)

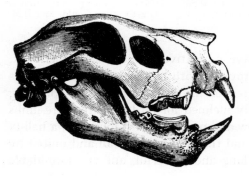

FIG. 501.—Super-family **Phalangeroidea,**
Family **Thylacoleonidæ. Thylacoleo.** This
remarkable Pleistocene marsupial (*T. carnifex*)
was another phalangeroid form. It was about
the size of a modern lion. The molars were
reduced and the rear premolars were specialised into powerful shearing teeth. (After
Flower.)

defensive weapon capable of disembowelling a dog. The tail is very long, usually thick and helps support the body while at rest. There is a large marsupium. The tree-kangaroos (*Dendrolagus*) differ from ordinary kangaroos, particularly in their shorter and thicker hind-limbs, in which the second and third toes have become nearly as large as the fourth (Fig. 493, p. 707).

The numerous, highly varied and vegetarian Macropodidæ range in size from the rabbit-sized rat-kangaroos (*Bettongia*) to the magnificent plain-dwelling Red Flier (*Macropus rufus*) (which has a blue-grey doe) and the Great Grey (Forester or Boomer) (*M. canguru*) which stands about six feet high. The new-born animal is little more than one inch long (see p. 908).

The aberrant and primitive Hypsiprymnodontidæ contains only one species, the Musk Rat-Kangaroo (*Hypsiprymnodon moschatus*), of dense North Queensland rain-forests. Alone among the kangaroos it possesses the first pedal digit, and shows certain similarities with the phalangers.

Among the Phalangeroidea has been placed the largest extinct marsupial yet discovered—*Diprotodon* (Fig. 499). This cumbersome Pleistocene animal was about as big as a modern rhinoceros, being perhaps six feet high and 10 feet long. *Diprotodon* was heavily quadrupedal with a massive head and neck. Anteriorly the upper jaw was armed with a pair of formidable chisel-shaped incisors with a frontal enamel deposition. These teeth had persistent pulps (p. 864), growing con-

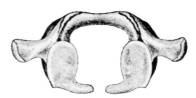

FIG. 502. — **Macropus: Atlas.** Note incomplete ossification of inferior arch.

tinuously as they wore away. Behind them lay two pairs of lesser incisors. The lower anterior pair of incisors was large and forwardly directed and the lower cheek teeth were transversely ridged for grinding. Petrified crushed vegetable material has been found with the bones. The animal was plantigrade, with minute digits : its arboreal ancestry was indicated by the structure of its hallux which appears to have been opposable. Hundreds of fossils were recovered from a single lake site where the animals bogged in mud (as do cattle to-day) in an attempt to reach water during a Pleistocene drought. Another fossil marsupial of identical antiquity and site is *Nototherium* (Fig. 500), an ox-sized lumbering, broad-headed, herbivorous form, possibly armed with a nasal horn. Some of its characters suggest a remote wombat affinity. *Thylacoleo* (Fig. 501) is another Australian Pleistocene phalangeroid. It was lion-sized, with peculiarly large posterior premolars, modified into shearing teeth, suggestive of a carnivorous diet.

Endoskeleton of Metatheria.—In marsupials the inferior arch of the atlas (Fig. 502) is often incompletely ossified, a gap being apparent in the macerated bone. Sometimes this gap becomes closed by ingrowths from the lateral parts of the arch, whilst at other times a small separate ossification is developed

therein, filling the opening.   There are always nineteen trunk vertebræ.   The
thoracic transverse processes are always well developed, and the ribs articulate

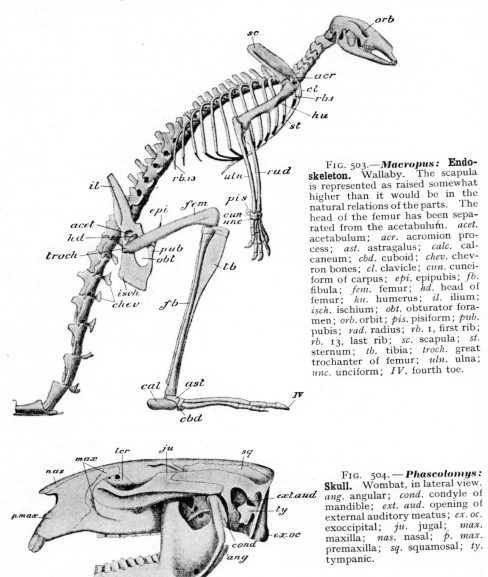

FIG. 503.—*Macropus:* **Endo-skeleton.** Wallaby. The scapula is represented as raised somewhat higher than it would be in the natural relations of the parts. The head of the femur has been separated from the acetabulum. *acet.* acetabulum; *acr.* acromion process; *ast.* astragalus; *calc.* calcaneum; *cbd.* cuboid; *chev.* chevron bones; *cl.* clavicle; *cun.* cuneiform of carpus; *epi.* epipubis; *fb.* fibula; *fem.* femur; *hd.* head of femur; *hu.* humerus; *il.* ilium; *isch.* ischium; *obt.* obturator foramen; *orb.* orbit; *pis.* pisiform; *pub.* pubis; *rad.* radius; *rb.* 1, first rib; *rb.* 13, last rib; *sc.* scapula; *st.* sternum; *tb.* tibia; *troch.* great trochanter of femur; *uln.* ulna; *unc.* unciform; *IV.* fourth toe.

FIG. 504. — *Phascolomys:* **Skull.** Wombat, in lateral view. *ang.* angular; *cond.* condyle of mandible; *ext. aud.* opening of external auditory meatus; *ex. oc.* exoccipital; *ju.* jugal; *max.* maxilla; *nas.* nasal; *p. max.* premaxilla; *sq.* squamosal; *ty.* tympanic.

with them as well as with the vertebral bodies.   Prominent metapophyses and
anapophyses are developed, largest in the lumbar region.   In most marsupials
but one sacral vertebra is present though in some a second is ankylosed with it.

The caudal region varies greatly in length ; it is short in the Koala and the wombats, long in the opossums, dasyures, phalangers, and kangaroos (Fig. 503).

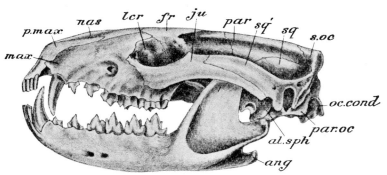

FIG. 505.—*Dasyurus: Skull.* Marsupial 'cat,' in lateral view. *al. sph.* ali-sphenoid; *ang.* angular process of mandible; *fr.* frontal; *ju.* jugal; *lcr.* lachrymal; *max.* maxilla; *nas.* nasal; *oc. cond.* occipital condyle; *par.* parietal; *par. oc.* par-occipital process; *p. max.* premaxilla; *s. oc.* supra-occipital; *sq.* squamosal; *sq'.* zygomatic process of squamosal.

Chevron bones are generally present, except in the Koala and the wombats.

In the *skull* (Figs. 504, 505, 506) the brain-cavity is relatively small. The pituitary fossa is not distinct, and there are no clinoid processes. The zygoma is complete, but the orbit is not completely bounded by bone behind. The extinct phalangeroid *Thylacoleo*, however, has a complete post-orbital bar (Fig. 501). The jugal extends beneath the squamosal root of the zygoma to form part of the outer wall of the glenoid fossa. The lachrymal foramen is usually on the anterior margin of the orbit, sometimes on the face. The palate usually presents vacuities in its posterior portion. The pterygoid is always small. The alisphenoid is large, and forms the anterior boundary of the tympanic cavity. In the kangaroos the *alisphenoid* (Fig. 506, *ali.*) extends backwards so as to join the greatly elongated paroccipital process. When an auditory bulla is developed, it is formed by that bone, the tympanic being always small, and never ankylosed to neighbouring bones. The internal carotid artery perforates the basisphenoid. The optic foramen is con-

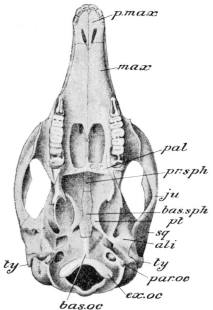

FIG. 506.—*Petrogale: Skull.* Rock Wallaby, in ventral view. *ali.* alisphenoid; *bas. oc.* basioccipital; *bas. sph.* basisphenoid; *ex. oc.* exoccipital; *ju.* jugal; *max.* maxilla; *pal.* palatine; *par. oc.* paroccipital; *p. max.* premaxilla; *pr. sph.* presphenoid; *pt.* pterygoid; *sq.* squamosal; *ty.* tympanic.

fluent with the sphenoidal fissure. In all except *Tarsipes* the angle of the mandible sends inwards a remarkable process (*ang.*), and is said to be *inflected*.

In the *pectoral arch* of the marsupials the coracoid process is, as usual, developed from a special bony centre, and a distinct suture is often recognisable between it and the scapula until a comparatively late stage. In the young condition (when the fœtus is attached to the teat) the coracoid is comparatively extensive and reaches the presternum ventrally. A clavicle is always present, except in the bandicoots, but may be incomplete. There is never a distinct centrale in the carpus. In the opossums the ilium has the primitive form of a straight, three-sided rod. In the kangaroos (Fig. 503, *il.*) it is still simple and three-sided, but somewhat curved outward. In the rest it is more or less compressed. In nearly all the marsupials there is a pair of elongated and compressed epipubic or marsupial bones (Fig. 503, *epi*), which articulate posteriorly with the anterior edge of the pubes. In the Thylacine they are represented only by small unossified fibro-cartilages. The fibula is always well developed, and in the young condition of some marsupials there is an accessory element situated outside its proximal end. This apparently corresponds to a bone known as the *parafibula* which occurs in some Lacertilia. In the phalangers (Fig. 498) and the Koala there is always a considerable range of movement between the fibula and the tibia, comparable in some degree to the movements of pronation and supination of the radius and ulna. The foot (Figs. 507, 508), as already stated, presents a much greater range of modification than the hand.

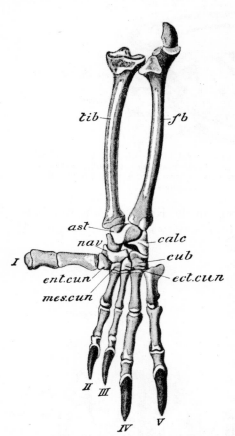

FIG. 507.—*Trichosurus:* **Hind-leg and pes.** Phalanger. *ast.* astragalus; *calc.* calcaneum; *cub.* cuboid; *ect. cun.* ecto-cuneiform; *ent. cun.* ento-cuneiform; *fb.* fibula; *mes. cun.* meso-cuneiform; *nav.* navicular; *tib.* tibia; *I—V*, digits. (After Owen.)

INFRA-CLASS EUTHERIA (PLACENTALIA, MONODELPHIA)

INTRODUCTION

The Eutheria and Metatheria are presumed to have arisen from some as yet untraced branch of the Jurassic pantotheres (p. 703). Since undoubted eutherians and metatherians are known from the Upper Cretaceous, they must have diverged along their separate lines of evolution during the early part of the Cretaceous period (p. 3). At the beginning of the Palæocene a great variety of eutherians made their appearance, implying either a very rapid evolutionary radiation, or perhaps more probably a rapid dispersal from an area, at present undiscovered, where they had been evolving during the Cretaceous. It must be remembered that only one Lower Palæocene mammalian fauna, that of the Puerco Beds of New Mexico, is adequately known. At the dawn of the Eocene (some 50 million years ago) additional diversification took place. Most of the orders of the infra-class Eutheria were present in the Eocene.

In all, Simpson (whose classification is here generally followed; see, however, p. 725) recognises twenty-six eutherian orders, ten of which have become extinct. The Eutheria includes all the more familiar mammals of to-day, including Man and his domesticated beasts. It embraces about 8,500 species.

The basic characters common to the group, which has in its fairly long history radiated into a considerable number of lines, are naturally relatively few. Although an allantoic placenta occurs in certain marsupials (p. 708), the chief eutherian character is nevertheless the highly organised allantoic arrangement, whereby

FIG. 508.—*Macropus:* **Pes.** Kangaroo, right. *a.* astragalus; *c.* calcaneum; *cb.* cuboid; *e³.* ento-cuneiform; *n.* navicular; *II—V,* digits. (After Flower.)

the young can be nourished in the uterus for a comparatively long time and be born in a far more advanced stage of growth than those of marsupials. The uterus tends gradually to lose its original double formation (*uterus duplex*) and becomes a single structure (*uterus simplex*). The urinary ducts pass to the bladder outside the genital ducts (cf. pp. 704, 892). A common sphincter is only rarely present and then only as a remnant, thus there is no longer any cloaca. In the brain a new structure appears—the *corpus callosum* (Fig. 486), which connects the large cerebral hemispheres. In the course of its evolution the brain has become more and more highly organised, especially by the remarkable development of the neopallial region of the hemispheres (pp. 679, 884).

The internal carotid enters the skull through the foramen lacerum medius or through the bulla. (In marsupials it passes medially to the middle ear to enter the skull through the basisphenoid.) The tympanic region in all but the most primitive forms is protected by a bony covering, or bulla, an outgrowth of the petrous bone to which the tympanic bone becomes attached in various ways to form a true *tympanic bulla*, as opposed to the *alisphenoid bulla* of those marsupials with protected ear region. Some Eutheria resemble marsupials in single features of the skull, but such resemblances have probably been secondarily acquired. They include the perforation of the palate in hedgehogs, the extension of the jugal back to the glenoid cavity in hyraxes, the confluence of the optic foramen with the sphenoidal fissure in some Lipotyphla, and the inflection of the angle of the lower jaw in some rodents. No eutherian possesses epipubic bones or a marsupial pouch (cf., however, monotremes, p. 688). The Eutheria all have the dental formula of $\frac{3 \cdot 1 \cdot 4 \cdot 3}{3 \cdot 1 \cdot 4 \cdot 3}$, or some derivative therefrom. (Some have lost all teeth, viz. Pholidota and some edentates.)

As mentioned above, most of the eutherian orders seem to have arisen during the Palæocene. Some (*e.g.* Tæniodonta, Tillodontia, Condylarthra, Dinocerata) had a comparatively short career and probably did not survive the Eocene. Others (Pyrotheria, Embrithopoda, Pantodonta) probably disappeared towards the end of the Oligocene. The Notoungulata and Litopterna survived until a few million years ago. Some of the above groups are still very imperfectly known, and the same can be said of the origins of many of the extant orders : on the material available it is not always easy to determine affinities.

Although the orders of Eutheria are so distinct to-day, their representatives in the early Cænozoic were much more alike, and it is sometimes a matter of dispute into which order some of the Palæocene forms should be placed. By comparing the most primitive members of the various orders it is possible to arrive at a conception of the characters of the hypothetical ancestral eutherian stock. They must have been small mammals, probably not larger than a rat, with a long trunk, arched back, rather short legs, and long, somewhat stout tail. The manus and pes were plantigrade, with five digits provided with claws. The clavicles were well developed, and the ulna and radius were free, as were the tibia and fibula. In the skull the face was as long as the small brain-case. The tympanic was ring-shaped and there was no bulla. The snout possessed a well-developed rhinarium and vibrissæ. The teeth were adapted for an insectivorous diet, with sharp interlocking cusps and cutting crests. There were three incisors, a moderately enlarged canine, four premolars, and three molars, which were of a pretritubercular type (p. 868). As regards soft parts, a good case can be made out that a cæcum was present in the gut. Both precaval veins may have been well-developed. The cerebral hemispheres were small (not completely covering the corpora quadrigemina)

and unconvoluted. The olfactory lobes were large. The perineum was probably poorly developed, and traces of a cloaca may have been present. The
testes were probably abdominal and the uteri separate (duplex). The number
of young produced at a birth was probably large. Numerous mammary glands
formed a series along the body between axilla pit and groin. No living eutherian possesses this combination of characters, but many have retained some
of them. Primitive characters are most numerous in the orders Menotyphla
and Lipotyphla (generally united into a single order, Insectivora), and thus the
other orders are often regarded as having an insectivore ancestry. It must be
emphasised, however, that the living insectivores, though primitive in some
respects, are specialised in others. Further, some such primitive characters
have survived in many other orders.

We will follow Simpson's arrangement of living and extinct orders into four
cohorts. The Insectivora, however, are divided into Lipotyphla and Menotyphla.

INFRA-CLASS EUTHERIA

Cohort Unguiculata

Orders Lipotyphla (Upper Cretaceous–Recent)
Menotyphla (Upper Cretaceous–Recent)
Primates (Palæocene–Recent)
Dermoptera (Palæocene-Recent)
Chiroptera (Eocene–Recent)
Tæniodontia (Palæocene–Eocene)
Tillodontia (Palæocene–Eocene)
Edentata (Palæocene–Recent)
Pholidota (Oligocene–Recent)

Cohort Glires

Orders Rodentia (Palæocene–Recent)
Lagomorpha (Palæocene–Recent)

Cohort Mutica

Order Cetacea (Eocene–Recent)

Cohort Ferungulata

Super-order Feræ
Order Carnivora (Palæocene–Recent)

Super-order Protoungulata
Orders Condylarthra (Palæocene–Eocene)
Notoungulata (Palæocene–Pleistocene)
Litopterna (Palæocene–Pleistocene)
Astrapotheria (Eocene–Miocene)
Tubulidentata (Pliocene–Recent)

Super-order Pænungulata
    Orders Hyracoidea [1] (Oligocene–Recent)
    Proboscidea (Eocene–Recent)
    Pantodonta (Palæocene–Eocene)
    Dinocerata (Palæocene–Eocene)
    Pyrotheria (Palæocene–Oligocene)
    Embrithopoda (Oligocene)
    Sirenia (Eocene–Recent)
Super-order Mesaxonia
    Order Perissodactyla (Eocene–Recent)
Super-order Paraxonia
    Order Artiodactyla (Eocene–Recent)

COHORT UNGUICULATA

This great assembly is composed of extinct and living orders in which archaic mammalian characters are notably retained. Among living mammals it includes the Lipotyphla (*e.g.* shrews, moles, and hedgehogs), Menotyphla (tree-shrews and elephant shrews) Chiroptera (bats), Dermoptera (Colugo or 'Flying Lemur'), Edentata (restricted to armadillos, sloths, and true ant-eaters among living beasts), Pholidota (pangolins) and the Primates (lemurs, lorises, tarsiers, monkeys, apes, and Man).

The older order Rodentia (rodents and rabbits), properly divisible into Rodentia, and Lagomorpha (p. 779), is often included among the above but its two groups are here included in a separate cohort Glires (p. 774).

Order Lipotyphla

This order, generally considered as a suborder of an order Insectivora, may be divided as follows:

    Sub-order Erinaceomorpha
        Super-family Erinaceoidea (Upper Cretaceous–Recent)
    Sub-order Soricomorpha
        Super-families Tenrecoidea (Palæocene–Recent)
                 Soricoidea (Palæocene–Recent)
                 Chrysochloroidea (Miocene–Recent)

The Lipotyphla have retained a large number of the characters of the Cretaceous stock from which all placental mammals have arisen. They are small mammals, the largest, *Solenodon* (Fig. 509), being only about the size of a cat. Some of the shrews, for example *Sorex minutus* and *Suncus etruscus* are

---

[1] There is considerable controversy about the affinities of this group. Recently discovered material has led Whitworth to place the order with the Perissodactyla in the Mesaxonia (p. 824).

the smallest living mammals, weighing only about three grammes (cf. p. 780). The manus and pes are plantigrade, and with few exceptions all five digits are retained. Clavicles have been lost only in *Potamogale*. In the vertebral column there may occur small bony nodules between the vertebræ on the ventral side which appear to be the remains of chevron bones (intercentra). An entepicondylar foramen is usually present in the humerus. The tympanic is usually ring-shaped. The cerebral hemispheres are small and smooth, and the olfactory lobes are large. Remains of a cloaca are often present. The testes are frequently abdominal in position, and there is never a fully developed scrotum. The uterus is bicornuate. The number of young produced at a birth may be very large: in *Tenrec* the average is 21. The mammary glands are usually numerous: three to six pairs, except in the Chrysochloroidea, where there are two pairs.

At the same time the Lipotyphla share a number of characteristic specialisations. The pelvic symphysis is reduced to a short contact between the ischia, or may be completely absent (as in Soricoidea). There is never any cæcum to the gut. The snout is prolonged to form a mobile proboscis, moved by muscles which are attached to the skull at the anterior edge of the orbit (in Erinaceomorpha) or pass back beneath the orbit as far as the squamosal (in Soricomorpha). The zygomatic arch is frequently incomplete: when it is present it is usually slender, and the jugal is greatly reduced. The eyes tend to be reduced in size, especially in the Soricomorpha, where the optic foramen is not separate from the sphenoidal fissure.

The Lipotyphla are predominantly insectivorous, and have sharp molar cusps and interlocking teeth. The incisors are frequently enlarged to function as forceps, notably in the shrews (Soricidæ), and the canines are then small or absent. The molar patterns fall into two main types. In the dilambdodont type the outer cusps (paracone and metacone) are both large, and usually form a W of high cutting crests. In the zalambdodont type, which characterises the Tenrecoidea (Fig. 509) and Chrysochloroidea (Fig. 510), the metacone is undeveloped, and the paracone forms a V: the protocone is reduced, together with the talonid of the lower molar, so that the zalambdodont molar teeth may closely resemble those of the Dryolestoidea of the Jurassic.

The Erinaceoidea are to-day represented by a single family, the Erinaceidæ, with a wide distribution in Europe, Asia, and Africa, but extinct in North America. The more primitive members of the group, found in South East Asia, are hairy (e.g. *Echinosorex = Gymnura*), but in the hedgehogs (e.g. *Erinaceus*) the hairs of the dorsal surface have become converted into spines and, owing to a remarkable development of the dermal musculature, the animal can roll itself into a spine-covered ball. A band of muscle passes down the sides of the body and over the neck and the root of the tail to form a sphincter round the edges of the spine-covered area. During contraction the

spiny skin is pulled over the head and tail by other skin muscles.   European
hedgehogs can kill vipers and are immune to their poison.

The Soricoidea include the families Soricidæ (shrews) and Talpidæ (moles
and desmans).   Shrews are world-wide except in the Australian region and most
of South America; moles are Holarctic and Oriental in distribution.   The
shrews have a higher metabolic rate than any other mammal, and are unable to

Fig. 509.—Infra-class **Eutheria,** Order **Lipotyphla,** Super-family **Tenrecoidea,** Family **Solenodontidæ. *Solenodon.*** The Lipotyphla (e.g. *S. paradoxus* above) and the Menotyphla (*e.g.* Fig.
514) are often united in a single polymorphic Order Insectivora.   Members of the genus *Solenodon*
are insectivorous, nocturnal, and gregarious, living by day in burrows and rock fissures.   The
females make nests.   They have well-developed inguinal and axillary glands and their saliva,
like that of some shrews, is said to be venomous.   (From Bourlière, and B.M. (N.H.) specimens.)

survive more than ten hours without food.   In some shrews (*Blarina*) the sub-
maxillary glands produce a poisonous saliva capable of killing a mouse.   The
most primitive moles, e.g. *Uropsilus* of China, are very much like shrews and
have no burrowing adaptations: their feet are unspecialised and pinnæ are
present.   The desman (*Desmana* = *Mygale*) is aquatic, possessing webbed feet
and a laterally compressed tail.   The remaining Talpidæ are specialised for
burrowing.   Moles have been recorded to burrow one hundred yards in a
single night.   The manus is very large and is held vertically at the side of the

head, with the palm outwards and the pollex ventrally. A *falciform* bone develops from the carpus on the medial side of the pollex, giving greater breadth. The humerus is very short and has its muscle crests powerfully developed. The clavicle is very short and thick, and articulates with the humerus as well as with the acromion process of the scapula. The humerus is entirely embedded in the body, the shoulder girdle having been carried forward to the neck region by elongation of the presternum. This aids in stream-lining. A prenasal bone is developed in the snout. The second, third, and fourth cervical vertebræ are fused. The hind limb pushes the body forward when burrowing, and the

Fig. 510.—Order **Lipotyphla,** Sub-order **Soricomorpha,** Super-family **Chrysochloroidea,** Family **Chrysochloridæ.** *Chrysochloris.* The fossorial golden moles of the African veldt (e.g. *C. trevelyani,* above) show in some respects a remarkable convergence with the marsupial mole of Australia (Fig. 497, p. 715). The eyes are small, or covered by skin. The ears are externally invisible and the legs are short and, particularly the fore-paws (A), specialised for burrowing. The fur is silky and iridescent. True moles belong to a different super-family (Soricoidea). (From *Cambridge Natural History.*)

sacrum is accordingly strongly constructed. The tail is short. The eyes are very small, and there is no ear-pinna.

The Tenrecoidea consist of two living families, the Tenrecidæ (= Centetidæ), found mainly in Madagascar, but with a few African representatives, and the Solenodontidæ, with a single genus, *Solenodon* (Fig. 509), in Cuba, Hayti and other West Indian islands. Fossil Solenodontidæ occurred in the Oligocene and Miocene of North America. The Tenrecidæ are varied in appearance. *Setifer* is spiny like a hedgehog, but it cannot roll up. *Microgale* is a small, shrew-like animal. *Hemicentetes,* which has spines mixed with hair, has reduced teeth and probably feeds on ants. *Limnogale* is aquatic, with webbed feet. All these are found in Madagascar, where the family has undergone an adaptive radiation. *Potamogale,* the otter-shrew of Africa, is also aquatic. It swims by its long, flattened tail and webbed feet, and has lost its lachrymal foramen and its clavicles. *Solenodon* (Fig. 509) is a relatively large, nocturnal animal with a long snout and a strongly developed tail. It uses its strong claws to break open dead wood to obtain insect food.

The golden moles (Chrysochloridæ) (Fig. 510) of East and South Africa, the only family in the Chrysochloroidea, are so different from the other Lipoty-

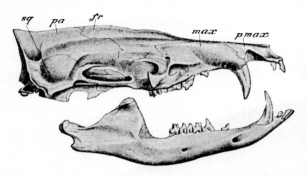

FIG. 511. — *Centetes*: **Skull.** Tenrec, lateral view. *fr.* frontal; *max.* maxilla; *pa.* parietal; *p. max.* premaxilla; *sq.* squamosal. (After Dobson.)

phla that some authorities have placed them in a separate order. In some of their fossorial adaptations they resemble the Talpidæ, which do not occur in Africa. Thus, the eyes are greatly reduced, pinnæ are absent, and the muscle crests on the humerus are strongly developed. However, the pectoral girdle is quite unlike that of the Talpidæ. The presternum is not markedly elongated, but the anterior ribs are concave to provide room for the humerus to be embedded in the body. The clavicles are long. The hand has only four digits, of which the second and third are provided with large claws. In these respects the golden moles resemble the marsupial *Notoryctes* (Fig. 497, 715). The skull is greatly modified. The face is turned down on the globular brain-case, and the whole skull is often very short and broad. Its sutures unite early. In some species the malleus is enormously enlarged, but the significance of this is unknown. The milk teeth are retained until the animal is mature, and function with the permanent molars.

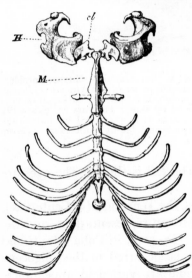

FIG. 512.—*Talpa*: **Sternum and part of shoulder girdle.** Mole. *cl.* clavicle; *H.* humerus; *M.* manubrium. (From *Cambridge Natural History*.)

Skeleton of the Lipotyphla.—The neural spine of the axis is usually well developed whilst those of the remaining cervical vertebræ are small or obsolete. The number of trunk-vertebræ varies in the different families from eighteen to twenty-four, and there is also great variation in the development of the various processes.

The number of sacral vertebræ ranges from two to seven. The caudal region is variable in length and frequently has chevron bones. These sometimes occur also in the lumbar region. The second, third, and fourth cervical vertebræ are fused in the mole. The presternum is usually an expanded, T-shaped bone, but in the moles it is greatly elongated.

The skull (Fig. 511) varies greatly in the different families. The cranial capacity is small, and the orbits and temporal fossæ are completely continuous. A postorbital constriction occurs in the Erinaceidæ, but only rarely in the Soricomorpha, in which the anterior part of the skull is tubular. The zygoma is often incomplete (Soricidæ, Tenrecoidea), and the jugal is small or absent. With few exceptions, the tympanic is ring-shaped and does not form a bulla. The palate is sometimes perforated.

In the *pectoral girdle* clavicles are always present except in *Potamogale*. The pectoral girdle of the moles has been described above. The humerus usually has an entepicondylar foramen, and often also a supracondylar foramen. In the moles (Fig. 512) it is short, greatly expanded at the extremities, and has a prominent deltoid ridge, and two synovial articular surfaces at the proximal end. One of these is for the glenoid cavity of the scapula; the other is for the clavicle. The radius and ulna are completely developed in all. They are usually distinct, but are sometimes fused distally. In the carpus the scaphoid and lunar sometimes coalesce, sometimes remain distinct; an os centrale is usually present. In the moles (Fig. 513) the manus is extremely broad, the breadth being increased by the presence of a large, curved, radial sesamoid (falciform bone).

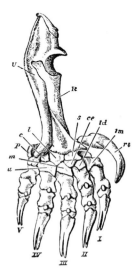

FIG. 513.—*Talpa:* **Forearm and manus.** Mole. *c.* cuneiform; *ce.* centrale; *l.* lunar; *m.* magnum; *p.* pisiform; *R.* radius; *rs.* radial sesamoid (falciform bone); *td.* trapezoid; *s.* scaphoid; *tm.* trapezium; *U.* ulna; *u.* unciform; *I—V.* digits.

In the *pelvis* the symphysis pubis is short or sometimes absent, the pubes remaining separated by a wide median ventral cleft. A third trochanter is sometimes represented by a ridge. The fibula usually, though not always, fuses distally with the tibia.

ORDER MENOTYPHLA

This order consists to-day of two very distinct families, the elephant-shrews (Macroscelididæ) of Africa and the tree-shrews (Tupaiidæ) (Fig. 514) of the Oriental region. The relationships of these animals are much disputed. The Macroscelididæ are often placed with the Lipotyphla as the 'Insectivora', and the Tupaiidæ were included by Simpson in the Primates. It has also been suggested that the Macroscelididæ should be raised to the rank of a distinct order. (For a discussion of the problem see, for example, Evans, Butler.) In spite of their differences, which are due largely to their adaptation to very different modes of life, the two families show a number of resemblances which are probably indicative of relationship. They may be regarded as survivors from the stock of primitive mammals from which the Primates have evolved.

FIG. 514.—Order **Menotyphla,** Family **Tupaiidæ.** *Tupaia.* The tree-shrews (e.g. *T. belangeri,* above) and the elephant shrews (Macroscelididæ) are often lumped with the Lipotyphla (Fig. 509) as an Order Insectivora. Including the pen-tailed species they are small, primitive, superficially squirrel-like eutherians that show certain resemblances with the 'lower' primates (p. 734) with which they are sometimes grouped. They are extremely active by day and some make relatively elaborate arboreal nests. They eat foliage, fruit, and insects, and sometimes small vertebrates. (From Zool. Soc. London photographs and skins from B.M. (N.H.).)

The Menotyphla differ from the Lipotyphla in several respects. The pubic symphysis is not reduced. A cæcum is present. The eyes are relatively large (Fig. 514). In the skull, the cranial cavity is larger, and extends forward between the large orbits. The jugal is well developed. A vertical plate of the palatine extends up the anterior medial wall of the orbit to meet the lachrymal, whereas in the Lipotyphla this part of the orbital wall is formed by an extension of the maxilla, and the palatine does not touch the lachrymal. The number of young produced at a birth is never more than three, and there are one to three pairs of mammary glands.

The Macroscelididæ are ground-living animals with enlarged hind limbs, resembling rabbits or jerboas in their manner of locomotion. The tibia is elongated, and is fused with the fibula at its lower end. The metatarsals are also elongated, and the pes is digitigrade. There is a large bulla, formed from several bones, including the tympanic and the alisphenoid. The last premolar is molariform, and the last molar is vestigial or absent. The testes are abdominal. Examples are *Rhynchocyon*, *Macroscelides*, and *Elephantulus*.

The Tupaiidæ are squirrel-like and climb trees with the aid of claws (Fig. 514). They resemble the lemurs in many features of the skull, but their feet are not prehensile. The tibia and fibula are free. The olfactory organ is smaller than in the Macroscelididæ, with fewer turbinal bones, and the olfactory lobes of the brain are reduced. The facial part of the skull is relatively shorter, and the eyes look somewhat forwards. As in lemurs, there is a postorbital bar, formed from the frontal and jugal bones. The ring-shaped tympanic is situated inside a bulla formed from the entotympanic, as in the Madagascan lemurs. The molar teeth are dilamb-dodont, resembling those of shrews. The testes descend permanently as in Primates. Examples are *Tupaia* and *Ptilocercus* (Fig. 515).

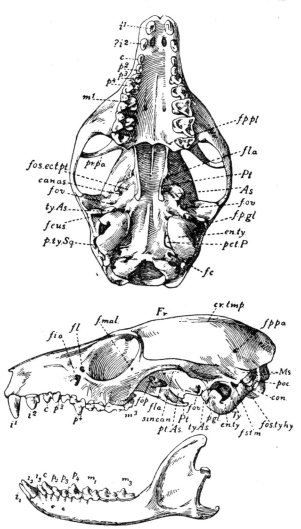

FIG. 515.—*Ptilocercus:* **Skull.** Tree-shrew, palatal and lateral views. $i.^1$ $i.^2$ incisors; *c.* canine; $p.^2, ^3, ^4,$ pre-molars; $M.^{1-3}$ molars. *As.* alisphenoid; *can. as.* alisphenoid canal; *con.* condyle; *cr. tmp.* temporal crest; *en. ty.* entotympanic; *f. c.* carotid foramen; *f. eus.* eustachian opening; *Fr.* frontal; *f. l. a.* foramen lacerum anterius; *f. mal.* malar foramen; *f. op.* optic foramen; *f. or.* foramen ovale; *fos. ect. pt.* ectopterygoid fossa; *fos. ty. hy.* tympano-hyoid fossa; *f. p. gl.* post-glenoid foramen; *fo. pl.* palatine foramen; *f. st. m.* stylomastoid foramen; *Ms.* mastoid; *p. ty. Sq.* post-tympanic process of squamosal; *Pt.* pterygoid; *Ty.* tympanic. (After Gregory.)

Anagale, from the Oligocene of Mongolia, is in some respects intermediate between the two living families, but it approaches the Primates in the flattening of its terminal phalanges, indicating the possession of nails. Some 'insectivores' from the Palæocene and Eocene may prove to belong to the Menotyphla, but their structure has not been sufficiently elucidated. The Leptictidæ, which range from the Upper Cretaceous to the Oligocene (e.g. *Ictops*), have hitherto been classed with the hedgehogs in the Lipotyphla, but recent studies of their skulls indicate that they probably stand near the base of the Menotyphla.

ORDER PRIMATES

There is still a considerable lack of knowledge as to many details of the structure of the earliest Primates, due to the rarity of their fossils, a consequence, probably, of their forest-living habits. 'Every scrap of fossilized material that has become available has been studied intensively because of Man's position in the order.' Yet a great deal of unnecessary confusion exists in the Primate literature. A major reason for this is that 'much of the work on primates has been done by students who had no experience in taxonomy and who were completely incompetent to enter this field, however competent they may have been in other respects . . . Most primates have alternative names . . . hardly two students use the same nomenclature for them. The importance of distinctions within the group has also been so exaggerated that almost every colour-phase, aberrant individual or scrap of bone or tooth has been given a separate name, and almost every really distinct species has been called a genus and a large proportion of genera have been called families. [Further] many studies of this order are covertly or overtly emotional' (Simpson).[1]

Linnæus included Man as a third genus in the Primates but many later authorities, including Cuvier, either declined to consider Man as an animal or regarded him as the unique occupant of a separate order. To-day no educated person has any doubt that *Homo sapiens* Linn. is a primate ; but there is still considerable argument as to his exact taxonomical position and relationships, as, indeed, there is concerning the origin of the Primates as a whole. There is, however, enough evidence to show the great antiquity of the group. Lemuriforms, for example, occur first in the Palæocene. Anthropoids, on the other hand, do not appear until the late Oligocene.

Absolutely diagnostic characters of a primate are not easy to find. The most primitive species (p. 736) still bear traces of their origin from the centralised Cretaceous 'insectivore' stock. There are, however, definite trends of evolution within the group, of which the beginning can be seen even in the

---

[1] Upon a single tooth later proved to be that of *Prosthenops*, an extinct peccary (p. 837), there was erected a 'new' genus and species with the resounding name *Hesperopithecus haroldcooki*, which was claimed to represent a North American Pliocene ape that resembled 'the human type more closely than it does any known anthropoid ape' (see Wood-Jones).

earliest forms. The dentition, for instance, never has the full eutherian formula of three incisors, a canine, four premolars, and three molars in each half of the upper and lower jaws. From the first it is reduced to two incisors, and (except in some early forms with four) to three premolars. Reduction may eventually proceed further by the loss of another premolar and a molar. The pattern of the molar teeth is at first trituberculo-sectorial, and in many later forms becomes quadri- or quinque-tubercular. The generalised nature of the primate diet has not resulted in the evolution of any great specialisation of tooth-pattern.

Primates were originally, and for the most part still are, arboreal. A return to a terrestrial habitat is a secondary and rare feature. This fundamental arboreality of the group has been held to have been of primary importance in the moulding of many of the most notable primate characteristics. Life away from the ground has allowed the drastic reduction of the olfactory receptor apparatus, olfactory bulbs, and rhinopallium. The consequent reduction of the snout allowed both eyes to look forward (in the manner of broad-faced, short-beaked nocturnal hunting birds) with the concomitant development of stereoscopic vision. Arboreal life also made possible the evolution of the grasping hand and opposable thumb. With all of these, and many other, novelties there came the great increase in size and complexity of the brain— especially in the neopallium of the cerebral hemispheres which grew so as ultimately to cover a large area of the cerebellum. The primate face has become more and more subcerebral as it became bent down on the basicranial axis, which became more inclined to the vertebral axis. Concurrently with the evolution of a grasping hand, the rounded articulation of the head of the radius with the humerus and of the distal extremity with the ulna allowed the hand to have a very free movement of supination, a characteristic primate feature, the primitive position of the mammalian hand being, of course, one of pronation.

Whilst the brain has become highly organised, with resulting modification of the skull, the rest of the body has retained a larger number of unspecialised features than is shown by many of the other orders of mammals. Progression is still plantigrade, and even in Man the number of digits remains the primitive five. Flat nails are characteristic of most primates, although claws occur on at least some of the fingers and toes of the lemuroids. The skull always has a complete orbital ring, and the eye-socket may either be confluent with the temporal fossa or separated by a bony partition. There is always a tympanic bulla formed by a flange from the petrosal with which the tympanic ring takes part in various ways. These have some value in classification.

The order is commonly divided into three sub-orders: the Lemuroidea, Tarsioidea, and Anthropoidea, but in this account the following condensed arrangement is preferred:

ORDER PRIMATES

Sub-order Prosimii
　Infra-order Lemuriformes
　　Families Plesiadapidæ (Palæocene–Eocene)
　　　　　　　Adapidæ (Eocene)
　　　　　　　Lemuridæ (Pleistocene–Recent)
　　　　　　　Indridæ (Pleistocene–Recent)
　　　　　　　Daubentoniidæ (?–Recent)
　Infra-order Lorisiformes
　　Family Lorisidæ (Miocene–Recent)
　Infra-order Tarsiiformes
　　Families Anaptomorphidæ (Palæocene–Oligocene)
　　　　　　　Tarsiidæ (?–Recent)
Sub-order Anthropoidea
　Super-family Ceboidea (Platyrrhina)
　　Families Cebidæ (Miocene–Recent)
　　　　　　Callithricidæ (?–Recent)
　Super-family Cercopithecoidea
　　Family Cercopithecidæ (Oligocene–Recent)
　Super-family Hominoidea
　　Families Parapithecidæ (Oligocene)
　　　　　　　Pongidæ (Oligocene–Recent)
　　　　　　　Hominidæ (Pleistocene–Recent)

It need hardly be said that the above classification, like all others, will most likely be modified as new data emerge.

SUB-ORDER PROSIMII

The Prosimii are the more primitive Primates. In the Palæocene and Eocene they formed practically the entire order. They had a wide distribution, many forms being known from Europe and North America. With the rise of the Anthropoidea in the Oligocene, the Prosimii were reduced in numbers, and are at present confined to Africa, Madagascar, and the eastern part of the Oriental Region (from Ceylon to Borneo). Three infra-orders may be distinguished: the Lemuriformes (Fig. 516) now confined to Madagascar; the Lorisiformes (Fig. 518), from the continent of Africa and the Oriental Region; and the Tarsiiformes (Fig. 519), represented to-day by a single genus from the East Indies. Fossils show that the Lemuriformes and Tarsiiformes were distinct groups even in the Palæocene.

INFRA-ORDER LEMURIFORMES

The lemurs share a number of generalised characters with the Tupaiidæ (p. 731), insectivores with whom they seem to have a common origin and which, in fact, may be more appropriately placed in the Primates.

To-day true lemurs (e.g. *Lemur* (Fig. 516)) exist in Madagascar only. Here

FIG. 516.—Order **Primates**, Sub-order **Prosimii**, Infra-order **Lemuriformes**, Family **Lemuridæ**. **Lemur.** The Ring-tailed Lemur (*L. catta*) is unusual in living among rocks. It inhabits southern and south-western Madagascar where trees are stunted and few. The animal has adapted itself to a mixed diet including especially prickly pears and often birds' eggs. It is about the size of a cat. The naked black area of the fore-arm covers the antebranchial ('carpal') gland (see also p. 847); nearby, on one or both limbs is a solid horny spur (not shown). Another gland, the brachial (not shown) occurs near the proximal end of the biceps muscle. (From photographs, and specimens from the B.M. (N.H.))

Pleistocene fossils (e.g. *Megaladapis*) also occur. In Madagascar too (and in Pleistocene deposits) is found the allied *Indri*. Elsewhere, other allies occur in the European and North American Palæocene (e.g. *Plesiadapis*) and Eocene (*Notharctus*, family Adapidæ). In Madagascar also still survives the Aye-aye (*Chiromys = Daubentonia*), yet another lemuroid of annectant family.

Compared with Anthropoidea, Lemuriformes show a number of distinguishing features, some explicable as primitive persistent characters, others as arboreal adaptations, and others as specialisations peculiar to the lemuroid line of evolution.   Primitive characters include the low brain-case (with its macrosmatic brain and uncovered cerebellum), the confluence under the postorbital rim of the orbital and temporal fossæ, the lateral instead of forward direction of the orbits (Fig. 517), the presence of four or even five ethmoturbinal bones (instead of the usual three), the backward extension of the jugal, the thickened hind border of the palate, the large nasal bones (wide at the back, instead of narrow and pointed), the *uterus duplex*, non-deciduous placenta, an entepicondylar foramen in the humerus and a third trochanter in the femur. The dentition is on the primitive trituberculosectorial plan, but subject to

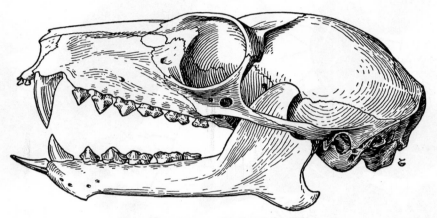

FIG. 517.—*Lemur:* **Skull and dentition.**

considerable specialisation in various forms.   The procumbent lower incisors and incisiform lower canines are specialisations that have arisen within the group.   The hands and feet are also specialised, in that the second pedal digit at least is always furnished with a sharp claw.   The second finger is likewise always clawed.   At least some of the digits have flat nails.   The tympanic ring is enclosed inside the bulla, where it lies free, as in the Tupaiidæ (Fig. 611). The aye-ayes (Daubentoniidæ) are notable for their short skull, single pair of enlarged incisors and reduced pre-molars.

INFRA-ORDER LORISIFORMES

The lorises are absent from Madagascar.   They occur in Africa (e.g. *Galago*, the bush-babies, and *Perodicticus*, the pottos, Fig. 518) and in Asia (e.g. *Loris*, the Slender Loris of India), including the East Indies.   They are poorly represented in the fossil record.   The oldest known form is *Progalago*, from the Miocene of Africa.

Though sharing many characters with the Lemuriformes, and often grouped with them in a sub-order Lemuroidea, the Lorisiformes are distinguished in several ways.   Thus the ring-shaped tympanic is not situated inside the bulla, but is attached to its edge to form a short bony auditory meatus. The ethmoid (*os planum*) appears in the medial wall of the orbit. Vibrissæ are reduced. In addition to the pair of mammary glands on the breast a second pair is present in the inguinal region. The eyes are enlarged and the face shortened, as in some Lemuriformes e.g. *Indri*. Also, as in Lemuriformes, the lower canine is incisiform.

FIG. 518.—Order **Primates**, Sub-order **Prosimii**, Infra-order **Lorisiformes**, Family **Lorisidæ**. ***Perodicticus.*** This family, including the pottos (e.g. *P. potto* above), bush-babies, and lorises is Asiatic and African in distribution, the present genus being confined to tropical Africa. Pottos are nocturnal. The present species possesses a peculiar defensive armoury of sharp vertebral spines that project through the skin. (Note toilet claw (cf. Fig. 483, p. 696). (From a photograph by Suschitzky.)

The galagos are leaping forms in which the calcaneum and navicular have become greatly lengthened. This has also happened, to a lesser degree, in some Lemuriformes, e.g. *Microcebus*.

INFRA-ORDER TARSIIFORMES

The tarsiers, to-day represented by only one genus, *Tarsius* (Fig. 519) of the East Indies, appear to have had a separate lineage dating from the Palæocene (Anaptomorphidæ, e.g. *Tetonius, Anaptomorphus*) and were formerly common in both the Old and New Worlds.

FIG. 519.—Order **Primates,** Sub-order **Prosimii,** Infra-Order **Tarsiiformes,** Family **Tarsiidæ.** *Tar-sius.* Celebesian Tarsier (*T. spectrum*). Tarsiers are rat-sized animals restricted to the Indo-Malayian region. They are essentially but not exclusively arboreal and inhabit rain-forests. Nocturnal and crepuscular (note orbits, Fig. 520) they cannot see well by day and generally sleep clinging to an almost vertical branch. They pro-gress by leaps, adhesion on impact being aided by peculiar digital pads (Fig. 607); the tail is not prehensile. They eat insects and small reptiles (tree geckos) and crustaceans on which they spring and capture by hand. Pre-18th century natura-lists sometimes placed these bizarre primates variously with opossums (marsupials) or jerboas (rodents). (From photographs.)

Tarsiers are of considerable in-terest in that they have been claimed anatomically to occupy an intermediate position between the lemurs and the anthropoids, and opinions have differed as to whether they are merely moderately aber-rant lemurs or representatives of an ancient stock of remote affinity thereto. *Tarsius* differs from lemurs and lorises in having the orbits (Fig. 520) directed forwards and almost completely separated from the temporal fossa, by the micros-matic brain, and by single olfactory foramina. They resemble Lorisi-formes in the arrangement of the tympanic ring, which remains out-side the bulla and forms the tubular external auditory meatus (Fig. 611). The structure of the nostrils and upper lip is nearer that of the anthropoids than of the lemurs, the jugal does not extend so far back, and the carotid artery enters the bulla wall.

There are specialised features which are sufficient to separate the tarsioids from the anthropoids. In the first place, the hind foot re-sembles that of *Galago* in having a greatly elongated navicular and calcaneum, a feature which occurs in all the early forms in which this structure is known, and one which alone is sufficient to prevent the line from being considered as directly ancestral. The digits of the hand have nails, as do all the toes except the second and third, which are clawed. The tibia and fibula are fused distally—a specialisation towards its peculiar saltatory progression. The great enlargement of the eyes (a specialisation for nocturnal habits) has caused considerable modification in the shape of the skull and, though the retinæ contain only rods, there are perhaps indications of a macula in the area where, in anthropoids, cones occur.

The head in general is more monkey-like than that of the lemurs. The enormous eyes have little mobility and in compensation the tarsier can rotate its head to a degree that enables the eyes to face backwards. The lemurine snout is replaced by a short face, with a relatively minute nose and large pinnæ. The olfactory areas of the brain are reduced, as might be anticipated, but the brain as a whole is large: the hemispheres, in accordance with the great occipital expansion correlated with unusually good vision, spread over part of the cerebellum:

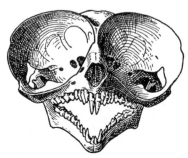

FIG. 520.—*Tarsius:* **Skull and dentition.** *T. spectrum* (see Fig. 519).

this last is relatively small and the mid-brain large. The placenta is deciduous and has similarities with that of higher forms. The external genitalia of both sexes are of primitive unspecialised pattern.

SUB-ORDER ANTHROPOIDEA

The rest of the Primates—the monkeys, apes, and Man—are included in the present group. Its precise origin remains in doubt, but fossils increasingly appear from the Oligocene onwards. Eocene remains are still unknown.

In the anthropoids the cranium is expanded as the cerebral hemispheres reach their greatest development. These overhang the cerebellum and the medulla as well and the neopallium is generally markedly convoluted with the development of the Sylvian fissure, and the central and other sulci. The occipital visual areas are notably well-developed. The optic tract exhibits a partial fibre-decussation; the eyes are forwardly directed and vision is binocular: the retina is variably, but often richly, supplied with cones and a macula lutea is generally present. The enhancement of the visual sense is correlated with a corresponding reduction in olfactory reception. The nose differs from that of the lemurs. In lemurs the muzzle or rhinarium has the primitive naked form, and the narial orifice is continued laterally as in most mammals. The rhinarium itself is hairless, and extends to the non-protrusible upper lip, which is restrained by a mucosal ligament. In the anthropoids the nostrils are completely ringed round by naked skin: there is no moist rhinarium. The upper lip lacks a ligament, and so is freely protrusible. The pinnæ are reduced and generally are pressed to the head. The tympanic bone is united with the squamosal. The sphincter colli is differentiated into muscles that enable a new facial mobility and permit the expression of crude emotion (Fig. 521).

The upper molars consist of the trigon of three cusps, to which a fourth (hypocone) has been added.   The cusps become joined by crests in various ways. In the lower molars the talonid and trigonid become equal in height and the paraconid is lost.   There are nearly always three molars, but in the Callithricidæ the last one is lost.   The bicuspid premolars are limited to three and later to two on each side.   The incisors lose their spike-like form and become broad cutting teeth.   With the exception of the primitive marmosets (Callithricidæ) the fingers and toes are all provided with flat nails and the pollex and hallux are opposable.   The foramen magnum tends to face downwards,

FIG. 521.—Order **Primates,** Sub-order **Anthropoidea:** New World Super-family **Ceboidea** (= **Platyrrhina**) and Old World Super-family **Cercopithecoidea** (= **Catarrhina,** minus gibbons, apes, and Man).   *Left:* Platyrrhine Spider Monkey *Ateles geoffroyi* (Family Cebidæ).   *Right:* Narrow-nosed Rhesus Monkey, *Macaca mulatta* (Family Cercopithecidæ).   (From photographs by Suschitzky.)

instead of backwards, in accordance with a semi-upright or upright gait. Other important characteristics are the highly efficient hæmochorial placentation, a *uterus simplex* and the occurrence of menstruation.   The last-named is not a widespread phenomenon.   Although common or perhaps universal in the Cercopithecoidea and Hominoidea, it is not ubiquitous in the Ceboidea.   It occurs in *Tarsius,* but not in the lemurs (nor in the tree-shrew *Tupaia,* sometimes included in the Prosimii).

Menstruation has been suggested in the dermopteran Colugo (*Cynocephalus*), as well as in the menotyphlan *Elephantulus.*   It has been reported in bats. Phenomena claimed as menstrual have sometimes proved to be merely cyclical (or even non-cyclical) uterine hæmorrhages, rather than the sudden and total destruction of the uterine mucosa specifically at the end of the luteal phase of the œstrous cycle (p. 896).

The Anthropoidea are generally subdivided into two groups—the Platyrrhina, or New World Monkeys, and the Catarrhina from the Old World (Fig. 521). There is, however, good reason for the creation of three divisions and so we must abandon the classical dichotomy.

SUPER-FAMILY CEBOIDEA (PLATYRRHINA)

This includes two exclusively New World (Central and South American) families, (1) Callithricidæ (marmosets) and (2) Cebidæ, composed of the capuchins (*Cebus*), spider monkeys (*Ateles*) (Fig. 521), howlers (*Alouatta*), woolly monkeys (*Lagothrix*) and others. Of these 'flat-nosed monkeys', with widely separated nostrils and a broad septum, *some species are deceptively narrow-nosed (catarrhine) in appearance*. The Platyrrhina have probably been isolated since the Eocene, and although they are more primitive than the Old World monkeys, the two stocks are obviously very similar in essentials. However, the tail in platyrrhines is almost always primitively long and is sometimes prehensile, the thumb is relatively unopposable and three premolars are retained, whereas the second premolar had already been lost in the earliest known (Oligocene) catarrhines. The tympanic ring is united with the petrosal. It resembles that of the lorises, whereas the tympanic bone of catarrhines is tube-like and resembles that of the tarsiers. A large bulla occurs ; this is absent in catarrhines. Within the group there is only the faintest suggestion of menstruation. The howlers have developed a large ossified laryngeal chamber that acts as a resonator.

Ceboidea are represented in the South American Miocene, but possibly very significantly, they remain undiscovered in North America, a fact that has led to the conjecture that they may have arisen independently from a once widespread tarsioid stock.

SUPER-FAMILY CERCOPITHECOIDEA

Early last century, Hemprich grouped the Old World monkeys, apes, and Man as the Catarrhina or narrow-nosed Primates, as opposed to the Platyrrhina of the New World (see above). However, the Old World monkeys, which form the family Cercopithecidæ, stand apart from the other catarrhine forms, and have been placed by Simpson in a separate super-family.

The Cercopithecoidea resemble the Hominoidea (see below) and differ from the Ceboidea (= Platyrrhina) in the reduction of the premolars to two, in the presence of a long tubular bony auditory meatus (Fig. 611, p. 853), and in the reduction of the turbinals and nasal fossæ (allowing of close-set nostrils). The thumb is opposable, except in the guerezas (*Colobus*) where it has atrophied. They are more primitive than the Hominoidea in the possession of a tail, which is often long, but never prehensile.   In some forms, such as some of the macaques or rhesus monkeys (*Macaca*) and the mandrill (*Mandrillus*), the tail is short. Ischial callosities (areas of bare skin on the buttocks, often brightly coloured) are well-developed.   Cheek-pouches are present, except in the guerezas and the langurs (*Semnopithecus*), which have complex lobulated stomachs.   The molar teeth have four cusps, which are arranged in two pairs, united by cross-crests (bilophodont).   Most cercopithecids are arboreal, but many are habitually terrestrial, *e.g.* baboons (*Papio*).   On the ground they walk on all fours in a *plantigrade* manner.

Cercopithecidæ were present in the African Miocene and perhaps earlier. By the Pliocene several living genera can be recognised.

Super-family Hominoidea

The extinct Egyptian Oligocene Parapithecidæ and the extant apes (Pongidæ) and Man (Hominidæ) are now separated from the other narrow-nosed anthropoids as a super-family Hominoidea.   They differ from the Cercopithecoidea in several respects.   The tail has disappeared.   The thorax is broad, with a flattened ventral surface, the sternum having become short and wide, whereas in cercopithecoids the thorax is narrow from side to side as in most mammals.   The lumbar region of hominoids is shorter than in cercopithecoids, and there are only 4 or 5 lumbar vertebræ, instead of 6 or 7.   The brain is proportionately larger than in cercopithecoids.   Ischial callosities have disappeared except in the gibbons, and cheek-pouches are never present.   The hair on the forearm points towards the elbow instead of towards the wrist. The molar teeth are characterised by the retention of an oblique crest from the protocone to the metacone, a survival from the trituercular stage (p. 865).

Family Pongidæ

The Pongidæ are to-day confined to the widely separated forests of Africa (*Gorilla* (Fig. 522); and the chimpanzee, *Pan*), Southern China, Indo-Malaya (*Hylobates*, gibbons), and the East Indies west of Wallace's Line (*Pongo*, the Orang-utan).   They are specialised in the elongation of the fore-limbs, which, especially in the gibbons, are used in swinging from branch to branch (*brachiation*).   Gibbons can walk in an upright position using the fore-limbs as balancing rods, but all other apes use their long forearms as crutches to help swing the trunk over the ground.

The Pongidæ are represented from the Lower Oligocene by the Egyptian *Propliopithecus*.   Several apes occurred in the Lower Miocene of East Africa, of which *Limnopithecus* appears to be related to the gibbons, while *Proconsul* and *Sivapithecus* represent the great apes.   Limb-bones of *Limnopithecus* and *Proconsul* show, however, that the brachiating habit had not been developed at that time, and the brain of *Proconsul* was probably more primitive than in existing apes. Several forms of ape have been found in the Miocene and Pliocene of Europe and India (*Pliopithecus*, *Dryopithecus*, *Sivapithecus* etc.). *Oreopithecus*, from the Lower Pliocene of Italy, resembled Man in the small size of its canine teeth. A much greater resemblance to Man is shown by the South African, possibly cave-dwelling, Australopithecinæ. These were almost

Fig. 522.—Order **Primates**, Sub-order **Anthropoidea**, Super-family **Hominoidea**, Family **Pongidæ.** *Gorilla.* The largest and heaviest of the primates, the Gorilla (*G. gorilla*) sometimes reaches a height of about six feet and a weight of more than 400 lbs. It usually lives in territorial family groups (10 to 15 animals) dominated by an old male that is probably polygamous. A mixed diet includes fruit, foliage, and seeds. Contrary to popular belief, gorillas generally prefer to retreat if the human intruder stands his ground. (From photographs.)

certainly bipedal, and approached man in the pelvis and the form of the teeth. They are regarded by many as primitive members of the family Hominidæ.

FAMILY HOMINIDÆ

The third family, the Hominidæ (if the Australopithecinæ are excluded) consists of only two genera—the extinct *Pithecanthropus* (= *Sinanthropus*), including the Java and Pekin 'men', and the genus *Homo*, first identifiable in the Pleistocene, containing two species, *H. neanderthalensis* and *H. sapiens*. The only surviving species is *H. sapiens* which embraces all the known 'races' of men—negroid, mongoloid, australoid, and caucasian, irrespective of colour and other superficialities.

Until recently, a third genus, *Eoanthropus* was recognised by most (but not all) authorities on the evidence presented by fragments of a skull and part of a lower jaw discovered in Pleistocene gravel at Piltdown in England. A few workers (*e.g.* Waterston and Miller) claimed that the jaw bore too great a resemblance to that of an ape to belong to a skull of such considerable cranial capacity as the one with which it was associated and, in fact, asserted that although the skull was human, the mandible was simian.

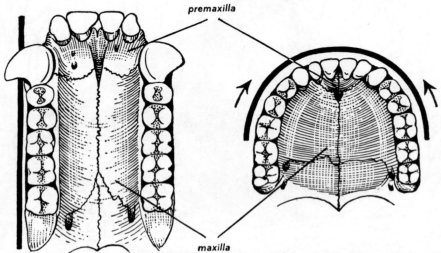

FIG. 523.—**Hominoidea: Jaw Structure and dentition in *Gorilla* and *Homo*.** Left, *Gorilla* (Pongidæ): The most anterior part of the face is formed by the premaxilla. The two elongated dental arcades are almost parallel and the incisors project markedly. A diastema is present. Right, *Homo* (Hominidæ): In Man alone among the Mammalia the premaxilla, although distinguishable on the palate by a premaxillo-maxillary suture, does not form an independent part of the face (as pointed out by Vesalius). Opinion is divided as to whether the premaxilla is *overgrown* by the embryonic maxilla (Wood Jones) or whether it is lost as a distinct facial element because of the fusion of both bones during early development. The general shortening of the dental arch in Man is, despite a certain broadening, associated with reduced tooth-size in a continuous series. Other dental characteristics in Man are the small size and frequent absence of the maxillary lateral incisors, the small, sexually undifferentiated canines, the reduction and arrangement of premolar roots, and the often crowded, relatively small molars. (Redrawn after Wood Jones.)

In 1953 exhaustive inquiries by means of modern fluorine-determination and other tests showed that the cranial fragments are probably of Upper Pleistocene age, but that the mandible is unquestionably that of a modern ape. The teeth of a young animal had been artificially abraded to simulate those of an adult man, and the jaw-bone had been stained by iron salts and potassium dichromate. Fragments from a second reputed individual were proved also to be fraudulent, as also were alleged implements found nearby. Inevitably the unmasking of this now-famous fraud was seized upon by fundamentalists to attempt to discredit all researches revealing the evolution of Man.

Actually, the erasure of '*Eoanthropus*' clarifies the problem of human ancestry. The work that led to the unmasking of the Piltdown fraud (see Weiner) was undertaken largely because the mandible and teeth of *Eoanthropus* could not be reconciled with those of indubitably genuine modern 'finds'.

Man, the sole living representative of the Hominidæ, differs anatomically from all other primate mammals in the following (among other) particulars:

(1) in his habitual bipedal orthograde posture and its associated morphological and physiological specialisations;

(2) in his distinctive external body-form, determined partly by the locomotor system, partly by subcutaneous fat;

(3) in the peculiarities of hair distribution and hair tracts.

(4) in the primitive morphological simplicity of the external genitalia in both sexes and the absence of 'sexual' skin, baculum, and ischial callosities;

(5) in the small canines which show very little sexual differentiation and do not project beyond the other teeth, but bite edge to edge like the incisors.

(6) in the lack of the premaxilla (*os incisivum*) which does not persist as a separate post-natal skeletal element.

(7) in the absolute size and structural complexity of the cerebrum.

(8) in the uniquely prolonged period of infancy and childhood and the slowness of skeletal maturation.

Man alone performs true ('heel and toe') walking: the arched foot was evolved for support, not prehension; the hallux cannot be abducted and is never a potential 'thumb'. The skull is balanced upon, not slung from, the spinal column, and the foramen magnum looks downwards and forwards: the balancing muscles attach to relatively little of the skull base, hence the occipital region protrudes. The large nasals remain permanently discrete: early in ontogeny the premaxilla becomes incorporated with the descriptive 'maxilla', so that a premaxillary-maxillary suture is lacking. The facial skeleton does not protrude muzzle-wise: the external nose and chin are prominent. The teeth have the maxillary premolars single- or double-rooted (triple-rooted in cercopithecids and anthropoid apes) and the mandibular premolars generally single-rooted (double-rooted in cercopithecids). A philtrum, superior labial tubercle and red everted lip-margins characterise the face. Coarse body-hair is confined to the scalp and beard areas, the eyebrows and eyelashes, the axillæ and the pubic region; and the disposition of hair tracts is much unlike that of anthropoid apes. Subcutaneous fat helps to mould the body contour, especially in the female, wherein the mammæ, even when non-lactating, are prominent surface features.

Postnatal development is extremely protracted, the successive periods of infancy, childhood and adolescence being unparalleled among mammals, Skeletal maturity is not attained until about the twenty-fifth year. This protracted period of dependence and immaturity is pre-eminently one of learning, permitting the acquisition of physical skills and the development of the specifically human intellect.

For Man is, uniquely, the rational animal, capable of forming abstract concepts and of enunciating his thought in articulate speech. Correlated with these higher faculties, and constituting the machinery of their expression, is the absolutely large and structurally complex cerebrum, with its characteristically extensive association areas and its intricacy of fibre-connexion.

Skeleton of the Primates.—The atlas is ring-like, the odontoid sub-conical. The spines of the cervical vertebræ are usually well-developed and simple. In Man they are short (with the exception of the seventh) and commonly bifid. In some forms they are trifid. The number of thoraco-lumbar vertebræ is usually nineteen, but there are only seventeen in Man, the Gorilla, and Chimpanzee, and sixteen in the Orang. In some lemurs there may be twenty-three or twenty-four. The number of sacral vertebræ varies from two to five. The sacrum of Man, which comprises five ankylosed verte-bræ, differs from that of other Primates in its greater relative breadth and in its backward curvature : it forms a well-marked angle (*sacro-vertebral angle*) with the lumbar region, an angle much less pronounced in other primates. The number of caudal vertebræ varies with the length of the tail—from four to about thirty-three. In Man there are but four vestigial caudal vertebræ, ankylosed to form the *coccyx*. In all forms wherein the tail is well developed chevron bones are present.

The human *skull* (Fig. 524) presents a marked contrast in certain respects to that of other mammals, but in some points is approached by that of the Simiidæ. An obtrusive characteristic of the human skull is the large size of the brain-case, the cubic content of the cranial cavity averaging 1500 cubic centi-metres in the European male. This great development is most marked in that part of the cavity which lodges the cerebral hemispheres, in adaptation to the large dimensions of which the cranium bulges out both anteriorly and posteriorly to such an extent that the entire length of the cavity greatly exceeds that of the basicranial axis. A result of the posterior bulging of the brain-case is that the foramen magnum (*f. m.*) is no longer situated at the posterior extremity of the skull as in other mammals, but assumes a position farther forwards towards the middle of the base. The anterior expansion, causing a strong arching forwards of the frontal region, brings about an alteration in the position of the ethmoidal cribriform plane. Instead of being perpendicular or inclined to the basi-cranial axis this becomes horizontal, and forms the middle part of the floor of the anterior cranial fossa. The fossa for lodgment of the cerebellum lies entirely beneath the posterior portion of the cerebral fossa ; the olfactory fossa is comparatively small.

The outer cranial surface is smooth and rounded, devoid of any prominent ridges or crests. The occipital crest of lower mammals is represented merely by

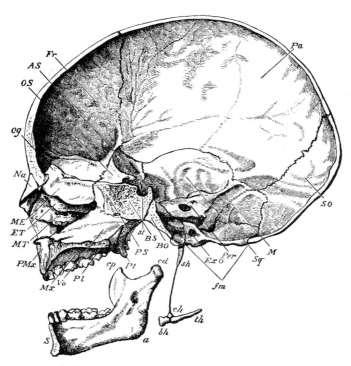

FIG. 524.—**Homo: Skull and hyoid apparatus.** Juvenile (at first dentition) with mandible displaced downwards to show its entire form. The lettering reads clockwise from the upper jaw: *P. mx.* anterior portion of maxilla; *MT.* maxillo-turbinal; *ET.* ethmo-turbinal; *ME.* ossified portion of the mesethmoid; *Na.* nasal; *cg.* crista galli of the mesethmoid; *OS.* orbitosphenoid, or lesser wing of the sphenoid; *AS.* alisphenoid, or greater wing of the sphenoid. *Fr.* frontal; *Pa.* parietal; *SO.* supraoccipital; *M.* mastoid portion of the periotic; *Sq.* squamosal; *Per.* petrous portion of the periotic; the large foramen below the end of the line is the internal auditory meatus, the small depression above it is the nearly-obliterated floccular fossa. *ExO.* exoccipital, the line points to the condylar foramen; *fm.* foramen magnum; *BO.* basioccipital; *BS.* basi-sphenoid; *st.* sella turcica; *PS.* presphenoid, ankylosed with the basisphenoid, forming the 'body of the sphenoid'; *Pt.* pterygoid; *Pl.* palatine; *Vo.* vomer; *Mx.* maxilla. *Lower Jaw:* s. sym-physis of mandible; *cp.* coronoid process; *cd.* articular condyle; *a.* angle. *Hyoid apparatus:* *sh.* stylohyal, or 'styloid process of temporal'; *ch.* ceratohyal, or lesser cornu of hyoid; *bh.* basihyal, or body of hyoid; *th.* thyrohyal, or greater cornu of hyoid. (After Flower.)

a rough raised line—the *superior curved line* of the occiput. The paroccipital processes are represented by slight eminences only—the *jugular eminences.* There is no auditory bulla ; the mastoid portion of the periotic projects down-wards as a prominent *mastoid process.* The periotic, tympanic, and squamosal early fuse into one bone—the *temporal bone.* The post-glenoid process is very slightly developed. The whole facial region is relatively small. The orbits, which are of moderate size, are directed forwards ; their bony margins are complete, and a plate of bone, developed partly from the jugal, partly from the alisphenoid, almost completely cuts them off from the temporal fossæ, leaving only a small, but characteristically wide, aperture of communication—the *spheno-maxillary fissure*. The interfrontal suture usually disappears early. The nasals rarely fuse in post-natal life. The suture between the premaxilla and the maxilla becomes obliterated early in fœtal life, so that the entire upper jaw appears to consist of a single bone. A peculiar spine, the *nasal spine*, is developed in the middle line below the nasal opening. The most marked feature of the mandible is the presence of a prominence, the *mental prominence*, in the lower part of the symphysial region (S.). The stylohyal nearly always becomes fused together with the tympanohyal to the periotic and tympanic, giving rise to a slender process, the *styloid process* (*sh.*) which projects downwards from the base of the skull.

None of the other primates has a cranial capacity approaching that of Man. Therefore, in them those modifications in the shape of the skull which are the concomitants of the great development of the human brain are accordingly not recognisable, or are much less strongly marked. The various fossæ of the cranium, however, as a rule occupy the same relative positions as in Man. The cerebellar fossa is entirely beneath the cerebral. The ethmoidal plane, and that of the foramen magnum (occipital plane), are usually both horizontal or nearly so. In all the Pongidæ, with the exception of the orangs, the frontals meet in the middle line below, over the presphenoid. In many monkeys the outer surface of the cranium is smooth and free from prominent ridges. In others, as in the baboons, the Orang, the Gorilla, and the Chimpanzee there are strongly developed occipital, sagittal, and supraorbital ridges. These are usually much more prominent in the male than in the female and increase in size with age. The paroccipital processes are always rudimentary, but there are well-marked post-glenoid processes. The mastoid does not form a distinct mastoid process in many forms. In the Cebidæ and marmosets alone is there a tympanic bulla. The entire facial region is relatively larger than in Man ; the premaxillo-maxillary region is always more prominent, and in the baboons projects forwards as a distinct muzzle. The orbit is separated from the temporal fossa as in Man. The nasals are usually fused in the adult. The nasal spine is never developed. The suture between the premaxilla and the maxilla becomes obliterated, if at all, only in old individuals. The mental prominence of the mandible is never developed, the anterior surface of the symphysial region sloping backwards and downwards from the alveolar margin. The stylohyal never gives rise to an ossified styloid process.

In the skull, as in many other respects, the lemurs occupy an intermediate position between the higher Primates and the lower orders of mammals. The

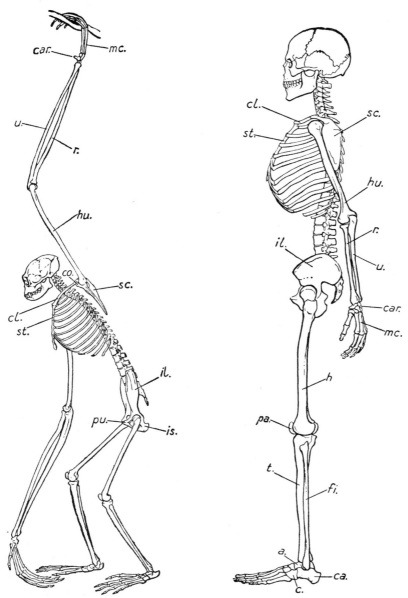

FIG. 525.—**Primates: Endoskeleton of *Hylobates* and *Homo.*** *a.* astragalus (talus); *ca.* calcaneum; *car.* carpus; *cl.* clavicle; *co.* coracoid; *fi.* fibula; *h.* femur; *hu.* humerus; *il.* ilium; *is.* ischium; *mc.* metacarpals; *pa.* patella; *pu.* pubis; *ra.* radius; *sc.* scapula; *st.* sternum; *t.* tibia; *u.* ulna. (After Young.)

occipital and ethmoidal planes are usually vertical. The tympanic forms a large bulla. The orbits, which are large, are usually separated from the temporal fossæ by a narrow rim of bone only. The lachrymal foramen is situated on the face outside the margin of the orbit. The facial region is usually elongated, and may form a prominent muzzle.

In all the Primates the *clavicle* is complete (Fig. 525), and in the *scapula* the spine, acromion, and coracoid process all are well developed. In Man and the higher apes the glenoid border of the scapula is much longer than the coracoid border. In the lower monkeys, on the other hand, these borders are nearly equal. The humerus is comparatively long and slender ; the tuberosities and ridges are not, as a rule, very strongly developed. In Man and the apes the bone is twisted around its long axis ; in the lower forms this torsion is absent. In Man and the higher apes the foramen above the inner condyle is absent but

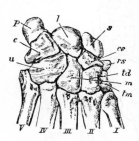

FIG. 526.—***Papio:***
Carpus. Baboon. *ce.* centrale; *c.* cuneiform; *l.* lunare; *m.* magnum; *p.* pisiform; *r. s.* radial sesamoid; *s.* scaphoid; *td.* trapezoid; *tm.* trapezium; *u.* unciform. (After Flower.)

it is present in many of the American monkeys and in most lemurs. Characteristic of the ulna of Man and the higher apes is the small upward extension of the olecranon process. The radius and ulna are discrete in all. In the higher forms the shafts of the two bones are bent apart, a wide interosseous space intervening and facilitating considerable freedom of pronation and supination. In the carpus (Fig. 526) the scaphoid and lunar are always distinct, and a centrale is present in all except some of the lemurs, the Gorilla, Chimpanzee, and Man. A pisiform is present, and in most a radial sesamoid. As compared with that of the other Primates, the carpus of Man is short and broad ; the trapezium has a saddle-shaped articular surface turned somewhat inwards. In Man, the Chimpanzee, Gorilla, and Orang the carpus articulates exclusively with the radius. In all the others it articulates also with the ulna. In Man the pollex has a remarkable and characteristic freedom of movement in opposition to the other digits.

The *pelvis* of Man is remarkable for its relative breadth, for the expanded form of the ilia and the deep concavity of their inner surfaces, and for the shortness of the pubic symphysis. In the higher apes some of these features are recognisable, though less pronounced ; but in the lower apes the ilia are long and narrow, and usually curved outwards. In the Old World monkeys the tuberosities of the ischia are strongly everted and roughened for the attachment of the ischial callosities.

The tibia and fibula are well developed and discrete in all. In nearly all the hallux (owing to the form and direction of the articulation between it and the internal cuneiform) is opposable to the other digits. This converts the foot into a grasping organ.   The human foot (Fig. 527) is distinguishable from that of the other Primates by the absence of this power of opposition and by the relative length of the tarsus, which exceeds that of the metatarsus.

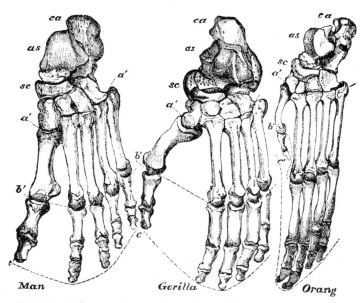

FIG. 527.—*Primates:* **Comparative anatomy of pes.**   Foot of *Homo, Gorilla,* and *Pongo* at the same absolute length to show the difference in proportions.   The line *a'a'* indicates the boundary between tarsus and metatarsus; *b'b',* that between the latter and the proximal phalanges; and *c'c'* bounds the ends of the distal phalanges; *as.* astragalus; *ca.* calcaneum; *sc.* scaphoid.   (After Huxley.)

ORDER DERMOPTERA

A single Oriental genus, *Cynocephalus* (= *Galeopithecus*) (Fig. 528), with only two species, forms the family Cynocephalidæ (= Galæopithecidæ) or 'flying lemurs'.

The 'flying lemurs' do not fly and are not lemurs : 'Colugo' is therefore a better group name.   The colugos are quite distinct and are aberrant 'insectivoran' derivatives.   They have close affinity with the Chiroptera within which group they have sometimes been included.

The most noticeable character of *Cynocephalus* is the hairy, muscular parachuting membrane or *patagium* which extends from the neck to the manus (embracing all the digits) and down the sides of the body to the ankle, and thence to the tip of the moderately long tail.   It may be compared to the similar, but not identical, structures in the gliding marsupials and rodents. The brain, like that of the 'insectivores,' is primitive in being macrosmatic, and in having the corpora quadrigemina uncovered by the cerebrum.   The dentition is peculiar.   The lower incisors are procumbent and comb-like, the molars multicuspidate.   The bulla is formed by the tympanic ring, which also forms the lower border of the spout-like external auditory meatus. In several characters the Dermoptera agree with the fruit-bats, the Tupaiidæ, and the lemurs, but how far these characters are merely convergent is indeterminate in the present state of knowledge. The order appears to have had a separate line of evolution from the Lower Eocene (cf. *Plagiomene* and its allies).

Fig. 528.—Order **Dermoptera,** Family **Cynocephalidæ.** *Cynocephalus.* The Colugo or so-called Flying Lemur (*C. variegatus*) does not fly and is unrelated to the lemurs. This East Indies form, which shows certain 'insectivoran' (p. 725) affinities, possesses gliding membranes that enclose neck, limbs, and tail. The feet, too, are webbed. Journeys of up to 70 yards, sometimes with the baby clinging to the mother's ventral surface, are made. Like other mammalian gliders (*e.g.* Fig. 498, p. 717) the Colugo turns sharply upwards as it reaches its target, thus presenting a flat surface at the point of impact. Strictly nocturnal, the Colugo lives almost entirely on fruit and leaves. The second surviving species (*C. volans*) occurs in the Phillipines (From a photograph by Walker, and skins from B.M. (N.H.).)

ORDER CHIROPTERA

The Chiroptera or bats (Fig. 529) are the only mammals capable of true flight. The fore-limbs have the segments greatly elongated (especially the fore-arm and the four ulnar digits), and these support a thin membranous fold of the integument which stretches to the hind-limbs and constitutes the wing. Curious arterio-venous connexions in the wings allow a speedy through-flow and a considerable short-circuiting of the capillary bed. The sternum is keeled for the attachment of the large pectoral flight muscles. The great development of these muscles is sometimes associated with an axillary or even a dorsal disposition of the mammary tissue.

There is often a cartilaginous rod (*calcar*) attached to the inner side of the ankle which helps to support a second membranous fold (inter-femoral membrane) extending between the hind-limbs, and sometimes involving the tail.

FIG. 529.—Order **Chiroptera**, Sub-order **Megachiroptera**, Family **Pteropidæ**. *Pteropus*. The nocturnal, large-eyed fruit-bats or flying-foxes of Indo-Malaya and Australasia (excluding New Zealand) congregate noisily by day in 'camps' that sometimes contain hundreds of thousands of bats. They use both thumb and pedal claws while feeding and changing position in camp. The biggest species (e.g. *P. giganteus*) are as large as a small cat and have a wing-spread of about five feet. They are nomadic pests, following the fruit-crops, and eating flowers as well. (Partly after a photograph by Suschitzky, and B.M. (N.H.) skins.)

The ulna is vestigial. The pollex, much shorter than the other digits, is directed forwards, and terminates in a well-developed curved claw. In the Megachiroptera, but not in the Microchiroptera, the second digit is also usually clawed, but the other digits are always clawless. The position of the hind-limbs is peculiar. Each is rotated outwards so that the knee is directed backwards instead of forwards as in other mammals. The five pedal digits are all provided with claws. So complete is the adaptation of the limbs for flight and suspension (in caves and trees) that bats are only able to shuffle along with great difficulty on the ground. In the Megachiroptera the muzzle is nearly always elongated, and the pinna of the ear simple. In the Microchiroptera the muzzle is generally short, the pinna usually complicated by the presence of an inner lobe or *tragus*, and often produced into remarkable arborescent appendages. The nose is also often provided with elaborate leaf-like or arborescent lobes (Fig. 530). The body is usually covered with soft fur, except in one group of Microchiroptera in which the integument is practically naked. The tail is sometimes short, sometimes well developed. In the Chiroptera the cerebral hemispheres are smooth and do not overlap the cerebellum. The olfactory centres are reduced as in the generality of flying animals. The dentition is complete, heterodont and diphyodont. The milk teeth are small hooked structures which help attach the young to the mother. The penis is large and pendent. The testes are abdominal but may descend seasonally, and often unilaterally, to a prominent situation in the groin. The uterus is simple or bicornuate. The placenta is deciduous and discoidal in the examples studied.

Sub-order Megachiroptera

These are generally big frugivorous Chiroptera with large eyes, long snout, without foliaceous nasal or auricular appendages and with the second digit of the manus usually ending in a claw. The tail, when present, is not enclosed in the inter-femoral membrane, but lies below it. The crowns of the molar teeth are devoid of sharp cusps. This sub-order comprises the fruit-bats or so-called flying-foxes (*Pteropus*) and other genera from the tropical and sub-tropical parts of Asia, Australia, and Africa. Indian and Australian fruit-bats (*Pteropus*) may have a wing-span of some five feet (Fig. 529).

Sub-order Microchiroptera

These are widely distributed, small, mostly insectivorous, Chiroptera usually with a short snout and, frequently, foliaceous nasal and auricular appendages. The second digit of the manus is always clawless. The tail when present is at least partially enclosed in the inter-femoral membrane. The crowns of the molar teeth have typically sharp cusps.

The sub-order includes all other bats (e.g. *Vespertilio, Miniopterus, Rhinolophus, Desmodus* (Fig. 530) and *Diphylla* (true vampires) and dozens of other genera). The little insectivorous forms have generally relatively small eyes, but they are never blind. They fly with assurance in apparently totally dark caves and in experimentally blackened rooms by means of an echo-location apparatus analogous to the sonic depth-sounding devices of Man (cf. the radar-like direction-finding apparatus of fishes, p. 335). Blindfolded bats do not collide with objects placed in their line of flight. As early as the late 18th century Spallanzani showed that only when the *ears* are obstructed do bats strike such obstacles, but it was not until 1920 that Hartridge suggested that they might find their way by means of echos from ultrasonic squeaking. Recent work with *Myotis* has revealed that bats can indeed appreciate frequencies as high as 100,000 cycles (cf. Man, with an upper range of about 20,000 cycles) and that only if *both* ears are left unobstructed do they successfully avoid wires stretched across their path. Efficiency varies in relation to the

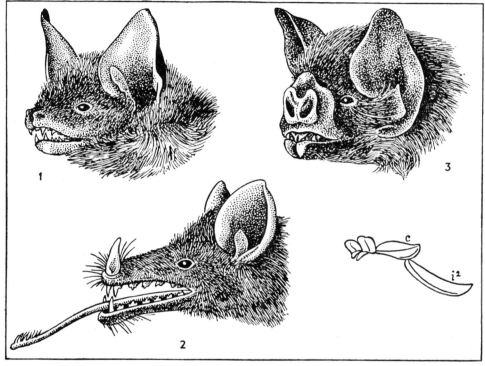

Fig. 530.—Order **Chiroptera,** Sub-order **Microchiroptera: Feeding adaptations.** 1. *Myotis lucifugus* (Family Vespertilionidæ) of North America, a generalised insect-eater. 2. *Chœronycteris mexicana* (Family Phyllostomatidæ), a tropical American form that lives mostly on nectar and pollen. It has a long snout, tactile vibrissæ, and brush tongue (cf. Fig. 426, p. 621). 3. *Desmodus rotundus* (Desmodontidæ), a tropical American true vampire which feeds on vertebrate blood. The flattened muzzle enables the highly specialised blade-like teeth deftly and almost painlessly to operate on the sleeping host. Below are shown a sharp, narrow upper incisor (i²) and canine (c). A small depression is scooped in the skin from which blood seeps; this is transferred by the vampire's tongue. The stomach is reduced. Little heavier than house mice, *D. rotundus* and its allies are unique among bats in their ability to move with gentle agility on a horizontal surface. (Redrawn after Wimsatt, Gregory.)

thickness of obstacles. Further, the more numerous the wires, the higher becomes the rate of vocalisation. The chiropteran apparatus of vocal emission, auditory reception and muscular reaction has evolved to a refinement that enables some species to turn sharply aside from obstacles less than ten inches distant. *Rousettus*, one of the large-eyed fruit-bats also possesses an echo location device. There is, incidentally, evidence that the nocturnal, cave-nesting South American nightjar *Steatornis caripensis* (Fig. 446, p. 643) guides itself by means of echo-location in a manner broadly comparable with that of bats (Griffin).

Among the Microchiroptera is the family Desmodontidæ which are true vampire bats from tropical America and the West Indies. Of these, *Desmodus* (Fig. 530) and *Diphylla* live solely on vertebrate blood. *Desmodus* painlessly scoops out a fragment of skin, exposing the capillaries with its obliquely flattened, razor-edged upper incisors, thereafter licking up the oozing blood. The œsophagus is narrow : the cardiac part of the stomach is expanded as a diverticulum, but the pyloric portion is small. In legend—and often in modern travellers' stories—the vampire is generally claimed to be a large animal, but *D. rotundus*, the commonest species, is a mere three inches long. *Desmodus* has in the past sometimes been sufficiently troublesome to livestock to cause the abandonment of settlements, and is the proved carrier of a form of rabies which may prove fatal to Man and domestic animals.

Often confused with the true vampires are the spear-nosed frugivorous, yet unfortunately named *Vampyrum* (= *Vampyrus*), and the long-tongued *Glossophaga*, both of which are harmless to Man. *Vampyrum* was so named in 1815 before the identity of the small, less conspicuous, blood-suckers was revealed. The archaic expression *vampir* originally referred to the hypothetical 'soul' which allegedly left a dead human individual to feast at night on the blood of living men. These belong to the Phyllostomatidæ.

Although the Microchiroptera are, excluding rodents, among the commonest mammals, their small fragile bones are rarely preserved as fossils. It is of great interest therefore that *Palæochiropteryx*, one of several genera from the Eocene of Europe, seems already as fully developed as any of the Microchiroptera. *Zanycteris* (known only from its teeth) may carry the sub-order as far back as the Palæocene, but it is probable that it and its congeners are really insectivores of uncertain affinity. In all, 17 families of bats are recognised.

Skeleton of the Chiroptera (Fig. 531).—The cervical region of the vertebral column is characterised by the absence of distinct neural spines, and the same holds good to a less extent of the trunk-vertebræ. The transverse processes of the lumbar region are also rudimentary. The tail varies in development. When it is elongated the component vertebræ have long, cylindrical bodies without processes. Sagittal and occipital crests are developed in the skull of some species. The facial region is rather elongated, especially in the Megachiroptera (Fig. 529). Postorbital processes of the frontal may be present or absent. The zygoma is long and slender and the malar small and applied to its outer surface. The long and narrow nasals are in some cases united ; the premaxillæ are small and absent in one of the false vampires (Megadermatidæ). The mandible has an angular process in the Microchiroptera, but not in the

Megachiroptera. The segments of the sternum are sometimes distinct, sometimes united. The presternum has a mesial keel developed in co-ordination with the great size of the pectoral muscles. The sternal ribs are ossified.

The *scapula* is large and oval in shape. The spine is near the anterior margin. The postscapular fossa is ridged for the origin of muscular fibres. The spine has a well-developed acromion. The coracoid is elongated and in some cases bifurcated. The clavicle is long. The procoracoid is represented by a separate ossification; there are rudiments of the sternal end of the coracoid between the clavicle and the first rib. The humerus and radius are both elongated. The ulna is reduced, and is sometimes represented by its proximal end only, ankylosed with the radius. A large sesamoid is developed in the tendon of the triceps muscle near the ulnar olecranon process. The carpal scaphoid and lunar are united, and sometimes the cuneiform, too, is united with them. The pisiform is small. There is no centrale. The ungual phalanges are absent in the nailless digits. The pelvis is small, and the symphysis pubis often deficient. The fibula is sometimes well-developed, sometimes rudimentary. The tuber calcanei is an inwardly curved process of the calcaneum, attached to which (by means of ligamentous fibres) is a slender rod of bone or cartilage, the *calcar* which supports the inter-femoral membrane.

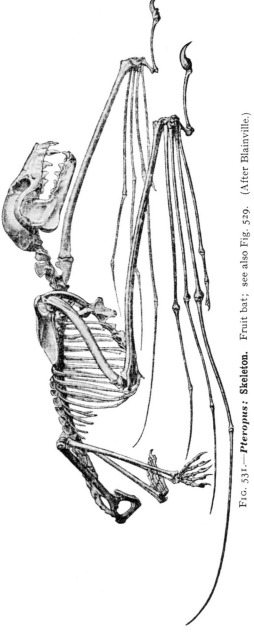

FIG. 531.—*Pteropus: Skeleton.* Fruit bat; see also Fig. 529. (After Blainville.)

ORDER TÆNIODONTIA

This order, of which representatives are known from the Palæocene (*Conoryctes, Ectoganus, Onychodectes, Psittacotherium*, etc.) to the Middle Eocene (*Stylinodon*), is, like the tillodonts, a very obscure one. It has no representation after the Eocene.

Earlier forms were primitive and somewhat insectivore-like, with a complete dentition and enamel-covered teeth. *Stylinodon*, the last mid-Eocene survivor, showed more distinctive characters in its very hypsodont, rootless teeth, whose enamel was confined to bands at the insides. These teeth were peg-like and without molar pattern. Later tæniodonts were probably herbivorous, but unable to compete with the radiating Ungulata.

Both the Tillodontia and Tæniodontia appear to have become specialised early along side lines which were, comparatively speaking, of short duration. Opinions differ as to whether they manifest any close mutual affinity.

ORDER TILLODONTIA

This is an archaic order of undetermined ancestry, which left no descendants and of which specimens occur only in the Lower and Middle Eocene of North America (e.g. *Esthonyx, Anchippodus, Tillotherium*). Some have grouped the Tillodontia with the rodents, though with little justification. The most progressive form known, the mid-Eocene *Tillotherium*, was the size of a bear. There were two pairs of incisors, of which the first was small, the second much enlarged, rootless, and rodent-like. The mandibular condyles, however, were transverse, and entirely unlike the condition found in rodents. The canines were small, the premolars and molars brachydont and bunodont. The braincase was small, the skull low, and the snout sharp. *Tillotherium* was plantigrade and pentadactyle : it was probably herbivorous, but perhaps omnivorous.

ORDER EDENTATA

This polymorphic yet geographically restricted group has undergone very considerable taxonomic rearrangement but the true affinities of some of its sub-divisions remain still in doubt. The group as a whole has sometimes been completely removed from any other and its independent reptilian origin has been suggested more than once. Such views cannot be sustained. There seems now to be adequate evidence that the edentates arose from proto-insectivoran ancestry about the beginning of the Cenozoic. As at present constituted the order contains the fossil North American Palæanodonta, and the Central and South American armadilloes, true ant-eaters, sloths and various extinct forms of close affinity. The arrangement followed below reduces the Xenarthra to sub-ordinal rank as follows :

Sub-order Palæanodonta (Palæocene–Oligocene)
Sub-order Xenarthra
   Infra-order Cingulata (Loricata)
      Super-families Dasypodoidea (Palæocene–Recent)
           Glyptodontoidea (Upper Eocene–Pleistocene)
   Infra-order Pilosa
      Super-families Megalonychoidea (Upper Eocene–Pleistocene)
           Myrmecophagoidea (Pliocene–Recent)
           Bradypodoidea (Recent)

SUB-ORDER PALÆANODONTA

This North American group (e.g. *Palæanodon, Metacheiromys, Epoicotherium*) appears to represent a primitive Palæocene offshoot from the ancestry that also gave rise to the Xenarthra, which found a southern refuge before the partition of the Americas. Four rare genera have been described.

Metacheiromys, an Eocene edentate about 18 inches long, probably lacked dermal armour but resembled to-day's armadilloes in many details. Interesting specialisations occurred in the enamel-covered canines (a unique feature in edentates) and in reduction and degeneration of teeth. The vertebræ had not acquired the xenarthran peculiarity of extra zygapophyses and there was no ischio-caudal symphysis.

SUB-ORDER XENARTHRA

This sub-order exhibits a great diversity of appearance and behaviour, but constitutes a natural and exclusive group, composed of essentially the Cingulata (= Loricata) containing armoured armadillos (Figs. 532, 533) and extinct glyptodons (Fig. 535), and the Pilosa, embracing ant-eaters (Fig. 537), sloths (Fig. 536), and extinct ground-sloths (Fig. 539).

The group consists almost entirely of South American forms. A few late-Tertiary animals penetrated northwards after the subsequent re-establishment of an inter-continental land-bridge (Figs. 491, 492, p. 705). However diverse, the Xenarthra are still unmistakably united basically by certain specialised characters which prove them a single natural group. Enamel is entirely absent from the teeth, except in an Eocene armadillo, *Utaëtus*, in which small enamel caps were just persisting. In the remainder, the teeth (see p. 871) are transformed to pillar-like persistently growing stumps (the armadillos), or are reduced in number (the sloths) or may be altogether absent (ant-eaters (Fig. 546)). A most noticeable character is the presence of an extra pair of zygopophyses upon the posterior dorsal and lumbar vertebræ (Fig. 540) a condition found elsewhere only in snakes and some lizards (e.g. Iguanidæ). Among other specialised characters are the frequent reduction (even absence) of the zygomatic arch, the frequent fusion of the coracoid process to the front border of the scapula so as to enclose a large foramen (Fig. 548) and articulation of several of the anterior caudal vertebræ to the ischium, producing an unusually long ischio-sacral region. The simple type of brain, on the other hand, and the persistently abdominal testes are primitive. All Edentata have heavily clawed feet.

The Xenarthra diverged widely. The Infra-order Cingulata are covered with bony plates bearing horny scutes, an unusual feature in mammals. In

FIG. 532.—Order **Edentata,** Sub-order **Xenarthra,** Infra-order **Cingulata,** Super-family **Dasypodoidea,** Family **Dasypodidæ.** *Chlamyphorus.* The fairy armadillos (e.g. *C. truncatus*) possess the armour characteristic of the group and in addition have a posterior shield that enables them to close the burrow. The protruding tail is armoured. (From B.M. (N.H.) skins.)

this group the teeth are more numerous than in the hairy Pilosa and the jugal arch is more complete. There is a considerable fusion of the vertebral column elements subserving the same mechanical junctions seen in chelonians. The super-families are the Dasypodoidea (Dasypodidæ, the armadillos, Fig. 532, and the Peltephilidæ); the extinct Glyptodontoidea (Glyptodontidæ, e.g. *Glyptodon*). The glyptodons (Fig. 535) had a peculiar protection involving the fusion of a mosaic of numerous small polygonal plates into a rigid hemispherical armour supported by blocks of fused vertebræ—*i.e.* cervical (excluding the first), fused dorsals, and finally a compacted group of posterior dorsals, lumbars, and sacrals connected posteriorly with the carapace. The tail, too, was armoured, sometimes with spikes. The head was protected by a bony casque and the zygomatic arch had a peculiarly elongated ventral down-growth. The clavicle was absent. These curious creatures survived from the Eocene until the Pleistocene and some penetrated northwards from South America as far as the southern United States. No doubt they represent a primitive offshoot from early armadillo stock.

FIG. 533.—Family **Dasypodidæ,** *Tolypeutes.* The Three-banded Armadillo (*T. conurus*) (and a few other species) possesses a hinged dorsal armour that allows it to curl protectively, the armoured head and tail fitting into place to form an impregnable sphere (Fig. 534). Most armadillos live in savannah or pampas. The fore-feet are peculiarly specialised for rapid digging. (From B.M. (N.H.) skins.)

In the armadillos (Dasypodidæ) the head (Fig. 533) is comparatively short, broad, and depressed. The number of complete digits of the fore-foot varies from three to five. These are provided with powerful claws, so as to form an efficient digging organ. The hind-foot always has five digits with smaller claws. The tail is usually well developed. The most striking external feature of the armadillos is their armour of bony dermal plates. This armour usually consists of a scapular shield of closely-united plates covering the anterior part of the body, followed by a series of transverse bands separated from one another by hairy skin, and a posterior pelvic shield. In the genus *Tolypeutes* these bands are movable, so that the animal can roll itself into a ball. The tail is also usually enclosed in rings of bony plates, and a number protect the dorsal surface of the head (Fig. 534).

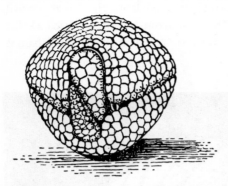

FIG. 534.—*Tolypeutes:* **Defensive mechanism.** (See also Fig. 533.) (From photograph by Eisentraut.)

The infra-order Pilosa contains the following hairy groups : The super-family Megalonychoidea, an extinct line of ground sloths consisting of the Megatheriidæ (e.g. *Megatherium*) the Megalonychidæ (e.g. *Megalonyx*) and Mylodontidæ (*Mylodon*, Fig. 536) : the super-family Myrmecophagoidea comprising the Myrmecophagidæ (e.g. *Myrmecophaga*, the Great Ant-eater (Fig. 537), *Tamandua*, the Lesser Ant-eater (Fig. 538)): the super-family Bradypodoidea comprising the Bradypodidæ (e.g. *Bradypus*, the Three-toed Sloth,

with nine cervical vertebræ (Fig. 539), and *Cholœpus*, the Two-toed Sloth, with six cervicals). The two last-named species are, with the exception of the dugongs among the Sirenia, the only mammals without the typical number of seven cervical vertebræ (p. 850).

FIG. 535.—Infra-order **Cingulata,** Super-family **Glyptodontoidea,** Family **Glyptodontidæ,** *Glyptodon.* This South American Pleistocene armadillo possessed a fused armour and was about nine feet long. The tail ended in a defensive 'mace'. (After Owen.)

In their limb structure the sloths (Bradypodidæ, Fig. 540) are perhaps more completely adapted to an arboreal life than any other mammalian group. They have a short, rounded head, ears with small pinnæ, and long, slender limbs, the anterior being much the longer. The digits, never more than three in number, are long, curved, and hook-like, and thus enable the animal to hand-climb, body downwards, among the branches. The three-toed sloth has three toes in both manus and pes : the two-toed sloth has two in the manus, three in the pes. The tail is rudimentary. The body is covered with long, coarse hairs, which differ from those of other mammals in being longitudinally fluted. On these hairs algæ grow abundantly, conferring obliterative greenish and bluish hues on the slow moving animals in the forest. Modern sloths live on leaves, but a former insectivorous life is evidenced by the reduction of the teeth and their enamel loss. This irreversible process has been compensated by the provision of a grinding surface by cement and by persistent pulps.

The ground sloths (e.g. *Megatherium, Nothrotherium, Mylodon* (Fig. 536)), which disappeared so recently as the Pleistocene, were once very common and latterly as big as oxen. They occurred in both American continents, and their fossils have been found in the West Indies.

The ant-eaters (Myrmecophagidæ) have a greatly elongated snout (Fig. 546), with the mouth as a small aperture at its extremity, small eyes, and auditory pinnæ which are sometimes small, sometimes well-developed. There are five digits in the fore-foot, of which the third has always a very large curved and pointed claw, rendering the manus an efficient digging organ. The toes of the hindfoot, four or five in number, are sub-equal, and provided with moderate-sized claws. In walking,

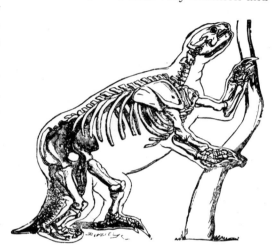

Fig. 536. — Infra-order **Pilosa**, Super-family **Megalonychoidea**, Family **Mylodontidæ**. *Mylodon.* This group flourished in both the Americas during the Pleistocene. *M. robustus* was as big as a small rhinoceros. (After Owen.)

the weight of the body rests on the dorsal surfaces of the second, third, and fourth digits of the manus and on a thick callous pad on the extremity of the fifth, and in the pes, on the entire plantar surface. The tail is always very long, and is sometimes prehensile. The body is covered with long hair. In the Two-toed Ant-eater (*Cyclopes*) the muzzle is short. There are four digits in the manus, of which the second and third only have claws, that of the third being the longer. The pes has four sub-equal clawed toes, forming a hook not unlike that of the sloths. The tail is prehensile.

Skeleton of Xenarthra.—In armadillos more or fewer of the cervical vertebræ are ankylosed together both by their bodies and neural arches. In the lumbar region the metapophyses are greatly prolonged. They are longer than the transverse processes and support the bony carapace. A remarkable peculiarity of the spinal column in armadillos is the fusion of a number of the anterior caudal vertebræ with the true sacrals to form the long sacrum which thus contains as many as ten vertebræ. The caudal region is of moderate length, with numerous chevron bones. In *Manis* and *Myrmecophaga* the neck-vertebræ are not united. In the posterior thoracic and lumbar regions of *Myrmecophaga* are developed complex accessory articulations between the vertebræ; the sacrum contains, in addition to the true sacral vertebræ, a number derived from the caudal region.

Fig. 537.—Order **Edentata,** Sub-order **Xenarthra,** Infra-order **Pilosa,** Super-family **Myrmeco-phagoidea,** Family **Myrmecophagidæ.** *Myrmecophaga.* The South American Giant Ant-eater or 'Ant-bear' seems to be rigidly insectivorous, feeding principally on ants which it gathers by means of its sticky protrusible tongue. Anterior pedal specialisations allow the animal to walk unimpeded by its powerful digging claws. (From B.M. (N.H.) skins.)

In the sloths none of the cervical vertebræ are ankylosed. In the three-toed sloths (Fig. 540) there is an important divergence from ordinary mammals in the number of vertebræ in the cervical region for there are nine or ten instead of seven. In the Two-toed Sloth (*Cholœpus hoffmanni*), there are six only. The neural spines of all the vertebræ are very short. A number of the anterior caudal vertebræ are united firmly, though not quite fused, with one another and with the true sacrals.

In the armadillos the sternal ribs, which are sub-bifid at their sternal ends, are ossified, and articulate with the sternum by means of well-developed synovial articulations. In the American ant-eaters there are similar synovial joints, and the sternal ends of the sternal ribs are completely bifid. In the sloths the sternum is long and narrow, and there are no costo-sternal synovial joints. The anterior sternal ribs are ossified and completely united with the vertebral ribs, but their posterior fellows are separated from the latter by intermediate ribs which are less perfectly ossified.

In the armadillos the *skull* (Fig. 545) is broad and flat, the facial region triangular. The tympanic (*ty.*) is in some developed into a bulla. The bony

FIG. 538.—Family **Myrmecophagidæ. *Tamandua.*** The South and Central American Collared Ant-eater (*T. tetradactyla*) is a forest-dwelling arboreal off-shoot from terrestrial stock (cf. Fig. 537), though its diet remains the same. The tail has become prehensile. (From photographs.)

auditory meatus is in some cases elongated. The zygoma is complete. The pterygoids are small, and do not develop palatine plates. The mandible has a well-developed ramus with a prominent coronoid process and a well-marked angular process.

In the ant-eaters (Figs. 546, 547) the skull is extremely long and narrow. The facial region is drawn out into a long, narrow rostrum, with the external nares at its extremity. The olfactory fossæ are correspondingly greatly developed. The rostrum is composed mainly of mesethmoid, vomer, maxillæ, and nasals; the premaxillæ are small. The zygoma is incomplete, and the orbit is not closed behind by bone, a postorbital process of the frontal being entirely absent. The pterygoids (*pter.*), in all but *Cyclopes*, develop palatine plates. There is no bony auditory meatus. The mandible is entirely devoid of ascending ramus and consists of two long and slender horizontal rami, with a very short symphysis.

In the sloths (Fig. 544) the cerebral component of the cranium is elevated

FIG. 539.—Order **Edentata,** Sub-order **Xenarthra,** Infra-order **Pilosa,** Super-family **Bradypodoidea,** Family **Bradypodidæ.** *Bradypus.* The three-toed Sloth (*B. tridactylus*) is another South American edentate that has become arboreal. It inhabits tropical forests and possesses very inefficient thermo-regulation: exposure to sun temperature of 35°–40° C. causes death from heat-stroke. The algæ which give the fur a green tinge (p. 844) are reported partly to support a fur-living population of mites, minute beetles, and moths. (From a photograph by Gross.)

and rounded, the facial short. The frontal region is elevated, owing to the development of extensive frontal air-sinuses. The premaxillæ are small, and not firmly connected with the maxillæ, so that they are commonly lost from the macerated skull. The jugal (*ju.*) develops a strong zygomatic process which bifurcates behind into two branches. Neither of these is connected with the vestigial zygomatic process of the squamosal, so that the zygomatic arch remains incomplete. There are, at most, the rudiments of postorbital processes of the frontals. The pterygoids develop vertical laminæ and form no

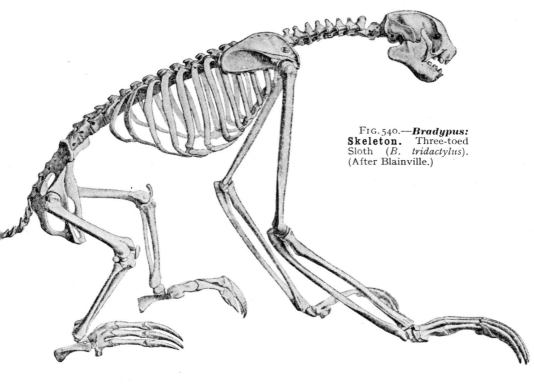

FIG. 540.—**Bradypus:**
Skeleton. Three-toed
Sloth (*B. tridactylus*).
(After Blainville.)

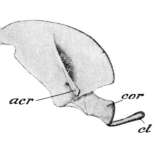

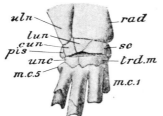

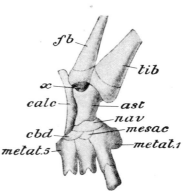

FIG. 541.—**Bradypus: Shoulder girdle.** Lateral view in three-
toed Sloth (*B. tridactylus*). *acr.*
acromion; *cl.* clavicle; *cor.*
coracoid.

FIG. 542.—**Bradypus:
Manus.** Right. *cun.* cuneiform;
lun. lunar; *m. c.* 1, first metacarpal; *m. c.* 5, rudiment of fifth
metacarpal; *pis.* pisiform; *rad.*
radius; *sc.* scaphoid; *trd. m.*
trapezoid and magnum united;
uln. ulna; *unc.* unciform.

FIG. 543.—**Bradypus: Pes.** *ast.*
astragalus; *calc.* calcaneum; *cbd.*
cuboid; *fb.* fibula; *meso.c.* meso-
cuneiform; *metat.* 1, vestige of first
metatarsal; *metat.* 5, vestige of fifth
metatarsal; *nav.* navicular; *tib.*
tibia; *x,* peg-like process at distal
end of fibula.

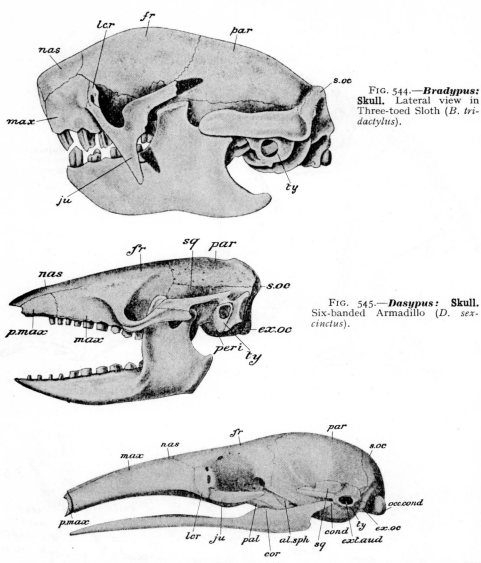

FIG. 544.—**Bradypus:** **Skull.** Lateral view in Three-toed Sloth (*B. tridactylus*).

FIG. 545.—**Dasypus:** **Skull.** Six-banded Armadillo (*D. sexcinctus*).

FIG. 546.—**Myrmecophaga:** **Skull.** Lateral view in Great Anteater. *al. sph.* ali-sphenoid; *cond.* condyle of mandible; *cor.* coronoid process of mandible; *ex. oc.* ex-occipital; *ext. aud.* external auditory meatus; *fr.* frontal; *ju.* jugal; *lcr.* lachrymal; *max.* maxilla; *nas.* nasal; *occ. cond.* occipital condyle; *pal.* palatine; *par.* parietal; *p. max.* premaxilla; *s. oc.* supra-occipital; *sq.* squamosal; *ty.* tympanic.

palatine plates. The ascending ramus and coronoid process of the mandible are both well developed.

In the ant-eaters and armadillos the bones of the *fore-limb* are short and powerful. The scapula in the ant-eaters is broad and rounded. Its anterior border unites with the coracoid process so as to convert the coraco-scapular notch into a foramen. In the middle of the spine there is a triangular process : a ridge on the postspinous fossa presents the appearance of a second spine. The fibres of origin of the subscapularis muscle extend on to the outer surface as far forward as this ridge, so that the part of the outer surface behind the ridge corresponds to a part of the subscapular fossa, which in other Theria is co-extensive with the inner surface. Except in *Cyclopes* the clavicles are vestigial. All the carpal bones are distinct.

In the armadillos the scapula (Fig. 548) has an extremely prolonged acromion (*acr.*), sometimes articulating with the humerus. A ridge (*sp'.*) representing a second spine is present. The clavicle is well developed. The humerus is short and powerful, with well-developed processes and ridges, and with a foramen (*entepicondylar foramen*) above the inner condyle. The carpus consists of the ordinary eight bones.

In the sloths (Fig. 540) the arm bones are comparatively long and slender. A coraco-scapular foramen is formed as in the ant-eaters. In the Three-toed sloths (Fig. 541) the acromion (*acr.*) is at first connected with the coracoid process, but becomes reduced and loses this connexion. In the two-toed sloth the connexion persists. The clavicle (*cl.*) is not directly connected medially with the sternum. Laterally it is directly connected with the coracoid process—a condition unique among the mammalia. The humerus is very long and slender, as are the radius and ulna, which are capable of a certain amount of pronation and supination. In the carpus (Fig. 542) the trapezoid and magnum are united in *Bradypus*, distinct in *Cholœpus* : in the former the trapezium is usually fused with the rudimentary first metacarpal. The first and fifth metacarpals are represented by rudiments only. The proximal phalanges of the three digits are early ankylosed with the corresponding metacarpals, so that it might readily be supposed that a normal component of each digit was absent.

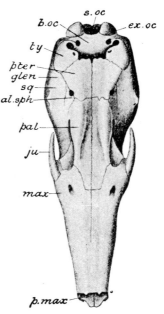

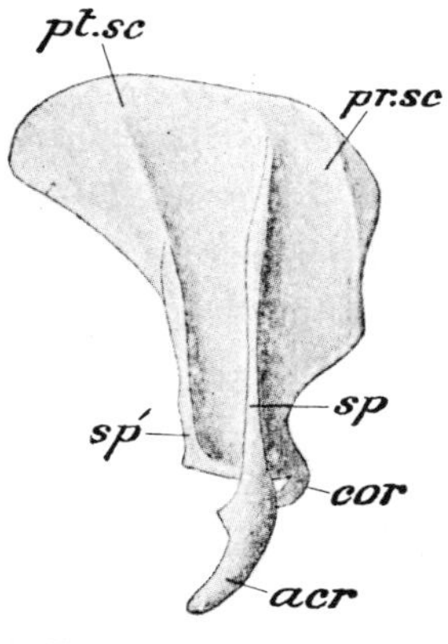

FIG. 547.—**Myrmecophaga: Skull.** Ventral view in Great Ant-eater. Letters as in Fig. 546. In addition, *b. oc.* basioccipital; *glen.* glenoid surface for mandible; *pter.* pterygoid.

FIG. 548.—**Dasypus: Shoulder girdle.** Six-banded Armadillo (*D. sexcinctus*). *acr.* acromion; *cor.* coracoid process; *pr. sc.* prespinous fossa; *pt. sc.* post-spinous fossa; *sp.* spine; *sp'.* ridge probably marking the anterior limit of origin of the subscapularis muscle.

The pelvis of the American ant-eaters is elongated, with a short symphysis pubis. The ischia unite with the spinal column. There is no third trochanter.

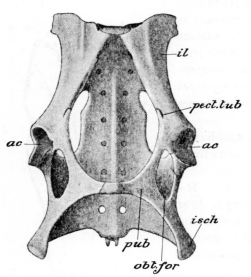

FIG. 549.—**Dasypus: Pelvis and sacrum.** Six-banded Armadillo (*D. sexcinctus*). *ac.* acetabulum; *il.* ilium; *isch.* ischium; *obt. for.* obturator foramen; *pect. tub.* pectineal tubercle; *pub.* pubis.

The tibia and fibula are nearly straight, and parallel. In *Cyclopes* the pes is modified to form a climbing organ.

In the sloths the pelvis is short and wide. The spines of the ischia unite with the anterior caudal vertebræ so that a sacro-sciatic foramen is formed as in ant-eaters. The femur is long and slender; it has no third trochanter. The tibia and fibula are also long and slender. At its distal end (Fig. 543) the fibula develops a peg-like process (*x*) which fits into a depression in the outer face of the astragalus. The calcaneal process is extremely prolonged in *Bradypus*, in which there is a tendency to ankylosis between the tarsal bones, and the proximal phalanges ankylose with the metatarsals.

In the armadillos the pelvis (Fig. 549) is extremely long, and both ilia and ischia are firmly fused with the spinal column. The femur has a prominent third trochanter. The bones of the pes are not specially remarkable.

ORDER PHOLIDOTA

The peculiar pangolins or scaly ant-eaters (Figs. 550, 551) of tropical Africa and Asia are often placed among the Xenarthra but ever since Huxley's day opinion has tended increasingly to accord them separate ordinal rank, at the same time retaining their undeniable connexions with the Edentata (in its original sense). Little is known of their phylogeny. Pleistocene remains are essentially similar to those of extant forms and the mid-Tertiary (European) species are known from fragments only.

The most noticeable character of living forms is their covering of imbricating horny scales over the head, body, and tail, among which scales grow a few scattered hairs. The lower body-surface is hair covered. The head is produced into a short, pointed muzzle. The tongue is long and teeth are entirely absent, as are also the jugal arch and clavicle. The skull is long and cylindrical and there is no bony separation of orbit and temporal fossa. The body and tail may be five feet long.

There is but one genus, *Manis*, which contains some seven species. The limbs are short and strong, and pentadactyle. The hind-feet are plantigrade, the fore-feet provided with strong curved claws. In walking, the weight rests

FIG. 550.—Order **Pholidota**, Family **Manidæ.** *Manis.* The pangolins (scaly ant-eaters) and the Aardvark (Order Tubulidentata) (Fig. 576) are often called the 'Old World edentates' but are probably better separated from armadillos, ant-eaters and sloths and, of course, from each other. The tropical pangolins (e.g. *M. javanica* above) are remarkably protected by an over-lapping armour (Fig. 551) and have developed a remarkable pedal specialisation that allows the possession of powerful digging claws without undue interference with walking (see convergence illustrated in Fig. 537). The tail may be prehensile (*e.g.* in *M. longicaudata*) and contain as many as 50 vertebræ, the largest number of any mammal (cf. four retained by Man). Some pangolins are arboreal. (From photographs and B.M. (N.H.) skins.)

FIG. 551. — *Manis:* **Defensive mechanism.** (From photograph by Lang.)

on the upper and outer side of the fourth and fifth digits. Some forms are expert climbers.

What resemblance there is to the edentate *Myrmecophaga* is probably due to convergent adaptation. Whilst a remote connexion with the American Edentata is not absolutely precluded, it is more convenient in the state of present knowledge to regard the Pholidota as a separate order.

COHORT GLIRES

In this great division are placed the orders Rodentia and Lagomorpha which were previously included in a single order Rodentia. Despite their familiarity to-day, and an abundance of Eocene fossils, there is still no certainty concerning the origin of either. It is probable that they represent early departures from the primitive eutherian insectivore stem. They show many adaptive parallels in morphology, physiology, and behaviour.

ORDER RODENTIA

This large and important order was formerly divided into two very unequal sub-orders, the numerous Simplicidentata and the few Duplicidentata (Lagomorpha) in which were placed only certain extinct Palæocene rabbit-like animals, as well as the pikas, hares, and rabbits, including the American cotton-tails. The Duplicidentata all possess a second pair of incisors, hence the name. It is now known, however, that many of the numerous similarities between the two groups are largely adaptive and that there are adequate grounds for the erection of a separate order Lagomorpha. Some authorities, indeed, believe that the two groups are related only to the extent that both are offshoots of early Eutherian stock and it has even been suggested (but not accepted) that the two orders arose independently from metatherians. Certainly both groups were clearly distinct in the Eocene period some 50 million years ago. The fact that these two widely differing, but apparently very similar, orders were so long combined in classification is a cogent warning to students against the unquestioning acceptance of systematic arrangements which are, in the state of current knowledge, inevitably no more than provisional.

The Rodentia, comprising almost three thousand living species, is numerically the largest of all the mammalian groups. Rodents are of enormous economic and medical importance in that the rats carry plague-fleas and do incalculable damage to stored foodstuffs and other goods, while plagues of mice periodically inflict incomputable injury upon crops in various countries.

No rodent has ever attained any great size. A capybara (*Hydrochœrus*), about the size of a small pig, is the largest living form, but its bulk may have been exceeded by two extinct beavers (*Trogontherium* and *Castoroides*). Most rodents are small and some, such as the Harvest-mouse (*Micromys minutus*), are among the smallest known mammals and weigh a mere 7 gms. (see also p. 727). The distribution of the group is almost global. Rodents are among the few eutherian mammals to occur in Australia, where they radiated successfully presumably after voyages thither on floating driftwood. Many rodents (such as the Lemming (*Lemmus lemmus*) and various species of rats and mice) can multiply rapidly to almost incredible numbers.

The characters of the order are as follows : Never more than a single pair of upper incisors is present. The incisors are chisel-shaped in wear owing to the absence of enamel on their posterior surfaces and, having persistently open roots, they grow throughout life and are always of great size. There is no anterior symphysis between the mandibles and special modifications of the mylohyoids and masseters permit the separation and return of the prominent lower incisors in a curious, almost scissor-action in feeding. Canines are never present, and there is a wide diastema between the incisors and the cheek-teeth into which the cheeks can be tucked so as to separate the front part of the mouth from the hind during the process of gnawing. This habit of gnawing, universal in the group, has induced noticeable modifications not only of the teeth, but of the whole skull and jaws. The glenoid cavities for the mandibular condyles are elongated in a fore-and-aft direction, an adaptation which enables the jaws to be moved forwards, and thereby the upper and lower incisors to be brought into contact for the purpose of gnawing. In this position, owing to the size of the incisors, the cheek-teeth are thrown out of action and cannot operate. For chewing, therefore, the jaws can be moved backwards when the lower incisor fits in behind the upper, and the upper and lower cheek-teeth can be brought into contact. The grinding-teeth vary in number, and frequently have persistently open roots. In some cases the milk dentition is suppressed.

To provide the necessary power for gnawing, the jaw-muscles are very greatly enlarged (Fig. 552). The increase in area for their attachments has produced considerable modifications in the skull and jaws which differ in different groups, and afford a basis for classification. The premaxillæ and maxillæ are enlarged, not only to house the great curved incisors, but also for the attachment of the anterior mass of the masseter muscle. This in some forms passes through the enormously enlarged antorbital vacuity, which may be as big as the orbit (in *Cælogenys*, the pacas), or it may pass over the edge of the jugal arch in front of the orbit (as in the enigmatic *Pedetes*). The fossæ for the pterygoid muscles may also be very large. The lower jaw may have the external border expanded into a flange for the insertion of the masseter. It is interesting to note a convergence in shape between rodents and *Phascolomys* (marsupial wombats). These have a single pair of persistently growing incisors and an enlargement of the masseter muscle inserted on to an everted mandibular flange. In many rodents the jugal extends back to the glenoid cavity, as in marsupials.

Additionally to its characteristic incisors and absent canines, the rodent dentition is peculiar as regards the cheek-teeth. Two premolars occur above and one below, though even fewer may be present. As few as one molar only

may occur in each maxilla and in each moiety of the mandible.   (The recently
described water-rat *Mayermys* from New Guinea has the unique dentition of
one cheek tooth only in each jaw, thus taking a further step beyond its allies
in the sub-family Hydromyinæ which may have as few as two.)   An average
number for many rodents is four molar teeth.   There is also a wide range of

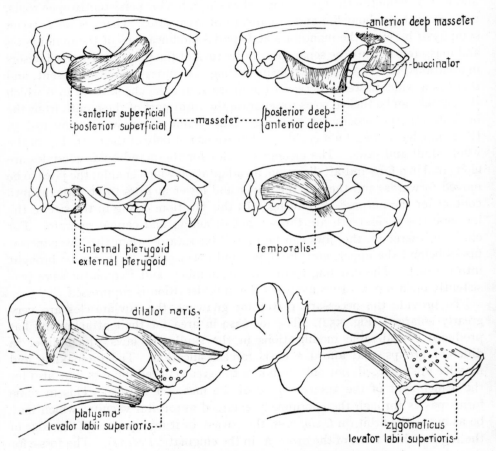

FIG. 552.—***Rattus*: Jaw musculature.**   (After E. Chase Green.)

difference in cheek-tooth crown-pattern as well as in size.   Thus, the squirrels
(Fig. 553B) possess teeth of the short-crowned brachydont and rooted type,
which, especially in the earliest species, can be referred to as the tritubercular
type.   The dentition exhibits gradations through various bilophodont patterns
(Fig. 553C) to the highly complicated multilophodont and hypsodont varieties
with permanently open roots, as, for example, in the capybaras (Fig. 553A).
     In the rest of their anatomy the rodents are not highly specialised.   They
are, for the most part, unguiculate, pentadactyle, and plantigrade.   A clavicle

is usually present and, as in all herbivorous mammals, the cæcum tends to be large. The brain is little, if at all, convoluted, and the cerebellum is not covered by the cerebral lobes.

The order is divided into three ill-defined sub-orders : 1. Sciuromorpha (squirrels, beavers, North American gophers, and allies); 2. Myomorpha (jerboas, voles and lemmings, rats and mice, hamsters and jumping-mice), and 3. Hystricomorpha (porcupines, guinea-pigs, chinchillas, viscachas, agoutis, capybaras, mole-rats, and allies).

A strong case, however, can be made that the above groups are essentially morphological grades and not phylogenetic divisions indicating close relationship of their contained forms. For example, Wood has shown that the New and Old World hystricomorphs (see below) are each derived independently from a world-wide sciuromorph stock. Rodents exist in great number and exhibit

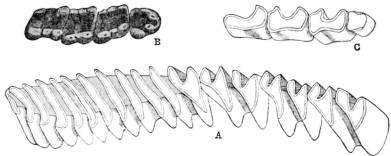

Fig. 553.—*Rodentia:* **Molar dentition.** *A, Hydrochœrus* (Capybara); *B, Sciurus* (squirrel); *C, Ctenodactylus* (of uncertain affinity, possibly a hystricomorph.) (From *Cambridge Natural History,* after Tullberg.)

an extraordinarily wide range of adaptive radiation. Some such as the beavers, are amphibious, with flattened swimming-tails. Some are burrowers to such an extent as to have acquired a mole-like appearance (e.g. *Spalax, Georychus*). The squirrels are tree-living. The Anomaluridæ (' flying '-squirrels) have proceeded a step further by the development of a parachuting membrane closely resembling that of the gliding marsupials. The Dipodidæ are saltatorial (hopping) forms, somewhat resembling kangaroos in their mode of progression.

The Sciuromorpha (of some 13 extinct and living families) are primitive in their retention of two upper and one lower premolars, and in the antorbital foramen not being enlarged. It does not transmit any part of the masseter muscle. In some classifications five super-families are recognised as follows : the Sciuroidea (squirrels, gophers, chipmunks, etc.), the Aplodontoidea (*Aplodontia,* the Sewellel), the Ischyromyidæ (Eocene and Oligocene rodents), the Castoroidea (beavers), the Geomyoidea (a purely North American group including the pocket-gophers, etc.), and the Anomaluroidea. The last-named includes *Anomalurus*, a West African ' flying-squirrel ', and possibly *Pedetes*, the Cape Jumping-hare. The last-named possesses a large infra-orbital opening, which, however, does not transmit any part of the masseter muscle, so that the skull in this respect resembles structurally, but not functionally that of the Myomorpha.

The Myomorpha (rats, mice, jerboas, hamsters, etc.) are differentiated into nine families and are characterised by the superficial portion of the masseter muscle passing forwards in front of the orbit, while its median portion runs, via the orbit, through the enlarged infraorbital opening. The sub-order Hystricomorpha (true porcupines, the guinea-pigs (*Cavia*), the Viscacha (*Lagostomus*) etc.) comprise some 19 families. They have the infraorbital canal enlarged to the greatest extent of all, and the median portion of the masseter is enlarged at the expense of the anterior superficial portion, which does not extend on to the face, but retains its more primitive attachment to the jugal arch. The tibia and fibula remain separate.

Skeleton of the Rodentia.—Among the rodents the jerboas are exceptional in having the cervical vertebræ ankylosed. Generally the transverse processes of the lumbar vertebræ are elongated. As in the Ungulata, the sacrum usually consists of one broad anterior vertebra followed by several narrower ones. The caudal region varies in length in the different families. In some it is very short, but in many (porcupines, squirrels, and beavers) it is elongated. The sternum of the rodents has a long and narrow body. Sometimes there is a broad pre-sternum. The posterior end is always expanded into a cartilaginous xiphisternum.

The *skull* is elongated, narrow in front, broader and depressed behind. The nasal cavities are very large, especially in the porcupines, with complex air sinuses in their upper part. In some the optic foramina fuse into one. An interparietal is often present. Paroccipital processes are developed. The orbit and the temporal fossa are always continuous. The nasal bones are large, and the nasal apertures are terminal or nearly so. The premaxillæ are always very large. A remarkable feature of the skull is the presence in many of a large opening corresponding to the infraorbital foramen. The middle part of the zygoma is formed by the jugal. The latter often helps to bound the glenoid cavity, as in the marsupials. The anterior palatine foramina are long. The periotic and tympanic may become ankylosed together, but not to the neighbouring bones. The coronoid process of the mandible is sometimes rudimentary or absent; the angle is often produced into a process.

The scapula of the rodentia is generally long and narrow. The spine sometimes has a metacromion process and a long acromion. The coracoid process is small. The clavicle varies as regards its development. Vestiges of the sternal end of the coracoid are sometimes distinguishable. The bones of the arm and forearm show considerable variation. The radius and ulna are in most instances distinct, though in close and firm apposition. The scaphoid and lunare are usually united ; a centrale may be present or absent. The pelvis and femur vary greatly : sometimes there is a third trochanter. The fibula may be distinct or fused with the tibia. In the jerboas the metatarsals of the three digits are fused (see Fig. 619).

ORDER LAGOMORPHA

As mentioned (p. 774) these forms (the hares, rabbits, and pikas or conies) were once included within the Rodentia (as the smaller sub-order Duplicidentata). They occur throughout Eurasia (including high arctic islands in the case of the hare *Lepus arcticus*) and North America. Hares have penetrated Africa as far as the Cape, and cotton-tails (*Sylvilagus*) occupy all tropical South America. The lagomorphs agree with the rodents in possessing a diastema, incisors with persistent pulps, cheek-pouches, enormous masseter muscles and relatively weak temporal muscles. They differ, however, in lacking the curious mandibular specialisation (p. 775), in their simpler, more restricted masseter muscle and in their additional small pair of upper incisors. There are always three upper and two lower premolars and three molars. The orbital foramina are small. Muscles never invade the infraorbital canal. The incisive foramina are large; and the maxillæ are curiously laterally fenestrated. The tail is invariably reduced and the hind-limbs are highly specialised for a saltatorial mode of progression. Some true rodents (agoutis, porcupines) also have reduced tails, and hind-limbs modified for jumping (jerboas). The apparently close similarity of rodent and lagomorph cheek-teeth is taxonomically misleading, being merely the result of convergent evolution. In the rodents the rows of lower cheek-teeth are more widely separated from each other than are their upper counterparts. In the lagomorphs the opposite is true.

The lagomorphs fall into two families : the Leporidæ (hares and rabbits) and the Ochotonidæ (pikas, *Ochotona*). Leporids are known from the Eocene and the second group from the Oligocene.

COHORT MUTICA

This division contains only those widely divergent and highly specialised mammals, the whales, whose phylogenetic history remains obscure. Their perfection of adaptation to a marine existence has, to a remarkable degree, obliterated evidence of their affinities to the other extant mammalian orders. Although an abundance of cetacean fossils is available from the Miocene, and archaic whales (Archæoceti) have been found in Eocene deposits, the early stages of cetacean evolution remain unknown.

Order Cetacea

Because their bodies are supported by water, and because of the manifold physiological advantages of homœiothermy, whales have been enabled to attain

Fig. 554.—Order **Cetacea**, Sub-order **Mysticeti**, Family **Balænopteridæ**, *Balænoptera*, and Sub-order **Odontoceti**, Family **Delphinidæ**. *Orcinus*. Among the micro-feeding Mysticeti or 'whale-bone' (baleen) whales the Blue, Sulphur-bottom, or Sibbald's Whale (*B. musculus*) grows to a length of more than 100 feet and may weigh 120 tons (cf. bull African elephant, 6 tons). It is perhaps the most massive animal that ever lived. A single Blue Whale (a rorqual) may yield about 135 barrels (22½ tons) of oil, 3½ tons of guano (from ground-up flesh) and about 336 lbs. of baleen.

The second extant sub-order is the Odontoceti (toothed whales). The Killer Whale (*O. orca*) eats fishes, birds, and marine mammals, attacking and eating the tongues of whales much bigger than itself (Andrews). In the stomach of a single Killer was found the remains of 13 porpoises and 14 seals. The species is harmless to Man but has attacked boats. *O. orca* is sexually dimorphic: the male (with a 'sharp' triangular dorsal fin reaching 5½ feet high) grows to a length of about 31 feet, and the female (with a slightly recurved dorsal fin) to about 18 feet. Although toothed whales of course produce oil (6 barrels from *Orca*) they are of relatively less commercial value. Some however (*e.g.* dolphins) have been hunted for food from earliest times, especially because they are considered as fish in certain countries and can therefore be eaten on fast days. Though rare in equatorial waters, both the above species are or were almost cosmopolitan in distribution. (From photographs and B.M. (N.H.) specimens.)

the greatest bulk of known animals, living or extinct. The Blue Whale (*Balænoptera musculus*), for example, grows to more than 100 feet long and may weigh about 120 tons (Fig. 554). This animal is capable of a speed of up to 18 knots. The great torpedo-shaped body is naked, the skin is very smooth, and structures likely to impede the even flow of water over the body surface, such as ear pinnæ, scrotum, and hind-limbs, have disappeared. The thrust propelling the whale's enormous bulk through the water is produced mainly by the up-and-down motion of the laterally expanded tail-flukes. The fore-limbs, or flippers, and the dorsal fin (when present) act as rudders and stabilisers. Dorsal fin and tail flukes are specialised skin folds supported by underlying fibrous tissue and are devoid of any bony skeleton. The Blue Whale, incident-ally, is sometimes called the 'Sulphur-bottom' because of a yellowish ventral colouration imparted by an adherent diatom population.

Modern Cetacea, which occur with an apparent suddenness in the early part of the Miocene, are characterised by the adaptation of many of their morpho-logical characters to their special mode of life. Some of these structures are new, some are normal mammalian structures much modified, and others indicate a complete loss of ancestral equipment. Examples of the first cate-gory include the formation of the horizontally expanded tail-flukes (Fig. 554), the single dorsal fin, and *baleen* or whalebone (Figs. 558, 559). Further examples are to be found in extra digits (hyperdactyly) and extra phalanges (hyperphalangy) (Fig. 564) which both serve to enlarge the surface of the flipper. Characters which have been modified from the normal include the development in the hypodermis of a thick insulating layer of dermal fat (the *blubber*)—which may constitute as much as 27 per cent of total weight—the very extensive breaking up of certain blood vessels into fine networks (*retia mirabilia*), the great obliquity of the diaphragm and its powerful musculature; the enclosure of the proximal elements of the fore-limb inside the body and the alteration of the hand to a skin-covered paddle; the peculiar shape of the scapula with extremely reduced prescapular fossa, forwardly directed acromion process and absence of spine; the relatively simple, bilobed liver and non-lobulated lungs; and the subdivisioning of the stomach into several digestive regions. The whole skeleton is naturally much modified. The skull has greatly elongated facial, and dorsoventrally compressed ('telescoped') cranial, portions. The nasal openings, often asymmetrical, are placed far back on the upper surface of the head. The tympanic bulla is loosely attached, and the cranial bones in general are much modified in shape. In the vertebral column the cervical vertebræ are shortened, compressed, and fused together to a greater or less extent (Fig. 561). (In *Balæna*, for example, there is complete fusion; in *Balænoptera*, complete separation.) The sternum is reduced. The features that have been lost are: hair, except for a very few facial bristles, finger-nails, except for traces in the fœtus; external ears; all skin-glands; the lachrymal duct and nicitating membrane in the eye; the heads of the ribs in some; the odontoid process in most, and, except for traces, the hind-limbs. Of all mammals the Cetacea show the greatest deviation from the ordinary.

The order falls into three sub-orders: 1. the extinct Archæoceti (e.g.

Protocetus, Basilosaurus = Zeuglodon) ; 2. the toothed Odontoceti, and 3. the baleen-bearing Mysticeti.

SUB-ORDER ARCHÆOCETI

The Archæoceti are first known from the Eocene and are of uncertain relationship. They give little indication of their original land-living ancestors

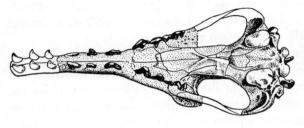

FIG. 555.—*Protocetus:* **Skull.** Palatal aspect in Middle Eocene Whale.

FIG. 556.—Order **Cetacea**, Sub-order **Archæoceti**, Family **Basilosauridæ. *Basilosaurus*** (= *Zeuglodon*). *Basilosaurus* was common in Eocene seas. It was serpentine in shape, and reached a length of about 55 feet. (From Romer, after Gidley.)

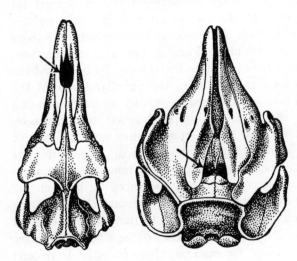

FIG. 557.—*Cetacea:* **Evolution of blow-hole.** *Left:* Dorsal view of the Eocene *Basilosaurus* (=*Zeuglodon*) showing primitive anterior position (arrowed). *Right:* Modern animal, in which the nostrils and surrounding bones have migrated posteriorly to the top of the skull. (Redrawn after Romer.)

beyond the slight suggestion of creodont-insectivore affinities. Archæocetes grew to a length of 70 feet and had already lost their hind-limbs. They comprise three families: the Protocetidæ, Basilosauridæ (= Zeuglodontidæ), and Dorudontidæ. The Protocetidæ (e.g. *Protocetus* (Fig. 555), *Eocetus*, *Pappocetus*) are known from the Middle Eocene and are of great interest because the dentition of *Protocetus* still showed a division into three incisors: a canine, three premolars, and three molars. The cheek-teeth had become elongated and sectorial, but one at least (the third premolar) retained an inner tubercle and is somewhat reminiscent of a creodont tooth.

In the Basilosauridæ *Prozeuglodon* had evolved still further. Its anterior teeth were simple cones. The posterior teeth (which, however, were still two-rooted) were elongated, with secondary serrations. The skull and skeleton as far as known, had advanced a long way towards the cetacean type. Members of this family (e.g. *Basilosaurus*, Figs. 556, 557) became unusually elongated, and were clearly a side-line. The Dorudontidæ (e.g. *Dorudon*) were shorter-bodied and persisted till the end of the Oligocene. While the Archæoceti were definitely whales, they were more primitive than modern whales in some respects. The head, for instance, had the front part elongated, as in other whales, but the cranial part was not compressed and the skull-bones bore a more usual relationship to one another than is the case in later forms.

Sub-order Odontoceti

The Odontoceti or toothed whales are represented by several extant families, of which may be mentioned the Iniidæ and Platanistidæ (the blind freshwater dolphins of South America and the Orient); the Physeteridæ (e.g. *Physeter*, the sperm whales); the Ziphiidæ (bottle-nosed and beaked whales); the Delphinidæ (a large heterogeneous assemblage of porpoises and dolphin, including the white Whale, Narwhal, Pilot Whale, and killer whales (Fig. 554)). The Agorophiidæ of the Upper Eocene, and Squalodontidae of the Miocene are two extinct families.

The freshwater dolphins retain a larger number of primitive characters than do other whales. Thus the cervical vertebræ are not fused, the interlocking processes of the thoracic vertebræ are more prominent, the number of double-headed ribs is large, and the hand is relatively simple and without increase in the number of phalanges. In the Ziphiidæ the snout is long and narrow but functional teeth are restricted to the lower jaw in which one pair (at most two pairs) persist and may in male animals be relatively massive. Two divergent throat grooves, and tail-flukes without a well-defined median notch in the hinder margin, are distinctive of the family. The Physeteridæ, represented by the Cachalot (growing to about 60 feet, and the biggest of all odontocetes) and the Pigmy Sperm (only about 12 feet long when adult), are characterised by the restriction of functional teeth to the lower jaw, by the long symphysial contact of the two rami of the latter and by the possession of a spermaceti organ. The last-named is a large receptacle situated in the snout to the right of the single nostril. It contains a large quantity of clear, colourless oil which in the air solidifies into a white, soft wax. Its function is uncertain.

A peculiar, and commercially valuable, intestinal product of the Physeteridæ is *ambergris*, a substance formerly used in Europe in pharmaceutical prepara-tions, and still so used in the Orient as also in cooking. It has been employed both in the East and West for centuries in the manufacture of perfumes. When used in minute quantities it adds to the pervasive and absorptive qualities of toilet 'washes' and perfumes. Ambergris is often said to be formed as a 'biliary concretion' in sick whales, but there is no evidence that such is the case. Its exact formation is still in doubt, but would appear to be pathological. Certainly, it is found in relatively few individuals. It has been variously considered to arise from intestinal irritation by the horny beaks of squid (the principal food of the sperm whales), or to be impacted, and otherwise altered, unvoided, fæcal material. In addition to occurring in the intestine of apparently healthy harpooned animals, or in carcases cast ashore, ambergris may be netted as flotsam, or picked up on beaches. When freshly voided it possesses a highly disagreeable odour, but after being well washed by the sea this may be lost and there may remain a not unpleasant, somewhat sweet, musty, earthy odour. As much as 926 lb. (65 × 30 inches) has been found in the intestine of a bull sperm whale only 49 feet long. The market price, which has been fairly stable for many years, varies from 2s. 6d. to 65s. per ounce according to quality.

In appearance, after floating and hardening, ambergris resembles a lump of dark, dull, often 'marbled', cobbler's wax. It is often impregnated with the undigested remnants of squid and cuttlefish. It has a specific gravity ranging from 0·780 to 0·926, melts at about 62° C. to a resinous dark yellow liquid, and is volatilised at 100° C. Ambergris dissolves in alcohol and ether (exhibiting iridescence) and liberates the *ambrein* which gives it its special quality.

The Delphinidæ display most pronouncedly the homodonty which characterises the group generally. The single, enormously elongated, spirally scored 'horn' of the Narwhal is at the one extreme of number of teeth, the Common Dolphin at the other with as many as fifty teeth in each row.

In the Odontoceti the skull shows a varying degree of asymmetry. The external nostril or blowhole is single and usually crescentic in outline. The upper jaw bones widen posteriorly to their snout portions and are squamous *above* the frontal bones, so that the latter are almost completely obliterated from dorsal view. The anterior ribs usually have capitulum and tuberculum. The sternum is formed of two or more sternebræ. The mandibular rami are wide at their articular end, gradually narrowing to the symphysis. The latter may be of considerable length (as in the river dolphins and sperm whales) or greatly shortened (as in the Common Porpoise and Pilot Whale).

SUB-ORDER MYSTICETI

The Mysticeti or baleen whales are rare in horizons earlier than the Lower Miocene. During this period a now-extinct family, the Cetotheriidæ, flourished. In these whales the compression of the skull had not proceeded to the extent found in later forms. The remaining extant families are the

Balænidæ (right whales, *Balæna*; and the Pigmy Right Whale, *Caperea*); the Eschrichtidæ (the Californian Grey Whale, *Eschrichtius*); and the Balænopteridæ (rorquals, *Balænoptera* (Fig. 554); and the Humpback *Megaptera*). These are represented by a few recent genera and many others now extinct.

The baleen whales have the very numerous, horny baleen (or whalebone) plates arranged in two series, one on each side of the upper jaw (Figs. 558, 559). The plates, roughly triangular in outline, have their shortest margin inserted transversely in the roof of the mouth and are spaced about a quarter of an inch apart. Of the two remaining, subequal margins the labial is smooth, while the

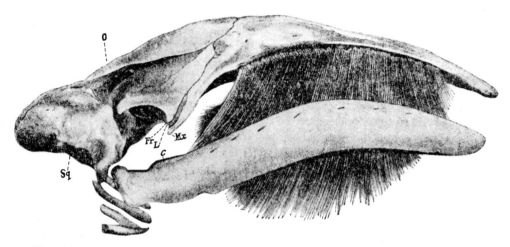

FIG. 558.—*Neobalæna:* **Adaptation to microphagy.** The genera *Balæna* and *Neobalæna* are composed of the Right Whales, including *N. marginata* (above), the Greenland and Southern 'whalebone' Whales, and others. The bigger species were the 'right' ones to kill for 'whalebone', since the baleen blades of the Greenland Whale (*B. mysticetus*) were as long as 15 feet (see also Fig. 559). During the late 19th-century heyday of voluminous corsetry, baleen fetched as much as £2,000 per ton. Baleen had many other common uses—*e.g.* as umbrella ribs—and it was woven into expensive fabrics that were guaranteed to 'stand of themselves'. Oil was relatively less prized during this period. *C.* coronoid process of mandible; *Fr.* frontal bone; *L.* lachrymal; *Mx.* maxilla; *O.* occipital; *Sq.* squamosal. (After Beddard.)

lingual is frayed out into a fringe of bristles. After water is taken into the buccal cavity the combination of these bristles forms an effective sieve for straining the plankton (usually crustacean *krill*) from the water that it is now forced from the mouth either by the action of a very muscular tongue (Balænidæ) or by the contraction of sub-cutaneous gular muscles (Balænopteridæ). As much as two tons of plankton have been found in the stomach of one Blue Whale.

Skeleton of Cetacea.—The cervical region (Fig. 561) (*cerv.*) is always very short, and the constituent vertebræ are often completely fused into a continuous bony mass (Fig. 560), or the atlas alone may be separate from the rest. Sometimes, however, all the vertebræ are complete and separate. In the latter case they have small arches and long transverse processes consisting of two narrow bars with a wide space between. The epiphyses are very distinct discs which often remain separate from the bodies up to a late period. The neural

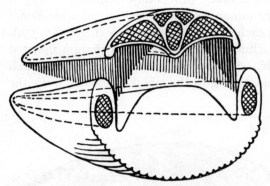

FIG. 559.—**Baleen plates: Relationship with tongue.** The twin sieves each consist of as many as 300 to 400 flexible horny blades embedded in the 'gum'. The baleen elements are longest and widest in the middle of each series, and become progressively shorter at each end. Each blade is in turn produced laterally into hair-like sieve processes. The water taken in through the open mouth is discharged through the sieve and leaves a vast trawl of krill behind. The tongue in baleen whales is immense compared with that of odontocetes. For *fœtal teeth* in Balænoptera, see Fig. 637, p. 874.

spines are well developed. The zygapophyses are poorly developed, and are absent in the posterior portion of the trunk. In the absence of hind-limbs there is no sacral region. The caudal region consists of numerous vertebræ beneath which, opposite the intervertebral spaces, are a series of chevron bones (*chev.*).

In the baleen whales only one pair of ribs articulates with the sternum, and none articulates with the body of the vertebra, but only with the transverse processes. In the toothed whales the anterior ribs (Fig. 561) have distinct tubercles and heads articulating respectively with transverse processes and vertebral bodies. The hinder ribs lack heads, and articulation is simply between tubercle and transverse process. The anterior ribs are linked with the sternum by ossified sternal ribs, while the posterior ones are progressively slender and imperfectly ossified. The *sternum* varies in shape. Sometimes it consists of a presternum and a series of several sternebræ without xiphisternum. Sometimes (Fig. 562) it is a continuous plate of bone, occasionally with median notches or fontanelles.

In the *skull* (Fig. 563) the brain-case is rounded, the jaws greatly elongated and often unsymmetrical. The parietals (*Pa.*) in most

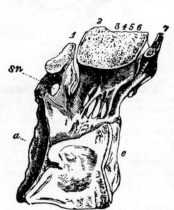

FIG. 560.—*Balæna:* **Vertebræ.** Section through middle line of united cervical vertebræ of Greenland Right Whale (*Balæna mysticetus*). *a.* articular surface for condyle; *e.* epiphysis of seventh cervical; *sn.* foramen in atlas for first spinal nerve; 1–7, arches of cervical vertebræ. (After Flower.)

Cetacea do not meet in the middle line above. They are generally separated by the supraoccipital (*S. O.*) and an interparietal (*I. P.*); there is thus no sagittal suture. A large supraorbital plate is developed from the frontal.

There are large and stout zygomatic processes of the squamosal, but the jugals are extremely small. In all the recent forms the maxilla (*Mx.*) is very large. It extends backwards in the toothed whales to overlap the frontal. In the baleen whales the extension is below the orbital process of the frontal. Forwards it extends nearly to the extremity of the snout. The premaxillæ (*P.Mx.*), which are long narrow bones, bound only a very small part of the oral border of the upper jaw. The nasals (*Na.*) are relatively small. The tympanic bone is very large. In the Mysticeti two bony pedicels connect it to the periotic. The anterior pedicel is absent in the Odontoceti and the posterior support does not involve bony fusion at the tympano-periotic junction. The lower jaw is remarkable for the absence of an ascending ramus. Baleen is keratinous. It is therefore in no way related to true bone (p. 73).

The *scapula* in most of the Cetacea is broad and flat and expanded into the shape of an open fan. The spine has practically disappeared. The acromion is a slightly curved laminar process with a narrow base of attachment. The coracoid also is compressed and parallel with the acromion. In some, both acromion and coracoid are absent. There is never any trace of a clavicle. The humerus is short and very stout. Its head is freely movable in the glenoid cavity, and its distal articulating surfaces are flat and oblique, meeting at an angle. The proximal ends of the radius and ulna are firmly united with the humerus and therefore allow of very little movement. At the distal

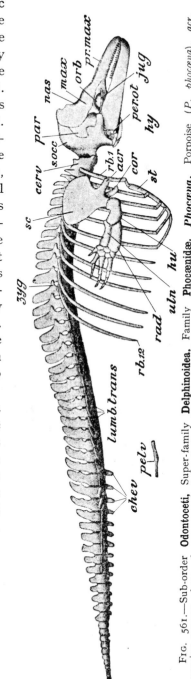

Fig. 561.—Sub-order **Odontoceti**, Super-family **Delphinoidea**, Family **Phocænidæ**. *Phocæna*. Porpoise (*P. phocæna*). *acr.* acromion process of scapula; *cerv.* united cervical vertebræ; *chev.* chevron bones; *cor.* coracoid process; *hu.* humerus; *hy.* hyoid; *jug.* jugal; *lumb. trans.* lumbar transverse processes; *max.* maxilla; *nas.* nasal; *orb.* orbit; *par.* parietal; *pelv.* vestige of pelvis; *per.ot.* periotic; *pelv.* vestigal pelvis; *pr.max.* pre-maxilla; *rad.* radius; *rb.* 1, first rib; *rb.* 12, twelfth rib; *sc.* scapula; *s. occ.* supraoccipital; *st.* sternum; *uln.* ulna; *zyg.* pre-zygapophysis.

end there are no complete synovial membranes. The manus is extremely modified. In all cetaceans it functions as a single unit with negligible in-

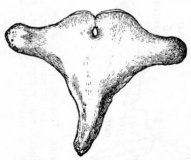

dividual mobility among the component elements. There are no synovial joints. The carpus is in some (whalebone whales) almost entirely cartilaginous, as also are the meta-carpals and phalanges. These cartilages are coalescent, or separated by intervals of fibrous tissues. In some of the carpal elements bone is deposited. In the toothed whales the carpals are completely ossified, and are of polygonal form. The phalanges are also ossi-

FIG. 562. — **Balœnoptera:**
Sternum. (After Flower.)

fied, with incomplete synovial articulations. In the Cetacea there are sometimes five digits, sometimes only four, of which the second is usually the longest (Fig. 564). A few species have considerably more than the customary number of

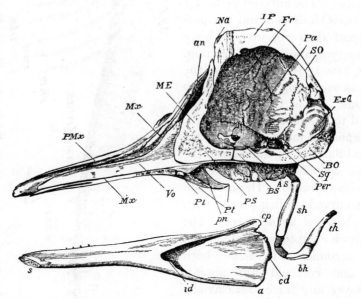

FIG. 563.—**Globicephala: Skull.** Sagittal section in a dolphin. *a.* angle of mandible; *an.* external nares; *A. S.* ali-sphenoid; *bh.* basi-hyal; *B. O.* basi-occipital; *B. S.* basi-sphenoid; *cd.* condyle of mandible; *c. p.* coronoid process; *Ex. O.* ex-occipital; *Fr.* frontal; *I. P.* inter-parietal; *M. E.* mesethmoid; *Mx.* maxilla; *Na.* nasal; *Pa.* parietal; *Per.* periotic; *Pl.* palatine; *P.mx.* premaxilla; *p. n.* posterior nares; *P.S.* pre-sphenoid; *Pt.* pterygoid; *s.h.* stylo-hyal; *S. O.* supraoccipital; *Sq.* squamosal; *t. h.* thyro-hyal; *Vo.* vomer. (After Flower.)

phalanges (*hyperphalangy*); sometimes as many as fourteen may occur. In whales with broad flippers (e.g. *Monodon, Delphinapterus* and *Phocæna*) the number of phalanges is reduced, and in those with long, narrow limbs (e.g.

Globicephala, Megaptera), the number is increased with maturity. It is of interest that whales are the only mammals that retain traces of discrete fourth and fifth distal carpals.

Vestiges of the *pelvis* are present in the form of a pair of long narrow bones (Fig. 561, *pelv.*), which lie parallel with the spinal column some little distance below the region where the chevron bones begin. These are completely isolated and appear to represent the ischia. A second pair of smaller bones which lie close to these in the whalebone whales are apparently vestiges of the femora. There may be additional vestiges representing the tibiæ.

Internal Adaptations of Cetacea.—Some whales can submerge for more than thirty minutes, and their submarine habits (unique as far as homœothermous animals are concerned) are made possible by a series of extraordinary morphological adaptations. To some degree the Cetacea have redeveloped piscine characteristics, *e.g.* in body-form, the almost total lack of bristles and absence of external ears; the long snout, lack of neck, and the broad, powerful tail. These characters mimic the typical fish form and make for smooth and unimpeded progress through water.

Even more remarkable adaptations, peculiar to the group, have developed internally. The so-called 'spout' or 'blow' was traditionally explained as a jet of water, and is generally held to be the condensation of warm air expired from the lungs through the dorsal blow-hole when the whale surfaces. Opinions differ, however, as to whether the blow is more conspicuous in polar than in tropical seas. A recent suggestion is that the 'blow' is composed of nitrogen-charged foam. Foam developed from a finely-divided emulsion of fat droplets (in mucus) and gas has been found in the middle ear and trachea of several species of whales. (In the ear it may subserve a sound-insulating function.) Fat has a high nitrogen absorption capacity : in the respiratory tract the fatty foam

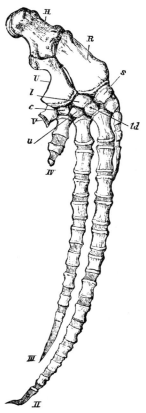

FIG. 564.—***Globicephala:*** **Hyperphalangy.** Dorsal surface of right anterior limb in a dolphin (*G. melas*). *c.* cuneiform; *H.* humerus; *l.* lunar; *R.* radius; *s.* scaphoid; *td.* trapezoid; *U.* ulna; *u.* unciform. (After Flower.)

may constitute an auxiliary excretory device. Audition may be improved by modifications of the Eustachian tubes as capacious, air-filled diverticula in the pterygoid and palatal regions. The blow-hole leads vertically to the nostrils which, varying from group to group, have moved backwards with corresponding modification of the dorsal cranial bones. The nostrils are equipped with valves which are closed during diving. The epiglottis is peculiar: it has become tube-like and intra-narial.

The remarkably prolonged submergence can be maintained only with the aid of special accessory respiratory arrangements, some of which are still incompletely understood. The muscles are heavily charged with *myoglobin* giving whale-meat its characteristically dark colour, and this device (Fig. 326) facilitates tissue oxidation during the tremendous dives. There is evidence, too, that the muscles can function anaerobically, thus setting up a large temporary oxygen debt that can be redressed later. The enormous system of *retia mirabilia* (Fig. 236, p. 342) also enables the storage of a huge oxygen volume that can be drawn upon during submersion. Whales avoid the 'diver's paralysis' ('bends', 'caisson sickness') that attacks Man when he ascends quickly from extreme depths. A submerged human diver continuously breathes compressed air. At the same time the nitrogen dissolves into his blood-stream. If he comes up too rapidly without 'staging', nitrogen is liberated and bubbles may block small blood vessels and lead to paralysis, cerebral anaemia, and death. As whales can inhale and submerge with only sufficient air to fill their lungs, there is a strict limit to the amount of nitrogen that can be dissolved into the circulation. It has been shown that the species that dive deepest have a relatively smaller lung capacity than others. Again, there is evidence that when a whale dives deeply, pressure causes the belly viscera to be thrust against the immense oblique diaphragm, which then compresses the lungs and forces air anteriorly into the trachea and forward passages. Meanwhile, the now comparatively empty alveoli contract and become thick-walled, and so gaseous exchanges between the lungs and blood remain at a minimum until the animal ascends above a certain level.

Whales lack a scrotum, and the testes are intra-abdominal. The elongated penis, operated by a correspondingly massive *ischio-cavernosus* muscle, is curled when not in erection. There is a bicornuate uterus, but usually only a single young one is produced at a time. The gestation period is more than a year in some forms and the new-born calf may be one-third of the mother's size. In the Blue Whale (*Balænoptera musculus* (Fig. 554)), which grows to about 100 feet long, the gestation period is said to be about a year. The neonatus weighs more than two tons and is some 23 feet long. It is reported to grow at a rate of about 200 lb. per day while suckling and to reach puberty at about four years of age. A single pair of teats occur in the inguinal area. The mammary glands are equipped with a remarkable muscular apparatus that pumps milk (containing up to 38 per cent fat, cf. p. 583) into the mouth of the calf. For the composition of other kinds of milk, see p. 849.

COHORT FERUNGULATA

This large group contains all mammalian groups not previously dealt with. It is divided into five super-orders. These are : 1. the Feræ (including only the Carnivora) ; 2. Protoungulata (four extinct orders and the Tubulidentata) ; 3. Pænungulata (four extinct orders and the Hyracoidea, Proboscidea, and Sirenia) ; 4. Mesaxonia (order Perissodactyla), and 5. Paraxonia (order Artiodactyla). It is possible that the constitution of this major group will be altered by future study, but convincing palæontological evidence is available that the Carnivora and hooved animals of widely differing kinds (the even-toed artiodactyles, *e.g.* deer, and the odd-toed perissodactyles, *e.g.* horses), arose, together with certain others, from a common Palæocene ancestry.

SUPER-ORDER FERÆ

The clear demarcation of the Carnivora from all other groups even before the Palæocene, their proved antiquity and their peculiar diversity, cannot be adequately expressed by mere ordinal rank and so they form the sole order of the present super-order.

ORDER CARNIVORA

The modern carnivores are relatively difficult to characterise. The fusion of the scaphoid, lunar, and centrale, however, is constant in modern carnivores. (These elements are said not to be fused in Miacidæ.) Other characteristic features are the almost universal retention of the full number of incisors and the well-developed canines. (Sloth-bears, *Melursus*, have lost the inner upper pair of incisors.) The post-canine dentition always shows a certain amount of reduction and a rather wide range of adaptive variation, as described below. The pedal digits are usually five, and are never less than four. The toes are armed with sharp claws which are often retractile. The brain is well-developed.

The present radiation of carnivores may be said to start mainly in the Oligocene period, but the line can be traced backward through late Eocene Canidæ to the Miacidæ of the Palæocene, until it becomes merged in the basal creodont-insectivore stock from which so many orders arose.

The group has been arranged as follows :

Sub-order Creodonta
    Families Arctocyonidæ (Lower Palæocene–Eocene)
        Mesonychidæ (Palæocene–Eocene)
        Oxyænidæ (Palæocene–Eocene)
        Hyænodontidæ (Eocene–Pliocene)
Sub-order Fissipedia
    Super-family Miacoidea
      Family Miacidæ (Palæocene–Eocene)

Super-family Canoidea
    Families Canidæ (Eocene–Recent)
        Ursidæ (Miocene–Recent)
        Procyonidæ (Miocene–Recent)
        Mustelidæ (Oligocene–Recent)
Super-family Feloidea
    Families Viverridæ (Oligocene–Recent)
        Hyænidæ (Miocene–Recent)
        Felidæ (Upper Eocene–Recent)
Sub-order Pinnipedia
    Families Otariidæ (Miocene–Recent)
        Odobenidæ (Miocene–Recent)
        Phocidæ (Miocene–Recent)

SUB-ORDER CREODONTA

Until their final extinction during the Pliocene, the sub-order Creodonta were the dominant flesh-eating mammals. They radiated into four families. Of these, the earliest, known from the Lower Palæocene, were the Arcto-cyonidæ. These were small animals primitive in general structure, with low skulls, small brains, and with a complete dentition. Shearing *carnassial* teeth were not yet developed, and the molars were usually of the tuberculo-sectorial pattern. The limbs and body were long and slender, with a long tail, the feet pentadactyle and plantigrade. From this centralised and unspecialised assembly arose (mostly during the Palæocene) the Mesonychidæ, Oxyænidæ (all of which disappeared about the end of the Eocene), and the Hyænodontidæ, which lived until the Oligocene.

The Mesonychidæ, like the Arctocyonoidea, developed no carnassials, but the cusps of the cheek-teeth became broad and blunt, and in some of the later forms developed a hypocone. The feet possessed flattened, fissured terminal phalanges which appeared to have borne small hooves.

The Oxyænidæ and Hyænodontidæ are characterised by having 'false' carnassials, in the sense that they are never the corresponding pair of teeth (fourth upper premolar and first lower molar) as those in the Miacoidea and modern carnivores. In the Oxyænidæ the carnassials are the first upper and second lower molars, in the Hyænodontidæ the second upper and third lower molars (Fig. 565). The two families in their day were the most successful of the earlier radiation, and gave rise to some large forms, though *Andrew-sarchus*, a mesonychid from the Lower Oligocene of Mongolia, reached the largest size of all, with a skull three feet in length.

SUB-ORDER FISSIPEDIA

The first true fissipedes arose in the Palæocene, possibly from the Arcto-cyonidæ. The group expanded during the Eocene, radiating into the modern families during the Oligocene. As in other fissipedes, and in contrast with creodonts, the Miacidæ possessed true carnassials which were developed from the fourth upper premolar and the first lower molar. The terminal phalanges were not fissured. Miacids differed from other Fissipedia, how-ever, in that the scaphoid, lunar, and centrale remained unfused.

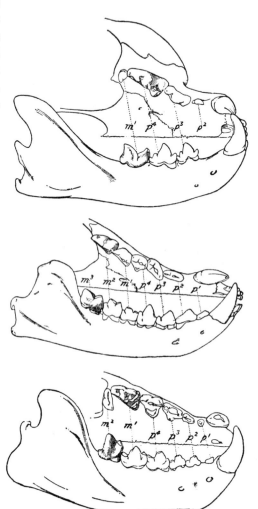

The modern Fissipedia are classi-fied on a number of anatomical characters such as the structure of the auditory bulla and the presence or absence of an alisphenoid canal. For practical quick identification of specimens, however, the most useful guide is the pattern of the molar teeth and the presence or absence of the flesh-cutting carnassial teeth (the last upper premolar and the first lower molar in all modern forms). In the classification adopted here we sepa-rate them into two superfamilies (1) the Feloidea (= Aeluroidea) com-posed of the Viverridæ, Hyænidæ, and Felidæ and (2) the Canoidea (Arctoidea) including the Canidæ, Procyonidæ, Mustelidæ, and Ursidæ. Of the above seven families the Viverridæ, Canidæ, and Mustelidæ are perhaps basic groups, possibly stemming independently from Miacidæ. Within the Canoidea, the history of the Family Canidæ (dogs, wolves, and foxes) is illustrated by a

FIG. 565.—**Carnivora: Comparison of creo-dont and fissipede dentition.** Upper and lower teeth of *Felis* (cat) (top figure); *Hyænodon* (middle figure) and *Oxyæna* (lower figure) show-ing the different arrangement of the carnassial teeth. The carnassials are shaded.

long series of fossils reaching back to the Tertiary. They are almost universally distributed although the Dingo (*Canis dingo*) of Australia was introduced there by colonising aborigines. Canine dentition is usually complete except

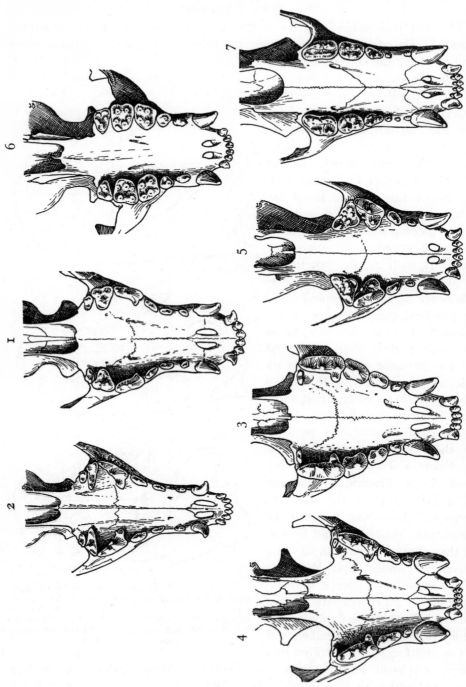

FIG. 566.—**Carnivora: Dentition in modern forms.** Upper jaw of 1. *Canis* (Dog); 2. *Viverra* (Civet); 3 *Hyæna*; 4. *Panthera* (leopard); 5. *Taxidea* (American Badger); 6. *Procyon* (Racoon); 7. *Ursus arctos* (Brown Bear).

for the absence of the last upper molar. The carnassial teeth are well-developed and the upper molars are bluntly triangular in pattern (Fig. 566). There are only four functional toes on the hind-feet. The claws are non-retractile.

The Viverridæ, surviving to-day as the civets, genets, mongooses (of various kinds), the Madagascar Fossa, and others, probably represents the basal feloidean stock. Essentially Asiatic and African in distribution, many of these small active animals are extremely cat-like in appearance and habits. The otter-civets (*Cynogale*) of the East Indies are adapted for fishing. The dentition and certain other features of extant forms show considerable similarity with those of ancestral miacids.

The Hyænidæ of Africa and Asia, an early offshoot from civet stock, feed mostly on carrion; the molar dentition is reduced to one in each jaw. The

FIG. 567.—Order **Carnivora,** Sub-order **Fissipedi.** Super-family **Feloidea,** Family **Felidæ.** *Acinonyx.* The Cheetah (*A. jubata*) is the fastest mammal. Although its speed is often exaggerated it can, in fact, reach 60 m.p.h. over very short distances. When travelling at speed over the veld the cheetah seems to remain—almost arrow-like—nearer the ground than shown in the above illustration which, however, is drawn in correct relationship from a photograph.

carnassials are well developed. The upper molar is reduced to a functionless vestige, transversely placed. The teeth as compared with those of the Felidæ are blunter and coarser, an adaptation to bone-crushing. There are never more than four pedal toes and the claws are non-retractile. The tympanic bulla has internally a rudimentary septum which partially divides it. The aberrant *Proteles,* the Aard-wolf or Earth-wolf of Africa is insectivorous and has teeth reduced to simple cones. Like the hyænas it is obviously a highly specialised viverrid offshoot and, following recent authors, it is here classified with the Hyænidæ.

The Felidæ are essentially carnivorous nocturnal hunters with large eyes, short high skulls, and retractable claws. They usually lie in wait for, or creep upon, their prey, finally securing it with a mighty spring. Unlike dogs, they are generally individualists in hunting and do not run a great deal. A striking exception, however, is the Cheetah (*Acinonyx*) (Fig. 567), which stalks and then pursues its prey and is the fastest living mammal over a very short distance. In 1937 cheetahs were tested against greyhounds in Britain, and the fastest were reported to cover a 355-yard lap at 55 m.p.h. The Cheetah moves with a series of bounds and catches the speediest gazelles. It occurs in Africa and Southern Asia and has been used as a so-called hunting-'leopard' or hunting-'dog' for centuries in India and Persia. Its claws are only partly retractile.

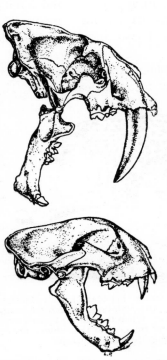

The teeth of the Felidæ are highly specialised for seizing, holding, tearing, and shearing, but not for grinding, meat. There are very well-developed carnassials. The Felidæ possess extremely small molars. The premolars, too, are reduced both in number and size to three above and two below. In some extinct Felidæ such as the sabre-toothed *Smilodon* remarkable dentitional, and associated cranial and muscular adaptations arose. The upper canines became immensely long, flattened, and blade-like as stabbing and slashing weapons (Fig. 568). The lower canines were markedly reduced. The cheek teeth were restricted in number, and lengthened antero-posteriorly into a carnassial scissors-like slicing apparatus. The mastoid process (to which the larger neck muscles were attached) became massive, suggesting that the upper canines were speared downwards by a powerful neck-thrust. Such a movement is quite different from the action employed by modern cats, which kill with both upper and lower canines as the jaws are closed (Fig. 568). The

FIG.   568.—**Felidæ: Dental specialisations.** *Above:* Sabre-tooth (*Smilodon*) (Sub-family Machaerodontinæ) of the Pleistocene (skull-length about 12 inches); *Below:* True cat (*Metailurus*) (Felinæ) of the Pliocene. (From Romer, after Zdansky.)

relatively reduced coronoid process of sabre-tooths allowed a wide gap, and a shift of the shearing carnassials (better developed than in modern cats) backwards towards the jaw articulation where they would exert greater power. *Smilodon* was extinguished only about 25,000 years ago.   There was, incidentally, an approximately parallel evolution among the marsupials (*e.g.* the South American Pliocene *Thylacosmilus*).   In the sabre-tooths the claws were completely retractile.   The tympanic bulla was smooth, inflated externally, and internally divided by a complete septum.

The Mustelidæ (stoats, otters, skunks, martens, wolverines, etc.) form a large group in which the post-carnassial upper molar, instead of being triangular, is expanded on the inner side (Fig. 566 [5]), sometimes, as in the European Badger (*Meles meles*), very much so.   The dental formula varies somewhat, but is not much reduced, except that there is never more than a single post-carnassial molar in either jaw. The claws are not retractile and the tympanic bulla is not inflated and has no internal septum. This group was well-developed in the Oligocene and one (*Megalictis*) as big as a bear occurred in the early Miocene.

The Procyonidæ (raccoons, Kinkajou, pandas, etc.) are American in distribution with the exception of the Panda (*Ailurus*) and the so-called Giant Panda (*Ailuropoda*), both of which are Oriental. The dentition, except for the loss of an anterior premolar and the last molar, shows little reduction. Carnassials are not developed as shearing-teeth and the upper molars are round in outline instead of triangular (Fig. 566 [6]). The claws are non-retractile. The Kinkajou (*Potos*) is a fruit-eating animal in which the crown surface of the molar teeth is degraded to a flat surface only obscurely tuberculated. It has a prehensile tail—a feature almost unique among carnivores. (The arboreal carnivorous Binturong (*Arctictis binturong*) of Indo-Malaya also has a prehensile tail.)

The Ursidæ (bears) appear to have arisen in the Pliocene. They. were probably the last of the Canoidea to appear. They have a fully plantigrade foot and non-retractile claws. Like the Procyonidæ, shearing carnassial teeth are not formed. The molar teeth are large, elongated, and much tuberculated (Fig. 566 [7]); the dentition, except for the last molar, is unreduced. The tympanic bulla is flat. With the plantigrade gait of bears there have arisen pedal and other specialisations that are to some degree convergent with those of Man. Thus, the ursine femur is long and superficially hominoid and the foot structure of bear and Man is somewhat alike. Should a person be so disposed he can sometimes compel himself to confuse the footprints of Man and bears. Moreover, bears sometimes produce grotesquely over-sized, composite footprints by superimposing the hind-foot partly over the print made by the adjacent fore-leg. Tracks of the Red Bear (*Ursus arctos isabellinus*) are almost certainly those that keep alive the Yeti ('Abominable Snow Man') legend of Tibetan shepherd and mountain romantic.

Bears of various species are commonly said to hibernate: certainly some retreat in winter into prepared dens but whether there is true hibernation (p. 883), involving a prolonged period of greatly lowered body temperature and general metabolism, is still uncertain.

SUB-ORDER PINNIPEDIA

Seals (Fig. 569) are in general piscivorous, but many species subsist largely on crabs, others on squids and some on euphausian plankton. As compared with the teeth, jaws, and associated muscles of fissipedes (see above) those of the Pinnipedia are simplified for grasping and tearing rather than chewing. There are no carnassial teeth. There are never more than two pairs of lower incisors in the adult; and never more than five pairs of lower post-canines (four premolars, one molar). The teeth are basically conical, with a single crown, although specialisations have appeared, ranging from an anterior and posterior additional cusp to an elaborate series of notches used for straining euphausians and other crustaceans by the Crab-eater seal. In the Walrus (of which there are two sub-species) the teeth are extremely aberrant: the upper canines may reach a length of $39\frac{1}{2}$ inches along the curve. The primary function of the tusks in both sexes is to tear clams from the ocean floor. The facial part of the skull is abbreviated, the cranial elongated.

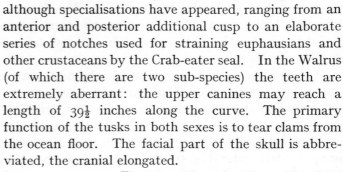

Fig. 569.—Order **Carnivora**, Sub-order **Pinnipedia**, Family **Phocidæ**. *Phoca*. A reptigrade or 'wriggling' seal (*P. vitulina*. (After Blainville.))

There are three families. The Otariidæ (sea-lions and fur seals) and Odobenidæ (walruses) are *gressigrade* or 'walking seals'. The members of both these families can turn the hind-feet forward for progression on land; the forelimbs are the primary swimming organs. The third family, the Phocidæ is composed of *reptigrade* or 'wriggling seals'. These have the hind-limbs (as far as the ankles) bound up with the short tail within the body covering. Such limbs are almost useless for terrestrial locomotion. In this group the hind-limbs are the primary swimming organs. The Otariidæ derive their name from the short, cartilaginous pinnæ which are absent in the other two families.

As yet no fossils linking land carnivores with pinnipedes have been discovered. Nor can it be said with assurance which of the three families is the oldest. The Pliocene *Semantor*, a long-tailed animal which was probably capable of walking, has been often thought to belong to a primitive pinnipede stock. Some modern authorities consider it to be more likely an otter (p. 796).

Skeleton of the Carnivora.—The atlas is very large, with wing-like lateral processes. The neural spine of the axis is elongated and compressed; the odontoid process conical. The other cervical vertebræ have small spines and large transverse processes. There are twenty or twenty-one thoraco-lumbar vertebræ. The most anterior thoracics have long, slender, backwardly-sloping spines. In the posterior thoracics large meta-

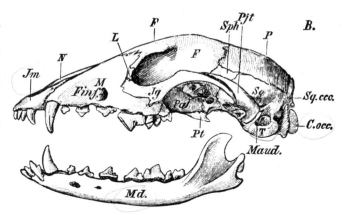

FIG. 570.—*Canis:* **Skull.** Dog. Lateral view. *C. occ.* occipital condyle; *F.* frontal; *F. inf.* infraorbital foramen; *Jg.* jugal; *Jm.* premaxilla; *L.* lachrymal; *M.* maxilla; *Maud.* external auditory meatus; *Md.* mandible; *N.* nasal; *P.* parietal; *Pal.* palatine; *Pjt.* zygomatic process of squamosal; *Pt.* pterygoid; *Sph.* ali-sphenoid; *Sq.* squamosal; *Sq. occ.* supra-occipital; *T.* tympanic. (After Wiedersheim.)

pophyses and anapophyses are developed. The transverse processes of the lumbar vertebræ are extremely long and the spines short. The sternum is long and narrow, composed usually of eight or nine pieces. The sternal ribs are almost uncalcified.

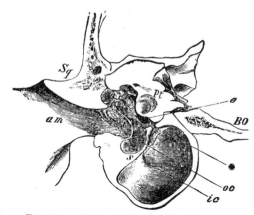

FIG. 571.—*Felis:* **Auditory bulla.** Tiger. Left, in section. * aperture of communication between the two chambers into which the cavity of the bulla is divided; *a. m.* external auditory meatus; *B. O.* basi-occipital; *e.* Eustachian tube; *i. c.* the inner chamber; *o. c.* the outer chamber; *Pt.* periotic; *s.* septum between the two chambers; *Sq.* squamosal. (After Flower.)

In the *skull* of the *Carnivora vera* (Fig. 570) there are prominent sagittal and lamboidal crests. The temporal fossæ are very deep; the orbits are not separated from them by bone. The relative development of the facial region varies in the different groups: in the bears and their allies, and in the dogs, it is elongated, whilst in the cats it is very short. The zygoma is strong and greatly arched outwards. The glenoid fossa is a transverse groove, to the shape of which the transversely elongated condyle is adapted. In the cats there is a large rounded tympanic bulla (Fig. 571), the cavity of which is divided into anterior and posterior parts by a septum. The anterior contains the auditory ossicles and the opening of the Eustachian tube. The bony auditory meatus is short. The paroccipital is closely applied to the posterior surface of the tympanic bulla. In the dogs the septum of the bulla is incomplete, the auditory meatus short, and the paroccipital process not applied to the bulla. In the bears and their allies the bulla (Fig. 572) is usually less dilated, and the septum is absent or represented by a ridge only, while the bony auditory meatus is elongated.

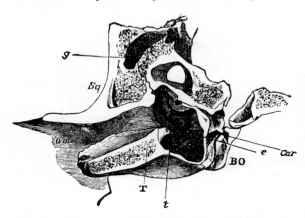

FIG. 572. — *Ursus:* **Auditory bulla.** Left, in section. *a. m.* external auditory meatus; *B. O.* basi-occipital; *Car.* carotid canal; *e.* Eustachian canal; *g.* glenoid canal ('foramen glenoideum which leads to a venous canal which runs upwards and backwards into the lateral sinus'; *Sq.* squamosal; *T.* tympanic; *t.* tympanic ring. (After Flower.)

The cranium in the Pinnipedia (Fig. 569) is broad, rounded, and rather compressed from above downwards. The orbits are large and relatively closely opposed.

In the *Carnivora vera* the spine of the *scapula* is situated at about the middle of the outer surface of the bone. The acromion is usually well developed, sometimes with a metacromion. The coracoid process is very small. The clavicle is never complete, sometimes entirely absent. There is a supra-condyloid foramen in the cats and some of the other groups, not in the dogs or bears.

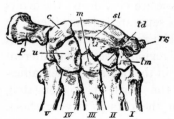

FIG. 573.—*Ursus:* **Carpus.** *c.* cuneiform; *m.* magnum; *p.* pisiform; *r. s.* radial sesamoid; *s. l.* scapholunar; *td.* trapezoid; *tm.* trapezium; *u.* unciform. (After Flower.)

The scaphoid and lunar are united (Fig. 573). There is no separate centrale. A radial sesamoid is usually present. There are five digits, though the pollex may be reduced in size, as in the dog, and it is vestigial in hyænas.

The *pelvis* is long and narrow. In the tarsus all the customary elements are developed. The hallux is fully formed in the bears, etc., but shorter than the other digits. In the cats and dogs it is represented only by a vestige of the metatarsal.

In the Pinnipedia (Fig. 569) both acromion and coracoid are short, and the scapula is curved backwards. There is no clavicle. The bones of the fore-limb are short and stout. The humerus has a prominent deltoid crest and has no foramen above its inner condyle. The ulna is greatly expanded at its proximal, and the radius at its distal, end. The manus is broad and expanded.

The scaphoid and lunar are united to form a scapho-lunar. The ungual phalanges are nearly straight, slender, and pointed. The ilia are short. The symphysis pubis is short and without firm union of the bones, an advantage in delivering the large precocious young. The femur is short, thick, and flattened. The fibula and tibia are commonly ankylosed proximally. The calcaneum is short and usually without a distinct calcaneal process. The lateral digits are usually the longest.

SUPER-ORDER PROTOUNGULATA

The term 'Ungulate' has been used to cover a multitude of hooved grazing animals, many of which are but remotely related. Further, modern evidence from fossils appears to indicate a much closer relationship between the Carnivora (p. 791) and the hooved 'ungulates' than was previously surmised. Hooved animals fall into a variety of widely divergent groups and it is probable that the even-toed cow is as unrelated to the odd-toed horse as it is to the cat. Hooves, like so many characters once considered to be fundamental, have arisen independently in several groups in response to special environmental conditions. In addition, grazing animals of apparently independent stems have evolved highly specialised grinding teeth of various kinds (as well as numerous muscular, articular, and alimentary adaptations), long necks and legs, and various social tendencies related to self-preservation.

Although Cretaceous strata have so far yielded no hooved grazing mammals, several unquestionably distinct groups had appeared by the early Tertiary. Of these, the Condylarthra were the most successful in the Palæocene. Before their extinction in the Eocene these probably gave rise to several other notable groups.

The super-order Protoungulata has been arranged as follows :

Super-order Protoungulata
  Order Condylarthra
    Families Hyopsodontidæ (Palæocene–Eocene)
      Phenacodontidæ Palæocene–Eocene)
      Didolodontidæ (Palæocene–Eocene)
      Periptychidæ (Palæocene)
      Meniscotheriidæ (Palæocene–Eocene)
  Order Tubulidentata
      Orycteropodidæ (Pliocene–Recent)
  Order Notoungulata
    Sub-orders Notioprogonia (Palæocene–Eocene)
      Toxodontia (Palæocene–Pleistocene)
      Typotheria (Eocene–Pleistocene)
      Hegetotheria (Eocene–Pleistocene)

Order Litopterna
    Families Macraucheniidæ (Upper Palæocene–Pleistocene)
        Proterotheriidæ (Upper Palæocene–Lower Pliocene)
Order Astrapotheria
    Sub-orders Trigonostylopoidea (Eocene)
        Astrapotherioidea (Eocene–Miocene)

ORDER CONDYLARTHRA

This order, an important basal group approaching the early Creodonta in some respects, is characterised by the foreshadowing of hooves—*i.e.* they are on the 'ungulate' line of evolution rather than on the 'unguiculate'. There is also a tendency for the third toe to become progressively larger than the others,

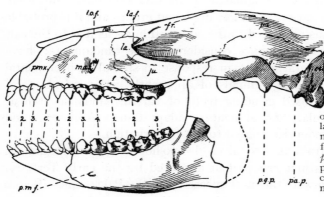

Fig. 574.—Order **Condylarthra**, Family **Hyopsodontidæ.** *Hyopsodus:* **Skull.** This North American Eocene condylarth was about the size of a hedgehog. It had clawed phalanges and may have been semi-arboreal. *fr.* frontal; *i.o.f.* infra-orbital foramen; *ju.* jugal; *la.* lachrymal; *la.f.* lachrymal foramen; *max.* maxilla; *m.f.* mental foramen; *na.* nasal; *oc.* occipital; *pa.* parietal; *pa.p.* paroccipital process; *pg.p.* postglenoid process; *pmx.* premaxilla; *sq.* squamosal. (After Matthews.)

thus producing a *mesaxonic* (p. 824), as compared with a *paraxonic* (p. 836), foot. These two characters suggest that the Perissodactyla arose from some early members of the group, although no direct ancestor has so far been discovered. The tooth pattern of such a form as the condylarth *Ectocion*, itself an Eocene form too late to be ancestral, could easily be modified into that of *Hyracotherium*, the earliest known horse (p. 826).

The chief characters of the early condylarths are mostly negative ones, as is to be expected in any very primitive group. The omnivorous, non-predaceous character of the teeth is unlike what was evolving in the allied creodonts, and there is none of the specialised features, such as the shortening of the jaws and reduction of the incisors found in the Primates. There is a general resemblance to the insectivores, but none of the specialisations of that order is observable. The astragalus, a diagnostically important bone (p. 859, Fig. 623), is of the creodont-carnivore type and the carpus is normally interlocking with the centrale retained.

In general, the Condylarthra are to be considered as primitive, and not far removed from the generalised ancestral stock of the Cretaceous period. They are probably ancestral to a number of later groups.

There are five families : the Hyopsodontidæ, Phenacodontidæ, Periptychidæ, Meniscotheriidæ, and Didolodontidæ. This last family contains only South American animals that appear to be a connecting link with the exclusively South American Litopterna (p. 805).

The Hyopsodontidæ (e.g. *Hyopsodus*, Fig. 574) are the more primitive forms, and have a general resemblance to insectivores and primates. *Hyopsodus*, with its sexitubercular molars and hedgehog-like skull, was formerly placed in one or other of the above orders until the discovery of its typically condylarth astragalus decided its truer position. The Mioclæninæ (e.g. *Mioclænus*) have tritubercular teeth, and both retain, among other primitive features, claws rather than hooves and an interlocking carpus.

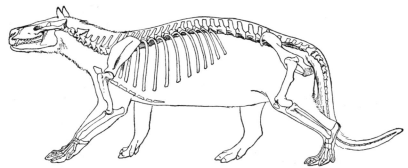

FIG. 575.—Order **Condylarthra,** Family **Phenacodontidæ.** *Phenacodus.* A North American (Upper Palæocene and Lower Eocene) and European (Lower Eocene) protoungulate which attained a length of about five feet. (Am. Mus. Nat. Hist.)

The Phenacodontidæ comprise several genera, among which are *Tetraclænodon*, which, in having blunt claws rather than hooves, somewhat bridges the gap between the condylarths and creodonts, and *Phenacodus* (Fig. 575), its direct descendant, which has become specialised in having a serially arranged carpus and by the loss of the clavicle. *Ectocion*, an Eocene genus, has, as already mentioned, a dentition approaching that of the early horses. In this family the feet are, as in the others, pentadactyle, but with a progressive tendency to tridactylism, to digitigradism, and to a broadening of the ungues into small flat hooves.

The Periptychidæ (e.g. *Periptychus, Conacodon, Ectoconus*) also have narrow hooves, and are a specialised side-line with enlarged premolars and multicuspid molars, which prevent them from appearing as ancestral to any later forms. Their earlier members are closely akin to the Hyopsodontidæ.

The Meniscotheriidæ (*Meniscotherium, Pleuraspidotherium*) retain a very primitive foot structure, but have become specialised in their very selenodont molars. On this ground they have been considered as ancestral to the Hyracoidea, though proof is still lacking.

The Didolodontidæ, with primitive bunodont molars and simple premolars, are on the line leading to the early Litopterna, such as *Diadiaphorus*.

ORDER TUBULIDENTATA

The relationship of this order is problematical. At one time it was grouped with the Edentata (Xenarthra and Pholidota), but now it appears possible that

FIG. 576.—Order **Tubulidentata,** Family **Orycteropodidæ.** *Orycteropus.* Only one species of Aardvark or 'Earth-pig' (*O. afer*), of perhaps three geographical races, survives over a wide area of African savannah. About the size of a small pig, the nocturnal Aardvark lives almost exclusively on termites. Mounds are breached with powerful hoof-like claws and the insects are gathered on its sticky tongue. The sub-maxillary glands are relatively enormous and the parotids highly developed. *Orycteropus* has remarkable auditory powers and its olfactory turbinals are perhaps more extensive than in any other mammal. Sensory vibrissæ, too, are highly developed. The animal lives in a system of subterranean galleries and, if surprised in the open, digs itself to safety in a few minutes. (From photographs and B.M. (N.H.) specimens.)

it is a very early independent offshoot of protoungulate ancestry. The order contains a single modern genus (*Orycteropus*, the Aardvark of Africa, Fig. 576) and a problematical Lower Eocene form, *Tubulodon*, from North America. *Orycteropus* is also known from the Pliocene of Europe and Asia and fragments of supposed orycteropods have been described from the Oligocene and Miocene of Europe.

The body of the Aardvark is thickset, with the head produced into a long muzzle. The fore-limbs are short and stout, with four digits, the palmar surfaces of which are placed on the ground in walking. The hind-limb has five digits and the body is covered with thick skin bearing scattered hairs. *Orycteropus* lives on termites and has the most strikingly developed turbinals of all the Mammalia. The tongue is long and the mouth small. Four to five peg-like teeth of peculiar structure are present in each jaw. They lack enamel, but possess a coating of cement and a body of vasodentine which is perforated by large numbers of fine tubules, whence the order takes its name. The teeth of *Tubulodon* also possess them. The structure of the rather primitive brain is stated to show some resemblance to that of *Anoplotherium*, an Eocene artiodactyle. The skeleton of the Aardvark is much like that of certain early condylarths.

SOUTH AMERICAN 'UNGULATA'

In South America there was an evolution of 'ungulates' of great diversity of form and of a range in time from the Palæocene to as late a period as the Pleistocene. They are grouped provisionally in four orders which have no connexion with one another beyond some remote condylarth ancestor. Although there are, on occasion, superficial resemblances to animals in other parts of the world, as, for instance, the curious convergence in foot-structure of certain Litopterna and the horses, or the proboscidean characters of the Pyrotheria, these four orders in reality have no special relationships with other ungulate groups. Each has pursued its own specialised line of evolution.

ORDER LITOPTERNA

This is a small order, consisting of two families, the Macraucheniidæ and Proterotheriidæ. The genus *Macrauchenia* had a three-toed foot with well-developed lateral toes, the neck long and camel-like, and the skull peculiar in the position of the nasal openings far back on the upper surface of the skull, suggesting the presence of a proboscis. In this order a series of genera show an evolution which closely parallels that of the horses. *Notodiaphorus*, an Oligocene form, had three toes with the lateral ones stout and still resting on the ground —about the stage, that is, of *Meso-hippus* among the horses (p. 826).

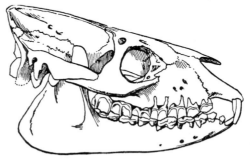

FIG. 577.—Order **Litopterna**, Family **Proterotheriidæ.** *Diadiaphorus.* South American Miocene–Pliocene. (After Scott.)

Diadiaphorus, in the Miocene, had the lateral toes much reduced, and can be compared with *Merychippus*, while *Thoatherium*, also Miocene, was monodactyle to a greater degree even than the modern horse, in that the splint-bones are reduced to mere nodules (see Fig. 615, p. 858).

The dentition of these animals has the perissodactyle-like feature of molarisation of the premolars, but unlike the horses, the teeth are usually low crowned. Although there is a superficial resemblance in the molar pattern

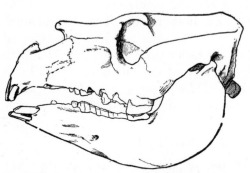

with the earlier horses, there are differences in detail. The tooth- and foot-structure combined are never in phase with that of any genus of horse, so that there is no real danger of confusion.

ORDER NOTOUNGULATA

Four sub-orders are recognised: The first, the Notioprogonia, contains the families Arctostylopidæ (occurring in Asia and North America, the only non-South American notoungulates), Henricos-

FIG. 578. — Sub-order **Toxodontia,** Family **Toxodontidæ. *Toxodon.*** A South American Pleistocene notoungulate about nine feet long. (After Scott.)

borniidæ, and the Notostylopidæ. This sub-order includes small and primitive forms confined to the Palæocene and Eocene. Some of them closely resemble the Condylarthra, and probably reveal the origin of the Notoungulates from that group. The second sub-order Toxodontia (Homalodotheriidæ, Toxodontidæ, etc.) reached considerable body size. The genus *Toxodon* (Fig. 578)

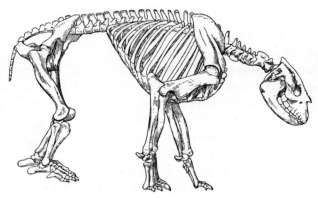

FIG. 579.—Order **Notoungulata,** Sub-order **Toxodontia,** Family **Homalodotheriidæ. *Homalodotherium.*** A South American Miocene notoungulate about six feet long. (After Riggs.)

of the Pleistocene was as large as a rhinoceros. The typical toxodonts had large cropping incisors and strongly curved hypsodont molar teeth.

The Family Homalodotheriidæ (considered to form a separate sub-order Entelonychia by some authors) is distinctive. The end forms of this line (e.g. *Homalodotherium*, Fig. 579) developed clawed feet resembling those of the chalicotheres of the Northern hemisphere. They became extinct towards the end of the Miocene or beginning of the Pliocene. The third sub-order, Typotheria (Mesotheriidæ, Interatheriidæ), also developed enlarged incisors and hypsodont molars. The final sub-order Hegetotheria (like the third) contained rodent-like forms of which some probably resembled rabbits in appearance and habits.

ORDER ASTRAPOTHERIA

This order includes two families only which, in spite of a general resemblance, are so different in basic structure that they are referred to two sub-orders. These are: (1) the Trigonostylopoidea (with the family Trigonostylopidæ)

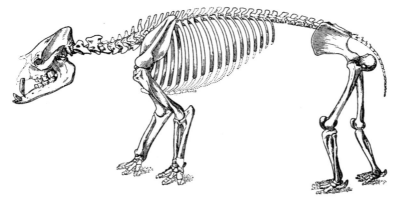

FIG. 580.—Order **Astrapotheria**, Sub-order **Astrapotheroidea**, Family **Astrapotheriidæ**. *Astrapotherium.* A South American Oligocene and Miocene animal about nine feet long. (From Scott, after Riggs.)

and (2) the Astrapotheroidea (single family Astrapotheriidæ). Of the latter the typical genus, *Astrapotherium* (Fig. 580), of Oligocene to Miocene age, was a large animal with a disproportionately big head, provided with great canine tusks and with retracted nasals suggesting the presence of a proboscis. The premolars were reduced and the molars greatly enlarged but not hypsodont. The whole dentition is suggestive of the amynodont rhinoceroses (p. 835).

SUPER-ORDER PÆNUNGULATA (SUBUNGULATA)

This widely diversified 'sub-' or 'near'-ungulate group probably had its origins in late Cretaceous or early Palæocene 'ungulate' forms, but diverged in several stems from the basic stock before the condylarth radiation which allowed the development of the Protoungulates and the Perissodactyla. Thus it forms a loose, though nevertheless related, assembly containing the peculiar little Hyrax, the elephants, the dugongs, as well as several extraordinary extinct orders.

The super-order is composed as follows :

Orders Hyracoidea (Oligocene–Recent)
    Embrithopoda (Oligocene)
Order Proboscidea
  Sub-order Mœritherioidea
    Family Mœritheriidæ (Eocene–Oligocene)
  Sub-order Elephantoidea
    Families Gomphotheriidæ (Oligocene–Pleistocene)
        Mammutidæ (Miocene–Pleistocene)
        Elephantidæ (Pliocene–Recent)
  Sub-order Deinotherioidea
    Family Deinotheriidæ (Miocene–Pleistocene)
  Sub-order Barytherioidea
    Family Barytheriidæ (Upper Eocene)
Orders Pantodonta (Palæocene–Oligocene)
  Dinocerata (Palæocene–Eocene)
  Pyrotheria (?Palæocene, Eocene–Oligocene)
  Sirenia
Sub-orders Trichechiformes (Eocene–Recent)
  Desmostyliformes (Oligocene–Miocene)

ORDER HYRACOIDEA

The Hyracoidea show a most curious mixture of primitive and specialised characters, and others, too, wherein they seem to resemble several different orders of mammals. The living forms of coneys are all small, hooved, rather rabbit-like animals of Africa and South-west Asia, and are included in a single family, the Procaviidæ (= Hyracidæ) with the genera *Procavia* (= *Hyrax*) and *Dendrohyrax*, the latter being semi-arboreal. Hyrax (Fig. 581) should not be confused with the pikas or conies (Lagomorpha) of North America and Central Asia (p. 779).

Manus and pes are plantigrade : the former bears four digits and a vestige of a pollex ; the latter bears three digits, of which the third is the longest. All digits terminate in small flat hooves, save the second pedal digit which is finished with a curved claw. The centrale persists in the carpus, and the astragalus differs greatly in shape from that of any other mammal in that the malleolus of the tibia has a large flat bearing on it. A clavicle is absent. The skull shows several peculiar features. The postorbital process arises largely from the parietal, and the postorbital bar is complete in *Dendrohyrax* but not in *Procavia* (Fig. 582). The jugal is a very stout bone, and extends backwards to take as large a share in the glenoid cavity as in any marsupial. The periotic and tympanic are ankylosed together, but not to the squamosal.

The tympanic forms a bulla and has a spout-like external auditory meatus. The seventh cervical vertebra is sometimes pierced by the vertebral artery. The scapula is triangular, as in Artiodactyla, and lacks an acromion. Dorso-lumbar vertebræ are as many as twenty-two. The radius and ulna are partially crossed, as in the Proboscidea.

FIG. 581.—Order **Hyracoidea,** Family **Procaviidæ.** *Procavia.* The hyraxes, 'dassies' or coneys (the 'feeble folk' of the Bible), are robust, tail-less, colonial, and immensely agile animals about the size of a hare. *Procavia* is diurnal and confined to Africa and a few areas of South-west Asia. It lives in rocky outcrops, often in arid or semi-arid country. A second genus of rock hyraxes is *Heterohyrax.* The tree-hyraxes (*Dendrohyrax*) are adapted to an essentially arboreal and nocturnal life and spend much of the day in tree-hollows. Rock and tree hyraxes thus live almost side by side in certain equatorial areas (*e.g.* Mt. Kenya) without competition. The manus of *Procavia* bears four flattened claws, the innermost being stouter and adapted for gripping laterally on difficult surfaces. The head is protected by prominent tactile vibrissæ and the body, too, bears elongated bristles on dorsal and lateral surfaces. (From B. M. (N.H.) specimens.)

The dentition includes a single pair of large curved upper incisors growing from persistent roots like those of rodents, but triangular in section. Canines are absent. There are four premolars and three molars which are lophodont and in pattern look like rhinoceros teeth in miniature. The lower jaw carries two pairs of incisors, which are spatulate and comb-like, as in some lemurs. It has a foramen which pierces the coronoid just behind the last molar, as in the South American typotheres (p. 807).

There is no gall-bladder.   The cæcum has a pair of cæcal pouches, a feature unknown in any other mammal.   The testes are abdominal.   There is a dorsal gland on the back not unlike that found in the peccaries.   This curious mixture of characters renders it difficult to suggest the affinities or origin of this order.   A remote affinity with the Proboscidea and Sirenia has been variously suggested.

The order is known as far back as the Oligocene of Egypt, where *Saghatherium* and *Megalohyrax* have been found.   Both are hyracoid in dentition, but neither appears to be on the direct line of evolution.   The latter form was of considerably larger size than the modern forms.   *Myohyrax* comes from

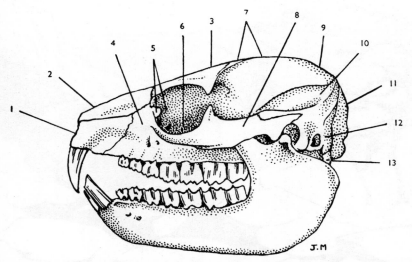

Fig. 582.—*Procavia :* **Skull and dentition.**   Male hyrax, in lateral view.   1, premaxilla; 2. nasal; 3. frontal; 4. maxilla; 5. lachrymal; 6. palatine; 7. parietal; 8. jugal; 9. interparietal; 10. squamosal; 11. supraoccipital; 12. mastoid; 13. paroccipital.   (From B.M. (N.H.) specimen.)

the Lower Miocene of Egypt and *Pliohyrax* from the Lower Pliocene of Greece. The order appears to have originated, like the Proboscidea, in North or Central Africa.   Rich deposits of hyracoid material from the Miocene of East Africa have thrown a great deal of light on the evolution of the group.   There is great similarity between it and perissodactyle evolution.   This had led Whitworth to include the order among the Mesaxonia, but these hyracoids do not resemble early Mesaxonia any more than do some of the South American ungulates, which certainly are not Mesaxonia.   Possibly it is best for the present to follow Simpson and leave the Hyracoidea among the Pænungulata.

ORDER EMBRITHOPODA

The order Embrithopoda is represented by *Arsinoitherium* (Fig. 583), a heavy animal the size of a rhinoceros from the Lower Oligocene of Egypt.   It has massive limbs and stumpy, five-toed feet. The skull is remarkable for the presence of a pair of large, forwardly directed nasal horns placed side by side and united at the bases, and of a pair of quite small frontal horns. The dentition is complete and without diastemata. The canines are incisiform and

FIG. 583.—Order **Embrithopoda**, Family **Arsinoitheriidæ.** *Arsinoitherium.* This remarkable genus, solitary in its order, is sometimes grouped with hyraxes (Fig. 581), proboscideans (Figs. 584, 587), and sirenians (Fig. 594) as 'subungulate'. *A. zitteli* (above) lived in the Egyptian Lower Oligocene and was about 11 feet long and larger than a modern rhinoceros. Relationship with the hyraxes is suggested by its molar pattern, but nothing is known of its ancestry and it left no descendants. The sharp horns, fused at the base, were supported by bony extensions from the nasals. The cartilaginous nasal septum, too, was ossified in their support in adults. The smaller posterior projections grew from the frontals. The dentition was complete (44 teeth) and points to a vegetarian diet. The animal probably possessed mobile lips adapted to cropping. (Redrawn after Andrews, Augusta.)

the cheek-teeth hypsodont. The molars are bilophodont. Beyond a faint suggestion in the molar pattern of some hyracoid affinity, nothing can be said as to the relations of this peculiar animal.

ORDER PROBOSCIDEA

This order includes the elephants (Fig. 584), mastodons, and their allies which are the largest recent land-animals. Except for an aberrant and extinct group of rhinoceroses (p. 835) they are probably the biggest land mammals ever to have existed.   Next to Man, they possess the greatest individual life-span of all mammals: they may live to an age of 70 compared with the 2 to 5 years of life of some of the smaller rodents.   Apart from their remote connexion with the Sirenia and possibly Hyracoidea, the Proboscidea occupy an isolated position.   At an early period of their history they acquired a number of

FIG. 584.—Order **Proboscidea,** Sub-order **Elephantoidea,** Family **Elephantidæ.** *Elephas.* The Hairy Mammoth (*E. primigenius*), not to be confused with the Mammutidæ (= Mastodons) of the Miocene–Pleistocene, existed from the Pleistocene until perhaps 15,000 years ago (earliest post-glacial).   It was a common animal of the European and Asiatic tundra, and frozen cadavers in a still edible condition have been uncovered by glacial retreat in Siberia during the present century. It is not generally known that an appreciable proportion of marketed ivory has come from the relatively indestructible tusks of *E. primigenius*.   (Redrawn after various authors.)

peculiar and adaptive characters which at once clearly distinguish them from other mammals, although they have retained to the present day several persistently primitive features, such as the pentadactyle hand and foot, a brain in which the cerebellum is not covered by the cerebral lobes (which are, however, well convoluted), permanently abdominal testes, and paired pre-caval veins.

The specialised features of the skeleton are perhaps mostly due to the original trend in trunk development.   The progressive and relatively enormous hypertrophy of the maxillary incisors necessitated a bulkier, heavier cranium for their carriage, which in turn requires a shortened cervical region and a corresponding modification of the muscular and ligamentous apparatus responsible for the support of skull and tusks. A single tusk of *Loxodonta*, the African Elephant, may weigh as much as 226 pounds, or reach a length of 11½ feet. At the same time an enlargement of the area of the skull became necessary for the insertion of cervical muscles and ligaments. This was brought about by a separation of the inner and outer tables of many of the bones of the skull, in particular the frontals and parietals (Fig. 585). The diplöe between the tables of bone became filled with air-cells which reduced weight. This caused an obliteration of most of the sutures between the bones.

The extraordinary elongated trunk has induced a shortening of the facial region proper, a recession of the nasal opening towards the top of the head, and a

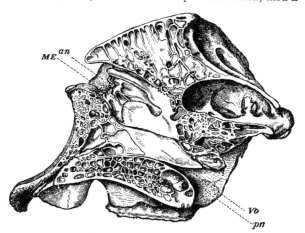

FIG. 585.—*Loxodonta*: **Skull pneumatization.** *L. africana.* African Elephant. Weight reducing adaptations are found in large Mesozoic reptiles. almost all birds (Fig. 387, p. 572) and among mammals (especially elephants and cetaceans). Pneumatic osteolysis is greater in the African than in the Asiatic elephant (*Elephas indicus*), being correlated " with the relatively greater size and weight of the tusks—which necessitate a relatively larger and heavier cranium for both their support and functional employment" (Cave). Tusks of *E. indicus* are never longer than 10 feet nor the weight apparently more than 161 lbs (cf. text). To the left of the mid-line: *an.* anterior nares; *M.E.* mesethmoid; *pn.* posterior nares; *Vo.* vomer. (After Flower.)

reduction in size of the nasal bones similar to the condition seen in the tapirs, but to a greater degree. The prehensile trunk represents a combination of upper lip and external nose, involving a functional specialisation of certain of the facial muscles. To carry the great weight of the head and body, the legs, simple in their general plan, have become pillar-like, with a loss of angulation. The carpals and tarsals are serial and compressed and, while the hand and foot are still pentadactyle, the digits are short, stout, and united by skin, with each toe ending in a small hoof. Progression is digitigrade, the back of the digits being supported by an elastic pad of tissue. In the fore-limb the ulna and radius are permanently crossed in pronation, and the ulna is unique in having its distal articulation with the carpus larger than that of the radius. The pelvis has broad ilia and is vertical in direction, an adaptation found in many heavy-bodied animals. Clavicles are absent.

The dentition is highly characteristic. In more recent elephants the upper tusks, which are the second pair of incisors, are the only ones to persist, the lower incisors having disappeared during the mastodont stage of evolution. The ivory of the tusks is solid, specialised dentine : enamel is absent save for a small cap on the point of the tusk, which soon becomes worn off. Premolars have not persisted beyond the mastodont stage. Of the six cheek-teeth, the three anterior are milk-teeth, which are soon worn down and pushed out by the three large molars at a very early period in life. Thenceforward the animal

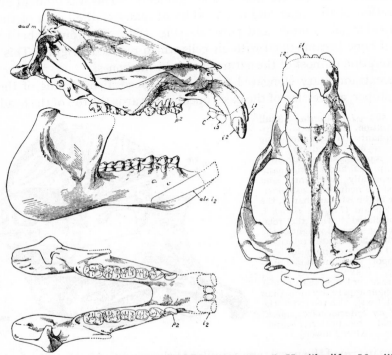

Fig. 586.—Order **Proboscidea,** Sub-order **Mœritherioidea,** Family **Mœritheriidæ.** *Mœritherium:* **Skull and lower jaws.** This animal, the earliest known proboscidean, was an Upper Eocene and Lower Oligocene Egyptian form that stood about 2 feet high at the shoulder. It was of 'normal, rather heavy mammalian build, with a head remarkable for the forward position of the eye and for the heavy lower jaw. The anterior teeth, with an enlarged i² both above and below, clearly form a special feeding mechanism, analogous to that of pigs and the hippopotamus, the forwardly directed incisors being used for grubbing in the ground' (Watson). There is some evidence that *Mœritherium* is of an ancestry allied to that of the Sirenia (Fig. 594) and, perhaps, the Hyracoidea (Fig. 581) (Andrews). (After Osborn.)

possesses only three molars in each half of the upper and lower jaws. Owing to their size, peculiar structure, and method of growth never more than two of the molars are in use at one time in each section of the jaws. They consist of a number of deep plates of enamel-covered dentine bound together by cement. The developing teeth lie at an angle to those in use and are at a higher level in the upper and lower jaws. As they slide down into the position of wear, they push the anterior teeth forwards until, after being nearly worn down, these fall out.

There are perhaps five extinct families, some deserving of sub-ordinal rank (see p. 808): 1. Mœritheriidæ (e.g. *Mœritherium*); 2. Gomphotheriidæ (e.g. *Gomphotherium, Palæomastodon*); 3. Mammutidæ (e.g. *Mammut = Mastodon*); 4. Deinotheriidæ (e.g. *Deinotherium*); and 5. Barytheriidæ (e.g. *Barytherium*). There still survive to-day two species of the family Elephantidæ (*Loxodonta* of Africa, and *Elephas* of Asia). This family contained also the mammoths (e.g. *Mammuthus*) and other extinct forms. The above are distinguished by differences in the arrangement of the tusks and in the degree of complexity of the molar pattern.

The Mœritheriidæ (*Mœritherium*, Upper Eocene and Lower Oligocene of Egypt) were the most primitive proboscideans (Fig. 586). The trunk was relatively small. They showed some points of similarity to the Sirenia, but

FIG. 587.—Sub-order **Elephantoidea**, Family **Gomphotheriidæ**. ***Palæomastodon*: Skull and dentition.** This genus, the largest member of which stood about 6 feet high at the shoulder, was a contemporary of the allied *Phiomia* and is so far known only from the African Oligocene. *ant. orb.* antorbital foramina; *e.a.m.* external auditory meatus; *exo.* exoccipitol; *fr.* frontal; *ju.* jugal; *lac.* lachrymal; *l. i.* lower incisor; *max.* maxilla; *n.* nasal; *nar.* external nares; *pa.* parietal; *par.* paroccipital process; *pmx.* premaxilla; *sq.* squamosal; *u.i.* upper incisor. (After Andrews.)

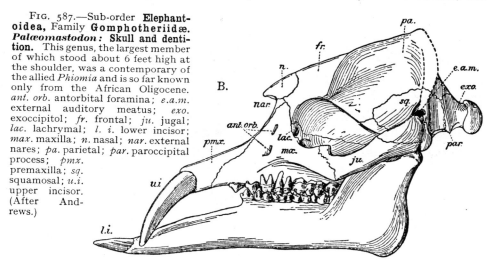

were probably not directly ancestral to the elephants. The dentition, while showing the beginning of proboscidean characters, was less highly specialised. In each upper jaw there were still three incisors (the second enlarged as a tusk) a canine, three premolars, and three molars. The lower jaw had only two pairs of incisors, the second being enlarged as tusks. It lacked the canine. The molars were bilophodont, except the third, which showed the beginning of a third ridge.

The Gomphotheriidæ existed in great numbers from the Oligocene to the Pleistocene. This group contained the African *Gomphotherium* (=*Trilophodon*) and existed in the Pleistocene of Eurasia and North and South America. In these, the upper tusks were large, downwardly turned, and had an enamel band on the outer side only. The lower tusks were present in early forms, and were either down-turned or procumbent with, or without, an enamel band. In later forms they disappeared. The molar-teeth varied widely in the number of ridges from three to as many as seven (in the third lower molar). The ridges, as compared with the true elephants, were lower, with the cusps more widely separated. Examples were *Palæomastodon* (Fig. 587), an early form from the Oligocene of Egypt, and *Stegomastodon*, a Pleistocene animal.

FIG. 588.—Order **Proboscidea**, Sub-order **Deinotherioidea**, Family **Deinotheriidea. Deino-therium.** The deinotheres (e.g. *D. giganteum* of the European Pliocene, above) are emphatically distinguishable from all other groups, including *Palæomastodon* (Fig. 587) and *Phiomia* (Family Gomphotheriidæ) with which they perhaps share a remote ancestry. The anterior parts of the lower jaw were thrust downwards almost at right angles (Fig. 589) and terminated in paired, decurved second incisors of doubtful function. The deinotheres appeared first in the Lower Miocene of Eurasia and Africa, and persisted to the Middle Pliocene (Europe and India) and the Middle Pleistocene (only 500,000 years ago) in Central Africa. During this long period their general structure remained extremely uniform, although there was a great increase in size, as in all proboscidean families. The deinotheres left no descendants. (Partly after Augusta.)

The extinct Mammutidæ contains only the single genus *Mammut* (= *Masto-don*). This family was possibly derived from the gomphotherian genus *Palæomastodon* (Fig. 587). *Mammut* had a few simple molars and huge upper tusks which converged outward and upward. The genus occurred from the Lower Miocene to the Pleistocene and lived in Europe, North America, and Asia.

The Deinotheroidea (*Deinotherium*, Fig. 588) (Lower Miocene–Middle Pliocene of Europe and Asia and Lower Miocene and Pleistocene of Africa) were characterised by the absence of upper tusks and the presence of a pair of downwardly turned lower tusks. The molar-teeth were partly bilophodont and partly trilophodont.

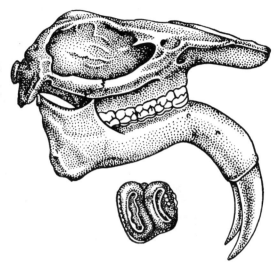

FIG. 589.—*Deinotherium:* **Skull and dentition.** The skull is low and broad, yet nearly four feet long. The projecting premaxilla, extending below the root of the trunk, bore no tusks (cf. *Palæomastodon*, Fig. 587) although the high position of the nostrils and other features suggest a long proboscis (Fig. 588). The cheek-teeth (insert) were primitive (cf. Fig. 590). In early (Lower Miocene) deinotheres the tusks were still only slightly decurved. (Redrawn after Gaudry and Andrews.)

The Barytheriidæ, sometimes considered as a separate order, is known by a single species, *Barytherium*, from the Upper Eocene of Egypt. Few fragments have been found beyond a lower jaw with bilophodont teeth, a trilophodont third molar, and a procumbent tusk-like incisor. The dentition was somewhat like that of *Deinotherium* (Fig. 589) but the humerus, almost the only non-cranial bone discovered, is said to diverge from the typically proboscidean shape.

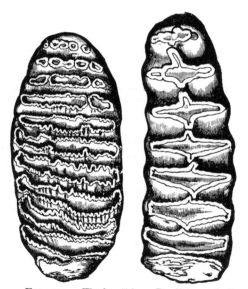

FIG. 590.—**Elephantidæ: Dentition.** Left: *Elephas* (Asian), Right: *Loxodonta* (African) elephants. (Cf. insert in Fig. 589.)

The Elephantidæ have totally lost the lower tusks and the enamel on the large upper tusks, except at the tip in the young stage. The ridges of the molars deepen and become progressively flattened into plates, the cusps in each ridge becoming obliterated. Cement is laid down between the plates. The ridges, or plates, increase in number to as many as twenty-seven. The pattern and the number of ridges are of use in classification, as, for example, in the living Indian Elephant *Elephas* and the African *Loxodonta* (Fig. 590).

The migration of the Proboscidea is interesting. They appear to have originated in North Africa, and thereafter to have migrated to Asia, whence a second radiation took place throughout that continent and throughout Europe. While some reached North, and later South America, others returned to Africa.

ORDERS PANTODONTA (AMBLYPODA) AND DINOCERATA

These two orders have been sometimes classed together as a single order (Amblypoda), but there are differences in dental structure that entitle them to be separated. Both in all probability arose from some early condylarthrous stock, but diverged from one another on specialised lines of foot-structure and dentition.

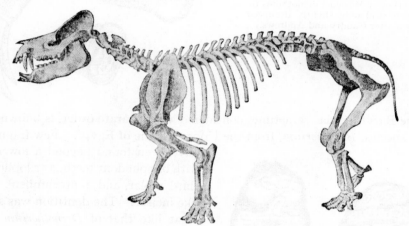

FIG. 591.—Order **Pantodonta,** Family **Coryphodontidæ.** *Coryphodon.* A North American and European (Upper Palæocene and Lower Eocene) pænungulate which grew to a length of about eight feet. (After Osborn.)

The Pantodonta is composed of the families Pantolambdodontidæ, Barylambdidæ, and Coryphodontidæ. *Pantolambda*, a Palæocene genus, represents a more primitive stage leading to *Coryphodon* (Fig. 591), the terminal genus of the Lower Eocene in Europe and North America. The order survived into the Middle Oligocene of Central Asia (e.g. *Hypercoryphodon*). *Coryphodon* attained the size of a rhinoceros. The feet have the carpals serially arranged, and the toes tend to become short and stout in adaptation to weight, but there is considerable variation within the order, some forms possessing tapir-like hooves (e.g. *Coryphodon*) while *Titanoides* possessed digging claws rather like those of chalicotheres, some creodonts, and notoungulates. The teeth are present in full series, and the canines large. The upper molars are triangular, and in *Pantolambda* have three cusps. In *Coryphodon* the pattern evolves into an aberrant type of bilophodont tooth. The order became extinct during the middle Oligocene.

The Dinocerata (uintatheres) were heavy, stump-footed animals reaching a large size. The skull in typical genera is characterised by the presence of three pairs of bony horn-cores placed on the nasals, parietals, and on the maxillæ just over the enlarged spear-like upper canines. The molar teeth are bilopho-

FIG. 592.—Order **Dinocerata**, Family **Uintatheriidæ**. *Uintatherium.* The ponderous, horned uintatheres, of unknown origin and without descendants, were once considered to be amblypods (Fig. 591) with which they share convergent features. The two groups are in fact separated by several deep-seated differences (*e.g.* molar structure). The latest (late Eocene) species had become as big as a modern African rhino. The brain was small, yet the depressed skull was about $2\frac{1}{2}$ feet long and bore pairs of bony protuberances on nasals, maxillæ, and parietals. It has been suggested that these 'horns' may have been covered with skin like those of the extant giraffe. The dentition was peculiar, with sabre-shaped upper canines, which, like the horns, were bigger in the male. Each such tooth was partly protected by an expansion of the lower jaw. The intermaxillaries were greatly reduced and there were usually no upper incisors. The lower incisors were small, as were the lower canines. *Uintatherium* was herbivorous and probably ingested great quantities of aquatic vegetation. Also inhabiting the then lush landscape of western North America was the collie-sized browsing horse *Orohippus* (Fig. 597, p. 827). (After various authors.)

dont superficially like those of *Coryphodon*, but with the two ridges converging medially. Any resemblance between the two forms is due to convergence rather than to any close affinity. The Dinocerata died out at the close of the Eocene without successors. Examples were *Uintatherium* (Figs. 592, 593) and *Eobasileus* (Fig. 593).

ORDER PYROTHERIA

The Pyrotheres are known from a single family (Pyrotheriidæ), with a short history from Eocene (*Carolozittelia*) to Oligocene (*Pyrotherium*). *Pyrotherium* was a large, elephant-like animal with a proboscis and with two pairs of large incisor tusks in the upper jaws and one pair in the lower. Each of the posterior premolars and the molars has two sharp transverse crests, somewhat as in kangaroos, tapirs, deinotheres, and some other groups. It was formerly maintained that the pyrotheres were allied to the mastodons and elephants, but the resemblance is convergent. Pyrotheres, like other South American ungulates, developed there from condylarth-like ancestors.

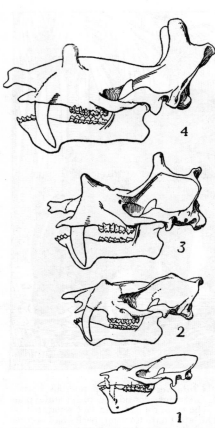

FIG. 593.—*Uintatheriidæ:* **Progressive specialisation.** The trend culminated in extinction during the Upper Eocene. 1. *Bathyopsis* (U. Palæocene); 2. *Elachoceras* (M. Eocene); 3. *Uintatherium* (M. Eocene; see also Fig. 592); 4. *Eobasileus* (Middle and Upper Eocene). (After Scott.)

ORDER SIRENIA

The dugongs, manatees (Figs. 594, 595) and their allies are fully aquatic and present a number of structural features convergent with those of the Cetacea. These include the thick, almost hairless, skin with an underlying layer of blubber, and the loss of external hind-limbs, external ears, and sacrum. The diaphragm, like the cetacean, is oblique and very muscular. The fore-limbs, though less highly modified, are paddle-like, and the tail is flattened and either rounded or rhomboidal in outline.

Lack of true affinity with the whales is shown by various features. Thus, the skeleton of the arm is more typically mammalian in its proportions and has the joints complete and the fingers little modified, beyond being bound together in a web of skin; the scapula is long and narrow, and without cetacean characters. The skull and dentition are specialised. The tympanic bone is ring-shaped. The cervical vertebræ are not ankylosed, and the whole skeleton is strong and its bone very dense.

The order is represented at the present day by the manatees (*Trichechus* = *Manatus*), which live in the fresh waters, or along the coasts of America and

Africa, and the dugongs or sea-cows (*Dugong* = *Halicore*) of the Indian Ocean and South Pacific and Australian coasts. A third genus and species, Steller's Sea Cow (*Hydrodamalis* = *Rytina*), of the North Pacific, only became extinct during the 18th century. To-day the order is confined to tropical and sub-tropical waters. Steller's sea-cow, however, was discovered among Kamchatka ice-floes. It was exterminated by hunters by the year 1768.

FIG. 594.—Order **Sirenia**, Sub-order **Trichechiformes**, Family **Trichechidæ**. *Trichechus*. Manatees (e.g. *T. manatus*, above) and dugongs are strictly vegetarian. The skin is thick and relatively hairless, but facial vibrissæ are well-developed. The hind-limbs have disappeared. The arms are converted into flippers, and the tail into a rounded horizontal fluke which enables a whale-like progression. The protruding upper lip is cleft: an adaptation to grazing. The nostrils are valvular and are closed under water. The inconspicuous mammary glands are thoracic in position. More active by night, sirenians are probably responsible for the mermaid myth: the females of at least some manatees nurse their young while browsing. According to Columbus (who saw three) such mermaids 'were not so beautiful as they had been painted, although to some extent they were like a man in the face'. (From photographs, New York Zool. Soc.)

Sirenians are of especial general interest since it is possible that from these tropical, vegetarian 'sea-cows' (which of course suckle their young) arose the traditional sailors' stories of mermaids inhabiting distant seas. The possession of both milk-glands and a superficially fish-like tail might easily have given rise to such legends. The famous 'song of the sirens', however, came from fishes, not sea-cows (see p. 346).

The manatees and dugongs are placed in separate families. In the manatees

(Fig. 594) the cheek-teeth are covered with enamel and are bilophodont, somewhat like those of the Proboscidea. There are
up to twenty in each half of the lower jaw and in
each maxilla. They are, however, not all in use
at any one time, but are continuously replaced
from the hind end. The premaxillary region is
small and little deflected. There are six cervical
vertebræ only. The fingers bear the remains of
nails. The dugong, on the other hand, has a
reduced dentition as far as the grinding-teeth are
concerned, never having more than six, and even
these are somewhat degenerate and without
pattern. The premaxillary region is, however,
enlarged into a down-turned rostrum, and bears,
in the male, a pair of stout tusks. The anterior
part of the mandible is covered by a horny pad,
under which can be found traces of the lower
incisors. There are no nails on the fingers, and
the normal seven cervical vertebræ are present.

The origin of the order and of its ancestral
form is unknown. The earliest known genera are
the Eocene *Prorastomus* of the West Indies, and
Protosiren and *Eotheroides* (=*Eotherium*) of
Egypt. *Eotheroides* is somewhat more advanced
than the other early genera which have a complete eutherian dentition, a rostrum but slightly
enlarged, and small tusks. Although the hind-
limbs have already gone, the pelvis is but little
reduced and these forms are clearly more primitive than, and functionally ancestral to, later
genera.

All the above are united in a sub-order,
the Trichechiformes. A second sub-order, the
Desmostyliformes, is represented by a sole
family and two genera, *Cornwallius* and *Desmo-
stylus*, found in Oligocene and Miocene deposits
of the Pacific coasts of North America and Japan
respectively. The chief characteristics of *Desmo-
stylus* lie in the peculiar dentition. There are
two procumbent lower incisors, the upper being
small or absent. The molars are columnar and formed of a number of closely
adpressed cylinders covered with a thick layer of enamel.

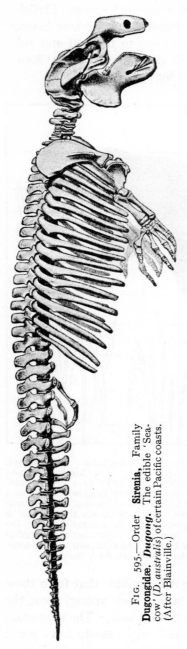

FIG. 595.—Order **Sirenia,** Family **Dugongidæ. *Dugong.*** The edible 'Sea-cow' (*D. australis*) of certain Pacific coasts. (After Blainville.)

Skeleton of Sirenia.—In the Sirenia (Fig. 595) the cervical vertebræ do not coalesce, with ·the exception of two of them in the manatees. In the manatees there are six cervical vertebræ only, and the neural arches are sometimes incomplete. In the trunk the thoracic vertebræ are numerous. All have well-developed facets for the heads of the ribs, and well-developed zygapophyses. The caudal vertebræ are numerous, depressed, with wide transverse processes. The ribs are numerous, but few are connected with the sternum. The sternum is a broad bone not composed of distinguishable segments.

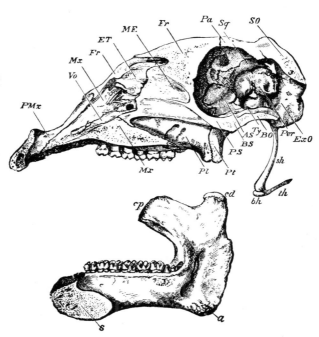

FIG. 596.—*Trichechus:* **Skull and dentition.** (*T. senegalensis* (¼ natural size.)) *PMx.* premaxilla; *Vo.* vomer; *Mx.* maxilla; *Fr.* frontal; *ET.* ethmoturbinal; *ME.* mesethmoid; *Fr.* frontal; *Pa.* parietal; *Sq.* squamosal; *SO.* supraoccipital; *ExO.* exoccipital; *Per.* periotic; *BO.* basioccipital; *Ty.* tympanic; *AS.* alisphenoid; *BS.* basisphenoid; *PS.* presphenoid; *Pt.* pterygoid; *Pl.* palatine; *Mx.* maxilla; *cp.* coronoid process of mandible; *cd.* condyle; *a.* angle; *s.* symphysis; *sh.* stylohyal; *bh.* basihyal; *th.* thyrohyal. (After Flower.)

The *skull* (Fig. 596) is characterised by its extreme hardness. The cranial cavity is rather long and narrow as compared with that of the Cetacea. Although the supraoccipital (*S. O.*) is produced forwards on the upper surface of the skull for a considerable distance, it does not separate the parietals (*Pa.*). The frontals develop broad supraorbital plates. The zygoma is stout. As in the Cetacea, the external nares are very wide, but they are situated relatively farther forwards. The nasals are vestigial. The tympanic and periotic are readily separable from the other bones. The premaxillæ are enormous in the dugongs. The mandible has a well-developed ascending ramus and coronoid process (*c. p.*).

The *scapula* of the Sirenia is much more like that of the terrestrial mammals than the scapula of Cetacea, and is nearer that of the Seals; it is narrow and curved backwards. The spine is situated about the middle; the acromion is directed downwards.   The coracoid is fairly well-developed, and of a conical shape.   A clavicle is absent, as in the Cetacea.   The skeleton of the arm also departs less from the ordinary mammalian type than does the cetacean.   The radius and ulna are ankylosed at their extremities.   The carpus has seven bones in the manatees : the pisiform is absent.   In the dugongs carpal coalescence takes place, so that the number of discrete elements is reduced in the adult. There are five digits, all of which possess the usual number of phalanges.

The *pelvis* is represented by a pair or more of vestiges widely separated from the spinal column.   They have a vertical position and probably represent the ilia.

SUPER-ORDER MESAXONIA

In this group is placed alone the Order Perissodactyla which are 'odd-toed', hooved animals including horses, tapirs, and rhinoceroses, and certain extinct forms.   In the *mesaxonic foot*, exemplified by the horse, the skeletal axis passes down the third digit.   The other digits are reduced and do not support any weight.   This compares with the *paraxonic foot* (Super-order Paraxonia, Order Artiodactyla, p. 837), exemplified by the cow, in which the skeletal axis passes between the third and fourth digits.

The utmost reduction that can take place in the number of digits in a perissodactyle is four.   (The second and fourth digit are represented in horses by the splint bones: metacarpals and metatarsals.)   In the artiodactyles the number of digits (as in the cow) can be reduced to two—the third and fourth. The tarsi also show points of difference, the shape of the astragalus (Fig. 623, p. 821) being in each case diagnostic.   Apart from the fusion of several of the tarsals in some artiodactyles (an unknown phenomenon among Perissodactyla) the artiodactyle cuboid bears always a distinctive articular surface for the calcaneum (Figs. 618, 860).

Further, whereas the perissodactyle has a third trochanter, twenty-two or twenty-three dorso-lumbar vertebræ, and a peg-like odontoid process, the artiodactyle lacks a third trochanter, has uniformly but nineteen dorso-lumbar vertebræ, and possesses a spout-like odontoid process.

Some, but not all, perissodactyles and artiodactyles have a complete post-orbital bar, the composition of which differs in the two orders.   In the horses (Fig. 597) a process of the squamosal runs between processes of the frontal and jugal bones alone, and the squamosal is excluded.   In their dentition the Perissodactyla manifest an almost complete molarisation of the premolar teeth : in the Artiodactyla all premolars (except occasionally the fourth) are simpler than the molars.   True horns with a bony horn-core never occur in the Perissodactyla.   Artiodactyla usually have a gall-bladder and a more or less complicated ruminating stomach.   Such structures never occur among Perissodactyla.

Both orders appear first in the Lower Eocene. The Perissodactyla largely replaced the pænungulates (p. 807) in the Oligocene and Miocene, radiating widely. They in turn were supplanted in the Pliocene and Pleistocene by the Artiodactyla (p. 837), and, but for the present protection extended to surviving species and the domestication of others, might well have become about extinct.

The group is arranged as follows :

ORDER PERISSODACTYLA

 Sub-order Hippomorpha
  Super-family Equoidea
   Families Palæotheriidæ (Eocene–Oligocene)
     Equidæ (Eocene–Recent)
  Super-family Brontotheriodea
   Family Brontotheriidæ (Titanotheridæ) (Eocene–Oligocene)
  Super-family Chalicotheriodea
   Family Chalicotheriidæ (Eocene–Pleistocene)
 Sub-order Ceratomorpha
  Super-family Tapiroidea
   Families Isectolophidæ (Eocene)
     Helaletidæ (Eocene–Oligocene)
     Lophiodontidæ (Eocene)
     Tapiridæ (Lower Eocene–Recent)
  Super-family Rhinocerotoidea
   Families Hyrachyidæ (Eocene)
     Hyracodontidæ (Eocene–Oligocene)
     Amynodontidæ (Eocene–Miocene)
     Rhinocerotidæ (Eocene–Recent)

ORDER PERISSODACTYLA

The order falls naturally into two divisions which arose from condylarthran (p. 802) ancestry. These are the sub-orders Hippomorpha and Ceratomorpha, each of which was distinct by the Upper Eocene. *Hyracotherium* (= *Eohippus*) of the Lower Eocene of Europe and North America belongs to the Hippomorpha and shows certain features that suggest that it is not far from the parent stock. Various species of *Hyracotherium* were between 10 and 20 inches tall and were not unlike the condylarthran *Phenacodus* (Fig. 575) in some respects. Also included among the Hippomorpha are the palæotheres which arose as an Eocene side-line from an ancestry similar to that of *Hyracotherium* and became extinct in the Oligocene after achieving certain notably equine characters (p. 826) before these were developed in the main Oligocene–Miocene radiation (Fig. 597).

With the main ordinal features held in common, different groups (the earliest representatives of which show a good deal of resemblance to one another) began to evolve on adaptive lines of their own.   Thus the terminal species of each acquired a highly distinctive external appearance.   The different trends of evolution are concerned chiefly with the structures of the feet and the teeth.   If the teeth of *Hyracotherium* (the earliest known horse), of *Homogalax* (a tapir), of *Eotitanops* (a brontothere), and of *Hyrachyus* (a rhinoceros) be compared, it can be seen that all start on the same general plan, with low crowned teeth, with premolars simpler than the molars, and with the six original cusps of the upper molars still clearly traceable.   Closer examination of the molars, however, shows that beginnings of differences which ultimately lead to great divergences in the final result (Fig. 598).   In *Hyracotherium*, which has the most primitive teeth of any perissodactyle, the protoconule and metaconule are only just beginning to elongate towards the paracone and metacone, and these two outside cusps are beginning to elongate in the anterio-posterior to form the beginning of an ectoloph.   In *Eotitanops* the intermediate cusps and the hypocone do not progress, but tend to disappear. The protocone is large and remains bunoid, while the paracone and metacone form a precociously enlarged ectoloph with a strongly marked W outer border. Already in the Eocene *Homogalax* shows the tapiroid structure of a bilophodont tooth in the joining of protocone, protoconule, and paracone into an anterior transverse crest and of hypocone, metaconule, and metacone into a corresponding hinder crest.   The ectoloph is hardly developed.   *Hyrachyus*, the earliest rhinoceros, is like the tapir in forming transverse crests, but the ectoloph is more strongly developed and is produced into a characteristic metaloph behind.

The horses gradually evolved very hypsodont teeth, the rhinoceroses rather less so, but in both cases a deposit of cement was acquired in the deep valleys between the cusps though to a much less degree in the rhinoceroses.   All other perissodactyles retained more or less brachydont teeth in which cement was not formed.

Throughout the order the premolars are at first simpler than the molars. During the course of evolution all the premolars, with the exception of the first, invariably became molariform.   In foot-structure the horses became functionally monodactylous.   The titanotheres, tapirs, and rhinoceroses show a less degree of reduction.

FAMILY EQUIDÆ

The horses present one of the most completely known phylogenies of all vertebrates.   In a condensed form it is as follows : There was a progressive increase in size and in height, due to a lengthening of the distal elements of the limbs (Figs. 597, 598).   Simpson has pointed out that as ancestral horses grew

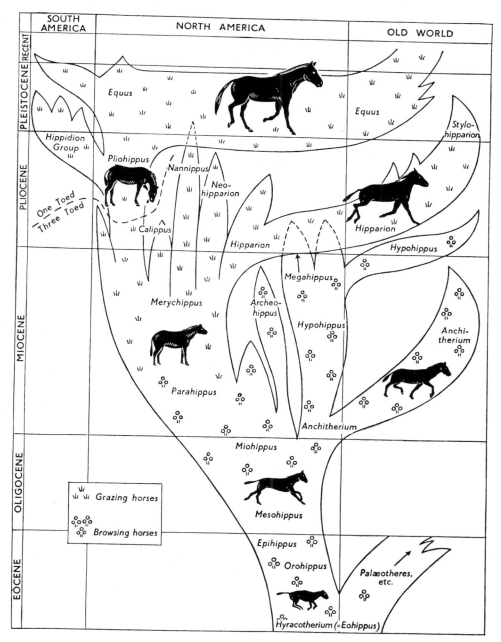

Fig. 597.—Order **Perissodactyla,** Sub-order **Hippomorpha,** Super-family **Equinoidea,** Family **Equidæ: Phylogeny and distribution of horses.** (Redrawn after Simpson.)

bigger, their proportions had to change and their 'running mechanism had to become different, stronger and more effective' if they were to maintain even the same speed as their already fast and agile ancestors. In fact, speed has increased to a fraction over 40 miles per hour (for about half a mile) in the selectively bred modern thoroughbred. Starting from a condition with four digits in the manus (there is no trace of a first digit (pollex) in the manus of any perissodactyle) and three sub-equal digits in the pes (here with traces of

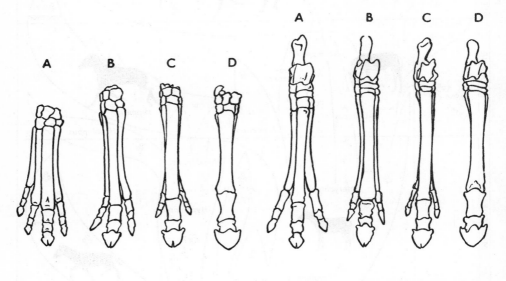

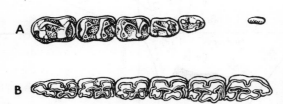

Fig. 598.—**Equidæ: Progressive specialisation of limbs and teeth.** *Upper left:* Manus; *Upper right:* pes. *A. Eohippus* (North American Lower Eocene), with four large toes retained in front and only three behind. *B. Miohippus* (North American Oligocene–Miocene) with only three functional toes. *C. Merychippus* (North American Miocene–Pliocene) with lateral digits reduced and *D.*

Modern *Equus. Lower: A.* Left lower cheek teeth of *Eohippus* (approx. ×1) and *B.* Pleistocene *Equus leidyi* (approx. ×½). (Redrawn from Romer, after various authors.)

the first and fifth digits, represented by nodules of bone) a gradual change took place whereby the central digit in both manus and pes became progressively longer and stouter. The lateral digits became thinner, failed to reach the ground, and finally became reduced leaving only the metacarpals and meta-tarsals as splint-bones. The ulna and fibula became reduced to their proximal halves. Progression, at first sub-digitigrade, became *unguligrade*. In the skull the profile of the top of the head became changed from a straight to a convex line, and the preorbital facial part became elongated. Up to the stage of *Mesohippus* (North American Oligocene) the postorbital bar was incomplete;

after that stage it became complete and progressively stouter. The teeth progressed from a brachydont and almost bunodont to a very hypsodont condition, with an increasing complication of crown pattern. The molars eventually acquired a coating of cement on their outsides as well as in the deep hollows between their cusps. The canines became proportionally smaller. The premolars, at first simpler than the molars, gradually became molariform and ultimately larger than the molars. A cingulum to the cheek-teeth, characteristic of the earliest forms, was soon lost.

A series of species can be selected to show these changes (Fig. 597), but the picture thus presented is only a partial one. Evolution did not of course proceed by a series of large jumps from the earliest type to the modern horse— the progress was gradual. Moreover, there was not a single line of evolution of one genus succeeding another, but a continual branching off of side-lines, the majority of which, after varying periods of existence, became extinct. It is not always easy, among these branches, to trace the actual line of descent of the living horses, though a reasonable approximation to the truth is probable.

Horse-like perissodactyles appeared first in the Lower Eocene. Of these, the chalicotheres, brontotheres and palæotheres became extinct whereas the main equine stem (typically represented by *Hyracotherium*) survived in North America although it died out in Europe (Fig. 598).

The name *Hyracotherium* has priority over the more familiar *Eohippus* ('dawn-horse'). Owen, who described the animal from English material, re- marked that the skull somewhat resembled that of a 'Hare or other timid Rodentia'. There was little about it that recalled a modern horse. Owen's *Hyracotherium* (hyrax-like animal) was later shown to be indistinguishable from the later described North American *Eohippus*. In Eurasia, during the Eocene, there was an expansion of lines from *Hyracotherium*, all of which became extinct by the Oligocene at the latest. The reason for this is unknown. No further horses occurred in Europe and Asia until the Miocene. One such early Miocene migrant from North America was *Anchitherium* ($=$ *Kalobathippus*) which colonised westward when the two continents were re-united. It was in turn extinguished before the beginning of the Pliocene (Fig. 597).

Meanwhile in North America *Hyracotherium* ($=$ *Eohippus*), of which genus a considerable number of species have been described, evolved by small increments in height and by a progressive molarisation of the premolars. By the Middle Eocene a new genus, *Orohippus*, is recognisable. In the Upper Eocene *Epihippus* replaced *Orohippus*. It is, however, questionable if it was a direct descendant of *Orohippus*. On the whole, the American horse genera during the Eocene formed a more direct line than those of Europe. In the succeeding Oligocene, horses were represented in America by the genus *Mesohippus*, which had increased to the size of a sheep. The feet were still three-toed, with the lateral elements touching the ground. The median digit, however, had become enlarged. All premolars except the first had now become molariform. To wards the close of the Oligocene another genus, *Miohippus*, arose. This is found together with the later species of *Mesohippus*, but persisted into the Miocene after the extinction of the parent genus. During the Miocene there was not one line of horses but several existing side by side. All of them were derived from *Miohippus* (e.g. *Archæohippus*, *Hypohippus*, and *Anchitherium*).

As mentioned above, *Anchitherium* re-established the stock in the Old World, a process to be repeated in the late Miocene and early Pliocene by *Hypohippus*, which in turn became extinct in Europe, as did related derivatives in North America. In fact all such side-lines died out, but *Parahippus*, derived directly from *Mesohippus*, persisted till the end of the Miocene, and during that time gave rise to the genus *Merychippus*. In this genus the teeth were greatly elongated in the sockets and there was formed a heavy deposit of cement not only between the cusps, but on the outside of the tooth as well. Cement was absent in the less advanced species of *Parahippus*, but had appeared in the later forms. The rapid development of this massive cement deposit went hand in hand with a changeover from browsing to grazing and the occupation of an ecological niche that was provided by the evolution of grasses that began to flourish at that time. Although they were less dramatic, other changes were manifest. *Merychippus* stood over three feet high and carried its weight on the central digit of each foot. Although considerable differences existed between species, members of the genus (even taking into account their small hooved lateral digits) probably looked not very unlike a modern pony.

This stock was unprecedentedly successful and gave rise to perhaps half a dozen Pliocene lines, including *Hipparion* which spread widely and successfully to Eurasia and Africa. (*Protohippus*, once considered to be a distinct and important line, is now accorded only sub-generic rank in *Merychippus*.) One undeniably valid stem derived from *Merychippus* was *Pliohippus*. In the more primitive species there were still retained jointed small lateral toes; in advanced forms these were lacking and the pes closely resembled that of modern horses, as did the lengthened teeth and skull except for relatively minor, though characteristic, details. From *Pliohippus* probably arose the earliest somewhat zebra-like late Pliocene or Pleistocene animals (sub-genus *Plesippus*) referable to the genus *Equus* which contains the horses of to-day.

Although the point of origin of the horses is unknown, there is little doubt that North America was the principal centre of equine evolution. Immigrations occurred both north-west and south to cross the periodically inundated land bridges in the region of the Bering Sea and Panama. In South America at the close of the Pliocene and during the Pleistocene there was a separate rapid evolution of horses represented by the genera *Hippidion*, *Onohippidium*, and *Parahipparion* (= *Hyperhippidium*), all derived from *Pliohippus*, and characterised by very long and slender nasal bones. These genera did not survive the Pleistocene.

A final invasion of South America, however, occurred during the Pleistocene and these spread widely throughout the continent. As in North America, they survived the Pleistocene Ice Age, but (again as in North America) mysteriously died out at the beginning of the Recent. Numerous conjectures have been made to account for the relatively sudden disappearance of their apparently enormous herds. They were seemingly still present when the 'Indians' arrived and were no doubt eaten—but many ungulates survived. They may have been attacked by a disease such as trypanosomiasis—but the above consideration should still apply. The ice-age was not responsible ; and there is no evidence that any other landscape change was sufficiently widespread to have seriously incommoded them. No new carnivorous enemy is thought to have assailed them : in fact, the sabre-toothed tiger and other probable predators died out at about the same time.

The family Equidæ continued in the Old World where it was domesticated by Man and then artificially selected to form the various familiar breeds which were in turn introduced throughout the world, including North and South America. At the present time, apart from domestic breeds, wild Equidæ are represented by *Equus przewalskii* of Central Asia and *E. asinus* of Africa (wild asses). In addition there are *E. hemionus* (the Oriental wild ass) and finally four striped species of African zebra (*E. quagga*, *E. zebra*, *E. burchelli*, and *E. grevyi*).

FAMILY BRONTOTHERIIDÆ (TITANOTHERIDÆ)

The titanotheres in their day were a large and important group and, although known chiefly from North America, had a wide distribution. Species have been found in Mongolia, Burma, and Europe. The family was polymorphic. A number of lines developed with differences of proportion in the skull, skeleton, horns, and teeth.

The terminal species attained a great size. Some stood eight feet at the shoulder. In spite of some specialisation of shape, all remained essentially undeveloped. The brain remained relatively small, the skull long and low, and the feet retained four rather unmodified digits in the manus and three in the pes. The teeth (Fig. 599) were incapable of chewing hard grasses, a condition that may have played a contributing part in the extinction of the family. In the upper molars the protocone remained a round but large cusp, the hypocone round but smaller, the protoconule and metaconule disappeared, while the para- and metacones became greatly enlarged, and together formed a high, W-shaped outer wall. The premolars remained rather small and less molarised than in other Perissodactyla.

The earliest brontotheres appeared in the lower Eocene. These were *Lambdotherium*, a genus that left no successors, and *Eotitanops*. Through the

Middle and Upper Eocene there arose a number of genera until the sub-order culminated in the Lower Oligocene in such large animals as *Brontotherium*, *Brontops* (Fig. 599), *Embolotherium*, and others.   In North America none is found later than the Lower Oligocene, but some, unearthed in Mongolia, have

FIG. 599.—Order **Perissodactyla,** Sub-order **Hippomorpha,** Super-family **Brontotherioidea,** Family **Brontotheriidæ.**   ***Brontops.***   The vegetarian brontotheres (= titanotheres) were perisso-dactyles sharing ancestry with the horses.   Best known from North America (though they occurred also in Eurasia) brontotheres arose in the Lower Eocene and disappeared during the Oligocene, leaving no descendants.   *Brontops* (North American Lower Oligocene) attained a length of about 14 feet.   Its skull was small and low, yet unusually broad owing to the extension of the massive zygomatic arches.   Outgrowths from the nasal bones produced the grotesque 'horns' that were possibly covered with skin like those of extant giraffes.   *Brontops*, representing the culmination of a trend towards gigantism possessed, unlike the horses, an 'unprogressive' dentition which was nevertheless adequate in the humid lush and grassy environment in which it lived.   These animals lived in a period of orogenic movement—a time of mountain-building that foreshadowed more stringent conditions to come.   A contemporary horse was the three-toed *Mesohippus* (Fig. 597) a browsing animal standing about 6 hands (i.e. 24 inches).   (Redrawn from various authors.)

persisted into the Middle Oligocene.   Thereafter the brontotheres appear to have become extinct.

FAMILY CHALICOTHERIIDÆ

The members of the former sub-order Chalicotheroidea (or order Ancylo-poda) are now generally believed to merit family rank only.   They show much resemblance to the titanotheres in tooth-structure and tooth pattern, but are characterised by a foot-structure unusual for a perissodactyle. There are three functional digits on manus and pes, the manus bearing additionally a splint of the fifth digit. The digits are subequal, and bear, instead of hooves, strong claws, a character which may entitle them to be erected into a distinct sub-order.

Examples are known from the Eocene to the Pleistocene from North America (e.g. *Eomoropus, Moropus*) and from Europe and Asia (e.g. *Chalicotherium, Macrotherium, Schizotherium*).

SUB-ORDER CERATOMORPHA

These—the tapirs and rhinoceroses—were once included in the unnatural assembly of 'Pachydermata' and widely separated from the horses with which they share an early Eocene ancestry. They form two super-families of unequal extent.

SUPER-FAMILY TAPIROIDEA

During the Eocene a number of small tapiroid forms evolved, which, like the European Eocene horse-lines, became extinct. A line, however, can be traced leading to the living forms, although the number of genera and species therein is comparatively few. The forest-living habits of tapirs have no doubt militated against their frequent preservation as fossils. Originally the distribution of the group was widespread over the Old and New Worlds, but now it is restricted to one species in the Old World (*Tapirus indicus* of the Malay Peninsula and Sumatra), and to four New World species (*T. terrestris* (Fig. 600), and *T. roulini, T. bairdi* and *T. dowi*).

The fossil Lophiodontidæ were members of a Lower Eocene to Oligocene radiation with characters intermediate between the tapirs and the rhinoceroses. The cheek-teeth were bilophodont, like those of the tapirs, but with a metaloph more like that of the rhinoceroses.

Of all living Perissodactyla, the tapirs are the least specialised. The feet have stout digits, four in the manus and three in the pes, the third digit in each case being somewhat enlarged. The skull is devoid of any postorbital bar. The anterior nasal openings are enlarged and recessed. The nasal bones are small and pointed upwards in correlation with the proboscis, which is characteristic of the group. The teeth are persistently brachydont and without cement. The molar teeth are bilophodont, and devoid of any complication in the way of extra cusps or crests. Modern tapirs do not seem to have advanced very much beyond the degree of tapiroid development already attained in the Miocene.

SUPER-FAMILY RHINOCERATOIDEA

The rhinoceroses were extremely common in the Tertiary but are today reduced to five species (Family Rhinocerotidæ). These are *Rhinoceros unicornis* (the one-horned Indian Rhinoceros), *R. sondaicus* (the Javan Rhinoceros, also one-horned), *Dicerorhinus sumatrensis* (the Sumatran Rhinoceros, two-horned and the smallest living species), *Diceros bicornis* (the African Rhinoceros,

FIG. 600.—Order **Perissodactyla,** Sub-order **Ceratomorpha,** Super-family **Tapiroidea,** Family **Tapiridæ.** *Tapirus.* The American *T. terrestris* ranges (as several sub-species) from southern Mexico to northern Argentine. The nearest living allies of tapirs are the rhinoceroses. Nocturnal, vegetarian, and amphibious, tapirs are superficially pig-like and adapted in shape for thrusting through undergrowth. The snout is remarkably flexible and the young (like those of so many forest-dwelling mammals and cursorial birds) are protectively striped (until the fourth or fifth month). (From photographs by Chapman, and B.M. (N.H.) skins.)

two-horned), and *Ceratotherium simum* (the White, or Square-lipped, Rhinoceros of Africa, also two-horned). In addition there are three extinct families. During the Oligocene to the Pleistocene period the rhinoceroses formed an especially large, varied, and important group. The characteristic tooth-structure has already been mentioned (p. 826). Manus and pes have never less than three functional toes. Two, one or no horns may be present. These are peculiar in being formed of a fused keratinous substance allied to hair, and neither true horn nor bone. From traditional times this substance has been valued in the Far East for its alleged aphrodisiacal properties. It possesses no such properties. Even to-day it fetches about 60s. per pound in Tanganyika, where 10–15 lb. are obtainable from a large example of *Diceros bicornis*.

In certain extinct forms the horns were confined to males. The super-family, soon after its beginning in the Lower Eocene, divided into four main lines of evolution : 1. Hyrachyidæ (the most primitive forms) ; 2. Hyraco-

FIG. 601.—Order **Perissodactyla,** Sub-order **Ceratomorpha,** Super-family **Rhinocerotoidea,** Family **Rhinocerotidæ.** *Baluchitherium.* This giant, aberrant, hornless rhinoceros of the Asiatic Oligocene and early Miocene was the biggest terrestrial mammal and, excluding certain dinosaurs (p. 508) probably the largest of all land animals. The most massive examples of *Baluchitherium* were perhaps 18 feet high at the shoulder and about 27 feet long. The skull was over four feet long, yet apparently small by comparison with body bulk. *Baluchitherium* was a browser with an essentially grinding dentition and a single pair of massive, blunt incisors. The long post-like legs were three-toed, with the lateral digits considerably reduced. (After various authors.)

dontidæ (light cursorial animals) ; 3. Amynodontidæ (about the size of a hippopotamus). The above-mentioned families became extinct during the Oligocene period. The remaining family 4. Rhinocerotidæ, began in the Eocene and spread out into many lines during the Oligocene and subsequent periods until the Pleistocene. Then the group became much reduced. The rhinoceroses were a very polymorphic family, and there is still much uncertainty as to their classification and as to the line of evolution of the living forms.   In certain cases genera can be distinguished by some peculiar character, as, for instance, *Elasmotherium* (a large Pleistocene animal with a large, forwardly directed, fronto-nasal horn and much folded cheek-teeth enamel), *Baluchitherium* (a Miocene rhinoceros with persistently primitive teeth and procumbent lower incisor tusks and the largest known land mammal (Fig. 601)), *Chilotherium* (a Pleistocene genus with an unusually broad mandibular symphysis), etc.

SUPER-ORDER PARAXONIA

This, like the Mesaxonia contains but one quite unmistakably defined order —the Artiodactyla.   The even-toed hooved animals that compose it are characterised essentially by the *paraxonic foot* (cf. p. 824) but also by other significant points of similarity.   While the Perissodactyla declined, the Artiodactyla flourished and radiated so that, despite their hunting by Man and the carnivores, many remain abundant to-day (*e.g.* wild pigs, various deer, etc). The order is arranged as follows :

ORDER ARTIODACTYLA

Sub-Order Suiformes
Infra-order Palæodonta
Families Dichobunidæ (Eocene–Oligocene)
Chœropotamidæ (Eocene–Oligocene)
Cebochœridæ (Eocene–Oligocene)
Leptochœridæ (Oligocene)
Entelodontidæ (Eocene–Miocene)

Infra-order Suina
Families Suidæ (Oligocene–Recent)
Tayassuidæ (Oligocene–Recent)

Infra-Order Ancodonta
Families Anoplotheriidæ (Eocene–Oligocene)
Anthracotheriidæ (Eocene–Pleistocene)
Hippopotamidæ (Pliocene–Recent)
Cænotheriidæ (Eocene–Miocene)

Infra-order Oreodonta
Families Agriochœridæ (Eocene–Miocene)
Merycoidodontidæ (Eocene–Pliocene)

Sub-order Tylopoda
Families Xiphodontidæ (Eocene–Oligocene)
Camelidæ (Eocene–Recent)

Sub-order Ruminantia
Infra-order Tragulina

Families Amphimerycidæ (Eocene–Oligocene)
       Hypertragulidæ (Eocene–Miocene)
       Protoceratidæ (Oligocene–Pliocene)
       Gelocidæ (Eocene–Oligocene)
       Tragulidæ (Miocene–Recent)
Infra-order Pecora
  Families Cervidæ (Oligocene–Recent)
       Lagomerycidæ (Miocene)
       Giraffidæ (Miocene–Recent)
       Antilocapridæ (Miocene–Recent)
       Bovidæ (Miocene–Recent)

ORDER ARTIODACTYLA

The 'even-toed' ungulates are represented at the present time by such animals as pigs, peccaries, hippopotamuses, camels, giraffes, sheep, oxen, deer, antelopes, etc. In the past there were, in addition, many other remarkable forms. As a whole, this order is larger and more varied than the Perissodactyla, and the division between its sub-orders is deeper and more marked. The division *within* some of its groups is still in dispute.

The Artiodactyla may be divided into three sub-orders—the Suiformes (pigs and peccaries), the Tylopoda (camels and llamas), and the Ruminantia (chevrotains, deer, giraffes, gazelles, cattle, Yak, buffaloes, goats, and sheep.

SUB-ORDER SUIFORMES

Some mammalogists consider that the earliest identifiable Artiodactyla (e.g. *Diacodexis, Bunophorus* of the American Lower Eocene) fall into the sub-order Suiformes whilst others consider them sufficiently distinct to occupy a sub-order by themselves. These primitive palæodonts have the upper molars still in the tritubercular condition and seem in several other ways not very remote from the archaic placental stem. However, the paraxonic feet and unmistakably diagnostic artiodactyle astragalus (Figs. 624, p. 861) at once reveal their true taxonomic position.

The Suiformes include the peccaries, pigs, wart-hogs, hippopotamuses and several extinct groups of highly debatable affinity. The teeth are 'bunodont'. The canines are triangular in section and in some forms become stout tusks. The molar teeth, while retaining bunoid cusps, exhibit a secondary specialisation in supernumerary cusps, additional to the original crown pattern. The limbs are short and carry invariably four digits. Of special interest among the archaic Suiformes are the giant pig-like entelodonts which were plentiful during the Eocene and Oligocene. These creatures stood more than five feet high, were sometimes 12 feet long and possessed small brains in skulls almost three feet long: the jaws were equipped with lance-like incisors, heavy canines, and simple cheek-teeth, a dentition perhaps adapted to the unearthing and grinding of roots.

The pigs became plentiful in the Old World in the late Tertiary. The peccaries arose from a common northern stock, and are represented in the North American Oligocene. They probably reached South America in relatively recent (Pleistocene) times.

The anthracotheres and the hippopotamuses (Ancodonta) (Fig. 602) are amphibious mammals that were plentiful in the Old World during the Tertiary. Extinct forms ranged in size from that of a rabbit to the modern Hippopotamus.

Perhaps admissible here, or perhaps under the next sub-order (Tylopoda) are the Oreodonta, an entirely North American group which had a long range from the Eocene to the Pliocene. These heavily-built, pig-like, animals had

Fig. 602.—Order **Artiodactyla,** Sub-order **Suiformes,** Infra-order **Ancodonta,** Family **Hippopotamidæ.** *Hippopotamus:* **Aquatic adaptations.** Although the body of *H. amphibius* may be 14 feet long and weigh more than two tons, the animal can conceal almost the whole of its bulk under water with little more than the most important exteroceptors exposed. (For comparable crocodilian adaptations, see Fig. 333, p. 500.)

four toes as well as strongly selenodont teeth which suggest ruminant affinity. The first lower premolars functioned as canines and the canines themselves were incisiform. In some forms the last premolar was molariform.

SUB-ORDER TYLOPODA

This sub-order consists of camels (extinct forms as well as the modern llamas, camels and dromedaries) and their allies. Some authorities believe that the Tylopoda should be included in the Sub-order Ruminantia.

Camels appeared as a distinct stock in the Eocene. They were common and almost exclusively North American in the Oligocene (e.g. *Poëbrotherium*) when they were about the size of a small sheep and had already lost the lateral digits and become didactyle. The development of the manual- and pedal-digits proceeded at an equal rate. The carpals and tarsals, unlike those of the Pecora, never fused, but the metacarpals and metatarsals soon fused into a cannon bone whose distal ends gradually became divergent, with smooth, unkeeled, articular surfaces for the phalanges.

The dentition of the living species is peculiar. In the upper jaw of the young there is the full number of incisors, but in the adult the third only is retained as an isolated recurved tooth similar in pattern to the upper and lower canines. The full number of lower incisors is retained as procumbent spatulate teeth. The premolars are reduced to the last two, and are small. The molars are very hypsodont, and their four cusps selenodont. In the neck vertebræ the vertebral artery takes the unusual course of piercing the anterior part of the transverse process, instead of traversing its whole length as is usual. The ruminating stomach is rather simpler than that of the Pecora, and does not contain special 'water-cells', as was once believed. Experimentally, a Dromedary can lose fluid equalling 25% of its body weight without being seriously weakened. Further, it can go for more than 17 days without drinking even when deprived of succulent plants. It loses relatively little fluid in its urine. Its body temperature ranges from 90° F. (at night) to 105° F.; and it starts to lose much sweat only near the upper limit. The massive concentration of fat in the hump ensures that heat-loss is little retarded elsewhere and the inflow of heat is slowed by its wool (Schmidt-Nielsen).

Like the horses, the camels became extinct in North America in the Pleistocene. Migrants from North America gave rise to the modern camels of the Old World and to the llamas of South America. The sub-order is now reduced to a few species. *Camelus dromedarius*, the one-humped Arabian Camel, is no longer found wild. The other camel is *C. bactrianus*, the two-humped Bactrian animal of Turkestan. In South America the representatives are the humpless Llama, *Guanaco*, Vicuna and Alpaca. The sub-order seems never to have been a large one, but there have been described several genera, some of them (as *Alticamelus*, a 'giraffe-necked' form) off the main line of descent.

SUB-ORDER RUMINANTIA

These form an exceedingly large and diverse group in which a few characters are held in common, as, for instance, the total loss of the upper incisors (p. 872). The upper canine is also usually lost, but, in the rarer cases where it persists, it is much enlarged. Flat, spatulate lower incisors are all present, as is the lower canine, which has the same shape as the incisors, and is closely pressed against them. The premolars are smaller than the molars, and the latter have four crescentic cusps. The feet have always a cannon bone. The lateral toes are usually lost and the feet absolutely didactyle. In some cases the second and fifth digits remain, but are never complete (Fig. 617, p. 860). In this group the ruminating stomach attains its highest development of four complete chambers (Fig. 639, p. 878). Horns of several types occur, but are absent in some species. The Ruminantia are sometimes divided into two principal groups or infra-orders, the Tragulina (chevrotains and their allies) and the Pecora (all other ruminants).

The Tragulina are the remarkable cud-chewing deerlets of tropical Asia (*Tragulus*) and Africa (*Hyemoschus*). Upper incisors are lacking. Particularly in males the upper canines are large and adapted to aggression. The molars are selenodont. The stomach is three-chambered as compared with the four-chambered organ of more advanced ruminants. Each limb has four hooved digits, and a cannon-bone (fused metatarsals) is present in the hind limbs. The lateral pedal digits are still complete, though slender as is the fibula, which is reduced in all other ruminants). The navicular, cuboid, and entocuneiform bones of the tarsus, however, are fused together. The odontoid process of the axis vertebra is conical, not spout-like. As a rule there are no horns, but these were present in at least one of the extinct families (Proto-ceratidæ). Superficially the chevrotains resemble large rodents—hence the name 'mouse-deer'.

The Pecora contains the families Cervidæ (deer), Giraffidæ (giraffes, okapi), Antilocapridæ (prong-buck) and Bovidæ (gazelles, Impala, Eland, Yak, cattle, buffaloes, goats, and sheep).

The Cervidæ date from the Oligocene. They usually have deciduous horns or antlers confined, with one exception (the Reindeer) to the males. Horns are absent in only two instances (*Moschus* and *Hydropotes*). The lateral toes are nearly always present, but are never complete. In some species the distal extremities of the metacarpals are retained (*telemetacarpal condition*), and in others, including most of the Old-World deer, the proximal elements alone persist (*plesiometacarpal condition*). In both cases the phalanges are much reduced in size and do not touch the ground. The skull has two orifices for the lachrymal duct and a very large antorbital vacuity. Except in *Moschus* there is no gall-bladder.

Moschus and *Hydropotes* are two rather aberrant forms in an otherwise fairly compact family. *Moschus*, the hornless Musk Deer, is placed by itself in a separate subfamily, the Moschinæ. The male has large upper canines. A gall-bladder is present. *Hydropotes*, the Chinese Water-deer, although placed in the second subfamily, the Cervinæ, differs from them in being hornless and in having large upper canines like *Moschus*, but in all other respects is a true deer. There are many genera of Cervidæ still living in the Old and New Worlds, but none in Africa south of the Sahara.

In the Giraffidæ the horns are non-deciduous, always covered with skin. They are simple and unbranched except in an extinct side-line represented by a few Pliocene genera such as *Vishnutherium*, *Sivatherium*, and *Bramatherium*, which had skin-covered palmate antlers. The upper canines are absent, as are all traces of lateral digits. Not even the lateral hoofs persist. The humerus has a characteristic double bicipital groove. The group may be traced from the Miocene, and is now represented by the Giraffe and Okapi.

The Antilocapridæ or prong-bucks of North America have been distinct from Bovidæ since at least the Miocene but are often included with them. In both groups there are neither upper canines nor incisors, and there is only one orifice to the lachrymal duct. The lateral digits are completely absent except for the persistence of small horny hooves which may contain a nodule of bone. A gall-bladder is present. Horns are universally present in males but in many genera of Bovidæ the females are hornless. Horns are never shed except in the prong-bucks, wherein a soft horny covering is discarded annually. The horns in the Bovidæ are never branched but are of many shapes: curved, or spiral, or circular. The Bovidæ comprises more than one hundred genera and a large number of subfamilies whose boundaries are not always satisfactorily definable.

GENERAL ORGANISATION OF MAMMALIA

Integument and General External Features.—Nearly all mammals are covered with hair (Fig. 603) developed in *hair-follicles*. Each individual hair is a slender rod, and is composed of two parts, a central part or *pith* (M) containing air, and an outer more solid part or *cortex* (R). Its outermost layer may form a definite cuticle (O). Commonly the cortical part presents transverse ridges so as to appear scaly. In one case only, *i.e.* sloths, is the hair fluted longitudinally. The presence of processes on the surface, by which the hairs when twisted together interlock firmly, gives a special quality to certain kinds of hair (wool) used for clothing— the *felting* quality as it is termed. A hair is usually cylindrical but there are many exceptions. In some it is compressed at the extremity, in others it is compressed throughout. The latter condition is observable in the hair of

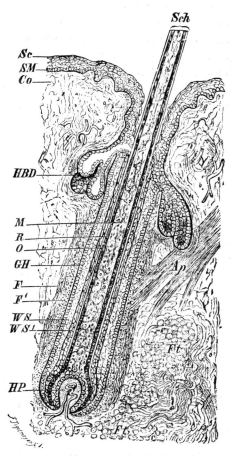

FIG. 603.—**Mammalia: Hair.** Longitudinal section (diagrammatic). *Ap,* band of muscular fibres inserted into the hair-follicle, *Co.* dermis; *F.* external longitudinal, and *F'.* internal circular fibrous layer of follicle; *Ft.* fatty tissue in the dermis; *GH.* hyaline membrane between the root-sheath and the follicle; *HBD.* sebaceous gland; *HP.* hair-papilla with vessels in its interior; *M.* medullary substance (pith) of the hair; *O.* cuticle; *R.* cortical layer; *Sc.* horny layer of epidermis; *SM.* Malpighian layer of epidermis; *WS. WS'.* outer and inner layer of root-sheath. (After Wiedersheim.)

negroes. Fur is usually composed entirely of one kind of hair. In some cases, however, there are two kinds. The hairs of the one sort may be very numerous and form the soft under-fur, while those of the other consist of longer and coarser hairs scattered over the surface as in *Ornithorhynchus*, the fur-seal (*Callorhinus*), and the mink (genus *Putorius* = polecats).

The principal function of hair is the part it plays in temperature regulation but it can be tactile, protective, and possess sexual functions as well. It has been secondarily reduced or almost lost in widely different animals, *e.g.* the almost hairless subterranean rodent, *Heterocephalus glaber*, and the Sirenia, Cetacea, and Man. Most, if not all rodents are born naked; the condition in the adult *H. glaber* of tropical East Africa is probably an example of pædomorphosis. In Man, and certain other animals (cetaceans, sirenians) that have become relatively hairless, heat loss is retarded by a compensatory layer of hypodermal fat (*blubber*) that arises in the superficial fascia. At the same time, the apparent hairlessness of Man is illusory. Except for the palmar and plantar surfaces, the lip borders, parts of the fingers and toes and external genitalia, the body of man is clothed by hair on the scalp, as eye-brows and -lashes, as secondary sexual characters in axillary and pubic regions and on chest and face (in the male); or, on the other hand, by widespread, short hair-down or *vellus*. In the neonatus, vellus normally replaces the fine *lanugo* which almost covers the fœtus from the fifth or sixth month until (usually) shortly before birth. Some of this is swallowed by the fœtus and may be voided by the neonatus in the meconium (fæces). It is of interest that the relatively hairless elephants also possess lanugo.

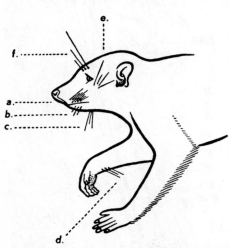

FIG. 604.—**Primates: Tactile vibrissæ.** Arrangement in a typical strepsirrhine monkey. *a.* mystacial; *b.* mental; *c.* inter-ramal; *d.* carpal; *e.* genal and *f.* supraorbital groups. (Redrawn after Osman Hill.)

Hair is also tactile in function and in most mammals (especially arboreal and nocturnal forms) it occurs also as specialised tactile *vibrissæ* on the facial region and sometimes near carpus and tarsus (Fig. 604). Groups of vibrissæ are richly innervated. These are absent in Man, but it is probable that eye-brows represent the supraorbital vibrissæ of ancestral mammals. The relative disappearance of hair may be associated with improved tactile acuity of the human skin.

In animals such as spiny anteaters (*Tachyglossus*), hedgehogs (*Erinaceus*) and porcupines (*Hystrix*) the hair in part assumes the form of defensive spines or quills. Also protective are the outwardly directed bristles in the nostrils and auditory meatus of many mammals, including Man, which serve to block the entrance of foreign substances and insects. Eyelashes have a similarly protective function. Hair too, probably subserves a threat function in combat, and, in specialised areas, assists in the retention of animal odours significant in courtship.

Hair, with the exception of eyelashes, grows at a slant and is distributed in *tracts* (Fig. 605). Primitively such tracts are directed caudally and ventrally on the trunk, and distally and postaxially on the limbs (*e.g. Myrmecobius*, *Dasyurus*, and, in addition, many relatively unspecialised eutherians). This

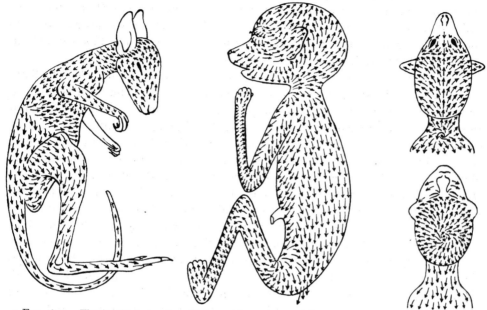

FIG. 605.—**Theria: Hair-tracts.** Hairs emerge with a slant in tracts characteristic of the group. The primitive arrangement appears to be backwards, perhaps related to the reduction of friction, as is the backward direction of feathers and scales. The primitive condition has been abandoned in numerous groups: there is sometimes a complete reversal of direction of specific tracts, seemingly related to toilet adaptations (Figs. 483, p. 696; Fig. 607, p. 846). The direction of hair tracts has been presumed by some authors as evidence of Neo-Lamarckian inheritance. *Left:* Marsupial (*Wallabia*) pouch young; *Centre:* Prosimii (*Loris*) juvenile; *Right upper and lower:* Head and neck region of *Pseudochirus* (marsupial possum) and *Homo* (Man) showing nuchal hair-whorls. (Redrawn after Wood Jones, Osman Hill.)

primitive distribution, however, is remarkably varied by the development of whorls and the complete reversal of direction of hair growth over extensive areas of body surface. Some such arrangements appear to be strikingly correlated with the combing or scratching habits (Wood Jones).

A hair, like a feather, is formed from the epidermis. The first rudiment of a developing hair usually takes the form of a slight downwardly projecting outgrowth, the *hair-germ*, from the lower layer of the epidermis, beneath which there forms a condensation of dermal tissue to form the rudiment of a *hair papilla*. In some mammals, however, the dermal papilla makes its appearance before the hair-germ. The hair-germ, which consists of a solid mass of epidermal cells, elongates, and soon its axial portion becomes condensed and cornified to form the shaft of the hair, while the more peripheral cells go to form the lining of the hair-follicle. They become arranged in two layers, the *inner* and *outer root-sheaths*. The epidermal cells in immediate contact with the hair-papilla retain their protoplasmic character and form the *hair-bulb*, by the activity of which the further growth of the hair is effected. Soon the upper end of the hair-shaft grows out beyond the surface of the epidermis, and the projecting part eventually becomes much longer than that which lies embedded in the follicle. At the same time the follicle grows downwards into the dermis. During its growth the hair is nourished by the blood-vessels in the dermal hair-papilla, which projects into its base.

Hair is erectile due to the action of unstriated *arrector pili* muscles which are innervated by the sympathetic nervous system (p. 119). Thus hair 'stands on end' during extreme fear, 'goose-pimples' are raised in cold and specific emotional states, or hair can be raised (as a bird's plumage is 'fluffed') as a heat conservation mechanism during cold weather. Hair follicles undergo cyclical activity by which old shafts are shed and replaced. In some mammals (*e.g.* Man, Domestic Cat) each follicle behaves independently of its neighbours, so that although each body hair (in Man) is replaced at least once, or perhaps twice, a year, there is no concerted seasonal moult such as occurs in the Arctic Fox (*Alopex lagopus*), Arctic Hare (*Lepus arcticus*), certain of the Mustelidæ and other forms. In such animals follicle behaviour is more or less synchronised. The white phase of the Arctic fox takes on brown fur during the summer. The 'blue' (bluish-grey) phase of the same species, on the other hand, does not change colour. There is some evidence that the 'blue' condition is recessive and the phasic one dominant. Blue animals remain conspicuous and at an apparent disadvantage during the winter; they constitute less than 5 per cent of the population in the rigorous climate of Baffin Land and the Canadian Arctic. The phases are probably about equal in Western Greenland. There is some evidence that 'blue' foxes have a lower reproduction rate. Their diet, too, is different.

Unlike that of many birds and other vertebrates, the mammalian exoskeleton is rarely brightly coloured although it is often boldly marked and in this way achieves an obliterative effect in shadowy situations (e.g. *Felis, Thylacinus, Equus,* and others). No mammal has developed green hair, although the sloth becomes greenish by special means (p. 768). Certain primates (Cercopithecidæ) possess a highly coloured posterior *sexual skin*, which becomes brighter in the female under the seasonal action of œstrogens, and which is no doubt important in sex recognition and stimulation. A few mammals possess scales. Thus in *Manis* (Fig. 550, p. 773) the greater part of the surface is covered with large, rounded, over-lapping horny scales of epidermal origin,

similar in their mode of development to those of reptiles. A similar phenomenon is seen in the integument of the ventral surface of the tail of *Anomalurus*,
the African 'flying' squirrel. Here the scales engage the tree-trunk at the end
of each glide and reduce skidding. Armadillos (Fig. 533, p. 763) are the
only mammals in which there occurs a bony *dermal exoskeleton*.

Also epidermal in their origin are the horny structures in the form of nails,
claws, or hoofs, with which the terminations of the digits are provided in all
the mammalia except the Cetacea. There seems little doubt that flattened
nails (*ungulæ*) arose by degeneration and specialisation from claws (*falculæ*)

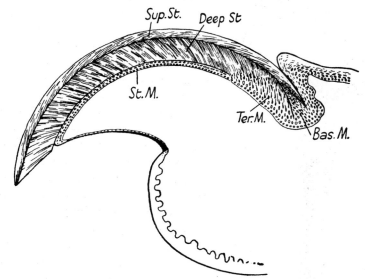

Fig. 606.—**Mammalia: Claw structure.** The claw (here in sagittal section) is composed of two
layers of which the deep stratum (*Deep St.*) is the major part, while the superficial stratum (*Sup.
St.*) merely forms a protective sheath. It is the latter stratum which persists in Primates to form
flat nails. The superficial stratum is formed from the basal part of the germinal matrix (*Bas. M.*)
and the deep stratum from the terminal part (*Ter. M.*). The rest of the claw-bed is made up of
the sterile matrix (*St. M.*). (After Le Gros Clark.)

which are common in the Reptilia and which occur in a few amphibians (e.g.
Xenopus, and the Japanese clawed newt, *Onychodactylus*).

Strong evidence presented by the form of the terminal phalanx shows that
Palæozoic theromorphs (p. 514) possessed clawed digits. The same is true
of their early mammalian descendants. There is, however, some developmental difference between the claws of at least some reptiles and mammals.
In Chelonia and Crocodilia the young claw develops from the whole of the
claw-bed, whereas in the Mammalia much of the claw-bed is sterile : the germinal matrix is restricted to the proximal segment which is, however, divided
into a basal and terminal matrix (Fig. 606). From the terminal matrix arise
oblique horny lamellæ which come to form the thick condensed *deep stratum*

or main body of the claw. From the basal matrix there grow lamellæ that become arranged horizontally to form the protective *superficial stratum*.

It is not improbable that relatively blunt, flattened nails arose with the broadening of the digital pads (Fig. 607) of ancestral primates. The assumption of nails was achieved by the reduction, and next the disappearance, of the terminal part of the germinal matrix and the deep stratum (Fig. 606) until only the thin superficial element, of changed shape, remained.

Evidence of such a transition is perhaps shown in extant primates. In the claws of marmosets (*Callithrix*) the deep stratum appears to have been greatly reduced; but this, on the other hand, may represent a secondary modification of nails. In lemurs, nails have arisen on all digits except the second toe which has remained clawed as a *toilet digit* (p. 843). In tarsiers, which have developed distal tactile pads of remarkable size, the nails in turn have been reduced to vestiges except for ungulæ that have become claw-like toilet-nails on the second and third toes (Fig. 607). Horns, too, are epidermal in origin, but those of rhinoceroses are peculiar: they appear to be formed by the agglutination of hair-like horny fibres (p. 834).

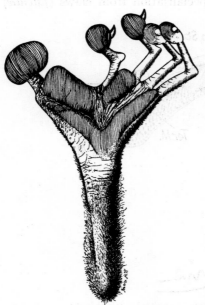

FIG. 607.— ***Tarsius*: Pes.** Both apical and plantar pads occur, as well as toilet claws (not present on manus) on the second and third digits. (After Osman Hill.)

Cutaneous glands are almost general in the Mammalia. The most constant are *sebaceous glands*, which open into the hair-follicles, and *sweat-* (*sudoriferous*) *glands*. Sebaceous glands are lobulated derivatives of the Malpighian layer and produce *sebum* which lubricates the adjacent hair-shaft skin. It is bacteriocidal in nature, and in addition probably helps render the skin impervious to moisture and to desiccation. Sweat-glands are relatively simple in structure. They are lacking in many mammals and occur chiefly on the plantar and palmar surfaces of others (*e.g.* arboreal animals).

In primates in particular sweat ducts emerge at the summit of *papillary ridges* which occur, often in association with *tactile pads*, of varying number and disposition. These ridges are the basis of finger-printing. Tactile pads occur on the palmar or plantar surfaces and sometimes, in addition, on the digits of the manus. The roughened surface of the touch pads, plus the secretions from sweat-ducts, probably augments the grasping power of the limb.

In many mammals there occur in various parts of the body multiple or single glands that secrete odorous material. These are often, but not invariably, situated in the genital region. Particularly notable in this respect are the *brachial glands* of certain primates (*e.g.* lemurs). These occur in the

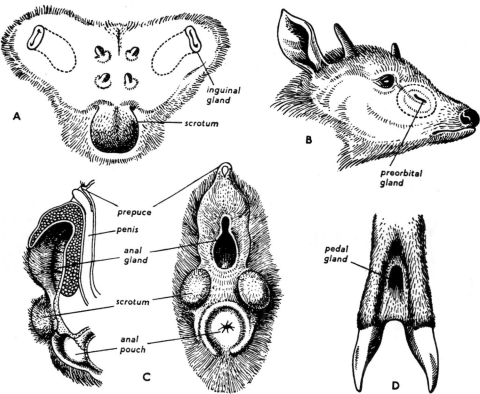

FIG. 608.—**Eutheria: Cutaneous glands and olfactory signals.** Mammals (and reptiles) that live on or near the ground make extensive use of olfactory signals. Among the ruminants alone, pedal, tarsal, metatarsal, carpal, caudal, inguinal, preputial, postcornual, occipital and preorbital glands have been described, all of which produce highly odorous secretions. Carnivores, rodents, and many other groups (see Fig. 609, p. 848) possess cutaneous glands of various kinds which are significant in courtship, and in the establishment of territory, and perhaps have other functions as well. For example, wild dogs (and lap-dogs) mark projections with urine mixed with preputial secretions. *A, Inguinal glands* of male Bush-buck (*Tragelaphus*); *B, Preorbital gland* of Four-horned Antelope (*Tetraceros*) (see also Fig. 609); *C, Anal gland* of male civet (*Viverra*); *D, Pedal gland* of Muntjac (*Cervulus*). (Redrawn from Bourliere, after Pocock.)

proximal region of the arm of the male. Also present in both sexes may occur an *antebrachial* or *carpal gland* in association with an erect horny spur of variable size and disposition. A variety of odoriferous glands has arisen in other orders (Figs. 608, 609).

Mammary glands, which secrete milk, are probably specialised sweat-glands. These arise along the mammary- or milk-lines which run from axilla to inguinal region on each side of the trunk. They differ considerably in number and distribution. From one (*e.g.* most Primates, Giraffes) to eleven (*Centetes*) pairs occur in eutherians, depending, in general, upon the number of young and their post-natal feeding requirements. Thus, *Cavia* has only one pair of mammary glands and produces 3 or 4 well-developed young after an unusually long period of gestation (67–68 days) for an animal of such size. The Common Rabbit, on the other hand, generally possesses four pairs of mammary glands and commonly produces about eight relatively helpless young after an intra-uterine period of only 30–32 days. Mammary glands may be restricted to the thoracic region (*e.g.* Chiroptera, Sirenia, p. 821, and all Primates except lemurs) or to the inguinal area (*e.g.* cetaceans, ungulates). When many young are produced the mammary glands are developed serially and extensively along thorax and belly. In a few mammals of arboreal or flying habit, certain nipples have taken on an accessory *anchoring* function (Wood Jones). Thus, in lemurs and rhinolophid bats, the young cling by means of both arms and legs and, at the same time, assist in maintaining their grip by grasping one or other of the otherwise apparently non-functional inguinal nipples with the mouth. When the parent comes to rest the young one reverses its position and feeds from a thoracic organ. The nipples open into the pouch of

FIG. 609.—**Ungulata: Territory establishment.** Male Blackbuck (*Antilope cervicapra*) marking a stick with preorbital secretion (see Fig. 608B). (Redrawn from Bourliere, after Hediger.)

marsupials that possess a functional marsupium. The number varies from two in the fossorial *Notoryctes* (p. 714) to about twenty in *Monodelphis henseli* (p. 711). In *Monodelphis* and *Marmosa* the nipples are distributed between axillæ and vent.

The complex group of events resulting in (1) the cellular synthesis of milk from precursors in the blood stream and its passage through the membranes of the alveolar cells, and (2) its discharge from the mammary gland, is *lactation* (see below). The apparatus of lactation is present in both sexes. In Man the phenomenon of 'witches'-milk' in boy as well as in girl babies exemplifies this when, occasionally, abnormal amounts of maternal œstrogen and prolactin (p. 849) escape into the fœtal circulation just before parturition. Further, milk production has been experimentally achieved in male rats and other mammals. In metatherians and eutherians each mammary gland opens to the exterior by a teat which is guarded by a sphincter apparatus of varying complexity.

In most of the Ruminantia (as well as the Tylopoda, p. 838) the two (*e.g.*

sheep and goats) or four (*e.g.* cattle) mammary glands are of remarkable size and are contained in an *udder* which is partitioned into *galactophoric sinuses* or milk-cisterns in which the fluid accumulates before final liberation through the teats. The careful selective breeding of domestic cattle and goats has resulted in milk production enormously in excess of the needs of the wild animal.

In the embryo, *milk streaks* develop into the mammary-lines on each side of the ventral mid-line. At definite points thereon appear centres of Malpighian-layer proliferation and these at length develop into functional or often supernumerary mammæ. (Supernumerary mammæ occasionally appear in both sexes in Man which may sometimes be functional in females.)

Mammary development and milk-secretion are largely under hormonal control, but neural influences may be also involved. There is evidence that the factors initiating the pubertal and subsequent seasonal growth of the mammary glands differ somewhat among species, but, in general, it can be said that œstrogens (liberated as a result of pituitary gonadotrophic stimulation) are always involved. In actual lactation, the anterior pituitary hormone, *prolactin* (see also p. 151) is important, together, probably, with other lactogens from the same (and possibly other) sources. Certainly the factors governing the initiation, discharge and inhibition of lactation are more complex than was formerly realised. Even the apparently well-established principle that a rise in œstrogen inhibits lactation has, perhaps unjustifiably, been called in question. As regards neural factors, it seems established that the mechanical stimulus of sucking causes a reflex discharge of prolactin (and possibly other anterior pituitary lactogens) and that, in cows at least, stimulation of the teat as well as other external factors may cause the liberation of posterior pituitary *oxytocin* which facilitates 'let-down'. It is undeniably true that fear and other unfavourable factors impede milk discharge, and so the nervous system is involved in yet another way. The basic composition of milk is approximately as follows (cf. c crop-milk', p. 583) :

TABLE IV. Composition of milk (expressed in percentages, modified after Davies).

Species.	Water.	Fat.	Sugar.	Casein.	Other Protein.	Ash.
Man	88·50	3·30	6·80	0·90	0·40	0·20
Rat	68·3	14·8	2·8	4·2	2·6	1·5
Cat	81·63	3·33	4·91	3·12	5·96	0·58
Porpoise . . .	41·11	48·50	1·33	11·19		0·57
Elephant . .	67·85	19·57	8·84	7·11	—	0·46
Ox	87·32	3·75	4·75	3·00	0·40	0·75
Goat	82·34	7·57	4·96	3·62	0·60	0·84

In addition to the above basic constituents, milk also contains both fat- and water-soluble vitamins, carotenoid pigments, enzymes, mineral salts (such as calcium phosphate and sodium chloride) and other materials. Before, and briefly after, parturition the maternal mammary glands contain a *colostrum* of high nitrogen, globulin and vitamin content. There is some evidence that maternal antibodies thus continue to be transferred to the offspring for a short period. The transition from colostrum to milk secretion proper occurs gradually during the days following birth.

Little is known concerning lactation in the Prototheria. Teats are absent. The milk glands consist of two groups of very large tubular follicles, the ducts of which open on the ventral body surface. In the ant-eater *Tachyglossus* (p. 695) the two areas on which the ducts open become depressed towards the breeding season to give rise to a pair of pouches—the *mammary pouches*. A large brood-pouch or *incubatorium* is subsequently formed, and in this the egg is deposited. When the young animal is hatched it is sheltered in the posterior deeper part of this incubatorium, while in the shallower anterior part lie the mammary pouches. In *Ornithorhynchus* mammary pouches are indicated only by extremely shallow depressions. No incubatorium is developed.

Endoskeleton.—The spinal column of mammals varies in the number of vertebræ which it contains, the differences being mainly due to variation in the length of the tail. The various regions are usually very distinct. In the *cervical* region the first two vertebræ are modified to form the *atlas* and *axis*. Owing to the absence of discrete cervical ribs, the posterior cervical vertebræ are much more sharply marked off from the anterior thoracic than is the case in reptiles and birds. The cervical vertebræ have double transverse process (or a transverse process perforated at its base by a foramen which transmits the vertebral artery) in all except the last. There are certain exceptions (such as many marsupials, some rodents, Hyrax and the hippopotamuses) where the seventh cervical vertebra is also perforated. The ventral portion of the transverse process in certain cases (*e.g.*, seventh and sometimes some of the others in Man) arises from a separate ossification, and this is regarded as evidence that this ventral part, even when not independently ossified, represents a cervical rib. Seven is the prevailing number of vertebræ in the cervical region. There are only three exceptions to this—the manatees and two genera of sloths (p. 764). Thus giraffes have the same number of cervical vertebræ as, for example, Man. The number of *thoracic* and *lumbar* vertebræ is far more variable. Usually there are between nineteen and twenty-three. Hyrax has a larger number of thoraco-lumbar vertebræ than any other mammal—from twenty-nine to thirty-one.

The thoracic vertebræ bear *ribs* which are connected, either directly or by intermediate ribs, with the *sternal ribs*, and through them with the *sternum*. Each rib typically articulates with the spinal column by two articulations —one articular surface being borne on its head and the other on its tubercle. The tubercle articulates with the transverse process, and the head usually with an articular surface furnished partly by the vertebra with which the tubercle is connected, and partly by that next in front. Thus the head of the first thoracic rib partly articulates with the vertebral body of the last cervical vertebra.

In all the Mammalia in which the hind-limbs exist (*i.e.* all save the Sirenia and the Cetacea) there is a *sacrum* consisting of closely united vertebræ, the number of which varies in the different orders. The *caudal* region varies greatly. In many long-tailed mammals there is developed a series of *chevron bones*—V-shaped bones which are situated opposite the inter-vertebral spaces.

The body of each vertebra ossifies from three centres—a middle, an anterior, and a posterior. Usually the two centres of ossification which form the neural arches also contribute to the formation of the bony body. The middle centre forms the body proper; the anterior and posterior form the epiphyses. The epiphyses are almost entirely absent in the monotremes. They have not been detected in dugongs (Sirenia). Between successive centra is formed a series of discs of fibro-cartilage—the *inter-vertebral discs*—represented in lower vertebrates in crocodiles and birds only. The anterior and posterior surfaces of the bodies are nearly always flat.

The *sternum* consists of a number of segments—the *presternum* in front, the *mesosternum*, or *corpus sterni* (composed of a number of segments or *sternebræ*) in the middle, and the *xiphisternum* behind. The sternum is formed in the fœtus in great part by the separating off of the ventral ends of the ribs. Some of the Cetacea and the Sirenia are exceptional in having a sternum composed of a single piece of bone. The sternal ribs, by which the vertebral ribs are connected with the sternum, are usually cartilaginous, but frequently undergo calcification in old animals. In some cases they soon become completely converted into bone.

The *skull* of a mammal (Fig. 610) contains the same chief elements and presents the same general regions as that of the reptiles and birds, but exhibits certain special modifications. But certain elements present in the skull of reptiles and birds are not represented (or are not certainly known to be represented) by separate ossifications in the Mammalia. Such are the supra-orbital, the prefrontal, the postorbital, the ectopterygoid and the quadrato-jugal. The bones of the skull, with the exception of the auditory ossicles, the lower jaw, and the hyoid, are all immovably united by means of sutures.

The palatine bones develop *palatine plates* separating off a posterior nasal passage from the cavity of the mouth, a condition found among the living reptiles only in the Crocodilia, and, to a less extent, in the Chelonia and some lizards.

The *zygomatic arch* is a strong arch of bone formed partly of the squamosal, partly of the jugal, and partly of the maxilla ; in position it represents the lower temporal arch of Amphibia, reptiles and birds, but is differently constituted.

The *orbit* in the skull of some mammals is completely enclosed by bone, constituting a well-defined cavity. In others it is not completely surrounded by bone behind, and so communicates freely with the *temporal fossa* which lies behind it.

The *periotic* bones (fused *prootic* and *opisthotic*) are not separately represented in the skull of mammals. Part of the periotic mass sometimes projects on the exterior at the hinder part of the lateral region of the skull, and is the

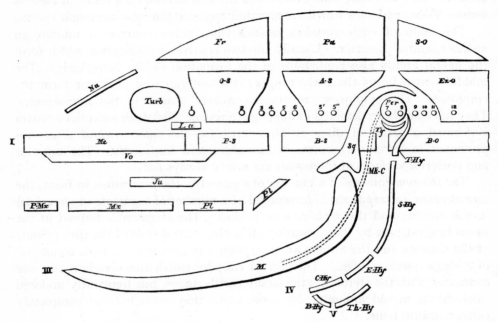

Fig. 610.—**Mammalia: Skull.** Relations of the principal bones. A.-S. ali-sphenoid; B-Hy. basi-hyal; B.-O. basi-occipital; B.-S. basi-sphenoid; C-Hy. cerato-hyal; E-Hy. epi-hyal; Ex.-O. ex-occipital; *Fr.* frontal; *Ju.* jugal; *La.* lachrymal; *M.* mandible; ME. mesethmoid; *Mx.* maxilla; *Na.* nasal; O.-S. orbito-sphenoid; *Pa.* parietal; Per. periotic; *Pl.* palatine; P.-S. presphenoid; *PMx.* premaxilla; *Pt.* pterygoid; S-Hy. stylo-hyal; S.-O. supra-occipital; *Sq.* squamosal; T-Hy. tympano-hyal; Th.-Hy. thyro-hyal; Turb. turbinal; *Ty.* tympanic; *Vo.* vomer. (Capitals—replacing bones; *italics*—investing bones.) The numbered circles indicate the points of exit of the cranial nerves; 1, olfactory; 2, optic; 3, oculo-motor; 4, trochlear; 5, 5′, 5″, the three divisions of the fifth nerve; 6, abducent; 7, facial; 8, auditory; 9, glosso-pharyngeal; 10, pneumogastric; 11, spinal accessory; 12, hypoglossal. (After Flower.)

mastoid portion. The rest is commonly called the *petrous* portion of the periotic, and encloses the parts of the internal ear. The mastoid portion contains only air cells. The *tympanic* bone, which represents the angular of reptiles and birds, sometimes forms a long tube, sometimes only a mere ring of bone. In other cases it not only gives rise to a tube—the *external auditory meatus*—but also forms the *bulla tympani*, a dilated bony process containing a cavity.

The tympanic cavity, in which lie the *auditory ossicles*, is hollowed out of the petrosal which is itself formed by the complete fusion of the pro-otic and opisthotic bones. In the primitive condition, as can be seen in some of the marsupials, 'insectivores', edentates, etc., this chamber has no bony covering, and the tympanic bone (*ectotympanic*) is an open ring lying loosely and supporting the ear-drum. When, as in most cases, a bony covering is formed, this structure is termed the *bulla*. It is not always formed in the same way in different groups. In those marsupials in which a bulla is present

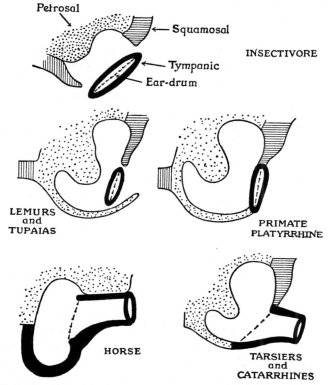

FIG. 611.—**Eutheria: Tympanic structure.** The tympanic bone is black; the petrosal dotted, the squamosal horizontally shaded and the basi-occipital vertically shaded. (For 'insectivores' see p. 726.)

it is always made from the alisphenoid, the tympanic forming the external auditory meatus. In the Primates it is formed chiefly by an outgrowth of the petrous bone, which may either grow round the tympanic ring so as to enclose it (as in the Tupaiidæ and Lemuridæ (Fig. 611), where it lies free in the cavity), or (as in the Lorisidæ and platyrrhine monkeys) it joins on to the edge of the tympanic ring, which thus forms part of the bulla wall and acts as the opening of the middle ear. Again, in the tarsiers and catarrhine monkeys it is further produced outwards to form a bony tube—the external auditory meatus. In other mammals the tympanic, as a rule, forms most of the bulla, but the entotympanic, squamosal, alisphenoid, and basisphenoid may also take some part either in the formation of the bulla or as supporting elements.

The *occipital* region presents two condyles for articulation with the atlas.

The *mandible* consists in the adult of one bone, the equivalent of the *dentary* of reptiles and birds, on each side. The two rami, as they are called, are in most mammals closely united at the symphysis. The mandible articulates with an articular surface formed for it by the *squamosal* bone, below the posterior root of the zygomatic arch.

The *hyoid* apparatus (Fig. 612) is a bony complex situated between the larynx and the base of the skull which serves to support the tongue and to suspend the larynx and trachea. It exhibits considerable variation in different mammals. It consists of a transverse, flattened *basihyal* or *corpus* ('body of hyoid') to which are articulated *anterior* and *posterior cornua* (or 'horns'). Each brief posterior cornu consists of a *thyrohyal* to which is attached the thyroid cartilage of the larynx. On each side of the pharynx extends an anterior cornu consisting of an articulated succession of three bones, the *ceratohyal, epihyal*, and *stylohyal* elements. In some mammals (*e.g.* Man) the last-named may unite with a *tympanohyal* as a *styloid process*.

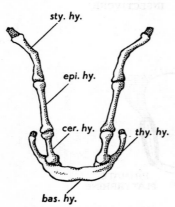

FIG. 612.—**Canidæ: Hyoid apparatus.** Extracranial portion (of dog). Front view. *Sty. hy.* stylohyal; *epi. hy.* epihyal; *cer. hy.* ceratohyal (these three constitute the 'anterior cornu'); *bas. hy.* basihyal or 'body' of hyoid; *thy. hy.* thyrohyal or 'posterior cornu'.

The ratio between cranial capacity and facial skeleton varies greatly in the different orders. The greater development of the cerebral hemispheres in the higher groups necessitates a more capacious cranium. This is brought about by the bulging upwards, forwards and backwards of the cranial roof, resulting in a great modification in the primitive relations of certain of the great planes and axes of the skull (Fig. 613). Taking as a fixed base line the *basicranial axis*—an imaginary median line running through the basioccipital, basisphenoid and presphenoid bones—it is found that the greatly expanded cranium in the higher mammals has effected a marked alteration in the relations to this axis 1. of the *occipital* plane or plane of the foramen magnum ; 2. of the *tentorial* plane or plane of the tentorium cerebelli (a transverse fold of the dura mater between the cerebral hemispheres and the cerebellum), and 3. of the *ethmoidal* plane or plane of the cribriform plate of the ethmoid. In the lower mammals (*A*) these are nearly at right angles to the basicranial axis. In the higher groups, by the bulging forwards and backwards of the cranial roof, the occipital and tentorial planes incline backwards and the ethmoidal forwards, until all three may become approximately horizontal. At the same time there is produced a change in the relations of the basicranial axis to the *basifacial axis*—a line passing along the axis of the face between the mesethmoid and the vomer. In the lower forms the angle at which the basifacial

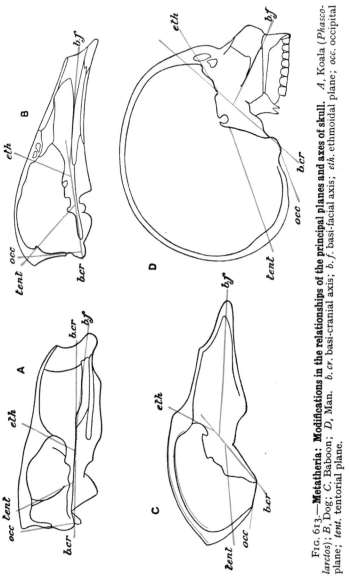

Fig. 613.—**Metatheria: Modifications in the relationships of the principal planes and axes of skull.** *A*, Koala (*Phascolarctos*); *B*, Dog; *C*, Baboon; *D*, Man. *b. cr.* basi-cranial axis; *b. f.* basi-facial axis; *eth.* ethmoidal plane; *occ.* occipital plane; *tent.* tentorial plane.

axis, when produced, meets the basicranial is an exceedingly open one. In the higher forms, owing to the downward inclination of the facial region, this angle decreases in size, though it is never reduced to less than a right angle.

The *pectoral arch* of the Mammalia has fewer distinct elements than that of reptiles and birds. The coracoid, which, in the last two groups, is a large bone, shares by means of its dorsal end in the bounding of the glenoid cavity. Its ventral end, articulating with the sternum, is in the adult never present as a distinct bone. In the young of many mammals it appears to be represented by a small ossification which enters into the glenoid facet. This very soon coalesces with the scapula. The coracoid process is a separate ossification in the young mammal, and, though in most instances it completely fuses with the scapula and with the smaller coracoid element, it is sometimes recognisable as a distinct element up to a late period (many marsupials, sloths). It appears to correspond to the bone called epicoracoid in the Prototheria (see p. 697). In fœtal marsupials the coracoid is represented by a well-developed cartilaginous element which extends inwards and meets the rudiment of the sternum.

In the scapula a *spine* is nearly always developed, and usually ends in a freely projecting acromion process. Unlike the main body of the scapula it is developed without any antecedent formation of cartilage, and is perhaps to be compared with the *cleithrum*, an investing bone occurring in some Amphibia and Reptilia (p. 397). A *clavicle* is well developed in many mammals, but is incomplete or absent in others. Its presence is characteristic of mammals in which the fore-limbs are capable of great freedom of movement. In the mammalian embryo there is, in the position of the clavicular bar, a bar of cartilage, which coalesces with its fellow in the middle line. The cartilaginous tract thus formed segments into five portions—a median (which coalesces with the presternum), two small inner lateral (which unite with the clavicles or are converted into the sterno-clavicular ligaments), and two long outer lateral (which give rise to the clavicles). The median and inner lateral portions appear to correspond to the episternum of reptiles and Prototheria. An additional small cartilage may represent the inner portion of the precoracoid of Amphibia. A piece of cartilage at the outer end of the clavicle proper is sometimes distinguishable—the *mesoscapular segment*.

The three elements of the *pelvic arch* unite to form a single bone, the *innominate*. The ilia unite by broad surfaces with the sacrum ; the pubes, and sometimes the ischia, unite in a *symphysis*. All three may take a share in the formation of the acetabulum, but the pubis is usually excluded by a small *cotyloid bone*. In both monotremes and marsupials (except in *Thylacinus* where they are cartilaginous) *epipubic* bones occur, the so-called 'marsupial' bones. They occur in both sexes and in unpouched as well as pouched species. They are large and flat, are only lightly joined to the rest of the pelvis, and spring upwards and outwards to taper and terminate in the muscles of the abdominal wall. It would seem that their function is to lend support for the abdominal wall : there is no evidence of any present or past function in relation to actual locomotion.

In the shank the inner or *tibial* element is always the larger ; the *fibula* may be vestigial. A large sesamoid bone—the *patella*—is almost universally formed in close relation to the knee-joint.

The most primitive type of extremity is the *plantigrade*, with five sub-equal digits, a flexible carpus and tarsus, and with the bones 'interlocking' (e.g. *Tritemnodon*, Fig. 614, and many primitive mammals). From a generalised pattern of this sort many modifications have been derived. As an adaptation to increasing speed, the *cursorial* patterns proceed through the subdigitigrade to the digitigrade, and finally to the unguligrade condition as the extreme adaptation along this line. This is accompanied by an increase in the length of the digits, either along the axis of the third toe—the *mesaxonic* pattern—or between the third and fourth toes—the *paraxonic* pattern. An early stage of a mesaxonic foot can be seen in the condylarth *Tetraclænodon*, and its final stage in horses or in the Litopterna (Fig. 615) where a functionally one-toed condition has been reached. Although these animals are morphologically three-toed, the second and fourth toes are still represented by splint bones. The paraxonic hand and foot, of which an early stage can be seen in the creodont *Mesonyx* (Fig. 616), has the axis passing between the third and fourth digits, which enlarge at an equal rate. The second and fifth toes, on the other hand, become equally reduced, and the first toe disappears. The final result can be seen in the more advanced Artiodactyla (*e.g.* a cow or sheep) where there is a complete reduction to two toes and a fusion of the two metapodials into the

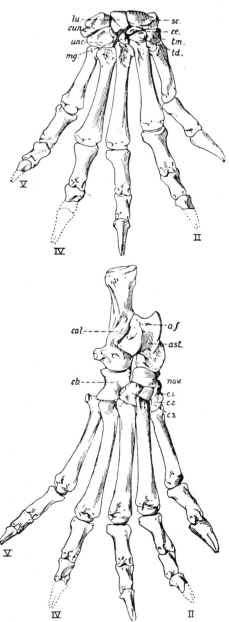

FIG. 614.—**Carnivora: Primitive plantigrade, pentadactyle limbs.** Carpus (upper) and tarsus (lower figure) of *Tritemnodon agilis.* *a. f.* astragalar foramen; *ast.* astragalus; *cal.* calcaneum; *cb.* cuboid; *ce.* centrale; *cun.* cuneiform; *c.* 1, 2, 3, ento-, meso, and ecto-cuneiforms; *lu.* lunar; *mg.* magnum; *nav.* navicular; *sc.* scaphoid; *td.* trapezoid; *tm.* trapezium. (After Matthew.)

characteristic 'cannon bone' (Fig. 617).   The bones of the carpus and tarsus, while retaining the characters of the interlocking type, are arranged to allow

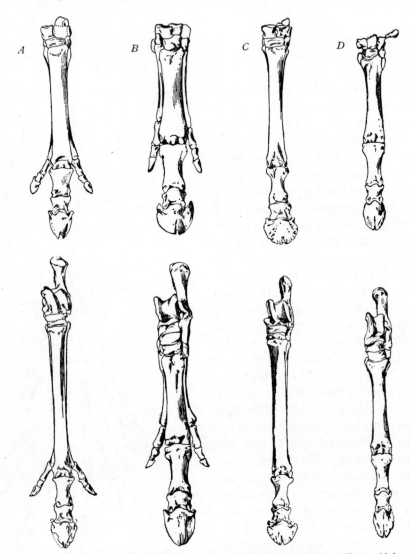

FIG. 615.—**Eutheria: Convergent adaptations in cursorial mammals.**   Two widely unrelated groups—Hippomorpha and Litopterna—illustrating a single-toed trend in fore- and hind-limbs. *A, Merychippus* (Miocene horse), three-toed stages; *B, Diadiaphorus* (Miocene–Pliocene litoptern), three-toed stages; *C, Pliohippus* (Pliocene horse), single toed stages; *D, Thoatherium* (Miocene litoptern), single-toed stages.   (Redrawn after Matthew.)

great flexion in the fore-and-aft direction, but little in the lateral.   In many artiodactyles some of the tarsalia are fused (Fig. 618).

In bulky animals such as the elephants, Dinocerata, etc., the carpals and tarsals become serially arranged with a great loss of flexibility, and the digits, while not reduced in number as a rule, are short and stout. Special habits, such as hopping (the kangaroos; *Macroscelides* among insectivores; *Dipus* and *Allactaga* among rodents (Fig. 619)); swimming (*e.g.* the Cetacea, Sirenia, seals); flying (*e.g.* the bats and to some extent the parachuting kinds of marsupials and rodents); digging (as in the moles and several other forms) all produce more or less profound modifications in the limbs, hands, and feet.

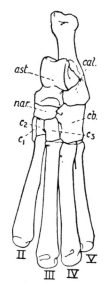

The generalised hand and foot has already been mentioned (see p. 100, Fig. 71). In the mammals the carpus contains three proximal bones: the *scaphoid, lunar,* and *cuneiform,* to which is added on the outer side, the *pisiform,* possibly a sesamoid, but equally possibly a true carpal element. The distal row consists of four bones: the *trapezium, trapezoid, magnum,* and *unciform.* The last named is a fusion of the fourth and fifth original elements of this row. In primitive mammals another bone is present, the *centrale,* which lies between the bones of the first and second rows. In reptiles there can be as many as three centralia, but in mammals there is never more than one, which may disappear either by fusion or loss.

The tarsus (Figs. 619, 623, 624) is usually rather more modified from the generalised pattern than is the carpus. There are only two proximal bones: the *astragalus* and *calcaneum,* which correspond to the lunar and cuneiform. The distal row is represented by the *ecto-, meso-,* and *entocuneiforms,* and the *cuboid,* which is formed by the fusion of the fourth and fifth cuneiforms and corresponds to the unciform of the hand. The centrale becomes a large and important bone, the *navicular.*

FIG. 616.—**Carnivora: Paraxonic carpus and tarsus.** *Mesonyx,* an Eocene Creodont. *ast.* astragalus; $C^1, {}^2, {}^3,$ ento-, meso-, and ectocuneiforms; *cal.* calcaneum; *cb.* cuboid; *cun.* cuneiform; *lu.* lunar; *mg.* magnum; *nav.* navicular; *pis.* pisiform; *sc.* scaphoid; *td.* trapezoid; *tm.* trapezium; *unc.* unciform.

The astragalus is also, in another sense, an important bone, because its shape differs in the various orders, but itself remains true to its particular type, subject only to differences in proportion, however much the rest of the foot may become modified. It is therefore a very useful guide to the affinity of any form, especially in the case of certain extinct mammals. The astragalus consists of a proximal grooved surface, the *trochlea* (which articulates proximally with the tibia and fibula), a *neck* and a *head* of varying shape (which articulates with the navicular and sometimes with the cuboid as well). In many early forms an *astragalar foramen* is present near the upper border of the trochlea. This foramen usually disappears in later mammals, but still occurs sporadically, as, for example, in *Orycteropus* (p. 804).

The main modifications of the astragalus are as follows. In the Condylarth–Creodont–Carnivore group the tibial trochlea is more or less grooved, obliquely pitched, with the inner (tibial) crest lower than the outer (fibular), or even absent; the neck is distinct and the head convex. In the Insectivora the trochlea is broad and shallow, but with well-defined crests of equal height, the neck is oblique and oval in section, the head convex. The primate astra-

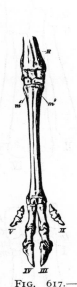

FIG. 617.—
Cervus: Manus.
C. elaphus. Red
Deer. m^2. m^5.
vestigial second
and fifth meta-
carpals; *R.* ra-
dius. (After
Flower.)

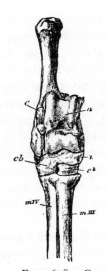

FIG. 618.—**Cervus: Tarsus.** Right,
dorsal surface. *a.*
astragalus; *c.* cal-
caneum; *cb.* cuboid;
c³. conjoined ecto-
and meso-cuneiform;
mIII, *mIV*, third
and fourth metatar-
sals; *n.* navicular.
(After Flower.)

FIG. 619.—
Dipus: Pes.
Jerboa. Let-
tering as in
Fig. 618.

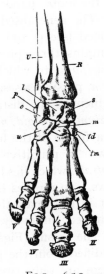

FIG. 620.—
Tapirus: Manus.
T. indicus. *c.* cunei-
form; *l.* lunar; *m.*
magnum; *p.* pisi-
form; *R.* radius;
s. scaphoid; *td.*
trapezoid; *tm.* tra-
pezium; *U.* ulna;
u. unciform. (After
Flower.)

galus has a concavo-convex trochlear surface, broader at the neck end than above, a somewhat oblique neck and a convex head. In the rodents the general appearance is like that of the insectivores, except that the trochlea extends backwards to the posterior margin of the bone. In the Perissodactyla the trochlea is deeply grooved and oblique, the neck short, and the head flattened. In the earlier forms there is a very small astragalo-cuboid facet. In more advanced forms, especially in the rhinoceroses and titanotheres, this becomes larger, though never to the extent that it does in the highly charac-teristic artiodactyle astragalus. Here the trochlea is deeply grooved in a straight line with the head and neck, with well-marked facets for both the cuboid and navicular. In this type also the sustenacular facet on the medial aspect (which articulates with the calcaneum) is a single large and flat surface instead of being divided, as in other astragali.

Other bones of the carpus and tarsus have their distinguishing characteristics, if rather less obvious than those of the astragalus, as, for example, the artiodactyle cuboid, which shows a constant difference from the cuboid of all other mammals in having a facet on its outer border for the calcaneum.

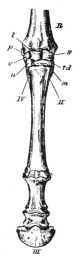
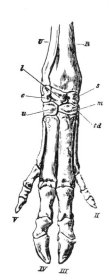
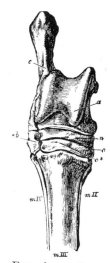

FIG. 621.— **Equus: Manus.** Horse. *c.* cuneiform; *l.* lunar; *m.* magnum; *p.* pisiform; *R.* radius; *s.* scaphoid; *td.* trapezoid; *u.* unciform; *II, IV,* vestigial second and fourth metacarpals. (After Flower.)

FIG. 622.— **Sus: Manus.** Pig. *c.* cuneiform; *l.* lunar; *m.* magnum; *R.* radius; *s.* scaphoid; *td.* trapezoid; *U.* ulna; *u.* unciform. (After Flower.)

FIG. 623.—**Equus: Tarsus.** Horse. Right. *a.* astragalus; *c.* calcaneum; *cb.* cuboid; *c.* united meso- and ento-cuneiform; *c³.* ecto-cuneiform; *n.* navicular; *mII, IV,* vestigial second and fourth metatarsals; *III,* third metatarsal. (After Flower.)

FIG. 624.—**Sus:** tarsus. Pig. Right. *a.* astragalus; *c.* calcaneum; *cb.* cuboid; *c³.* ecto-cuneiform; *c².* meso-cuneiform; *mII— V,* metatarsals; *n.* navicular. (After Flower.)

The external form of the limbs and the mode of articulation of the bones vary in the different orders of the Mammalia, in accordance with the mode of locomotion. In most the habitual attitude is that which is termed the *quadrupedal* wherein the body is supported in a horizontal position by all four limbs. In quadrupedal mammals the manus and pes sometimes rest on the ventral surfaces of the entire metacarpal and metatarsal regions as well as on the phalanges (when the limbs are said to be *plantigrade*); or on the ventral surfaces of the phalanges only (*digitigrade*); or on the hoofs developed on the terminal phalanges (*unguligrade*). Many of the quadrupeds have the extremities prehensile with the manus and pes converted into grasping organs.

This is most marked in quadrupeds that pass the greater part of their life among the branches of trees. In the sloths the modification goes so far that both hands and feet are converted into mere hooks by means of which the animal suspends itself body downwards from the branches of trees (Fig. 539, p. 768).

Certain mammals, again, have their limbs modified for locomotion through the air. The only truly *flying* mammals are bats, in which the digits of the fore-limb are greatly extended so as to support a wide delicate fold of skin constituting the wing. In the so-called 'flying' squirrels and 'flying' phalangers and other gliders there is no active flight, and the limbs undergo no special modification. The 'flying' organ in these cases is merely a parachute or *patagium* in the form of lateral flaps of skin extending along the sides of the body between the fore- and hind-limbs (Fig. 498, p. 717; Fig. 528, p. 754).

Finally, there are several groups of *swimming* mammals. Most mammals, without any special modification of the limbs, are able to swim, and some of the quadrupeds, such as the tapirs and hippopotamuses, spend a great part of their life in the water. But there are certain mammals in which the limbs are specially modified to assume the form of flippers or swimming paddles and for these locomotion on land becomes almost, sometimes quite, impossible. Such are the whales and porpoises, the dugongs and manatees, and, in a less degree, the seals and walruses (Fig. 554, p. 780; Fig. 594, p. 821).

Alimentary Canal and Associated Structures.—*Teeth* are present in nearly all mammals, but in some they do not occur in the adult condition (whalebone whales, *Ornithorhynchus*). In *Tachyglossus* teeth are absent throughout life. In some of the ant-eaters teeth are developed in the fœtus and are discarded *in utero*—the adult animal being devoid of them (p. 871).

Teeth, already described in the general account of the Craniata (p. 103), are developed partly from the epidermis and partly from the underlying dermis. In the mammals each tooth is lodged in a socket (*alveolus*) in the jaw. The part of the tooth developed from the epidermis is the enamel. The remainder of the tooth—dentine, cement, and pulp—is formed from the subjacent meso-dermal tissue (Fig. 625).

Along the oral surface of the jaw is formed a ridge-like ingrowth of the ectoderm—the *dental lamina*—and from it a bud is given off in the position to be occupied by each of the teeth. This bud becomes constricted off as a conical cap of cells—the *enamel-organ*—which remains in continuity with the dental lamina by a narrow isthmus. The cap-like form of the enamel-organ is brought about by its growth over a concentration of dermal tissue—the *dental papilla*. The dental papilla has a rich blood supply. On the surface of this papilla, in contact with the enamel-organ, a layer of cells (*odontoblasts*) becomes arranged rather like an epithelium. This layer of odontoblasts is the dentine-forming layer. The cells of the enamel-organ which are in contact with the dental papilla become long and cylindrical to form *ameloblasts*. This layer of ameloblasts forms the *inner enamel epithelium*. The cells on that part of the surface of the enamel organ which is not in contact with the dental papilla form a layer of cubical cells, which is called the *outer enamel epithelium*. Between these two layers the remaining cells of the enamel organ become modified: those in contact with the inner enamel-epithelium form a distinct

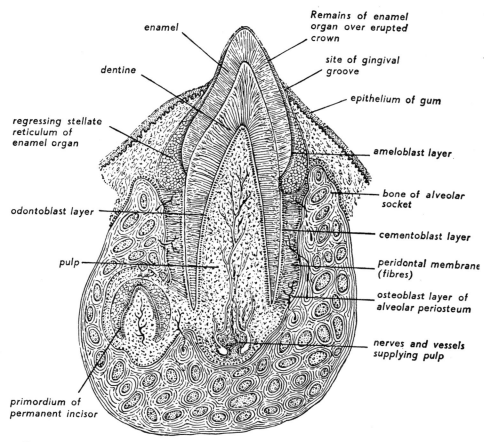

FIG. 625.—**Primates: Tooth structure.** Semi-schematic, showing an erupting 'milk' incisor and primordium of adjacent permanent tooth. In the deciduous tooth the root is not yet fully formed but the arrangement of its tissues indicates how it will be attached within the alveolar socket. (Modified after Patten.)

layer (the *stratum intermedium*), while the remainder become vacuolated and form a loose tissue known as the *stellate reticulum*. Around the enamel organ and dental papilla there develops a layer of connective tissue—the *dental follicle*. This contains many blood vessels.

The hard part of the tooth begins to develop by the formation of a cap of *predentine* (produced by the odontoblasts); and of a layer of *enamel matrix* which is laid down on the surface of this (produced by the *ameloblasts*). The predentine and enamel matrix calcify to form the *dentine* and *enamel*. Additional layers are added until the crown of the tooth is complete. The enamel organ then degenerates, but the dental papilla remains as the *pulp* of the fully-developed tooth. Roots are formed, and the crown of the tooth then erupts into the mouth cavity. The roots of the teeth consist of dentine over which a layer of *cement* is deposited. This is formed by the cells of the dental follicle. There is no enamel on the roots. (In some mammals cement is also formed on the surface of the enamel on the crown, *e.g.* modern horses, rabbits, some rodents, some artiodactyles, and the elephants.) In mammals the roots of the teeth generally open at their bases by small foramina through which nerves

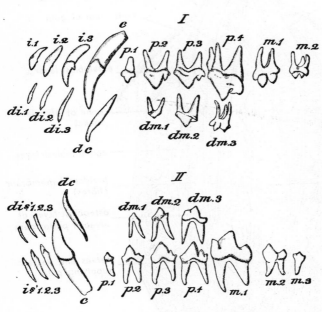

FIG. 626.—*Canis:* **Deciduous and permanent dentition.** Upper (*I*) and lower (*II*) jaws of dog, with the symbols by which the different teeth—incisors, canines, premolars and molars—are commonly designated. The prefix '*d*', or sometimes '*m*', indicates deciduous or milk teeth. (After Flower and Lydekker.)

and blood vessels enter the pulp. However, in the teeth of some (*e.g.* the molar teeth of modern horses and elephants) the formation of roots is delayed, and the enamel organ which persists around the sides and within the folds of the crown continues to add to its height long after the tooth has erupted and come into use. In other mammalian teeth (*e.g.* the incisors of rodents and elephants, and all the teeth of rabbits) roots are never formed and the crowns of the teeth continue to grow throughout life. Such teeth are said to have 'persistent pulps'.

Usually mammals have two distinct sets of teeth developed, the *deciduous* (milk) and *permanent* dentitions (Fig. 626). Sometimes there is only one set present. Accordingly *diphyodont* and *monophyodont* dentitions are distinguished. In nearly all of the latter, however, another set is developed, though the teeth early become absorbed or remain as functionless vestiges. The milk-teeth in mammals with typical diphyodont dentition sometimes disappear at an early stage (*e.g.* seals), and sometimes persist and do not become replaced by the permanent teeth till long after birth (*e.g.* Man). Some mammals have the teeth indefinite in number, *e.g.* the dolphins and porpoises. Such teeth are all uniform in appearance (*homodont*) (Fig. 627) and not divided into functional varieties (Fig. 628). Where they are divided into functional varieties they are said to be *heterodont*.

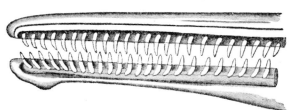

FIG. 627.—*Lagœnorhynchus:* **Homodont dentition.** Adaptation in dolphins to fishing. (After Flower and Lydekker.)

In the typical eutherian dentition there are forty-four teeth, *viz.* three incisors on each side, one canine, four premolars and three molars both above and below. The upper incisors (Fig. 626) are lodged in the premaxillæ. The lower incisors are placed opposite. The upper canine is the most anterior tooth of the maxilla, situated on or immediately behind the premaxillo-maxillary suture and has usually a characteristic shape. The lower canine bites in front of the upper. The premolars are distinguished from the molars by having milk predecessors. The molars have no teeth preceding them, and are sometimes looked upon as persistent teeth of the first set. As a rule in heterodont dentitions the incisors have cutting edges, the canines are pointed and conical, the premolars and molars have broad surfaces with ridges and tubercles for crushing the food, and may have from two to four roots.

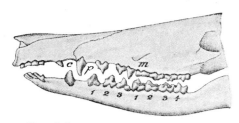

FIG. 628.—*Perameles:* **Dentition.** Marsupial bandicoot. (After Owen.)

The crown surface of the molar teeth of mammals shows a wide range of pattern which, used with caution and due regard to the possibility of convergence, is of great use in classification. With very few exceptions these patterns can be expressed as modifications of a relatively simple type, and this type itself can be explained as a modification of a simple ancestral reptilian cone. This basal type of mammalian molar pattern is termed the *tritubercular*, with respect to the upper molar and *trituberculo-sectorial* with respect to the lower. The theory of its origin, due originally to Cope, and subsequently added to and amended by Osborn, is known universally as the *Cope–Osborn theory of trituberculy*. The theory in its modified form will be more easily understood if a brief and condensed history of its origin is first given.

Cope saw that the molar teeth of the earliest eutherian mammals commonly possessed a triangular crown with three main *cusps*, and that later forms tended to have molars with from four to six cusps. These he regarded as derived from the earlier triangular type. Osborn greatly developed this hypothesis and, on the assumption that the principal cusps are homologous throughout the Mammalia, gave them names that have been in universal use

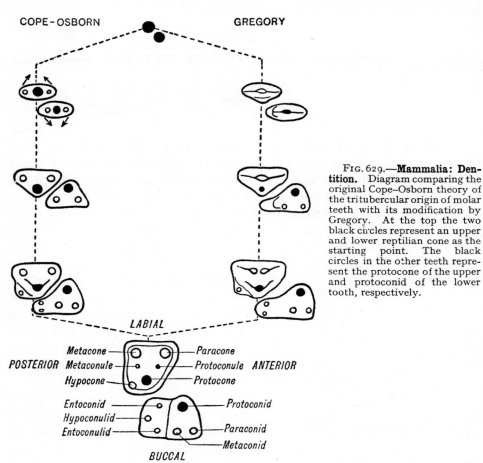

FIG. 629.—**Mammalia: Dentition.** Diagram comparing the original Cope–Osborn theory of the trituttbercular origin of molar teeth with its modification by Gregory. At the top the two black circles represent an upper and lower reptilian cone as the starting point. The black circles in the other teeth represent the protocone of the upper and protoconid of the lower tooth, respectively.

ever since. Osborn's view as to the method of origin of the individual cusps, which has since been modified in some important respects, was as follows (Fig. 627). Starting with a simple reptilian cone, this was assumed to have elongated in an antero-posterior direction and two subsidiary cones to have arisen one on the front and one on the hind border, thus producing a triconodont tooth. These two cusps were then supposed to have rotated in opposite directions in the upper and lower jaws to form triangular or *tritubercular* teeth. The apex of the triangle, or *trigon*, points inwards in the upper tooth and outwards in the lower. The cusp at the apex of the triangle, being supposed to represent the original reptilian cone, was named the *protocone* in the upper and *protoconid* in the lower tooth.[1]

At a very early stage criticism was directed against the view that the protocone of the mammalian tritubercular tooth represents the original reptilian cone largely because in ontogeny it is not the first cusp to be formed, nor is there any known evidence to support the hypothesis of the rotation of the subsidiary cusps to form the triangles. Within the premolar series, and still more in their deciduous predecessors, there is usually a transition from behind forwards from a tooth that resembles a molar in many respects to one that is more like a canine or an incisor. If the single cusp of the canine is traced backwards through the successive teeth, it is seen to correspond to the paracone of the molar, and not to the protocone. This is the essence of the 'premolar analogy' theory. The protocone of the molar is represented on the more anterior teeth as an inner shelf at the base, or is even completely absent, and it was therefore thought probable that this cusp is secondary in origin to the paracone, a statement which is consistent with the embryological evidence. Further evidence for the same theory is found in the fact that in some groups the premolars evolve from simple peg-like teeth to a molariform condition. This process is called the *molarisation* of the premolars. Further, in this evolution the original cusp becomes the paracone of the molar rather than the protocone.

Further study of the dentitions of Mesozoic mammals has led to modifications of Osborn's theory. It is widely held that, whereas in the lower molar the protoconid does represent the tip of the originally simple reptilian tooth, this is not true of the protocone of the upper molar. According to some investigators the original upper molar cusp was the paracone, but others think it was an 'amphicone', which split to form the paracone and metacone. However, the names which Osborn gave to the cusps have become so widely applied to Cenozoic mammals that it is generally agreed to continue to call the lingual cusp of the tritubercular tooth the protocone, even though it may not have arisen as Osborn supposed.

In many early forms of tritubercular teeth, in Cretaceous and Palæocene mammals, the paracone and metacone were far removed from the buccal edge of the crown, which was occupied by a wide shelf bearing a number of *styles*. This type of upper molar, which is retained by the living opossums, may be

---

[1] The suffix *-id* designates a cusp on the lower molar. Of the other two cusps, the antero-external was named the *paracone* and the postero-external the *metacone*. A fourth cusp arising later on the cingulum on the postero-internal side, termed the *hypocone*, produces a quadri-tubercular tooth, and by the evolution of two smaller intermediate cusps, an anterior, the *protoconule*, and a posterior, the *metaconule*, the six cusped tooth, which underlies the molar pattern of so many mammals, comes into being. Like the upper, the lower molar consists of a triangle, or *trigonid*, and in addition a posterior shelf, the *talonid*, on which a number of cusps arise to produce the trituberculo-sectorial pattern, termed the *entoconid*, *hypoconulid*, and *hypoconulid*.

called *pretritubercular*. It is not very different from the *dilambdodont* teeth of Soricoidea and *Tupaia*. It is probable that the more typical tritubercular tooth has evolved from the pretritubercular condition by reduction of the buccal shelf to a cingulum, so that the paracone and metacone come to stand near to the buccal edge of the tooth. At the same time the protocone enlarged. On the other hand, in the *zalambdont* teeth of some Lipotyphla and the marsupial mole (p. 714), the protocone was reduced and the paracone was displaced towards the lingual side, so that in extreme cases it occupies the position taken by the protocone in tritubercular teeth. The upper molars of Dryolestoidea appear to resemble those of zalambdodont Lipotyphla, but this resemblance is almost certainly secondary.[1]

It is certain that, in whatever manner the tritubercular tooth may have arisen, the subsequent sexi-tubercular tooth has been derived from it. This is borne out by an enormous amount of direct fossil evidence, and it is possible to show that such diverse tooth-patterns as that of an artiodactyle, a perissodactyle, or a carnivore can be derived from the tritubercular type.

Further terms are in use to designate different parts of a tooth. If the cusps remain separate and rounded, the tooth is termed *bunoid*, if they join to form ridges, these ridges are termed *lophs*, and the tooth is *lophodont*. A tooth with crescentic cusps is *selenodont*. Any tooth may have a combination of these characters, in which case it is called *buno-lophodont*, *buno-selendont*, etc. Additional pillars such as can be seen in the molar of a horse, or on the outer border or *ectoloph* of many teeth, are called *styles*—e.g. the *proto-*, *meso-*, and *metastyle*, etc. A tooth with a low crown is termed *brachydont*, and with a high crown and deep socket termed *hypsodont*.

As already stated, the crown pattern of the teeth of mammals is largely used as a guide to their affinities. Generally speaking, it is a fairly dependable one, and starting from the more primitive and generalised forms of dentition, such as is shown by the early insectivores, creodonts, and condylarths, the major groups of mammals usually have trends of evolution on their own recognisable lines. Thus, for example, the Carnivora, the Artiodactyla, and Perissodactyla have all ultimately acquired dental patterns which are sufficiently distinctive. Other groups, such as the Proboscidea, Cetacea, and Xenarthra, have patterns that are both distinctive and diagnostic. At the same time exceptions occur, due presumably to some unusual and specialised kind of food, such as in *Proteles* (an insect- and worm-eating hyæna), or *Potos* (a fruit-eating procyonid), both of which animals have their dentition modified away from the usual carnivore type. These two are examples of a dentition that has degenerated, but there are many instances of tooth resemblance, more or less close, among unrelated animals due to convergence, the result of similar

---

[1] For a discussion of this question, and a full account of the history of the tritubercular theory, see Gregory, and for details of the Mesozoic forms, both Simpson and Butler.

feeding habits. Thus a permanently growing gnawing incisor is not absolutely diagnostic of a rodent, but can be found in the primate, *Chiromys* (*Daubentonia*) (p. 737), in *Tillotherium* and even in the artiodactyle *Myotragus*. A bilophodont form of molar tooth occurs in many diverse orders of mammals. The difficulty of assessing the true affinity of some mammals on the evidence of their teeth alone increases when the earlier and more primitive forms are considered : and to decide whether a Palæocene or an Eocene tooth is to be ascribed to an insectivore, a primate, a condylarth or a creodont is difficult, and sometimes impossible. Precaution therefore must be taken against regarding as evidence of affinity a similarity of pattern, which may be the result of convergence due to a similarity of habit.

A comparison of the wide adaptive radiation of the teeth of the marsupials into insectivorous, carnivorous, rodent, and herbivorous types of dentition with that obtaining in placental mammals of corresponding habits is instructive.

The number of the various sets of teeth in the jaws is conveniently expressed by a *dental formula*, in which the kind of tooth (incisor, canine, premolar, molar) is indicated by the initial letter (*i.*, *c.*, *p.*, *m.*), and the whole formula has the arrangement of four vulgar fractions, in each of which the numerator indicates the teeth of the upper, the denominator those of the lower jaw. Thus :

$$i. \frac{3 \cdot 3}{3 \cdot 3}, \ c. \frac{1 \cdot 1}{1 \cdot 1}, \ p. \frac{4 \cdot 4}{4 \cdot 4}, \ m. \frac{3 \cdot 3}{3 \cdot 3} = 44 \ ;$$

or, in a simpler form, since the teeth of the right and left sides are always numerically similar,

$$i. \frac{3}{3}, \ c. \frac{1}{1}, \ p. \frac{4}{4}, \ m. \frac{3}{3} = 44.$$

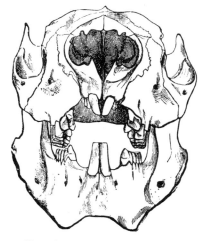

FIG. 630.—*Phascolarctos:* **Skull.** Koala, in front view, illustrating diprotodont and herbivorous dentition. (After Flower.)

Tachyglossus has no teeth at any stage. In *Ornithorhynchus* ridged teeth are present in the young and are functional for a time, but they are replaced by broad horny plates formed essentially by a down-growth of epidermis. One of these occurs on each upper, and one on each lower, jaw (Fig. 481, p. 695).

In marsupials the milk-dentition remains in a degenerate condition. With the exception of one (the last premolar) the milk teeth remain in an imperfect state of development, though they persist, as functionless vestiges, to a comparatively late stage.

In the adult marsupial dentition the number of upper and lower incisors is always dissimilar, except in *Phascolomys*. With regard to the arrangement of these teeth, the order falls into two series, termed respectively *diprotodont* and *polyprotodont*. In the former (Figs. 630, 631) the two anterior incisors are large and prominent, the rest of the incisors and the canines being smaller or absent. In the latter (Figs. 632, 633), the incisors are numerous and sub-equal and the canines large. There are typically three premolars and four molars.

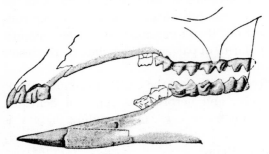

FIG. 631.—*Macropus:* **Dentition.** Kangaroo.

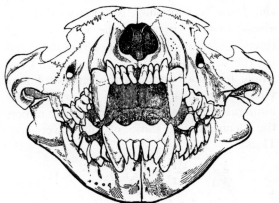

FIG. 632.—*Sarcophilus:* **Skull.** Tasmanian Devil, in front view, illustrating polyprotodont and carnivorous dentition. (After Flower.)

A good example of the diprotodont arrangement is the kangaroo (*Macropus*, Fig. 631), which has the dental formula—

$$i. \frac{3}{1}, c. \frac{1}{0}, p. \frac{2}{2}, m. \frac{4}{4} = 34.$$

The canine is very small and lost early. Of the polyprotodont forms the Australian *Dasyurus* (Fig. 495, p. 713) has the formula—

$$i. \frac{4}{3}, c. \frac{1}{1}, p. \frac{2}{2}, m. \frac{4}{4} = 42;$$

and the American opossums (*Didelphys*) (Fig. 633)—

$$i. \frac{5}{4}, c. \frac{1}{1}, p. \frac{3}{3}, m. \frac{4}{4} = 50.$$

The Xenarthra, though not by any means all toothless, always have some peculiarity of dentition. When teeth are present in the adult the anterior series is absent and the teeth are imperfect, wanting roots and devoid of enamel. The tooth-characters differ widely in the different groups. In the sloths there are five teeth above and four below on each side; no second series is known. In the American ant-eaters there are no teeth in the adult. In the armadillos, on the other hand, the teeth are numerous, though simple and rootless, and, in one genus at least, two series occur. The scaly ant-eaters (Pholidota) lack teeth. In the Tubulidentata (aardvark) (Fig. 634) again, there are five teeth on each side which are heterodont and diphyodont, and of peculiar structure, being perforated by numerous minute, parallel, vertical canals. The pulp of

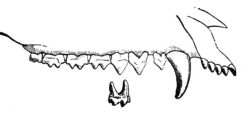

FIG. 633.—*Didelphys:* **Dentition.** Upper jaw of opossum (*D. marsupialis*), showing the condition typical of marsupials, in all of which there is no succession except in the last premolar, the place of which is occupied in the young animal by a molariform tooth represented in the figure below the line of the other teeth. (After Flower and Lydekker.)

FIG. 634.—*Orycteropus:* **Dentition.** Section of lower jaw and teeth of Aardvark. (After Owen.)

each tooth, entire at its base, is divided distally into a number of parallel columns.

In the Mesaxonia the dentition is heterodont and diphyodont, and the teeth are very rarely devoid of roots. In the Artiodactyla the premolars and molars differ from one another in pattern; the first upper premolar is almost always without a milk predecessor. The Suidæ (Fig. 635) are among the very few recent mammals which possess the primitive and typical dentition, the formula of which is—

$$i. \frac{3}{3}, c. \frac{1}{1}, p. \frac{4}{4}, m. \frac{3}{3} = 44.$$

The upper incisors are vertical, the lower greatly inclined forwards. The canines are greatly developed, especially in the male, and grow from persistent pulps; both the upper and lower are bent upwards and outwards and work against one another in such a manner that the upper wears on its anterior and external surface, the lower at the extremity of the posterior surface. The premolars are compressed, with longitudinal cutting edges, and the molars are provided with numerous tubercles or cusps arranged for the most part in transverse rows (bunodont type). The first permanent premolar has no predecessor, the formula of the milk dentition being—

$$i. \frac{3}{3}, c. \frac{1}{1}, m. \frac{3}{3} = 28.$$

In the typical ruminants there are no teeth on the premaxillæ, the lower incisors and canines, which resemble them in shape, biting against a thickened callous pad on the opposed surface of the upper jaw. The upper canines are also usually absent. There are three premolars and three molars in both upper and lower series, all characterised by the presence of column-like vertical folds

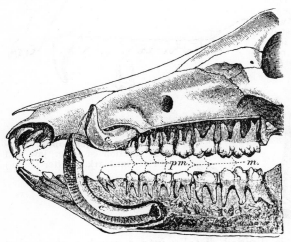

FIG. 635.—*Sus:* **Dentition.** The slashing canines of the boar possess persistent pulps. The Melanesians of the New Hebrides knock out the upper canine, thus allowing the lower ones to grow circularly without interruption. After about eight years the lower tusk may re-enter the jaw near its own socket or it may avoid the bone and form a full circle or more. (After Flower and Lydekker.)

of enamel. The interstices between these may be filled up with cement—the worn surface of the tooth presents a pattern of the selenodont type. In the camels there are a pair of upper incisors and a pair of large canines in each jaw.

In the Perissodactyla the molars and premolars form a continuous series of large teeth with ridged or complexly-folded crowns, the posterior premolars often differing little in size and structure from the molars. In the horse (Fig. 636) the formula is—

$$i. \frac{3}{3}, c. \frac{1}{1}, p. \frac{4}{4}, m. \frac{3}{3} = 44,$$

but the first premolar is a small tooth which is soon lost. A fold of the enamel dips downwards (*i.e.* towards the root) from the extremity of the incisor teeth like the partly inverted finger of a glove ; the canines are small in the female, and may not appear on the surface. There is a wide interval in both jaws between the canines and premolars. The premolar and molar teeth present a complicated pattern due to folds of the enamel, which differ in their arrangement in the upper and lower jaws ; their roots become completed only at a late period.

In the Hyracoidea the dental formula is—

$$i. \frac{1}{2}, c. \frac{0}{0}, p. \frac{4}{4}, m. \frac{3}{3} = 34.$$

The upper incisors are not unlike the larger pair of the rabbit in shape, though prismatic and pointed, instead of compressed and chisel-like ; they grow from persistent pulps. The lower incisors are elongated, inclined forwards, and trilobed at the extremities. The premolars and molars form a continuous series,

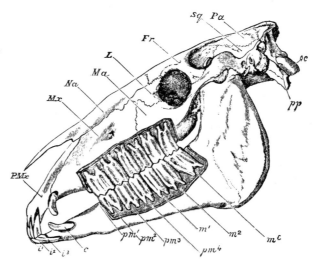

FIG. 636.—*Equus:* **Skull and teeth.** Side view in Horse with the bone removed to expose the whole of the teeth. *c.* canine; *Fr.* frontal; *i*^{1}. *i*^{2}. *i*^{3}. incisors; *L.* lachrymal; *Ma.* jugal; *Mx.* maxilla; *m*^{1}. *m*^{2}. *m*^{3}. molars; *Na.* nasal; *o.c.* occipital condyle; *Pa.* parietal; *p.m.*^{1}. situation of the vestigial first premolar, which has been lost in the lower, but is present in the upper jaw; *pm*^{2}. *pm*^{4}. *pm*^{1}. remaining premolars; *Pmx.* premaxilla; *p. p.* par-occipital process; *Sq.* squamosal. (After Flower and Lydekker.)

separated by an interval from the incisors, and in pattern closely resemble those of some of the Perissodactyla.

The elephants (Fig. 584, p. 812) have extremely specialised teeth. There are no canines and no lower incisors. The single pair of upper incisors are developed into the enormous tusks (Fig. 588, p. 816), which grow continuously from persistent pulps throughout the life of the animal ; they are of elongated conical form, and usually become curved. The tusks are composed of solid dentine. Enamel occurs on the apices only, and is early worn away. The molars (Fig. 590) are very large, and their worn surfaces are marked with prominent transverse ridges. There are six molars altogether on each side, but only one or two are functional at once, the more posterior moving forward and taking the place of the more anterior as these become worn out and shed.

When teeth are developed in the Cetacea they are nearly always numerous, homodont, and monophyodont. In the sperm-whales they are confined to the lower jaw. In the whalebone-whales, though teeth are developed in the foetal condition (Fig. 637), they become lost either before or soon after birth, and are succeeded in the adult by the triangular plates of baleen or whalebone (Fig. 558, p. 785), which hang vertically downwards from the palate.

Of the Sirenia, the dugongs and manatees have a heterodont dentition ; in *Hydrodamalis* (Dugongidæ) teeth were absent. In the two former sirenians there are incisors and molars with a wide diastema beween them. In the manatees there are two rudimentary incisors on each side, in both upper and lower jaw. These disappear before adulthood. There are altogether eleven molars on each side above and below, but not more than six of these are in use at once, the more anterior when worn out being succeeded by the more posterior. They have enamelled crowns with transverse ridges, and are preceded by milk-teeth. In the dugongs there are no mandibular incisors in the adult, and only one tusk-like mandibular pair. These are large in the male (in which they grow from persistent pulps) and but little developed in the female, remaining concealed in their sockets. In the young there are rudimentary mandibular incisors, and also a rudimentary second pair in the maxillæ.

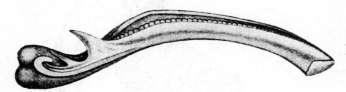

FIG. 637.—*Balænoptera:* **Fœtal jaw and teeth.** Right Whale. Inner Aspect of left jaw. Natural size. (After Julin.)

There are either five or six molars on each side, both above and below. These are cylindrical teeth devoid of enamel, and with persistent pulps.

In the Fissipedia (Fig. 565) the dentition is complete, heterodont, and diphyodont, and all the teeth are provided with roots. The incisors are relatively small, chisel-shaped teeth. There are nearly always three of them on each side in both jaws. The canines are always large and pointed. The presence of carnassials, consisting of the last premolar in the upper and the first molar in the lower jaw, is characteristic. In front of the carnassial the teeth are compressed and pointed; behind it they have broad surfaces. In the cat family (Felidæ) the formula is—

$$i. \frac{3}{3}, c. \frac{1}{1}, p. \frac{3}{2}, m. \frac{1}{1} = 30.$$

The lower carnassial is thus the last of the series. In the dogs (Canidæ) the formula is usually—

$$i. \frac{3}{3}, c. \frac{1}{1}, p. \frac{4}{4}, m. \frac{2}{3} = 42,$$

and in the bears (Ursidæ) it is the same. (For the pattern of the molar teeth see Fig. 566, p. 794.)

In the Pinnipedia there are always fewer than $\frac{3}{3}$ incisors, and carnassials are not developed. The premolars and molars have a compressed, conical, pointed form. The prevailing dental formula of the seals is—

$$i.\ \frac{3}{2},\ c.\ \frac{1}{1},\ p.\ \frac{4}{4},\ m.\ \frac{1}{1} = 34.$$

In the Walrus the adult formula is—

$$i.\ \frac{1}{0},\ c.\ \frac{1}{1},\ p.\ \frac{3}{3},\ m.\ \frac{0}{0} = 18.$$

The upper canines take the form of large, nearly straight tusks.

In the large order of the rodents the dentition is remarkably uniform, and, in all its general characters, resembles what has already been described in the Rabbit (Lagomorpha) except that in the lagomorphs a second, smaller pair of incisors is present in the upper jaw. The number of premolars and molars varies in rodents from—

$$p.\ \frac{0}{0},\ m.\ \frac{1}{1}\ \text{to}\ p.\ \frac{3}{2},\ m.\ \frac{3}{3},$$

and they may develop roots.

In the two 'insectivoran' orders (see p. 725) the dentition is heterodont, complete, and diphyodont. All the teeth are rooted. There are never fewer than two incisors on either side of the lower jaw. The canines are not of large size. The crowns of the molars are beset with pointed tubercules.

In the Chiroptera (bats) the dentition is complete, and the teeth are all rooted. There is a milk-series which, if not resorbed, differs entirely from the permanent teeth (see p. 756). In the insectivorous Chiroptera the molars are provided with pointed cusps, while in frugivorous forms (*e.g.* 'flying foxes', *Pteropus*) they are longitudinally grooved or excavated.

In the Primates the teeth are heterodont and diphyodont, and always, with the exception of *Daubentonia* (p. 737), with roots. (In *Daubentonia* the incisors are persistently growing.) There are almost invariably two incisors on each side of the jaws, and, in all but the marmosets, three molars. The dentition of Man differs from that of the rest of the order in the teeth forming a continuous series not interrupted by a diastema, and in the comparatively small size of the canines (Fig. 523, p. 746).

The *mouth* in mammals is bounded by fleshy *lips*. On the floor of the mouth is situated the *tongue*, which is usually well developed, but varies in size and shape in different orders. In some herbivorous animals it can be curled around grass and thus helps pull the 'feed' into the mouth. Its surface is covered with papillæ of different kinds. These are sometimes horny, serving either the initial grinding of food, or for the toilet of the hairy coat. Thus the tongue- and lip-margins in many mammals are equipped with raised processes which can be moved up and down along the interspaces of the teeth (and on the surfaces of the teeth) in cleansing action. In association with the papillæ of the tongue are special *end organs* of taste ('taste buds') which are often arranged in zones. The sense of taste differs profoundly among various groups. The roof of the mouth is formed in front by the *hard palate*, consisting of the horizontal palatine plates of the maxillary and palatine bones covered with mucous membrane bearing *palatal rugæ*. Behind the hard palate there projects backwards the soft muscular fold of the *soft palate* which divides the cavity of the pharynx into two chambers, an upper and a lower. In some forms the soft palate also bears taste buds. In the Primates a free-hanging *uvula* occurs. During deglutition or swallowing both *uvula* and soft palate are raised to close off the nasopharynx and prevent the entrance of food thereto. In front of the opening, leading from the lower division of the pharynx into the larynx, is a cartilaginous plate (*epiglottis*) a primitive form of which is found in certain lower vertebrates (see p. 362). The epiglottis, anatomically part of the larynx, assists the reflex swallowing mechanism by preventing the food from entering the trachea and so causing aspiration pneumonia.

It will be recalled that various prominent structures in the oral and pharyngeal region are in part derived from the gill-pouches of ancestral vertebrates (Fig. 73, p. 106). Thus, the tympanum, middle ear, and Eustachian tube are all partly derived from the first pharyngeal pouch. Again, connective tissue around the regressing second pharyngeal pouch becomes infiltrated by lymphoid material which comes to constitute the *palatine (faucial) tonsil*. Adjacent and above, the small *supratonsillar fossa* is a permanent remnant of the originally extensive second pouch. (The lingual, and pharyngeal tonsils ('adenoids'), are separate and unassociated with gill-clefts.) The thyroid and parathyroids (p. 152), as well as the thymus (Fig. 638), are also essentially pharyngeal pouch derivatives.

The *œsophagus* is always a simple, straight tube down which the food is propelled by peristaltic contractions of the muscular walls, which, like the act of deglutition, are reflex and involuntary. The opposite action, *retroperistalsis*, enables ruminants to regurgitate stomach contents for more leisurely mastication (see below), and many other animals to expel injurious substances accidentally swallowed. Highly-trained showmen can control the normally involuntary deglutition reflex and make a living as sword-swallowers : actually they are non-swallowers, for if they allowed the swallow reflex to operate they would wound their throats internally. Retroperistalsis in Man is sometimes used by 'spiritualist' fakers to regurgitate in dimly lit seances 'ectoplasm', *i.e.* previously-swallowed filmy cloth, or other material.

The *stomach* varies greatly in different mammalian orders. In the majority of mammals it is a relatively simple sac, as in the rabbit (p. 669). But in certain groups it is complicated by the development of internal folds, and may be divided by constrictions into several functionally different chambers. Such complication reaches its extreme in the Ruminantia especially, in the Tylopoda (but not Suiformes) and Cetacea. In a typical ruminant (Fig. 639) such as sheep or ox, the stomach is divided into four chambers—the *rumen* (or *paunch*), the *reticulum*, the *psalterium*, and the *abomasum* (or *rennet stomach*). The epithelium of both reticulum is highly reminiscent of that of the œsophagus.

The œsophagus opens into the rumen close to its junction with the reticulum. The rumen is much larger than the rest. Its mucous membrane is beset with numerous short villi. The reticulum, which is much smaller than

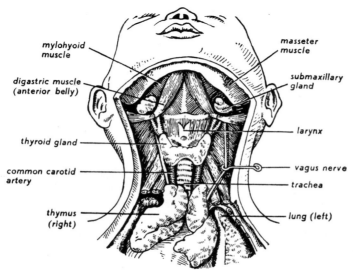

mylohyoid muscle

digastric muscle (anterior belly)

thyroid gland

common carotid artery

thymus (right)

masseter muscle

submaxillary gland

larynx

vagus nerve

trachea

lung (left)

FIG. 638.—**Primates: Pharyngeal region.** Relationships and some certain gill-pouch derivatives (see also Fig. 73). Modified from Patten, after Bien.

the rumen, has its mucous membrane raised up into a number of anastomosing ridges. This gives its wall the appearance of a honeycomb with shallow cells. From the aperture between reticulum and rumen to that by which it communicates with the psalterium there runs a groove bounded by a pair of muscular ridges. These are capable of closing together in such a way as to convert the groove into a canal. The mucous membrane of the psalterium is raised up into numerous longitudinal leaf-like folds. The abomasum, smaller than the rumen, but larger than the reticulum, has a smooth vascular and glandular mucous membrane. The ruminant swallows herbage without mastication. The habit enables timid herbivores to snatch and swallow at intervals food that can be digested later in safer circumstances. It has arisen, with convergent specialisations, in the grazing Quokka Wallaby (Fig. 640).

In ruminants the food is swallowed, saturated by copious salivation and passes into the rumen and reticulum, where it lies until, having finished feeding, the animal begins ruminating or chewing the cud.   In this process the sodden

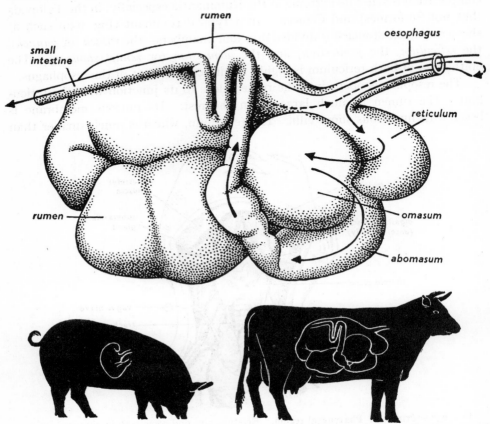

FIG. 639.—**Rumination and digestion.   Comparison between ruminant (*Bos*) and non-ruminant (*Sus*) tracts.** *Above:* Cow: Arrowed lines trace the course of foodstuffs in regurgitation (by retroperistalsis, broken line) and subsequently down through the four compartments.   Rumen and recticulum are connected by a wide aperture and together they constitute a fermentation chamber with a capacity of some 40 gallons.   Here micro-organisms split cellulose and sugars to utilisable fatty acids (absorbed through walls of rumen) as well as carbon dioxide and methane (discharged by belching).   Bacteria and protozoa in the rumen also synthesise amino-acids, proteins and vitamins of the B. complex.   This material is pushed peristaltically in a semi-fluid mass into the osmasum.   Here fluid is extracted, and the food passes into the abomasum where characteristic gastric digestion occurs.   An œsophageal groove (not shown) runs from the cardia to the reticulo-omasal orifice and permits the by-pass of milk in young ruminants.   The omasum is also called the psalterium or manyplies.   *Below:* Comparison of structure, mass and position of gastric apparatus in pig and cow.   (Redrawn after various authors.)

food is returned in rounded *boluses* from the rumen to the mouth.   It now undergoes mastication.   When fully masticated it is swallowed again in a semi-fluid condition, and passes along the groove into the reticulum, or over the unmasticated food contained in the latter chamber, to strain between the leaves of the psalterium (omasum) and enter the abomasum. (In some ruminants the psalterium is absent.) In the rumen and reticulum of deer, cattle, sheep, etc., there exists a dense population of protozoa and bacteria which attack and break down the enzyme-resistant cellulose which forms the major part of the diet. Fermentation produces acetic, butyric and propionic acids which are neutralised by sodium bicarbonate secreted in the saliva.

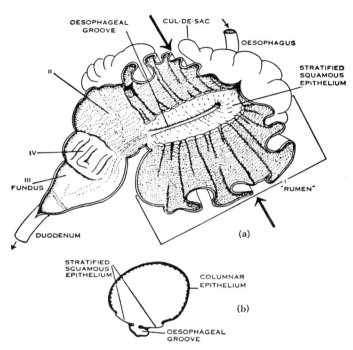

FIG. 640.—**Marsupialia: Digestion.** A ruminant-like digestion has arisen by parallel evolution in the grazing marsupials (*e.g.* the Quokka, *Setonix brachyurus*) although the stomach is not divided into four compartments like that of eutherian mammals (Fig. 639). In *Setonix* the œsophagus leads into a putative rumen (I). An *œsophageal groove*, by-passing the extensive sacculated main fermentative region (of tubular glands), passes through an area of stratified squamous epithelium like that of the rumen, reticulum and omasum of sheep. Region III may be analogous to the abomasum; the functions of II and IV are still unknown. These and other complexities are associated with the possession of a dense bacterial population (demonstrably concerned with fatty acid production) and a very small cæcum. (After Moir, Somers, and Waring.)

Absorption takes place in the rumen, and liberated gases (*e.g.* methane and carbon dioxide) are regurgitated.

Meanwhile, food residues, fluid and micro-organisms descend the alimentary tract. In the omasum fluid is absorbed. In the abomasum, the protozoa and probably the bacteria, are destroyed by secreted hydrochloric acid. The abomasum produces also digestive enzymes, and further absorption takes place in the small intestine. In ruminants the cæcum is relatively small; in Georgian times those of sheep were prepared for use as condoms (Huxley). In ruminants the colon too, is comparatively unimportant ; but in non-ruminating herbivores such as horses both cæcum and colon are enormous. All material passing from ileum to colon enters the cæcum which, in the horse, may be some four feet long and hold as much as eight gallons. In horses the cæcum has a fluid-storing and digestive function. The large colon in horses is principally absorptive in function although some bacterial (but not enzymatic) digestion occurs therein.

In the camels the stomach is not so complicated as in the more typical ruminants. There is no distinct psalterium, and the rumen is devoid of villi. Both the rumen and the reticulum have connected with them a number of pouch-like diverticula, the openings of which are capable of being closed by sphincter muscles. In the Cetacea the stomach is also divided into compartments. In porpoises the œsophagus opens into a spacious paunch, the cardiac compartment of the stomach, which has a smooth, thick, mucous membrane. This is followed by a second median chamber of considerably smaller dimensions. This has a glandular mucous membrane, which is thrown into a number of complex folds. A long and narrow third, or pyloric, compartment follows upon this, terminating in a constricted pyloric aperture. Beyond this the beginning of the small intestine is dilated into a bulb.

A cæcum (see above), situated at the junction of the large and small intestines, is usually present, but varies greatly in extent in the different orders and even families. In general it is much larger in vegetarian than in carnivorous forms. Among the former it is those that have a simple stomach (such as in the rabbit) that have the largest cæcum. The hyraxes (p. 808) differ from the rest of the class in the possession of four definite cæca, of which there is a posterior *pair*, each carrying a *vermiform appendix*. The cæcum is simple in monotremes, absent in the sloths, some Cetacea, and a few Carnivora. It is relatively enormous (about 250 cm. long) in the marsupial Koala, *Phascolarctos* (which eats almost only *Eucalyptus* leaves), next relatively largest in two other marsupials (*Trichosurus*, *Didelphys*), and big in all phalangers (p. 716). In Man and a few other animals (civets, some rodents, monkeys) the distal end of the cæcum has degenerated into an appendix vermiformis. The mere *proportion* of vegetable material ingested is not, however, the only factor governing the size of the cæcum.

The Prototheria resemble reptiles, birds, and the Amphibia, and differ from most mammals in the retention of a cloaca. Into this not only the rectum but the urinary and genital ducts open. In the marsupials a common sphincter muscle surrounds both anal and urinogenital apertures. In the female there is a definite cloaca. In nearly all the Eutheria the apertures are distinct, and separated from one another by a considerable space—the *perinæum*.

Associated with the alimentary canal is the *liver* (Fig. 461, p. 669). It consists of two parts or main divisions (right and left) incompletely separated from one another by a fissure termed the *umbilical*, owing to its marking the position of the fœtal umbilical vein. Typically each of these main divisions is divided by a fissure into two parts, so that *right lateral* and *right central* and *left lateral* and *left central* lobes are clearly distinguishable. When a gall-bladder is present, as is the case in the majority of mammals, it is attached to, or embedded in, the right central lobe. A *portal fissure* crosses the right central lobe near the anterior border. Through this the portal vein (from the hepatic portal vessels arising at the small intestine) and hepatic artery pass into the liver and bile vessels pass out. Hepatic veins drain into the postcaval which lies in contact with, or embedded in, the right lateral lobe near its anterior border. Given off from this lobe, between the postcaval and the portal fissure, is a small *Spigelian* lobe, of varying extent. The term *caudate lobe* is applied to a process of the right lateral lobe (of considerable extent in most mammals), which has the postcaval vein in intimate relation to it. This is often closely applied to the kidney. A gall-bladder is absent in the Cetacea, the perissodactyles, the Hyracoidea, and some rodents. It is present in fruit-bats (*Epomophorus*).

Blood-vascular System.—The blood of mammals is warm, with a temperature always of from 35° to 40° C. except in the Prototheria (p. 690). The *red corpuscles* or *erythrocytes* are non-nucleated : in form they are most usually biconcave discs, always circular in outline, except in the Camelidæ, in which most of them are elliptical. The relative numbers of red cells differ widely among various groups and particularly in relation to altitude and therefore oxygen pressure.

The general statements which have been given with regard to the *heart* of the rabbit (p. 670) hold good for the Mammalia in general. The sinus venosus is never distinct from the right auricle. Of its valves, which are more completely retained in the Edentata than in the other orders, the right gives rise to the Eustachian valve. This is a membranous fold, often fenestrated in the adult, extending from the right wall of the postcaval to the edge of the foramen ovale (*annulus ovalis*). The left becomes merged in the auricular septum, helping to complete the annulus ovalis behind. Each auricle has an auricular appendix. The right auriculo-ventricular aperture has a three-cusped tricuspid valve, and the left a two-cusped bicuspid, or mitral, with chordæ tendineæ and musculi papillares. In all mammals the openings of the pulmonary artery and aorta are provided with three-lobed semilunar valves.

The single aortic arch, situated in all mammals on the left side, varies greatly in the way in which it gives off the main arterial trunks. Sometimes a single large trunk passes forward from the arch of the aorta and gives rise to both carotids and both subclavians. Sometimes there are two main trunks—*right* and *left innominate arteries*—each giving rise to the carotid and subclavian of its own side. Sometimes there is a right innominate giving off right carotid

and right subclavian.   The left carotid and left subclavian come off separately
from the arch of the aorta.   In the rabbit and many other types an innominate
may give origin to the right subclavian and both carotids, with the left subclavian coming off separately.

In monotremes and marsupials, in most pænungulates, and in the Rodentia,
'Insectivora' and Chiroptera, both right and left precavals persist ; in the others
the left aborts, its vestige giving rise to the coronary sinus.   In the monotremes
the openings of all three cavals are provided with valves, only vestiges of which
exist in the other groups.   In the monotremes all the pulmonary veins open by
a common trunk.   In the Metatheria and Eutheria the four veins sometimes
open separately, sometimes the two veins of each side unite to form a single
lateral trunk.   In *Tachyglossus* there is an abdominal vein corresponding to
that of amphibians and reptiles.

The following are some of the principal variations in the structure of the
heart which occur in the different groups of mammals : In the Monotremata
there is a deep fossa representing the fossa ovalis in the auricular septum.
The auriculo-ventricular valves depart from the structure typical of mammals
and approach the corresponding valves in the heart of birds.   In the Marsupiala
the fossa ovalis and annulus ovalis are absent.   In the uterine fœtus of the
kangaroos the auricles communicate by a fissure, but all trace of this becomes
lost before the adult stage is reached.

In the Cetacea, Eustachian and Thebesian valves are both absent.   In
some of the Cetacea the apices of the ventricles are separated by a slight
depression.   In the Sirenia a corresponding cleft is much deeper and wider, the
apex of the heart being distinctly bifid.

In the ungulata, Eustachian and coronary valves are absent ; in some there
occurs a cartilage, or bone (*os cordis*), often double, at the base of the heart.
(This is a 'visceral' bone of the nature of the *os penis* (p. 74), the diaphragmatic
ossification in camels and the mandible and hyoid.)   The Eustachian valve is
absent in most of the Carnivora.   In the Pinnipedia an inter-auricular aperture
often persists in the adult.

The *Mammalian Heart-beat*.—The heart-beat is myogenic in origin even
though the rate and other factors can be controlled by outside influences
(p. 116).   In the human fœtus, rudimentary heart beats begin after about three
week's gestation and perhaps two weeks before nervous elements arise.   (In the
chick embryo the heart rudiment begins rhythmical contractions after about 36
hours, but ganglion cells do not appear until after the sixth day of development.)

In mammals a system of specialised cardiac tissue is responsible for the
initiation and propagation of the heart-beat.   The neuromuscular *sinu-
auricular node* (S.A. node), embedded in the wall of the right auricle with a
special blood supply of its own, is the *pace-maker*.   From this an *excitation wave*
arises and is transmitted in all directions through auricular cardiac muscle and

to the *auriculo-ventricular node* (A.V. node).   Thence the *auriculo-ventricular bundle* (*of His*) and its right and left branches convey the contraction impulse simultaneously to right and left ventricles.   The branches of the A.V. bundle break up into numerous conducting fibres of the *Purkinje network*.   These specialised pathways make possible the synchronised contractions that occur in the healthy animal (see also p. 109).

The cardiac blood supply in mammals comes from right and left *coronary* arteries which arise from the aorta near its origin.   These terminate in an unusually rich distribution of capillaries.   Anastomotic arrangements of three kinds feature in the intrinsic circulation of the heart.

Special peripheral or sub-peripheral anastomoses, too, occur as *climatic thermal adaptations* in many animals. Such creatures can probably swiftly lose heat, or ensure its retention, by means of arterio-venous *retes* at the base of, or within, the various extremities.   Thus, aquatic or other animals that are heavily insulated by fur or fat appear to avoid serious overheating during severe exercise by means of heat-loss through relatively uninsulated limbs or tail into which the blood-flow is reflexly regulated according to the state of the internal and external environments.   Such anastomoses have arisen in whales, sirenians, seals, certain amphibious rodents, and various strictly terestrial animals as well (*e.g.* sloths).

Hibernation.—Many small mammals (*e.g.* bats, rodents) undergo hibernation involving a reduced cardiac and respiratory rate and greatly lowered general metabolism and temperature (cf. æstivation, p. 375).   In true hibernation the animal, deeply hidden in a relatively constant environment, becomes, except for respiration, almost independent of external conditions.   The North American ground squirrel (*Citellus beecheyi*) can be experimentally hibernated irrespective of season.   In winter, animals placed in a temperature of 5·5° C. will hibernate (brain temperature, about 9° C.) within three days.   Animals put into a 7° C. environment during the summer need from 9 to 26 days before entering deep hibernation.   Although during deep hibernation (oral temperature, 5·8° C.) there is an average 90 per cent reduction 'in the amplitude of general brain wave activity', squirrels are nevertheless susceptible to external stimuli.   They can discriminate between sounds.   At brain temperatures of 6·1° C. they vocalise when touched.   Muscle tone, too, is maintained (Strumwasser).

Lymphatic System.—This is very highly developed, ramifying richly throughout the body.   It comprises lymph capillaries, lymph vessels, and adenoid tissue associated therewith in the form of lymph glands (*lymph nodes*).   Those lymphatic vessels (*lacteals*) which occur in the villi of the intestine and absorb the products of fat metabolism, as also the lymphatic vessels from the hindlimbs and lower trunk, pour their lymph into a receptacle on the posterior abdominal wall (*receptaculum chyli*) from which a tube (*thoracic duct*) runs headwards to open into the great veins of the precaval system by a valvular aperture.   Brief accounts of tissue fluid and lymph are given elsewhere (p. 77).

Respiratory System.—The respiratory organs resemble those of rabbits in the general features mentioned (p. 676) but in the Cetacea, the epiglottis and arytenoids are prolonged to form a tube, which extends into the nasal chambers and is embraced by the soft palate.   Thus a continuous passage is formed leading from the nasal chambers to the larynx, and giving rise to the condition of an *intranarial epiglottis*.   In the remaining orders a similar condition occasionally occurs.   The epiglottis is produced upwards into the respiratory division of the pharynx behind the nasal chamber.   In marsupial pouch-young, in which the intranarial condition is complete, it is obviously associated with the passive absorption of the milk while breathing is being carried on continuously through the nostrils (p. 908).   Some Cetacea and Artiodactyla, are exceptional in possessing a *third bronchus*, which passes to the right lung anteriorly to the ordinary bronchus of that side and to the pulmonary artery.   In connection with various parts of the respiratory system there are cavities containing air.   The connection of the tympanic cavity with the pharynx by means of the Eustachian tube has been already mentioned.   Air-sinuses, connected with the nasal chambers, extend into the bones of the skull, especially into the maxillæ and frontals, where they may reach large dimensions, and are known as the *maxillary antra* and *frontal sinuses*.   In the howler monkeys (*Alouatta*, p. 743), pharyngeal air-sacs occur, and the hyoid has become enormously developed (and bell-shaped) to house them.

Nervous System.—The brain of mammals (Fig. 467, p. 678) is distinguished by its relatively large size, and in particular by the large size and complex structure of the *cerebral hemispheres* of the fore-brain.

The cerebral hemispheres of opposite sides are connected together across the middle line in all mammals, except the monotremes and marsupials, by a band of nerve-tissue termed the *corpus callosum*—a structure not present in reptiles and birds.   The hemispheres, in all but certain of the lower and smaller mammals, are not smooth, but marked by a number of grooves (*sulci*) separating winding ridges (*convolutions*).   The *lateral ventricles* in the interior of the hemispheres are of large size and somewhat complex form.

The *optic lobes*, which are relatively small, are divided into four parts, and are hence called the *corpora quadrigemina*.   The *pineal body* is always small. Connecting the lateral parts of the cerebellum, which, in the higher mammals, attains a high degree of development, is a transverse flattened band (*pons Varolii*) crossing the hind-brain on its ventral aspect.

In the monotremes and marsupials (Figs. 641, 642) there is no corpus callosum, while the anterior commissure (*ant. com.*) is of relatively large size, and, unlike the corresponding commissure in lower vertebrates, contains fibres connecting together areas of the non-olfactory regions (*neopallium*) of the hemispheres. The *hippocampi* extend along the whole length of the lateral ventricles. The layer of nerve-cells in each hippocampus gives origin, as in Eutheria, to numerous fibres, which form a layer on the surface, the *alveus*, and become arranged in a band—the *tænia hippocampi*. In the Eutheria, as we have seen in the Rabbit, the tæniæ unite mesially to form the body of the *fornix* (see p. 680). In the monotremes and marsupials, on the other hand, there is no such union ; the fibres of the tænia run towards the foramen of Monro, where they become divided into several sets. Of these one set, con- stituting the great majority of the fibres, pass into the hippocampus of the opposite side, giving rise to a *hippocampal commissure* (*hip. com.*, cf. Figs. 641,

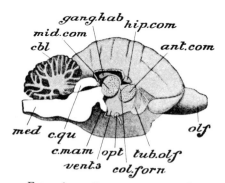

Fig. 641.—*Tachyglossus:* **Brain.** Spiny Ant-eater, sagittal section. *ant. com.* anterior commissure; *cbl.* cerebellum ; *c. mam.* corpus mammillare; *col. forn.* column of the fornix; *c. qu.* corpora quadrigemina; *gang. hab.* habenular gang- lion; *hip. com.* hippocampal commissure; *med.* medulla oblogata; *mid. com.* middle commissure; *olf.* olfactory bulb; *opt.* optic chiasma; *tub. olf.* tuberculum olfactorium; *vent.* 3, third ventricle.

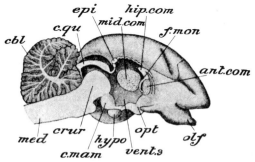

Fig. 642.—*Petrogale:* **Brain.** Rock Wallaby, sagittal section. *ant. com.* anterior commissure; *cbl.* cerebellum ; *c. mam.* corpus mammillare; *c. qu.* corpora quadrigemina; *crur.* crura cerebri; *epi.* epiphysis, with the posterior commissure imme- diately behind; *f. mon.* position of foramen of Monro; *hip. com.* hippocampal commissure, con- sisting here of two layers continuous behind at the splenium, somewhat divergent in front where the septum lucidum extends between them; *hypo.* hypophysis; *med.* medulla oblongata; *mid. com.* middle commissure; *olf.* olfactory bulb; *opt.* optic chiasma; *vent.* 3, third ventricle.

642). The great development of these may lead to its being mistaken for a corpus callosum. The fibres entering into the formation of this commissure correspond, however, not to the fibres of the corpus callosum, which is the commissure of the neo-pallium, but, as proved by their mode of origin, to the fibres of the fornix, and they connect together only the hippocampi, the *fasciæ dentatæ*, or specialised lower borders of the hippocampi, and an area of the hemisphere in front of the anterior commissure (*precommissural area*) : they thus constitute an *olfactory* or *archipallial* commissure, since all these parts belong to the olfactory region or *archipallium* of the hemispheres. In the monotremes (Fig. 643) the hippocampal commissure is only very slightly bent downwards at its posterior extremity. In most marsupials (Fig. 645) it bends sharply round posteriorly and runs forward again, becoming thus folded into two layers, dorsal and ventral, continuous with one another at a posterior bend or *splenium*, similar to the splenium of the corpus callosum. The dorsal layer of the hippocampal commissure becomes almost completely replaced in the

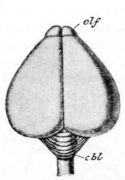

FIG. 643.—*Ornithorhynchus:*
Brain. Platypus, dorsal view (natural size). *cbl.* cerebellum; *olf.* olfactory bulbs.

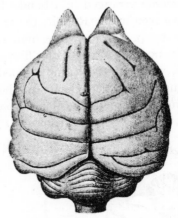

FIG. 644.—*Tachyglossus:*
Brain. Spiny Ant-eater, dorsal view. Natural size.

Eutheria by the fibres of the corpus callosum, and the ventral part persists in the shape of the *psalterium* or *lyra*.

In *Ornithorhynchus* (Fig. 643) the hemispheres are smooth; in *Tachy-*

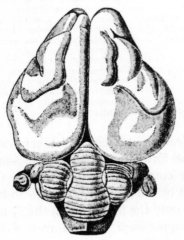

FIG. 645.—*Macropus.* **Brain.** Kangaroo, dorsal view. (After Owen.)

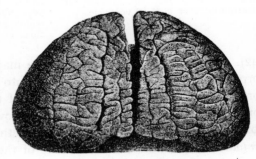

FIG. 646.—**Odontoceti: Brain.** Whale (*Kogia grayi*), dorsal view. (After Haswell.)

glossus (Fig. 644) they are somewhat convoluted. In the lower marsupials there are no convolutions (*Notoryctes*, Koala, phalangers), while in more advanced forms convolutions are numerous, though the sulci are not deep

(*Macropus*, Fig. 645). Among the Eutheria, from the rodents and lower insectivores to the higher primates there is a great range in the development of the fore-brain. In the lower types of mammalian brain the cerebral hemispheres are relatively small, do not over-lap the cerebellum, and have smooth, or nearly smooth, surfaces. In the higher types the relative development of the hemispheres is immense. Their backward extension causes them to cover over all the rest of the brain. The cortex is thrown into numerous complicated convolutions separated by deep sulci (Fig. 646). This development of the cerebral hemispheres reaches its maximum in Man.

Organs of Special Sense.—These have the same general structure and arrangement as in reptiles and birds. Jacobson's organs, however, are developed only in the 'lower' families of mammals (see p. 139). The *olfactory mucosa* is of great extent, owing to the development of the convoluted ethmoturbinal bones over which it extends. In the toothed Cetacea (alone among mammals) the nasal chambers lose their sensory functions—the olfactory nerves being vestigial or absent. *Taste-buds* occur in the tongue and palate.

In essential structure the *eye* of the mammal resembles that of the Vertebrates in general (see p. 139). The sclerotic is composed of condensed fibrous tissue. The pecten of birds and reptiles is absent. In most mammals there are three movable eyelids. Two, the upper and lower, are opaque and usually covered with hair. The third is anterior, translucent, and hairless. This, the *nictitating membrane*, is vestigial in higher types—it can be seen in Man as a small pink fold in the inner canthus of each eye. The secretions of a *lachrymal*, a *Harderian*, and a series of *Meibomian* glands moisten and lubricate the conjunctival surfaces of the eye-ball and its lids. In moles, and certain other burrowing Insectivora and rodents, and in *Notoryctes* among the marsupials, the eyes are imperfectly developed and functionless. In whales the eyes are small, or even vestigial (e.g. *Platanista*), but often elaborately modified. The cornea is extremely flattened and the lens rounded in an almost piscine manner. An unusually thick sclera and specialised *lid muscles*, derived from the four recti, provide protection against pressures. The Harderian glands secrete a fatty material which lubricates the eye-surface. Lachrymal glands and ducts have disappeared.

The *ear* of a mammal is more highly developed than that of other vertebrates, both in respect of the greater complexity of the membranous labyrinth and in the greater development of the accessory parts. A large external *auditory pinna*, supported by cartilage, is almost invariably present, except in the Monotremata, Cetacea, and Sirenia. This is a widely open funnel, of a variety of shapes in different groups. It assists the collection of sound waves. By the action of a system of muscles it is usually capable of being turned about in different directions. Enclosed by its basal part is the opening of the *external auditory passage* (Fig. 93, p. 144). This, the length of which varies, leads inwards to the *tympanic membrane*, which separates it from the cavity of the middle ear (*tympanic cavity*).   The wall of the external auditory passage is sometimes entirely membranous or cartilaginous, but sometimes in part osseous.   In *Tachyglossus* it is strengthened by a series of incomplete rings of cartilage.   The tympanic cavity, enclosed by the periotic and tympanic bones, communicates with the upper or respiratory division of the pharynx by a longer or shorter tubular passage (*Eustachian tube*).   On its inner wall are the *fenestra ovalis* and *rotunda*, and across its cavity, from the tympanic membrane to the fenestra ovalis, runs the chain of auditory ossicles—the *malleus* (hammer), the *incus* (anvil) and the *stapes* (stirrup).   These, the smallest bones in the body, vary somewhat in form in different mammals. The stapes is usually perforated by a considerable foramen and a minute artery, as in the rabbit, but, in the monotremes, certain marsupials, and *Manis* among the Pholidota, it approximates more towards the rod-like shape of the columella auris of amphibians, reptiles, and birds.   The *membranous labyrinth* of the internal ear of a mammal is characterised by the special development of the *cochlea* which (except in the monotremes) is spirally coiled to a greater or less extent.   In cetaceans the entrance to the long meatus (which often contains a substantial wax plug) is very small.   The tympanic membrane is thickened and the auditory ossicles are fused into a single rigid column connecting tympanum and periotic.   The tympanic bulla is held to the periotic by a pair of thin, flattened bones.   The petrosal does not unite with the skull. The cochlea is not truly spiral, making but one and a half turns.

Endocrine Organs.—See pp. 147–154, 889, 905.

Urinogenital System.—The *kidneys* of mammals are compact organs of oval shape.   On the inner side is a slit or *hilum*, by which vessels and ducts enter or leave the interior (Fig. 99, p. 154).   The substance of the kidney consists of two distinctly marked portions—a central portion or *medulla*, and an outer part or *cortex*.   The latter is marked by numerous minute tubules, each of which ends in an indented expansion (*Bowman's capsule*).   Into this enters an arteriole which leads to a tiny canalicular knot (*glomerulus*) of capillaries, the walls of which are one cell thick.   As the blood flows through this tuft of vessels, fluid and solutions are transferred through its walls and through the capsule into a *proximal convoluted tubule* where vital glucose, salts and fluid are selectively reabsorbed.   The concentrated urine now flows into the *descending loop of Henle*, the first section of a hairpin-shaped structure of uncertain function. The succeeding *ascending loop* leads into a *distal convoluted* tubule from which, possibly, more fluid and dissolved substances may be taken into the tissue spaces and back into circulation.   In any case, the residual urea, sodium chloride, potassium, uric acid, and traces of a considerable number of other substances flow down a final, wider *collecting tubule* (made up from several renal units) towards the centre of the kidney (Fig. 100, p. 155).   In *Procavia*

(p. 808), which inhabits hot, rocky areas, there exists a mechanism that allows such a high degree of fluid retention that the urine is voided in viscid streaks. In some mammals (cf. Amphibia, p. 451) the antidiuretic hormone (from the pars neuralis, p. 151) operates by increasing the tubule reabsorption of water.

The numerous apertures of the collecting tubules open into the *pelvis* of the ureter. They are situated on the summits of papillæ, which are the apices of a series of pyramidal masses into which, in most cases, the substance of the kidney is completely divided. In many mammals, however, there is no such division of the kidney substance, and all the ducts open on the surface of a single papilla. In others again (ox, bears, seals, Cetacea) the division is carried so far that the kidney is divided externally into a number of distinctly separated lobules. Each kidney possesses a duct (*ureter*) which leads, in all the Theria, into a large median sac, the *urinary bladder*. This is situated in the posterior or pelvic part of the cavity of the abdomen. From this a median passage, the urinogenital passage or *urethra* (into which in the male the *vasa deferentia* open) leads to the exterior. Only in the monotremes do the two ureters and the bladder all have separate openings into the urinogenital division of the cloaca.

The *testes* only exceptionally retain their original position in the abdominal cavity (as in cetaceans, elephants, Hyracoidea, some Lipotyphla (p. 726), Macroscelididæ (p. 731)). In the majority of mammals they descend the *inguinal canal* (in the posterior abdominal wall) to lie in the *perinæum* (space between the urinogenital and anal apertures) or to be received into a pendulous pouch of skin, sometimes double—the *scrotum*.

The testes are oval bodies composed essentially of three elements: 1. a fibrous connective tissue *tunica albuginea*; 2. *seminiferous tubules*, and 3. aggregated *Leydig* or *interstitial cells* which secrete the male sex hormone. The two last-named components are under the influence of gonadotrophic hormones from the anterior pituitary gland (p. 150). The spermatozoa from each testis are discharged from the convoluted seminiferous tubules into a plexiform *rete testis* whence they migrate into the proximal *head* and next the *tail* of the convoluted *epididymis*. From here they pass to the *vas deferens*, a narrow canal which enters the abdomen. Each vas now takes a curved course, ascending in Man (for example) above the level of the bladder. Passing downward, the vas expands into an *ampulla* and, additionally, gives off a complicated glandular *seminal vesicle*. This pair of structures, prominent in the prostate region, do not, in fact, store seminal fluid: they produce fructose, which is apparently utilised by the descending spermatozoa. (The usual sites of sperm-storage are the epididymides and the ampullæ.) Paired *ejaculatory ducts* allow access of spermatozoa into the median unpaired urethra and penis (see below).

A small diverticulum of the proximal part of the urethra (the *uterus masculinus*) may be the rudiment of the Müllerian duct (p. 159). Surrounding this part of the urethra is the large alveolar *prostate gland* (in close association with the ejaculatory ducts) which is under both nervous and endocrine (sex hormone) control. Prostatic secretion, together with that of a pair of small racemose *Cowper's* or *bulbo-urethral glands* is added to the spermatozoa. The ducts of the latter glands open into the urethra near the base of the penis.

The *penis*, present in all male mammals, varies greatly in form but is essentially composed internally of sinusoidal erectile tissue arranged in longitudinal columns. In general, two such columns lie in close apposition and form the dorsal *corpora cavernosa penis* which is attached proximally to the ischia (except in monotremes, marsupials, and some edentates). A third column of erectile tissue, the *corpus spongiosum* or *corpus cavernosum urethræ*, is perforated by the urethra. It lies below and is often dilated at its extremity to form the *glans*. In some species there develops an osseous element, the *os penis* (*os priapi*), or *baculum*, in the fibrous septum between the parallel columns of the corpora cavernosa. This 'visceral' bone is widespread among rodents, carnivores, bats, and primates except Man (p. 75), but it does not occur in whales, as is often stated. Its homologue may occur in the clitoris where this structure is well-developed (e.g. *Lemur*, Fig. 647).

FIG. 647.—*Lemur*: **Female external genitalia.** (After Osman Hill.)

During sexual excitement, nerve impulses cause the dilation of the arterioles and capillaries from which the above-mentioned sinuses are filled. At the same time, the plain muscle of each sinus wall is relaxed and there is a contraction of the circular muscles that regulate outflow. Thus, blood flow is impeded, resulting in turgidity and erection. Many species of several mammalian orders (e.g. Carnivora) possess horny penile spines or *copulatory grapples*, and analogous structures have arisen in the elasmobranch fishes and Reptilia as well (pp. 256, 550).

The *ovaries* are compressed, oval bodies which retain their primary position in the abdomen or pass backwards into its posterior (pelvic) region. Each organ is attached at its *hilus* to the *suspensory ligaments* of the uterus. In the monotremes, large *Graafian follicles* project on the surface of the ovary. In all groups the ovary is wholly, or at least partly, ensheathed in specialised peritoneum formed of cubical cells—the *germinal epithelium*. In the mare (*Equus*) this epithelium is restricted to an *ovulation fossa* into which ovulation inevitably occurs. Within, the ovary is composed of chiefly fibrous connective tissue *ovarian stroma*, in which lie the oocytes enclosed in the Graafian follicles in various stages of maturation and atresia, and, after ovulation, endocrine *corpora lutea* (see p. 152). After its regression, each *corpus luteum* persists as a scar-like *corpus albicans*.

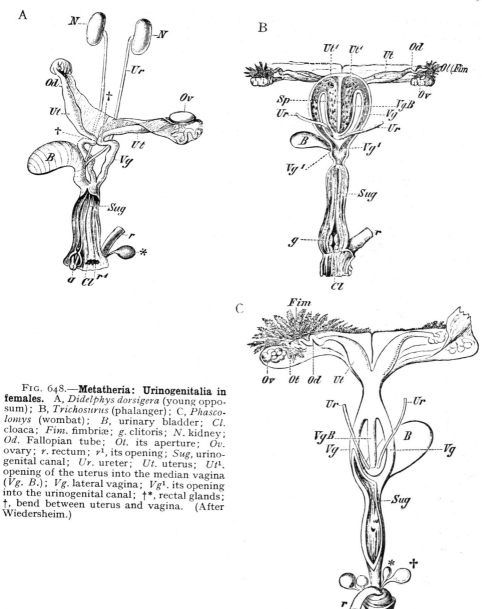

FIG. 648.—**Metatheria: Urinogenitalia in females.** A, *Didelphys dorsigera* (young opposum); B, *Trichosurus* (phalanger); C, *Phascolomys* (wombat); *B*, urinary bladder; *Cl.* cloaca; *Fim.* fimbriæ; *g.* clitoris; *N.* kidney; *Od.* Fallopian tube; *Ot.* its aperture; *Ov.* ovary; *r.* rectum; *r¹*, its opening; *Sug*, urinogenital canal; *Ur.* ureter; *Ut.* uterus; *Ut¹.* opening of the uterus into the median vagina (*Vg. B.*); *Vg.* lateral vagina; *Vg¹.* its opening into the urinogenital canal; †*, rectal glands; †, bend between uterus and vagina. (After Wiedersheim.)

The ciliated *oviducts* usually have dilated funnel-like abdominal openings, the edges of which are generally fimbriated and arranged in a way that allows direct access of ova from bursting follicles into the adjacent oviducal funnel. In some mammals (e.g. *Pteropus*), the ovaries are almost completely *encapsulated* by which means the ovum is extruded into a bursa and is thus compelled to enter the conjoined oviduct. In some bats (Microchiroptera), but not the megachiropteran *Pteropus*, only one ovary is functional.

In monotremes the two oviducts are distinct throughout their length, and open separately into an *urinogenital sinus*. In nearly all mammals, however,

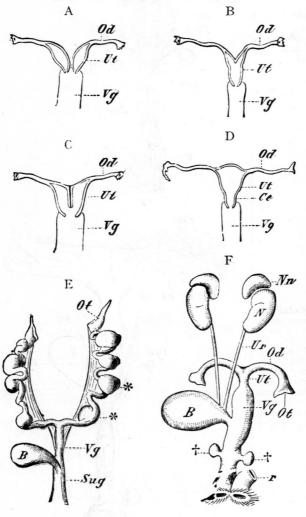

FIG. 649.—**Eutheria. Urinogenitalia in females.** A, B, C, D, illustrate the different degrees of coalescence of the oviducts. *A*, two distinct uteri. *B*, bicornuate uterus. *C*, uterus with a median partition. *D*, complete coalescence. *E*, female reproductive organs of one of the *Mustelina* with embryos (**) in the uterus. *F*, female reproductive organs of the Hedgehog. *B*, urinary bladder; *Ce*. cervix uteri (neck of uterus); *N*, *Nn*, kidneys and adrenal bodies; *Od*. Fallopian tube; *Ot*. ostium tubæ (abdominal opening of Fallopian tube); *r*. rectum; *Sug*. urinogenital canal; *Ur*. ureter; *Ut*. uterus; *Vg*. vagina; ††, accessory glands. (After Wiedersheim.)

more or less coalescence takes place. In marsupials this coalescence is confined to the proximal parts of the vagina. In opossums (Fig. 648) the two oviducts are merely in close apposition at one point behind the uteri, and there is no actual coalescence. In the rest of the marsupials (B, C) the anterior portions of the oviduct in the region (vagina) posterior to the uteri unite to form a median chamber which may send backwards a median diverticulum (*median vagina*, *Vg.*, *B*), and in this way communicate behind with the urinogenital passage. In the Eutheria there is a single median *vagina* (Fig. 649, *Vg.*) formed by the union of the posterior parts of the two oviducts. In some cases the two uteri (*A. ut.*) remain distinct ; in others their posterior portions coalesce (B, C), the anterior parts remaining separate, so that there is formed a median *corpus uteri* with two horns or *cornua*. In Primates and some of the Edentata the

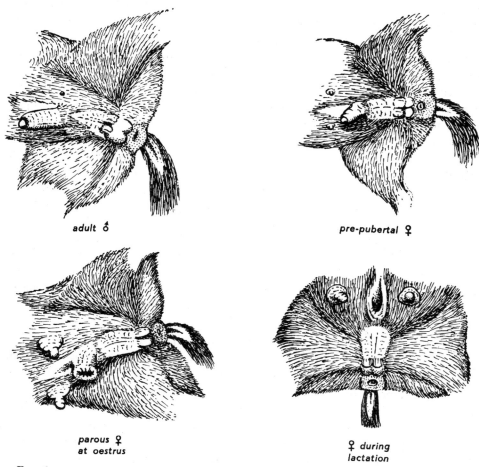

adult ♂

pre-pubertal ♀

parous ♀
at oestrus

♀ during
lactation

Fɪɢ. 650.—*Crocuta:* **External genitalia.** The aberrations depicted occur in the Spotted species (*C. crocuta*) but not in other Hyænidæ. (Redrawn after Harrison Matthews.)

coalescence goes still further. In these there is an undivided uterus (D) in addition to an undivided vagina. The only parts of the oviducts which remain distinct from one another are the narrow anterior parts or Fallopian tubes.

The capacious urinogenital sinus of monotremes extends from the cloaca anterior to the entire length of the bladder (Fig. 487, p. 700). The paired Müllerian ducts enter separately the extreme anterior end of the chamber; the ureters pierce the dorsal wall a little closer to the cloacal aperture. The bladder opens independently into the ventral surface of the urinogenital sinus, being unconnected with the ureters.

In all mammals there is, in the *vestibule* or *urinogenital passage* (through which the vagina communicates with the exterior by the aperture of the *vulva*) a small erectile body—the *clitoris*—the homologue of the penis. This is only sometimes perforated by the urethral canal (p. 701). In many mammals, including Man, the vagina is first almost enclosed by the *hymen*, a mucosal fold with a central circular or elliptical aperture. Its function may be to prevent the reflux of urine into the genital tract of the juvenile.

Among the eutherians the external female genitalia of the Spotted Hyæna (*Crocuta crocuta*) and at least one mole (i.e. *Talpa europea*) are not developed in the usual way although the internal elements fall into the general pattern. The external peculiarities of the female Spotted Hyæna gave rise to the ancient belief that the species changed sex every year. Both sexes of the Spotted (but not of other species of) hyæna are externally very similar and male-like (Fig. 650) : in both the nipples are surrounded by areolæ which in the mature but non-parous female are practically indistinguishable from those of the male. Both sexes possess an almost identical *phallus* and their external similarity is further emphasised by posterior perineal swellings in the female resembling the male scrotal prominences. Although slightly smaller in the female, the *glans* and *prepuce* in both sexes are almost identical. The *meatus* is similar in position, and is the only external means of communication possessed by bladder and urethra, uterus, and vagina (Fig. 651). In both sexes the glans is armed with horny spines (*copulatory grapples*) such as occur in several orders of mammals.

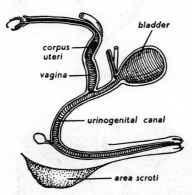

FIG. 651.—*Crocuta:* **Internal genitalia.** (Redrawn after Wood Jones.)

At the approach of the breeding season the external meatus of the female enlarges from a slit 2 mm. long to a longitudinal opening some 15 mm. in the ventral surface of the phallus. Insemination and parturition occur through this genito-urinary aperture. Although it has been often claimed that the urogenital canal extends right to the *os uteri* (and that therefore the typical eutherian vagina is absent), Matthews has shown that a vagina does occur as a slightly expanded part of the tract a little less than half-way down the utero-vaginal canal. Its entrance is guarded by a hymeneal fold. Thus, the reproductive tract in the Spotted Hyæna retains the original embryonic connection with the urogenital sinus which in turn finds outlet through the female phallus. Copulation occurs in essentially the position assumed by other pronograde mammals, and according to Grimpe 'amid loud laughter, which is characteristic of hyænas' (cited by Wood Jones).

In the mole, *Talpa europea*, both sexes are externally male-like during their first year. The female phallus is only slightly smaller than, and differently shaped from, that of the male. Through this phallus discharges the urinary canal from the bladder. There is no external genital opening. The single wide internal uterovaginal chamber ends blindly, showing no sign of its original, bilateral embyronic structure or of the former junction of the Müllerian ducts with the urinary tract. During the first œstrus (second season after birth) an amazingly rapid transformation occurs in the female genitalia. The perineum becomes hyperæmic and a transverse vulval orifice appears immediately posterior to the base of the phallus. By virtue of its formation this is necessarily without labia. The internal genital tract shows even more profound seasonal modification. There develops a vulvovaginal canal, lined with mucosa, which joins the external orifice and completes the formation of a reproductive tract that is still, however, in no way connected with the urinary tract. After parturition the vulval apparatus regresses, loses its connection with the uterovaginal canal and disappears, sometimes without an obvious scar. The process is repeated seasonally.

Remarkable temporary (or in some species permanent) genital changes take place also during the breeding season of marsupials. During early eutherian development the ureteric elements pass towards the kidneys lateral to the Müllerian ducts which will give rise to the Fallopian tubes. These ducts remain separate anteriorly, but unite posteriorly to form a median *corpus uteri* to communicate with the vagina. In the Metatheria, on the other hand, the presumptive ureters pass *between* the genital elements. This prevents a median fusion into a single corpus. As development proceeds, the primitive marsupials come to possess twin uteri, and corresponding lateral vaginæ opening separately into the urogenital sinus and likewise externally at the cloacal aperture. The penis, too, is correspondingly bifid at its termination.

Before pregnancy in some marsupials a remarkable and temporary sagging occurs in the anterior parts of the female ducts so that each forms a vaginal *cul-de-sac* between and below the ureters where they enter the bladder.

After high tubal fertilisation the embryos descend into the small twin uteri. Here they establish a brief placental connection, but soon migrate posteriorly, not down the lateral ducts, but into the median *cul-de-sacs*. The thin double septum separating these pouches disintegrates and the young are entrapped in a posteriorly closed, greatly dilated chamber distended below the ureters.

An extraordinary development now occurs. The posterior point of the elongated brood-chamber ruptures, extravasation of blood occurs and a birth passage forms through the tissues between chamber and median urinogenital sinus. Through this temporary corridor the minute embryos escape after an extremely short gestation period. The membranes and cords remain in the passage and are incorporated with the scar tissue on the site of the former canal. The temporary passage has no epithelium and little definite structure ; the rent that formed it heals rapidly so that in *Dasyurus* (for example) the rupture is repaired within two days of parturition (Hill). In some marsupials (e.g. *Potorous*, a genus of rat-kangaroos) parturition is by way of the lateral vaginæ.

In more progressive marsupials the phenomenon differs considerably. The arboreal phalanger, *Trichosurus*, has the *cul-de-sacs* already present in the 22 mm. embryo and in the adult these are separated by only a fragile septum which ruptures early in pregnancy and remains permanently open during successive seasons. Nevertheless, there still remains to be formed the temporary median birth-passage during each parturition. In some of the Macropodidæ the median brood chamber and birth canal have become permanent structures, the latter with a muscular wall and epithelial lining, but still not permanently joining the urinogenital sinus. Others of the same family appear to have gone a step further and retain the final aperture as a permanent feature. Yet even in these forms (as far as is known) the sperms still ascend the original lateral ducts.

The spermatozoa of most mammals seem to be extremely short-lived (see below) but in some temperate zone Microchiroptera (members of the genera *Myotis, Rhinolophus*) there has been evolved a mechanism for sperm preservation in the female tract after copulation in late summer or autumn until the following spring, when ovulation and fertilisation occur. In addition to spermatozoa, the male *Myotis* provides also a considerable amount of mucus from accessory sexual (probably urethral) glands, and this fills and dilates the vagina as a congealed, sperm-containing plug—the *bouchon vaginal*. The encapsulated spermatozoa are freed and make their way to the uterus in time for a post-winter fertilisation. In some species the *bouchon* still occludes the vagina after pregnancy has begun and luteinisation is completed.

Breeding Seasons.—Most mammals, like other vertebrates, breed at more or less specific times of the year although many (*e.g.* Man, Baboon, Giraffe, elephants) have no particular mating season. Those which reproduce at regular periodic intervals have evolved by natural selection a mechanism which is influenced by naturally recurring stimuli and inhibitors (*e.g.* changes in day-length, temperature, food-supply, psychical factors, etc.) and such influences, operating via the exteroceptors, central nervous system and anterior pituitary in conjunction with an internal rhythm of reproduction, ensure that, in general, the copulation will occur at a period appropriate for the launching of the young at the time of year most propitious for their survival.

The females undergo an *œstrus cycle*. *Anœstrus*, a period of sexual quiescence, is succeeded by *proœstrus* during which there is a progressive increase in the production of œstrogen, endometrial proliferation and, in some species uterine bleeding superficially like that of menstruation (see below). Next comes *œstrus*, or *heat*, involving further uterine changes, a readiness to mate, and usually ovulation. Immediately after ovulation, the corpus luteum develops. Its *progesterone* operates synergistically with œstrogen, further preparing the endometrium for the reception of the blastocyst and pregnancy. If fertilisation does not occur, there may be a progesterone-induced *pseudo-pregnancy* during which non-pregnant females often exhibit maternal behaviour. In any case, œstrus will be ultimately followed by some degree of endometrial degeneration and a period of quiescence and rehabilitation varying in duration among different species.

Monœstrus animals (*e.g.* dog, *Dasyurus*, Koala, bigger kangaroos) have a single cycle each sexual season, *polyœstrus* animals (*e.g.* sheep, rat, goat, rat-kangaroos, p. 719) may have several. In polyœstrus groups a period of *diœstrus* intervenes between cycles. Although, in general, parturition is followed by a *lactation anœstrus* (during which ovulation and conception rarely occur), some mammals undergo immediately, or almost so, a *post-partum œstrus* and copulation (*e.g.* the wallaby, *Setonix*, seals and many rodents). In the Common Hare (*Lepus europæus*) an astonishing *pre-partum ovulation* occurs, and the female may conceive again before delivery and thus achieve *super-fœtation*.

Attempts to relate precisely the sexual rhythm of the Primates that undergo true menstruation with the œstrous cycle in other animals have not been conspicuously successful. True menstruation is the post-ovulatory destruction and discharge of pseudopregnant endometrium and is widely spread only in 'catarrhines' (p. 743), but occurs in certain other Primates and perhaps in *Elephantulus*, the African elephant-shrew. It is not impossible that true menstruation may occur in several other groups but it must be remembered that different types of uterine hæmorrhage may occur (*e.g.* cow, bitch, and intermenstrual hæmorrhage in women). There is, incidentally, no evidence of the relatively early cessation of female reproductive activity (i.e. *menopause*) in any animal other than Man.

In most, but not all (p. 896) mammals the period at which fertilisation can take place is strictly limited. Thus in the rabbit, in which induced ovulation occurs ten hours after copulation (p. 898) ova remain fertile for only six hours, though they live for much longer. In women ovulation usually occurs between the twelfth and fourteenth day of the cycle : the basis of the possibly 'safe period' which falls into about the week immediately before menstruation. The life of spermatozoa in the female tract of most mammals is brief (*e.g.* from seventeen to forty hours in most species investigated, including Man, but up to seven days in horses).

Development and Associated Phenomena.—The ova of mammals, like those of vertebrates in general, are developed from germinal epithelium. Each of these, surrounded by smaller unmodified cells of the epithelium, sinks into the stroma of the ovary, in which it becomes embedded, the small cells forming a *Graafian follicle* which encloses it. Soon spaces filled with fluid appear among the follicle cells, and these eventually coalesce to form a single cavity containing *liquor folliculi* of high œstrogen content. This cavity, which in some mammals is crossed by strings of cells, separates an outer layer of the follicle cells (the *membrana granulosa*) from the mass (*cumulus proligerus*) surrounding the ovum, except on one side where they coalesce. A basement membrane is formed externally to the follicle cells, and the stroma around this becomes vascular, and forms a two-layered investment for the follicle. The cells immediately surrounding the ovum become arranged as a definite layer of cylindrical cells—the *corona radiata*. A thick membrane, the *zona radiata*, perforated by numerous radially arranged pores, into which project processes from the cells of the corona, invests the ovum. Beneath this there is a delicate vitelline membrane. In marsupials the ovum contains yolk which is soon extruded. The ovum of placental mammals is devoid of yolk.

As the ovum approaches maturity the *liquor folliculi* in the cavity of the follicle increases in quantity and œstrogen content. The follicle becomes greatly distended. The follicle has meanwhile approached the surface of the ovary, on which it comes to project as a rounded prominence. Eventually the middle region of the projecting part of the wall of the follicle thins out and ruptures, setting free the ovum, which passes into the body cavity and then to the Fallopian tube.

Ovulation may be *spontaneous* or *induced*. In the great majority of mammals (including Man) it occurs as a spontaneous event in the œstrous cycle (p. 896), or it may be induced by sexual excitement, or more usually, copulation (Mink, Rabbit, Ferret, Domestic Cat, *Pteropus*, etc.). Some animals that normally ovulate after copulation may sometimes do so spontaneously.

In a relatively few mammals endometrial implantation of the blastocyst may be delayed for as long as four months. Like ovovivipary (p. 549) delayed implantation is adaptive and of little phylogenetic significance. Thus, it has arisen in widely unrelated animals (*e.g.* Nine-banded Armadillo, Roe Deer, the wallaby *Setonix*, and in Carnivora such as seals, bears, Mink, Weasel, badgers, Stoat). Although delayed implantation occurs in Roe Deer (*Capreolus capreolus*) and Mink (*Mustela vison*), it is unknown in Red Deer (*Cervus elaphus*) and Ferret (*Mustela furo*). In the Roe Deer delayed implantation allows individuals to mate during July and August and yet delay parturition until after the winter and so drop their young in spring pastures after a prolonged interuterine period of between nine and eleven months. Spring mating individuals, on the other hand, parturate after only five months.

Transuterine migration occurs in numerous species (rodents, Primates, Chiroptera, Carnivora, horse, cow.) This involves the implantation on the opposite side (or even cornu) of the uterus from the tube along which the blastocyst passed.

Multiple pregnancy represents the primitive mammalian condition. This has been abandoned, however, in many mammals, including particularly flying or arboreal forms (*e.g.* Primates). The restriction of the number of ova extruded during each œstrous cycle is reflected in the reduction of functional mammary glands (p. 848) and often in the evolution of a simple, fore-shortened uterus. This principle is well shown in Man and in many other animals. A fascinating situation in this respect is presented by some, but not all, armadillos. In the genus *Dasypus* there has arisen an extraordinary secondary specialisation in the production of identical quadruplets in *Dasypus novemcincta* and eight or even twelve monovular young in *D. hybrida*. Not all of such fœtuses (the nidation of which is maintained by a single corpus luteum) survive gestation. *D. hybrida* commonly produces from seven to twelve young, however, and these must be maintained by four mammary glands—one inguinal, and one pectoral pair. The prolonged period of gestation (eighteen weeks in *D. novemcincta*) probably reduces the dependence of the neonatal young (which are protected in burrows) on lactation. It is probably only in *Homo*, *Bos*, and *Dasypus* that identical (*i.e. monovular*) twinning has been shown unequivocally to occur.

The unfertilised mammalian *ovarian* ovum may naturally undergo several parthenogenetic divisions (rodents, dog, one record in Man): ova perhaps possess an intrinsic capacity to divide. Experimental parthenogenesis has been achieved in rabbits (Pincus).

Most of the differences between the early stages of development of a higher mammal (Fig. 652) and those of a reptile or bird are correlated with the absence of food yolk. One of the most striking of these is in the mode of cleavage. In the case of the large ovum of birds, as we have seen, the segmentation is of the incomplete or *meroblastic* type, being confined to a small disc of protoplasm—the *germinal disc* on one side of the ovum. In the mammals, except in the monotremes, cleavage is complete or *holoblastic*, the entire ovum taking part in the process of segmentation. The cleavage is nearly or quite regular, the cells into which the ovum divides being of equal, or approximately equal, size. The result, in the Eutheria, is the formation of a sphere of cells, which soon become distinguishable into an outer layer the *trophoblast*, and the *inner cell-mass* or *embryonal knot*. In the marsupials, so far as known, the stage of a solid cellular sphere or morula does not occur. A central cavity is present from the outset. In the Eutheria, by imbibition of liquid, a cavity, which is formed in the interior of the sphere, increases rapidly in size. The stage now reached is called the *blastodermic vesicle*. During the growth in size of the internal cavity the central mass of cells remains in contact with one side only of the trophoblast, where it spreads out as a stratum several cells deep. From it are derived the embryonal ectoderm and the entire endoderm of the vesicle.

The outer layer is apparently the equivalent of the extra-embryonal ectoderm of the bird and reptile, and has been termed the *trophoblast* or *trophoblastic ectoderm*, because of the part which it plays in the nutrition of the fœtus. Immediately beneath it, throughout its extent, a thin layer of flattened cells appears—the *peripheral endoderm*. This is continuous with a similar layer formed on the inner surface of the embryonic cell-mass—the *embryonic endo-*

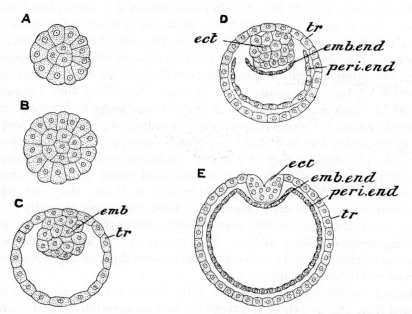

FIG. 652.—**Eutheria: Development.** Sections of the embryo at successive stages in the segmentation and formation of the layers. *A* and *B*, formation of enclosing layer (trophoblast) and inner cell-mass destined to give rise to the embryo; *C*, blastodermic vesicle with embryonic cell-mass (*emb.*) separated from trophoblast (*tr.*) except on one side; *D*, blastodermic vesicle in which peripheral and embryonic portions of endoderm have become established: the break here represented on each side between the two does not occur. *E*, stage in which the embryonic ectoderm has broken through the trophoblast and become joined to it peripherally.

derm—and is formed by outgrowth from it. The rest of the cell-mass gives rise to the *embryonic ectoderm*. The part of the trophoblast lying over this embryonic ectoderm, known as the *covering layer* or *Rauber's layer*, has a widely different fate in different Eutheria : it may thin out and disappear.

A *primitive knot* and *embryonic shield* are formed as in reptiles. The primitive knot has simply the appearance of the somewhat enlarged anterior extremity of a *primitive streak* (Fig. 653, *pr.*) which is developed very much in the same way as in the bird. Its formation is due to the same cause as in the bird, *viz.* active proliferation of cells leading to the development of the beginnings of the mesoderm. A dark median streak, the *head-process*, appears in front of the primitive knot, and in some mammals there is an invagination on the surface of the latter leading to the formation of a neurenteric canal and of a notochordal canal which gives rise to the rudiment of the posterior part of the notochord. In the region of the anterior part of the primitive streak, the primitive knot and the head-process, the mesoderm coalesces with the endoderm ; but there does not appear to be any breaking through into the underlying space such as occurs in reptiles (p. 551). A *medullary groove* (*rf*) and *canal* are formed in front of the primitive streak, and a row of mesodermal somites (Fig. 654) make their appearance on each side of the former. The embryo becomes folded off from the blastoderm as in the bird, and at length the body of the young mammal is constricted off from the 'yolk-sac' so that, ultimately, the two come to be connected only by a narrow yolk-stalk (Figs. 655, 656): the yolk-sac is a thin-walled sac containing a coagulable fluid in place of yolk. A *vascular area* early becomes established around the embryo on the wall of the yolk-sac.

The most important of the points of difference between a mammal and a bird, as regards the latter part of the history of the development, are connected with the fate of the *fœtal membranes*. The amnion is in many mammals developed in the same way as in the bird, *i.e.* by the formation of a system of folds of

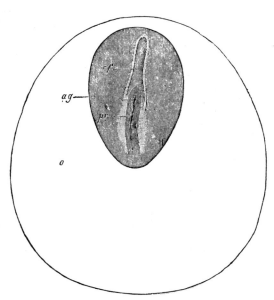

Fig. 653.—**Eutheria: Development.** Embryonic area of seven days' embryo Rabbit. *ag.* embryonic area; *o.* place of future vascular area; *pr.* primitive streak; *rf.* medullary groove. (From Balfour, after Kölliker.)

the extra-embryonal somatopleure which arise from the blastoderm around the embryo, and grow upwards and inwards, eventually meeting in the middle over the body of the embryo, and uniting in such a way as to form two layers. Of the two layers thus formed the outer, consisting of trophoblastic ectoderm and somatic mesoderm, simply constitutes a part of the extra-embryonic somatopleure which forms a complete investment for the entire ovum, and is known as the *chorion* (Fig. 655, *2* and *3*). In the account of the development of the bird it has been referred to as the *false amnion* or *serous membrane*. The inner layer or true amnion, as in the bird, forms the wall of the *amniotic cavity* (*4* and *5, ah.*) which becomes tensely filled with fluid (the *liquor amnii*) over the body of the embryo. This serves the purpose of protecting the delicate embryo from the effects of shocks. As in the case of the bird, the folds giving rise to the amnion and serous membrane may consist from the first (except the head-fold, which, being formed from the pro-amnion, consists solely of ectoderm and endoderm) of somatic mesoderm as well as ectoderm (trophoblast : or mesoderm may extend into them later). Thus, either from the first, or as a result of outgrowth which takes place subsequently, the chorion contains mesoderm as well as ectoderm. The ectodermal cells—

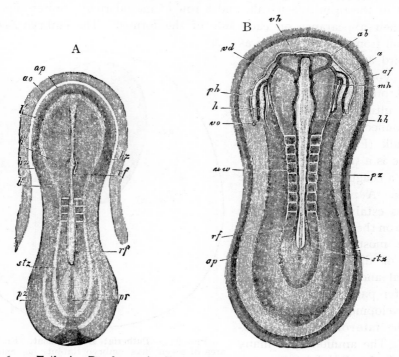

FIG. 654.—**Eutheria: Development.** Embryo Rabbit, of about nine days, from the dorsal side. *a.* aorta; *ab.* optic vesicle; *af.* fold of amnion; *ao.* area opaca; *ap.* area pellucida; *h., hz.* heart; *h', h'.* medullary plate in the region of the future fore-brain; *h''.* medullary plate in the region of the future mid-brain; *hh* and *hh'''.* hind-brain; *mh.* mid-brain; *ph.* pericardial section of body cavity; *pr.* primitive streak; *pz.* lateral zone; *rf.* medullary groove; *uw.* somites; *stz.* vertebral zone; *vd.* pharnyx; *vo.* vitelline vein. (From Balfour, after Kölliker.)

trophoblast cells—of the chorion may enter into close relationship with the mucous membrane of the wall of the uterus, and send out processes or *primary villi* (Fig. 656, *EK*) by means of which the ovum becomes intimately attached, and by means of which perhaps nourishment is absorbed.

In certain mammals the history of the amnion is very different from that above described. In the hedgehogs and Man, for example, a cavity appears in the ectoderm of the embryonic area. This is destined to give rise to the cavity of the amnion. The ectoderm, which forms its roof, is entirely tropho-blastic or chorionic ; that which forms its floor is partly destined to become amniotic ectoderm, partly embryonal ectoderm. After the mesoderm has begun to become differentiated, the margins of the amniotic part of this ectodermal floor begin to grow upwards, giving rise to a layer which extends over the roof on the inner side of the chorionic ectoderm and eventually forms a complete layer—the ectodermal layer of the amnion.

FIG. 655.—**Eutheria: Fœtal membranes.** Stages in formation. In 1, 2, 3, 4 the embryo is represented in longitudinal section. 1, Embryo with zona pellucida, blastodermic vesicle, and embryonic area; 2, embryo with commencing formation of yolk-sac and amnion; 3, embryo with amnion about to close; 4, embryo with villous chorion, larger allantois, and mouth and anus; 5, embryo in which the mesoderm of the allantois has extended round the inner surface of the chorion and united with it to form the fœtal part of the placenta; the cavity of the allantois is aborted. *a.* ectoderm of embryo; *a'.* ectoderm of non-embryonic part of the blastodermic vesicle; *ah.* amniotic cavity; *al.* allantois; *am.* amnion; *ch.* fœtal part of placenta; *chz.* placental villi; *d.* in 1 zona radiata, in 2 and 3 chorion; *d'.* processes of zona radiata and chorion; *dd.* embryonic endoderm; *df.* area vasculosa; *dg.* stalk of umbilical vesicle; *ds.* cavity of umbilical vesicle; *e.* embryo; *hh.* pericardial cavity; *i.* non-embryonic endoderm; *Kh.* cavity of blastodermic vesicle; *Ks.* head-fold of amnion; *m.* embryonic mesoderm; *m'.* non-embryonic mesoderm; *r.* space between chorion and amnion; *sh.* subzonal membrane (chorion); *ss.* tail-fold of amnion; *st.* sinus terminalis; *sz.* villi of chorion; *vl.* ventral body wall. (From Foster and Balfour, after Kölliker.)

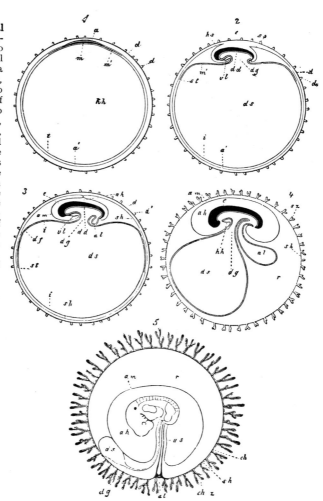

In the moles (*Talpa*) spaces appear in the layer of ectoderm of the embryonal area, and these subsequently coalesce to form a single cavity—the primitive amniotic cavity. This, however, has only a temporary existence, the amnion arising later by the formation of a series of folds. In *Mus, Arvicola*, and others the amnion is developed as a cavity in the embryonic knot. In other mammals the amnion arises in the manner already described. The portion of the trophoblast immediately overlying the embryonic part of the ectoderm eventually disappears.

The allantois has, in all essential respects, the same mode of development as in the bird, arising in most cases as a hollow outgrowth from the hinder part of the alimentary canal. This, growing out into the space (extra-embryonic cœlom) between the chorion and the amnion, becomes in all the Eutheria

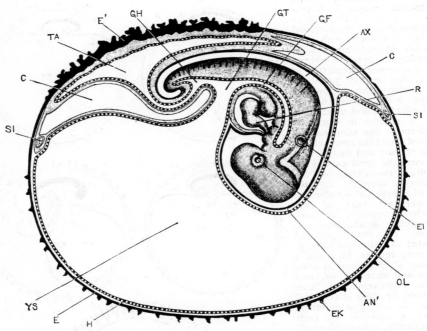

Fig. 656.—**Eutheria: Development.** Rabbit embryo and blastodermic vesicle at the end of the tenth day. The embryo is represented in surface view from the right side, the course of the alimentary canal being indicated by the broad dotted line; the blastodermic vesicle is shown in median longitudinal section. The great part of the tail has been removed. *AN'*. pro-amnion; *AX*. cavity of aminion. *C*. extra-embryonic portion of cœlom; *E*. ectoderm; *E'*. thickened ectoderm by which the vesicle is attached to the uterus and from which the fœtal part of the placenta is derived; *EI*. auditory vesicle; *EK*, ectodermal villi; *GF*. fore-gut; *GH*. hind-gut; *GT*. mid-gut; *H*. endoderm; *O*, extra-embryonic cœlom; *OL*. lens of eye; *R*. heart; *SI*. sinus-terminalis; *TA*. allantoic cavity; *YS*. yolk-sac. (From A. M. Marshall, in part after Van Beneden and Julin.)

applied to the former, and unites with it to contribute towards the formation of the *placenta*.

Chorio-allantoic placentæ are also classified into the following five types according to the degree in which both maternal and fœtal tissues are present:

1. *Epitheliochorial* (*e.g.* pig, horse), in which the maternal uterine epithelium is in simple apposition with the fœtal chorion.

2. *Syndesmochorial* (*e.g.* sheep), in which the uterine epithelium disappears

so that the chorion is in contact with the endometrium or glandular epithelium of the uterus. Such placentæ are usually cotyledonary.

3. *Endotheliochorial* or *Vasochorial* (*e.g.* cat, dog), in which the epithelium and the endometrium of the uterus disappear and the chorion is in intimate contact with the endothelial wall of the maternal capillaries.

4. *Hæmochorial* (*e.g.* Man), in which the maternal epithelium, endometrium and endothelium disappear, so that the chorionic epithelium is surrounded by circulating maternal blood.

5. *Hæmoendothelial* (*e.g.* many rodents), in which the trophoblastic epithelium disappears, as well as the maternal epithelium, endometrium, and endothelium, so that only the fœtal endothelium separates the two blood streams.

Probably in most eutherian mammals gonadotrophic hormones are secreted perhaps by the cytotrophoblast, but they are not identical with those of the anterior pituitary (p. 150). Chorionic gonadotrophin itself cannot cause ovarian luteinisation. It probably does not normally pass through the placenta into the fœtus except in very small quantities. It is possible that placental gonadotrophin augments the action of pituitary luteinising hormone in maintaining the corpus luteum during pregnancy. Its liberation in the urine of pregnant animals, including Man, makes possible the Aschheim-Zondek and the more modern tests for pregnancy.

In many mammals the yolk-sac, through the medium of the chorion, enters into a close relationship with the uterine wall. A connection, the so-called *yolk-sac placenta*, is established through which nourishment and antibodies can be conveyed to the embyro. This rarely persists after the true (allantoic) placenta has become established.

The stalk of the yolk-sac, with the corresponding narrowed part of the allantois and the vessels which it contains, forms the *umbilical cord* by which the fœtus is connected at the umbilicus with the yolk-sac and placenta. This is enclosed in a sheath formed by the ventral portion of the amnion. The part of the allantois which remains within the cavity of the body develops into the urinary bladder, together with a cord, the *urachus*, connecting the bladder with the umbilicus. In some mammals the *umbilical* cord contains a sphincter muscle in the umbilical ring (rabbit, Cavy, cow, horse and sheep). In rat, dog, cat, Man, pangolins and Macaque no such muscle occurs.

In Man, and some other eutherian mammals, the head of the neonatus is occasionally cloaked with a *caul*—a fragment of the thin, translucent amniotic membrane. To be born with, or subsequently to carry on the person, a caul, betokens (in various communities) good fortune, long life, powers of clairvoyance, a religious career, safety in mines from fire-damp, and, at sea, immunity from drowning. In Leeds, in 1889, a miracle was reported whereby a caul was found to bear the words *British and Foreign Bible Society*. Great excitement prevailed, and some still held to a supernatural theory even after it was shown that after detachment, the caul had lain for some hours on a Holy Bible, on the cover of which the above title was deeply indented. In Napoleonic times the market value of cauls was sometimes as high as 30 guineas, but by early in the present century prices had declined to about £1. During the First World War the price rose again to from £3 to £5. Cauls are still occasionally carried by sailors and are purchasable on the water-fronts.

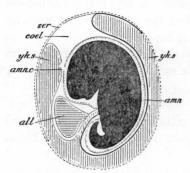

Fig. 657.—Metatheria: **Apla-cental arrangement.** Embryo and fœtal membranes of *Bettongia* (a rat-kangaroo). *all.* allantoic cavity; *amn.* amnion; *amn. c.* cavity of amnion; *cœl.* extra-embryonic cœlom; *ser.* serous membrane (chorion); *yk. s.* yolk-sac. (After Semon.)

In monotremes the ovum is relatively enormous (diameter of vitellus about 2·5 mm. in *Ornithorhynchus* and about 4·5 mm. in *Tachyglossus*); and in marsupials comparatively large. The ovum is 0·25 mm. in diameter in *Dasyurus* and 0·14 mm. in *Didelphys* compared with 0·087 mm. in *Mus* and 0·15 mm. in sheep—the last-named being the largest recorded for a eutherian.

After fertilisation the marsupial ovum becomes enclosed in a thick shell-membrane with a layer of albumen. The first cleavage of the ovum (*Didelphis*), or the fourth (*Dasyurus*), involves a separation of the embyro-forming part of its substance from that destined to give rise only to the trophoblastic ectoderm. Further divisions take place in such a way as to give rise, not to a solid morula as in the Eutheria, but to a hollow blastodermic vesicle with a wall composed of a single layer, the cells on one side of which form the embyronic area. An elaborate allantoic placenta is not developed except in *Perameles*, *Phascolarctos*, and *Phascolomys* (p. 716). The intra-uterine development of the fœtus is abbreviated, and birth takes place when the young animal is still relatively very small and incompletely developed.

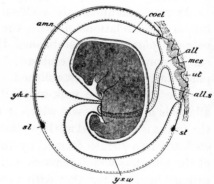

Fig. 658.—Metatheria: **Placentation.** Embryo and placenta of *Perameles* (a marsupial bandicoot). Letters as in Fig. 658. In addition, *all. s.* allantoic stalk; *mes.* mesenchyme of outer surface of allantois fused with mesenchyme of serous membrane; *s. t.* sinus terminalis; *u.t* uterine wall. (After J. P. Hill.)

In all marsupials, so far as known, the embyro is covered, except in a limited area, by the compressed and expanded yolk-sac. In the great majority (Fig. 657) the allantois (*all.*) is small, and is completely enclosed with the embryo in the yolk-sac. In native 'cats' (*Dasyurus*) there is a well-developed yolk-sac placenta. Only in bandicoots (e.g. *Perameles*), the Koala and the wombats, so far as known, is the outgrowth of the allantois to the chorion followed by the establishment of an intimate relationship between the chorion and the uterine wall, with the formation of interlocking ridges and depressions. The whole constitutes a placenta of the same essential character as that of the Eutheria, though devoid of actual villi (Fig. 658).

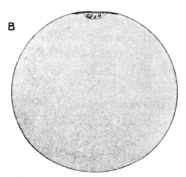

FIG. 659.—**Mammalia: Comparative embryology.** *A*, Blastula stage in a eutherian. *B*, Transition stage between the morula and blastula in a monotreme. Both represented in diagrammatic section. (After Semon.)

The Prototheria, unlike all the rest of the Mammalia, are oviparous. In *Tachyglossus* only a single egg, as a general rule, is laid in a season. This is placed in a temporary incubatorium, formed as already described (p. 695) in the mammary region of the ventral surface. The young animal soon emerges from the egg, and remains enclosed in the marsupium till it reaches an advanced stage of development. *Ornithorhynchus* develops no marsupium : its two eggs are deposited in its burrow. In *Tachyglossus* the eggshell is composed of keratin ; in *Ornithorhynchus* it contains carbonate of lime.

The ova of the Prototheria (Fig. 659) are very much larger than those of other mammals, their greater dimensions being due to the presence of a large proportion of food-yolk. The segmentation, unlike that of all the Theria, is meroblastic, and the blastoderm eventually forms a complete investment of two layers, to the yolk. An embryonic area is differentiated at one pole, and on it appears a primitive streak with a primitive knot and head-process. The young of all monotremes possess a *caruncle* as well as an egg-tooth (p. 651).

FIG. 660.—*Macropus:* **Mammary foetus.** Young kangaroo attached to the teat. (Natural size.)

The gestation period of mammals varies widely. It is about twelve days in *Didelphys* and *Dasyurus*, sixteen in *Trichosurus* and thirty-eight to forty in the bigger kangaroos. Among eutherians it varies between about three weeks in some smaller rodents to approximately one year in the whale *Physeter* and in *Equus zebra*, thirteen months in *Tapirus indicus*, fourteen in the Giraffe, eighteen in *Rhinoceros bicornis* and nineteen to twenty-two months in *Elephas maximus* (see also p. 281).

Post-natal Behaviour in Marsupials.—It was often erroneously thought that marsupials are 'born in the pouch' as a growing expansion of the teat (Fig. 660). The new-born young of the largest living kangaroo is only 1·3 inches long. Once the neonatus attaches itself to the nipple the latter expands slightly, so that if forcible removal is attempted, the neonatal buccal tissues may rupture and bleed, thus creating an understandable impression of origin *in situ*. This is particularly so in the case of the smaller marsupials. For example, the neonatus (32 hours ± 8) of the Yellow-footed Pouched Mouse (*Antechinus flavipes*) has a vertex-rump measurement of less than 5 mm. The head is 3 mm., the fore-limbs 2 mm. and the hind-limbs 1 mm. in length. The total weight is a mere 0·0164 gr. (Marlow, unpublished).

Marsupial parturition, first observed by Europeans in 1804, has now been described in *Didelphys*, several species of *Macropus*, in *Phascolarctos* and possibly others. Most observers have stated that the neonatus travels unaided to the pouch. In *Macropus*, however, the female sometimes licks a 'pathway' on her fur along which the young one ascends. In captive Great Grey Kangaroos, the female has been reported to assist the neonatus with either lips or paws (Hediger). There is evidence that if the young becomes dislodged during its ascent she makes no attempt to retrieve it.

The relatively long and powerful fore-limbs of the new-born kangaroo are already equipped with claws which no doubt assist in the upward 'swimming' movement over or through the mother's fur. The swelling of the nipple within the juvenile's mouth helps to keep the *mammary fœtus* in position during its helpless stage. Milk, expressed from the mammary gland by the contraction of the *cremaster muscle*, is thus forced down the œsophagus of the young animal which breathes unobstructedly through its nostrils by virtue of the continuous passage established between the nasal cavities and the larynx, as already described (p. 884). An opposing view, however, is that in at least some species the neonatus extracts milk by its own efforts.

REFERENCES

Adrian, E. D. (1935) *The Mechanism of Nervous Action.* Oxford.

Adrian, E. D. (1947) *The Physical Background of Perception.* Waynflete Lectures, 1946. Oxford.

Allee, W. C. (1951) *The Social Life of Animals.* New York.

Allee, W. C., Emerson, O., Park, T., and Schmidt, K. P. (1949) *Principles of Animal Ecology.* Philadelphia.

Allison, A. C. (1953) 'The Morphology of the Olfactory System in the Vertebrates', *Biol. Rev.*, **28**, 195.

Amoroso, E. C. (1952) 'Placentation', in *Marshall's Physiology of Reproduction*, 3rd edition, ed. A. S. Parkes. London.

Andrewartha, H. G., and Birch, L. C. (1954) *The Distribution and Abundance of Animals.* Chicago.

Ariëns Kappers, C. U. (1929) *The Evolution of the Nervous System.* Haarlem.

Ariëns Kappers, C. U., Huber, G. C., and Crosby, E. C. (1936) *The Comparative Anatomy of the Nervous System of Vertebrates, Including Man.* New York.

Augusta, J., and Borian, Z. (N.D.) *Prehistoric Animals.* Revised edition. London.

Baldwin, E. (1948) *An Introduction to Comparative Biochemistry.* 3rd edition. Cambridge.

Baldwin, E. (1952) *Dynamic Aspects of Biochemistry.* 2nd edition. Cambridge.

Barclay, A. E., Franklin, K. J., and Prichard, M. M. L. (1944) *The Fœtal Circulation and Cardiovascular System, and the Changes that they undergo at Birth.* Oxford.

Barcroft, J. (1932) 'La fixité du milieu intérieur est la condition de la vie libre' (Claud Bernard), *Biol. Rev.*, **7**, 24.

Bargmann, W., and Scharrer, E. (1951) 'The site of origin of the hormones of the posterior pituitary', *Amer. Sci.*, **39**, 255.

Barrington, E. J. W. (1942) 'Gastric Digestion in the Lower Vertebrates', *Biol. Rev.*, **17**, 1.

Beach, F. A. (1948) *Hormones and Behavior.* New York.

Berrill, N. J. (1955) *The Origin of Vertebrates.* London.

Best, C. H., and Taylor, N. B. (1950) *The Physiological Basis of Medical Practice*, 5th edition. New York.

Blum, H. F. (1951) *Time's Arrow and Evolution.* Princeton.

Boyd, J. D. (1950) 'Development of Thyroid and Parathyroid Glands and the Thymus', *Ann. Roy. Coll. Surg. Eng.*, **7**, 455.

Boyd, W. C. (1950) *Genetics and the Races of Man.* Boston.

Brambell, F. W. R., Hemmings, W. A., and Henderson, M. (1951) *Antibodies and Embryos.* London.

Bretschneider, L. H., and de Wit, J. J. D. (1947) *Sexual Endocrinology of Non-mammalian Vertebrates*. Amsterdam.

Brody, S. (1945) *Bioenergetics and Growth*. New York.

Brooks, C. E. P. (1949) *Climate through the Ages*. Revised edition. London.

Brough, J. (1958) 'Time and Evolution', in *Studies on Fossil Vertebrates*, ed. T. S. Westoll. London.

Burrows, H. (1949) *Biological Action of Sex Hormones*. 2nd edition. Cambridge.

Buxton, P. A. (1923) *Animal Life in Deserts*. London.

Cannon, W. B. (1939) *The Wisdom of the Body*. 2nd edition. New York.

Carleton, H. M., and Drury, R. A. B. (1957) *Histological Technique*. 3rd edition. Oxford.

Carter, G. S. (1931) 'Aquatic and aerial respiration in animals', *Biol. Rev.*, **6**, 1.

Clark, W. E. Le G. (1949) *The Tissues of the Body*. 2nd edition. Oxford.

Clark, W. E. Le G. (1957) 'Inquiries into the anatomical basis of olfactory discrimination', *Proc. Roy. Soc. Lond.*, **B**, **143**, 299.

Clark, W. E. Le G. (1959) *The Antecedents of Man*. Edinburgh.

Clark, W. E., Le G., and Medawar, P. B. (1945) *Essays on Growth and Form*, presented to D'Arcy Wentworth Thompson. Edited by W. E. Le Gros Clark and P. B. Medawar. Oxford.

Colbert, E. H. (1955) *Evolution of the Vertebrates*. New York.

Collins, F. D. (1954) 'The Chemistry of Vision', *Biol. Rev.*, **29**, 453.

Creed, R. S., Denny-Brown, D., Eccles, J. C., Liddell, E. G. T., and Sherrington, C. S. (1932) *Reflex Activity of the Spinal Cord*. Oxford.

Dakin, W. J. (1935) Presidential Address: 'The Aquatic Animal and its Environment', *Proc. Linn. Soc. N.S.W.*, **30**, 7.

Darlington, C. D., and Maller, K. (1949) *The Elements of Genetics*. London.

De Beer, G. R. (1937) *The Development of the Vertebrate Skull*. Oxford.

De Beer, G. R. (1951) *Embryos and Ancestors*. 2nd edition. London.

De Beer, G. R., and Swinton, W. E. (1958) 'Prophetic Fossils', in *Studies on Fossil Vertebrates*. Ed. T. S. Westoll. London.

Dobzhansky, T. (1951) *Genetics and the Origin of Species*. 3rd edition. Columbia.

Downey, H. (1938) *Handbook of Haematology*, **11**. New York.

Edwards, J. G. (1928) 'Studies on aglomerular and glomerular kidneys. I. Anatomical', *Amer. J. Anat.*, **42**, 75.

Edwards, J. G. (1929) 'Studies on aglomerular and glomerular kidneys. III. Cytological', *Anat. Rec.*, **44**, 15.

Edwards, J. G. (1933) 'The Renal Unit in the Kidney of Vertebrates', *Amer. J. Anat.*, **53**, 55.

Edwards, J. G., and Condorelli, L. (1928) 'Studies on Aglomerular and Glomerular Kidneys. II. Physiological', *Amer. J. Physiol.*, **83**, 383.

Euler, U. S. v. (1954) 'Visceral Functions of the Nervous System', *Ann. Rev. Physiol.*, **13**, 349.

Fisher, R. A. (1929) *The Genetical Theory of Natural Selection*. Cambridge.

Ford, E. B. (1945b) 'Polymorphism', *Biol. Rev.*, **20**, 73–88.

Foxon, G. E. H. (1955) 'Problems of the Double Circulation in Vertebrates', *Biol. Rev.*, **30**, 196.

Fraser, Elizabeth A. (1950) 'The Development of the Vertebrate Excretory System', *Biol. Rev.*, **25**, 159.

Fulton, J. F. (1951) *Physiology of the Nervous System*. 3rd edition. New York.

Gabriel, M. L., and Fogel, S. (1955) *Great Experiments in Biology.* New York.

Gamow, G. (1948) *Biography of the Earth, Its Past, Present and Future.* New York.

Garstang, W. (1922) 'The Theory of Recapitulation: a Critical restatement of the Biogenetic Law', *J. Linn. Soc. Lond. (Zool.)*, **35**, 81.

Gilbert, P. W. (1957) 'The Origin and Development of the Human Extrinsic Ocular Muscles', *Carnegie Inst. Wash. Pub.*, **XXXVI**, 49.

Goodrich, E. S. (1930) *Studies on the Structure and Development of Vertebrates.* London.

Goodrich, E. S. (1935) 'The Study of Nephridia and Genital Ducts since 1895', *Quart. J. micr. Sci.*, **83**, 113.

Grassé, P.-P. (1954) *Traité de Zoologie.* Paris.

Gray, J. (1944) 'Studies in the Mechanics of the Tetrapod Skeleton', *J. exp. Biol.*, **20**, 88.

Gray, J. (1953) *How Animals Move.* Cambridge.

Green, J. D. (1947) 'Some Aspects of the Anatomy and Function of the Pituitary Gland with Especial Reference to the Neurohypophysis', *Alexander Blain Hosp. Bull.*, **6**, 128.

Green, J. D. (1951) 'The Comparative Anatomy of the Hypophysis, with Special Reference to its Blood Supply and Innervation', *Amer. J. Anat.*, **88**, 225.

Gregory, W. K. (1934) 'A Half Century of Trituberculy, the Cope–Osborn Theory of Dental Evolution', *Proc. Amer. phil. Soc.*, **73**, 169.

Gregory, W. K. (1936) 'On the Meaning and Limits of Irreversibility of Evolution', *Amer. Natur.*, **LXX**, 517.

Gregory, W. K. (1951) *Evolution Emerging.* London.

Gregory, W. K., and Raven, H. C. (1941) 'Studies on the Origin and Early Evolution of Paired Limbs. Part 1. Paired Fins and Girdles in Ostracoderms, Placoderms, and other Primitive Fishes', *Ann. N.Y. Acad. Sci.*, **42**, 275.

Ham, A. W. (1953) *Histology.* 2nd edition. London.

Hardy, A. C. (1954) 'Escape from Specialization', in *Evolution as a Process.* London.

Harris, G. W. (1955) *Neural Control of the Pituitary Gland.* London.

Harrison, R. J. (1948) 'The Development and Fate of the Corpus Luteum in the Vertebrate Series', *Biol. Rev.*, **23**, 296.

Hess, W. R. (1948) *Die funktionelle Organisation des vegetativen Nervensystems.* Basel.

Hill, E. S. (1958) 'A Brief Review of Australian Fossil Vertebrates', in *Studies on Fossil Vertebrates*, ed. T. S. Westoll. London.

Holmes, W., and Moorhouse, D. E. (1956) 'The Peri-renal Tissue of *Protopterus.* A Contribution to the History of the Adrenal', *Quart. J. Micros. Sci.*, **97**, 123.

Hörstadius, S. (1950) *The Neural Crest.* London.

Huggett, A. St. G., and Hammond, J. (1952) 'Physiology of the Placenta', in *Marshall's Physiology of Reproduction*, 3rd edition, ed. A. S. Parkes. London.

Huxley, J. (1941) *Evolution. The Modern Synthesis.* London.

Huxley, J., Hardy, A. C., and Ford, E. B. (Eds.). (1954) *Evolution as a Process.* London.

Jarvik, E. (1960) *Théories de l'évolution des vertébrés, reconsidérés à la lumière des récentes découvertes sur les vertébrés inférieurs.* Paris.

Jones, F. Wood (1943) *Habit and Heritage.* London.

Krogh, A. (1939) *Osmotic regulation in aquatic animals.* Cambridge.

Krogh, A. (1948) *The Comparative Physiology of Respiratory Mechanisms.* Pennsylvania.

Kuntz, A. (1946) *The Autonomic Nervous System.* 3rd edition. London.

Lack, D. (1954) *The Natural Regulation of Animal Numbers.* Oxford.

Lorenz, K. (1952) *King Solomon's Ring.* London.

Lowenstein, O. (1950) 'Labyrinth and Equilibrium', *Symp. Soc. exp. Biol.*, **4**, 60.

Marshall, F. H. A. (1952–) *Physiology of Reproduction*, ed. A. S. Parkes, 3rd edition. London.

Maximow, A. A., and Bloom, W. (1948). *A Text-book of Histology.* Philadelphia and London.

Mayr, E. (1942) *Systematics and the Origin of Species.* New York.

Mayr, E., Linsley, E. G., and Usinger, R. L. (1953) *Methods and Principles of Systematic Zoology.* New York.

Morton, J. E. (1960) 'The Functions of the Gut in Ciliary Feeders', *Biol. Rev.*, **35**, 92.

Murray, P. D. F. (1936) *Bones.* Cambridge.

Neal, H. V., and Rand, H. W. (1936) *Comparative Anatomy.* Philadelphia.

Neal, H. V., and Rand, H. W. (1939) *Chordate Anatomy.* Philadelphia.

Needham, J. (1950) *Biochemistry and Morphogenesis.* Cambridge.

Nicol, J. A. C. (1960) 'The Regulation of Light Emission in Animals', *Biol. Rev.*, **35**, 1.

Nordenskiold, E. (1928) *The History of Biology.* New York.

Oakley, K. P., and Muir-Wood, H. M. (1949) *Succession of life through Geological Time.* 2nd edition. Brit. Mus. (Nat. Hist.), London.

Patten, B. M. (1949) 'Initiation and Early Changes in the Character of Heart Beat in Vertebrate Embryos', *Physiol. Rev.*, **29**, 31.

Patton, H. D. (1950) 'Physiology of Smell and Taste', *Ann. Rev. Physiol.*, **12**, 469.

Pfaffmann, C. (1951) 'Taste and Smell', in *Handbook of Experimental Psychology*, ed. S. S. Stevens. London.

Prosser, C. L. (1952) *Comparative Physiology.* New York.

Pumphrey, R. J. (1950) 'Hearing', *Symposia Soc. for Exp. Biol.*, **IV**.

Rand, H. W. (1950) *The Chordates.* Philadelphia.

Rhodes, F. H. T. (1954) 'The Zoological Affinities of the Conodonts', *Biol. Rev.*, **29**, 419.

Robertson, J. D. (1957) 'The Habitat of the Early Vertebrates', *Biol. Rev.*, **32**, 156.

Rochon-Duvigneaud, A. (1943) *Les veux et la vision des vertébrés.* Paris.

Roe, A., and Simpson, G. G. (1958) *Behavior and Evolution.* Yale.

Romer, A. S. (1941) *Man and the Vertebrates.* Chicago.

Romer, A. S. (1942) 'Cartilage an Embryonic Adaptation', *Amer. Natur.*, **LXXVI**, 394.

Romer, A. S. (1945) *Vertebrate Palæontology.* 2nd edition. Chicago.

Romer, A. S. (1955a) *The Vertebrate Body.* 2nd edition. Philadelphia and London.

Romer, A. S. (1955b) 'Fish Origins—Fresh or Salt Water?' in *Papers in Marine Biology and Oceanography.* London.

Romer, A. S. (1958) 'The Texas Permian Redbeds and their Vertebrate Fauna', in *Studies on Fossil Vertebrates*, ed. T. S. Westoll. London.

Romer, A. S., and Grove, B. H. (1935) 'Environment of the Early Vertebrates', *Amer. Midl. Nat.*, **13**, 805.

Rǔǔd, J. T. (1954) 'Vertebrates without Erythrocytes and Blood Pigment', *Nature*, **173**, 848.

Schmidt-Nielsen, K. (1960) *Animal Physiology.* New Jersey.

Selye, H. (1949) *A Textbook of Endocrinology.* 2nd edition. Montreal.

Sherrington, C. S. (1947) *Integrative Action of the Nervous System.* Cambridge.

Sholl, D. A. (1956) *The Organization of the Cerebral Cortex.* London.

Simpson, G. G. (1944) *Tempo and Mode in Evolution.* New York.

Simpson, G. G. (1945) 'The Principles of Classification and a Classification of the Mammals', *Bull. Amer. Mus. Nat. Hist.*, **85**, 1.

Simpson, G. G. (1949) *The Meaning of Evolution.* New Haven.

Simpson, G. G. (1953) *The Major Features of Evolution.* New York.

Singer, C. (1950) *A History of Biology.* Revised edition. New York.

Smith, H. W. (1953). *From Fish to Philosopher.* Boston.

Thompson, D'A. W. (1948) *On Growth and Form.* Cambridge.

Thorpe, W. H. (1956) *Learning and Instinct in Animals.* London.

Tinbergen, N. (1951) *The Study of Instinct.* Oxford.

Tinbergen, N. (1953) *Social Behaviour in Animals.* New York.

Turner, C. D. (1955) *General Endocrinology.* 2nd edition. Philadelphia.

Tyler, A. (1941) 'Artificial Parthenogenesis', *Biol. Rev.*, **13**, 291.

Waddington, C. H. (1956) 'Physiological Mechanisms in Development', *Physiol Rev.*, **34**, 1–24.

Walls, G. L. (1942) 'The Vertebrate Eye and its Adaptive Radiation', *Cranbrook Inst. Sci. Bull.*, **19**.

Waterlot, G. (1953) 'Classe des Graptolites', in *Traité de Paléontologie*, **III**, 968.

Watson, D. M. S. (1942) 'On Permian and Triassic Tetrapods', *Geol. Mag. Lond.*, **79**, 81.

Watson, D. M. S. (1951) *Palæontology and Modern Biology.* Yale.

Weichert, C. K. (1951) *Anatomy of the Chordates.* New York.

Weddell, G., Palmer, E., and Pallie, W. (1955) 'Nerve Endings in Mammalian Skin', *Biol. Rev.*, **30**, 159.

Westoll, T. S. (1943) 'The Origin of the Primitive Tetrapod Limb', *Proc. Roy. Soc. Lond.*, (B), **131**, 373.

White, E. I. (1958) 'Original Environment of the Craniates', in *Studies on Fossil Vertebrates*, ed. T. S. Westoll. London.

White, W. J. (1945) *Animal Cytology and Evolution.* Cambridge.

Willmer, E. N. (1946) *Retinal Structure and Colour Vision.* Cambridge.

Witschi, E. (1956) *Development of Vertebrates.* Philadelphia and London.

Woolley, P. (1959) 'The Effect of Posterior Lobe Pituitary Extracts on Blood Pressure in Several Vertebrate Classes', *J. Exp. Biol.*, **33**, 453.

Young, J. Z. (1938) 'The Evolution of the Nervous System and of the Relationship of Organism and Environment', in *Evolution, Essays Presented to E. S. Goodrich*, ed. G. R. de Beer. Oxford.

Young, J. Z. (1950) *The Life of Vertebrates.* Oxford.

Zeuner, F. E. (1944) 'The Pleistocene Period. Its Climate, Chronology, and Faunal Successions', Ray Society, London.

Zeuner, F. E. (1950) *Dating the Past.* 2nd edition. London.

PROTOCHORDATES

Barrington, E. J. W. (1937 'The Digestive System of *Amphioxus*', *Phil. Trans. Roy. Soc.*, **228**, 269.

Barrington, E. J. W. (1938) 'The Structure and Function of the Digestive System in *Amphioxus* (*Branchiostoma*) *lanceolatum*', *Phil. Trans. Roy. Soc.*, **B**, **228**, 269.

Barrington, E. J. W. (1941) 'Observations on Feeding and Digestion in *Glossobalanus minutus*', *Quart. J. Micr. Sci.*, **82**, 227.

Bateson, W. (1884) 'Note on the Later Stages in the Development of *Balanoglossus kowalevskii* (Agassiz) and on the Affinities of the Enteropneusta, *Proc. Roy. Soc., Lond.*, **38**, 23–30.

Berrill, N. J. (1950) *The Tunicata*. Ray Society, London.

Berrill, N. J. (1955) *The Origin of Vertebrates* London.

Bone, Q. (1958) 'Nervous control of cilia in *Amphioxus* (*Branchiostoma*)', *Nature*, **181**, 193.

Bone, Q. (1959) 'The Problem of the "Amphioxides" Larva', *Nature*, **180**, 1462.

Bone, Q. (1960). 'The Origin of the Chordates', *J. Linn. Soc. Lond.* (*Zool.*) **44**: 252.

Bullock, T. H. (1945) 'Anatomical Organization of the Nervous System of Enteropneusta', *Quart. J. micr. Sci.*, **86**, 55.

Burdon-Jones, C. (1951) 'Observations on the Spawning Behaviour of *Saccoglossus horsti* Brambell and Goodhart, and of other Enteropneusta', *J. mar. biol. Ass. U.K.*, **21**, 625.

Burdon-Jones, C. (1952) 'Development and Biology of the Larva of *Saccoglossus horsti* (Enteropneusta)', *Phil. Trans. Roy. Soc. Lond.*, **B**, **236**, 553.

Burdon-Jones, C. (1954) 'The Habitat and Distribution of *Rhabdopleura normani* Allman' (Pub. Biol. St. 12, 1–17) *Univ. Bergen Arb. naturv. R. Wr. II, Bergen.*

Burdon-Jones, C. (1956) 'Nachtrag zu Enteropneusta', in Kükenthal and Krumbach, *Handbuch der Zoologie*, **111**, 57.

Burdon-Jones, C. (1956). 'Observations on the Enteropneust, *Protoglossus koehleri* (Caullery & Mesnil)', *Proc. Zool. Soc. Lond.*, **127**, 35.

Burdon-Jones, C., and Patil, A. M. (1960) 'A Revision of the Genus *Saccoglossus* (*Enteropneusta*) in British Waters', *Proc. Zool. Soc. Lond.*, **134**, 635.

Burdon-Jones, C. (1962) 'The Feeding Mechanism of *Balanoglossus gigas*', *Bol. Fac. Filos. Ciên. S. Paulo* (*Zool.*), **24**, 255.

Carlisle, D. B. (1950) 'Gonadotrophin from the Neural Region of Ascidians', *Nature*, **166**, 737.

Carlisle, D. B. (1951) 'On the Hormonal and Neural Control of the Release of Gametes in Ascidians', *Jour. Exp. Biol.*, **28**, 463.

Carlisle, D. B. (1958) 'Niobium in ascidians', *Nature*, **181**, 933.

Colwin, A. L., and Colwin, L. H. (1953) 'The Normal Embryology of *Saccoglossus kowaleskyi*', *J. Morph.*, **92**, 401.

De Beer, G. R. (1951) *Embryos and Ancestors*. Rev. ed., Oxford.

Garstang, W. (1929) 'The Morphology of the Tunicata and its Bearing on the Phylogeny of the Chordata', *Quart. Jour. Micr. Sci.*, **72**, 51.

Gilchrist, J. D. (1917) 'On the Development of *Cephalodiscus*', *Quart. Jour. Micr. Sci.*, **62**, 189.

Gregory, W. K. (1946) 'The Role of Motile Larva and Fixed Adults in the Origin of the Vertebrates', *Quart. Rev. Biol.*, **21**, 348.

Hardy, A. C. (1954) 'Escape from Specialization', in *Evolution as a Process*, p. 1–22. London.

Hatschek, B.   (1881)   'Studien über Entwicklung des *Amphioxus*', *Arb. zool. Inst. Univ. Wien*, **4**, 1.

Holmes, W.   (1953)   'The Atrial Nervous System of *Amphioxus (Branchiostoma)*', *Quart. J. micr. Sci.*, **94**, 523.

Horst, C. J. Van Der   (1927–36)   'Hemichordata', in Bronn's *Klassen u. Ordnungen des Tierreichs*, IV.

Horst, C. J. Van Der   (1932)   'Enteropneusta', in Kükenthal and Krumbach, *Handbuch der Zoologie*, III.

Jorgensen, C. B.   (1950)   'Quantitative Aspects of Filter Feeding in Invertebrates', *Biol. Rev.*, **30**, 391.

Knight-Jones, E. W.   (1952)   'On the Nervous System of *Saccoglossus cambrensis* (Enteropneusta)', *Phil. Trans. Roy. Soc. Lond.*, (B) **236**, 315.

Knight-Jones, E. W.   (1953)   'Feeding in Saccoglossus (Enteropneusta)', *Proc. Zool. Soc. Lond.*, **123**, 637.

Komai, T.   (1949)   'Internal Structure of the Pterobranch *Atubaria heterolopha* Sato, with an Appendix on the Homology of the "Notochord"', *Proc. Japan. Acad.*, **25**, 19.

Komai, T.   (1951)   'The Homology of the "Notochord" found in Pterobranchs and Enteropneusts', *Amer. Nat.*, **85**, 270.

Kozlowski, R.   (1947)   'Les affinités des graptolites', *Biol. Rev.*, **22**, 93.

Krijgsman, B. J.   (1956)   'Contractile and Pacemaker Mechanisms of the Heart of Tunicates', *Biol. Rev.*, **31**, 288.

Lohmann, H., Huus, J., and Ihle, I. F. W.   (1933)   'Tunicata', in Kükenthal and Krumbach, *Handbuch der Zoologie*, V.

Newell, G. E.   (1951)   'The Stomochord of Enteropneusta', *Proc. Zool. Soc.*, **121**, 741.

Orton, J. H.   (1913)   'The Ciliary Mechanism on the Gills and the Mode of Feeding in *Amphioxus*, Ascidians and *Solenomya togata*', *Jour. Mar. Biol. Ass.*, **10**, 19.

Spengel, J. W.   (1893)   'Die *Enteropneusten* des Golfes von Neapel und der Angrenzenden Meeres-abschnitte', in *Fauna und Flora des Golfes von Neapel*, **18**, 1–7.

Thomas, I. M.   (1956)   'Accumulation of Radio-active Iodine by *Amphioxus*', *J. mar. biol. Ass. U.K.*, **35**, 203.

Waterlot, G.   (1953)   'Classe des Pterobranches', in *Traite de Paléontologie*, **III**, 963.

Webb, D. A.   (1939)   'Observations on the Blood of Certain Ascidians with Special Reference to the Biochemistry of Vanadium', *Jour. Exp. Biol.*, **16**, 499.

Willey, A.   (1894)   'Amphioxus and the Ancestry of the Vertebrates', *Columbia Univ. Biol.*, Ser. 2, 180.

Whitear, M.   (1957)   'Some Remarks on the Ascidian Affinities of the Vertebrates', *Ann. Mag. Nat. Hist.*, **10**, 338.

AGNATHANS

Applegate, V. C.   (1950)   *Natural History of the Sea Lamprey in Michigan.*   U.S. *Fish & Wildlife Serv. Spec. Sci. Rep.*, **55**. Washington.

Balabai, P. P.   (1956)   *Morphology and Phylogenetic Development of Jawless Vertebrates.*   Kiev. (In Russian.)

Barrington, E. J. W.   (1936)   'Proteolytic Digestion and the Problem of the Pancreas in the Ammocoete Larva of *Lampetra planeri*', *Proc. Roy. Soc. Lond.*, **B, 121**, 221.

Barrington, E. J. W. (1945) 'The Supposed Pancreatic Organs of *Petromyzon fluviatilis* and *Myxine glutinosa*', *Quart. Journ. Micr. Sci.*, **85**, 391.

Baxter, E. W. (1956) Observations on the Buccal Glands of Lampreys (Petromyzonidæ)', *Proc. Zool. Soc. Lond.*, **127**, 95.

Baxter, E. W. (1957) 'The Development of the Intestinal Blood-system of Lampreys (Petromyzonidæ), with an Account of the Origin of Vascular Couples', *Proc. Zool. Soc. Lond.*, **129**, 371.

Bigelow, H. B. and Schroeder, W. C. (1948) *Fishes of the Western North Atlantic.* Sears Foundation Mar. Res., New Haven.

Brodal, A., and Fänge, R. (1963) (ed.). *The Biology of Myxine.* Oslo.

Cole, F. J. (1905–25) 'A Monograph on the General Morphology of the Myxinoid Fishes, Based on a Study of *Myxine*, I–VI, *Trans. Roy. Soc. Edinburgh*, **41**, **45**, **46**, **48**, **49**, **54**.

Damas, H. (1935) 'Contribution à l'étude de la Métamorphose de la Tête de la Lamproie', *Arch. Biol., Paris*, **46**, 171.

Damas, H. (1944) 'Recherches sur le Développement de *Lampetra fluviatilis*. Contribution à l'étude de la Céphalogenèse des Vertébrés', *Arch. Biol., Paris*, **55**, 3.

Fontaine, M., *et al.* (1958) 'Formes actuelles des cyclostomes', in P. P. Grassé, *Traite de Zoologie*, **13**. Paris.

Goodrich, E. S. (1909) 'Vertebrata Craniata, I. Cyclostomes and Fishes', in Lankester's *Treatise on Zoology*, **IX**. London.

Gregory, W. K. (1936) 'The Transformation of Organic Designs: a Review of the Origin and Deployment of the Earlier Vertebrates', *Biol. Rev.*, **11**, 311.

Hagelin, L. O. (1959) 'Further Aquarium Observations on the Spawning Habits of the River Lamprey (*Petromyzon fluviatilis*)', *Oikos*, **10**, 50.

Heintz, A. (1939) 'Cephalaspida from Downtonian of Norway', *Skr. norske VidenskAkad. Oslo*, Mat.-Nat. Kl. 1939, No. 5, 1.

Heintz, A. (1958) 'The Head of the Anaspid *Birkenia elegans*, Traq.', in *Studies on Fossil Vertebrates*, ed. T. S. Westoll. London.

Holmgren, N. (1946) 'On Two Embryos of *Myxine glutinosa*', *Acta Zool., Stockh.*, **27**, 1.

Johnels, A. G. (1948) 'On the Development and Morphology of the Skeleton of the Head of *Petromyzon*, *Acta Zool, Stockh.*, **29**, 139.

Johnels, A. G. (1950) 'On the Dermal Connective Tissue of the Head of Petromyzon', *Acta Zool., Stockh.*, **31**, 177.

Kiaer, J. (1924) 'The Downtonian Fauna of Norway. I. Anaspida', *Skr. VidenskSelsk., Khrist.*, Mat.-Nat. Kl., 1924, **6**, 1.

Leach, W. J. (1951) 'The Hypophysis of Lampreys in Relation to the Nasal Apparatus', *J. Morph.*, **89**, 217.

Lindström, T. (1949) 'On the Cranial Nerves of the Cyclostomes, with Special Reference to the *N. Trigeminus*', *Acta Zool., Stockh.*, **30**, 315.

Marinelli, W., and Strenger, A. (1954–56) *Vergleichende Anatomie und Morphologie der Wirbeltiere; Lfg. 1, Lampetra fluviatilis; Lfg. 2, Myxine glutinosa.* Vienna.

Moy-Thomas, J. A. (1939) *Palæozoic Fishes.* London and New York.

Parrington, F. R. (1958) 'On the Nature of the Anaspida', in *Studies on Fossil Vertebrates*, ed. T. S. Westoll. London.

Pietschman, V. (1933–35) 'Cyclostomata', in Kükenthal and Krumbach, *Handbuch der Zoologie*, **6**, Hft 1. Berlin and Leipzig.

Robertson, J. D.   (1957)   'The Habitat of the Early Vertebrates', *Biol. Rev.*, **32**, 156.

Stensiö, E. A.   (1927)   'The Downtonian and Devonian vertebrates of Spitzbergen. Pt. 1.   Cephalaspidæ', *Skr. Sval. og Ishavet*, No. XII, *Norske Vid. Akad. Oslo*, 1.

Stensiö, E. A.   (1932)   *The Cephalaspids of Great Britain*.   British Museum (Nat. Hist.), London.

Stensiö, E. A.   (1950)   'La cavité labyrinthique, l'ossification sclérotique et l'orbit de *Jagorina*', in George, A., *Paléontologie et transformisme*, 9.   Paris.

Stensiö, E.   (1958)   'Les Cyclostomes fossiles', in P.-P. Grassé, *Traite de Zoologie*, **13** (1).   Paris.

Sterba, G.   (1952)   *Die Neunaugen*.   Leipzig.

Stetson, H. C.   (1928).   'A Restoration of the Anaspid *Birkenia elegans* Traquair', *J. Geol.*, **33**, 458.

Strahan, R.   (1960)   'Speculations on the Evolution of the Agnathan Head', *Proc. Centenary and Bicentenary Congr. Biol. Singapore 1958*, 83.

Strahan, R.   (1963)   'The Behaviour of Myxinoids', *Acta Zool., Stockh.*, **44**, 73.

Watson, D. M. S.   (1954)   'A Consideration of Ostracoderms', *Phil. Trans. Roy. Soc. Lond.*, B, **238**, 1.

Westoll, T. S.   (1945)   'A New Cephalaspid Fish from the Downtonian of Scotland, with Notes on the Structure and Classification of Ostracoderms', *Trans. Roy. Soc. Edinb.*, **31**, 341.

Westoll, T. S.   (1958)   'The Lateral Fin-fold Theory and the Pectoral Fins of Ostracoderms and Early Fishes', in *Studies on Fossil Vertebrates*, ed. T. S. Westoll.   London.

White, E. I.   (1935)   'The Ostracoderm *Pteraspis* Kner, and the Relationships of the Agnathous Vertebrates', *Philos. Trans.*, **225**, 381.

White, E. I.   (1946)   '*Jamoytius kerwoodi*, a New Chordate from the Silurian of Lanarkshire', *Geological Magazine*, **83**, 89.

Whiting, H. P.   (1957)   'Mauthner Neurones in Young Larval Lampreys (*Lampetra* spp.)', *Quart. J. Micr. Sci.*, **98**, 163.

PLACODERMS AND FISHES

Atz, J. W.   (1952)   'Internal Nares in the Teleost, *Astroscopus*', *Anat. Rec.*, **113**, 105.

Atz., J. W.   (1952)   'Narial Breathing in Fishes and the Evolution of Internal Nares', *Quart. Rev. Biol.*, **27**, 366.

Barrington, E. J. W.   (1942)   'Gastric Digestion in the Lower Vertebrates', *Biol. Rev.*, **17**, 1.

Bertelesen, E., and Marshall, N. B.   (1956)   'The Miripinnati, a New Order of Teleost Fishes', *Dana Report*, **42**, 1–34.   Copenhagen.

Bodemer, C. W.   (1957)   'The Origin and Development of the Extrinsic Ocular Muscles in the Gar Pike (*Lepisosteus osseus*)', *J. Morph.*, **100**, 83.

Bodemer, C. W.   (1958)   'The Origin and Development of the Extrinsic Ocular Muscles in the Trout (*Salmo trutta*)', *J. Morph.*, **102**, 119.

Brækkan, O. R.   (1956)   'Function of the Red Muscle in Fish', *Nature*, **178**, 747.

Brough, J.   (1936)   'On the Evolution of Bony Fishes during the Triassic Period', *Biol. Rev.*, **11**, 385.

Clark, E.   (1959)   'Functional Hermaphroditism and Self-fertilization in a Serranid Fish', *Science*, **129**, 215.

Dean, B.   (1895)   *Fishes, Living and Fossil*.   New York.

Duthie, E. S. (1939) 'The Origin, Development and Function of the Blood Cells in Certain Marine Teleosts. 1, Morphology', *Jour. Anat.*, **73**, 396.

Foxon, G. E. H. (1950) 'A Description of the Coronary Arteries in Dipnoan Fishes and Some Remarks on their Importance from the Evolutionary Standpoint', *J. Anat.*, **84**, 121.

Gilbert, P. W. (1958) 'The Structural and Functional Relationship of Mother to Developing Young in Two Ovoviviparous Elasmobranchs', *Anat. Rec.*, **132**, 442.

Goodrich, E. S. (1906) 'Notes on the Development, Structure and Origin of the Median and Paired Fins of Fish', *Quart. J. micr. Sci.*, N.S., **50**, 333.

Goodrich, E. S. (1909) 'Vertebrata Craniata, I. Cyclostomes and Fishes', in Lankester's *Treatise on Zoology*, **IX**. London.

Gray, J. (1953) 'The Locomotion of Fishes', in *Essays in Marine Biology*, ed. Elmhirst, R., 1. London.

Greenwood, P. H. (1956) 'A New Species of *Clariallabes* (Pisces, Clariidæ) from the Nile', *Proc. Zool. Soc. Lond.*, **127**, 555.

Greenwood, P. H. (1958) 'Reproduction in the East African Lung-fish *Protopterus æthiopicus* Haeckel', *Proc. Zool. Soc. Lond.*, **30**, 547.

Greenwood, P. H., and Thompson, K. S. (1960) 'The Pectoral Anatomy of *Pantodon buchholzi* Peters (a freshwater flying fish) and the Related Osteoglossidae', *Proc. Zool. Soc. Lond.*, **135**, 283.

Harden Jones, F. R., and Marshall, N. B. (1953) 'The Structure and Functions of the Teleostean Swim-bladder', *Biol. Rev.*, **28**, 16.

Harris, J. E. (1936, 1938) 'The Role of the Fins and the Equilibrium of the Swimming Fish', *J. Exp. Biol.*, **13**, 476; **15**, 32.

Hoar, W. S. (1955) 'Phototactic Responses of Sockeye Salmon Smolts Following Injury to the Pineal Organ', *J. Fish. Res. Canada*, **12**, 178.

Holmes, W. (1950) 'The Adrenal Homologues in the Lungfish *Protopterus*', *Proc. Roy. Soc.*, **B**, **137**, 549.

Jarvik, E. (1942) 'On the Structure of the Snout of Crossopterygians and Lower Gnathostomes in General', *Zool. Bidr. Uppsala*, **21**, 235.

Jenkin, P. M. (1927) 'Note on the Sympathetic Nervous System of *Lepidosiren paradoxa*', *Proc. Roy. Soc. Edinb.*, **48**, 55.

Kerr, J. G. (1932) 'Archaic fishes—*Lepidosiren, Protopterus, Polypterus*—and Their Bearing upon Problems of Vertebrate Morphology', *Jena. Z. Naturw.*, **67**, 419.

Kerr, T. (1952) 'The Scales of Primitive Living Actinopterygians', *Proc. Zool. Soc. Lond.*, **122**, 55.

Kerr, T. (1955) 'The Scales of Modern Lungfish', *Proc. Zool. Soc. Lond.*, **125**, 335.

Lowenstein, O., and Roberts, T. D. M. (1949) 'The Equilibrium Function of the Otolith Organs of the Thornback Ray (*Raja clavata*)', *Jour. Physiol.*, **110**, Nos. 3 and 4, 392.

Lowenstein, O., and Roberts, T. D. M. (1951) 'The Localization and Analysis of the Responses to Vibration from the Isolated Elasmobranch Labyrinth. A Contribution to the Problem of the Evolution of Hearing in Vertebrates', *Journ. Physiol.*, **114**, 471.

Matthews, L. H. (1950) 'Reproduction in the Basking Shark, *Cetorhinus maximus* (Gunner)', *Phil. Trans. Roy. Soc. Lond.*, **B**, **234**, 247.

Millot, J. (1945) 'Les nouveaux cœlacanthes', *La Nature* (Paris), **3228**, 121.

Millot, J. (1955) 'First Observations on a Living Cœlacanth', *Nature*, **175**, 362.

Millot, J., and Anthony, J. (1954) 'Tubes rostraux et tubes nasaux de *Latimeria* (Cœlacanthidæ)', *C.R. Acad. Sci. (Paris)*, **239**, 1241.

Millot, J., and Anthony, J. (1956) 'Considérations préliminaires sur le squelette axial et le système nerveux central de *Latimeria chalumnæ* Smith', *Mém. Inst. Sci. Madagascar* (A), **11**, 176.

Millot, J., and Anthony, J. (1956) 'L'Organe rostral de *Latimeria* (Crossoptérygien cœlacanthidé)', *Ann. Des Sc. Nat., Zool.*, **11**, 381.

Millot, J., and Anthony, J. (1958) 'Crossoptérygiens Actuels', in *Traité de Zoologie*, ed. P. P. Grassé.

Morris, D. (1955) 'Sticklebacks as Prey', *Brit. J. Animal Behav.*, **111**, 2.

Moy-Thomas, J. A. (1939) *Palæozoic Fishes*. London.

Moy-Thomas, J. A. (1939) 'The Early Evolution and Relationships of the Elasmobranchs', *Biol. Rev.*, **14**, 1.

Norman, J. R. (1963) *A History of Fishes*. 2nd edition revised by P. H. Greenwood. London.

O'Donoghue, C. H., and Abbott, E. (1928) 'The Blood Vascular System of the Spiny Dogfish', *Trans. Roy. Soc. Edin.*, **55**, 823.

Ørvig, T. (1960) 'New Finds of Acanthodians, Arthrodires, Crossopterygians, Ganoids and Dipnoans in the Upper Middle Devonian Calcareous Flags (Oberer Plattenkalk) of the Bergisch Gladbach–Paffrath Trough, (1)', *Paläont. Z.*, **34**, 295.

Parker, T. J. (1886) 'On the Blood Vessels of *Mustelus antarctica*', *Proc. Roy. Soc., Lond.*, **XL**, 472.

Parker, W. N. (1892) 'On the Anatomy and Physiology of *Protopterus annectens*', *Trans. Roy. Irish Acad.*, **30**, 109.

Rayner, D. H. (1941) 'The Structure and Evolution of the Holostean Fishes', *Biol. Rev.*, **16**, 218.

Rayner, D. H. (1958) 'The Geological Environment of Fossil Fishes', in *Studies on Fossil Vertebrates*, ed. T. S. Westoll. London.

Romer, A. S. (1946) 'The Early Evolution of Fishes', *Quart. Rev. Biol.*, **21**, 33.

Romer, A. S. (1955) 'Herpetichthyes, Amphibioidei, Choanichthyes or Sarcopterygii?', *Nature*, **176**, 126.

Scott, T. D. (1962) *The Marine and Fresh Water Tides of South Australia*. Adelaide.

Smith, H. W. (1931) 'Observations on the African Lung-fish, *Protopterus æthiopicus*, and on Evolution from Water to Land Environments', *Ecology*, **12**, 164.

Smith, H. W. (1936) 'The Retention and Physiological Role of Urea in the Elasmobranchii', *Biol. Rev.*, **11**, 49.

Smith, J. L. B. (1939) 'A Living Cœlacanthid Fish from South Africa', *Trans. Roy. Soc. S. Africa*, **28**, 1.

Smith, J. L. B. (1939) 'The Second Cœlacanth', *Nature*, **171**, 99.

Stensiö, E., and Orvig, T. 'On the Scales of the Elasmobranchs. An Introduction to the Lepidomorial Theory', *Acad. Sci.* Stockholm. (In press.)

Stensiö, E. A. (1921) *Triassic Fishes from Spitzbergen*. Vienna.

Stensiö, E. A. (1932) 'Triassic Fishes from East Greenland', *Medd. Grønl.*, **83**, 1.

Taning, A. V. (1932) In Schmidt *et al.*, *Dana's Togtomkring Yorden* 1928–30 ('Dana's Cruise around the World'), p. 283.

Traquair, R. H. (1899) 'Reports on Fossil Fishes', *Trans. Roy. Soc. Edinb.*, **39**, 827.

Trewavas, E., White, E. I., Marshall, N. B., Tucker, D. W. (1955). 'Herpeti-chthyes, Amphibioidei, Choanichthyes or Sarcopterygii?' *Nature*, **176**, 126.

Trewavas, E. (1958) 'The Cœlacanth Yields its Secrets', *Discovery*, May, 196.

Watson, D. M. S. (1937) 'The Acanthodian Fishes', *Phil. Trans. Roy. Soc. Lond.*, **B, 228**, 49.

Watson, D. M. S. (1959) 'The Myotomes of Acanthodians', *Proc. Roy. Soc.*, **B, 151**, 23.

Westoll, T. S. (1945) 'The Paired Fins of Placoderms', *Trans. Roy. Soc. Edinb.*, **61**, 381.

Westoll, T. S. (1949) 'On the Evolution of the Dipnoi', in *Genetics, Palæontology and Evolution*. Princeton.

White, E. G. (1936) 'A Classification and Phylogeny of the Elasmobranch Fishes', *American Museum Novitates*, No. 837, April.

White, E. I. (1954) 'More about Cœlacanths', *Discovery*, **15**, 332.

Whitley, G. P. (1940) *The Fishes of Australia. I. Sharks.* Sydney.

Whitley, G. P. (1960) *Fresh Water Fishes of Australia.* Brisbane.

AMPHIBIANS

Dawson, A. B. (1951) 'Functional and Degenerate or Rudimentary Glomeruli in the Kidney of Two Species of Australian Frog, *Cyclorana* (*Chiroleptes*) *Platy-cephalus* and *Alboguttatus* (Günther)', *Anat. Rec.*, **109**, 471.

de Groot, B., and van Oordt, G. J. (1951) 'The Endocrine Activity of Bidder's Organ of the Male Toad, *Bufo bufo* (L.)', *Acta Endocrinol.*, **13**, 24.

Francis, E. T. B. (1934) *The Anatomy of the Salamander.* London.

Gadow, H. (1909) *Amphibia and Reptiles.* Cambridge Natural History. London.

Gordon, M. S., Schmit-Nielsen, K., and Kelly, H. M. (1961) 'Osmotic Regulation in the crab-eating frog (*Rana cancrivora*)', *J. Exp. Biol.*, **38**, 659.

Gordon, M. S. (1962) 'Osmotic Regulation in the green toad (*Bufo viridis*)', *J. Exp. Biol.*, **39**, 261.

Gray, J., and Lissman, H. W. (1946) 'The Co-ordination of Limb Movements in the Amphibia', *J. Exp. Biol.*, **23**, 133.

Gregory, W. K., and Raven, H. C. (1941) 'The Origin and Early Evolution of Paired Fins and Limbs', *Ann. N.Y. Acad. Sci.*, **42**, 273.

Griffiths, I. (1956) 'Status of *Protobatrachus massinoti*', *Nature*, **177**, 342.

Kingsbury, B. F., and Reed, P. H. D. (1909) 'The Columella Auris in Amphibia', *J. Morph.*, **20**, 549.

Marshall, A. M. (1939) *The Frog.* Rev. ed. London.

Noble, G. K. (1931) *The Biology of the Amphibia.* New York and London.

Romer, A. S. (1947) 'Review of the Labyrinthodontia', *Bull. Mus. comp. Zool. Harv.*, **99**, 1.

Sarasin, P. and F. (1887) 'Zur Entwicklungsgeschichte und Anatomie der Ceylonesischen Blindwühle *Ichthyophis glutinosus*', in Sarasin and Sarasin, *Ergebnisse naturwissenschaftlicher Forschungen auf Ceylon.* 2. Wiesbaden.

Watson, D. M. S. (1918) 'On Seymouria the most primitive known reptile', *Proc. Zool. Soc. Lond.*, **2**, 267.

Watson, D. M. S. (1919) 'The Structure, Evolution and Origin of the Amphibia. The " Orders " Rachitomi and Stereopondyii', *Phil. Trans. Roy. Soc. Lond.*, **B, 209**, 1.

Watson, D. M. S. (1919 and 1925) 'Evolution and Origin of Amphibia', *Phil. Trans. Roy. Soc.*, **209** and **214**.

Watson, D. M. S. (1926) Croonian Lecture. 'The Evolution and Origin of the Amphibia', *Phil. Trans. Roy. Soc. Lond.*, **B**, **214**, 189.

Watson, D. M. S. (1939) 'The Origin of Frogs', *Trans. Roy. Soc. Edinb.*, **60**, 195

Watson, D. M. S. (1956) 'The Brachyopid Labyrinthodonts', *Bull. Brit. Mus. Nat. Hist., Geol.*, **2**, 315.

Westoll, T. S. (1943) 'The Origin of Tetrapods', *Biol. Rev.*, **18**, 78; *Proc. Roy. Soc.*, **B**, **131**, 373.

White, E. I. (1935) 'On the Ostracoderm *Pteraspis*, and the Relationships of the Agnathous Vertebrates', *Phil. Trans. Roy. Soc.*, **225**, 381.

White, T. E. (1939) 'The Osteology of *Seymouria*', *Bull. Mus. Comp. Zool. Harvard*, **85**.

REPTILES

Bellairs, A. D'A. (1958) *Reptiles*. London.

Bellairs, A. D'A. (1959) 'Reproduction in Lizards and Snakes', *New Biology*, No. 30, 73.

Bogert, C. M. (1943) 'Dentitional Phenomena in Cobras and other Elapids with Notes on Adaptive Modifications of Fangs', *Bull. Amer. Mus. of Nat. Hist.*, **LXXXI**, 285.

Broom, R. (1932) *The Mammal-like Reptiles of South Africa*. London.

Bullock, T. H., and Cowles, R. B. (1852) 'Physiology of infra red receptor: the facial pit of pit vipers', *Science*, **115**, 541.

Carr, A. (1952) *Handbook of Turtles*. New York.

Colbert, E. H. (1951) *The Dinosaur Book*. New York.

Colbert, E. H. (1951) 'Environment and Adaptations of Certain Dinosaurs', *Biol. Rev.*, **26**, 265.

Colbert, E. H. (1958) 'The Beginning of the Age of Dinosaurs', in *Studies on Fossil Vertebrates*, ed. T. S. Westoll. London.

Crompton, A. W. (1958) 'The Cranial Morphology of a New Genus and Species of Ictidosaurian', *Proc. Zool. Soc. Lond.*, **130**, 183.

Dawson, W. R., and Bartholomew, G. A. (1958) 'Metabolic and Cardiac Responses to Temperature in the Lizard *Dipsosaurus dorsalis*', *Physiol. Zool.*, **XXXI**, 100.

Ditmars, R. L. (1952) *Snakes of the World*. New York.

Eakin, R. M., Quay, W. B., and Westfall, J. A. (1961) 'Cytochemical and cytological studies of the parietal eye of the lizard, *Sceloporus occidentalis*', *Zeits. f. Zellforschung*, **53**, 449.

Edinger, T. (1949) 'The Brain of *Pterodactylus*', *Amer. Journ. Sci.*, **239**, 665.

Foxon, G. E. H., Griffith, J., and Price, M. (1956) 'The Mode of Action of the Heart of the Green Lizard, *Lacerta viridis*', *Proc. Zool. Soc. Lond.*, **126**, 145.

Gadow, H. (1909) *Amphibia and Reptiles*. Cambridge Natural History. London.

Goldby, F., and Gamble, H. J. (1957) 'The Reptilian Cerebral Hemispheres', *Biol. Rev.*, **32**, 383.

Gray, J. (1946) 'The Mechanism of Locomotion in Snakes', *J. Exp. Biol.*, **23**, 101.

Gregory, W. K. (1958) 'On Interacting Causal Networks Converging towards Observed Results in Evolution', in *Studies on Fossil Vertebrates*, ed. T. S. Westoll. London.

Khalil, F. (1947) 'Excretion in Reptiles', *Jour. Biol. Chem.*, **171**, 611.

Klauber, L. M. (1956) *Rattlesnakes*. Berkeley.

Moyle, V. (1949) 'Nitrogenous Excretion in Chelonian Reptiles', *Biochem. J.*, **44**, 581.

Pope, C. H. (1956) *The Reptile World*. London and New York.

Romer, A. S. (1956) *Osteology of the Reptiles*. Chicago.

Romer, A. S., and Price, L. (1940) 'Review of the Pelycosauria', *Geol. Soc. Amer.*, *Special Paper* No. 28.

Smith. M. (1954) *The British Amphibians and Reptiles*. London.

Stresemann, E. (1927–1934) 'Sauropsida; Aves, etc.', in Kükenthal and Krumbach *Handbuch der Zoologie*, **7**.

Swinton, W. E. (1934) *The Dinosaurs*. London.

Watson, D. M. S., and Romer, A. S. (1956) 'A Classification of Therapsid Reptiles', *Bull. Mus. Comp. Zool.*, **114**, 37.

White, F. A. (1956) 'Circulation in the reptilian heart (*Caiman sclerops*)', *Anat. Rec.*, **125**, 417.

BIRDS

Auber, L. (1956) 'The Distribution of Structural Colours and Unusual Pigments in the Class Aves', *Ibis*, **99**, 463.

Allen, C. M. (1956) *Birds and their Attributes*. London.

Archey, G. (1941) 'The Moa, a Study of the Dinornithiformes', *Bull. Auckl. Int. Mus.*, **1**, 1.

Bailey, R. E. (1952) 'The Incubation Patch of Passerine Birds', *Condor*, **54**, 121.

Bartholomew, G. A., Jr., and Dawson, W. R. (1954). 'Body Temperature and Water Requirements in the Mourning Dove, *Zenaidura macroura marginella*', *Ecology*, **35**, 182.

Bartholomew, Jr., G. A., and Dawson, W. R. (1954) 'Temperature Regulation in Young Pelicans, Herons, and Gulls', *Ecology*, **35**, 466.

Bartholomew, G. A., Howell, T. R., and Cade, T. J. (1957) 'Torpidity in the White-throated Swift, Anna Hummingbird and Poor-will', *Condor*, **59**, 145.

Beddard, F. E. (1898) *The Structure and Classification of Birds*. London.

Breneman, W. R. (1955) 'Reproduction in Birds: the Female', *Mem. Soc. Endoc.*, **4**, 94.

Broom, R. (1906). 'On the Early Development of the Appendicular Skeletons of the Ostrich with Remarks on the Origin of Birds', *Trans. S. Afr. Phil. Soc.*, **16**, 355.

Collias, N. (1950) 'Hormones and Behaviour with Special Reference to Birds and the Mechanism of Hormone Action', in *Steroid Hormones*, ed. by E. S. Gordon, p. 277. Wisconsin.

Cottam, P. A. (1957) 'The Pelecaniform Characters of the Skeleton of the Shoebill Stork, *Balæniceps rex*', *Bull. Brit. Mus. (Nat. Hist.) Zool.*, **5**, 51.

De Beer, G. R. (1954a) '*Archæopteryx* and Evolution', *The Advancement of Science*, **42**, 160. London.

De Beer, G. R. (1945b) *Archæopteryx lithographica*. London.

De Beer, G. R. (1956) 'The Evolution of Ratites', *Bull. Brit. Mus. (N.H.) Zool.*, **4**, 59.

Edinger, T. (1941) 'The Brain of *Pterodactylus*', *Amer. Journ. Sci.*, **239**, 665.

Edinger, T. (1951) 'The Brains of the Odontognathæ', *Evol.*, **5**, 6.

Forbes, T. R. (1947) 'The Crowing Hen: Early Observations on Spontaneous Sex Reversal in Birds', *Yale Jour. Biol. and Med.*, **19**, 955.

Fox, D. C. (1955) 'Astaxanthin in the American Flamingo', *Nature*, **175**, 492.

Friedmann, H. (1955) 'Recent Revisions in Classification and their Biological Significance', in *Recent Studies in Avian Biology*. Illinois.

Friedmann, H., and Kern, J. (1956) '*Micrococcus cerolyticus*, Nov. Sp., an Ærobic Lipolytic Organism Isolated from the African Honey-guide', *Canad. Jour. Microbiol.*, **2**, 515.

Friedmann, H., and Kern, J. (1956) 'The Problem of Cerophagy or Wax-eating in the Honey-guides', *Quart. Rev. Biol.*, **31**, 19.

Grassé, P.-P. (1950) *Traité de Zoologie*. Oiseaux, **15**. Paris.

Gregory, W. K. (1935) 'Remarks on the Origins of the Ratites and Penguins', with discussion by Robert Cushman Murphy, *Proc. Linn. Soc. New York*, **45–46**, I, 18.

Gregory, J. T. (1952) 'The Jaws of the Cretaceous Toothed Birds', *Ichthyornis* and *Hesperornis*. *Condor*, **54**, 73.

Griffin, D. R. (1958) *Listening in the Dark*. Yale.

Heilmann, G. (1936) *The Origin of Birds*. London.

Horton-Smith, C. (1926) *The Flight of Birds*. London.

Howard, H. (1950) 'Fossil Evidence of Avian Evolution', *Ibis*, **92**, I.

Huxley, J., Webb, C. S., and Best, A. T. (1939) 'Temporary Poikilothermy in Birds', *Nature*, **143**, 683.

Jenkin, P. M. (1957) 'The Filter-feeding and Food of Flamingoes (Phœnicopteri)', *Phil. Trans. Roy. Soc. Lond.*, **B**, **240**, 401.

Lack, D. (1947) *Darwin's Finches*. Cambridge.

Lorenz, K. (1935) 'Der Kumpan in der Umwelt des Vogels', *J. Ornith.*, **83**, 137.

Lorenz, K. (1937) 'The Companion in the Birds' World', *Auk*, **54**, 245.

Marsh, O. C. (1880) 'Odontornithes. A Monograph on the Extinct Toothed Birds of North America', *U.S. Geol. Expl. 40th Parallel, Washington*, **7**, 201.

Marshall, A. J. (1954) *Bower Birds: Their Displays and Breeding Cycles*. Oxford.

Marshall, A. J. (1960) (Ed.) *The Biology and Comparative Physiology of Birds*. London and New York.

Mayr, E., and Amadon, D. (1951) 'A Classification of Recent Birds', *Amer. Mus. Nov.*, **1496**, I.

Mayr, E. (1955) 'Comments on Some Recent Studies in Song-bird Phylogeny', *Wilson Bull.*, **67**, 33.

McDowell, S. (1948) 'The Bony Palate of Birds. I. The Palæognathæ', *Auk*, **65**, 520.

Newton, A. (1893) *A Dictionary of Birds*. London.

Pearson, O. P. (1953) 'Use of Caves by Hummingbirds and Other Species at High Altitudes in Peru', *Condor*, **55**, 17.

Pearson, O. P. (1954) 'The Daily Energy Requirements of a Wild Anna Hummingbird', *Condor*, **56**, 317.

Peters, J. L. (1931 onwards) *Checklist of the Birds of the World*. Harvard.

Pumphrey, R. J. (1949) 'The Sense Organs of Birds', *Smithsonian Rep. for* 1948 305.

Romanoff, A. L., and Romanoff, A. J. (1949) *The Avian Egg*. London.

Simpson, G. G. (1946) 'Fossil Penguins', *Bull. Amer. Mus. Nat. Hist.*, **87**, I.

Steiner, H. (1918) 'Das Problem der Diastataxie des Vogelflügels', *Jena Z. Naturw.*, **55**, 221.

Stresemann, E. (1927–1934) 'Sauropsida; Aves, etc.', in Kükenthal and Krumbach, *Handbuch der Zoologie*, **7**. Berlin.

Stresemann, E. (1959) 'The Status of Avian Systematics and its Unsolved Problems', *Auk*, **76**, 269.

Sturkie, P. (1954) *Avian Physiology*. New York and London.

Swarth, H. S. (1934) 'The Bird Fauna of the Galapagos Islands in Relation to Species Formation', *Biol. Rev.*, **9**, 213.

Thomson, J. A. (1923) *The Biology of Birds*. London.

Tucker, B. W. (1938a) 'Functional Evolutionary Morphology: the Origin of Birds', in *Evolution: Essays on Aspects of Evolutionary Biology*, ed. G. R. de Beer. Oxford.

Udvardy, M. D. F. (1953) 'Contributions to the Knowledge of the Body Temperature of Birds', *Zool. Bid. Fran. Upp. Band*. Sweden.

Wetmore, A. (1951) 'A Revised Classification of the Birds of the World', *Smith. Misc. Coll.*, **117**, 1.

MAMMALS

Abbie, A. A. (1941) 'Marsupials and the Evolution of Mammals', *Austral. Jour. Sci.*, **IV**, 77.

Ashley-Montague, M. F. (1955). 'Time, Morphology, and Neoteny in the Evolution of Man', *Amer. Anthrop.*, **57**, 13.

Austin, C. R., and Bishop, M. W. H. (1957) 'Fertilization in Mammals', *Biol. Rev.*, **32**, 296.

Barnett, C. H., Harrison, R. J., and Tomlinson, J. D. W. (1958) 'Variations in the Venous Systems of Mammals', *Biol. Rev.*, **33**, 442.

Bartholomew, G. A. (1956) 'Temperature Regulation in the Macropod Marsupial *Setonix brachyurus*', *Physiol. Zool.*, **XXIX**, 1.

Beddard, F. E. (1920) *Mammalia*, **10**, Cambridge Natural History. Cambridge.

Bensley, R. A. (1938) *Anatomy of the Rabbit*. 6th edition. Toronto.

Bourlière, F. (1954) *The Natural History of Mammals*. London.

Bradley, O. C. (1927). *Topographical Anatomy of the Dog*. Edinburgh.

Burrell, H. (1927) *The Platypus*. Sydney.

Butler, P. M. (1939) 'Studies of the Mammalian Dentition. Differentiation of the Post-canine Dentition', *Proc. Zool. Soc. London*, **B**, **109**, 1–36.

Butler, P. M. (1946) The evolution of carnassial dentitions in the mammalia. *Proc. Zool. Soc. London*, **116**, 198.

Butler, P. M. (1956) 'The Skull of *Ictops* and the Classification of the Insectivora', *Proc. Zool. Soc. Lond.*, **126**, 453.

Butler, P. M. (1956) 'The Ontogeny of Molar Pattern', *Biol. Rev.*, **31**,30.

Cave, A. J. E. (1959) 'Pneumatic Osteolysis in the Elephant Skull', *Proc. Zool. Soc. Lond.*, **132**, 655.

Clarke, R. (1954) 'A Great Haul of Ambergris', *Nature*, **174**, 155.

Clark, W. E. Le Gros (1940) 'Palæontological Evidence Bearing on Human Evolution', *Biol. Rev.*, **15**, 202.

Clark, W. E. Le Gros (1949) *History of the Primates*. London.

Clark, W. E. Le Gros (1954) *Early Forerunners of Man*. London.

Cowie, A. T., and Folley, S. J. (1957) 'Neurohypophysial Hormones and the Mammary Gland', in *The Neurohypophysics*, ed. H. Heller. London.

Davison, A. (1937) *Mammalian Anatomy, with Special Reference to the Cat*. 6th edition. Philadelphia.

Edinger, T. (1948) 'Evolution of the Horse Brain', *Mem. Geol. Soc. Amer.*, **25**, 1.

Elton, C. S. (1942) 'Voles, Mice and Lemmings', in *Problems in Population Dynamics*. Oxford.

Flower, W. H. (1885) *Osteology of the Mammalia*. 3rd edition. London.

Flower, W. H., and Lydekker, R. (1891) *Mammals, Living and Extinct*. London.

Fraser, F. C., and Purves, P. E. (1955) 'The " Blow " of Whales', *Nature*, **176**, 1221.

Gilbert, P. W. (1947) 'The Origin and Development of the Extrinsic Ocular Muscles in the Domestic Cat', *J. Morph.*, **81**, 151.

Grassé, P.-P. (1955) *Traité de Zoologie*. Mammalia, **17**. Paris.

Gregory, W. K. (1910) 'The Orders of Mammals', *Bull. Amer. Mus. Nat. Hist.* New York.

Gregory, W. K. (1947) 'The Monotremes and the Palimpsest Theory', *Bull. Amer. Mus. Nat. Hist.*, **88**, 1.

Griffin, D. R. (1958) *Listening in the Dark*. Yale.

Hamilton, W. J. (1949) 'The Bacula of Some North American Vespertilionid Bats', *Journ. Mammalogy*, **30**, 97.

Huxley, J. (1957) 'Material of Early Contraceptive Sheaths', *Brit. Med. Jour.*, **1**, 581.

Irving, L. (1939) 'Respiration in Diving Mammals', *Physiological Reviews*, **19**, 112.

Jones, F. Wood (1916) *Arboreal Man*. London.

Jones, F. Wood (1923) *The Mammals of South Australia*. Adelaide.

Jones, F. Wood (1929) *Man's Place Among the Mammals*. London.

Jones, F. Wood (1941) *The Principles of Anatomy as Seen in the Hand*. London.

Jones, F. Wood (1944) *Structure and Function as Seen in the Foot*. London.

Jones, F. Wood (1944–1945) 'Some Curiosities of Mammalian Reproduction', *J. Obst. Gynæ. Brit. Emp.* Oct. Dec. 1944, Feb. 1945. Also, Sherratt and Hughes, Manchester.

Jones, F. Wood (1948) *Hallmarks of Mankind*. London.

Kermack, K. A., and Mussett, F. (1958). 'The Jaw Articulation of the Docodonta and the Classification of Mesozoic Mammals', *Proc. Roy. Soc., Lond.*, **B**, **148**, 204.

Kermack, K. A., and Mussett, F. (1959) 'The Jaw Articulation in Mesozoic Mammals', *Proc. XV Intl. Congr. of Zool.*, Sect. V, paper 8.

Kermack, D. M., Kermack, K. A., and Mussett, F. (1956) 'New Mesozoic Mammals from South Wales', *Proc. Geol. Soc. Lond.*, **1533**, 31.

Krapka, J. (1939) 'Parthenogenic Cleavage in the Human Ovary', *Anat. Rec.*, **75**, 19.

Matthews, L. H. (1939) 'Reproduction in the Spotted Hyæna, *Crocuta crocuta* (Erxleben)', *Phil. Trans. Roy. Soc. Lond.*, **B**, **230**, 1.

Moir, R. J., Somers, M., and Waring, H. (1956) 'Studies on Marsupial Nutrition', *Aust. J. Biol. Sci.*, **9**, 293.

Osborn, H. F. (1929) *Titanotheres*. Washington.

Osborn, H. F. (1929) 'The Titanotheres of Ancient Wyoming, Dakota and Nebraska', Vol. 2, U.S. *Geol. Surv. Mon.*, **55**, 703.

Osborn, H. F. (1936) 'Proboscidea. A Monograph of the Discovery, Evolution, Migration and Extinction of the Mastodonts and Elephants of the World. 1', *Amer. Mus. Nat. Hist.*

Parrington, F. R., and Westoll, T. S. (1940) 'On the Evolution of the Mammalian Palate', *Phil. Trans. Roy. Soc.*, **B**, **230**, 305.

Parry, H. J. (1954) 'A Comparative Study of the Umbilical Sphincter', *Proc. Zool. Soc. Lond.*, **124**, 595.

Patten, B. M. (1953) *Human Embryology*. 2nd edition. London.

Patterson, B. (1956) 'Early Cretaceous Mammals and the Evolution of Mammalian Molar Teeth', *Fieldiana Geol.*, **13**, 1.

Pilgrim, G. E. (1941) 'The Dispersal of the Artiodactyla', *Biol. Rev.*, **16**, 134.

Pincus, G. (1936) *The Eggs of Mammals*. New York.

Pincus, G. (1939a) 'The Comparative Behaviour of Mammalian Eggs *in vivo* and *in vitro*. IV. The Development of Fertilized and Artificially Activated Rabbit Eggs', *J. Exp. Zool.*, **82**, 85.

Pincus, G. (1939b) 'The Breeding of Some Rabbits Produced by Recipients of Artificially Activated Ova', *Proc. Nat. Acad. Sci., Wash.*, **25**, 557.

Ride, W. D. L. (1957) 'The Affinities of *Plagiaulax* (Multituberculata)', *Proc. Zool. Soc. Lond.*, **128**, 397.

Ride, W. D. L. (1961) 'On the evolution of Australian Marsupials'. *The Evolution of Living Organisms* (ed. G. W. Leeper). Melbourne.

Scholander, P. F., and Schevill, W. (1955) 'Counter-current Vascular Heat Exchange in the Fins of Whales', *J. App. Phys.*, **8**, 279.

Schmidt-Nielsen, K., and Schmidt-Nielsen, B. (1952) 'Water Metabolism of Desert Mammals', *Physiol. Rev.*, **32**, 135.

Schmidt-Nielsen, K. (1959) 'The Physiology of the Camel', *Sci. Amer.*, **201**, 140.

Sharman, G. (1959) 'Marsupial Reproduction'. In Bodenheimer's *Biogeography and Ecology in Australia*. Den Haag.

Simpson, G. G. (1928a) *A Catalogue of the Mesozoic Mammalia in the Geological Department of the British Museum (Natural History)*. London (British Museum).

Simpson, G. G. (1929) 'American Mesozoic Mammalia'. *Mem. Peabody. Mus. Nat. Hist.* Pt. I. New Haven and London.

Simpson, G. G. (1933). 'The "Plagiaulacoid" Type of Mammalian Dentition', *J. Mammal.*, **14**, 97.

Simpson, G. G. (1937) 'The Beginning of the Age of Mammals', *Biol. Rev.*, **12**, 1.

Simpson, G. G. (1941) 'The Function of Saber-like Canines in Carnivorous Mammals', *Amer. Mus. Nov.*, **1130**, 1–12.

Simpson, G. G. (1945) 'The Principles of Classification and a Classification of Mammals', *Bull. Amer. Mus. Nat. Hist.*, **85**, 1.

Simpson, G. G. (1951) *Horses*. New York and Oxford.

Simpson, G. G. (1953) *Evolution and Geography*. Condon Lectures, Oregon.

Storr, G. M. (1958) 'Are Marsupials "Second-Class Mammals"?', *W.A. Nat.*, **6**, 179.

Strumwasser, F. (1957) 'Regulatory Mechanisms, Brain Activity and Behavior during Deep Hibernation in the Squirrel (*Citellus beecheyi*)', *Amer. J. Phy.*, **196**, 23.

Watson, D. M. S. (1916) 'The Monotreme Skull: a Contribution to Mammalian Morphogenesis', *Phil. Trans. Roy. Soc. Lond.*, **B**, **207**, 311.

Watson, D. M. S. (1946) 'The Evolution of the Proboscidea', *Biol. Rev.*, **21**, 1.

Weddell, G. Palmer, E., and Pallie, W. (1955) 'Nerve Endings in Mammalian Skin', *Biol. Rev.*, **30**, 159.

Whitworth, T. (1954) 'The Miocene Hyracoids of East Africa', in *Fossil Mammals of Africa*, **7**. British Museum (N.H.).

Young, J. Z. (1957) *The Life of Mammals*. Oxford.

INDEX

All numbers refer to pages: words in italics are names of genera and species: words in thick type are names of higher divisions: numbers in thick type refer to a definition of the term or a main section dealing with it.